TABLE OF ATOMIC WEIGHTS, 1961 (*Continued*)

Element	*Symbol*	*Atomic Number*	*Atomic Weight*
Neon	Ne	10	20.183
Neptunium	Np	93	
Nickel	Ni	28	58.71
Niobium	Nb	41	92.906
Nitrogen	N	7	14.0067
Nobelium	No	102	
Osmium	Os	76	190.2
Oxygen	O	8	15.9994 (±0.0001, nat.)
Palladium	Pd	46	106.4
Phosphorus	P	15	30.9738
Platinum	Pt	78	195.09
Plutonium	Pu	94	
Polonium	Po	84	
Potassium	K	19	39.102
Praseodymium	Pr	59	140.907
Promethium	Pm	61	
Protactinium	Pa	91	
Radium	Ra	88	
Radon	Rn	86	
Rhenium	Re	75	186.2
Rhodium	Rh	45	102.905
Rubidium	Rb	37	85.47
Ruthenium	Ru	44	101.07
Samarium	Sm	62	150.35
Scandium	Sc	21	44.956
Selenium	Se	34	78.96
Silicon	Si	14	28.086 (±0.001, nat.)
Silver	Ag	47	107.870 (±0.003, exp.)
Sodium	Na	11	22.9898
Strontium	Sr	38	87.62
Sulfur	S	16	32.064 (±0.003, nat.)
Tantalum	Ta	73	180.948
Technetium	Tc	43	
Tellurium	Te	52	127.60
Terbium	Tb	65	158.924
Thallium	Tl	81	204.37
Thorium	Th	90	232.038
Thulium	Tm	69	168.934
Tin	Sn	50	118.69
Titanium	Ti	22	47.90
Tungsten	W	74	183.85
Uranium	U	92	238.03
Vanadium	V	23	50.942
Xenon	Xe	54	131.30
Ytterbium	Yb	70	173.04
Yttrium	Y	39	88.905
Zinc	Zn	30	65.37
Zirconium	Zr	40	91.22

nat. = Variation in atomic weight due to natural variation in the isotopic composition.
exp. = Experimental uncertainty of magnitude given.

Adopted 1961 by the International Union of Pure and Applied Chemistry.

STANDARD METHODS OF CHEMICAL ANALYSIS

The first four editions of STANDARD METHODS OF CHEMICAL ANALYSIS were prepared under the Editorship of Dr. Wilfred W. Scott, Professor of Chemistry at the University of Southern California. After his death, the Fifth Edition was edited by Dr. N. Howell Furman, then Professor of Chemistry at Princeton University. Professor Furman also edited Volume I of the Sixth Edition, and was Advisory Editor of Volume II, which was edited by Dr. Frank J. Welcher of Indiana University. The present Volume III was also prepared under the Editorship of Dr. Welcher.

STANDARD METHODS OF CHEMICAL ANALYSIS

SIXTH EDITION

Volume Three—Instrumental Methods

Part A

FRANK J. WELCHER, Ph.D., *Editor*

Professor of Chemistry, Indiana University

IN COLLABORATION WITH MANY CONTRIBUTORS
(SEE LIST ON PAGES FOLLOWING)

D. VAN NOSTRAND COMPANY, INC.

Princeton, New Jersey

Toronto **London**

New York

D. VAN NOSTRAND COMPANY, INC.
120 Alexander St., Princeton, New Jersey (*Principal office*)
24 West 40 Street, New York 18, New York

D. VAN NOSTRAND COMPANY, LTD.
358 Kensington High Street, London, W.14, England

D. VAN NOSTRAND COMPANY (Canada), LTD.
25 Hollinger Road, Toronto 16, Canada

Published simultaneously in Canada by
D. VAN NOSTRAND COMPANY (Canada), LTD.

PRINTED IN THE UNITED STATES OF AMERICA

PREFACE

The first five editions of STANDARD METHODS OF CHEMICAL ANALYSIS were prepared to provide proven methods of analysis to the practical chemist who was required to determine the composition and quality of many materials. Originally such analysis was comparatively simple. Little or no significance was attached to the presence of trace amounts of various substances which might have been present in a sample. As a result there was little demand for highly sensitive methods, and many component substances were not even determined, although their value today is unquestioned. Further, the number of special materials then requiring examination was not nearly so large as it is at the present time, nor was speed so important a factor.

In the science and technology of today, however, all this has changed: the modern analytical chemist faces a challenging diversity of new and increasingly complex materials; simultaneously, he is called upon to furnish information about constituents which, only a short time before, were either unknown or considered unimportant. To complicate his task further, he must comply as best he can with demands for greater sensitivity, greater reliability, and greater speed. Confronted by these conditions, analytical chemists and their colleagues in allied fields have, understandably, turned to research to develop the techniques, instruments, procedures, and reagents to cope with their problems adequately. The combined efforts of thousands of analytical chemists throughout the world have contributed to a clearer understanding of the scope, advantages, and limitations of each of the many methods now available. This understanding, in turn, has created new difficulties. A few decades ago there was little question as to choice of a reliable method for a particular analysis. Today the analytical chemist must explore numerous possibilities before arriving at a satisfactory selection of a useful or superior method for a given purpose. Therefore, in order that STANDARD METHODS OF CHEMICAL ANALYSIS continue to fulfill its function as a practical aid to the analytical chemist the contents of this work must be expanded to conform to the developing trends in analytical chemistry today.

Although many of the classical procedures of analysis remain among the more useful methods for specific problems, in recent years chemists have initiated a major trend toward the use of the so-called instrumental methods of analysis. Many advantages result from the use of these methods: frequently they are far more rapid than the older methods; in many cases they are adaptable to automatic determinations; they may in some instances be used for determinations without destruction of the sample; some may be applied to exceedingly small volumes, as 2 to 5 cubic microns or to a single plant or animal cell; they may be applied to quantities of a sample that could not be so examined a few years ago; and they may be used for the analysis of mixtures which would defy analysis, at least in reasonable time, by classical procedures.

To treat this subject of instrumental analysis adequately, a new Volume III has been added to the Sixth Edition of STANDARD METHODS OF CHEMICAL ANALYSIS. This volume contains a brief discussion of each of the important instrumental techniques, and the applications of these techniques to the analysis of special materials.

The original idea upon which earlier editions have been based has not been fundamentally altered in preparing the Sixth Edition. The work is to remain a convenient source of practical analytical information for use in the chemical laboratory. Because some of the instrumental techniques are still so recent, slight changes in the criteria for inclusion of material have been necessary for Volume III. In previous editions, and also in Volumes I and II of this edition, methods have been regarded as standard if they have been accepted as standards by certain groups or organizations, or if they are of proven value, widely accepted, and readily applied. With these limitations, however, many of the useful instrumental methods might not properly qualify for inclusion in Volume III. Because of the present importance of many techniques, and the potential significance of many others, a complete coverage of all instrumental methods in Volume III has been attempted, although some of them cannot be regarded as standard.

Perhaps few instrumental methods could properly be called standard in the sense that they have been standardized by a particular group or have been accepted as such through long and successful usage. In the preparation of this book, therefore, the original idea of a standard method has been in some sense modified, and all instrumental methods which are used widely or effectively, or even those which show promise of usefulness in certain areas are included. In brief, the criterion for the inclusion of an instrumental technique or method has been that mentioned above; namely, that the technique be widely used, or, if not widely used, at least effectively used for various purposes for which a noninstrumental method might for any reason be inferior. Further, a method has been included if it shows considerable promise of becoming useful in the forseeable future.

A problem has also arisen in connection with what procedure might be called instrumental as relates to inclusion in this volume. Actually, almost all analytical methods require the use of one or more instruments, such as in weighing, melting point determination, etc. In general, however, methods for measuring physical constants have not been included. Some physical constants, such as refractive index and specific rotation may be very important in solving some analytical problems, and have been included. The determinations of many physical constants are included in some chapters of Volume II, and are not repeated here.

Since the number of specific determinations which might conceivably be required is virtually unlimited, it is not possible to give anything like complete coverage for the analysis of a special material by giving only a limited number of so-called standard methods. These have been included where they exist, but in addition many methods have been presented because they are known to be useful in solving special problems and because they are helpful in suggesting possible approaches for the development of still other methods which may be required now or in the future.

Since many techniques are relatively recent, and their applications in analysis have not, in general, been standardized or even fully explored, the design of Volume III has been such, it is hoped, as to stimulate interest in the extension of these approaches to the solution of current and developing analytical problems. There is no question as to the usefulness of the many new instrumental methods, but the consensus seems to be that few of the numerous methods described in the chemical literature can be presented as standard methods in the accepted sense of the term. Therefore, Volume III is not, as has been the case in earlier editions, a compilation of standardized methods of analysis. Rather, it is intended to provide the analyst with a general understanding of the principles, instrumentation, scope, advantages, and limitations of each of the instrumental techniques, and then to illustrate by generally proven methods the application of these techniques to the analysis of special materials. To accomplish this Volume III has been divided into two parts: Part I consists of a general discussion of each technique; and Part II comprises a series of chapters describing the application of these methods to the analysis of special materials. The special materials included are generally the same as those of Volume II. A number of materials, however, have received adequate coverage in Volume II and have not been included in Volume III. These are: commercial acids and bases; bituminous substances; coal and coke; explosives and propellants; gas analysis-vacuum techniques; poisons; vitamins; and the bacterial and biological examination of water. New chapters have been added on foods and semiconductors.

The editor wishes to acknowledge the valuable assistance given by Dean Virgil Hunt of the Indianapolis Regional Campus in making available the many facilities of his department to aid in the completion of this book. A number of people have also rendered invaluable aid in preparing the manuscript, attending to correspondence, and preparing the index. These are: Janet Boling, Patricia Van Noy, Oka Negley, and Susanne Bennett.

Permission to reproduce material from many books, journals, and industrial publications has generously been granted by the following: Academic Press, Inc.; American Association for the Advancement of Science; American Chemical Society; American Instrument Co., Inc.; *American Journal of Public Health;* American Public Health Association, Inc.; American Society for Testing and Materials; American Water Works Association; *The Analyst; Analytica Chimica Acta; Analytical Chemistry;* Applied Physics Corp.; *Applied Spectroscopy;* Archer-Daniels-Midland Co.; Associated Electrical Industries, Ltd.; Association of Official Agricultural Chemists; *ASTM Bulletin;* Baird-Atomic, Inc.; Barnes Engineering Co., Instrument Division (formerly Connecticut Instruments Co.); Beckman Instruments, Inc.; The Bendix Corp.; British Standards Institution; *Canadian Journal of Chemistry;* Canadian National Research Council; *Corrosion;* E. I. düPont de Nemours and Co.; R. J. Eastman of Stanford University; Eberbach Corp.; Farrand Optical Co.; Federation of Societies for Paint Technology and the *Official Digest;* Fisher Scientific Co.; FMC Corporation; General Radio Co.; General Services Administration, Standardization Division; *Industrial and Engineering Chemistry;* Instrument Society of America; International Atomic Energy Agency; Interscience Publishers, Inc.; *Journal of Analytical Chemistry; Journal of Applied Polymer Science; Journal of Polymer Science; Journal of the American Chemical Society; Journal of the American Water Works Association; Kautschuk und Gummi Kunststoffe;* S. M. Klainer of Clark University; Maclaren and Sons, Ltd.; *Materie Plastiche ed Elastomeri;* McGraw-Hill Book Co.; Mechrolab, Inc.; National Association of Corrosion Engineers; Nuclear Materials and Engineering; *Nucleonics;* Oxford University Press; Pergamon Press; The Perkin-Elmer Corp.; Plenum Press; Radio Corporation of America; C. Reichert, AG; *Rubber Age; Rubber Chemistry and Technology; Rubber World;* O. C. Rudolph and Sons, Inc.; E. H. Sargent and Co.; *Science;* C. L. Sia of Clark University; *Soviet Rubber Technology;* Spartan Books, Inc.; *Spectrochimica Acta; SPE Transactions;* Technical Association of the Pulp and Paper Industry; Technicon Instruments Corp.; G. K. Turner Associates; the United States Pharmacopoeial Convention, Inc.; Varian Associates; Water Pollution Control Federation; John Wiley and Sons, Inc.

The task of assembling and integrating the material for this book has been greatly facilitated by the remarkable cooperation of all collaborators in every phase of the undertaking. The editor wishes to thank all contributors for their efforts in bringing this volume to its final form, and for making available the highly specialized information which it contains to all who may have need of it.

CONTRIBUTORS *Sixth Edition—Volume Three*

P. Bruce Adams
Corning Glass Works

L. W. Aurand
North Carolina State University

Allen J. Bard
University of Texas

Richard C. Barras
Atlantic Refining Co.

S. A. Bartkiewicz
Humble Oil and Refining Co.

Roger G. Bates
National Bureau of Standards

Hugh F. Beeghly
Jones and Laughlin Steel Corp.

E. W. Blank
Colgate-Palmolive Research Center

David F. Boltz
Wayne State University

John A. Brabson
Tennessee Valley Authority

E. J. Brooks
Naval Research Laboratory

Robert J. Bryan
Los Angeles Air Pollution Control District

Vincent E. Caldwell
Pittsburgh Plate Glass Co.

William J. Campbell
Department of the Interior

Paul Close
Owens-Illinois Technical Center

John G. Cobler
Dow Chemical Co.

J. William Cook
Department of Health, Education and Welfare

S. Dal Nogare
E. I. duPont de Nemours and Co.

Donald G. Davis
Louisiana State University

John A. Dean
University of Tennessee

Joseph B. DiGiorgio
Sacramento State College

Jan Doležal
Charles University
Prague, Czechoslovakia

John C. Evans
Dow Chemical Co.

Robert B. Fischer
California State College at Palos Verdes

Robert Fisher
Universität Graz
Graz, Austria

Harlan Foster
E. I. duPont de Nemours and Co.

Owen R. Gates
Naval Research Laboratory

Roland S. Gohlke
Dow Chemical Co.

S. Mark Henry
Bristol Myers Corp.

Harold W. Hermance
Bell Telephone Laboratories

William G. Hime
Portland Cement Association

Emanuel Horowitz
National Bureau of Standards

R. Norman Jones
National Research Council of Canada

W. C. Jones, Jr.
Esso Research and Engineering Co.

Philip F. Kane
Texas Instruments, Inc.

Brian H. Kaye
I. I. T. Research Institute

Gerson Kegeles
Clark University

R. M. Kelley
Colgate-Palmolive Research Center

Duane V. Kniebes
Institute of Gas Technology

Richard M. Kniseley
Iowa State University

Stephen H. Laning
Pittsburgh Plate Glass Co.

George W. Leddicotte
University of Missouri

Gabor B. Levy
Photovolt Corp.

Ralph B. Lingeman
Indiana University Medical Center

Donald C. Malins
Department of the Interior

Helmut K. Mangold
University of Minnesota

James D. McGinness
Sherwin-Williams Research Center

Virgil C. Mehlenbacher
Swift and Co.

M. G. Mellon
Purdue University

C. M. Mitchell
Canadian Department of Mines and Technical Surveys

John Mitchell, Jr.
E. I. duPont de Nemours and Co.

L. N. Mulay
Pennsylvania State University

A. Wendell Musser
Veterans Administration

John L. Parsons
Consultant to the Paper and Allied Industries

Dennis G. Peters
Indiana University

James W. Robinson
Louisiana State University

Howard G. Ross
Ford Motor Co.

James W. Ross, Jr.
Orion Research, Inc.

Edward J. Rubins
University of Connecticut

Ward B. Schaap
Indiana University

Harold F. Schaeffer
Westminster College

Harald H. O. Schmid
University of Minnesota

Robert D. Schwartz
Shell Development Co.

Paul J. Secrest
Sherwin-Williams Research Center

William L. Senn, Jr.
Esso Research Laboratories

W. D. Shults
Oak Ridge National Laboratory

E. L. Steel
General Dynamics Corp.

D. P. Stevenson
Shell Development Co.

Hans J. Stolten
General Aniline and Film Corp.

Richard D. Strickland
Veterans Administration

Michael J. Taras
Detroit Department of Water Supply

Domenic J. Tessari
Sherwin-Williams Research Center

Max Tryon
National Bureau of Standards

Harold V. Wadlow
Bell Telephone Laboratories
Holmdel, New Jersey

P. A. Wadsworth
Shell Development Co.

Alan Walsh
Commonwealth Scientific and Industrial Research Organization
Melbourne, Australia

Dean I. Walter
Naval Research Laboratory

Alfred Weissler
Air Force Office of Scientific Research

Wesley W. Wendlandt
Texas Technological College

Charles E. White
University of Maryland

William P. Whitney
Corning Glass Works

Sidney Williams
Department of Health, Education and Welfare

J. B. Willis
Commonwealth Scientific and Industrial Research Organization
Melbourne, Australia

Jaroslav Zýka
Charles University
Prague, Czechoslovakia

CONTENTS

Part I

INSTRUMENTAL METHODS

VISIBLE SPECTROMETRY

ULTRAVIOLET SPECTROMETRY

INFRARED SPECTROMETRY

RAMAN SPECTROMETRY

FLUOROMETRIC ANALYSIS

ATOMIC ABSORPTION SPECTROMETRY

FLAME EMISSION SPECTROMETRY

EMISSION SPECTROMETRY

X-RAY EMISSION AND ABSORPTION

ELECTRON PROBE X-RAY MICROANALYZER

X-RAY DIFFRACTION

CHEMICAL MICROSCOPY

ELECTRON MICROSCOPY

REFRACTOMETRY

POLARIMETRY AND SPECTROPOLARIMETRY

TURBIDIMETRY AND NEPHELOMETRY

POTENTIOMETRIC TITRATIONS

CONDUCTOMETRIC TITRATIONS

POLAROGRAPHY

AMPEROMETRIC TITRATIONS

CHRONOPOTENTIOMETRY

ELECTROGRAVIMETRIC ANALYSIS

COULOMETRIC METHODS

HIGH FREQUENCY METHODS

ELECTROGRAPHY AND ELECTROSPOT TESTING

ELECTROMETRIC METHODS OF pH DETERMINATION

CRITICAL SOLUTION TEMPERATURES

ELECTROPHORESIS

GAS CHROMATOGRAPHY

THIN-LAYER CHROMATOGRAPHY

SEDIMENTATION ANALYSIS

PARTICLE SIZE ANALYSIS

Part II

INSTRUMENTAL METHODS FOR INDUSTRIAL PRODUCTS AND OTHER SPECIAL SUBSTANCES

AIR POLLUTANTS

ALLOYS: IRON, STEEL, FERRO-ALLOYS, AND RELATED PRODUCTS

ALLOYS: NONFERROUS

AMINO ACID ANALYSIS

PORTLAND CEMENT

Part I

INSTRUMENTAL METHODS

Chapter 1

VISIBLE SPECTROMETRY

By D. F. Boltz
Department of Chemistry
Wayne State University
Detroit, Michigan

and

M. G. Mellon
Department of Chemistry
Purdue University
Lafayette, Indiana

Visible spectrometry involves the determination of the light absorptive capacity of a chemical system. Inasmuch as light is the aspect of radiant energy of which a normal person is aware through the usual sensations resulting from stimulation of the retina of the eye,[1] the region of the electromagnetic spectrum which is encompassed in visible spectrometry is approximately 380 to 750 mμ.

Chemical systems which exhibit a selective light absorptive capacity are colored, and, hence, the terms colorimetric analysis and colorimetry are often applied to the measurement of such systems when the objective is to determine the concentration of the constituent responsible for the color. In physics, colorimetry refers to the measurement of color. The determination involves neither the nature of the colorant nor its amount. A spectrophotometric curve for the colored system is the basis for calculating the trichromatic coefficients, x, y, and z; or the dominant wavelength, luminance, and excitation purity. In chemistry, a preferable term is absorptimetry.

As will be noted later, visible spectrometry may be applied to determine a constituent constituting the major part of the sample. However, this technic has been used very largely to determine trace quantities of constituents. Thus, many methods are applicable to amounts of a few parts per million, and some are used to 0.01 p.p.m. or less.

Like other areas of molecular spectroscopy, visible spectrometry has a wide range of applications. Included are most of the elements, many anions, functional groups, and innumerable compounds. The treatise by Snell and Snell is a representative sampling of the possibilities.[2]

The main practical problems in the methodology of visible spectrometry are: (1) to prepare a suitable colored solution; and (2) to measure the light absorptive capacity of this solution, or to compare it with that of a colored solution of known concentration. Let us examine in more detail the chemical problem, the development of a stable, intensely colored solution.

[1] Jones, L. A., *et al.*, The Science of Color, Thos. Y. Crowell Co., New York, 1953.
[2] Snell, F. D., and Snell, C. T., Colorimetric Methods of Analysis, 3rd Ed., D. Van Nostrand Co., Princeton, N.J., Vol. 2, 1949; Vol. 2A, 1959; Vol. 3, 1953; Vol. 3A, 1961; Vol. 4A, 1954

FUNDAMENTALS

PREPARATION OF THE COLORED SOLUTION

Although some desired constituents are self-colored, it is usually necessary to develop a color by the addition of one or more color-forming reagents. Thus, the permanganate ion is sufficiently self-colored; in contrast, since the iron (II) ion is very weakly colored, a complexant, such as 1,10-phenanthroline, is used to form a system suitable for the determination of very small amounts of iron.

The measured system usually contains the desired const tuent either as such or in the form of some ion or compound. In many instances, however, one measures some system known to be chemically equivalent to the desired constituent. For example, ozone may be determined through its action on iodide to liberate an equivalent amount of iodine which is then complexed with starch.

Chromogenic Processes.—Chemical processes used to prepare suitable colored solutions are often called chromogenic reactions, and the color-forming reactants chromogenic reagents. The methodology by which a suitable colored solution is prepared is chemical in nature and requires the careful attention of the analyst. As important as the measurement step is in visible spectrometry, the results will not be valid unless the colored solution being measured has been properly prepared.

The real chemical problem is to transform all of the desired constituent, or something chemically equivalent to it, into the colored state. With an extremely small amount of a specific substance, this conversion may not be rapid or stoichiometric. Usually a large excess of reagent must be used to accelerate the reaction and ensure maximum conversion to the colored species. The advantage of using a very soluble colorless chromogenic reagent is obvious. If a chromogenic reagent possesses some self-color, the amount of reagent being used must be rigorously controlled; or, in some cases, the preferential extraction of the colored constituent by an immiscible solvent eliminates the additive effect of the reagent to the resultant color. Extraction with a solvent of lower dielectric constant also often shifts favorably the equilibrium and results in a more efficient conversion to the colored form. Sometimes heating the solution decreases the time required for development of maximum color.

Usually, one develops a colored system, the absorbing capacity of which is directly proportional to the amount of the desired constituent. In some cases advantage is taken of a decolorizing reaction with a standard colored solution. Thus, calcium may be precipitated and separated as calcium oxalate. Following dissolution in sulfuric acid, the solution of oxalate ions is added to a known amount of a standard solution of permanganate. The decrease in the absorbance of the permanganate, resulting from the reduction by the oxalate ions, is directly related to the amount of oxalate, and, hence, to the amount of calcium.

The effect of other substances present in the sample must be known. These diverse substances may interfere by developing a color with the chromogenic reagent, by precipitating, by inhibiting the chromogenic reaction of the desired constituent, or by consuming the reagent even though no colored substances result.

The optimum conditions under which the chromogenic reagent reacts with the desired constituent should also be known. Thus, if important, the optimum pH range, temperature, the sequence of operations, and the time intervals involved in the treatment of sample should be specified.

Ideally, colored systems suitable for measurement should have the following properties:

Sensitivity.—The solution should be intensely colored. Hence, small changes in concentration, *e.g.*, 1–2 mg./liter, must cause an easily detectable change in intensity. Such intensely colored systems are a necessity for the determination of trace amounts of constituents. By very careful dilution the useful range for a given method can be extended, as shown by Mehlig[3] in the determination of iron. In this way he analyzed ores containing up to 57 percent of iron, and the results were practically as reliable as those by the dichromate titrimetric method. Mention will be made later of the use of differential spectrophotometry for large percentages of desired constituents.

Reproducibility.—Both the hue and intensity of the colored solution must be reproducible. The effect of the order of addition of reagents, the pH, and other solution variables should be clearly delineated.

Stability.—The intensity of the colored solution should remain constant long enough to enable reliable measurements to be made.

Specificity.—Only the desired constituent or some entity definitely related to it should develop a color.

Conformity to Beer's Law.—If the colored solution conforms to Beer's law, the measurement may be facilitated, both for single and polycomponent systems. If it does not conform, adequate precautions must be taken. A later discussion will consider this topic in more detail.

MEASUREMENT OF THE COLORED SOLUTION

Once a stable colored solution has been prepared, the next concern of the analyst is measuring the light absorptive capacity of the system and relating the measurement to the concentration of the desired constituent. We shall consider the fundamentals of the measurement step in respect to the following topics: (1) laws of absorption; (2) terminology used in spectrophotometry; (3) instrumentation; (4) presentation of data; (5) sources of error; and (6) special spectrophotometric technics.

Laws of Absorption.—There are two fundamental laws related to the absorption of monochromatic radiant energy by homogeneous, transparent systems. Bouguer's law expresses the relationship between the light absorptive capacity and thickness of the absorber. Each layer of equal thickness absorbs an equal fraction of the light which traverses it. Thus, a beam of monochromatic radiant energy of radiant power P_0 upon passing through an absorber of thickness b decreases in radiant power according to the following expression: $dP = -k_1 P_0 \, db$. (See Fig. 1-1.) There are no known exceptions to this law for homogeneous systems. The second law, formulated by Beer, expresses the relationship between light absorptive capacity and the concentration of the absorber in a solution. Hence, the fraction of the monochromatic radiant energy absorbed on passing through a solution is directly proportional to the concentration c of the absorber and can be expressed mathematically as follows: $dP = k_2 P_0 \, dc$. These two laws can be combined to give the following exponential form, $P = P_0 \, e^{-k_3 bc}$, or $P =$

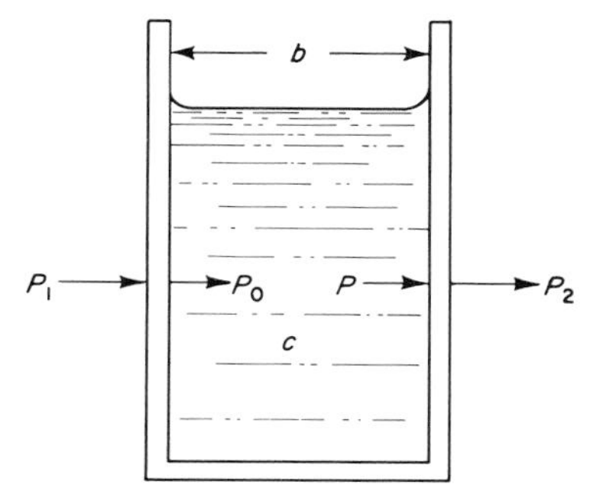

FIG. 1-1. Transmission of Light Through a Colored Solution. P_1, Radiant Power Incident on First Surface of Medium; P_0, Radiant Power Entering Sample Solution of Concentration c and Thickness b; P, Radiant Power Leaving Solution and Incident on Second Surface; P_2, Radiant Power Leaving Last Surface of Medium.

[3] Mehlig, J. P., Ind. Eng. Chem., Anal. Ed., **9**, 162, 1937.

$P_0 10^{-abc}$ where $a = k_3/2.3$. In logarithmic form, this combined expression may be written $\log P_0/P = abc = A$ (absorbance).

In applying this to analytical determinations, b is known and A, or P/P_0, the transmittance, is measured. Thus, one can calculate a for a solution of known concentration and a specific wavelength. Knowing A, a, and b for an unknown solution, its concentration c can be calculated provided that Beer's law is applicable.

If a colored system does not show conformity to Beer's law it is necessary to prepare a calibration graph using a series of standard solutions, and plotting either transmittance or absorbance values against concentration. The absorbance reading obtained with a solution of unknown concentration can be interpreted by reference to this calibration

TABLE 1-1. RECOMMENDED SPECTROPHOTOMETRIC TERMINOLOGY

Term	*Symbol*	*Definition*
Radiant power	P	The rate at which energy is transported in a beam of radiant energy, *i.e.*, radiant flux.
Transmittance	T	The ratio of the radiant power transmitted by the sample (P) to the radiant power incident on the sample (P_0) both being measured at the same spectral position and with the same slit width.
Absorbance	A	The logarithm to the base 10 of the reciprocal of the transmittance $A = \log_{10} (1/T) = -\log T$.
Absorptivity	a	The ratio of the absorbance to the product of concentration and length of optical path. A constant characteristic of $a = A/bc$ substance and wavelength.
Molar absorptivity	ϵ	The absorptivity expressed in units of liter/(mole cm.). The concentration is in mole per liter and the cell length in centimeters.
Path length	b	Internal cell length, centimeters.
Millimicron	$m\mu$	A unit of length equal to one thousandth of a micron. One micron is equal to 10^{-6} meter.
Resolution	—	The ratio of the average wavelength of two spectral lines, which can just be detected as a doublet, to the difference in their wavelengths.
Spectral band width	—	The range of wavelengths of radiant energy emerging from the exit slit of the monochromator.
Half-intensity band width	—	The range of wavelength of radiant energy at a point on the spectral transmittance curve where the transmittance is just one-half of the maximum transmittance value.
Visible	—	Radiant energy which is perceived by the normal human eye (approximately 380 to 780 $m\mu$).
Slit width	S.W. (S.S.W.) (E.S.W.)	The slit width is the mechanical distance (mm.) between the sides of the narrow aperture which permits radiant energy to enter and to leave the monochromator. Sometimes the width of the image of the exit slit along the wavelength scale is called the spectral slit width ($m\mu$) and the width of the image at which the intensity is half of the maximum is termed the effective slit width ($m\mu$).

graph. Care must be taken to follow the same procedure in preparing the colored solution from the unknown samples as was used in preparing the standard colored solutions for constructing the calibration graph. If possible, it is desirable to limit measurements to a narrow concentration range. Apparent deviations from Beer's law may be attributed to either the failure to use monochromatic radiant energy or to chemical effects. Thus, a calibration graph is applicable to a specific instrument inasmuch as the finite spectral slit width depends on the relative energy distribution of the light source and the spectral response curve of the photocell. Chemical effects which can cause errors in absorbance measurements include association, dissociation, shifts in equilibrium with changes in ionic strength or pH, solute-solvent interaction, and consumption of reagent by diverse ions. Polymerization and hydrogen bonding effects can sometimes be eliminated by selecting a different solvent.

Terminology.—Certain spectrophotometric terms and symbols are introduced in the brief discussion of the Bouguer-Beer law. As it is exceedingly important that chemists be consistent in their usage a selected list of recommended terms, symbols, and definitions is summarized in Table 1-1.[4]

INSTRUMENTATION

Although visual colorimetric comparisons utilizing either the balancing or standard series technics are applicable for many routine determinations, the use of photoelectric filter photometers and spectrophotometers is now so widespread in modern analytical technology that only the latter method of measuring colored solutions will be considered. The basic components of photoelectric instruments follow: (1) an intense source of radiant energy of the visible region; a tungsten filament bulb is usually used; (2) a filter, or monochromator, to isolate the wavelength region to be used in irradiating the colored solution; (3) a pair of optically matched cells—one for the colored solution, the other for the blank or reference solution; and (4) a photometer, comprising a photoelectric detector which converts radiant energy to electrical energy and a meter to indicate the resulting electric current. The main distinguishing feature of a spectrophotometer is the use of a monochromator to select nearly monochromatic radiant energy. From a practical operational viewpoint of the analyst, let us examine some of the concepts of instrumentation involved.

Sources.—The emitting capacity of an incandescent tungsten lamp, the source used for visible spectrometry, depends upon the temperature of the filament and upon the wavelength of the radiant energy emitted. Figure 1-2 illustrates relative intensities *vs.* wavelength for several operating temperatures. It is obvious that, other factors being comparable, an instrument so equipped will be less sensitive in the far blue than in the red region of the spectrum.

In a single-beam instrument the stability of the output of the source is very important. Either a fully charged, high capacity storage battery or an a.c. supply with a transformer or voltage regulator, is necessary to provide constant intensity.

Filters and Monochromators.—Nearly all modern instruments employ one of two means to isolate and pass a limited portion of the visible spectrum to be incident upon the sample. These means are filters and monochromators. In general, the former isolates a wider band than the latter although some interference filters have a narrower half-intensity band width than some inexpensive monochromators. Filter photometers employ filters, and spectrophotometers employ monochromators.

In the use of filter photometers, selecting the proper filter and obtaining reproducible photometric readings are the principal considerations in the measurement process. Re-

[4] Hughes, H. K., *et al.*, Anal. Chem., **24**, 1349, 1952.

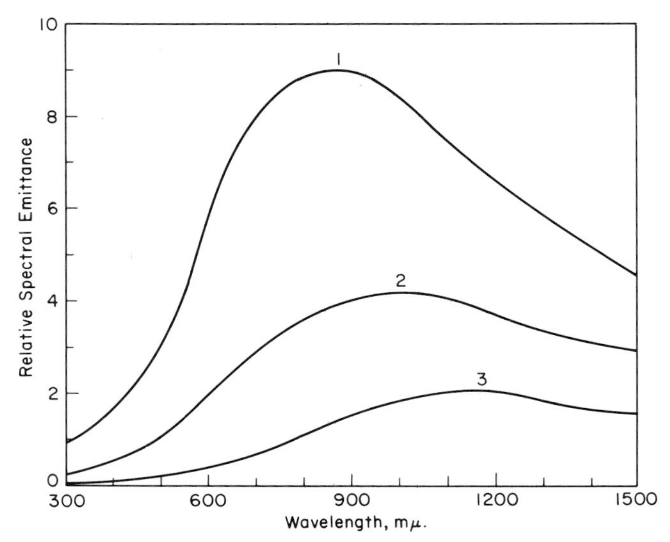

FIG. 1-2. Relative Spectral Emittance of a Tungsten Lamp at Temperatures of (1) 3500°K., (2) 3000°K., and (3) 2500°K.

producible photometric readings depend chiefly on either maintaining the source at a constant radiant power, or compensating for any fluctuations in light intensity. Most modern filter photometers have two photocells so arranged in an electrical circuit that one photocell monitors the source and the other photocell measures the energy transmitted by the colored solution. The resulting readout of a properly designed balanced circuit compensates almost completely for fluctuations in source intensity.[5]

The nominal wavelength and band width of the filter are important characteristics in selecting the appropriate filter to be used in measuring a specific colored solution. The nominal wavelength of the filter should correspond as closely as possible to the wavelength at which the colored solution exhibits maximum absorptivity. Maximum sensitivity is realized the closer these two wavelengths are to each other and the smaller is the half-intensity band width. Optical interference filters with half-band widths corresponding to 1.5, 2.5 mμ, and with nominal wavelengths throughout the visible region are commercially available.[6] The color of tinted glass and dyed gelatin filters should be complementary to that of the solution to be measured (See Table 1-2). The half-band width of absorption filters is quite large, often exceeding 50 mμ.

The preparation of an analytical calibration graph by plotting the transmittance on a log scale, or absorbance on a linear scale, *vs.* concentration is recommended in using filter photometers.

A monochromator consists of entrance and exit slits and a dispersive device, either a prism or grating, so arranged that radiant energy of a relatively narrow spectral band width is obtained. The resolution of the monochromator is a measure of the approach to monochromaticity. In most commercial spectrophotometers the entrance and exit slits have the same slit widths so that the distribution of energy of the transmitted beam

[5] Mellon, M. G., Ed., Analytical Absorption Spectroscopy, John Wiley and Sons, New York, 1950.

[6] Boltz, D. F., and Schenk, G. H., in Handbook of Analytical Chemistry, L. Meites, Ed., pp. 6-6 to 6-85, McGraw-Hill Book Co., New York, 1963.

Table 1-2. Guide in Selecting Color of Filter

Color of Solution	*Color of Filter*
Orange	Blue-green
Yellow	Blue
Purple	Green
Red	Blue
Violet	Yellow-green
Green	Purple
Blue-green	Red-orange
Blue	Yellow

is triangular, as shown in Fig. 1-3. The sensitivity of the photoelectric detector and the radiant power of the source are additional factors affecting the resolution of the spectrophotometer. The use of electron multiplier phototubes as detectors and electronic amplification of the photocurrents permit the better spectrophotometers to have spectral band widths of 0.2 to 1 mμ in the visible region. One advantage of the high resolution characteristic of good spectrophotometers is that the Bouguer-Beer relationship is based on the use of monochromatic radiant energy and, therefore, this relationship is more nearly applicable. Thus, the preparation of a series of standard solutions to prepare a calibration graph is obviated. The possibility exists of selecting a wavelength at which other absorbers do not interfere, and one can analyze a polycomponent mixture by making absorbance measurements at several selected wavelengths on the colored system.

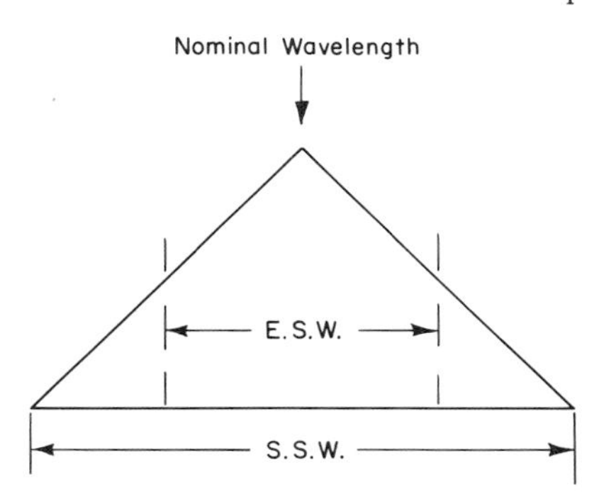

Fig. 1-3. Distribution of Radiant Energy Transmitted by a Monochromator Having Entrance and Exit Slits of Equal Widths.

Absorption Cells.— Glass absorption cells are suitable for absorbance measurements in the visible region although silica cells can also be used. For best results it is recommended that the entrance and exit sides of the cells be plane parallel surfaces. When cylindrical cells are used, the entrance and exit sides are curved and there may be slight deviations from Beer's law. Slightly lower absorbance readings may be obtained at higher concentrations due to refraction, the effect being more pronounced if the incident beam is divergent. A precaution in the use of cylindrical cells is to position each cell in the same manner for each reading so that the optical path through the cell and its contents is the same; the magnitude of this error depends on the ratio of the beam width to cell diameter and is normally small.[7] Much larger errors are likely to result by rotation of cylindrical absorption cells having variations in wall thickness.

Cell thicknesses of 1, 2, and 5 cm. are quite common. The cells with 5-cm. optical path length are suitable for measuring solutions of low absorbance provided an adequate amount of the solution is available. Cell systems are also available for insertion into rectangular cells in order to reduce the path length in measuring high absorbance systems, or when small amounts of sample are available. A special cell adapter of Teflon can be inserted in a 1-cm. rectangular cell so that the cell aperture is in alignment with

[7] Meites, L., Anal. Chim. Acta, **27**, 131, 1962.

the optical beam of Beckman spectrophotometers. Only 0.3 ml. of solution is needed for this modified cell.

Photometers.—The most essential component of the photometer is the detector of radiant energy which produces a signal proportional to the radiant power impinging upon it. There are three types of photoelectric detectors being extensively employed in modern visible spectrometry.

The photovoltaic cell, often called a barrier-layer cell, consists of a conductor in close contact with a semiconductor. Electrons are transferred at the interface from the semiconductor to metal when the semiconductor is irradiated. The electric current produced is proportional to the radiant power of the incident beam and to the area of the photosensitive surface being irradiated. This detector has a low impedance, and has sufficient sensitivity that either a microammeter or a balanced circuit using a galvanometer as a null point detector can be used to measure the current output of the cell. Because of its low impedance, electronic amplification is not feasible unless a regenerative feedback type of amplifier is used. This detector is relatively inexpensive and is most widely used in filter photometers or cheap spectrophotometers. In using this detector it should be kept in mind that the current is a linear function of the radiant power only under conditions of moderate irradiation and low external electric resistance. If this detector is subjected to a powerful beam of radiant energy, it exhibits a fatigue effect; the current output decreases with time of irradiation. The spectral response of the photovoltaic cell is very similar to the spectral sensitivity of the human eye.

The photoemissive type detector consists of a photosensitive cathode containing an alkali metal oxide, such as cesium oxide, and an anode mounted in an evacuated glass tube. The spectral response of the phototube depends on the nature of the material used as coating for the photocathode. Cathode coatings of cesium-antimony and cesium-cesium oxide on silver with spectral responses corresponding to about the 200–650 and 250–1200 mμ ranges, respectively, are suitable for measurements in the visible region. Radiant energy striking the photocathode causes photoelectrons to be emitted. The number of electrons is proportional to the radiant power of the incident beam and the maximum velocity of the electrons is directly proportional to the reciprocal of the wavelength, *i.e.*, frequency, of the incident radiant energy. These electrons are collected by the anode and a photocurrent is generated. The high impedance characteristic of this phototube facilitates electronic amplification so that beams of very low radiant power can be measured.

The electron multiplier phototube has a number of photosensitive electrodes (dynodes) each charged at a successively higher potential and so arranged that the electrons ejected from the photocathode travel successively from one electrode to the next, the photocurrent being increased in each step by the secondary emission of electrons. An amplification factor of about 10^8 is obtainable with this type of phototube and the current output can also be amplified electronically.

Instrument Design.—The mechanical, optical, and electrical systems constitute the principal design features to be considered in comparing commercial instruments used for photometric measurements. As indicated previously, the use of either a filter or a monochromator to isolate and transmit a narrow band of radiant energy from the incident light determines whether the instrument is classified as a filter photometer or a spectrophotometer. Both filter photometers and spectrophotometers may employ either a single-beam or a double-beam optical system. With the single-beam instruments a beam of radiant energy is first passed through a reference medium and either mechanical, optical, or electrical compensation is used to adjust the readout to a 100 percent transmittance or zero absorbance setting. The beam is then passed through the sample to obtain the photometric reading. The stability of the source is very important for reliable photometric measurements with a single beam instrument.

Double beam instruments utilize a beam splitting device to produce two optical beams; one beam passes through the reference cell, the other beam passes through the sample cell. Some instruments have a detector for each beam so that the ratio of the two photocurrents being produced can be measured. Other instruments use a single detector which alternately receives the signal from the reference and sample beams. A rotating sector is often employed as a beam splitter in spectrophotometers and not only alternately transmits and reflects the incident monochromatic, but does so at a definite frequency, perhaps 30 or 60 cycles per second. An a.c. amplifier tuned to this chopping frequency gives a high amplification with a minimum of noise. One commercial spectrophotometer utilizes a vibrating mirror to reflect alternately the single beam through the sample and reference absorption cells in order to obtain a double beam system. The double beam system compensates for any source fluctuations and is amenable to automatic recording. It should be pointed out that it is possible for double beam instruments to be used so that the reference beam monitors only the source and that both the reference and sample solutions could be measured alternately in the same optical path. Schematic diagrams of typical instruments for absorptimetric measurements are shown in Figs. 1-4, 1-5, and 1-6.

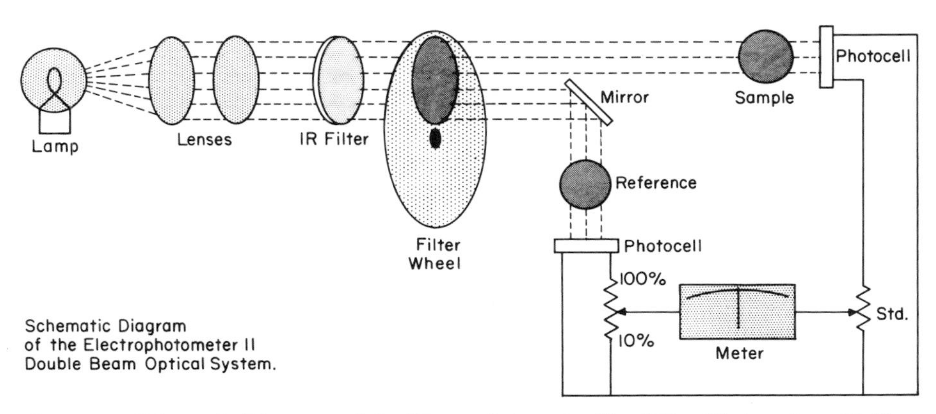

FIG. 1-4. Schematic Diagram of the Electrophotometer II, a Filter Photometer with Two Photovoltaic Cells and a Balanced Circuit which Permits Compensation for Source Fluctuations. (Reprinted through courtesy of Fisher Scientific Co.)

Another distinctive aspect of instrumentation is the nature of obtaining the photometric reading. Direct reading instruments indicate the magnitude of the output of the photoelectric detector on a deflection type meter. Constancy of the radiant power of the source and linearity for the current-irradiance ratio for the photoelectric detector are essential for reliable photometric measurements. Employment of the null balance principle in which the d.c. unbalance voltage from a potentiometer bridge circuit is detected by an electronic amplifier as the null point detector permits more precise photometric measurements. In general, the limit of the error in terms of full scale is about 1 percent for deflection type meters and about 0.3 percent for slidewires. The unbalance of the output signals from the reference and sample beams can also be counterbalanced automatically by a servosystem. A mechanical link with the servomotor records the magnitude of the compensation necessary to restore photometric balance. Thus, by synchronizing the wavelength drive with the attentuation of the output signal, an absorption spectrum is automatically recorded. Details on collimating and dispersive

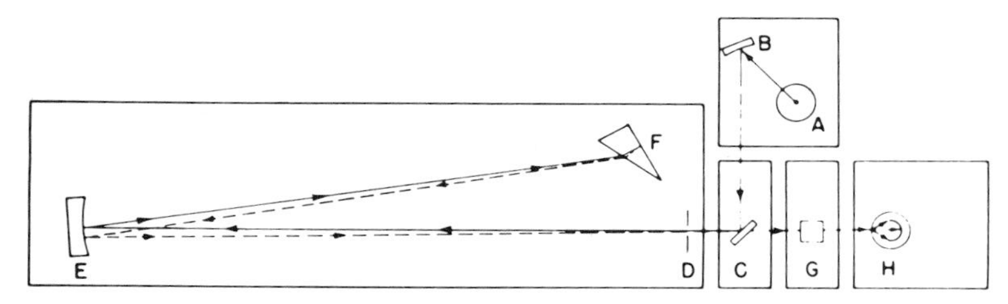

FIG. 1-5. Optical Diagram of Beckman DU Spectrophotometer, a Single Beam Spectrophotometer Having an Auto-Collimating Monochromator with Quartz Littrow Prism, Curved Bilateral Entrance and Exit Slits, and Two Interchangeable Photoemissive Type Detectors. DU is a Registered Trademark of Beckman Instruments, Inc. (Courtesy Beckman Instruments, Inc.)

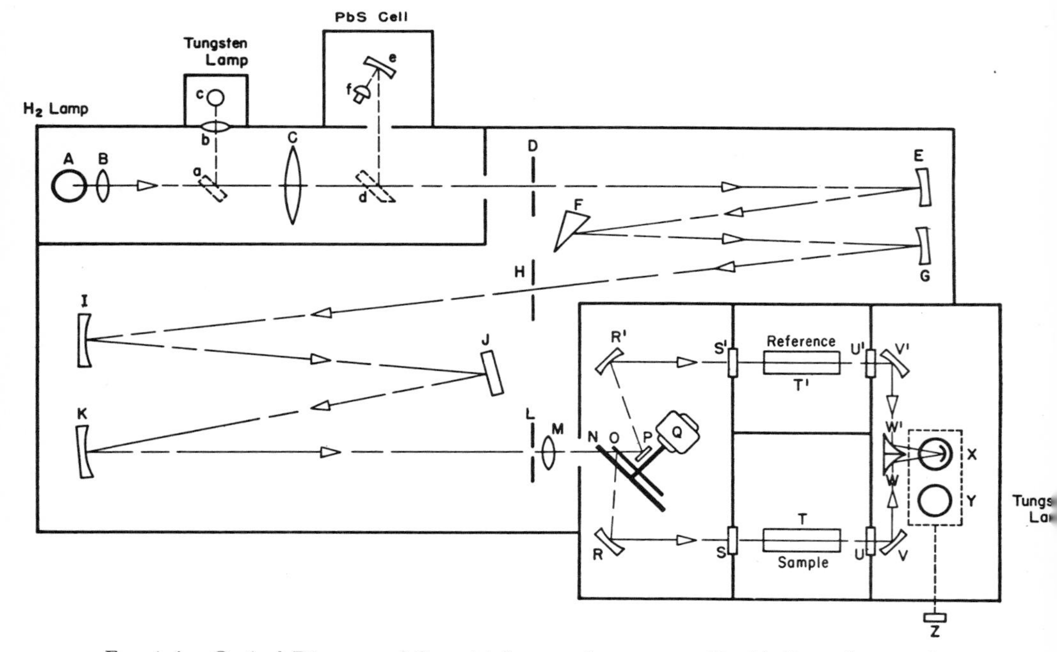

FIG. 1-6. Optical Diagram of Cary 14 Spectrophotometer, a Double Beam Spectrophotometer with a Double Monochromator Consisting of a Quartz Littrow Prism and an Echellete Grating. The Chopped Beams from the Reference and Sample Cells Irradiate Alternately a Single Electron Multiplier Phototube. (Courtesy Applied Physics Corp.)

devices, slit mechanisms, d.c. and a.c. amplifiers, and servomechanisms can be found in comprehensive references.[8,9,10]

Calibration.—In visible spectrometry, regardless of the manufacturer or the cost of the spectrophotometer, the authors recommend the calibration of the instrument in

[8] Bair, E. J., Introduction to Chemical Instrumentation, McGraw-Hill Book Co., New York, 1962.

[9] Malmstadt, H. V., Enke, C. G., and Tores, E. C., Jr., Electronics for Scientists, W. A. Benjamin, Inc., New York, 1962.

[10] Strobel, H. A., Chemical Instrumentation, Addison-Wesley Publishing Co., Reading, Mass., 1960.

certain biological substances have been observed to coat the absorption cells with a film of material which can not easily be removed by rinsing with water. Occasionally substances are light-sensitive and will exhibit a diminution of color when irradiated.

SPECIAL SPECTROPHOTOMETRIC TECHNIQUES

Differential Technique.—When colored solutions having absorbance values above 1 and transmittance of less than 10 percent, are to be measured, the photometric error can be minimized by using a differential technique, commonly called the "transmittance ratio method." [15,16] In using this precision method, the 0% T setting is made with phototube in total darkness and the 100 percent setting is made using a colored solution just slightly less concentrated than the most dilute solution to be measured. By this technique, spectrophotometric results have an accuracy comparable with titrimetric and gravimetric methods.[17]

Bastian has determined copper in copper-base alloys (60–80 percent copper) with an average deviation of about 1.5 parts per thousand by using this differential technique. Figure 1-12 shows the effective scale expansion resulting from using this differential method.

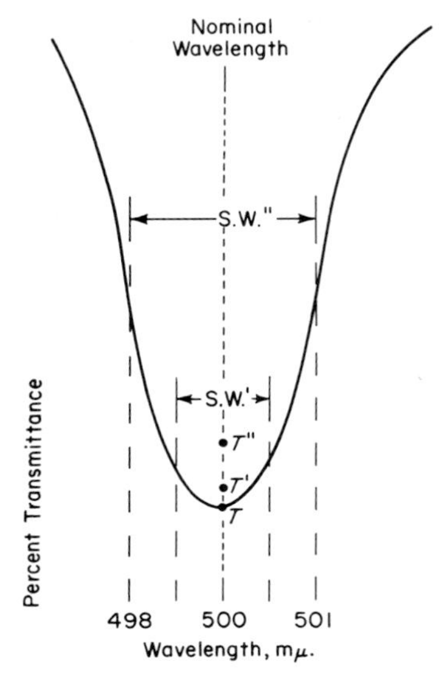

Fig. 1-11. Diagram Illustrating Finite Slit Width Effect. T' and T'' Show the Deviation of the Measured Transmittance Values from the True T Value as a Function of the Slit Width Being Used.

Multicomponent Analysis.—Under the proper conditions it is possible to determine the concentrations of two or more colored components of a solution. Ideally, each colored species would exhibit maximum absorptivity at a wavelength where the other components are optically transparent. In practice, usually one is concerned with conditions wherein each component has its maximum absorptivity at a wavelength where the other components have low absorptivities. The following procedure illustrates the application of spectrophotometric analysis to a two-component system.[18]

1. Determine the absorbance-wavelength spectrophotometric curves for standard solutions of each component. Use the same reference solution.

2. Determine the two wavelengths at which there is a maximum difference in absorbances. A plot of the ratios of absorptivities, $a\text{I}/a\text{II}$, of the two components at 5-mμ intervals is the best method of determining the appropriate wavelength, corresponding to the maximum and minimum found in the plot.

3. Plot absorbance *vs.* concentration to test for conformity to Beer's law for each component.

[15] Hiskey, C. F., *et al.*, Anal. Chem., **21,** 1440, 1949; **22,** 1464, 1950.
[16] Willard, H. H., Merritt, L. L., Jr., and Dean, J. A., Instrumental Methods of Analysis, 4th Ed., D. Van Nostrand Co., Princeton, N. J., 1965.
[17] Bastian, R., *et al.*, Anal. Chem., **21,** 972, 1949; **22,** 160, 1950.
[18] Boltz, D. F., Selected Topics in Modern Instrumental Analysis, Prentice-Hall, Inc., 1952

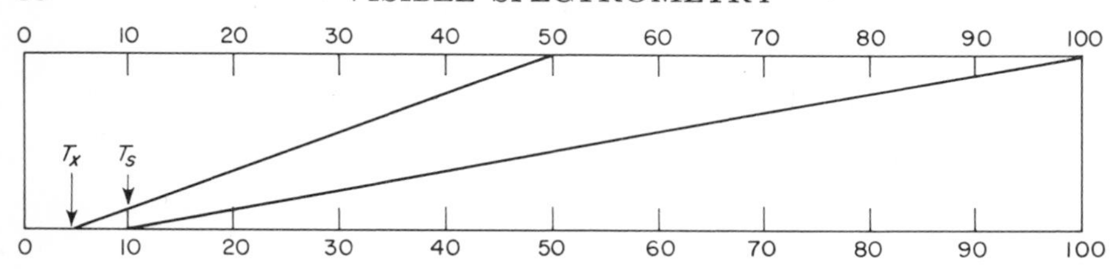

Fig. 1-12. Diagram Illustrating Scale Expansion by Using Differential Spectrophotometric Technique. (Standard and Unknown Solutions Give Transmittance Readings of 10 (T_S) and 5% (T_X), Respectively, by Conventional Technique. When the Standard Solution is Used as Reference in Adjusting the 100% Setting, the Transmittance Reading for the Unknown Solution is 50%. Thus, a 10 × Scale Expansion is Obtained by the Differential Technique.)

4. Calculate the absorptivities for each component at the selected wavelengths. Let x and y designate the two wavelengths and I and II designate the two absorbers. The following four expressions are applicable:

$$A_x^I = a_x^I bc^I \quad \text{(at } x \text{ wavelength)}$$
$$A_y^I = a_y^I bc^I \quad \text{(at } y \text{ wavelength)}$$
$$A_x^{II} = a_x^{II} bc^{II} \quad \text{(at } x \text{ wavelength)}$$
$$A_y^{II} = a_y^{II} bc^{II} \quad \text{(at } y \text{ wavelength)}$$

5. Prepare known mixtures of I and II and measure the absorbance at the two wavelengths. Plot the observed absorbances at each wavelength *vs.* the calculated absorbances. A linear plot indicates that the absorbances are additive.

6. Assuming that the absorbances are additive, the following equations apply:

$$A_x = a_y^I bc^{II} + a_x^{II} bc^{II}$$
$$A_y = a_y^I bc^I + a_y^{II} bc^{II}$$
$$(A = \text{total (measured) absorbance})$$

7. Solve these simultaneous equations for c^I and c^{II}

Typical examples of polycomponent systems are permangante-dichromate, cobalt-copper-iron thiocyantes, and vanadium-titanium-molybdenum peroxyacids.[18]

APPLICATIONS

In selecting a colorimetric method to be used in determining a constituent of a specific material, one must be especially concerned with the approximate concentration of the desired constituent and the effect of other substances present in the sample. Inasmuch as spectrophotometry is concerned so extensively with determining small amounts, it is imperative that the absorber have intrinsically high absorptivity—a large molar absorptivity. Sandell[19] has proposed a convenient method of expressing sensitivity in terms of the gamma (10^{-6} gram) of an element per milliliter of solution which gives a change in absorbance of 0.001 (approximately 0.2 percent in transmittance). Table 1-3 illustrates these two methods of expressing sensitivity.

The optimum concentration range for most colorimetric methods corresponds to

[19] Sandell, E. B., Colorimetric Determination of Traces of Metals, Interscience Publishers, New York, 1950.

solutions giving absorbance readings in the 0.1 to 1 region when using most visible spectrophotometers. However, it is desirable to determine the optimum concentration range for a specific method and a specific instrument by preparing a plot of percent

TABLE 1-3. COMPARISON OF SENSITIVITY; SPECTROPHOTOMETRIC METHODS FOR THE DETERMINATION OF PHOSPHORUS

Method	Wavelength, mμ	Optimum Concentration Range, p.p.m.	Molar Absorptivity, liter mole-cm.	Sensitivity, v./ml. = 0.001A
Heteropoly Blue[20]	830	0.1–1.2	26,800	0.00115
Modified Heteropoly Blue[21]	725	0.1–1.3	22,700	0.00137
Molybdovanadophosphate[22]	460	3–40	720	0.0431
Modified Molybdovanado-phosphate[23]	315	0.15–1.5	20,600	0.00150
Molybdophosphate[24]	400	2–25	1,300	0.0238
Modified UV. Molybdo-phosphate[25]	310	0.1–1.2	25,400	0.00122
Indirect UV. Method[26]	230	0.05–0.6	57,400	0.000541

transmittance *vs.* logarithm of the desired constituent concentration.[27,28] This Ringbom plot has a virtually linear segment of the curve corresponding to the optimum concentration range.

Foreign substances in the sample which interfere in photometric methods usually do so by forming a colored product with the reagents, if not self-colored, or they impart a turbidity to the solution. In the case of self-colored interferences it is possible to use in the reference cell a solution containing the same concentration of interfering substances as in the sample solution, and, thus, externally to compensate for the absorbance of the interfering substance. Frequently this reference solution is the sample solution diluted sufficiently to take into account the increase in volume of the analytical sample due to the addition of reagents.

When the interference reacts with the chromogenic reagents, or the desired constituent, or imparts a turbidity, the ultimate solution to the problem is to separate the desired constituent from the interfering substance. The possibility of transforming the interfering substance to a noninterfering substance should also be considered as a means of circumventing an analytical separation. Extraction, ion exchange, columnar and paper chromatography, distillation, electrodeposition, and precipitation methods of separation require special precautions in working with trace amounts.

[20] Boltz, D. F., and Mellon, M. G., Ind. Eng. Chem., Anal. Ed., **19,** 873, 1947.
[21] Lueck, C. H., and Boltz, D. F., Anal. Chem., **28,** 1168, 1956.
[22] Kitson, R. E., and Mellon, J. G., Ind. Eng. Chem, Anal. Ed., **16,** 379, 1944.
[23] Michelson, O. B., Anal. Chem., **29,** 60, 1965.
[24] Boltz, D. F., and Mellon, M. G., Anal. Chem., **20,** 749, 1948.
[25] Wadelin, C., and Mellon, M. G., Anal. Chem., **25,** 1668, 1953.
[26] Lueck, C. H., and Boltz, D. F., Anal. Chem., **30,** 183, 1958.
[27] Ayres, G. H., Ind. Eng. Chem., Anal. Ed., **21,** 652, 1949.
[28] Ringbom, Z. anal. Chem., **115,** 132, 1939.

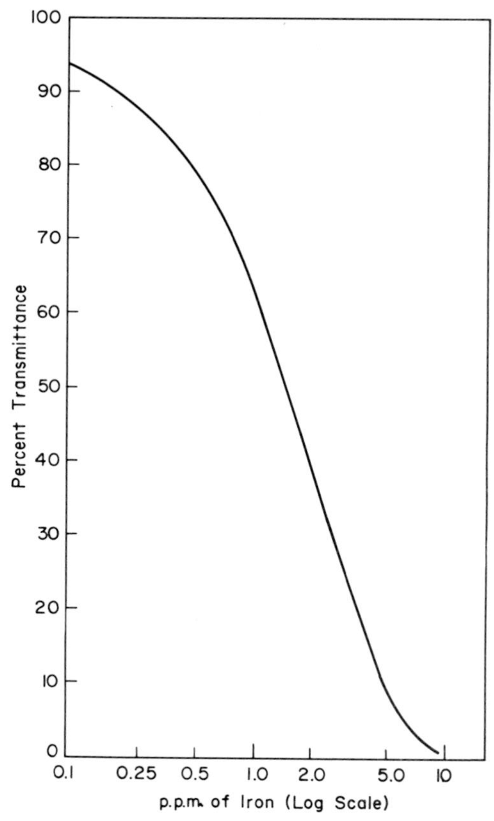

FIG. 1-13. Ringbom Plot. The Optimum Concentration Range Corresponds to the Virtually Linear Section of this Graph, *i.e.* 1–4 p.p.m. of Fe. The Percentage Relative Error per 1% Error in Transmittance Can Be Obtained from the Slope of this Graph from the Expression,

$$\frac{\%\ \text{Rel. Error}}{1\%\ \text{Trans. Error}} = \frac{230}{\Delta T/\Delta \log C}$$

A number of compilations[6,29,30,31,32,33,34] and reference works[5,12,19,35,36,37] should be

[29] American Society for Testing and Materials, 1964 ASTM Standards, Part 32, Philadelphia, 1964.

[30] Boltz, D. F., and Mellon, M. G., Anal. Chem., **36,** 256 R, 1964.

[31] Mellon, M. G., Anal. Chem., **21,** 3, 1949; **22,** 2, 1950; **23,** 2, 1951; **24,** 2, 1952; **26,** 2, 1954.

[32] Mellon, M. G., and Bly, D. D., 1959 Supplement to the Bibliography of Spectrophotometric Methods of Analysis for Inorganic Ions, Am. Soc. Testing and Materials, Spec. Tech. Publ. 125-A, Philadelphia, 1959.

[33] Mellon, M. G., and Boltz, D. F., Anal. Chem., **28,** 559, 1956; **30,** 554, 1958; **32,** 194, 1960; **34,** 232 R, 1962.

[34] Standard Methods for the Examination of Water and Wastewater, 11th Ed., Am. Public Health Assn., Inc., New York, 1960.

[35] Bauman, R. P., Absorption Spectroscopy, John Wiley and Sons, New York, 1962.

[36] Boltz, D. F., Ed., Colorimetric Determination of Nonmetals, Interscience Publishers, New York, 1958.

[37] Charlot, G., Colorimetric Determination of Elements, American Elsevier Publishing Co., New York, 1964.

consulted for detailed procedures and as primary sources of information. Some extensively used visible spectrophotometric methods are listed in Table 1-4.

TABLE 1-4. SELECTED LIST OF REPRESENTATIVE VISIBLE SPECTROMETRIC METHODS

Desired Constituent	Method or Reagent	Wavelength of Measurement, mμ	Concentration Range, p.p.m.
Aluminum	Aluminon	525	0.04–4
Ammonia	Nessler	580	2–25
Arsenic	Heteropoly Blue	840	0.3–3
Cobalt	Nitroso-R salt	425	0.1–10
Copper	Neocuproine	454	1–10
Fluoride	Zr Alizarin Red S	525	0.5–1.2
Iron	1,10-Phenanthroline	510	0.5–5
Magnesium	8-Quinolinol	400	1–5
Manganese	Periodate	545	1–25
Molybdenum	Thiocyanate	465	0.1–5
Nickel	Dimethylgloxime	445	0.2–5
Nitrate	Phenoldisulfonic acid	410	0.1–2
Phosphate	Heteropoly Blue	830	0.1–1.2
Silicate	Heteropoly Blue	820	0.1–1.5
Titanium	Peroxytitanic acid	410	7–60
Vanadium	Peroxyvanadic acid	460	20–150
Acetaldehyde	Schiff	560	1–5
Glycine	Ninhydrin	565	0–0.4
Salicylic acid	Iron (III) chelate	515	0.1–2
Urea	Diacetyl monoxime	480	8–22

A number of methods using visible spectrometry have been applied to the analysis of special materials, and are discussed or described elsewhere in Standard Methods of Chemical Analysis. These methods, listed by the type of material analyzed, are:

1. Chapter 47, Volume III, Instrumental Methods in Clinical Medicine.
   a. Albumin
   b. Acid phosphatase
   c. Alkaline phosphatase
   d. Bilirubin
   e. Calcium
   f. Carbon dioxide
   g. Chloride
   h. Total cholesterol
   i. Creatinine
   j. Glucose
   k. Hemoglobin
   l. Phosphate
   m. Protein
   n. Serum glutamic-oxalacetic transaminase
   o. Urea nitrogen
   p. Uric acid
2. Chapter 48, Volume III, Natural Fats.
   a. Copper
   b. Gossypol
   c. Iron
   d. Nickel
   e. Rancidity in fats
   f. Sesamol and sesamin
   g. Tocopherols
   h. Water-insoluble combined lactic acid
3. Chapter 49, Volume III, Fertilizers.
   a. Ammonia nitrogen
   b. Nitrate nitrogen
   c. Phosphorus

4. Chapter 50, Volume III, Foods.
   a. Additives
   b. Arsenic
   c. Calcium in flour
   d. Chemical preservatives
   e. Copper
   f. Iron in flour
   g. Lactic acid
   h. Lactose
   i. Lead
   j. Nitrates in meat and meat products
   k. Nitrites in meat and meat products
   l. Starch and sugar
   m. Vitamins

   Chapter 33, Volume IIB, Natural Fats.
   a. Determination of reconstituted fatty acids, page 1470
5. Chapter 59, Volume III, Rubber and Rubber Products.
   a. Amine antioxidants
   b. Antioxidants
   c. Organic acid in SBR
   d. Phenolic antioxidants
   e. Tetramethylthiuram disulfide accelerators
   f. Zinc oxide filler
6. Chapter 61, Volume III, Soaps and Synthetic Detergents.
   a. Biodegradability in detergents
   b. Copper in soap
   c. Iron in syndets
   d. Sodium carboxymethylcellulose in syndets
   e. Surfactants
7. Chapter 63, Volume III, Water Analysis.
   a. Color of water

   Chapter 48, Volume IIB, Water Analysis.
   a. Aluminum, page 2401
   b. Arsenic, page 2402
   c. Boron, page 2406
   d. Cadmium, page 2407
   e. Chlorine, residual, page 2416
   f. Chromium, page 2423
   g. Copper, page 2426
   h. Cyanide, page 2430
   i. Fluoride, page 2431
   j. Iron, page 2435
   k. Lead, page 2436
   l. Magnesium, page 2440
   m. Manganese, page 2441
   n. Nitrogen, pages 2449, 2453, 2454
   o. Nitrate, pages 2445, 2447
   p. Nitrite, page 2448
   q. Phenols, page 2464
   r. Phosphate, page 2467
   s. Selenium, page 2474
   t. Silicon, page 2476
   u. Sulfide, page 2486
   v. Anionic surfactants, page 2489
   w. Tannin and lignin, page 2492
   x. Zinc, pages 2496, 2499
8. Chapter 64, Volume III, Determination of Water.

Visible spectrometry is used to determine water in bauxite, cereals, gases, halides, hydrocarbons, jet fuels, ketones, sawdust, and soya bean mash.

Chapter 2

ULTRAVIOLET SPECTROMETRY

By David F. Boltz
Department of Chemistry
Wayne State University
Detroit, Michigan

The ultraviolet region of the electromagnetic spectrum is frequently subdivided into the far or vacuum ultraviolet region, approximately 10 to 200 mμ, and the near ultraviolet region which extends from 200 mμ to 400 mμ. This classification is somewhat arbitrary. Oxygen and water vapor absorb below 195 mμ and must be eliminated from the optical path if absorbance measurements are to be made in the far ultraviolet region. Purging of the optical system with nitrogen gas permits absorbance measurements to be made to about 170 mμ, but below this wavelength it is necessary to evacuate the monochromator. There have been many recent interesting advances in vacuum ultraviolet spectrometry, especially in respect to the development of suitable sources, monochromators, and detectors. However, there have not been sufficient analytical applications to warrant including a discussion of vacuum ultraviolet spectrometry in this chapter. Kaye has reviewed certain fundamental considerations when working in the 170 to 200 mμ region of the ultraviolet region, has tabulated many references to the far ultraviolet spectra of inorganic and organic compounds, and has pointed out some of the potential analytical applications of far ultraviolet spectrometry.[1]

The utilization of near ultraviolet absorption spectra as an analytical tool has increased extensively as recording ultraviolet spectrophotometers have become more available, and as ultraviolet spectra have been collected and documented. Inasmuch as the fundamental principles of spectrophotometry have already been discussed in Chapter 1, "Visible Spectrometry," and are applicable to the ultraviolet region, this chapter will be confined primarily to a consideration of: (1) the nature of the ultraviolet absorption process; (2) ultraviolet spectrophotometers; (3) special methodology; and (4) specific analytical applications.

ORIGIN OF ULTRAVIOLET ABSORPTION SPECTRA

It is not within the scope of this introduction to ultraviolet spectrometry to discuss the principles of molecular spectroscopy involving group theory, quantum mechanics, etc. The analytical chemist is interested in the nature of the process responsible for absorption spectra and the correlation of characteristic spectra with specific structures and substances. However, the rigorous mathematical treatment of the spectral properties and electronic states of complex molecular species is not essential for the utilization of these absorption spectra in chemical analysis. Hence, only a few descriptive generalizations related to the nature of the absorption process will be given.

Ultraviolet absorption spectra are attributed to a process in which the outer electrons

[1] Kaye, W. L., Appl. Spectroscopy, **15**, 89, 130, 1961.

of atoms, or molecules, absorb radiant energy and undergo transitions to higher energy levels. These electronic transitions are quantized and depend on the electronic structure of the absorber. The magnitude of these discrete energy changes increases as the spectral position of the corresponding absorbance maximum goes from the visible to the shorter wavelength region. Thus, whereas perhaps 50,000 calories per mole may be involved for an absorption band in the visible region, 100,000 calories per mole are required for an absorption band in the ultraviolet region. The wavelength at which an ultraviolet absorbance maximum is found depends on the magnitude of the energy involved for a specific electronic transition. The molar absorptivity depends on the rate at which the absorber is absorbing radiant energy from the incident beam. When the absorber is in the gaseous state, the vibrational and rotational transitions may also contribute to the characteristic absorption spectrum. The fine vibrational structure characteristic of a vapor usually disappears when the substance is dissolved in a solvent due to perturbation by the solvent molecules. The effect of the solvent on ultraviolet absorption spectra of certain solutes is often quite pronounced.

In the case of inorganic ions and molecules, the transitions may be between two electronic states of the individual atoms, or there may be a partial electron transfer from ligand to the central ion resulting in a charge-transfer absorption spectrum. It is possible for both the electronic transitions and the electron transfer process to contribute to the absorption spectrum of a substance. The ultraviolet absorption spectra of the hexahalide complexes of a number of metal ions have been explained on the basis of the molecular orbital configurations, and are examples of electron transfer spectra.[2] Perhaps certain peroxy complexes owe their ultraviolet absorptivity to the electron transfer between the ligand and the interacting metal ion.

Several types of transitions involving both bonding and nonbonding electrons are possible with organic substances. The transitions of electrons which form single bonds (σ electrons) from one orbital to a higher energy orbital give absorption bands in the far ultraviolet. Thus, *n*-heptane is optically transparent in the near ultraviolet region, and is an excellent solvent for organic ultraviolet spectrometry. It can be used as a solvent for measurements as low as 170 mμ provided a short cell thickness, *e.g.*, 0.03 mm., is used and dissolved oxygen is removed.[1] The transitions of the electrons which form double and triple bonds (the π electrons) gives absorption bands in the ultraviolet region. The olefins in vapor phase have an absorbance maximum at about 180 mμ in the far ultraviolet. Aromatic hydrocarbons have characteristic ultraviolet absorption spectra due to their π electrons. If there is conjugation of double bonds, the orbital size is extended and the absorbance maximum shifts to a longer wavelength.

Butadiene has an absorbance maximum at 217 mμ, and isoprene has an absorbance maximum at 220 mμ. A 3-mμ displacement toward the longer wavelength is the result of the substitution of a methyl group for a hydrogen.[3] Such a shift of an absorbance maximum to a higher wavelength is called a *bathochromic* shift. A displacement to a lower wavelength is a *hypsochromic* shift. If there is an enhancement in absorptivity as the result of structural modification, the term *hyperchromic* effect is applicable. If there is a diminution in absorptivity, the term *hypochromic* effect is used. Organic molecules containing hetero atoms (nitrogen, oxygen, and sulfur) have nonbonding electrons which may undergo transitions to high energy molecular orbitals to give ultraviolet absorption spectra.[4] Ketones exhibit an absorbance maximum at about 280 mμ and have additional maxima in the far ultraviolet. Acetone is reported to have absorbance maxima at 277

[2] Jorgensen, C. K., Absorption Spectra and Chemical Bonding in Complexes, Pergamon Press, New York, 1962, pp. 146–172.

[3] Woodward, J., J. Am. Chem. Soc., **64,** 72, 1942.

[4] Sidman, J. W., Chem. Revs., **58,** 689, 1958.

and 190 mμ for two different transitions involving nonbonding electrons.[5] Charge transfer spectra are also observed for organic and complexes[6,7] Mesitylene forms a 1:1 complex with iodine.

A group of atoms giving an absorbance maximum in the visible region was called a chromophore, or chromophoric group, by the early organic chemists working with dyes. Any group of atoms whose electronic transitions involve sufficient energy that their maximum absorptivity occurs in the ultraviolet region are also called chromophores. In an analogous manner, any substituent which has an appreciable effect either on the position of the absorbance maximum and/or on the magnitude of the absorptivity is called an auxochrome group. The relative acidic nature of the auxochrome group, the polarity of the substituent, the possibility of resonance-stabilization, hydrogen bonding, and steric hindrance may affect the spectral position and shape of an absorbance maximum due to a specific chromophore. The polarity of the solvent may also influence the spectral position and absorptivity due to a certain electronic transition.

ULTRAVIOLET SPECTROPHOTOMETERS

Upon the introduction of the Beckman DU® spectrophotometer with its quartz optics and ultraviolet accessory unit, the chemist was able for the first time to obtain reliable ultraviolet absorption spectra conveniently and within a reasonable time. With the advent of automatic recording and many improvements in instrumentation, there are now a number of excellent commercially available ultraviolet spectrophotometers which are capable of meeting all of the requirements of the analytical chemist. Certain characteristic design and operational features of ultraviolet spectrophotometers will be considered.

Hydrogen discharge lamps with quartz windows provide a continuous spectrum of radiant energy in the 185- to 375-mμ region. In one type of discharge lamp, the hydrogen in the tube is bombarded by electrons being emitted by a heated cathode filament; the excited electrons of the gas then emit the continuum when they return to their ground state. A deuterium lamp produces an ultraviolet continuum having a very high radiant power, several times that of the hydrogen lamp. The d.c. voltage of the electric supply to these lamps is rigorously controlled by electronic voltage regulators to ensure a controlled discharge. Most ultraviolet sources are surrounded by a jacket through which cooling water flows. These ultraviolet lamps have a limited life expectancy which depends somewhat upon operating conditions. Deterioration of the ultraviolet lamp is often indicated by the necessity of using much wider slit widths and a higher wavelength cut-off. A collimating mirror or lens is mounted opposite the exit window of the source lamp in order to condense the energy and provide rectilinear radiant energy to the monochromator. Several source units also incorporate a mercury discharge lamp which can be used to periodically check the accuracy of the wavelength scale. Most commercial spectrophotometers are designed so that the ultraviolet lamps and the tungsten lamp, for visible spectrometry, can be rapidly interchanged. All of the instruments cited in Table 2-1 employ the hydrogen discharge lamp-tungsten lamp combination unless otherwise designated.

Monochromators for radiant energy of the ultraviolet region cannot have glass optics so that either prisms of quartz or fused silica, or echlette gratings must be used as the dispersive device. Littrow prisms are quite extensively used in prism monochromators because they provide the maximum dispersion with a minimum expenditure of optical

[5] Rao, C. N. R., Ultraviolet and Visible Spectroscopy, Butterworths, London, 1961.
[6] Andrews, L. J., Keefer, R. M., J. Am. Chem. Soc., **74**, 4500, 1952.
[7] Benesi, H. A., Hildebrand, J. H., J. Am. Chem. Soc., **71**, 2703, 1949.

TABLE 2-1. SELECTED LIST OF ULTRAVIOLET SPECTROPHOTOMETERS

Manufacturer and Model	*Design Features*
Bausch and Lomb, Spectronic 505	Double grating monochromator Range: 200–700 mμ Double beam, photomultiplier, recording, mercury lamp for wavelength check, automatic change in rate of wavelength scan in proportion to change in absorbance
Beckman DU-2	Single prism monochromator Range: 210–1000 mμ Single beam, photomultiplier (or red and blue sensitive phototubes) null balance readout
Beckman DB	Single prism monochromator Range: 205–770 mμ Double beam, photomultiplier, direct readout or recording
Beckman Std. DK-2A	Single prism monochromator Range: 185–3500 mμ Double beam, photomultiplier, recording
Beckman Far UV DK-2A	Single prism monochromator Range: 160–3500 mμ Double beam, special photomultiplier recording
Cary 11	Double prism monochromator Range: 200–800 mμ Double beam, dual photomultipliers recording
Cary 14	Double, prism-grating monochromator Range: 186–2600 mμ Double beam, single photomultiplier, recording
Cary 15	Double prism monochromator Range: 185–800 mμ Double beam, dual photomultipliers, recording
Hilger Uvispek	Single prism monochromator Range: 185–,1000 mμ Single beam, interchangeable photoemissive detectors, null-balance readout
Hitachi Perkin-Elmer 139	Single grating onochromator Range: 195–800 mμ Single beam, transistorized power supply, photomultiplier, direct readout
Perkin-Elmer 202	Single prism monochromator Range: 190–390, 350–750 mμ Double beam, photomultiplier optical-null recording
Shimadzu QV-50	Double prism monochromator Range: 175–2700 mμ Double beam, dual photomultipliers, recording, deuterium lamp, scale expander
Unicam SP 500	Single prism monochromator Range: 185–1000 mμ Single beam, interchangeable photoemissive detectors, null-balance readout

TABLE 2-1 (cont.)

Manufacturer and Model	*Design Features*
Unicam SP 700	Single prism monochromator (Grating for near infrared) Range: 186–3600 mμ Double beam, photomultiplier, recording
Unicam SP 800	Single prism monochromator Range: 190–850 mμ Double beam, photomultiplier, optical null balance recording
Zeiss PMQ II	Single prism monochromator Range: 200–1100 mμ Single beam, photomultiplier, direct readout
Zeiss RPQ 20 A	Single prism monochromator Range: 200–2500 mμ Double beam, photomultiplier, ratio recording

NOTE.—Lower wavelength limit may require purging optical system with nitrogen. When instrument is used for near infrared measurements, a different detector may be used.

material (see Fig. 2-1). The back surface of the prism is aluminized normal to the optic axis. Synthetic quartz is usually used for optics when measurements are to be made below 200 mμ. Double Littrow prism, Littrow prism-echlette grating, single grating, and double grating monochromators have been utilized in commercial spectrophotometers.

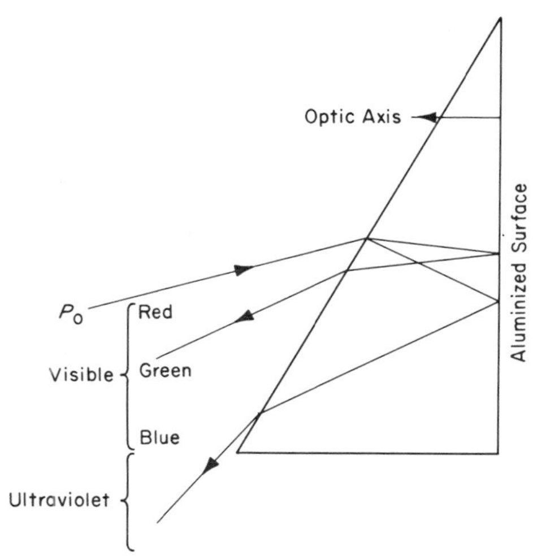

FIG. 2-1. Littrow Prism.

Two important considerations in evaluating the performance of spectrophotometers which are related to the design of the monochromator are (1) the amount of stray radiant energy, and (2) the resolution. The radiant energy which reaches the detector at wavelengths which do not correspond to the spectral position selected is termed "stray radiation." Double monochromator instruments usually have less than 0.001 percent stray radiant energy except at the very extremes of their wavelength range where it is unlikely to exceed 0.1 percent. Well designed single monochromator instruments have less than 0.1 percent stray radiant energy except in extreme lower wavelength region; this value may then approach 1 percent. Resolution is considered to be the difference in wavelengths of two absorbance maxima which can just be detected as being two discrete absorption bands. Double monochromators have resolutions of the order of 0.1 mμ in the near ultraviolet region, while the resolving power of single monochromators will be about 0.2–0.5 mμ. The resolution of a spectrophotometer depends on the use of narrow slit widths and is, therefore, dependent on the radiant power of the source, the sensitivity of the detectors, and the gain of the amplifier. Front-surfaced, aluminized mirrors are used for collimating and condensing optical beams in order to minimize selective absorption and reflection losses.

Absorption cells for ultraviolet spectrometry are fabricated with silica optical windows. The sample and reference absorption cells should be matched in respect to optical path-length and transmittance at specific wavelengths. It is especially important to remember that even though two cells have identical lengths, transmittance characteristics may be quite different in the ultraviolet region, unless they were purchased as matched cells. Several of the commercial spectrophotometers have electrical compensation systems coupled to the wavelength scanning mechanism so that by adjustment of a number of "multipots," each corresponding to a specific wavelength, it is possible to compensate electrically to zero absorbance, and thus eliminate variations in the spectral transmittance of the two absorption cells. This compensation method also corrects for differences in the spectral response characteristics of the two phototubes used to monitor the reference and sample beams and for differences in the optical efficiency of two optical paths in the case of certain instruments. Therefore, it is especially important in ultraviolet spectrophotometric measurements to mark each cell and consistently use one as the reference cell and the other one as the sample cell. For spectrophotometric measurements below 200 mμ, absorption cells with special silica windows are available. Absorptions cells with 1-cm., internal optical path length are used extensively. Cells with path lengths of 0.1, 0.5, 2.5, and 10 cm. are available commercially.

Ultraviolet spectrophotometers use either vacuum photoemissive phototubes or electron multiplier phototubes as detectors. The photocathode surfaces are coated with antimony-cesium or other elements having high sensitivity to ultraviolet radiant energy. The photocurrent output of these detectors is amplified. In the case of many single beam instruments, a d.c. amplifier is employed with either the output read on a deflection type meter or the resulting voltage drop across a resistor balanced by a potentiometer calibrated in transmittance and/or absorbance. In double beam operation, the chopping of the optical beams gives a signal which favors the utilization of a.c. amplification. The ratio of two signals may give a direct readout on a meter or the difference in signal can cause the pen motor of a recorder to adjust the slide wire position in order to attenuate the reference signal. The magnitude of the potentiometer slidewire of adjustment is proportional to difference in the output from the two signals. Several instruments attenuate the reference optical beam in order to obtain null balance recording. In general, the use of photomultipliers, a.c. amplification, and double beam operation can give a photometric accuracy of about 0.005 absorbance unit in the middle of the 0–1 absorbance range. Better resolution is also obtainable in examining solutions exhibiting high ultraviolet absorptivities with these highly sensitive photometers. Several instruments incorporate a scale expansion device which permits one to expand the readout by definite factors, *e.g.*, 10×. Hence, weak absorption spectra can be expanded in order to improve the delineation of the absorbance maxima or transmittance minima.

SPECIAL METHODOLOGY IN ULTRAVIOLET SPECTROMETRIC ANALYSIS

The general procedure for preparing a solution for ultraviolet measurements is quite similar to that followed in visible spectrometry. However, there are several unique aspects related to ultraviolet absorbers and these shall be considered. Because the solutions exhibiting ultraviolet absorptivity may be colorless, one can not estimate the concentration of absorber by visual examination. Thus, prepared solutions may be much too concentrated for reliable measurements and a number of trial and error dilutions are necessary. The interference due to substances other than the desired constituent exhibiting ultraviolet absorptivity must likewise be considered, as well as the transparency of the solvent in the ultraviolet region. Suitable solvents have been tabulated in Table 2-2.

TABLE 2-2. SELECTED LIST OF SOLVENTS FOR ULTRAVIOLET SPECTROMETRY

Solvent	Lower Wavelength Limit,[a] $m\mu$	Solvent	Lower Wavelength Limit,[a] $m\mu$
Acetic acid	270	Ethyl acetate	260
Acetone	330	Ethyl formate	265
Acetonitrile	212	Glycerol	230
Amyl acetate	260	*n*-Hexane	210
Benzene	280	*n*-Heptane	210
Butanol	220	Isooctane	210
n-Butyl acetate	260	Methanol	210
Carbon tetrachloride	260	Methylcyclohexane	210
Chloroform	240	Methyl formate	260
Cyclohexane	210	*i*-Propyl alcohol	210
1,2-Dichloroethane	235	Pyridine	300
Dichloromethane	233	Sulfuric acid (96%)	210
Diethyl ether	220	Tetrachloroethylene	295
N,*N*-dimethylformamide	270	Toluene	285
p-Dioxane	220	Water	210
Ethanol	220	*m*-Xylene	290

[a] Based on the use of 1-cm. absorption cells.

Certain solutes have a tendency to plate out on the inside of the fused silica absorption cells, and, in the case of colorless solutes, serious errors may result unless special care is taken to keep the cells scrupulously clean and to check with blank determinations. Impurities on the outside of the absorptions cells due to skin oils and perspiration deposited by handling in the filling operation can be troublesome.

The influence of the solvent on the ultraviolet absorption spectrum of a substance has been indicated previously and this phenomenon can be utilized in certain practical applications. For example, phenols can be determined by a differential technic in which the difference in the spectra obtained with alcoholic and basic aqueous solutions not only indicates the concentration of the phenolic compound but is helpful in identifying the phenolic compound.[8] High molecular weight materials have been examined by

[8] Wexler, A. S., Anal. Chem., **35**, 1936, 1963.

ultraviolet spectrometry by dispersing them in melted polyethylene and pressing between metal foil to give a film suitable for mounting between two metal rings.[9] The potassium bromide pellet technic has also been used in preparing samples for ultraviolet spectrometric measurements but scattering is a problem.[10] A potential source of error is related to the property of certain metal chelates and organic substances to fluoresce when irradiated with ultraviolet radiant energy.[11] Placement of the absorption cell several centimeters from the phototube minimizes this error.

ANALYTICAL APPLICATIONS

Ultraviolet spectrophotometric methods have been applied rather extensively to the identification of aromatic hydrocarbons, vitamins, steroids, heterocyclics, and conjugated aliphatics. In biochemical and pharmaceutical research, ultraviolet absorption spectra are often used to identify degradation products and to test for purity. The detection of characteristic ultraviolet absorption bands of contaminants is used as a guide to purity while the constancy of molar absorptivity at a specific wavelength upon additional purification steps is indicative of purity. In qualitative analysis, the correlation of ultraviolet absorption bands with specific structures is made chiefly by analogy. Table 2-3 lists several common chromophoric groups and the approximate wavelengths of maximum absorbance. The analytical chemist seldom uses an ultraviolet absorption spectrum as singular confirmation of a specific substance as being present in a solution. Because of the influence of solvent, pH, temperature, and other solution variables on absorption spectra, and the fact that quite dissimilar substances may give almost identical ultraviolet spectra, it is necessary to utilize additional diagnostic techniques and methods in the identification of specific absorbers. One technique consists of comparing the relative magnitude of the absorbance maxima and minima at specific wavelengths for the spectra of solutions for which one is trying to ascertain whether the ultraviolet absorption spectra are due in the same absorber. The changing of solvents, especially in respect to dielectric strength and acid-base character, or the use of mixed solvents, is another approach by which one can obtain further evidence as to the identicalness of two solutes on the basis of their similarity of spectra.

In qualitative analytical studies, collections of spectra and indexes of ultraviolet spectra are extremely useful. Thus, The American Petroleum Institute Project 44, and the Sadtler,[12] and the Lang[13] collections of spectra are available. Several volumes entitled "Organic Electronic Spectral Data,"[14,15] the ASTM E-13 IBM cards[16] and an Index[17] are recommended for those concerned with the identification of organic compounds.

Many inorganic substances can be determined by ultraviolet spectrometry. A sensitive method for determining lead in bone ash involves the measurement of the tetrachloro-

[9] McDonald, F. R., Cook, G. L., Applied Spectroscopy, **15,** 110, 1961.

[10] Friedel, R. A., Queiser, J. A., Fuel, **38,** 369, 1959.

[11] Stearns, E. I., Analytical Absorption Spectroscopy, M. G. Mellon, Ed., John Wiley, New York, 1950, p. 306.

[12] Sadtler Research Laboratories, Sadtler Standard Spectra; Ultraviolet, Philadelphia, Pennsylvania.

[13] Lang, L., Absorption Spectra in the Ultraviolet and Visible Region, Vols. II, III, and IV, Academic Press, Budapest, Hungary, 1961, 1962, 1963.

[14] Kamlet, M. J., Ed., Organic Electronic Spectral Date, Vol. 1, 1946–52, Interscience Publishers, New York, 1960.

[15] Ungnade, H. E., Organic Electronic Spectral Date, Vol. 2, 1953–55, Interscience Publishers, New York, 1960.

[16] Am. Soc. Testing and Materials, Committee E-13, J. Opt. Soc. Am., **47,** 672, 1957.

[17] Hershenson, H. M., Ultraviolet and Visible Spectra: Index for 1930–54, 1956; Index for 1955–59, 1961; Academic Press, New York.

TABLE 2-3. SELECTED LIST OF CHROMOPHORIC GROUPS[5,18,19]

Group	*Approximate Wavelength of Absorbance Maximum, mμ*
C≡N	170
C≡C	180
C=C	190
C=N	190
—COOH	210
C=C—C=C	220
$—NO_2$	270
$C_6H_5^-$ (Phenyl)	270
C=O	280
$C_{10}H_7^-$ (Naphthyl)	310
C_9H_7N (Quinoline)	310
C=S	330
N=N	370
—ON=O	370

lead(II) ion at 271 mμ after the iron(III) and copper(II) ions have been removed by extracting with triiso-octylamine.[20] A Teflon-coated, stainless steel absorption cell with sapphire windows has been used to determine fluorine in fluorine-oxygen mixtures by measuring the absorbance due to the fluorine at 278 mμ.[21] Ammonia has been determined indirectly by a method in which ammonia is oxidized by hypobromite and the differential absorbance of the sample relative to that of a reference standard is measured at 330 mμ.[22] Other ultraviolet spectrometric methods for the metals and nonmetals are listed in Table 2-4.

Ultraviolet spectrometry has been applied very extensively to the determination of organic substances. Unsaturated hydrocarbons, alcohols, ethers, and amines exhibit near ultraviolet absorptivity, especially if conjugation of multiple bonds exists. Alpha-eleostearic acid absorbs strongly at 270 mμ, while other fatty acids have characteristic ultraviolet absorption spectra. Hence, the analysis of fats, oils, and soaps involves numerous ultraviolet methods.[23,24,25] Monosubstituted and disubstituted acetylenic compounds have been determined by forming mercury(II) addition compounds and measuring the ultraviolet absorbance of these addition compounds.[26] Vitamin A can be assayed by measuring its absorbance at 324 mμ. Steroids, enzymes, pharmaceuticals, and many other substances of interest to the biochemist can be determined by ultraviolet spectrometry. Often analytical separations are necessary prior to spectrophotometric measurement. In the analysis of ACP tablets, it is necessary to extract the aspirin from the chloroform solution with a sodium bicarbonate solution, leaving the phenacetin and caffeine in the chloroform. The aspirin is extracted from the acidified aqueous solution with chloroform,

[18] Jaffe, H. H., Orchin, M., Theory and Applications of Ultraviolet Spectroscopy, John Wiley, New York, 1962.
[19] Schilt, A. A., Treatise on Analytical Chemistry, Part I, Vol. 5, Kolthoff, I. M., and Elving, P. J., Eds., Interscience Publishers, New York, 1964, pp. 2945–2979.
[20] Ilcewicz, F. H., Holtzman, R. B., Lucas, H. F., Jr., Anal. Chem., **36,** 1132, 1964.
[21] Kaye, S., Koency, J. E., Anal. Chem, **36,** 1838, 1964.
[22] Howell, J. A., Boltz, D. F., Anal. Chem., **36,** 1799, 1964.
[23] Brice, B. A., Swain, M. L., J. Opt. Soc. Am., **35,** 532, 1945.
[24] Brice, B. A., Swain, M. L., Schaeffer, B. B., Ault, W. C., Oil and Soap, **22,** 219, 1945.
[25] Kass, J. P., Protective and Decorative Coatings, J. J. Mattiello, Ed., Volume IV, John Wiley, New York, 1944, p. 362.
[26] Siggia, S., Stahl, C. R., Anal. Chem., **35,** 1740, 1963.

TABLE 2.4. SELECTED LIST OF ULTRAVIOLET SPECTROPHOTOMETRIC METHODS FOR INORGANIC SUBSTANCES

Constituent	*Method or Reagent*	*Wavelength, mμ*	*Reference*[a]
Al	8-Hydroxyquinaldine	389	(1)
As	12-Molybdoarsenic acid	370	(2)
Au	Bromoaurate	380	(3)
B	Chromotropic acid	316.5	(4)
Be	Sulfosalicylate	317	(5)
Bi	Iodide	337	
	Thiourea	322	(6)
Br	Palladium(II) sulfate	230, 390	(7)
BrO^-	—	330	(8)
Ca	Naphthalhydroxamate	339	(9)
Cl_2			(10)
Cl^-	Palladium(II) sulfate	230, 390	(11)
Ce	Hydrogen peroxide	304	
	Peroxydisulfate	320	(12)
Co	Thiocyanate	312	(13)
	Hydrogen peroxide	260	(14)
	Isonitrodimedon		(15)
Cu	Dipyrophosphatocuprate(II)	241	(16)
Cd	Diethyldithiocarbamate	262	(17)
Fe	Iron(III) perchlorate	240, 260	(18)
	Iron(III) chloride	342.5	(19)
Hg	Thiocyanate	281	(20)
I^-	Iodine	352	(21)
Ir	EDTA	313	(22)
K	Tetraphenylborate	266, 274	(23)

[a] Parenthetical numbers refer to the following list of references:

1 Hynek, R. J., Wrangell, L. J., Anal. Chem., **28,** 1520, 1956.
2 Desesa, M. A., Rogers, L. B., Anal. Chim. Acta, **6,** 534, 1952; Anal. Chem., **26,** 1381, 1954.
3 McBryde, W. A. E., Yee, J. H., Anal. Chem., **20,** 1094, 1948.
4 Kuemmel, D. F., Mellon, M. G., Anal. Chem., **29,** 378, 1957.
5 Meek, H. V., Banks, C. V., Anal. Chem., **22,** 1512, 1950.
6 Lisicki, N. M., Boltz, D. F., Anal. Chem., **27,** 1722, 1955.
7 Chapman, F. W., Jr., Sherwood, R. M., Anal. Chem., **29,** 172, 1957.
8 Howell, J. A., Boltz, D. F., Anal. Chem., **36,** 1799, 1964.
9 Banerjee, D. K., Budke, C. C., Miller, F. D., Anal. Chem, **33,** 418, 1961.
10 Spurny, Z., Talanta, **9,** 885, 1962.
11 Chapman, F. W., Jr., Sherwood, R. M., Anal. Chem., **29,** 172, 1957.
12 Medalia, A. I., Byrne, B. J., Anal. Chem., **23,** 453, 1951.
13 Lundquist, R., Markle, G. E., Boltz, D. F., Anal. Chem., **27,** 1731, 1955.
14 Telep, G., Boltz, D. F., Anal. Chem., **24,** 945, 1952.
15 Vanden Bossche, W., Hoste, J., Anal. Chim. Acta, **18,** 564, 1958.
16 Nebel, M. L., Boltz, D. F., Anal. Chem., **36,** 144, 1964.
17 Havlena, E. J., Boltz, D. F., Anal. Chim. Acta, **30,** 565, 1964.
18 Bastian, R., Weberling, R., Palilla, F., Anal. Chem., **28,** 459, 1956.
19 Desesa, M. A., Rogers, L. B., Anal. Chim. Acta, **6,** 534, 1952; Anal. Chem., **26,** 1381, 1954.
20 Markle, G. E., Boltz, D. F., Anal. Chem., **26,** 447, 1954.
21 Custer, J. J., Natelson, S., Anal. Chem., **21,** 1005, 1949.
22 MacNevin, W. M., Kriege, O. H., Anal. Chem., **28,** 16, 1956.
23 Pflaum, R. T., Howick, L. C., Anal. Chem., **28,** 1542, 1956.

TABLE 2-4 (cont.)

Constituent	*Method or Reagent*	*Wavelength, mμ*	*Reference*[a]
Mg	8-Quinolinol	380	(24)
Mo	Peroxymolybdic acid	338	(25)
	Thiocyanate	320	(26)
	Chloranilic acid	350	(27)
Nb	Thiocyanate	385	(28)
	Hydrogen peroxide	342	(29)
NH_3	Indirect, Hypobromide	330	(30)
Ni	β-Mercaptopropionic acid	330	(31)
	Diethyldithiocarbamate	325	(32)
NO_3^-	—	210	(33)
Pb	Chloroplumbite	270	(34)
PO_4^{-3}	Molybdovanadophosphoric acid	315	(35)
	Indirect	230	(36)
	Modified molybdophosphoric acid	310	(37)
Rare earths	Direct		(38)
Re	Hexachlororhenate	281.5	(39)
Sb	Iodide	330	(40)
Sc	8-Quinolinol	378	(41)
Si	Indirect, molybdosilicic acid	230	(42)
Ta	Pyrogallol	325	(43)
	Hydroquinone	375	(44)
Te	Iodotellurite	335	(45)
Ti	Ascorbic acid	360	(46)
Tl	Hydrochloric acid	245	(47)
	Indirect, iodine	352	(48)
NO_2^-	4-Aminobenzenesulfonic acid	270	(49)

[a] Parenthetical numbers refer to the following list of references:

24 Weber, W. J., Morris, J. C., Stumm, W., Anal. Chem., **34,** 1844, 1962.
25 Telep, G., Boltz, D. F., Anal. Chem., **22,** 1030, 1950.
26 Markle, G. E., Boltz, D. F., Anal. Chem., **25,** 1261, 1953.
27 Waterbury, G. R., Bricker, C. E., Anal. Chem., **29,** 129, 1957.
28 Lauw-Zecha, A. B., Lord, S. S., Jr., Hume, D. N., Anal. Chem., **24,** 1169, 1952.
29 Telep, G., Boltz, D. F., Anal. Chem., **24,** 163, 1952.
30 Howell, J. A., Boltz, D. F., Anal. Chem., **36,** 1799, 1964.
31 Lear, J. B., Mellon, M. G., Anal. Chem., **25,** 1411, 1953.
32 Cluett, M. L., Yoe, J. H., Anal. Chem., **29,** 1265, 1957.
33 Hoather, R. C., Rackham, R. F., Analyst, **84,** 548, 1959.
34 Merritt, C., Jr., Hersheson, H. M., Rogers, L. B., Anal. Chem., **25,** 572, 1953.
35 Kuhns, L. J., Braman, R. S., Graham, J. E., Anal. Chem., **34,** 1700, 1962.
36 Lueck, C. H., Boltz, D. F., Anal. Chem., **30,** 183, 1958.
37 Wadelin, C., Mellon, M. G., Anal. Chem., **25,** 1668, 1953.
38 Banks, C. V., Klingman, D. W., Anal. Chim. Acta, **15,** 356, 1956.
39 Meloche, V. W., Martin, R. L., Anal. Chem., **28,** 1671, 1956.
40 Elkind, A., Gayer, K. H., Boltz, D. F., Anal. Chem., **25,** 1744, 1953.
41 Umland, F., Puchelt, H., Anal. Chim. Acta., **16,** 334, 1957.
42 Trudell, L., Boltz, D. F., Anal. Chem., **35,** 2122, 1963.
43 Dinnin, J. I., Anal. Chem., **25,** 1803, 1953.
44 Waterbury, G. R., Bricker, C. E., Anal. Chem., **29,** 1474, 1957.
45 Johnson, R. A., Kwan, F. P., Anal. Chem., **23,** 651, 1951.
46 Hines, E., Boltz, D. F., Anal. Chem., **24,** 947, 1952.
47 Merritt, C., Jr., Hersheson, H. M., Rogers, L. B., Anal. Chem., **25,** 572, 1953.
48 Haddock, L. A., Analyst, **60,** 394, 1935.
49 Pappenhagen, J. M., Mellon, M. G., Anal. Chem., **25,** 341, 1953.

TABLE 2-4 (cont.)

Constituent	*Method or Reagent*	*Wavelength, mμ*	*Reference*[a]
	Chloro-*p*-phenylenediamine	354	(50)
U	Thiocyanate	375	(51)
	Benzohydroxamic acid	380	(52)
V	Peroxyvanadic acid	290	(53)
	Tungstovanadic acid	392	(54)
W	8-Quinolinol	358	(55)
Zn	1,10-Phenenthroline	270	(56)
Zr	Mandelic acid	250	(57)
	Chloranilic acid	350	(58)

[a] Parenthetical numbers refer to the following list of references:

50 Kuemmel, D. F., Mellon, M. G., Anal. Chem., **28,** 1674, 1956.
51 Newell, J. E., Anal. Chem., **23,** 445, 1951.
52 Meloan, C. E., Holkeboer, P., Brandt, W. W., Anal. Chem., **32,** 791, 1960.
53 Telep, G., Boltz, D. F., Anal. Chem., **23,** 901, 1951.
54 Wallace, G. W., Mellon, M. G., Anal. Chem, **32,** 204, 1960.
55 Eberle, A. R., Anal. Chem., **35,** 669, 1963.
56 Kruse, J. M., Brandt, W. W., Anal. Chem., **24,** 1306, 1952.
57 Hahn, R. B., Weber, L., Anal. Chem., **28,** 414, 1956.
58 Bricker, C. E., Waterbury, G. R., Anal. Chem., **29,** 559, 1957.

and the absorbance of the extract is measured at 277 mμ. The caffeine and phenacetin are determined by simultaneous spectrophotometry by measuring the absorbance at 250 and 275 mμ.[27] Simultaneous spectrophotometric analysis of a three-component mixture of *o*-, *m*-, and *p*-cresol[28] and a six-component mixture of benzene, toluene, ethyl benzene, *o*-xylene, *m*-xylene and *p*-xylene[29] illustrate the ultimate potentiality of this method. Representative ultraviolet methods for organic substances have been tabulated in Table 2-5. The biennial reviews on ultraviolet spectrometry appearing in *Analytical Chemistry* should be consulted for additional specific analytical applications.[30,31]

Methods using ultraviolet spectrometry have been discussed or described elsewhere in Standard Methods of Chemical Analysis. These methods are listed below, and are grouped according to the type of material analyzed.

1. Chapter 50, Volume III, Foods.
   a. Benzoic acid
   b. Sorbic acid
2. Chapter 51, Volume III, Organic Functional Groups.
   a. Determination of acetylenic compounds as mercuric acetate complexes
   b. Alkanes
   c. Alkenes
   d. Alkynes
   e. Aromatic hydrocarbons
   f. Benzene in poly(methyl vinyl ether-maleic anhydride)
   g. Trace quantities of carbon disulfide in benzene
   h. Carbonyl compounds
   i. Microgram quantities of divinyl sulfone in aqueous media

[27] Jones, M., Thatcher, R. L., Anal. Chem., **23,** 957, 1951.
[28] Carney, G. E., Sanford, J. K., Anal. Chem., **25,** 1417, 1953.
[29] Tunnicliff, D. D., Brattain, R. R., Zumwalt, L. R., Anal. Chem., **21,** 890, 1949.
[30] Hirt, R. C., Anal. Chem., **28,** 579, 1956; **30,** 589, 1958; **32,** 225R, 1960; **34,** 276R, 1962.
[31] Hirt, R. C., Vandenbelt, J. M., Anal. Chem., **36,** 308R, 1964.

TABLE 2-5. SELECTED LIST OF ULTRAVIOLET SPECTROPHOTOMETRIC METHODS FOR ORGANIC SUBSTANCES

Constituent	*Method or Reagent*	*Wavelength*	*Reference*[a]
Acetic anhydride		252	(1)
Acetone	—	280	(2)
Alkylbenzene sulfonates	—	225	(3)
Amino acids and peptides	Copper(II) complexes	208–255	(4)
Ascorbic acid	—	245, 265	(5)
Barbiturates	—	260	(6)
Benzaldehyde	—	283	(7)
Benzoic acid	—	274	(8)
Butadiene	—	217	(9)
Caffeine	—	272	(10)
Chloroform	Fujiwara	366	(11)
Furfural	Bisulfite	276	(12)
5-Ketogluconate	1-Methyl-1-phenylhydrazine sulfate	350	(13)
Parathion	—	274	(14)
Penicillin G	—		(15)
Phenols	Differential		(16, 17, 18)
Phthalic anhydride	—	276	(19)
Salicylate	Malonic acid	307	(20)
Styrene		250–260	(21)
Sugars	Glycosylamine	370–380	(22)
2,4,6-Trinitrotoluene	—	227	(23)
Vitamin A		325	(24)
Vanillin		347	(25)

[a] Parenthetical numbers refer to the following list of references:

1 Bruckenstein, S., Anal. Chem., **28,** 1920, 1956.
2 Barthauer, G. L., Jones, F. V., Metler, A. V., Ind. Eng. Chem., Anal. Ed., **18,** 354, 1946.
3 Weber, W. J., Morris, J. C., Stumm, W., Anal. Chem., **34,** 1844, 1962.
4 Cherkin, A. W., Wolkowitz, H., Dunn, M. S., Anal. Chem., **28,** 895, 1956.
5 Danglish, C., Biochem. J. (London), **49,** 635, 1951.
6 Stevenson, G. W., Anal. Chem., **33,** 1374, 1961.
7 Rees, H. L., Anderson, D. H., Anal. Chem., **21,** 989, 1949.
8 Murnieks, R., Gonter, C. E., Anal. Chem., **34,** 197, 1962.
9 Rosenbaum, E. J., Stanton, L., Anal. Chem., **19,** 794, 1947.
10 Kogan, L., DiCarlo, F. J., Maynard, W. E., Anal. Chem., **25,** 1118, 1953.
11 Mantel, M., Malco, M., Stiller, M., Anal. Chem., **35,** 1737, 1963.
12 Harris, J. F., Zoch, L. L., Anal. Chem., **34,** 201, 1962.
13 Schramm, M., Anal. Chem., **28,** 963, 1956.
14 Hirt, R. C., Gisclard, J. B., Anal. Chem., **23,** 185, 1951.
15 Levy, O. B., Shaw, D., Parkinson, E. S., Fergus, D., Anal. Chem., **20,** 1159, 1948.
16 Smullin, C. F., Wetterau, F. P., Anal. Chem., **27,** 1836, 1955.
17 Wadelin, C. W., Anal. Chem., **28,** 1530, 1956.
18 Wexler, A. S., Anal. Chem., **35,** 1936, 1963.
19 Shreve, O. D., Heether, M. R., Anal. Chem., 23, 441, 1951.
20 Stevenson, G. W., Anal. Chem., **32,** 1522, 1960.
21 Nietzel, O. A., Desesa, M. A., Anal. Chem., **29,** 756, 1957.
22 Timell, T. E., Glaudemans, C. P. J., Currie, A. L., Anal. Chem., **28,** 1916, 1956.
23 Schroeder, W. A., *et al.*, Anal. Chem., **23,** 1740, 1951.
24 Ewing, D. T., Sharpe, L. H., Bird, O. D., Anal. Chem., **25,** 599, 1953.
25 Englis, D. T., Wullermann, L. A., Anal. Chem., **29,** 1151, 1957.

j. Mercaptobenzothiazole in antifreeze solutions containing borax
k. Trace quantities of basic nitrogen in gasoline
l. Nonylphenyl in nonylcyclohexanol
m. Phenanthrene in anthracene
n. Determination of *m*-phenylenediamine and *m*-nitroaniline in heterogeneous reaction mixtures
o. Polyunsaturated fatty acids
p. Toluene in poly(methyl vinyl ether)

3. Chapter 48, Volume III, Natural Fats.
   a. Differentiation between bleached and unbleached lard
   b. Chlorophyll in fats and oils
   c. Color in fats
   d. Conjugated dienoic acid in castor oil
   e. Eleostearic acid in tung oil
   f. Polyunsaturated fatty acids in fats (also Volume IIB, page 1470)
4. Chapter 54, Volume III, Paint, Varnish, and Lacquer.
   a. Benzoic acid in alkyd resins and esters
   b. Dibasic acids in alkyd resins
   c. Inhibitor content of vinyl monomers
   d. Melamine content of nitrogen resins
   e. Composition of unsaturated fatty acids in oils
   f. Phthalic acid isomers in alkyd resins and esters
   g. Phthalic anhydride of alkyd resins and esters containing other dibasic acids
5. Chapter 39, Volume IIB, Pesticides.
   a. Sevin, page 1902
   b. Thiram, page 1910
6. Chapter 57, Volume III, Petroleum and Petroleum Products.
   a. Aromatic fractions in petroleum
   b. Conjugated diolefins
   c. Olefins
7. Chapter 57, Volume III, Plastics.
   1. Determination of additives in polymers
   2. Determination of structure of polymers

   Chapter 41, Volume IIB, Plastics.
   1. Combined styrene in styrene plastics, page 2062
   2. 2,6-di-*tert*-butyl-*p*-cresol in ethylene plastics, page 2084
   3. Methyl salicylate in plastics, page 2091
   4. Styrene monomer in styrene plastics, page 2056
8. Chapter 59, Volume III, Rubber and Rubber Products.
   1. Accelerators
   2. Antioxidants
   3. Determination of copolymer composition
   4. Lead
   5. Sulfur
   6. Zinc oxide

   Chapter 43, Volume IIB, Petroleum and Petroleum Products.
   1. Antioxidants in synthetic rubber, pages 2183, 2185
   2. Bound styrene in polymers, page 2194
9. Chapter 61, Volume III, Soaps and Synthetic Detergents.
   1. Germicides in soaps and detergents
   2. Nonionics of alkylphenoxypolyethylene-ethanol type

3. Sodium alkylbenzenesulfonate
4. Sodium toluenesulfonate
5. Sodium xylenesulfonate

10. Chapter 63, Volume III, Water Analysis.
    1. Alkylbenzenesulfonates
    2. Nitrate
11. Chapter 64, Volume III, Determination of Water.
    1. In gases
12. Chapter 47, Volume IIB, Vitamins.
    1. Vitamin A and other Vitamins, page 2340
13. Chapter 42, Volume IIB, Poisons.
    1. Alkaloids, pages 2124, 2125
    2. Barbiturates, page 2131

Chapter 3

INFRARED SPECTROMETRY

By J. C. Evans
Chemical Physics Research Laboratory
The Dow Chemical Co.
Midland, Michigan

INTRODUCTION

The term infrared spectrometry normally denotes the study of absorption spectra between the approximate wavelength limits of 0.8 and 1000 μ, where μ is the micron unit (1 μ = 10,000 A = 10^{-4} cm.). A more significant unit is the wavenumber, ω, which is the number of waves per cm. The units are related;

$$\omega = \frac{1}{\text{Wavelength in cm.}} = \frac{1}{\lambda}\ (\text{cm.}^{-1}\ \text{units})$$

Since the frequency, ν, of the electromagnetic radiation is given by

$$\nu\ (\text{in cycles per second}) = \frac{C}{\lambda},$$

where C = velocity of electromagnetic radiation (cm. per sec.), then

$$\nu = C\omega.$$

Now when a molecule absorbs or emits radiation of this frequency, ν, the quantum of energy exchanged is $h\nu$, where h is Planck's constant, and so the wavenumber is directly proportional to the energy change. Other advantages of the use of the wavenumber unit are apparent when comparisons with Raman spectra are necessary and when integrated band intensities must be measured. However, for historical and practical reasons the wavelength unit is still widely used and commercial instruments are available with spectral recording linear either in wavelength or in wavenumber.

For convenience of nomenclature the infrared spectrum is usually divided into regions, the division recommended by the Triple Commission for Spectroscopy being the following: the "near infrared" is the region between 12,500 and 4000 cm.$^{-1}$ (0.8 to 2.5 μ); the "mid-infrared" is between 4000 and 200 cm.$^{-1}$ (2.5 to 50 μ); and the "far infrared" lies between 200 and 10 cm.$^{-1}$ or 50 to 1000 μ. The mid-infrared will be of major concern here.

Absorption spectra in the infrared originate in transitions between vibrational and rotational levels of the lowest, or ground, electronic energy state of the molecule. Exceptions to this statement are known, of course, since many molecules possess absorption bands in the near infrared which arise from transitions to excited electronic states. Pure rotational transitions, which normally involve small energy changes, occur in the far infrared, but, for molecules in the vapor phase, transitions between vibrational levels are accompanied by transitions between rotational levels and fine structure is observed in the vibrational absorption bands. In condensed phases, this fine structure is rarely observed and, because the majority of studies of practical analytical interest involves condensed phase spectra, this discussion will be concerned mainly with vibrational energy.

It is a good approximation in treating vibrational energy levels to ignore the electronic energy and to treat the vibrating molecule as a number of point masses held together by Hooke's law forces; *i.e.*, for small displacements the restoring force is proportional to the displacement. For a molecule with N atoms the number of coordinates needed to specify the positions of the nuclei in space is $3N$; this number is the total number of degrees of freedom possessed by the molecule. The atoms are combined so they do not move independently and three coordinates are required to specify the center of mass position and describe the translational motion of the molecule as a unit. Three more are needed to describe the rotational motion of the molecule about its center of mass, so that there are, in general, $3N - 6$ coordinates left to describe the motions of the atoms relative to one another for a fixed orientation of the molecule, *i.e.*, the vibrational degrees of freedom number $3N - 6$. Linear molecules require only two rotational coordinates and have $3N - 5$ vibrational degrees of freedom.

Although a vibrating system of point masses held together by Hooke's law forces apparently moves in a very complex manner, classical mechanics shows that the displacements of the masses from their mean positions are always the sums of displacements of a special set of vibrations, in general of different frequencies, during each of which the masses move in straight lines and in phase; when the nuclei are in phase they pass through their mean positions and turning points simultaneously. The number of such special vibrations is equal to the number of vibrational degrees of freedom, and these vibrations, in terms of which all possible vibrational motion of the molecule may be expressed, are known as the *normal* or *fundamental modes* of the molecule. The nuclear displacements actually undergone when the molecule is carrying out one and only one of these normal modes may be described in terms of the *normal coordinate* of that mode. Much of the usefulness of the infrared spectrum in qualitative analysis arises from the fact that frequently a normal mode is localized largely in a group in the molecule and it is then a good approximation to describe the normal coordinate in terms of the stretching or bending of one or a few bonds, *e.g.*, —O—H stretching.

Classical mechanics, then, provides a convenient description of the fundamental frequencies of a molecule and also expressions, relating the frequencies to the masses of the atoms and the forces binding them, which may be used to derive values for the Hooke's law constants (the force constants), if the frequencies are known; *i.e.*, information about the binding forces may be derived from the vibrational spectrum. In order to obtain a fuller understanding, the application of quantum mechanics must be made. With the same harmonic oscillator approximation, implied by the use of Hooke's law forces, the essential result is the same as before—the vibrational motion is a superposition of the $3N - 6$ normal modes. The additional fact, absent in the classical picture, emerges that the vibrational energy values are restricted to certain values; *i.e.*, the vibrational energy is quantized, and the total vibrational energy can have only values which satisfy

$$\text{Total energy } E \text{ (ergs)} = \sum_i E_i = h\nu_1(v_1 + \tfrac{1}{2}) + h\nu_2(v_2 + \tfrac{1}{2}) + \cdots$$

where ν_i is the frequency (cycles per second) of the ith normal mode, and v_i is the vibrational quantum number, which may take integral values only: 0, 1, 2, 3 $\cdots$. Expressed in wavenumber units,

$$\frac{E}{hc}\,(\text{cm.}^{-1}) = \omega_1(v_1 + \tfrac{1}{2}) + \omega_2(v_2 + \tfrac{1}{2}) + \omega_3(v_3 + \tfrac{1}{2}) + \cdots.$$

When all the v_i are zero, the molecule is in its ground vibrational state but still possesses its zero point vibrational energy of $\Sigma \frac{\omega_i}{2}$; that is, the molecule still vibrates even at the lowest attainable temperature.

In order that the vibrating molecule should interact with the oscillating electric field of the incident electromagnetic radiation of the appropriate frequency, and undergo a transition between two of its energy levels, the molecular electrical dipole moment must change its magnitude or its orientation with respect to a fixed coordinate system during the motion. The intensity of the absorption band is determined by the magnitude of this dipole moment change, which may be zero if symmetry dictates. For the harmonic oscillator model, only transitions in which the vibrational quantum number changes by ± 1 are allowed to be infrared active; overtones and combination tones, which require a change of 2 or more, should not appear. However, some of these transitions are always observed in the infrared spectra of molecules, indicating that the motion is not truly harmonic. Usually these overtones and combination tones give rise to weak absorption bands, but, occasionally, one may fall near a fundamental, and quantum mechanical resonance (Fermi resonance) between the two excited vibrational levels may occur. The overtone or combination tone absorption band is then enhanced in intensity by the resonance.

Such complications and the large number of fundamental modes possessed by even the small molecule—*e.g.*, for a molecule of 10 atoms the number of fundamentals is 24, and many, if not all, will be infrared active depending on the molecular symmetry—means that a large amount of information is contained in the infrared spectrum. This information being determined by the atomic masses and bonding forces makes the vibrational spectrum a highly characteristic property of the molecule so that it is not surprising that infrared spectrometry is the physical tool most widely used by organic chemists.

At first sight, the fact that during the normal vibrations all the nuclei take part suggests that few resemblances between the spectra of different molecules should be expected unless the structures are very closely related. However, it was recognized early that certain groups of atoms give rise to absorption bands at or near the same frequencies even when contained in quite dissimilar molecules. The reason for this has already been mentioned—the normal mode to a good approximation involves atomic movement only in the group in question and a group vibration exists. In general, a group vibration will arise whenever the group, if it were completely separated from the molecule, has a frequency which is sufficiently different from any vibrational frequency of the remainder of the molecule. This requirement may be relaxed if two normal modes of comparable frequency are confined to parts of the molecule which are well separated physically so that appreciable coupling of the modes cannot occur. This concept of splitting the molecule up into a few well-chosen groups is very useful and allows qualitative predictions of the spectrum of a molecule to be made. Conversely, it enables a picture of the molecular structure of an unknown to be built on the basis of its infrared spectrum, and this is probably the most widely used application of infrared spectrometry. The limitations of the concept must, however, always be kept in mind.

INSTRUMENTATION

As befits such a widely used analytical tool, infrared spectrometry is well served by commercial instrument makers who offer a wide variety of instruments ranging from those designed for use at the organic chemist's bench to the more sophisticated instruments suitable for detailed study of the finer aspects of infrared spectra. This discussion will deal briefly only with the general features of the essential components of spectrometers; the reader is referred to the operating manual of his own instrument for design details and specific operating instructions.

BASIC COMPONENTS

The basic components are shown in block form in Fig. 3-1. Radiation from a source is collected by condensing optics, passed through the sampling space and focused onto

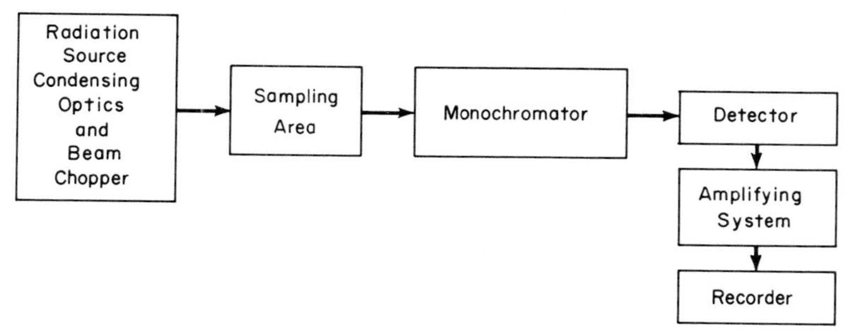

FIG. 3-1. Schematic Diagram of the General Infrared Instrument.

the entrance slit of a monochromator, which isolates a narrow spectral range and focuses this onto the detector. The electrical signal generated by the detector is amplified and recorded. Two main types of instrument are used—the single-beam and the double-beam spectrometers. In the former, the energy transmitted by the sample is recorded as the spectrum is scanned, while the latter measures directly the ratio of the energy transmitted by the sample to the energy incident upon the sample, and records this as the spectrum is scanned.

Infrared Sources.—Infrared sources are hot bodies which emit continuously throughout the infrared, and which approximate a black body radiator in their emission properties. The Nernst filament (a small rod of mixed rare earth oxides heated by passage of an electric current to about 1800°C.), the Globar source (a rod of silicon carbide operating at about 1200°C. through electrical heating), and a small spiral of nichrome wire heated electrically to about 1200°C. are some of the more common sources used. For all of these the radiation intensity falls off rapidly with increasing wavelength, and in all instruments designed for continuous scanning over a wide frequency range this fall-off in energy is compensated for by programming the slits to open continuously. Fortunately, this does not result in loss of resolution because the dispersion of prism materials and gratings used increases with wavelength and more than compensates for the widening slits.

Monochromators.—Monochromators used are basically one of two designs illustrated in Fig. 3-2. The Littrow arrangement is most frequently encountered; the Ebert design has some advantages in flexibility, however, and uses the simpler spherical reflectors instead of the off-axis paraboloid collimator, which must be of high quality for good performance. Prisms or gratings are used but the latter, because of the need for separating orders, always require the aid of a prism or of filters. Several gratings are used to cover a useful spectral range although a grating may be used in more than one order.

Detectors.—Thermocouples are the most widely used detectors, but the equally sensitive Golay cell, a pneumatic type detector, has a larger area, which means that simpler condensing optics or wider slits can be used. In the far infrared where wide slits must be used, the Golay cell is the better choice. The noise level in these wide range thermal detectors is of the order of 10^{-9} to 10^{-10} watt, which sets the limit on the energy they can detect. Their low efficiency is the chief limitation on the performance of infrared instruments.

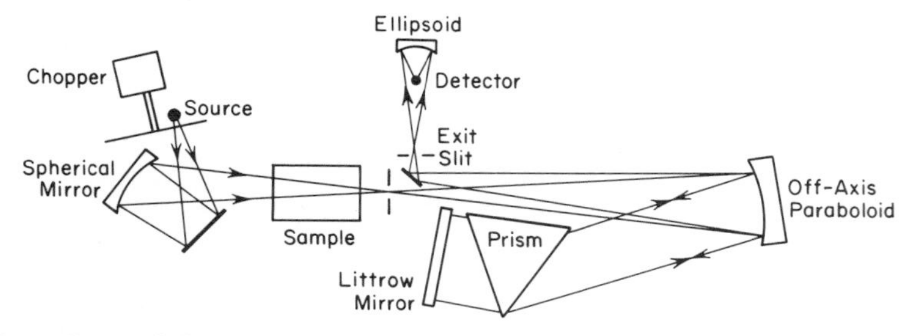

FIG. 3-2 *a*. Essential Optics of a Single-beam Spectrometer with Littrow Monochromator.

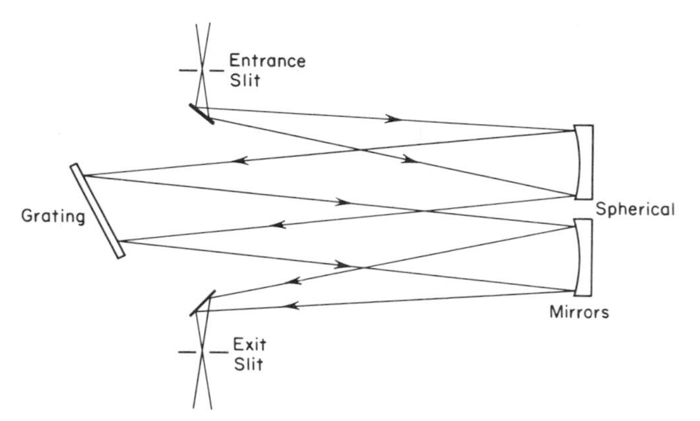

FIG. 3-2 *b*. Ebbert Monochromator.

Amplifiers.—Because all bodies at room temperature emit radiation in the infrared, a direct current amplifying system is not desirable and alternating current amplification is used. The radiation beam is chopped at a suitable, constant frequency, usually of the order of 10 cycles per sec., to provide the a.c. signal for the detector. A sharply tuned, linear-response amplifier amplifies only this frequency, rejecting all other frequencies and the d.c. background signal. After amplification the signal is rectified and used to drive the recorder.

SINGLE- AND DOUBLE-BEAM INSTRUMENTS

Single-beam Instrument.—Figure 3-2a illustrates the essential components of the single-beam instrument, which measures directly the amount of energy transmitted by the sample and the spectrometer optics. The position of the recorder pen on the chart is a function of the sample transmission, the monochromator slit widths, and the amplifier gain. In order to measure the transmittance T of the sample at any wavelength, where

$$T = \frac{\text{radiant power transmitted by sample}}{\text{radiant power incident on sample}} = \frac{I}{I_0}$$

a "blank" measurement of I_0 must also be made. For solution work, in which the solute spectrum is of interest, a measurement of the solvent transmission under exactly the same conditions must be made; for gas phase work the empty cell must be measured. Usually the I_0 is set first at a convenient position on the recorder chart by suitable adjustment of slit width and amplifier gain, and I is measured immediately afterward in order to minimize any effects due to amplifier instability and source variations.

The single-beam instrument yields the most accurate transmittance measurements and is particularly useful for quantitative analysis. For this reason most commercial double-beam instruments may also be operated single-beam. The single-beam is a simpler and more reliable system than the double-beam and, unlike the double-beam, any malfunction is immediately apparent. Scanning a wide frequency range is not convenient with the single-beam system unless it is operated with a mechanism for opening the slits to maintain a fairly flat I_0 line. A minor irritation is that even with careful flushing of the instrument with dry air free of carbon dioxide or with dry nitrogen some absorption usually remains in the water and carbon dioxide bands.

Double-beam Instrument.—The double-beam system was introduced to facilitate the rapid recording of survey spectra covering a wide range; most instruments used in qualitative analysis are of this type. Two designs are in use, the widely used optical-null system and the electrical beam-ratioing system that has been used for ultraviolet, visible, and near infrared instruments for some time but which is only recently being applied to the mid-infrared region.

The optical-null, double-beam instrument differs essentially from the single-beam in the optics between source and monochromator entrance slit and in the method of recording the signal from the detector. Figure 3-3 illustrates the important optical

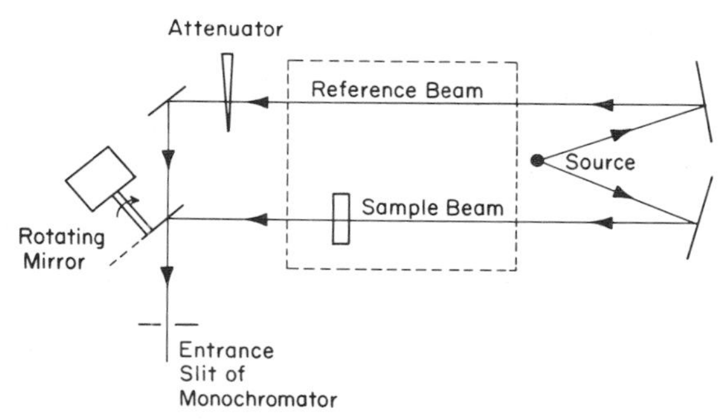

FIG. 3-3. Schematic Diagram of Optical Paths in the Optical-null, Double-beam Spectrometer.

features. Radiation from the source is split into two equal beams, sample and reference, which, after passing through the sampling area, are focused alternately onto the entrance slit of the monochromator. A rotating, semicircular, front-surfaced plane mirror provides the beam switching at a frequency of about 15 cycles per sec. If the radiant energies in the two beams are equal, as is the case in the absence of sample, the detector produces a d.c. signal which is not amplified. An a.c. signal is produced only when the beams are of unequal intensity. This signal is amplified and fed to a servomotor which varies the

When all the v_i are zero, the molecule is in its ground vibrational state but still possesses its zero point vibrational energy of $\sum_i \frac{\omega_i}{2}$; that is, the molecule still vibrates even at the lowest attainable temperature.

In order that the vibrating molecule should interact with the oscillating electric field of the incident electromagnetic radiation of the appropriate frequency, and undergo a transition between two of its energy levels, the molecular electrical dipole moment must change its magnitude or its orientation with respect to a fixed coordinate system during the motion. The intensity of the absorption band is determined by the magnitude of this dipole moment change, which may be zero if symmetry dictates. For the harmonic oscillator model, only transitions in which the vibrational quantum number changes by ± 1 are allowed to be infrared active; overtones and combination tones, which require a change of 2 or more, should not appear. However, some of these transitions are always observed in the infrared spectra of molecules, indicating that the motion is not truly harmonic. Usually these overtones and combination tones give rise to weak absorption bands, but, occasionally, one may fall near a fundamental, and quantum mechanical resonance (Fermi resonance) between the two excited vibrational levels may occur. The overtone or combination tone absorption band is then enhanced in intensity by the resonance.

Such complications and the large number of fundamental modes possessed by even the small molecule—*e.g.*, for a molecule of 10 atoms the number of fundamentals is 24, and many, if not all, will be infrared active depending on the molecular symmetry—means that a large amount of information is contained in the infrared spectrum. This information being determined by the atomic masses and bonding forces makes the vibrational spectrum a highly characteristic property of the molecule so that it is not surprising that infrared spectrometry is the physical tool most widely used by organic chemists.

At first sight, the fact that during the normal vibrations all the nuclei take part suggests that few resemblances between the spectra of different molecules should be expected unless the structures are very closely related. However, it was recognized early that certain groups of atoms give rise to absorption bands at or near the same frequencies even when contained in quite dissimilar molecules. The reason for this has already been mentioned—the normal mode to a good approximation involves atomic movement only in the group in question and a group vibration exists. In general, a group vibration will arise whenever the group, if it were completely separated from the molecule, has a frequency which is sufficiently different from any vibrational frequency of the remainder of the molecule. This requirement may be relaxed if two normal modes of comparable frequency are confined to parts of the molecule which are well separated physically so that appreciable coupling of the modes cannot occur. This concept of splitting the molecule up into a few well-chosen groups is very useful and allows qualitative predictions of the spectrum of a molecule to be made. Conversely, it enables a picture of the molecular structure of an unknown to be built on the basis of its infrared spectrum, and this is probably the most widely used application of infrared spectrometry. The limitations of the concept must, however, always be kept in mind.

INSTRUMENTATION

As befits such a widely used analytical tool, infrared spectrometry is well served by commercial instrument makers who offer a wide variety of instruments ranging from those designed for use at the organic chemist's bench to the more sophisticated instruments suitable for detailed study of the finer aspects of infrared spectra. This discussion

Some instruments possess refinements which improve performance or versatility. Accurate following of a spectrum requires a slow scanning speed. A device which measures the error voltage, or unbalance, in the reference attenuator servoloop, and which slows the scanning speed in a manner proportional to this error voltage, enables the instrument to follow the spectrum more accurately in the regions of rapidly changing transmittance. This automatic speed suppression system permits the use of high scanning speed in regions without absorption, and ensures that the speed is low enough to follow absorption bands accurately.

Another feature of great value for difference spectra work in which the material in the reference beam absorbs in some regions of the spectrum, is the automatic servoenergy control. The servoloop gain, which is proportional to the amplifier gain and to slit width, must be held within rather narrow limits for proper instrument performance. These limits are soon exceeded when absorption in the reference beam becomes appreciable. Frequent adjustment of slit or amplifier gain is necessary to correct for this. The automatic servoenergy control device measures the reference beam energy and uses this to drive a second servosystem which either controls the amplifier gain setting or the slit width setting so that the servoenergy remains constant.

A desirable feature in quantitative analysis, particularly of low concentrations when very weak bands must be measured, is the expansion of the transmittance scale (ordinate expansion). Several expansion factors are usually available. Signal and noise are, of course, both increased to the same extent so that some improvement in signal-to-noise ratio, either by opening the slits to increase signal or by slowing the attenuator response (and hence scan speed) to reduce noise, must be made if the scale expansion is to be effective.

Examples of the applications of all of these refinements are given in the instrument manuals, which also describe tests designed to measure instrument performance. Frequency calibration, transmittance accuracy, and general instrument performance are conveniently checked by running spectra for comparison with standard spectra reproduced in the manuals.

SAMPLE HANDLING

Samples in the vapor, liquid, or solid phases may be examined by the infrared method, which is applicable to almost any sample. The quantity necessary for normal recording is usually much less than is available, but, when this is not the case, microspectrometric techniques can be used. Little sample preparation is usually required, although the interpretation of the spectrum of an unknown mixture will obviously be facilitated if the sample is first subjected to a separative method and its components are examined separately. A practical point which may require some preliminary attention is the possible reaction between sample and cell window material. Most frequently the presence of water is a nuisance because the commonly used cell materials are the water-soluble, alkali halides. Alternative cell materials are available; Table 3-1 collects most of these with an indication of their useful regions.

Vapor Phase.—Sampling areas of most commercial instruments will accommodate a simple once-through vapor cell about 10 cm. long. Such cells can be made of glass or metal, with windows sealed on with a cement or stopcock grease; they are also available commercially. Materials of low volatility can be examined with cells of this type if they are heated, but the effects of cell thermal emission in optical-null instruments must be kept in mind. Improved sensitivity at ambient temperature can be obtained by the use of long-path cells, which are also available commercially. These employ multiple-reflection within a reasonable volume of gas; paths of up to 40 meters may be obtained.

TABLE 3-1. SOME MATERIALS, AND THEIR APPROXIMATE LONG WAVELENGTH CUT-OFF, USED IN INFRARED SAMPLING TECHNIQUES

Material	Approximate Cut-off, μ	Material	Approximate Cut-off, μ
Glass	2.5	CsBr	40.0
Quartz	3.5	TlBr: TlI	40.0
LiF	6.0	CsI	50.0
Sapphire	6.5	Irtran[a] 1 (MgF_2)	9.0
CaF_2	9.0	Irtran 2 (ZnS)	14.7
BaF_2	11.0	Irtran 3 (CaF_2)	11.5
NaCl	16.0	Irtran 4 (ZnSe)	21.8
AgCl	22.0	Irtran 5 (MgO)	9.4
KBr	25.0		

[a] Polycrystalline materials having high resistance to thermal shock as well as to attack by a wide variety of chemical reagents (Eastman Kodak Company).

Analyses of trace amounts of material in air, of the order of parts per million, are possible with these cells.

In quantitative analytical work using vapor phase infrared spectra, it is particularly important to ensure that the total pressure be maintained constant; this is usually done by adding dry nitrogen gas to bring the total pressure up to a convenient standard value near atmospheric. This is important because the analysis usually involves a measurement in the rotational fine structure of a resolved vibrational band. These rotational lines are very narrow and their widths are pressure sensitive. Unless the spectral slit width is considerably less than the width of the line or band being measured, the relation between absorption and concentration is not linear. Analysis under variable pressure conditions is not possible because the variable line widths are less than the slit widths attainable with analytical instruments.

Liquid and Solution Phases.—Cells for use with pure liquids must usually be of short path length. Qualitative liquid phase spectra are easily obtained merely by squeezing a capillary film of the liquid (about 0.01 mm. or less in thickness) between two plates of infrared transmitting material, usually sodium chloride, potassium bromide, or silver chloride. Sealed cells of known thickness are also used when the viscosity of the liquid allows such thin cells to be filled properly; for liquids of high volatility, sealed cells are essential to avoid loss of sample and the appearance of holes, which lead to meaningless relative band intensities, in the liquid during the scan. Cells of known thickness may be of two types, demountable or sealed permanently. Essentially, both types consist of two plates separated by a spacer of about the desired thickness with two holes for filling. Several designs are available commercially in a range of thicknesses. Cells of continuously variable path length are also available. These are particularly useful for difference spectra work because they allow the solvent compensation to be made exactly.

Solution spectra are obtained whenever possible with solvents of high transmission over a wide spectral range. The solvent pair, carbon tetrachloride and carbon disulfide, is very convenient for the regions usually scanned routinely; carbon tetrachloride for the 4000–1330 cm.$^{-1}$ range and carbon disulfide for the 1330–450 cm.$^{-1}$ range. This pair is widely used in organic structural analysis work. Concentrations of about 10 percent (0.1 g. in 1 ml.) in cells of 0.1 mm. thickness requiring volumes of solution of approximately 0.2 to 0.5 ml. are suitable for survey work, but if solubility is limited, the combination of a 1 percent solution in a 1-mm. cell is still very useful. Numerous other solvents or solvent mixtures with more limited frequency ranges free from absorption can be used for polar materials which are insoluble in the preferred pair; methylene chloride, chloroform, acetonitrile, nitromethane, acetone, and dimethylformamide are a few. These find use not for survey runs but in quantitative analysis, which should always be done in solution if possible, and which usually involves a measurement of one or only a few absorption bands.

The thickness and an indication of the quality of a cell may be obtained by recording its interference pattern—the spectrum of the empty cell is scanned. If the cell is of good quality, a wave-like pattern similar to that drawn in Fig. 3-4 will be recorded. The

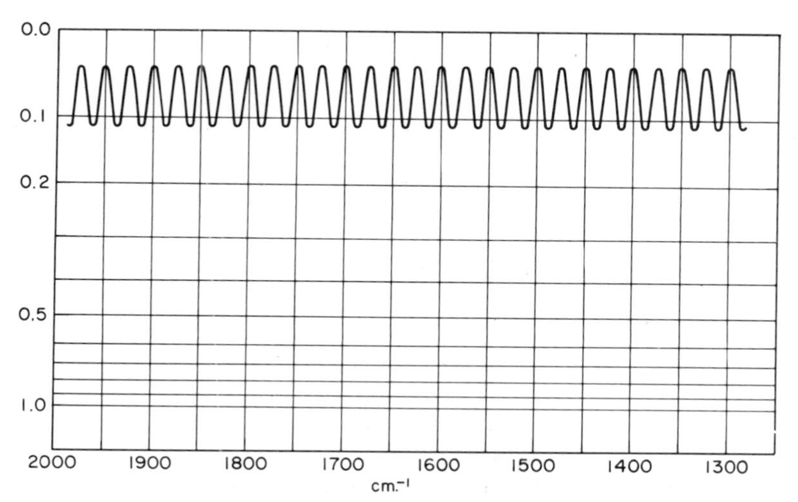

FIG. 3-4. Part of the Interference Pattern of a 0.200-mm. Cell.

better the quality of the cell the greater is the ordinate separation between maxima and minima and the smoother is the curve; subsidiary peaks between the main ones indicate nonplanarity of the inside plate-faces. Fogged windows or departure from parallelism of the inside surfaces will destroy the interference pattern, which arises from interference between the radiation which has been reflected twice within the cell and that which is transmitted directly. The phase relation between these depends on the wavelength of the radiation and the length of the cell. Cancellation or reinforcement will occur to produce maxima and minima in the transmitted energy. At a maximum in transmission,

$$2b = n\lambda$$

where b, the cell length, and λ, the wavelength, are in microns, and n is an integer. To obtain the cell length, measurements of the wavelengths of two widely separated transmission peaks are made. Then,

$$2b = n_1\lambda_1 \quad \text{and} \quad 2b = n_2\lambda_2$$

The values of n_1 and n_2 cannot be determined, but this is unnecessary because the difference $d = n_1 - n_2$ is the number of complete fringes or cycles of the pattern. Thus,

$$b = \frac{d}{2} \frac{\lambda_1 \lambda_2}{\lambda_2 - \lambda_1} \times \frac{1}{1000} \text{ mm.}$$

which is convenient when the instrument records linearly in wavelength and

$$b = \frac{d}{2} \frac{1}{\omega_1 - \omega_2} \text{ cm.}$$

for an instrument recording linearly in wavenumber. Several measurements, agreeing to within about 0.2 percent, should be made with different choices of ω_1 and ω_2, and the cell length should be checked frequently by this method when quantitative analysis is desired.

Aqueous solutions deserve special mention.[1] Thin layers of about 0.07 mm. or less can be examined with barium fluoride cells in certain regions, shown in Fig. 3-5, while

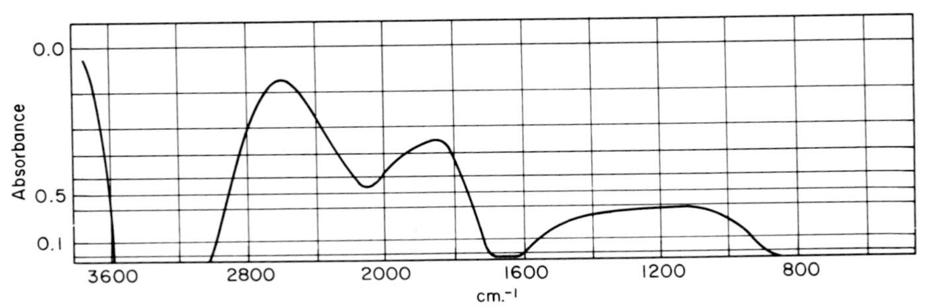

Fig. 3-5. Infrared Absorption Spectrum of Water, 0.025-mm. Film.

for capillary films the range can be extended to about 400 cm.$^{-1}$ with silver chloride plates. In the interesting region centered at 1200 cm.$^{-1}$ the transmission is low, but a convenient way of raising the pen on the chart is to insert a screen in the reference beam and to adjust the gain and slit width to ensure adequate servoloop energy. Alternatively, an equivalent barium fluoride cell in the reference beam may be used but such use necessitates the use of automatic servoenergy control because the reference beam energy varies considerably during the total scan.

This method of compensating for loss of energy by placing a wire screen or one of the adjustable type screens available commercially is of wide-spread application. Transmissions reduced to a few percent by intense scattering, small sample size, or broad absorption may be expanded to full scale.

Solids.—Very infrequently is it possible to obtain a solid sample in a layer already thin enough for direct recording of its spectrum. Films of plastics and resins are an important exception; their preparation and examples of spectra are fully described in Volume II.[2] If the solid is soluble in carbon tetrachloride and carbon disulfide, the solution technique is probably the best method, if the application allows, because it will yield reproducible spectra so essential for identification and structure studies. Quantitative analysis should be done in solution.

[1] Potts, W. J., and Wright, N., Anal. Chem., **28,** 1255, 1956.
[2] Cobler, J. G., in Standard Methods of Chemical Analysis, 6th Ed., Vol. IIB, F. J. Welcher, ed., D. Van Nostrand Co., Inc., Princeton, 1963, p. 2034.

A simple technique applicable to those solids that can be melted without decomposition or oxidation is to melt a small quantity between two infrared transmitting plates to form a capillary film, which is then allowed to solidify. With proper temperature control, single crystals may be obtained; even without careful control, fairly large regions of oriented material are usually obtained. Since the spectrometer, particularly grating instruments, polarizes the radiation appreciably, orientation effects which are not reproducible between samples appear in the spectra—relative band intensities change with sample and with the orientation of the sample in the beam.

Film casting techniques similar to those used for polymer film preparation may sometimes yield a thin layer of very fine crystals which are smaller than the wavelength of the radiation. Light losses by reflection and refraction at the crystal faces which become serious for particles comparable in size to the wavelength are not then important, and spectra of reasonable quality may be obtained. This rarely occurs at wavelengths shorter than about 5 μ. Both reflection and refraction losses depend on the difference in refractive index between the crystalline material and the medium surrounding it. In addition, the refractive index varies with wavelength—gradually in regions of no absorption, but sharply near and within an absorption band. The usual result in the case of a solid surrounded by air, a lower refractive index medium, is that the recorded absorption band is distorted (the Christiansen effect) as drawn in Fig. 3-6.

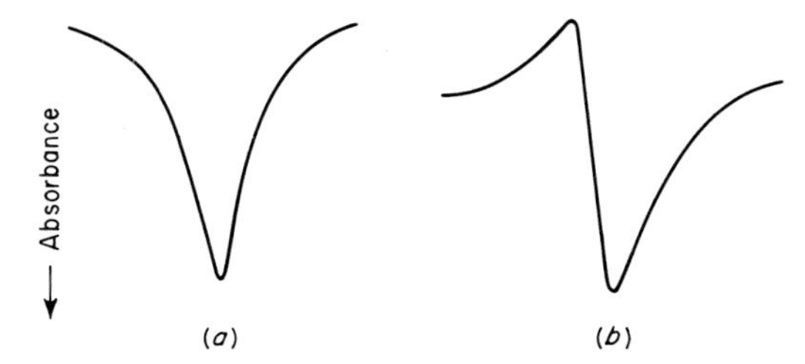

FIG. 3-6 *a*. Expected Band Shape. *b*. Band Distorted by Christiansen Effect

Two general methods have been widely used to overcome these difficulties, and both aim at embedding the finely divided solid in a medium of similar refractive index. The older method, the mull method, requires that the solid be ground to a fine-particle size and suspended in an oil, usually mineral oil (Nujol) or fluorinated hydrocarbon. Mineral oil has prominent absorption bands in the 2900, 1470, and 1380 cm.$^{-1}$ regions but only a few weak features below 1380 cm.$^{-1}$, while fluorinated oil is free of absorption in thin layers above 1330 cm.$^{-1}$. A small quantity (about 5 mg.) of the solid is ground, with an agate pestle and mortar, vigorously for several minutes until the particles are fine enough to adhere in a very thin solid film to the mortar. A small drop of mulling agent is added and ground into the solid layer until all the solid has been raised from the mortar surface into suspension in the oil. Efficient transfer of the mull, even from a large mortar, with which it is easier to grind effectively, may be made with a rubber policeman to a flat alkali halide plate. Another flat plate is placed on top and the two plates are squeezed together with a rotary motion to spread the mull evenly. A satisfactory mull should appear almost transparent to visible light with but little scattering. Handling of soft and rubbery materials by this technique is facilitated by lowering the temperature of the sample in a dry box with liquid nitrogen or solid carbon dioxide.

The other general method of obtaining solid phase spectra employs a solid matrix, prepared by fusing a suitable infrared transmitting material, usually potassium bromide, to a clear glass, at room temperature, under vacuum, by applying pressure of about 10–30 tons per square inch with a small laboratory press. A few milligrams of the sample are mixed with about 0 5 g. of dry, powdered potassium bromide, and the mixture is then ground to a fine-particle size, usually by shaking it vigorously in a small capsule containing a steel ball. A few minutes' shaking usually suffices, depending on the hardness of the solid. The mixture is transferred—quantitative transfer is possible if desired—to the die and a disc usually about half an inch in diameter is pressed under vacuum. Removal of the air is necessary to avoid splitting of the disc by the compressed air trapped in pockets when the pressure is lowered; this will render the disc cloudy. Several alkali halides have been used in addition to potassium bromide, *e.g.*, potassium iodide, potassium chloride; silver chloride and polyethylene have also found application.

Which solid-sampling method to use is largely a matter of personal choice. The disc technique is easier to standardize. One may readily attempt quantitative analysis with this method, although an alternative solution method should be preferred if one can be found. The disc technique succeeds also with soft rubbery material. One disc will suffice to cover the potassium bromide region, but careful drying and handling are necessary to keep the spectrum free from water absorption bands. The method, when used with ionic samples, may lead to errors because ion exchange between the sample and disc material may occur readily and the spectrum observed may be that of the potassium salt or the bromide rather than of the desired salt. This occurrence is less likely with the mull technique, although it does sometimes happen. It can be avoided by suitable choice of plate material.

In addition to these simple general techniques of sample handling, there are other special techniques which facilitate the recording of spectra. For all of them, equipment designed to be compatible with commercial instruments is available and is fully described, with examples of applications, in manufacturers' literature. Variable path solution cells are most useful for use in the reference beam in difference spectra studies. When the amount of material available is small, as, for example, is the case for cuts emerging from vapor-phase chromatographic columns, microtechniques are available. Usually these employ a beam-condensing unit, utilizing mirrors or lenses, which reduces the aperture of the beam at the sampling area, allowing a small cell to be used. Solids and liquids of low volatility may be handled in miniature potassium bromide discs about 0.5 mm. in diameter containing microgram quantities of sample, or they may be examined in solution in microcells. Volatile liquids may also be dissolved or they may be examined in very long path-length but small-volume gas cells, which are available from several manufacturers.

A useful technique, which requires a special attachment, makes use of the fact that, under conditions of total reflection at a boundary between two media of different refractive indexes, the radiation penetrates a short distance into the medium of lower refractive index. The reflected radiation, when examined spectrally, shows the absorption spectrum of the medium of lower refractive index. This is known as attenuated total reflection (ATR), and it has wide application for samples which are difficult to examine by the usual absorption techniques, such as resin coatings on metal or paper. Samples which cannot be made thin enough for direct absorption, aqueous solutions, for example, can be studied. By varying the angle of incidence at the boundary, the depth of penetration can be adjusted to provide convenient intensity of the bands in the ATR spectrum. Simple units employ one reflection at the surface between the infrared-transmitting material, such as silver chloride, germanium or KRS-5 (thallium bromide–thallium iodide), while other units make use of multiple internal reflection to increase sensitivity; both types are available commercially in several designs.

APPLICATIONS

Qualitative Analysis.—Of the three main divisions of the infrared spectrum, the mid-infrared (4000–200 $cm.^{-1}$) has proved to be the most useful for analytical purposes. The reason is that this region contains most of the fundamental modes of organic molecules. This is not to say that it contains all the fundamental modes; many fundamentals lie below 200 $cm.^{-1}$, especially those for heavier atom-containing molecules, and there is one above 4000 $cm.^{-1}$—that of the hydrogen molecule. The near infrared region contains largely the combination and overtone bands of the hydrogen stretching modes; the bands are weaker in general and are not of great diagnostic value, although they frequently provide convenient bands for quantitative analysis of a mixture which is qualitatively understood. Instruments and techniques used in the near infrared, *e.g.*, quartz cells, are similar to those used in the ultraviolet-visible regions and most ultraviolet-visible instruments are designed to cover the near infrared also.

Literature abounds describing the application of spectrometry in the mid-infrared region to chemical analysis. Much of it comprises studies of the spectra of series of related molecules, their purpose being to discover group frequencies or to examine the small variations of group frequencies and to correlate these variations with structural differences. A large number of group frequencies has been studied in this fashion and much of the information has been collected, discussed, and often presented in tabular form in several very useful texts (see bibliography, items 3 to 12). Little would be accomplished by reproducing the minute fraction of such available material that this brief discussion would allow, and we shall be content to describe in general terms the procedure which might be followed in determining the structure of an unknown compound by use of its infrared spectrum. The strongest bands of the spectrum are first selected for consideration with due regard being given to the possible effects in solution spectra of solute-solvent and solute-solute interactions, which are in general small except when hydrogen bonding occurs, and, in the case of solid phase spectra, to the possible effects of intermolecular forces and polymorphism. Polymorphs may yield quite different spectra, and mixtures of polymorphs can be confusing. With the aid of correlation tables the possible structural groups present may be determined. Overlap of group frequencies and the possibility of interaction leading to unexpected displacements of group frequencies tend to make this process ambiguous. Some possibilities may be eliminated if other information from the sample origin—chemical properties and other spectroscopic methods—is available. Weaker infrared bands may provide additional information and, at this stage, comparison with standard spectra of several possibilities may well lead to positive structural determination or identification.

This last step depends, of course, on the availability of a large number of standard spectra. Large collections are available, details of which may be found in the bibliography. It cannot be overemphasized that sample and standard spectra should be compared under the same phase conditions.

Quantitative Analysis.—The fundamental law governing absorption of radiation of wavenumber ω in solution is

$$I = I_0 \exp(-K_\omega C b),$$

where I_0 = intensity of radiation incident at wavenumber ω,
I = intensity of radiation transmitted at wavenumber ω,
C = concentration (moles solute per liter solution),
b = cell length in cm. and
K_ω = absorption coefficient.

Rewriting, we obtain

$$\log_e \left(\frac{I_0}{I}\right) = K_\omega Cb$$

or, expressed in terms of common logarithms,

$$\log_{10} \left(\frac{I_0}{I}\right) = \epsilon_\omega Cb$$

where ϵ_ω is the molecular extinction coefficient or molar absorptivity in units of liter cm.$^{-1}$ moles^{-1}. These relations are associated with the names of Beer, Lambert, and Bougier.

Previously, the transmittance T was defined as $\frac{I}{I_0}$. Another quantity, the *absorbance*, or optical density, A, is defined as

$$A = \log_{10} \frac{I_0}{I} = \log_{10} \frac{1}{T}$$

so that

$$A = \epsilon_\omega Cb$$

If this relation is valid, the absorbance A is directly proportional to the concentration of the solute. Instruments for the visible, ultraviolet, and near infrared frequently are provided with a logarithmic cam in the light attenuator servosystem so that absorbance is recorded linearly on the chart; this refinement is also available with mid-infrared instruments, but only for the 0 to 1 absorbance range, because they must operate at a higher noise level. However, most charts are printed with absorbance units as the ordinate even though a linear transmission system is used.

Beer's law deviations frequently occur and result in a nonlinear but smooth relation between the absorbance and concentration. Intermolecular interactions involving equilibria which change with concentration are frequently the cause of deviations; instrumental effects may also be responsible. These arise when the spectrometer spectral slit width in cm.$^{-1}$ is comparable with the width in cm.$^{-1}$ of the absorption band under study. Grating instruments can usually be operated with sufficiently narrow slits to avoid this but it is of the utmost importance to ensure that the same slit conditions are employed for samples and standards. It is then possible to plot the nonlinear absorbance *vs.* concentration curve and to use this as a calibration curve. Other systematic and reproducible errors, such as the choice of I_0, are also corrected for by this procedure.

Absorbance is measured at the peak of the band chosen to be the measure of the component of interest. An isolated band is desirable. The simplest method is to measure directly at the one wavelength the transmissions of a series of standard mixtures; a single-beam instrument will give the best reproducibility. Sufficient time for the sample to attain equilibrium temperature should be allowed because infrared absorption bands are, in general, rather sensitive to temperature, *e.g.*, about 1 percent change in absorbance per degree centigrade. This delay also allows the recording system plenty of time to reach the correct position so that a longer than normal response time with corresponding improvement in signal-to-noise ratio is possible. The I_0 value is obtained by reading the transmission of the same cell full of solvent while the zero percent transmission is measured by placing an object opaque at the frequency of interest in the beam. Modern instruments are not normally plagued by scattered light but tests described in the instrument manual should be made to eliminate the possibility of an error contribution from this factor. A Beer's law plot should be used for the analysis A systematic error may be present in this method because I_0 may not be measured correctly. Figure 3-7*a* shows the ideal situation where this error is absent, while Fig. 3-7*b* shows the more usual condition where background absorption arising from differences in reflection and scattering between solvent and solution is present. A practical method of dealing with this difficulty is the baseline method which requires that a straight line be drawn across the base of the band such that it touches at two points tangentially.[3] This is a reproducible approximation to the I_0 value unless the neighboring bands arise from other components in the mixture, in which case the transmission maxima to which the tangent is drawn would vary considerably in frequency, and large errors would arise. Often there is a choice of

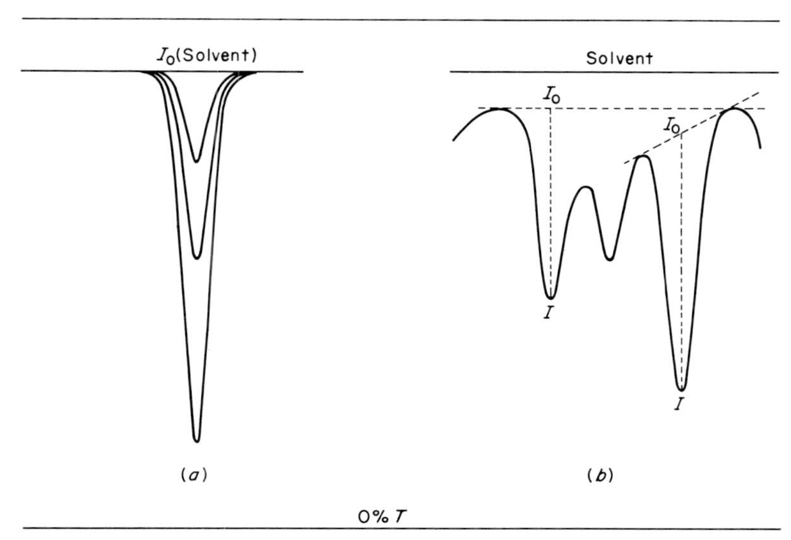

FIG. 3-7 *a*. The Ideal Situation. *b*. The Usual Situation. Several baseline constructions may be chosen. Two are drawn.

tangent line available and if all are reproducible over the range of concentration covered by the analysis, any of the possible baselines may be used. The nonlinear absorbance *vs.* concentration curves are all different but so long as samples and standards are measured using the same baseline construction the analyses will be valid. This method requires that at least a small region of the spectrum be scanned. This should be done slowly enough to follow the true spectrum. The slit conditions must be kept the same for samples and standards.

For multicomponent mixtures it is sometimes not possible to find bands which are not overlapped by bands of the other components present. If Beer's law holds for all components, the absorbances for n bands (one for each of the n components of the mixture) can be related to the n concentration terms by a set of n linear equations. A_1, the total absorbance at wavenumber ω_1, is given by $A_1 = A_{11} + A_{12} + \cdots A_{1n}$, where A_{12} = absorbance of component 2 at frequency of band 1; then $A_1 = a_{11}c_1 + a_{12}c_2 + \cdots a_{1n}c_n$. All the coefficients, a_{ij}, which number n^2, must be determined by measuring absorbances of the pure compounds. When Beer's law is not obeyed these relations are not valid and sets of calibration curves for each analytical frequency must be employed. A successive approximation method is then used to read off the required concentrations. Limitations of this technique are severe because some of the calibration

[3] Wright, N., Ind. Eng. Chem., Anal. Ed., **13,** 1, 1941.

curves must be derived for frequencies on the sides of absorption bands and these frequencies must be reproduced each time very accurately to avoid introducing large errors. In such cases a preliminary separation of the mixture is advisable.

Uncertainties.—Errors due to uncertainties in concentration need not be significant unless small quantities are being analyzed and very volatile solvents are used. Cell length uncertainty is about 0.2 percent if the cell is measured interferometrically, but this may be eliminated by using the same cell for samples and standards. The main errors arise in the photometric measurement.

It may be shown that the best precision is obtained, if the absorbance is measured in the approximate range of 0.3 to 0.6, *i.e.*, about 50 to 25 percent transmission.[4] In this range an uncertainty of ± 0.3 percent of full scale in the transmittance measurement corresponds to an uncertainty of about ± 1 percent of the measured absorbance and, hence, of the solute concentration. Errors in determining I, I_0 and the zero transmission all contribute. Reproducibility tests have shown that under favorable conditions short term reproducibility of absorbance measurements is better than ± 0.5 percent of the measured absorbance, whereas long term reproducibility is closer to ± 1 percent.[5] Accuracy of concentration determination may approach ± 0.5 percent of the measured concentration, if samples and standards are run consecutively under exactly the same slit width setting and other instrumental conditions in the same cell, with proper control of sample temperature. Intensity values are not transferable between instruments; each instrument must have its own absorbance *vs.* concentration curve determined experimentally.

Double-beam, optical-null instruments do not in general perform as well as single-beam instruments in quantitative absorbance measurement, although results well within ± 1 percent of the quantity measured may be attained.[6] Considerably higher accuracy may be obtained with the double-beam instrument if the difference spectra method is employed.[6,7] This technique reduces the uncertainty in the baseline (I_0), it compares sample and standards directly, thus eliminating long term variations in absorbance readings, and it effectively expands the absorbance scale by allowing the measurements to be made in the lower absorbance region. Sensitivity may then be increased by ordinate scale expansion accompanied by the use of wider slits and slowed response to improve the signal-to-noise ratio.

Methods for Special Materials.—Since no single example of an analysis could possibly be typical of all of the wide variety of problems to which the method of quantitative infrared spectrometry may be applied, none is included here. The reader is referred to the Coblentz Society collection of several hundred standard methods of analysis. An index[8] gives the location of each method—either in Analytical Chemistry or Applied Spectroscopy—and each method includes details of wavelengths used, range of concentration analyzed, accuracy attainable, and instrumental method used. Recommended practices for general techniques of infrared quantitative analysis are to be found in the ASTM Proceedings.[9]

The applications of infrared methods in the analysis of special materials listed elsewhere in Standard Methods of Chemical Analysis are as follows:

1. Chapter 42, Volume III, Air Pollutants.
   a. Determination of carbon monoxide in air pollution studies

[4] Robinson, D. Z., Anal. Chem., **23**, 273, 1951.
[5] Childers, E., and Struthers, G. W., Anal. Chem., **25**, 1311, 1953.
[6] Schurmann, R., and Kendrich, E., Anal. Chem., **26**, 1263, 1954.
[7] Robinson, D. Z., Anal. Chem., **24**, 619, 1952.
[8] Smith, A. Lee, and Kiley, L. R., Applied Spectroscopy, **18**, 38, 1964.
[9] American Society for Testing and Materials, Proceedings, **59**, 611, 1959.

b. Qualitative and semiquantitative detection of hydrocarbons in air pollution studies

2. Chapter 43, Volume III, Alloys: Iron, Steel, Ferro-alloys and Related Products.
   a. To monitor carbon monoxide and carbon dioxide in effluent stack gases in steelmaking
   b. Determination of gaseous compounds in effluent gases from steelmaking and heat treating
3. Chapter 46, Volume III, Portland Cement.
   a. Inorganic compounds (possibilities)
   b. Lignosulfonates in cement, concrete, paste, and mortar
   c. Organic components in cement
4. Chapter 52, Volume III, Gases.
   a. Method for recording carbon monoxide concentration in air or combustion products
   b. Hydrocarbons in gas streams
5. Chapter 48, Volume III, Natural Fats.
   a. *Trans*-isomers in fats (also Volume IIB, page 1478)

   Chapter 33, Volume IIB, Natural Fats.
   a. Fats, oils, and waxes, page 1478
6. Chapter 51, Volume III, Organic Functional Groups.
   a. Amines and amides
   b. Analysis of acid chlorides for free fatty acid content
   c. Alcohols
   d. Alkanes
   e. Alkenes
   f. Alkynes
   g. Aromatic hydrocarbons
   h. Determination of 2-butyne-1,4-diol in 2-butene-1,4-diol
   i. Degree of chain branching in alkylbenzene sulfonates
   j. Estimation of ethylene oxide chain length in alkylphenol ethoxylates
   k. Ethylene-propylene copolymers
   l. Analysis of hydrolyzed methyl vinyl ether-maleic anhydride copolymers
   m. Determination of moisture in *N*-methyl-pyrrolidone
   n. Determination of nonylphenoxypropionitrile in nonylphenol
   o. Analysis of propargyl halides for residual propargyl alcohol
   p. Determination of 2-pyrrolidone in *N*-vinyl pyrrolidone
   q. Determination of 2,6-toluenediisocyanate and 2,4-toluenediisocyanate in mixtures
   r. Determination of *N*-vinyl pyrrolidone in 2-pyrrolidone
   s. Analysis of isomeric xylenes

   The following methods using the near infrared are also given:
   a. Analysis of acetic acid–acetic anhydride mixtures
   b. Determination of primary and secondary amines in the presence of tertiary amines
   c. Determination of aliphatic formates
   d. Determination of aromatic aldehydes in the presence of aromatic ketones
   e. Determination of hydroxyl values of alcohols
   f. Determination of terminal unsaturation
   g. Determination of water in organic materials
7. Chapter 54, Volume III, Paint, Varnish, and Lacquer.
   a. Cellulose nitrate content of lacquers

b. Unreacted isocyanate in urethane intermediates
c. Oil content of resin-modified oil varnishes
d. Poly(vinyl acetate) in vinyl resins
e. Qualitative analysis of materials used in paints, varnishes, and lacquers

Chapter 37, Volume IIB, Paint, Varnish, and Lacquers.
a. Identification of oils, pages 1644, 1663
b. Pigments, organic and inorganic, page 1685
c. Identification of polymers, resins, and oils, page 1628
d. Analysis of solvents, page 1703
e. Spectra given, page 1708–21

8. Chapter 39, Volume IIB, Pesticides.
a. Aldrin, page 1845
b. DDT, page 1865
c. Sevin, page 1902

9. Chapter 57, Volume III, Petroleum and Petroleum Products.
a. Characterization of aromatic fractions in petroleum analysis

10. Chapter 58, Volume III, Plastics.
a. Additives in polymers
b. Epoxides in epoxy resins
c. Composition of polymers
d. Determination of structure of polymers
e. Identification of plastics
f. Quantitative analysis of polymers
g. Used to follow molecular changes which occur in thermal treatment of polymers
h. Used to follow polymerization or curing reactions

Chapter 41, Volume IIB, Plastics.
a. Ester plasticizers in plastics, page 2059
b. Identification of plastics, page 2036
c. Determination of styrene-butudiene rubber, page 2066

11. Chapter 59, Volume III, Rubber and Rubber Products.
a. Identification of accelerators
b. *cis*-1,4-content of polyisoprene
c. Determination of composition of ethylene-propylene copolymers
d. Identification of inorganic fillers
e. Analysis of natural rubber—SBR mixtures
f. Analysis of NBR *N*-phenolic blends
g. Identification of polymers
h. Determination of structural characteristics of polyurethane rubber
i. Determination of structural characteristics of silicone rubbers
j. Determination of structural characteristics in rubber analysis

Chapter 43, Volume IIB, Rubber and Rubber Products.
a. Identification of rubber polymers, pages 2168, 2176
b. Identification of rubber polymers, page 2191

12. Chapter 60, Volume III, Semiconductors.
a. Determination of oxygen in semiconductors

13. Chapter 61, Volume III, Soaps and Synthetic Detergents.
a. Estimation of branching in chain alkylaryl sulfonates
b. Identification of surface active agents
c. Determination of ester in ethanolamide fatty acid derivatives
d. Determination of alkylbenzenesulfonates in sewage

14. Chapter 48, Volume IIB, Water Analysis.
    a. Anionic surfactants in water
15. Chapter 64, Volume III, Determination of Water.
    a. Determination of water in alcohols, amines, liquid chlorine, Freon, gases, glycerol and glycols, hydrocarbons, hydrogen fluoride, mercaptans, fuming nitric acid, and sulfur dioxide

SELECTED BIBLIOGRAPHY

Excellent, detailed accounts of infrared instrumentation and sampling techniques are given in references 1 and 2.

1) Potts, W. J., Jr., Chemical Infrared Spectroscopy, Vol. 1: Techniques, John Wiley and Sons, New York, 1963.
2) Brugel, W., An Introduction to Infrared Spectroscopy, John Wiley and Sons, New York, 1962.

Some of the references 3 to 12 also contain discussions of experimental methods but they are primarily concerned with the interpretation of spectra, some largely in terms of group frequencies; others, on a less empirical basis.

3) Bellamy, L. J., Infrared Spectra of Complex Molecules, 2nd Ed., Methuen, London, 1958.
4) Jones, N., and Sandorfy, C., "The Application of Infrared and Raman Spectrometry to the Elucidation of Molecular Structure," Chapter IV in Chemical Applications of Spectroscopy, Vol. IX of Techniques of Organic Chemistry, A. Weissberger, ed., Interscience Publishers, New York, 1956.
5) Rao, C. N. R., Chemical Applications of Infrared Spectroscopy, Academic Press, New York, 1963.
6) Nakanishi, K., Practical Infrared Absorption Spectroscopy, Holden-Day Inc., San Francisco, 1962.
7) Nakamoto, K., Infrared Spectra of Inorganic and Coordination Compounds, John Wiley and Sons, New York, 1963.
8) Flett, M. St. C., Characteristic Frequencies of Chemical Groups in the Infrared, Elsevier Publishing Co., New York, 1963.
9) Phillips, J. R., Spectra-Structure Correlations, Academic Press, New York, 1964.
10) Colthup, N. B., Daly, L. H., and Wiberly, S., Introduction to Infrared and Raman Spectroscopy, Academic Press, New York, 1964.
11) Davies, M., ed., Infrared Spectroscopy and Molecular Structure; An Outline of the Principles, Elsevier Publishing Co., New York, 1963.
12) Szymanski, H. A., Theory and Practice of Infrared Spectroscopy, Plenum Press, New York, 1964. See especially the chapter on instrumentation by N. L. Alpert.

Collections of standard spectra mainly for the 2.5- to 16-micron region include the following:

13) The Coblentz Society collection of several thousand spectra, available through the Sadtler Research Laboratories, Philadelphia, Pennsylvania.
14) A Catalog of Infrared Standard Spectra, collected and published by the Sadtler Research Laboratories.
15) Documentation of Molecular Spectroscopy System (DMS) available from Spex Industries Inc., Hollis, New York.
16) American Petroleum Institute, Project 44 collection (mainly hydrocarbon spectra) and the Manufacturing Chemists Association Research Project collection (nonhydrocarbon spectra) are complementary. Chemical Thermodynamics Properties Center, Agricultural and Mechanical College of Texas, College Station, Texas.
17) National Bureau of Standards Collection, NBS, Washington, D. C.
18) American Society for Testing and Materials—Wyandotte Chemical Corporation System. An index of collections 13 to 17 and the general literature in the form of punched cards suitable for searching and correlating infrared data with chemical structure by machine methods. Spectra are not reproduced. Also available is a molecular formula list of compounds with references to published spectra of all compounds in the Wyandotte—ASTM system, ASTM, Philadelphia, Pennsylvania.

19) Hershenson, H. M., Index of Published Infrared Spectra, Academic Press, New York. Literature references only. Two volumes, for 1945–1957 and for 1958–1962.
20) An Index of Published Infrared Spectra, Vols. 1 and 2, H. M. Stationery Office, London, 1960. Up to 1957. Includes information on physical state, spectral region, and instrumentation.

Several small collections, of the order of a hundred spectra, of related compounds are available:

21) Miller, F. A., Wilkins, C. H., Carlson, G. L., Bentley, F. F., and Jones, W. H., "Infrared Spectra of Inorganic Ions," Spectrochim. Acta, **16,** 135, 1960, and Anal. Chem., **24,** 1253, 1952.
22) Nyquist, R. A., Infrared Spectra of Plastics and Resins, Dow Chemical Company, Midland, Michigan, 1960.
23) DuVall, R. B., Infrared Spectra of Plasticizers and other Additives, Dow Chemical Company, Midland, Michigan, 1962.
24) Erley, D. S., and Blake, B. H., Infrared Spectra of Gases and Vapors (Commonly Found as Industrial Air Contaminants), Dow Chemical Company, Midland, Michigan, 1964.
25) Infrared Spectra of Steroids, Vol. 1 by K. Dobriner, E. R. Katzenellenbogen, and R. N. Jones, 1953, Vol. 2 by G. Roberts, B. S. Gallagher, and R. N. Jones, 1958, Interscience Publishers, New York.

Chapter 4

RAMAN SPECTROMETRY

By R. Norman Jones
Division of Pure Chemistry
National Research Council of Canada
Ottawa, Canada

and

Joseph B. DiGiorgio
Department of Chemistry
Johns Hopkins University
Baltimore, Maryland

INTRODUCTION

Since the analytical chemist should regard Raman spectrometry primarily as an adjunct to infrared spectrometry, it is necessary that we include some mention of infrared spectrometry in this chapter, though this does not infringe upon the more detailed discussion of the infrared technique given in Chapter 3. Both Raman spectrometry and infrared spectrometry are methods for determining the internal vibrations of molecules, and their use in analysis is based on the specificity of these vibrations. The methods are predominantly applicable to the qualitative and quantitative analysis of covalently bonded molecules rather than to ionic structures. Nevertheless, they can give information about the lattice structure of ionic molecules in the crystalline state and about the internal covalent structure of complex ions and the ligand structure of coordination compounds both in the solid state and in solution.

Both the Raman and the infrared spectrum yield a partial description of the internal vibrational motion of the molecule in terms of the normal vibrations of the constituent atoms. Neither type of spectrum alone gives a complete description of the pattern of molecular vibration, and, by analysis of the difference between the Raman and the infrared spectrum, additional information about the molecular structure can sometimes be inferred. Physical chemists have made extremely effective use of such comparisons in the elucidation of the finer structural details of small symmetrical molecules, such as methane and benzene, but the mathematical techniques of vibrational analysis are not yet sufficiently developed to permit the extension of these differential studies to the Raman and infrared spectra of the more complex molecules that constitute the main body of both organic and inorganic chemistry.

The analytical chemist can use Raman and infrared spectra in two ways. At the purely empirical level they provide "fingerprints" of the molecular structure and, as such, permit the qualitative analysis of individual compounds, either by direct comparison of the spectra of the known and unknown materials run consecutively, or by comparison of the spectrum of the unknown compound with catalogs of reference spectra.

By comparisons among the spectra of large numbers of compounds of known structure, it has been possible to recognize, at specific positions in the spectrum, bands which can be identified as "characteristic group frequencies" associated with the presence of localized units of molecular structure in the molecule, such as methyl, carbonyl, or hydroxyl groups. Many of these group frequencies differ in the Raman and infrared spectra. The use of group frequencies in this manner is to be regarded as a technique more properly for molecular structure determination than for chemical analysis in the narrower sense, but the analyst must be familiar with the group frequencies in order to apply Raman and infrared techniques with maximum efficiency to the qualitative recognition of individual compounds and to the quantitative analysis of mixtures.

Theoretically, the normal modes of vibration of a molecule involve the simultaneous motions of all the atoms; they depend on the masses of all the atoms and on the forces acting between them. Any change in the molecular structure will, therefore, alter the normal vibrations; it follows that no two substances can have identical Raman or infrared spectra. In practice caution must be used in identifying substances by comparison of the spectra, since molecules with related but not identical structures may have extremely similar spectra over limited ranges of wavenumber; structure identification based solely on the similarity of Raman or infrared spectra should be claimed, therefore, only after the measurements have been extended over the maximum measurable wavenumber range. It is also important that the comparisons be based on spectra determined under the same physical conditions of measurement. In the case of organic solids this requires that the unknown and the standard comparison sample should have been recrystallized from the same solvent.

Raman spectra are difficult to obtain, and the analyst will be well advised to use infrared spectra in preference to Raman spectra under most circumstances, for reasons that will become apparent later in this chapter. The techniques of ultraviolet spectrometry and proton magnetic resonance spectrometry are also easier to apply; hence, it is also advisable to investigate their feasibility to deal with the problem on hand before turning to the Raman method. In this chapter we shall indicate the types of problems for which the Raman technique is best suited, and shall discuss the basic principles of Raman spectrometry using photoelectric instruments of commercial manufacture.

THE NATURE OF RAMAN SPECTRA

In 1928, Sir C. V. Raman first reported his discovery of the phenomenon that today bears his name,[1] proving Smekal's earlier prediction of such an effect.[2] Raman observed that when a transparent medium was irradiated with an intense source of monochromatic light, and the scattered radiation was examined spectoscopically, not only was light of the exciting frequency, ν, observed (Rayleigh scattering), but also some weaker bands of shifted frequency were detected. He further noted that, while most of the shifted bands were of lower frequency, $\nu - \Delta\nu_i$, there were some at higher frequency, $\nu + \Delta\nu_i$. By analogy to fluorescence spectrometry, the former Raman bands are called Stokes bands and the latter anti-Stokes bands. The Stokes and anti-Stokes bands are equally displaced about the Rayleigh band; however, the intensity of the anti-Stokes bands is much weaker than the Stokes bands and they are seldom observed. In this chapter we shall deal only with the more intense Stokes bands. The geometric arrangement for observing the Raman effect is shown diagrammatically in Fig. 4-1.

The spectral position of a Raman band is dependent on the exciting frequency, but the displacement of the Raman band is independent of the exciting frequency and the positions of Raman bands are recorded as wavenumber displacements. By convention

[1] Raman, C. V., Indian J. Phys., **2,** 387, 1928.
[2] Smekal, A., Naturwissenschaften, **11,** 873, 1923.

the positions of Raman bands are expressed as wavenumbers (ν) but more correctly they are wavenumber differences ($\Delta\nu$). It is often expedient to overlook this fact, particularly when comparisons with infrared spectra are being made.

The magnitude of Raman displacements corresponds to the vibrational and rotational region of the electromagnetic spectrum (*ca.* 50–4000 cm.$^{-1}$). Raman bands arise from the same energy levels as are observed in the infrared for vibrational and rotational modes of vibration, but in this chapter we shall be concerned only with the vibrational Raman effect.

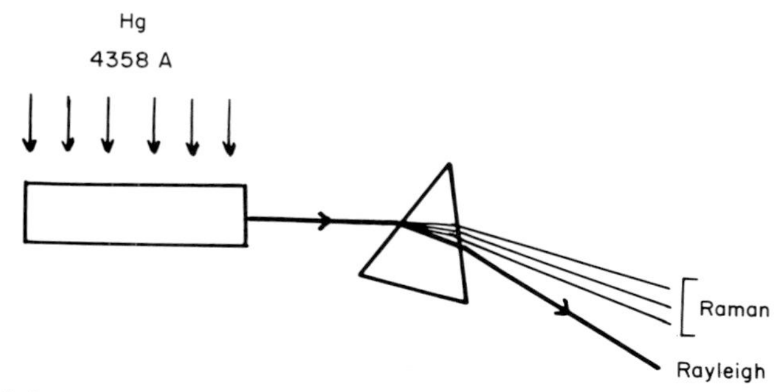

FIG. 4-1. Optical System to Observe a Raman Spectrum. The Rayleigh scattering is at the wavelength of the exciting line.

The motions of the atoms in a polyatomic molecule are very complex, but they can be treated as a superposition of a set of fundamental or normal vibrations.[3,4] For a nonlinear molecule containing N atoms, there are 3 N degrees of freedom and these can be separated into translational, rotational, and vibrational degrees of freedom. There are 3 degrees of translational freedom and 3 degrees of rotational freedom (2 degrees of rotational freedom for a linear molecule). The remaining $3\,N - 6$ ($3\,N - 5$ for a linear molecule) degrees of freedom are the vibrational degrees of freedom and each corresponds to one of the normal modes of vibration of the molecule. All possible vibrations of a complex molecule can be represented as a linear combination of its $3\,N - 6$ normal modes. In a normal mode of vibration all of the atoms move in phase with one another. Each normal mode is associated with a corresponding frequency, which occurs in the infrared region of the electromagnetic spectrum. However, the presence of a normal mode at a certain frequency does not necessarily mean that an infrared or Raman band will be observed at that position.

The factor that determines whether or not a band is observed in the infrared or Raman spectrum is the electrical nature of the normal vibration. For a band to be allowed in the infrared, the normal mode must produce a change in the dipole moment during the vibration, while for a band to be allowed in the Raman spectrum there must be a change in the polarizability of the molecule during the vibration. This can be illustrated by considering two of the normal modes of vibration for benzene. The out-of-plane C—H deformation mode at 671 cm.$^{-1}$ (Fig. 4-2*a*) involves a change of dipole moment during this vibration, but there is no change in the polarizability of the molecule; this vibration is, therefore, infrared active and Raman inactive. In the symmetrical breathing mode at 991 cm.$^{-1}$ (Fig. 4-2*b*) the molecule suffers no change in dipole moment, but

[3] Herzberg, G., Molecular Spectra and Molecular Structure, Vol. II, Infrared and Raman Spectra of Polyatomic Molecules, D. Van Nostrand, Princeton, 1945.

[4] Wilson, E. B., Jr., Decius, J. C., and Cross, P. C., Molecular Vibrations, McGraw-Hill, New York, 1955. Both these works afford a thorough treatment of molecular vibrations.

there is a change in the polarizability; this vibration is accordingly infrared inactive but Raman active.

In the example cited the infrared and Raman selection rules are mutually exclusive; *i.e.*, a band allowed in the infrared is forbidden in the Raman and vice versa. This condition is true for all molecules that have a center of symmetry. In molecules with

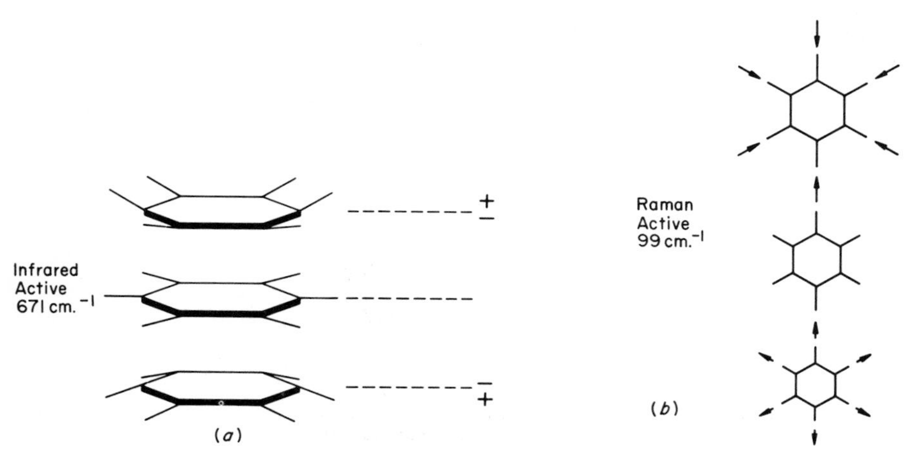

FIG. 4-2. (*a*) Normal Vibration of the 671 cm.$^{-1}$ Infrared Active Out-of-plane C—H Deformation Vibration of Benzene. (*b*) Normal Vibration of the 991 cm.$^{-1}$ Raman Active Breathing Vibration of Benzene.

different elements of symmetry certain bands may be active in the Raman, infrared, both, or neither. For a complex molecule that has no symmetry save identity, all of the normal modes are allowed in both the infrared and Raman spectra. This does not mean, however, that they will all be observed. In both types of spectra, weak bands can be obscured by neighboring strong bands, while others may be intrinsically too weak to be observed even though they are theoretically "allowed." Thus, the infrared and Raman spectra of a compound do not necessarily exhibit the same bands differing only in intensity. Figure 4-3 shows a comparison of the Raman and infrared spectra of a typical steroid. It can be seen that in general the strong bands in the infrared correspond to weak bands in the Raman and vice versa. This complementary nature of infrared and Raman is due to the electrical characteristic of the vibration. If a bond is strongly polarized, a small change in its length, such as occurs during a vibration, will have only a small additional effect on the polarization. Vibrations involving polar bonds (C—O, N—O, O—H) are, therefore, comparatively weak Raman scatterers. Such polarized bonds, however, carry their charges with them during the vibrational motion, and unless neutralized by symmetry factors, this results in a large net dipole change and high infrared intensity. Conversely, relatively neutral bonds (C—C, C—H, C═C, C≡C) suffer larger changes in polarizability during a vibration, though this is less easy to visualize. The dipole moment is not similarly affected and vibrations that predominantly involve this type of bond are strong Raman scatterers but weak in the infrared.

Raman radiation is always optically polarized, and by examining the polarization of the individual Raman bands additional information may be obtained, which is useful in identifying the type of normal vibration responsible for the band. In Fig. 4-4, where

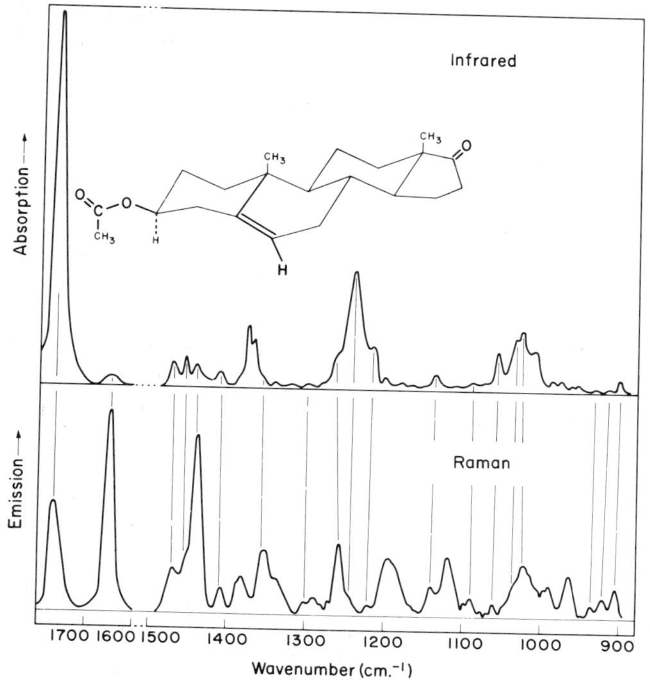

FIG. 4-3. Comparison of the Infrared and Raman Spectra of 3β-acetoxy-Δ^5-androsten-17-one in Carbon Disulfide Solution; see also Fig. 4-7. (Courtesy Spartan Books.)

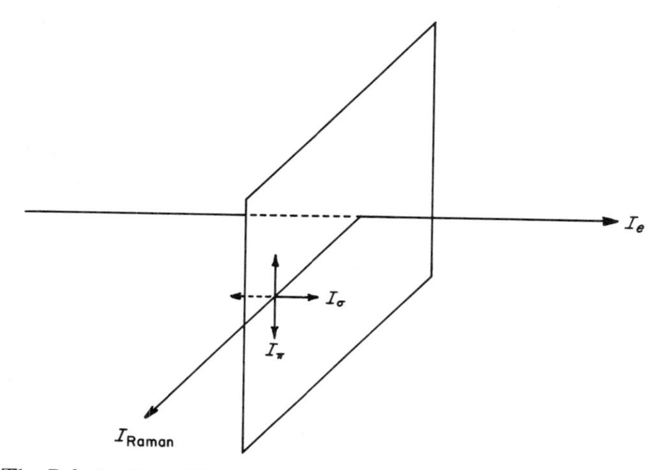

FIG. 4-4. The Polarization of Raman Radiation. If the exciting radiation is incident along the z-axis, ρ is the ratio of the intensity of radiation scattered perpendicular to the xy-plane to that scattered parallel to the xy-plane.

I_e is the direction of the exciting radiation beam, the Raman scattering will be observed in the plane perpendicular to this direction. If I_π and I_σ are the intensities of the scattered radiation polarized parallel and perpendicular to this plane respectively, the ratio

$$\rho = \frac{I_\sigma}{I_\pi} \tag{1}$$

is known as the *depolarization ratio;* its theoretical significance is discussed in detail elsewhere.[5,6]

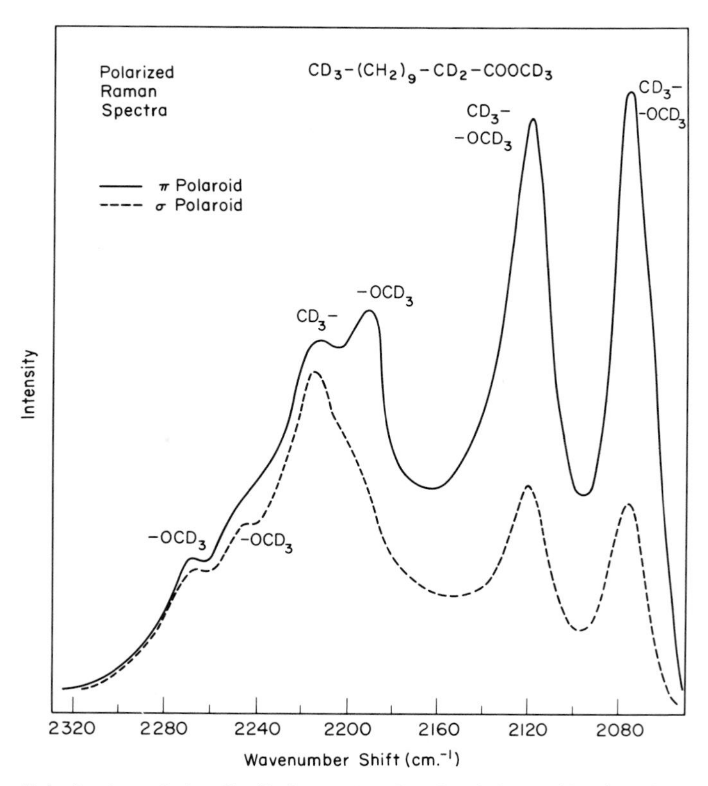

FIG. 4-5. Polarization of the C—D Stretching Bands of CD_3—$(CH_2)_9$—CD_2—$COOCD_3$. (From R. Norman Jones and R. A. Ripley, Can. J. Chem., **42,** 305, 1964; reprinted with permission.)

If the exciting radiation is nonpolarized, the depolarization ratio (ρ) will have a value of 6/7 for all nontotally symmetrical vibrations. For totally symmetric vibrations ρ will be less than 6/7 and may be as low as zero.

This is illustrated in Fig. 4-5 where part of the Raman spectrum of the deuterated

[5] Mizushima, S., "Raman Effect," Handbuch der Physik, S. Flügge, Ed., Vol. XXVI, Springer-Verlag, Berlin, Gottingen, Heidelberg, 1958, pp. 196–208 (in English).

[6] Evans, J. C., Infrared Spectroscopy and Molecular Structure, M. Davies, Ed., Elsevier, New York, 1963, p. 206.

methyl laurate $CD_3\cdot(CH_2)_9\cdot CD_2\cdot COOCD_3$ is shown. This is the region of the spectrum associated with C—D stretching vibrations. The band at 2216 cm.$^{-1}$ which is associated with the asymmetric C—D stretching vibration of the terminal CD_3— group is depolarized, whereas the neighboring band at 2196 cm.$^{-1}$ associated with the —OCD_3 group of the ester is strongly polarized.

Experimentally it is sometimes difficult to measure the depolarization ratio accurately, due to the considerable loss of intensity when polarizers are used. Then we can say only that a band is strongly ($\rho \leq 0.4$) or weakly ($\rho = 0.4$–0.8) polarized or that it is depolarized ($\rho \geq 0.8$). Strongly polarized bands are not commonly observed in the Raman spectra of complex compounds due to the lack of symmetry, though they are quite common in small molecules.

In many Raman spectrometers, the radiation source is cylindrically symmetrical about the sample cell, and it is convenient to polarize the incident light as described by Edsall and Wilson.[7] A cylinder of Polaroid film is placed around the sample cell with the direction of polarization either perpendicular or parallel to the cell axis. In this case the apparent depolarization ratio is

$$\rho_{\text{app}} = \frac{I_{\text{par}}}{I_{\text{per}}} \tag{2}$$

The apparent depolarization ratio must be corrected for a "convergence error" which is due to the incident radiation not being strictly normal to the tube. This oblique irradiation gives apparent depolarization ratios that are larger in magnitude than they would be if the sample were illuminated only with radiation normal to the cell. Procedures have been described to correct for this effect.[8,9] It is to be noted that the intensity symbols of Eq. (2) differ from those of Eq. (1). This is to emphasize that Eq. (1) refers to a system irradiated with unpolarized light and Eq. (2) to the comparison of two systems irradiated with light polarized in mutually perpendicular planes.[7] In either case the maximum depolarization ratio is 6/7 in the absence of any convergence error. Care must be taken when dealing with other optical arrangements; thus, for the system of Fig. 4-4, with light plane polarized at 90° to the scattered beam, the maximum depolarization ratio becomes 3/4.

EXPERIMENTAL TECHNIQUE

Excitation of Raman Spectra.—The intrinsic weakness of the Raman effect necessitates the use of an intense source of monochromatic light for its excitation. The most widely used source at present is the mercury blue line at 4358 A. There are many factors that have to be considered when choosing an exciting line. The intensity of Raman radiation is proportional to the fourth power of the frequency of the exciting line,[10] and it is therefore advantageous to use as short a wavelength source as possible. However, if the wavelength of the exciting line is too short other problems are created; fluorescence and photodecomposition of the sample are enhanced. With colored samples the wavelength of the exciting line must be chosen so that it will not be absorbed too strongly by the sample.

The 4358 A line is a good compromise in the present state of the Raman technique. The photomultiplier detectors used in contemporary spectrometers have high sensitivity in this wavelength region. The Toronto-type low pressure mercury arc is an excellent

[7] Edsall, J. T., and Wilson, E. B., Jr., J. Chem. Phys., **6**, 124, 1938.
[8] Elson, E. L., and Edsall, J. T., Biochemistry, **1**, 1, 1962.
[9] Koningstein, J. A., and Bernstein, H. J., Spectrochim. Acta, **18**, 1249, 1962.
[10] Zubov, V. A., Optics and Spectroscopy, **14**, 304, 1963.

source of the 4358 A line when used with appropriate filters. One convenient filter arrangement for this purpose consists of a dual system of saturated aqueous potassium nitrite solution and aqueous rhodamine solution.[11] Other types of sources for the 4358 A line have been described using high pressure[12] and medium pressure[13] mercury arcs. A high-power Toronto-type mercury arc has been described by Janz, Mikawa, and James.[14] Siebert[15] has described another filter suitable for isolating the 4358 A line, while Simon *et al.*[16,17,18] have described numerous filters for isolating particular mercury lines.

The mercury green line (5461 A) has been used by Noack and Jones[19] to examine the Raman spectrum of biacetyl, which absorbs strongly at 4358 A, and they describe suitable filters for isolating the 5461 A line. The long-wave excitation of Raman spectra has been reviewed by Stammreich,[20] and the use of long wavelength lines of helium,[21] helium, argon, krypton, or xenon,[22] and sodium vapor[23] have also been reported. The recent surge of interest in lasers should have important consequences for Raman spectrometry. Their high intensity could overcome the handicap of the inverse fourth power dependence on the wavelength, permitting the excitation of strong Raman spectra under conditions where fluorescence will be less serious. It seems probable that within the next few years continuous gas lasers operating in the red, or in the near infrared, may replace the 4358 A mercury lamp for the generation of Raman spectra and this could lead to a re-evaluation of the technique.

Note Added in Proof.—Since the above was written this technique has developed rapidly. One Raman spectrophotometer, manufactured by the Perkin-Elmer Corp., using 6328 A radiation from a helium neon laser source is in commercial production, and it is to be expected that other instruments will soon be available. It is not yet feasible to say how these instruments will compare with those using the conventional sources, but it would appear to be largely a matter of time before laser sources with sufficient power to overcome any deficiencies become routinely available. The 6328 A laser source has undoubted advantages for the measurement of certain colored substances and photosensitive compounds. For further discussion see Koningstein, J. A., and Smith, R. G., J. Opt. Soc. Am., **54,** 1061, 1964.

Sample Preparation.—Qualitative measurements of Raman spectra can be made on solids, liquids, solutions, and gases. The measurements on gases require elaborate apparatus; most practical analytical applications are concerned with measurements on pure liquids and, to a lesser extent, on solutions and solids. When preparing samples for Raman analysis, it is extremely important that the material be entirely free of fluorescent impurities. If fluorescent materials are present in the sample, the fluorescence

[11] Jones, R. N., Krueger, P. J., Noack, K., Elliott, J. J., Ripley, R. A., Nonnenmacher, G. A. A., and DiGiorgio, J. B., Proc. Xth Colloquium Spectroscopicum Internationale, Spartan Books, Washington, 1963, pp. 461–486.

[12] Brandmüller, J., and Moser, H., Angew. Phys., **8,** 95, 142, 1956.

[13] Simon, A., Kriegsmann, H., and Steger, E., Z. physik, Chem., **205,** 190, 1956.

[14] Janz, G. L., Mikawa, Y., and James, D. W., Appl. Spectroscopy, **15,** 47, 1961.

[15] Siebert, H., Z. anorg. u. allgem. Chem., **308,** 314, 1961.

[16] Simon, A., and Hamann, H., Z. physik. Chem., **209,** 222, 1958.

[17] Simon, A., and Hamann, H., Z. physik. Chem., **216,** 50, 1961.

[18] Simon, A., Jentzsch, D., Schnurrbusch, K., and Hamann, H., Z. physik. Chem., **215,** 340, 1960.

[19] Noack, K., and Jones, R. N., Z. Elektrochemie, **64,** 707, 1960.

[20] Stammreich, H., Pure and Appl. Chem., **4,** 97, 1962.

[21] Delhaye, M., Spectrochim. Acta, Suppl. 1957, 485.

[22] Stammreich, H., Spectrochim. Acta, **8,** 41, 1956.

[23] King, F. T., and Lippincott, E. R., J. Opt. Soc. Am., **46,** 661, 1956.

radiation will obscure the much weaker Raman radiation. The Raman spectrometer itself provides the best test for the absence of such interfering impurities.

The purification of samples for Raman spectra can prove extremely difficult. With liquids, distillation *in vacuo* or filtration through a column of alumina or activated charcoal often suffices, but in some cases these procedures may have to be repeated several times. Repeated recrystallization or sublimation will sometimes clean up solids but it may also be necessary to convert the sample to a derivative and then convert back again to the original compound after purification. Some compounds fail to respond to any of these procedures. For best results the purification should be carried out immediately prior to the determination of the Raman spectrum. It is also essential that all apparatus and solvents used in preparing samples for Raman spectrometry be free of fluorescent materials. If the samples are colored, special techniques can sometimes be employed such as long wavelength excitation.

Sample Phases and Cells. **Liquids.**—In the early development of Raman spectrometry a very large amount of material was required compared to that needed for analysis by ultraviolet or infrared techniques. It was not uncommon to have liquid cells of 100-ml. capacity. This was indeed a serious limitation to the general application of the Raman technique. It was undoubtedly one of the reasons for the trend away from Raman spectrometry as an analytical tool that began in the early nineteen-forties, when infrared methods of analysis were greatly improved.

Much of the subsequent discussion of instrumental technique in this chapter will center around the Cary Model 81 Raman Spectrophotometer which is described in detail on page 73. This instrument is the most widely used at the present time and is best adapted for analytical work where the quantity of sample available must be kept as small as possible. This spectrometer is provided with three sizes of cells, each with its own ancillary optics. The cells are in the form of cylindrical glass tubes 250 mm. long, closed at one end. The largest has an outside diameter of 19 mm. and a volume of 65 ml. The intermediate size is 7 mm. in outside diameter with a volume of 5 ml., and can be modified to take advantage of multiple reflections to give a five-fold increase in the Raman intensity.[24] The smallest cell is 2 mm. in outside diameter with a volume of about 0.2 ml. This capillary cell has the advantage of a reasonably small sample size (*ca.* 200 mg.), but its utilization introduces other complications that will be discussed later. A cavity type microcell with a volume of less than 1 ml. has been described by Mizushima *et al.*[25] We have used the capillary cell for qualitative work with the Cary Model 81 instrument almost exclusively, and have obtained excellent results for both pure liquids and solutions. Special techniques for filling and manipulating this type of cell have recently been described.[26] When the sample to be examined is a liquid, it should usually be used without dilution in order to obtain as strong a signal as possible. Although solids can be measured in the solid phase, they can usually be more conveniently investigated in solution, provided a suitable solvent is available.

As in infrared spectrometry there are a number of factors to consider when choosing a solvent. Since Raman spectra are usually determined at high concentration, the sample must be very soluble in the solvent, and the refractive index of the solution is important especially when using the capillary technique. It is desirable in both Raman and infrared spectrometry to choose a solvent that has a simple spectrum so that it obscures as little as possible of the spectrum of the solute. Generally speaking the Raman

[24] Tunnicliff, D. D., and Jones, A. C., Spectrochim. Acta, **18,** 569, 1962.
[25] Mizushima, S., Shimanouchi, T., and Sugita, T., J. Am. Chem. Soc., **72,** 3811, 1950.
[26] Jones, R. N., DiGiorgio, J. B., Elliott, J. J., and Nonnenmacher, G. A. A., J. Org. Chem., **30,** 1822, 1965.

spectra of the common solvents are simpler than their corresponding infrared spectra. Since Raman and infrared spectra are often compared with one another, it is advantageous to use the same solvent for both types of spectra. Solutions suitable for Raman spectrometry can frequently be investigated in the infrared in cells of 0.1 mm. path length directly without concentration or dilution. The most widely used solvents for Raman spectrometry are carbon disulfide, carbon tetrachloride, chloroform, acetonitrile, and water, and their obscuration ranges are shown in Fig. 4-6, together with their

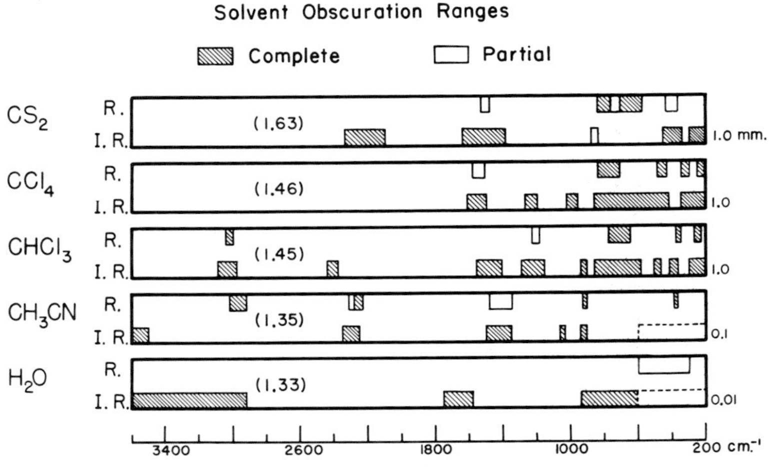

FIG. 4-6. The Obscuration Ranges of the Most Useful Solvents for Raman Spectrometry in Solution. The infrared obscuration at the indicated path lengths is given for comparison.

blackout regions for infrared spectra at the indicated path lengths. Other useful solvents are methylene dichloride, tetrachloroethylene, and deuterium oxide.[26] Above 850 cm.$^{-1}$ carbon disulfide, carbon tetrachloride, and chloroform obscure the Raman spectrum less seriously than the infrared spectrum, and this is of particular importance for the region 1650–1500 cm.$^{-1}$ where the C=C stretching bands occur. Raman obscuration below 850 cm.$^{-1}$ tends to be more severe than in the infrared, but by using more than one solvent, spectra can be obtained down to about 250 cm.$^{-1}$; spectra of neat liquids can be measured to 175/100 cm.$^{-1}$, depending on the instrumental conditions. The most dramatic difference between Raman and infrared solvent obscuration regions is for aqueous solutions; Raman spectra measured in water are free from significant solvent obscuration below 3200 cm.$^{-1}$ This offers a marked advantage over infrared spectrometry and favors the use of Raman techniques for the study of aqueous solutions. The Raman spectrum of an aqueous solution of a monosaccharide derivative is shown in Fig. 4-7.

Gases.—For theoretical reasons it is often desirable to determine infrared and Raman spectra in the gas phase so that intermolecular interactions are reduced to a minimum. The low concentration of a species in the gas phase requires the use of complex multiple reflection cells; Stoicheff has described the construction of such a cell for high resolution Raman spectroscopy of gases.[27] A multiple reflection gas cell is available for the Cary Model 81 Raman instrument along with the necessary additional power supply. Brand-

[27] Stoicheff, B. P., Can. J. Phys., **32**, 330, 1954.

müller and Moser also describe various types of cells for use with gases in their excellent monograph on Raman spectrometry.[28]

Solids.—A recent trend in Raman spectrometry has been toward the development of better techniques for determining the Raman spectra of solids. The solid sample can be in the form of a single crystal, a pellet of compressed powder, or a pellet of compressed powder dispersed in potassium bromide. This method resembles the well known potassium bromide pellet technique used in infrared spectrometry except that concentrations

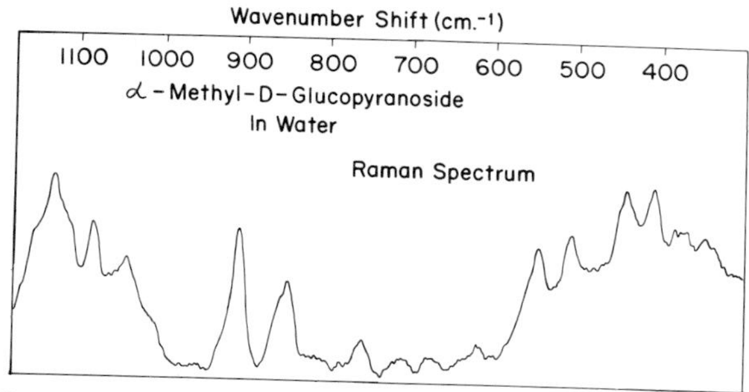

FIG. 4-7. The Raman Spectrum of α-Methyl-D-glucopyranoside in Water. This is a direct transposition of the recorder chart. The steroid spectrum shown in Fig. 4-3 has been corrected for background variation by tangent construction to the bases of the bands.

in the range of 10 to 100 percent are used compared to about 1 percent or less in infrared spectrometry. Some Raman work on solids has been reported by Schrader *et al.*,[29] Ferraro *et al.*,[30] and Tobin.[31] Nelson and Mitchell[32] describe an improved powder technique which uses as little as 20 mg. of material; with this method, the spectrum can be determined to within 40 cm.$^{-1}$ of the exciting line. These authors found that the optimum amount of material is 120 to 160 mg. and that this amount is independent of the compound used or whether or not it is diluted with potassium bromide. They also point out that dilution with potassium bromide may improve the spectra of colored substances. Other types of cells designed for special purposes such as high pressure gases,[33] low temperatures,[34,35] and high temperatures[14] have also been described.

QUANTITATIVE ANALYSIS

To carry out quantitative analysis with the Raman technique, a method of measuring the intensity must be devised. This involves the determination of an absolute light intensity and in this respect Raman spectrometry bears a closer resemblance to emission spectrography than to infrared absorption spectrophotometry where it is only necessary to compare intensity ratios. As with emission spectrography it is customary to choose a standard band with which to compare all other Raman bands; however, the choice

[28] Brandmüller, J., and Moser, H., Einführung in die Ramanspektroskopie, Steinkopff Verlag Darmstadt, 1962, pp. 298–309.
[29] Schrader, B., Nerdel, F., and Kresze, G., Z. anal. Chem., **170**, 43, 1959.
[30] Ferraro, J., Mack, G., and Ziomek, J., Spectrochim. Acta, **17**, 802, 1961.
[31] Tobin, M. C., Developments in Applied Spectroscopy, **1**, 205, 1962.
[32] Nelson, D. C., and Mitchell, W. N., Anal. Chem., **36**, 555, 1964.
[33] Stryland, J. C., and May, A. D., Rev. Sci. Instr. **31**, 414, 1960.
[34] Bouttier, L., Mem. serv. chim. etat, **41**, 79, 1956.
[35] Janz, G. J., and Wait, S. C., Appl. Spectroscopy, **11**, 47, 1957.

of a proper band is not easy and great attention to detail is necessary to obtain reproducible results.

The 459 cm.$^{-1}$ band of carbon tetrachloride is the most widely used intensity standard in Raman spectrometry; the 313 cm.$^{-1}$ band of carbon tetrachloride and the 801 cm.$^{-1}$ band of cyclohexane have also been used. There are objections to the 459 cm.$^{-1}$ carbon tetrachloride band because it is a strongly polarized band and its intensity is dependent on the degree of convergence of the exciting radiation. The isotopic isomers of chlorine also make the band appear as a multiplet under high resolution.[28]

At present there is considerable theoretical interest in the absolute measurements of Raman band intensities and an extensive literature is accumulating on this subject. Most of this work is directed toward obtaining an absolute measurement of the Raman intensity, free of all instrumental variables, in a form that will permit study of the relationship between Raman band intensities and the electrical characteristics of the normal vibrational modes. We shall not review this work here as it is not particularly relevant to analytical applications. Those interested should consult the publications of Bernstein,[36,37] Michel and Gueibe,[38] Venkateswarlu and Thyagarajan,[39] Krushinskii,[40,41] Rea,[42,43] Ryason,[44] Thompson,[45,46,47] Naberukhin,[48] and Brandmüller and Moser.[49]

Bernstein and Allen[37] express the area beneath an isolated Raman band in terms of the "standard intensity," (S), in which corrections have been applied for the instrumental and environmental factors affecting the measurement.

$$S = \frac{I}{I_{459}} \cdot \frac{1+\rho_{459}}{1+\rho_{\text{obs.}}} \cdot \frac{n^2}{n^2_{\text{CCl}_4}} \cdot \frac{\sigma_{\Delta\nu}}{\sigma_{459}} \cdot \frac{M}{d} \cdot \left(\frac{d}{M}\right)_{\text{CCl}_4} \cdot \frac{\Delta\nu}{459} \cdot \left(\frac{\nu - 459}{\nu - \Delta\nu}\right)^4 \cdot \frac{(1 - e^{-1.44\Delta\nu/T})}{(1 - e^{-1.44\times 459/T})} \tag{3}$$

where I and I_{459} are the integrated intensities of the band at $\Delta\nu$ and the standard 459 cm.$^{-1}$ band of carbon tetrachloride, respectively; $\rho_{\text{obs.}}$ and ρ_{459} are the respective observed depolarization ratios; n and n_{CCl_4} the refractive indexes; $\sigma_{\Delta\nu}$ and σ_{459} the spectral sensitivity of the photomultiplier tubes; M the molecular weight; d the density; $\Delta\nu$ the Raman wavenumber displacement; and T the absolute temperature.* The evaluation

[36] Bernstein, H. J., Pure and Appl. Chem., **4,** 23, 1962.
[37] Bernstein, H. J., and Allen, G., J. Opt. Soc. Am., **45,** 237, 1955.
[38] Michel, G., and Gueibe, R., Bull. soc. chim. Belges, **70,** 323, 1961.
[39] Venkateswarlu, K., and Thyagarajan, G., Z. für Physik, **154,** 70, 81, 1959; **156,** 561, 566, 569, 1959.
[40] Krushinskii, L. L., and Shorygin, P. P., Optics and Spectroscopy, **11,** 80, 1961.
[41] Krushinskii, L. L., Optics and Spectroscopy, **14,** 406, 1963.
[42] Rea, D. G., J. Opt. Soc. Am., **49,** 90, 1959.
[43] Rea, D. G., J. Mol. Spectroscopy, **4,** 507, 1960.
[44] Ryason, P. R., J. Mol. Spectroscopy, **8,** 164, 1962.
[45] Jesson, J. P., and Thompson, H. W., Proc. Roy. Soc., **268 A,** 68, 1962.
[46] Facer, G. H. J., and Thompson, H. W., Proc. Roy. Soc., **268 A,** 79, 1962.
[47] Tare, S. A., and Thompson, H. W., Spectrochim. Acta, **18,** 1095, 1962.
[48] Naberukhin, Yg. I., Optics and Spectroscopy, **13,** 278, 1961.
[49] Brandmüller, J., and Moser, H., *op. cit.*, pp. 235–280.

* Bernstein and Allen included an additional term (R) in their original expression to take care of reflection losses; however, an analytical treatment by Rea[42,43] has indicated that this factor has no effect under the conditions of his analysis, a conclusion with which Bernstein now concurs.[50]

[50] Bernstein, H. J., personal communication.

of S required that I and I_{459} be separately measured under identical conditions, *i.e.*, the carbon tetrachloride is used as an external standard. It is also necessary to determine the refractive index and density of the sample if they are not already known. This procedure has been employed only where large samples are available and cells are used with volumes of the order of 50 ml. The Raman radiation that is examined is generated in the bulk of the sample, and radiation reflected at the walls of the cell does not enter the spectrometer. It is to be noted that Bernstein and Allen's "standard intensity" is a band area measurement, and is primarily intended for the study of isolated bands such as are commonly encountered in the spectra of simple symmetric molecules. It is not very meaningful to attempt to evaluate S for the overlapping band systems that more frequently occur in the Raman spectra of complex molecules.

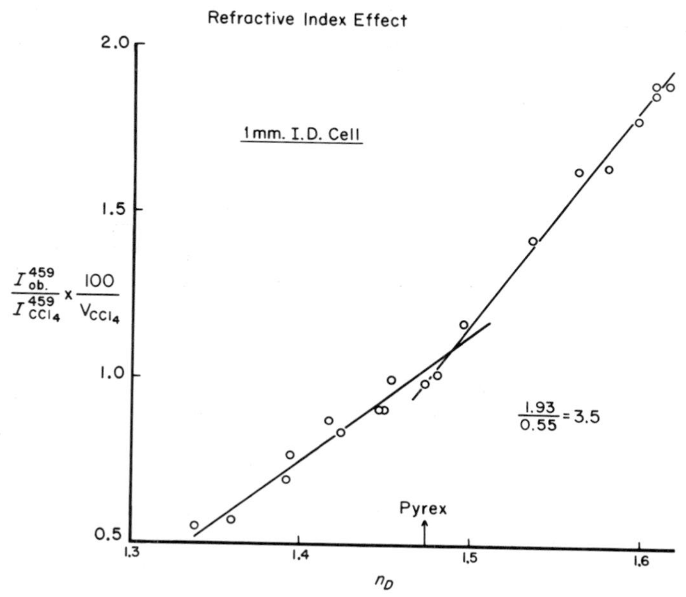

FIG. 4-8. The Peak Raman Intensity of the 459 cm.$^{-1}$ Band of Carbon Tetrachloride in Solutions of Different Refractive Index. A small component of this effect may be due to intrinsic differences in the absolute band intensity, but most result from the change in the optical behavior of the sample cell. (Courtesy Spartan Books.)

When using capillary cells, the reflection of the Raman radiation from the walls of the cell becomes an important factor, and the Raman radiation entering the spectrometer is strongly affected by the refractive index of the solution. Under these conditions the cell acts as a light-pipe and the higher the refractive index of the solution relative to that of the cell material, the greater is the efficiency of the transfer of Raman radiation into the spectrometer.

The refractive index effect for two cell sizes has been described in more detail elsewhere,[26] but the practical effect is shown in Fig. 4-8. When using a 1-mm. I.D. capillary cell, the relative efficiency increases more than threefold in going from a solution of low refractive index (n_D 1.33) to one of high refractive index (n_D 1.63). It is also of interest to note the discontinuity in this graph near the point where the refractive index of the solution and the cell are the same. New glasses with refractive indexes as low as 1.27[51] may lead to a further increase in efficiency.

To reduce the complication of this refractive index effect, an internal standard method must be employed, in which carbon tetrachloride (*ca.* 10 percent) is added to the sample so that the sample and the standard band are measured at the same refractive index. In using this technique it is assumed that the intrinsic intensity of the band, either peak height or area, is not affected by the surrounding medium. This is not strictly true, but the errors involved by this assumption will be less than those encountered with the external standard technique, and can be allowed for in quantitative analysis by establishing working calibration curves. If a solvent other than carbon tetrachloride is used, one of its bands can be used as the internal reference standard.

For codifying data run in various solvents, it is useful to establish an approximate ratio between the secondary solvent bands and the primary standard band of carbon tetrachloride. In our laboratory we employ the "apparent Raman scattering coefficient" ($k_A{}^{\Delta\nu}$) for this purpose where

$$k_A{}^{\Delta\nu} = \frac{i_A{}^{\Delta\nu}}{i_S{}^{\Delta\nu'}} \cdot \frac{\sigma_{\Delta\nu'}}{\sigma_{\Delta\nu}} \cdot \frac{g_S}{g_A} \cdot \frac{N_S}{N_A} \cdot \beta \cdot 100 \tag{4}$$

in which i_A and i_S are the observed peak heights for the substance A at a Raman shift $\Delta\nu$, and the corresponding value for the standard band S at $\Delta\nu'$, respectively; σ is the spectral sensitivity, g the amplification factor of the recorder, N the mole fraction, and β a factor to convert from the intensity scale of a secondary band to the standard 459 cm.$^{-1}$ band of carbon tetrachloride. The 459 cm.$^{-1}$ band of carbon tetrachloride has been assigned the arbitrary value of 100 units.

The β values for a number of solvents have been determined and the methods for evaluating them have been discussed by Jones *et al.*[26]

The value of β will be influenced to some extent by the internal field effects in the particular solvent-solute system, but the evaluation of the apparent Raman scattering coefficient is useful for coordinating Raman spectra measured in different solvents. The β-constants will also depend on certain instrument parameters, notably the spectral slit width and the amplifier time constant. They should be determined by each operator for his own spectrometer under standardized conditions. Solutions in water and in deuterium oxide present a special difficulty owing to the absence of any sharp solvent bands that can be used for secondary standards. We have found it convenient to add 10 percent by weight of acetonitrile to the water in some cases, and use the sharp and highly characteristic C≡N stretching band at 2253 cm.$^{-1}$ as an internal intensity standard.

METHODS OF RECORDING RAMAN SPECTRA

Most Raman data in the present literature are at best semiquantitative and were obtained by photographic methods. The monographs of Kohlrausch[52,53,54] attest to the large interest in Raman spectrometry from its inception in 1928 until the advent of

[51] Schröder, J., Angew. Chem., Intern. Ed. Eng., **3**, 376, 1964.

[52] Kohlrausch, K. W. F., Der Smekal-Raman-Effekt, Springer, Berlin, 1931.

[53] Kohlrausch, K. W. F., Der Smekal-Raman-Effekt, Ergänzungband 1931–37, Springer, Berlin, 1938.

[54] Kohlrausch, K. W. F., "Ramanspektren," in Eucken-Wolf, "Hand- and Jahrbuch der Chemischen Physik," Vol. 9, Section VI, Akademische Verlagsgesellschaft, Leipzig, 1943. Reprinted by Edwards Bros., Ann Arbor, Michigan, 1945.

modern infrared techniques in the early 1940's. Hibben's monograph[55] lists almost 2000 references to the Raman literature up to 1939. Although this work was almost all done by the photographic plate method, many useful structure-spectra correlations were established.

Photographic techniques have the advantage that the entire spectrum is determined simultaneously, and variations in the exciting radiation intensity are automatically taken into account. This method has several operational disadvantages; the plates have to be developed and a comparator must be used to measure the band positions. If intensity data are required, a densitometer tracing must be obtained. While these techniques have been used for a long time in emission spectrometry, and instruments have been designed to measure the plates automatically, it is more convenient if the quantitative data can be obtained directly from the spectrometer. Where long exposures are necessary to observe weak lines, the stronger lines become overexposed and tend to blur the photographic plate. This can mask weak lines that are located near strong bands. To record bands of widely different intensities, several exposures are necessary.

The current resurgence of interest in Raman spectrometry is due largely to the introduction of photoelectric recording and the greater possibilities it provides for quantitative measurements. With photoelectric recording only a small portion of the spectrum is scanned at any one time. If intensity measurements are to be meaningful, the intensity of the exciting radiation must be maintained constant throughout the entire scanning of the spectrum, or a means of monitoring the exciting radiation and correspondingly correcting the Raman signal for any fluctuations must be employed. This latter technique is the more reliable and is used on the Cary Model 81 instrument. With the sensitive photomultiplier tubes that are now available, the time to scan a complete spectrum can be reduced to minutes and the Raman signal of the more intense bands can be electrically attenuated to give a complete spectrum recorded on precalibrated paper. Recognizing these obvious advantages of the photoelectric method, we will restrict our discussion to commercial instruments of this type.

COMMERCIAL PHOTOELECTRIC INSTRUMENTS

Cary Model 81.—In North America the Cary Model 81 Raman spectrophotometer, manufactured by the Applied Physics Corporation, Monrovia, California, is the most widely used commercial Raman instrument. The design of this instrument has been discussed in detail by Cary.[56] Two of the innovations responsible for its sensitivity are the use of an image slicer and dual phototubes to utilize as large a fraction as possible of the Raman radiation. Coupled with these is the use of an efficient grating spectrometer, which incorporates a dual slit system developed by Shurcliff.[57] A schematic diagram of the Model 81 optical system is shown in Fig. 4-9. The other components are discussed below.

Lamp.—A three-kilowatt, low pressure, Toronto-type mercury arc in the form of a helix is used for the excitation source. The helix is constructed of Corning 1720 non-darkening glass, and is equipped with water-cooled Pyrex electrodes.

Filter Jacket.—A cylindrical glass filter jacket is located between the Toronto arc and the sample cell. A thermostatted solution is circulated through the filter system to isolate the 4358 A line and to keep the sample cool. A modified filter system has been

[55] Hibben, J. H., The Raman Effect and Its Chemical Applications, Reinhold, New York, 1939.

[56] Cary, H., "Raman Spectrograph Design," presented at the Symposium on Molecular Spectroscopy, Ohio State University, June 1953. Reprints available from the Applied Physics Corporation, Monrovia, California.

[57] Shurcliff, W. A., J. Opt. Soc. Am., **39**, 1048, 1949.

described by Jones *et al.*[11,26] which uses a double-walled filter jacket. A thermostatted aturated aqueous potassium nitrite solution is circulated through the outer chamber and a static aqueous solution of Rhodamine (0.009 percent, 5 DGN extra) is in the sinner chamber. This combination efficiently isolates the 4358 A line and maintains its stability over a long period.

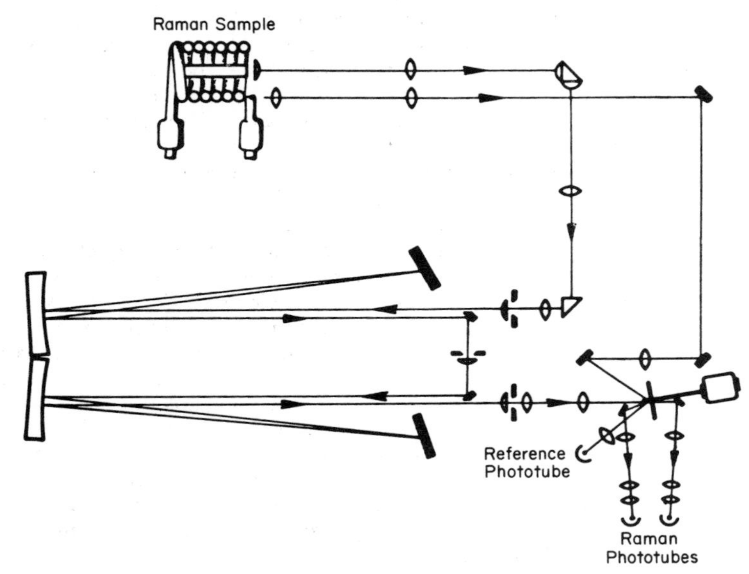

FIG. 4-9. Cross-sectional Diagram Through the Optical System of the Cary Model 81 Raman Spectrophotometer. (Courtesy The Applied Physics Corp.)

Cells.—There are three sizes of liquid cells (0.2, 7, and 65 ml.), a solid sample holder, and a multiple reflection gas cell with their associated cell optics available for the instrument.

Monochromator.—The dispersing system of the Model 81 uses a dual grating, twin slit, double monochromator collimated by off-axis spherical mirrors in a Czerny-Littrow arrangement, with corrector lens to flatten the field. The focal length is 1000 mm. and aperture is 100 × 100 mm. The gratings are ruled 1200 lines per mm. and blazed for 4500 A in the first order. Slit curvature is matched at 4600 A. A wavenumber accuracy of 0.5 cm.$^{-1}$ and a reproducibility of 0.1 cm.$^{-1}$ are achievable with this instrument.

Slits.—The maximum height of the Shurcliff twin slits is 10 cm., but they can be masked down to 5 or 2.5 cm. by means of a panel control for higher resolution work. The continuously variable slit aperture can be opened to 1.5 mm., which corresponds to a spectral slit width of 30 cm.$^{-1}$ When determining Raman spectra below 200 cm.$^{-1}$, one of the twin slits can be masked off to eliminate a diffraction band that occurs around 175 cm.$^{-1}$ when both slits are used. Although this introduces a 50 percent loss in intensity, it permits one to scan closer to the exciting line, and measurements can be made to within 100 cm.$^{-1}$ without undue difficulty.

Photodetectors.—The instrument is equipped with three matched 1P28 photomultiplier tubes. The Raman signal is chopped at 30 c.p.s. by a 180° rotating sector mirror and directed alternately on two of the phototubes. The Raman phototube signals are then combined and corrected for fluctuation in the exciting radiation, which is monitored by the third phototube. Photometer sensitivity can be varied over a factor of 1000 in steps of 2 and 2.5, and continuously by a factor of 3. An additional factor of 2000 is available by changing the dynode voltage through a five-position switch. An optical attenuator with an optical density of about 3 is also provided to allow the Rayleigh line to be scanned. The time constant of the recorder is continuously variable from 0.5 to 60 sec.

Data Presentation.—This instrument has a linear wavenumber scale and the chart paper is directly geared to the wavelength scan mechanism. There are 14 scanning speeds available from 0.005 cm.$^{-1}$/sec. to 10 cm.$^{-1}$/sec.; a quick-return speed of 50 cm.$^{-1}$/sec. is also provided. The chart paper is 12 in. wide and there are five presentations of 10, 20, 50, 100 and 200 cm.$^{-1}$/in. available by means of manually changed gears. A metric presentation is also available. A choice of marking intervals at 100 or 1000 cm.$^{-1}$ is provided.

Other Instruments.—Two other photoelectric Raman instruments are described in detail by Brandmüller and Moser.[58] The C. A. Steinheil Co., of Munich, Germany, manufactures a Raman instrument that uses three prisms in its monochromator; another instrument, using two prisms, is produced by Hilger and Watts, Ltd. of London, England.

RESONANCE RAMAN EFFECT

When the frequency of the exciting line approaches an electronic absorption band of the compound being examined, the intensity of the Raman spectrum is markedly enhanced. This is known as the resonance Raman effect. Although much attention has been directed toward a better understanding of this phenomenon in the last decade, a satisfactory explanation is still lacking.[59,60,61] Nevertheless, the potential use of this effect for the analysis of small amounts of suitable samples is very promising. Schrötter[62] has detected as little as 10^{-7} mole fraction concentrations under suitable conditions. Some further examples will be covered in the next section.

APPLICATIONS

Advantage and Limitation of Raman Spectrometry.—Both infrared and Raman spectrometry are related to the vibrational modes of the molecules being examined and one wonders why both techniques are needed. There are several reasons why one technique may be favored over the other. Raman spectrometry is, in general, restricted to weakly absorbing, nonfluorescent materials; on the other hand infrared is not readily adaptable to the study of aqueous solutions. At present infrared has the advantage of a considerably smaller sample requirement.

Overtone and combination bands tend to complicate the infrared spectrum, but they are usually weak in the Raman spectrum so that the Raman spectrum appears simpler. The linear relationship of intensity and concentration in the Raman technique makes identification of major components of a mixture easier than in the infrared where the intensity is logarithmically dependent on the concentration. Analysis of multicomponent mixtures—especially of conjugated systems, dienes, styrenes, and cyclic paraffins, where the infrared spectra are often very similar—is simpler with Raman techniques.

[58] Brandmüller, J., and Moser, H., *op. cit.*, pp. 207–216.
[59] Rea, D. G., J. Mol. Spectroscopy, **4,** 499, 1960.
[60] Shorygin, P. P., Pure and Appl. Chem., **4,** 87, 1962.
[61] Sushchinskii, M. M., and Zubov, V. A., Optics and Spectroscopy, **13,** 434, 1962.
[62] Schrötter, H. W., Z. Electrochem., **64,** 853, 1960.

While the Raman technique is less specific for polar substituent groups on organic molecules, it is more sensitive to structural changes in the skeletal structure.[11] A potential advantage of this will be in the analysis of organic compounds that carry polar groups but differ only in skeletal structure. An illustration of the advantage of Raman over infrared spectrometry is shown in Fig. 4-10. The C≡C stretching band at about

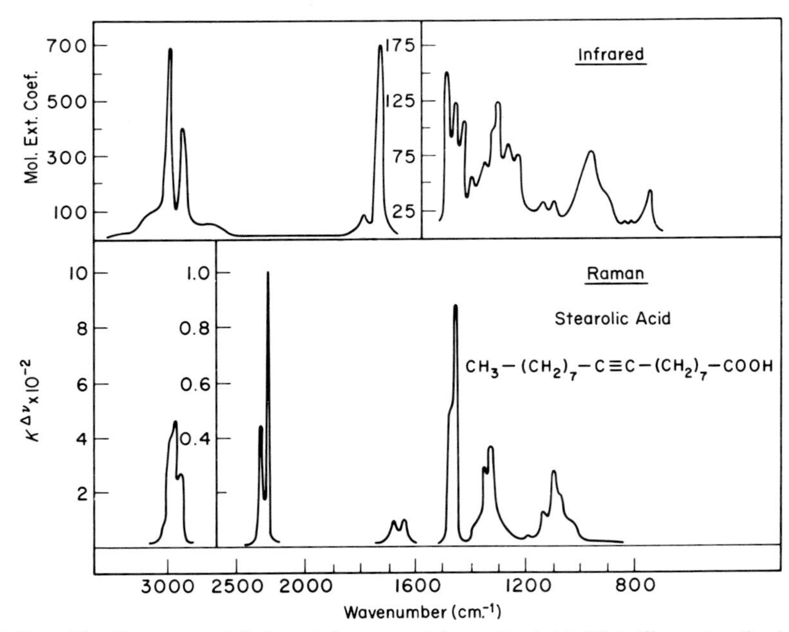

FIG. 4-10. The Raman and Infrared Spectra of Stearolic Acid. This illustrates the intense scattering by the —C≡C— bond giving rise to the doublet near 2300 cm.$^{-1}$. This band is absent from the infrared spectrum. Note also the absence from the Raman spectrum of the broad underlying infrared band at 3200–2900 cm.$^{-1}$ and the strong 930 cm.$^{-1}$ infrared band. These are associated with the C—O vibrations in the hydrogen bonded carboxylic acid dimer group. (Courtesy Spartan Books.)

2300 cm.$^{-1}$ of stearolic acid is completely absent from the infrared spectrum, even in the neat liquid at a pathlength of 3 mm. However, in the Raman spectrum this band is one of the strongest. This illustrates the advantage of Raman spectrometry in examining olefins and acetylenes.

Example of Raman Spectrometry as an Analytical Tool.—The use of Raman in analytical work has recently been reviewed by A. C. Jones and Tunnicliff.[63] Here we shall give only a few examples of the use of Raman as an analytical tool and refer the reader to this review article for a more complete bibliography.

The Raman spectra of hydrocarbons were reviewed by Sheppard over a decade ago,[64,65] and more recently by Rea[66] and Sushchinskii.[67] Rea's paper deals specifically

[63] Jones, A. C., and Tunnicliff, D. D., Anal. Chem., **34,** 261 R, 1962.
[64] Sheppard, N., J. Institute of Petroleum, **37,** 95, 1951.
[65] Sheppard, N., and Simpson, D. M., Quart. Rev., **6,** 1, 1952; **7,** 19, 1953.
[66] Rea, D. G., Anal. Chem., **32,** 1638, 1960.
[67] Sushchinskii, M. M., Molecular Spectroscopy, E. Thornton and M. W. Thompson, Eds., Pergamon Press, London, 1959, pp. 305–317.

with correlations of acyclic monoolefins, while Sushchinskii deals with various hydrocarbon structural units. The latter paper makes extensive use of depolarization ratios.

Raman spectrometry has a great advantage over infrared for the study of aqueous solutions. The early literature on this subject is to be found in Hibben's monograph.[55] Recently Edsall *et al.* have reported the Raman spectra of aqueous solution of sulfhydryl compounds[8] and diamines.[68] Deno and Wisotsky have studied the protonation equilibrium and base strength of weak organic bases in aqueous sulfuric acid.[69]

Tunnicliff and A. C. Jones[70] have developed a general scheme of quantitative Raman analysis, which largely avoids the effect of instrumental variables and sample composition on the intensities of the scattering coefficients. They use the solvent as an internal standard, which may be a multi-component solvent of constant composition. The procedure uses the measured peak heights of suitable bands in each component as well as in the solvent which do not markedly interfere with one another. The authors point out, however, that the technique could also be used employing band areas.

Nicholson[71] has reported a procedure for analysis on an eight-component mixture, which consists of benzene and various di-, tri-, and tetra-isopropylbenzenes. The average deviations in concentrations determined on synthetic mixtures of these components was about 1 percent. Concentrations of 0.001 percent benzene in carbon tetrachloride were readily detected.

Brandmüller and Glatzer[72] made use of the resonance Raman effect to determine the concentration of pyridine in various solvents and of the solvents in pyridine. The lower limit of detectability of solvents in pyridine is: water 0.07 percent; methanol 0.25 percent; ethanol 0.17 percent; formic acid 0.09 percent; and carbon tetrachloride 0.15 percent. The application of Raman spectrometry to the determination and identification of organic compounds is considered in Chapter 51, Volume III, Organic Functional Groups.

CONCLUSION

We have endeavored to review the basic theory and experimental techniques of Raman spectrometry. The advantages and limitations have been discussed and we have tried to stress the limitations rather than the advantages, as this seemed the most prudent thing to do at the present juncture. It is easy to visualize quantitative analytical problems for which Raman spectrometry would appear ideally suited on theoretical grounds, but, given the present state of the art, the analyst would usually be better advised to examine the applicability of other instrumental techniques before resorting to quantitative Raman spectrometry.

It is reasonable to expect that better techniques will soon be developed through the perfection of intense longer wavelength light sources that could alleviate the most serious limitations associated with fluorescing impurities, large sample size, and inconvenient cell geometry. The Raman technique might then recapture some of the prominence it held three decades ago. The main promise probably lies more in the field of molecular structure determination than conventional quantitative analysis. At present, the organic chemist relies almost exclusively on infrared spectrometry as a means to probe the vibrational behavior of complex organic compounds. In so doing he obtains a very unbalanced picture. This will only be righted when our knowledge and utilization of Raman spectra as tools for structure analysis come into better balance with the infrared technique.

[68] Ghazanfar, S. A. S., Edsall, J. T., and Meyers, D. V., J. Am. Chem. Soc., **86,** 559, 1964.
[69] Deno, N. C., and Wisotsky, M. J., J. Am. Chem. Soc., **85,** 1735, 1963.
[70] Tunnicliff, D. D., and Jones, A. C., Spectrochim. Acta, **18,** 579, 1962.
[71] Nicholson, D. E., Anal. Chem., **32,** 1634, 1960.
[72] Brandmüller, J., and Glatzer, G., Anal. Physik, **4** [7], 229, 1959.

Chapter 5

FLUOROMETRIC ANALYSIS

By Charles E. White
Department of Chemistry
University of Maryland
College Park, Maryland

and

Alfred Weissler
Air Force Office of
Scientific Research
Washington, D. C.

GENERAL SURVEY

In fluorescence analysis, the amount of light *emitted* characteristically under suitable excitation is used as a measure of the concentration of the responsible species. Thus the method is closely related to colorimetric or spectrophotometric analysis, in which the amount of light *absorbed* characteristically is used to measure the concentration of the dissolved species.

Advantages.—The main advantage of fluorescence methods is their high sensitivity, about 1 part in 10^8, or 0.01 μg./ml., in many determinations both inorganic and organic. This is two or three orders of magnitude better than absorption methods, where the sensitivity is limited by the necessity of detecting a very small fractional decrease in the light transmitted by the solution.

In fluorescence, the situation is inherently more favorable. Inasmuch as zero concentration corresponds to darkness (neglecting reagent blanks) and the sensitivity depends on detecting the first faint emission of light as the concentration is increased, advantage can be taken of highly sensitive detectors such as photomultipliers, and high intensity ultraviolet sources for excitation. Combining these with sophisticated electronic and optical techniques has led to a remarkable achievement; under favorable conditions, it was possible to detect Rhodamine 5DGN down to the extremely low concentration of 1 part in 10^{12}, in an instrument designed for tracing ocean currents with a fluorescent dye marker.[1]

The fluorometer characteristics affect not only the sensitivity, but also the precision. An analytical precision of 1 part per 100 is a reasonable goal in careful work with a good instrument, except for the lowest concentration ranges. The *accuracy* can be equally good, if the possible sources of error are well understood and have been systematically eliminated in the procedure used.

Fluorometric methods possess greater specificity than spectrophotometric methods,

[1] Pauli, D. C., A Dye Concentration Measurement System for Tracer Studies of Circulation in the Ocean, Pneumodynamics Corp., Washington, D. C., 1960. See also (a) Leaf, W. B., Tracing Water Movement, in Feb. 1963 issue of Undersea Technology, and (b) Quarterly Progress Reports 1 and 2 on Contract AT (30-1)-2664, AEC Biomedical Division, 1961.

because there is a choice of wavelength not only for the radiation emitted but also for the light which excites it. This suggests the possibility of determining simultaneously two constituents which both emit the same fluorescence color, if their respective excitation wavelengths are separated sufficiently far. Still another property, the pH, is available to give increased specificity; by shifting the pH as well as the excitation and emission wavelengths, one can often determine several closely related substances in the same solution, without separations.[2,3]

Another attractive feature of fluorometry is that it is one of the newer methods and its potentialities are still largely unexplored. Interest in it is increasing steadily, however, and hundreds of papers are published each year on new or improved methods and instrumentation.

Limitations.—The fact that fluorescence analysis has been developed relatively recently is a disadvantage in some ways. One of them is the fact that only a relatively short time has been available for the thorough cross-checking, in different laboratories, of possible sources of error.

Some possible sources of error deserve mention here—a more extended discussion is given later. (a) The fluorescence intensity may be strongly dependent on pH, so that careful buffering is necessary (see Fig. 5-1). (b) Because an appreciable time may be

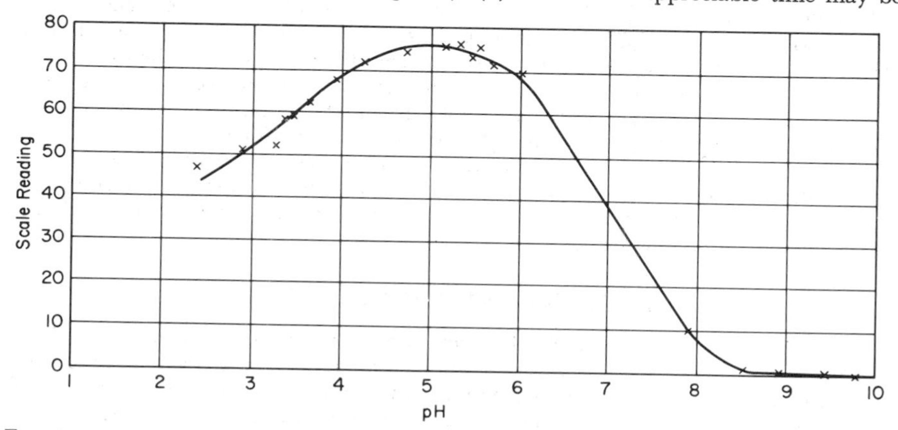

FIG. 5-1. The Effect of pH on the Fluorescence Intensity of the Al-PBBR Chelate; see footnote 25. (Courtesy Analytical Chemistry.)

required for the formation of the fluorescent complex, the intensity may not reach its maximum value for many minutes (see Fig. 5-2). (c) The ultraviolet light used for excitation may cause photochemical changes or destruction of the fluorescent molecule, giving a gradual decrease in the intensity reading.[4] The combination of the opposing factors in (b) and (c) may require that the fluorescence be measured at a precise time after addition of the reagents (see Fig. 5-3). (d) The presence of dissolved oxygen may cause increased photochemical destruction, or else a more generalized kind of "quenching" (*i.e.*, reduction of the fluorescence intensity). In the fluorometric determination of boron with benzoin, the harmful effects of oxygen can be avoided, and the sensitivity increased, by bubbling hydrogen through the solutions before mixing.[5] (e) Even small amounts of

[2] Airth, R. L., and Foerster, G. E., Anal. Biochem., **3,** 383, 1962.
[3] Himes, R. H., and Rabinowitz, J. C., J. Biol. Chem., **237,** 2903, 1962.
[4] White, C. E., Weissler, A., and Busker, D., Anal. Chem., **19,** 802, 1947.
[5] Elliott, G., and Radley, J. A., Analyst, **86,** 62–69, 1961.

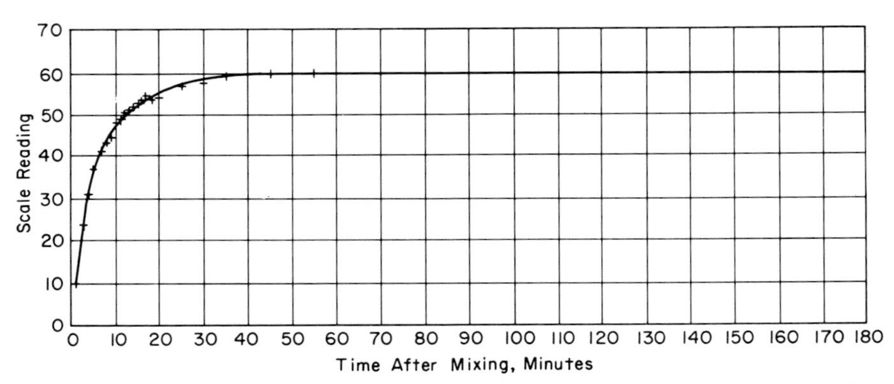

FIG. 5-2. The Effect of Time, After Mixing, on the Fluorescence Intensity of the Al-PBBR Chelate; see footnote 25. (Courtesy Analytical Chemistry.)

iodide or nitrogen oxides are efficient quenchers, and therefore interfere. (f) The increase of fluorescence intensity with the concentration is less than linear in the higher ranges, for various reasons (see Fig. 5-4). Among these are "concentration quenching" and the absorption of the exciting radiation before it reaches the entire bulk of the solution.

A second type of disadvantage is that fluorometry is not usually suited for the determination of the major constituents of a sample, because for larger amounts the accuracy is considerably less than that attainable by gravimetric or volumetric methods.

A third type of limitation is the fact that not all elements and compounds exhibit definite fluorescence, so that the extent of applicability of this analytical technique is limited. Where it may be used, however, fluorometry is very often the method of choice, especially for small concentrations.

THEORETICAL BACKGROUND

What are the types of substance which are fluorescent enough to provide a basis for an analytical method? Among organic substances, fluorescence is shown mainly by aromatic compounds (such as benzene, naphthalene, anthracene, and their derivatives) rather than the aliphatic series. Among the metal ions, only a few show intrinsic fluorescence, such as uranium and thallium, but many others can be determined fluorometri-

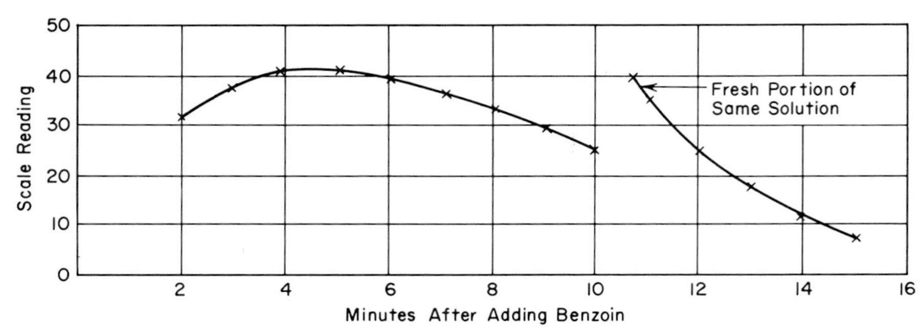

FIG. 5-3. An Illustration of Decomposition, With Time, of the Boron-benzoin Chelate Affected by Air and Light.[4] (Courtesy Analytical Chemistry.)

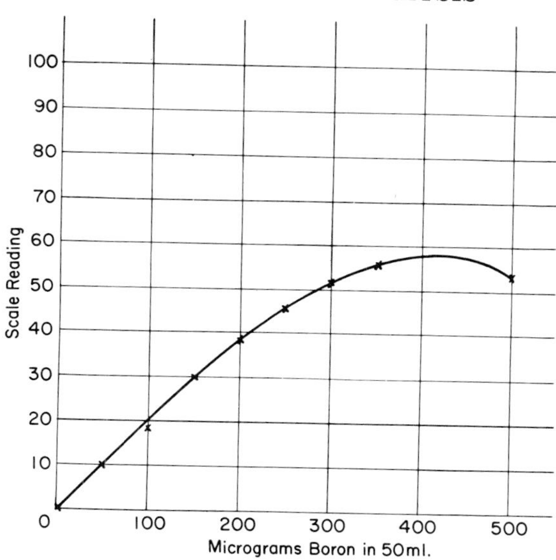

FIG. 5-4. The Relationship of Fluorescence Intensity to Concentration of the Boron-benzoin Chelate.[4] (Courtesy Analytical Chemistry.)

cally by adding a specific reagent which reacts with the metal to form a fluorescent complex.

Such fluorogenic organic reagents often have a molecular structure of the following type: they contain two or more aromatic rings, joined by an unsaturated linkage containing either oxygen or nitrogen. In addition, there are usually hydroxyl, amino, or sulfonate groups. Some examples are benzoin as a reagent for boron, trihydroxyazobenzenesulfonate for aluminum, and 1-amino-4-hydroxyanthraquinone for beryllium. See Fig. 5-17, page 99 for a more complete list, with structural formulas.

To understand the formation of a strongly fluorescent complex from a nonfluorescent or weakly fluorescent reagent, an intuitive approach is that the metal ion undergoes chelation involving the oxygen or nitrogen in the bridging linkage. This makes the entire molecule more rigid, which prevents the excitation energy from being dissipated in ways other than by the emission of fluorescent light.

A deeper understanding of the relation of structure to fluorescence can be achieved by a closer look at the processes of excitation and emission. When a molecule absorbs a quantum of ultraviolet or visible light, one of the electrons in the molecule is raised to a higher energy level. Fluorescence occurs when the electron simply drops back into its ground level, with emission of the excess energy in the form of light;[5a] this process takes place usually in less than a millionth of a second. Other possibilities (which compete with fluorescence for the excess energy) include photochemical reactions, phosphorescence, and degradation of the energy into heat by collisional deactivation.

The processes of molecular excitation and emission described above are analogous to those occurring in atoms, as encountered in emission spectrographic analysis for the

[5a] The emitted light is usually somewhat longer in wavelength than that absorbed, because some of the energy is transferred to vibrational excitation. Generally, the absorption spectrum and the emission spectrum are mirror images of each other, and the absorption band of longest wavelength usually intersects the emission band.

elements. One difference is that the allowed energy levels for an electron in an atom are classified into types such as *s*, *p*, *d*, and *f*, while the allowed electron levels in a molecule are classified into types such as *sigma* and *pi*. Sigma electrons are those in single bonds, formed by the on-axis overlap of electron clouds; pi electrons are characteristic of aromatic systems and multiple bonds, formed by the off-axis overlap of electron clouds.

Each energy level can be occupied by two electrons, which must have opposite spins, designated as plus and minus. If all the electrons are "paired" in this way, the system is in a *singlet* state. However, an atom or molecule may contain two unpaired electrons, both having the same spin; it is then in a *triplet* state. The lowest energy level available, the "ground state," is usually a singlet state. If the absorption of energy causes one of the electrons to be raised to a higher vacant level, without change of spin, the result is an *excited singlet* state; with change of spin, which is a much less probable process, the result is an *excited triplet* state (see Fig. 5-5).

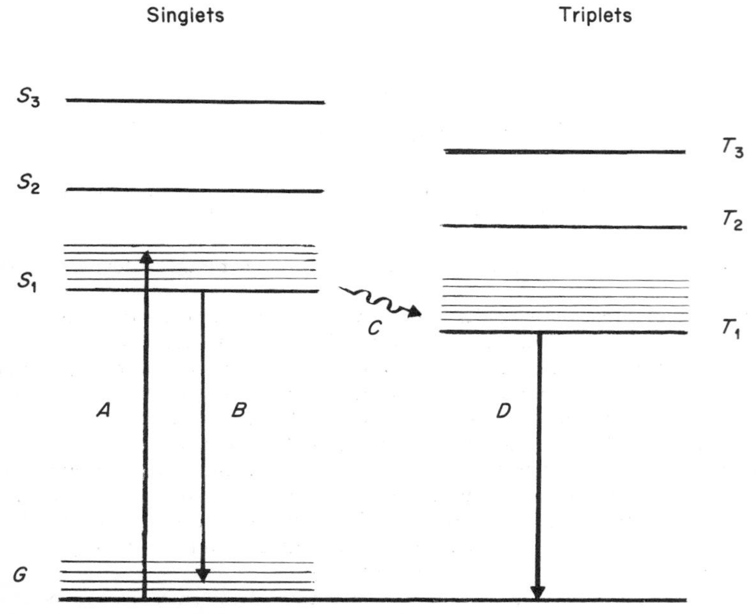

FIG. 5-5. Electron Energy Level Diagram, Showing Vibrational Sublevels of Singlet and Triplet States. Transition *A* represents light absorption; *B*, fluorescence; and *C* and *D* together, phosphorescence.

Thus there are possible in the molecule a variety of electron-energy transitions, accompanied by the absorption or emission of light. For example, one of a pair of pi electrons can be excited to a higher pi level, designated as pi-star, π^*, in which the electron cloud is shifted to an anti-bonding configuration. The resulting state is a π,π^* singlet if no change of spin has occurred, but a π,π^* triplet if the spin has flipped over to the opposite sign.

Characteristically, fluorescence is the light emission from a π,π^* singlet. If the excited state is a π,π^* triplet, the lower probability of a spin-flipping transition back to the ground state causes the light emission to be greatly delayed, sometimes for as long as several seconds, and the result is phosphorescence.

No fluorescence occurs if the excitation results in an n,π^* state. The n electrons are the pair of nonbonded electrons associated with oxygen or nitrogen atoms in the molecule; they are also responsible for dative bond formation. When one of the n-electrons is raised (by light absorption) to a π^* level, the characteristics of the resulting n,π^* state are such that other energy-dissipating processes compete successfully against the emission of light.

With this background, there is a clearer rationale for the formation of fluorescent complexes of metal ions with organic reagents. The reagent should be an aromatic molecule containing oxygen or nitrogen atoms, which is itself nonfluorescent or only weakly fluorescent; the presence of available nonbonding electrons makes it more probable that the absorption of exciting light will give a nonfluorescent n,π^* state. But if a complex is formed between this molecule and a metal ion, the n-electrons are utilized to form a bond with the metal thus becoming more firmly bound and less available for excitation. The π,π^* state then becomes much more probable upon excitation, and the result is a strong fluorescence.

LINEARITY

The use of fluorescence in quantitative analysis requires that there be a definite relationship (preferably linear) between concentration and fluorescence intensity. Such a relationship does indeed exist on the basis of theory as well as experiment. It is related to the familiar Lambert-Bouguer-Beer law, from which it can be derived as follows.

The light intensity absorbed by a solution is of course

$$I_0 - I \tag{1a}$$

or, since $I = I_0 e^{-acL}$,

$$I_0 - I_0 e^{-acL} \tag{1b}$$

or

$$I_0(1 - e^{-acL}) \tag{1c}$$

where I_0 = intensity of incident light,
I = intensity of transmitted light,
a = absorptivity (or extinction coefficient) multiplied by 2.303, the conversion factor for natural logarithms,
c = concentration of absorbing species, and
L = length of optical path.

The intensity of fluorescence emitted is found by multiplying the quantum yield for fluorescence by the amount of light absorbed:

$$F = \phi \times I_0(1 - e^{-acL}) \tag{2}$$

where F = fluorescence intensity

ϕ = quantum yield for fluorescence (ratio of light emitted to light absorbed).

Reabsorption and scattering of the light have been neglected in the above equations; also it is assumed that a single molecular species is responsible for both the absorption and the emission, and that the degree of dissociation does not vary with the concentration.

Mathematically, an exponential expression such as e^{-acL} is equivalent to a series of the form:

$$e^{-acL} = 1 - acL + \frac{(acL)^2}{2} - \frac{(acL)^3}{6} + \cdots \frac{(acL)^n}{n!} \quad (3)$$

If the magnitude of acL is small enough, all terms after the first two can be discarded, giving

$$e^{-acL} = 1 - acL \quad (4)$$

For example, a value not exceeding 0.05 for the exponent will give an error of only 0.1% in Eq. (4).

Next, if Eq. (4) is substituted into Eq. (2), the result is

$$F = \phi \times I_0(1 - 1 + acL) \quad (5a)$$

or

$$F = \phi \times I_0 acL \quad (5b)$$

For a given fluorescent compound, solvent, temperature, etc. in a cell of definite dimensions in a specific instrument, all the other factors are constant, giving simply

$$F = Kc \quad (6)$$

where K is the proportionality constant into which all the other factors are lumped.

The fluorescence intensity is thus a linear function of concentration, subject to the conditions of low concentration and low light absorption, as well as the other assumptions mentioned. The approximations made are such that the ratio F/c decreases if c increases beyond its range of validity. This causes the curve to flatten off at higher concentrations, or even to turn downward in some cases (see Fig. 5-4).

CALCULATION OF RESULTS

In every set of fluorometric determinations, the analyst should run a blank and two standards of known composition which cover the range of concentrations expected. The blank reading should of course be subtracted from all the other readings; the blanks must be kept relatively low, because high blanks cause a great increase in the analytical error. If there is known to be a linear dependence of fluorescence upon concentration, then from Eq. (6) it is evident that

$$F_s = Kc_s \quad (7a)$$

and

$$F_x = Kc_x \quad (7b)$$

where the subscripts s and x refer to the standard and unknown, respectively. The standard used should be one which is close to the unknown in composition. Dividing Eq. (7b) by (7a) gives

$$c_x/c_s = F_x/F_s \quad (8a)$$

or

$$c_x = c_s(F_x/F_s) \quad (8b)$$

Therefore, the concentration of the unknown is found by multiplying the concentration of the standard by the ratio of the fluorescence intensity of the unknown to that of the standard (both corrected by subtraction of the blank). This is exactly the form of the equation used for calculating the results in colorimetric analysis from the measured absorbances of the unknown and standard solutions.

However, if experience has cast doubt on the reliability of the linear relation in the particular analysis, it is necessary to run a series of standard samples through the procedure and use the results to construct a calibration curve. Even so, a standard and a blank must be included with each succeeding set of unknowns, in order to make sure that the calibration curve has remained valid and that errors have not crept into the technique.

APPARATUS

Apparatus for the observation and measurement of fluorescence and phosphorescence extend from the simple view box[6] to a sophisticated spectrofluorometer or phosphorimeter. In all cases the instruments consist of a source of radiation to raise the molecules to a higher energy state, a filter or monochromator to separate the exciting radiation from the emitted radiation, and an instrument to measure the energy of the latter. The exciting radiation may vary in wavelength anywhere from the x-ray region of one or two tenths of a millimicron (mμ) to the red region of the visible spectrum. Since x-ray fluorescence as a means of analysis is discussed in another section of this book (Chapter 9), it will not be considered here.

Instruments for the measurement of fluorescence have been described in the biannual reviews on fluorometric analysis[7] and in a review article on instrumentation for fluorometry.[8] The design of fluorometers is constantly changing and current industrial literature must be consulted for the latest improvements. General principles and a few examples will be discussed here. Our attention will be concerned with fluorescence excited or emitted in the approximate radiation range of 200 to 800 mμ.

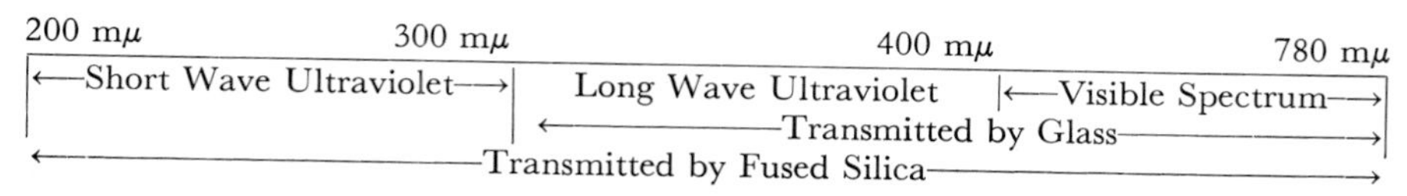

FIG. 5-6. Radiant Energy Involved in Fluorometric Analysis.

Radiation below 300 mμ is injurious to the eyes and adequate protection must be provided when it is used. Radiation below 300 mμ, in contact with air, produces ozone and oxides of nitrogen. These gases should not be inhaled over long periods of time. For the observation of visual fluorescence any exciting wavelength from 200 to 600 mμ may be used. Since ultraviolet radiation is relatively easy to separate from visible radiation by filters, the region from 300 to 400 mμ is most often chosen for excitation. This range of the spectrum not only avoids the objection noted above, but it is also transmitted by glass and by quartz, so that fused silica containers are unnecessary.

Sources of Exciting Radiation.—At the present writing the most popular sources for exciting fluorescence are the 360BL lamps, mercury vapor lamps, and the xenon arc lamp. A tungsten lamp may be used for substances having a strong excitation band above 450 mμ. Both the desired excitation band and emission band may be isolated by means of interference filters. However, since the desired excitation band is usually in the ultraviolet, the tungsten lamp is not in general use, but may have specific applications. It gives a band spectrum and does not have the sharp line limitation of the mercury vapor lamps.

[6] White, C. E., J. Chem. Educ., **28**, 369, 1951.
[7] White, C. E., and Weissler, A., Anal. Chem., **36**, 116R, 1964.
[8] Lott, P. F., J. Chem. Educ., **41**, A327, and **41**, A421, 1964.

The 360BL lamp is similar to the ordinary fluorescent lighting tube but contains a phosphor which emits an abundance of radiation in the 350 to 360 mμ region of the spectrum. These lamps are usually of 5 or 15 watts and operate with a simple starter and ballast. The phosphor in the 360BL lamp emits visible light, which must be excluded by means of a filter. These lamps may be purchased with either a clear or a blue glass envelope. Since an auxiliary filter is almost always necessary, there is but little advantage in the use of the built-in filter on the tube except for demonstration purposes. A number of commercial fluorometers are equipped with this type of lamp.

Mercury vapor lamps provide the only practical type of metallic arc used in fluorometry. These are designed to operate at high pressure or low pressure. The high pressure type has been made with a mercury arc at a pressure of about 8 atmospheres, surrounded by a protective envelope. The emission of this lamp is at wavelengths of 350 mμ and higher. All of the strong mercury vapor emission lines at 365, 398, 436, 546, 579, 690, and 734 mμ are present and may be isolated with suitable filters. The 253.6 mμ emission is not obtained with this lamp in any appreciable amount because of the absorption of this wavelength both by the mercury vapor and by the glass envelope.

This lamp may be obtained with a clear envelope in the General Electric model number H100A4, or with a blue glass envelope in the H100B4. The figure 100 designates the power (in watts). Other models operate at higher voltage levels and must be water cooled; these lamps require a special base and a transformer.

The low pressure mercury vapor lamp gives a strong emission at 253.6 mμ as well as at the longer wavelengths. This lamp is provided with a fused silica envelope and a fused silica Woods glass filter to absorb much of the visible light. This low pressure lamp finds use in exciting the fluorescence of scheelite ($CaWO_4$) and the lanthanide salts. Other mercury vapor lamps are described in the commercial literature and in various references.[9]

The hydrogen arc, the deuterium arc and the xenon arc all find some use in fluorescence analysis. Of these the xenon arc is the most favored at the present time. In contrast to the many strong lines of the mercury arcs, the xenon arc gives a smooth energy curve with a very strong peak at 470 mμ. Figure 5-7 illustrates three methods for obtaining this curve. The wavelength-response curve of the xenon lamp varies with the grating. The xenon arc is used most extensively as the source of a spectrofluorometer used for studying the excitation spectra of fluorescent substances. For routine use with a filter instrument a 360BL lamp or a mercury vapor lamp is more convenient.

Measurement of the Fluorescence Radiation.—If the emission is in the visible spectrum it may be estimated by visual comparison with standards. In any range of the spectrum the intensity of the emission may be measured with a phototube, a barrier layer cell, or with a photographic plate and densitometer. By far the most common procedure is to use a phototube or an electron multiplier phototube attached to a microphotometer or a recorder. Since phototubes vary greatly in their sensitivity at various wavelengths, and in their response per microwatt input, care must be taken in their selection. The electron multiplier phototube usually gives a much greater response than the phototube for a given photosensitive surface, and is, therefore, used more widely. However, the ordinary phototube is sufficiently sensitive for many measurements and requires a lower voltage system, which is less sensitive to line fluctuations.

The R.C.A. (Radio Corporation of America)[10] electron multiplier phototubes, 931A

[9] White, C. E., Chapter 3, in Selected Topics in Instrumental Analysis, Boltz, D. E., Ed., Prentice-Hall Co., Englewood Cliffs, New Jersey, 1952.

[10] Booklet ICE-269, Radio Corporation of America Electron Tube Division, Harrison, New Jersey.

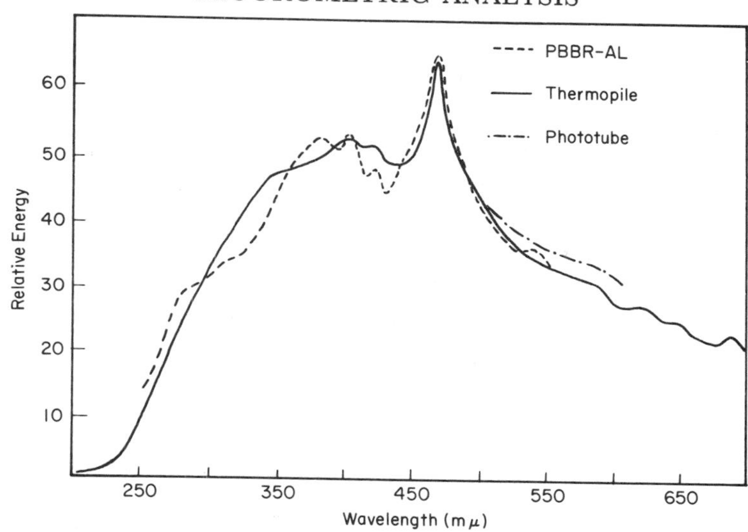

FIG. 5-7. Relative Spectral Energy Distribution of a Xenon Arc, Attenuated by a Monochromator Blazed at 300 mμ, Measured on a Constant Response Thermopile, a Standardized Phototube, and With a Solution of Al-PBBR Chelate. (Courtesy Analytical Chemistry.)

(S-4 surface), 1P21 (S-4 surface) and 1P28 (S-5 surface) are in common use. The photoresponse of several electron multiplier phototubes is given in Fig. 5-8, which shows a set of curves obtained by averaging results from groups of tubes; hence the performance of a single tube may vary somewhat from them. The curves show that phototubes can be selected to give a good response from 300 to 800 mμ.

Data furnished by the manufacturer to show the microampere response per microwatt input must also be considered in choosing a phototube. For example the 1P21 and 931A both have the same response curve, but the 1P21 is designed for measuring far lower light levels. For measurement of fluorescence spectra from 550 to 700 mμ, an electron multiplier tube such as R.C.A. 7102 (S-1 surface) may be used. This tube requires cooling with Dry Ice® and a special high voltage attachment. Both of these requirements are troublesome, so that the tube is commonly used only to obtain the emission spectrum curve. However, for quantitative measurements of a fluorescence up to 650 mμ, a 1P28 tube may be used even though it is not particularly sensitive to longer wavelengths. An electron multiplier phototube, R136, which is especially sensitive at a band in the red and which operates at room temperature, is being imported from Japan.[11]

Fluorometers.—Fluorometers are generally filter instruments and are used for routine measurements of fluorescence from 350 to 780 mμ. There are a number of good fluorometers manufactured in this country.[8] The choice of instrument is governed by the use. Care should be exercised to choose one with a stable electrical measuring device, a stable excitation source, ease of change of filters, ease of placement and change of samples, adequate cooling of the lamp so that the sample or phototube does not become heated, and a shutter between the exciting source and the sample and another between the sample and the phototube. The advertising pages of the issue of the Journal of

[11] American Instrument Co. Inc., 6030 Georgia Avenue, Silver Spring, Maryland, C-156-62104 Page 18, Bull. 2392A.

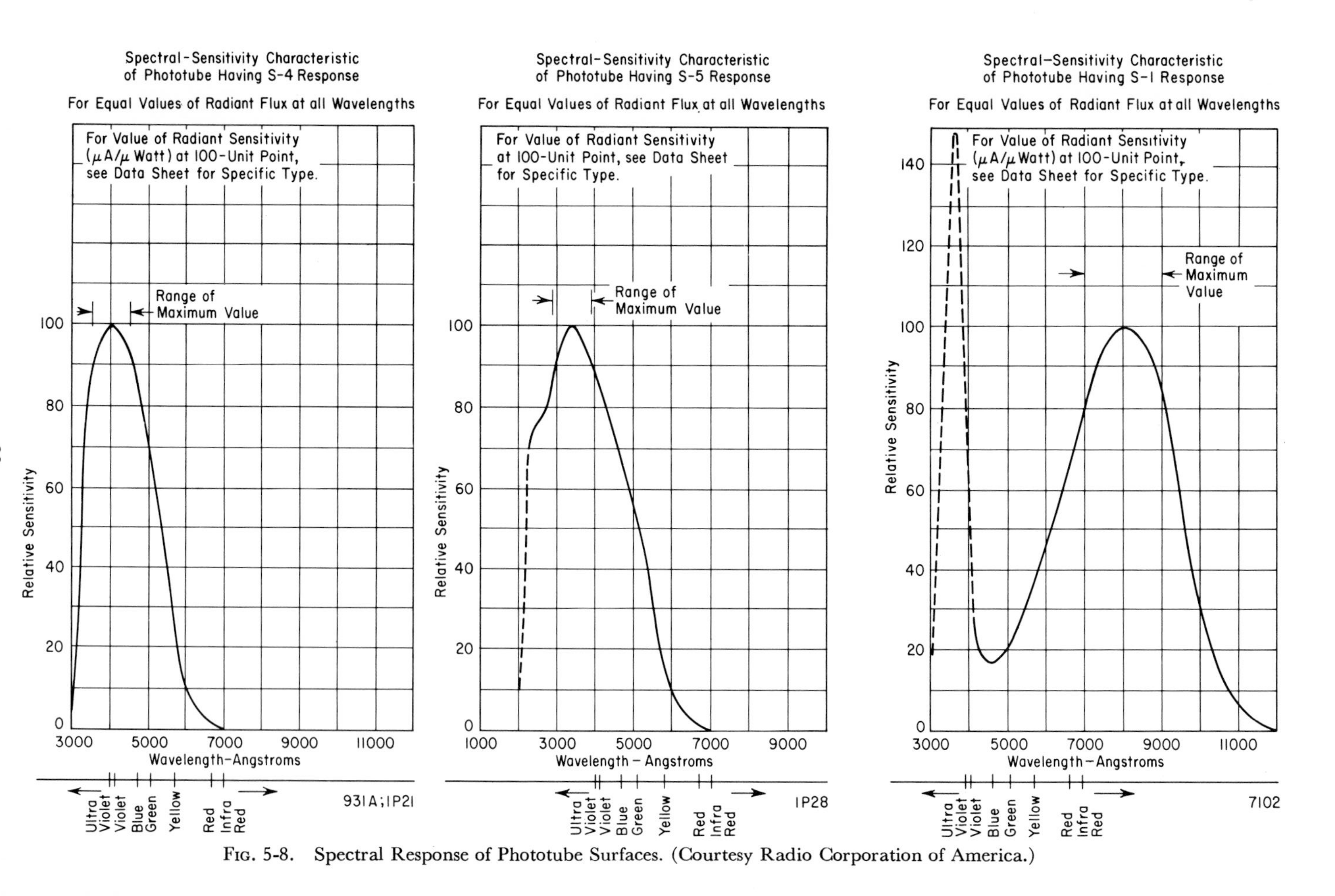

FIG. 5-8. Spectral Response of Phototube Surfaces. (Courtesy Radio Corporation of America.)

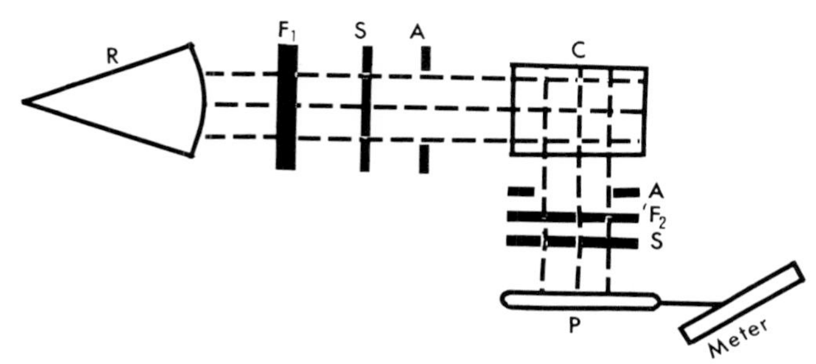

FIG. 5-9. Block Diagram of a Simple 90° Axis Fluorometer, Top View. *R*, radiation source; F_1 and F_2, filters; *S*, shutters; *A*, apertures or slits; *C*, sample container.

Chemical Education cited in footnote 8 give a good review of available fluorometers.

Figure 5-9 shows components of a fluorometer in a typical arrangement, of which there are many variations. For example, there may be a lens system between the source and the sample and another between the sample and the phototube. The detecting unit may be at a 45° angle to the source, and it may measure the emission from the surface of the sample. The shutters are necessary to protect the sample from long exposure to the exciting radiation and to protect the phototube from exposure while changing samples. A balanced circuit is often used to compensate for changes in the excitation source. An arrangement that permits the fluorescence to be observed from the top of the cuvet is often useful. The fluorescence should be observable as a uniform beam through the entire solution; if it is weaker at the far side from the source, the solution is too concentrated and proper results cannot be obtained.

Another arrangement of the components is in the vertical axis or transmission fluorometer,[12] Fig. 5-10. This instrument has long been used for solid samples. It also has some advantages for solutions; for example, the depth of the solution is easily controlled and more concentrated solutions can be used than in the right-angle arrangement. A disadvantage lies in the fact that the secondary filter must remove a large amount of exciting radiation, not only the scattered radiation as in the right-angle arrangement. A commercial transmission instrument for solids is available.[13] Automatic recording fluorometers are used for continuous

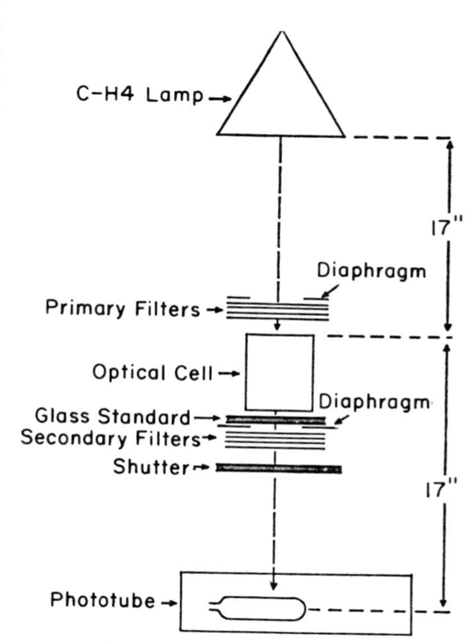

Fig. 5-10. Block Diagram of a Vertical Axis Fluorometer.[12] (Courtesy Analytical Chemistry.)

[12] Fletcher, M. H., Anal. Chem., **35**, 278 and 288, 1963.
[13] Ball Bros., Boulder, Colorado.

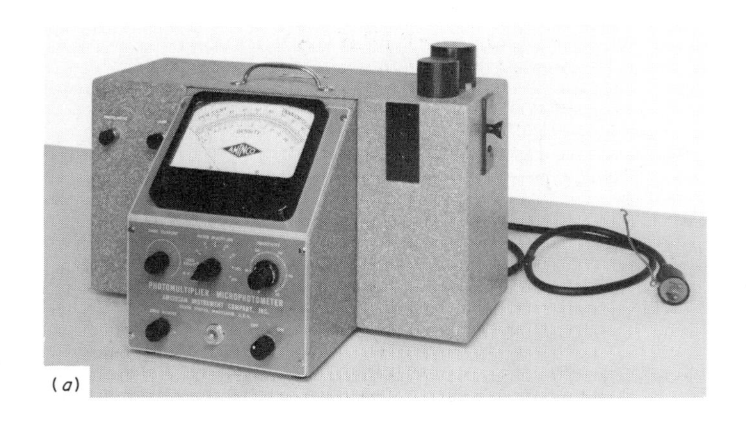
AMINCO
PHOTOMULTIPLIER MICROPHOTOMETER
AMERICAN INSTRUMENT COMPANY, INC.
(a)

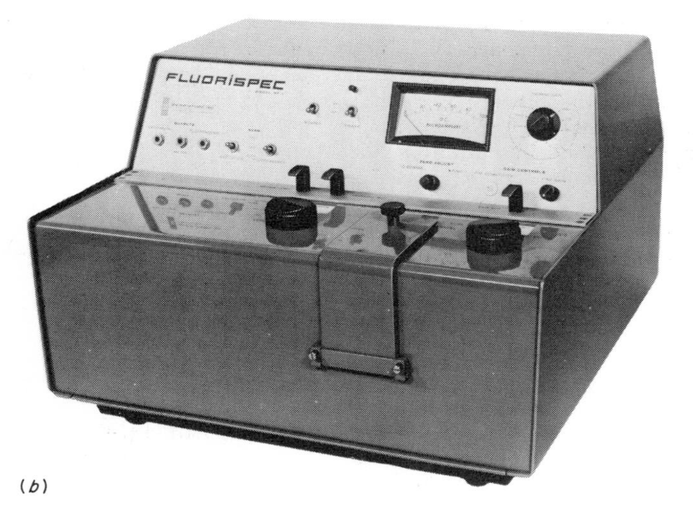
FLUORISPEC
(b)

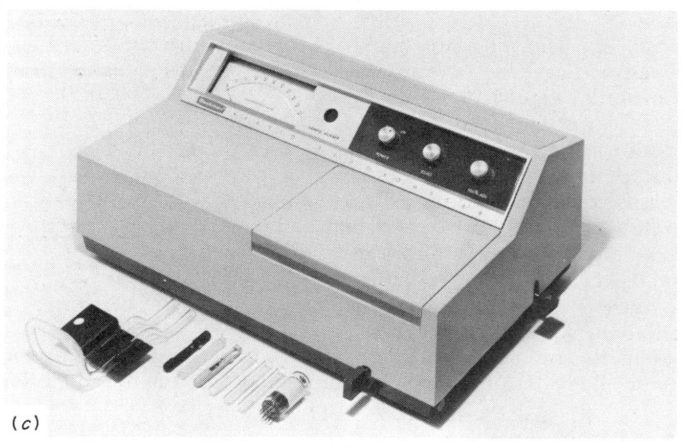
(c)

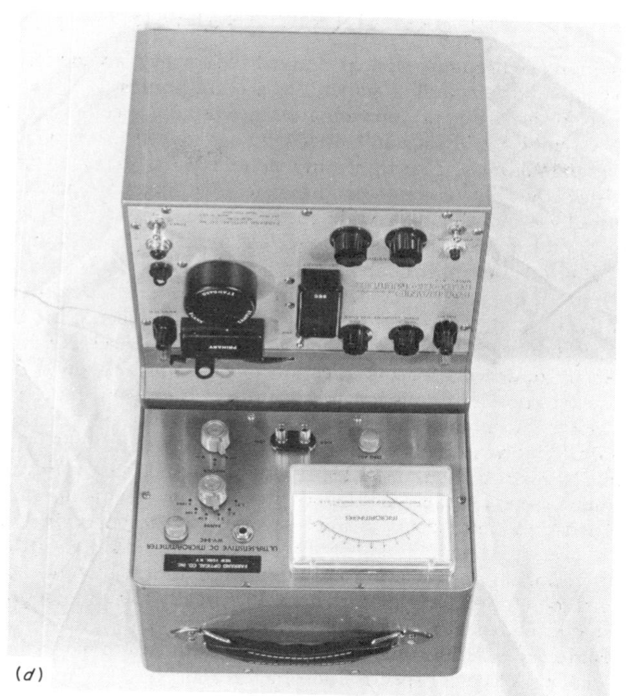

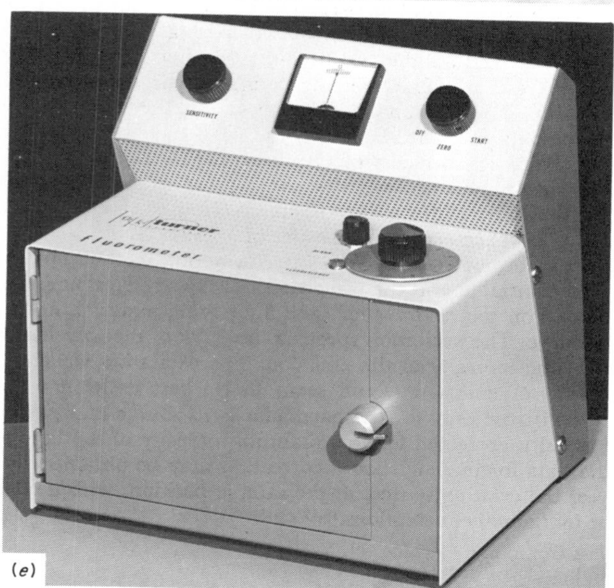

FIG. 5-11. Typical Fluorometers. (*a* Courtesy American Instrument Co., Inc.; *b* Courtesy Baird-Atomic, Inc.; *c* Courtesy Beckman Instruments, Inc.; *d* Courtesy Farrand Optical Co., Inc.; *e* Courtesy G. K. Turner Associates.)

determinations in flow-through systems. Some fluorometers are designed to measure the fluorescence of solids, including papers, as well as liquids.

The filters used for a particular determination are usually specified in the description of the method. Corning[14] or Eastman[15] filter catalogs give transmission curves for the filters of these manufacturers. The transmittance curves for many of these filters have also been published by Sill.[16] Narrow band interference filters are also useful. The primary filter is usually a nickel-cobalt oxide glass, as Corning No. 5874, which transmits radiation in the band from 330 to 380 mμ, as well as some wavelengths in the red region; the latter is not desirable but unavoidable unless a very dense glass is used. The secondary filter should remove the scattered incident light, but transmit the emitted fluorescence. An estimate of the proper secondary filter may be made by placing the filter in front of the fluorescing solution in a fluorescence view box,[6] where the relative transmission can be observed. Accurate criteria for the selection of filters are obtained from the determination of the excitation and emission spectra of the fluorescent material.

Several late model fluorometers are illustrated in Fig. 5-11. The American Instrument Company fluorometer provides for cooling with liquid nitrogen, which will increase the intensity of some samples a thousand fold; it also accommodates a dozen samples. The Turner instrument is very widely used and provides for a run-through sample. The Baird instrument is new and seems to have several good features, including a double monochromator grating system. Each of these instruments has features which are of value for specific applications. The journal cited in footnote 8 should be consulted for other instruments too numerous to picture here. Practically all manufacturers of spectrophotometers have provided attachments for fluorometry.

Spectrofluorometers.—A fluorometer constructed with two monochromators is called a spectrofluorometer. A typical spectrofluorometer and phosphorimeter is shown both schematically and as assembled in Fig. 5-12. The excitation source is usually a xenon arc which is dispersed by a prism or grating blazed for high efficiency at shorter wavelengths such as 300 mμ, and another prism or grating blazed at 400 or 500 mμ to disperse the emitted fluorescence. The fluorescence intensity is measured with a phototube attached to a microphotometer and a recorder or an oscilloscope. The spectrofluorometers most commonly used in the past several years have been the Farrand and the Aminco-Bowman. Baird Instruments of Cambridge, Massachusetts, has recently produced a similar spectrofluorometer. The Aminco-Bowman (American Instrument Company) model shown here may also be used as a phosphorimeter, which can measure the decay time of phosphorescence of the order of a millisecond.

With the spectrofluorometer two types of information can be obtained easily, the wavelength of best excitation and the wavelength of the strongest emission. Two curves are generally plotted on the recorder for each fluorescing material, an excitation curve and an emission curve. The excitation spectrum is a plot of the wavelength of the exciting source against the intensity of the emission. The excitation wavelength producing the greatest intensity of emission would seem to be best exciting wavelength, however this statement is true only for the particular light source and grating. This curve becomes more useful if corrected for the quantum intensity of the light source at each wavelength. The data for making such a correction may be obtained by measurement of the intensity of the exciting source, at the sample position, with a constant response thermopile,[17] or by fluorescent solutions.[18,19]

[14] Corning Glass Company, Corning, N. Y.
[15] Eastman Kodak Co., Rochester, N. Y.
[16] Sill, C. W., Anal. Chem., **33**, 1584, 1961.
[17] White, C. E., Ho, M., Weimer, E. Q., Anal. Chem., **32**, 438, 1960.
[18] Argauer, R. J., White, C. E., Anal. Chem., **36**, 368, 1964.
[19] Parker, C. A., Rees, W. T., The Analyst, **85**, 587, 1960.

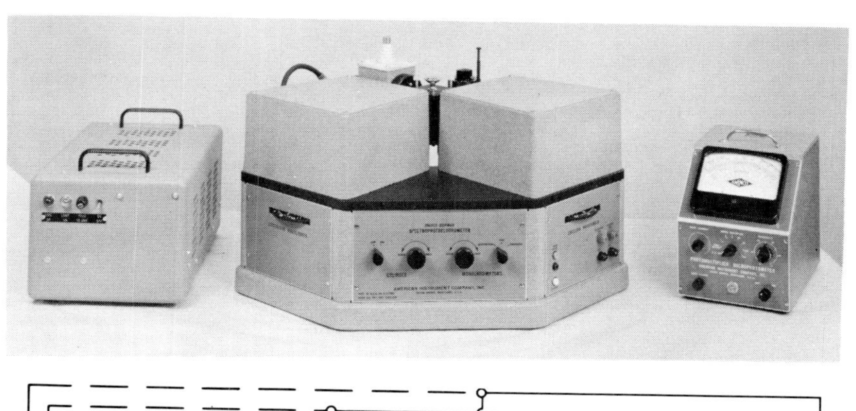

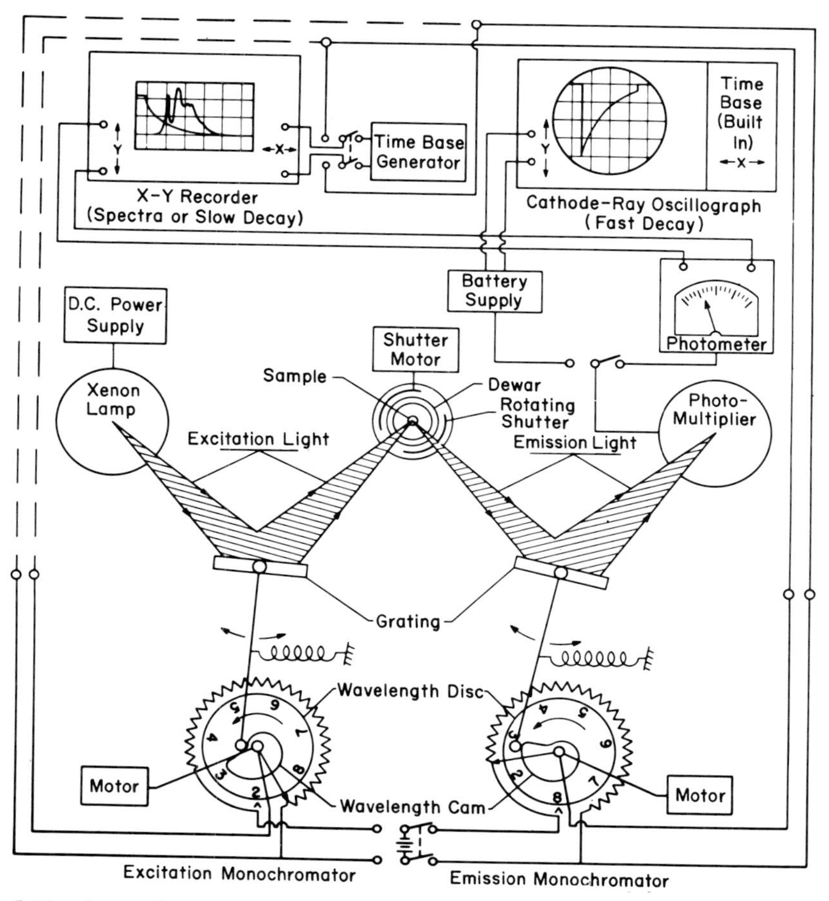

FIG. 5-12. Spectrofluorometer and Phosphorimeter; *a*, Schematic, *b*, Assembled. (Courtesy American Instrument Co., Inc.)

The correct or true excitation curve is a representation of the absorption curve and consequently the wavelength of the maximum absorption also serves as a good excitation wavelength. This does not mean that the excitation curve determined by fluorescence is not useful. It shows immediately the best excitation point for the instrument and for practical use on this particular instrument does not have to be corrected. In addition, the excitation curve may be obtained on much more dilute solutions than can the absorption curve. In the case of metal chelates the excitation curve represents the absorption curve of the chelated ligand, whereas the absorption curve is a sum of the values of its chelated and unchelated forms.

Figure 5-13 shows the corrected and uncorrected excitation curves of quinine sulfate as determined on the Aminco-Bowman spectrofluorometer. Curve *A* is traced on the

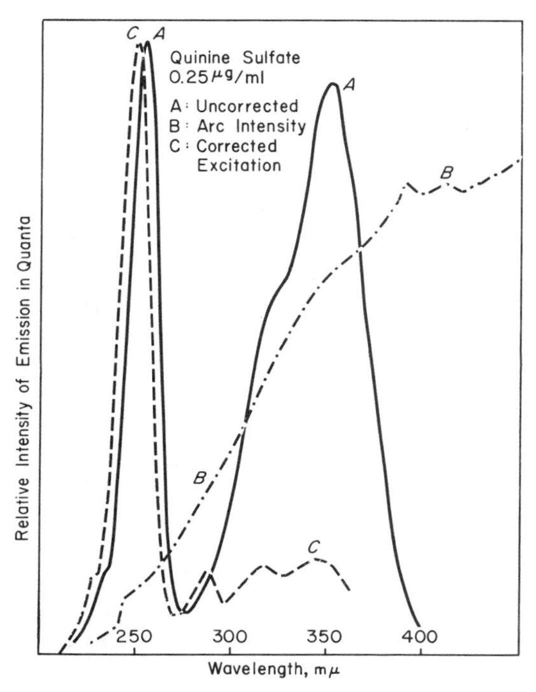

Fig. 5-13. Excitation Curve of Quinine Sulfate, 0.25 μg./ml. *A*, as recorded with a spectrofluorometer; *C*, corrected curve; *B*, relative intensity of the xenon arc at the sample holder.

recorder with the emission set at 450 mμ. Since the intensity is measured at a single wavelength value, the intensity values recorded in energy units are directly proportional to the number of quanta. The uncorrected curve shows that on this instrument 350 mμ is apparently the best excitation point. The corrected curve shows that if a source giving strong 250 mμ radiation is used, this wavelength would be the better choice.

The emission spectrum is a plot of intensity of fluorescence over the wavelength span with the excitation at a particular setting. Since the emission is in most cases independent of the excitation, it does not matter what exciting wavelength is used provided it is shorter than the shortest emission.

The emission curve plotted by the recorder on an instrument such as the Aminco-

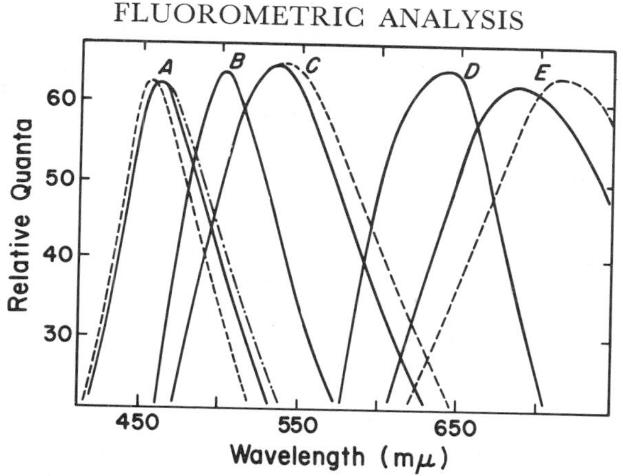

Fig. 5-14. Fluorescence Emission Standards.[18] Curve *A*, quinine sulfate; curve *B*, 3-aminophthalimide; curve *C*, *m*-nitrodimethylaniline; curve *D*, PBBR-aluminum chelate; curve E, 4-dimethylamino-4′-nitrostilbene. (Courtesy Analytical Chemistry.)

Bowman is attenuated by the emission grating and the response of the phototube, and must be corrected for these two factors. This may be accomplished by a correction factor obtained by measurement of the radiation from a standardized lamp, projected through the sample compartment, dispersed by the grating, and measured with the phototube. This correction may also be accomplished by fluorescent solutions, such as those illustrated by the curves in Fig. 5-14. Figure 5-15 shows that if the fluorescence emission is

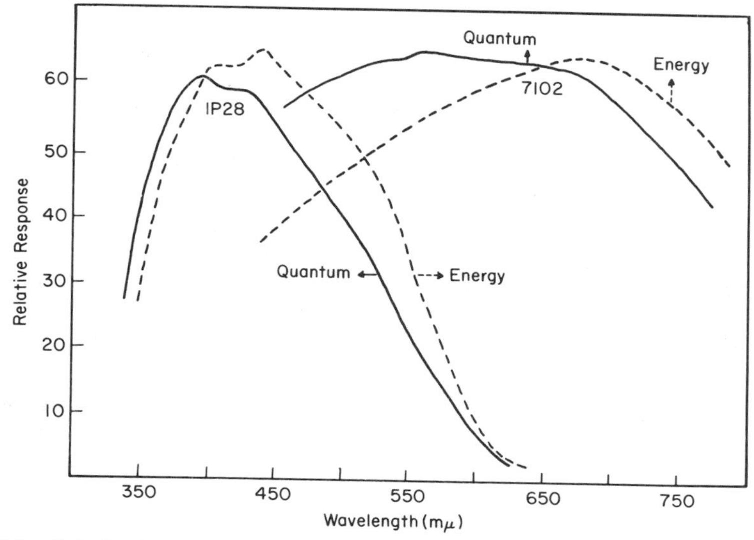

Fig. 5-15. Relative Response of the R.C.A. 1P28 and R.C.A. 7102 Electron Multipliphototubes-emission Unit of the Aminco-Bowman Spectrophotofluorometer.[18] The energy curve of the R.C.A. 7102 tube has been multiplied by a factor of 6.1. (Courtesy of Analytical Chemistry.)

expressed in terms of quanta instead of energy, the results obtained in the Aminco-Bowman instrument with the R.C.A. 1P28 and R.C.A. 7102 tubes need but little correction when operated in the ranges from 350 to 450 mμ and 550 to 650 mμ, respectively. The correction factors discussed above have been programmed for computers and hence the corrected curves are easily obtained.[20] The precaution given under the discussion of excitation is again appropriate here. The emission maximum plotted by the recorder is the best emission to measure on the instrument but in reporting the work, the corrected curve should be given, since it may be applied to any instrument.

Because the above corrections are a nuisance, several manufacturers, including Perkin Elmer, Turner, and Zeiss, have produced instruments which give automatically a correct excitation or emission curve. This feature increases greatly the complication and the cost of the instruments. The emission spectrum of a compound can be predicted, since it is usually the mirror image of the absorption spectrum if both are plotted in wavenumbers. This mirror image is also found from a plot of the corrected excitation and emission curves from the grating instrument. Here the excitation curve of longest wavelength usually overlaps the emission curve of shortest wavelength. A technique for the simultaneous recording of excitation and emission spectra gives promise of being useful in the identification of compounds.[21]

The development of the potassium bromide[22] solid pellet technique of fluorescence analysis will increase the demand for fluorometers and spectrofluorometers capable of measuring the fluorescence of solids. Many of the instruments are now equipped for both solids and liquids.

REPORTING FLUORESCENCE SPECTRA

The following suggestions for reporting fluorescence spectra have been abstracted from an article[23] by an active group of research workers abroad.

1. "The spectrum should be corrected or, if the correction is not vital to the work being reported, reference should be made to a correction curve of the instrument.

2. "The spectrum should be plotted as relative quanta per unit interval on the vertical scale *vs.* wavenumbers in reciprocal microns or reciprocal cms. If possible the absolute fluorescence efficiency should be quoted or quantitative comparison should be given with a suitable standard solution, such as quinine sulfate in 0.1 *N* sulfuric acid at a stated concentration and optical density per cm.

3. "The spectra should be corrected for background fluorescence of the cuvette, scattered light, and Raman emission, or the total background should be recorded on the graph from a measurement on the pure solvent.

4. "The following experimental details should be given: the spectrum of the exciting light; if a monochromator is used, the light source and the band width; or if filters are used, their transmission curves and the nature of the light source; the geometrical arrangement and the path lengths of the exciting and fluorescent light through the liquid; the optical density per cm. of solution for the frequency of the exciting light and an estimate of distortion of the spectrum by self absorption, purity and concentration of solute, and nature of the solvent, temperature of the solution and a statement of whether it is aerated or air-free; the type of analyzing monochromator and the band width at an appropriate frequency."

[20] Drushel, H. V., Sommers, A. L., Cox, R. C., Anal. Chem., **35,** 2166, 1963.
[21] Schachter, M. M., Haenni, E. O., 11th Anachem Conf. Detroit, Mich. October 23, 1963.
[22] Van Duuren, B. L., Bardi, C. E., Anal. Chem., **35,** 2198, 1963.
[23] Chapman, J. H., Foster, Th., Kortum, G., Parker, C. P., Lippert, E., Melhuish, W. H., and Nebbia, G., Appl. Spectroscopy, **17,** 171, 1963.

The above suggestions are good and should be followed as far as practicable, however, when a grating is used, as in most spectrofluorometers in the United States, it seems unnecessary to convert the wavelength readings to wave numbers. For results from instruments with prisms, this conversion is highly desirable.

SELECTION OF AN EXCITATION WAVELENGTH FOR ANALYSIS

The best excitation wavelength to choose for a particular determination is governed by several considerations. It should be at a strong absorption band of the compound. It should be at a strong intensity point of the instrument's radiation source. It should be easily separated from the emission either by a grating, prism, or filter. For a filter instrument the spread between excitation and emission bands needs to be much greater than when a grating or prism is used. Since most fluorescing solutions contain colloids there is considerable scattering of the exciting light. If the wavelength of the exciting radiation is within 50 mμ of the emission, the scattered exciting radiation joins the emission and is registered on the phototube. Therefore in any instrument the excitation wavelength must be reasonably separated from the emission. Compounds and metal chelates often have broad absorption bands and any position in the band may be chosen to satisfy best the above limitations. If possible, the wavelength region of least decomposition of the sample should be chosen. There is generally less decomposition at the longer wavelength.

The following examples illustrate these points. Quinine sulfate has a much stronger absorption band at about 250 mμ than at 350 mμ. A low-pressure mercury vapor lamp with quartz optics gives a very strong emission at 254 mμ. This is an excellent source of excitation if a quartz container is used for the sample. The high pressure mercury vapor lamp gives a strong radiation at 350 mμ which is not absorbed by ordinary glass; hence, for convenience and safety of the eyes, the high pressure lamp is very satisfactory for excitation of quinine sulfate. The aluminum chelates of several 2,2′-dihydroxyazo dyes have good excitation points in the ultraviolet as well as in the visible near their emission wavelengths. Since the ultraviolet region is easily separated from the visible emission with ordinary filters, the high-pressure mercury vapor lamp with an emission wavelength at 360 mμ is usually chosen for the excitation. The boron chelate with benzoin has good absorption from 320 to 390 mμ. Since this chelate is subject to decomposition by radiation it is better to use the 390 mμ excitation.

PRECAUTIONS

Since fluorescence analysis is especially applicable to trace quantities of substances, care must be taken to eliminate contamination of the samples. Common solvents often contain large amounts of fluorescent substances. Commercial methyl and ethyl alcohols must be redistilled. Dimethylformamide must be redistilled; a middle fraction of this distillate is usually better than those at the extremes. Rubber and cork stoppers contain fluorescent materials which are extracted if the solvent touches them. Grease from stopcocks and other sources is a fluorescent contaminant. Filter papers contain a fluorescent material which is extracted by solvents.[9] A liquid shaken against a ground glass stopper will remove traces of glass which causes scattered radiation. In spectrofluorometry, Raman lines from the solvent may interfere. Solutions often extract materials from containers, such as boron from Pyrex glass and some plastics. All glass contains aluminum, calcium, and silica which may be extracted. Many reagents contain aluminum in appreciable amounts.

The concentration of the reagent is an important consideration in fluorescence. Concentrations should be expressed in micromoles so that the ratio of reagent to metal ion may be estimated easily. For a quantitative analytical procedure the reagent must be in molar excess to the ion in question. However, too large an excess may result in absorption of the exciting energy by the unchelated reagent and not permit penetration of the entire solution by the exciting radiation. Large temperature changes between unknown and standard should be avoided. Solutions should not be exposed to ultraviolet radiation for long periods.

FLUORESCENT METAL CHELATES

The term *chelate* is derived from the Greek meaning a crab's claw. A metal chelate is a combination of a metal with an organic molecule to which the metal ion is attached at one point by a primary bond and to another part of the molecule with a secondary bond. Typical cases are illustrated by the combination of a metal ion with a 2,2′-dihydroxyazo dye or with 8-quinolinol (Fig. 5-16). This combination usually results in the metal ion being a member of a five- or six-membered ring.

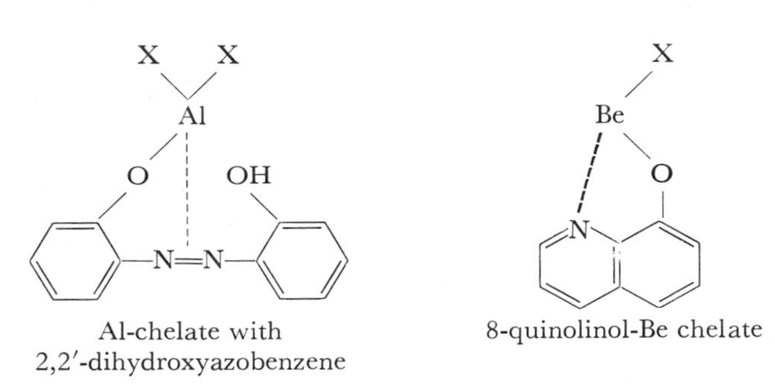

FIG. 5-16. Typical Fluorescent Metal Chelates.

Solvent molecules or other available units may complete the coordination sphere of the metal ion. This combination does not appear to be the origin of the fluorescence, since the original molecule is slightly fluorescent. However, the fluorescence band is shifted, usually to longer wavelengths, and is greatly intensified in the chelate. Apparently after being raised to an excited state by the absorption of energy, the original molecule may lose the excitation energy as molecular vibration. In the chelate the parts of the molecule are held more rigidly by the metal ion and much more of the energy then appears as fluorescence. In some cases, such as in the zirconium-flavonol chelate, the fluorescence is at shorter wavelengths than that of the unchelated ligand. In a number of cases the metal chelate is soluble in an organic solvent which is immiscible with water and may be extracted. The fluorescence is often far more intense in a nonpolar organic solvent than it is in water. This technique is practiced in the extraction of aluminum-8-quinolinol from water with chloroform, gallium-Rhodamine B from 6 *N* hydrochloric acid with benzene, magnesium-2,2′-dihydroxyazobenzene from water with amyl alcohol.[24] In addition to the compounds illustrated in Fig. 5-16, the compounds in Fig. 5-17 have been widely used for chelate formation in fluorometric analysis.

The formulas in Fig. 5-17 illustrate some interesting points. Formula III chelated with aluminum gives a yellow fluorescence. If one more benzene ring is added, as in

[24] Diehl, H., Olsen, R., Spielholtz, G. I., Jensen, R., Anal. Chem., **35**, 1144, 1963.

I

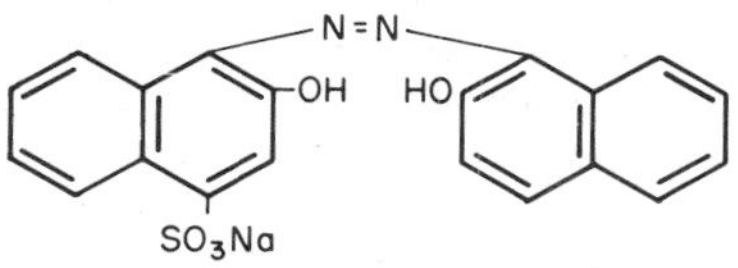

2,2′ Dihydroxy-1,1′-azonaphthalene-4-sulfonic acid, sodium salt (Pontachrome B.B.R.). Reagent for Al. Red fluorescence.

II

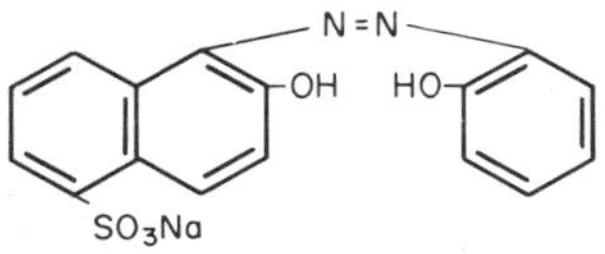

2,2′ Dihydroxy-1,1′-naphthalene-azobenzene-5-sulfonic acid, sodium salt (Pontachrome Violet S.W.). Reagent for Al. Orange fluorescence.

III

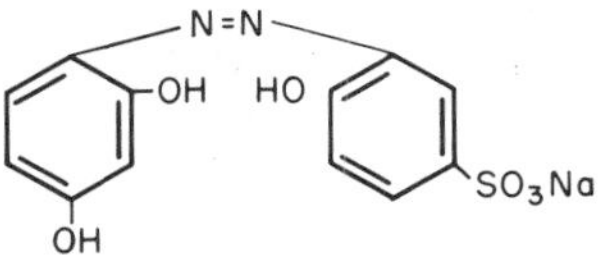

2,4,2′-trihydroxyazobenzene-5′-sulfonic acid, sodium salt (Acid Alizarin Garnet R). Reagent for Al. Yellow fluorescence.

IV

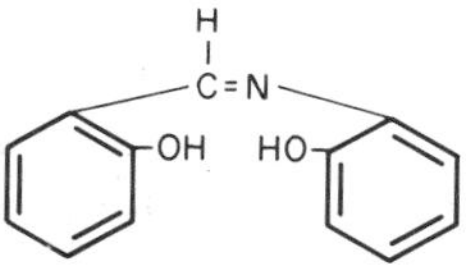

Salicylidene-*o*-aminophenol Reagent for Al, Ga. Green fluorescence.

V

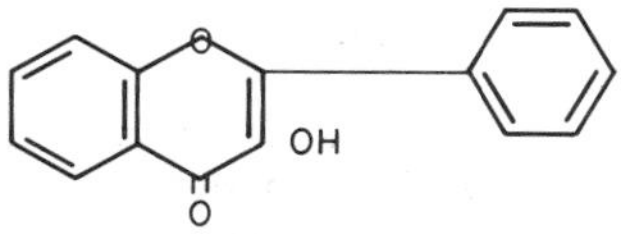

3-Hydroxyflavone (flavonol). Reagent for Zr, Sn. Blue-white fluorescence.

VI

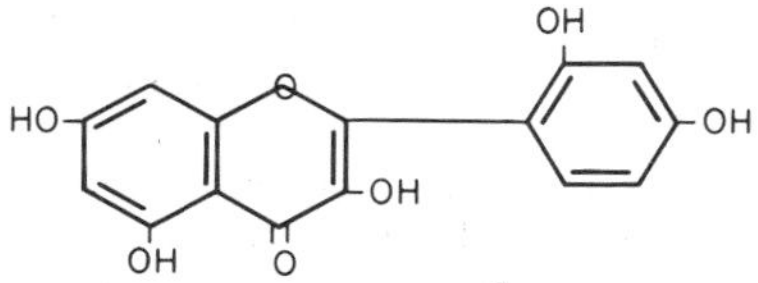

2′,3,4′,5,7 Pentahydroxyflavone (morin). Reagent for Al, Be. Bluish fluorescence.

VII

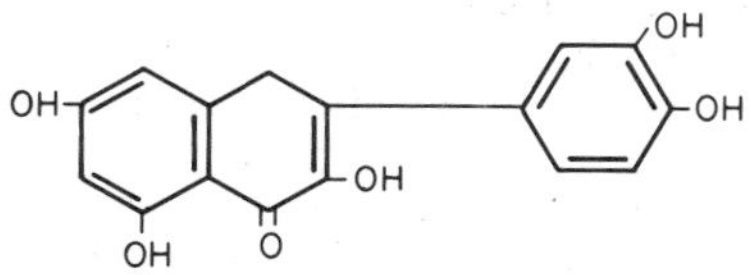

3,3′,4′,5,7 Pentahydroxyflavone (quercetin). Reagent for Zr on paper. Blue-white fluorescence.

VIII

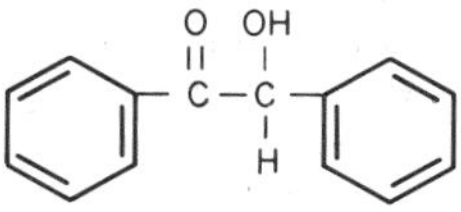

Benzoin. Reagent for B, Zn, Ge, Si. Blue-white fluorescence.

IX

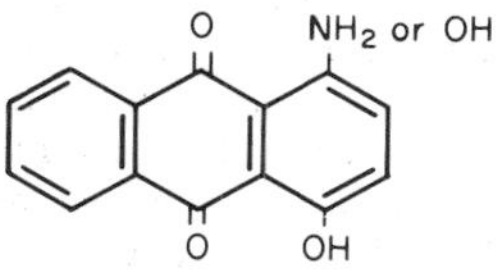

1-amino-4-hydroxyanthraquinone or 1,4-dihydroxyanthraquinone. Reagent for Be, Th. Red fluorescence.

X

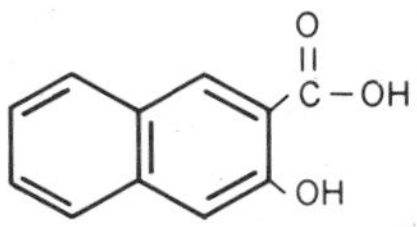

2-Hydroxy-3-naphthoic acid. Reagent for Al, Be. Blue fluorescence.

Fig. 5-17. Typical Fluorometric Reagents for Metal Ions.

formula II, the color of the chelate is shifted to longer wavelengths and becomes orange. If another benzene ring is added, as in formula I, the fluorescence is shifted further to the red. Compounds V to VII all chelate with the ions of aluminum, beryllium, thorium, and zirconium. Since flavonol has only one OH group it can be assumed that in both morin and quercetin the metal replaces the hydrogen of the OH group in the 3-position and unites with a secondary bond to the carbonyl oxygen. In solution with the metal ions, morin gives a stronger fluorescence than its isomer quercetin, but on paper quercetin fluoresces with zirconium more intensely than morin. Compound IX forms fluorescent chelates with a number of ions, but if additional OH groups are substituted on the molecule it becomes more highly colored and the chelates are not fluorescent.

REPRESENTATIVE FLUOROMETRIC DETERMINATIONS

In this section, some typical fluorometric procedures are given in detail, in order to illustrate the principles discussed previously.

DETERMINATION OF ALUMINUM IN STEEL

This method provides a good example of the advantages of fluorometric analysis in speed, sensitivity, and accuracy. It is suitable for the range 0.001% to 1% of acid-soluble aluminum in steel.[25] The principle is the formation of the complex of aluminum with the azo dye 2,2′-dihydroxy-1,1′-azonaphthalene-4-sulfonic acid, sodium salt (Pontachrome Blue Black R, also Superchrome Blue Conc., Eastman #3302). After removal of iron and other interferences by mercury cathode electrolysis, the fluorescence of the complex is measured at pH 4.9 in a carefully buffered solution.

***Reagents.* Pontachrome BBR, 0.1% Solution.**—Dissolve 0.50 g. of the dye in 500 ml. of 95% ethyl alcohol and allow to stand a few days before using.

Dilute Sulfuric Acid 1:9.—Pipet 100 ml. of the concentrated acid into several hundred milliliters of water in a 1-liter volumetric flask, cool, and dilute to the mark.

Ammonium Acetate, 10%.—Dissolve 50.0 g. in water and dilute to 500 ml.

Standard Solution of Aluminum, 1.00 ml. = 0.0100 mg.—Dissolve 0.1769 g. of potassium aluminum sulfate crystals in water, and dilute to 1 liter. If desired, this solution can be diluted tenfold to give a solution containing 1.00 μg. per milliliter.

Procedure.—Dissolve a 1.00-g. sample in 25.0 ml. of 1:9 sulfuric acid, transfer to a 500-ml. volumetric flask without filtering, and dilute to the mark. Mix well, and allow any residue to settle. (If the aluminum content is over 0.10%, use a 0.100-g. sample.) Electrolyze a 10-ml. aliquot, containing 0.020 g. of steel, for 1 hour in a small motor-stirred mercury cathode cell at a current of about 0.5 ampere. Draw off the solution and rinsings into a 50-ml. volumetric flask which contains 5.0 ml. of 10% ammonium acetate plus 1.50 ml. of 0.1% PBBR solution. After 1 hour, measure the fluorescence intensity at 630 mμ in the unknowns and in a blank and standards treated similarly, including the electrolysis. Standards of 10 and 20 μg. are prepared from the aluminum standard solution, and must contain the same amounts of acid, buffer, and dye as the unknowns and blank. Calculate the results using Eq. (8b); the calibration curve is linear up to 25 μg. of Al in the 50-ml. volume.

Procedures are also given in the original paper for the determination of aluminum in bronzes and in minerals, and for acid-insoluble alumina in steel.

The related azo dye 2,4,2′-trihydroxyazobenzene-5′-sulfonic acid, sodium salt (Acid Alizarin Garnet R) may be used in place of PBBR, with some gain in sensitivity.[26]

[25] Weissler, A., and White, C. E., Ind. Eng. Chem., Anal. Ed., **18,** 530, 1946.
[26] Powell, W. A., and Saylor, J. H., Anal. Chem., **25,** 960, 1953.

DETERMINATION OF BERYLLIUM IN SILICATES

Here again fluorometric analysis offers great advantages over conventional procedures. The method[27] is highly sensitive: 0.001 μg. of beryllium in 25 ml. can be detected, and 0.25 μg. can be determined with a precision of better than 1 percent. The calibration curve is practically linear up to 0.50 μg. in the 25 ml. volume used. The basis of the method is the formation of the fluorescent complex of beryllium with morin (2′,4′,3,5,7-pentahydroxyflavone). Interferences such as iron and rare earths are eliminated by complexing with triethanolamine and diethylenetriaminepentaacetate.

Reagents.[27] **Sodium Hydroxide-DTPA-TEA.**—Dissolve 60 g. of sodium hydroxide and 320 g. of anhydrous sodium perchlorate in 250 ml. of water and filter through a double 7-cm. glass fiber filter in a No. 2 Buchner funnel. Dissolve 13.0 g. of recrystallized diethylenetriaminepentaacetic acid and 10.0 ml. of 20% triethanolamine in 50 ml. of water and about 20 ml. of the sodium hydroxide solution. When all solid material has dissolved, add the remainder of the sodium hydroxide, dilute to 500 ml., and store the solution in a polyethylene bottle. Acidify a small portion and test for the presence of hypochlorite or chlorine. Any oxidizing capacity must be eliminated by treatment with small portions of sodium sulfite.

Piperidine Buffer.—Transfer 15.0 g. of purified DTPA to a 500-ml. volumetric flask with about 200 ml. of distilled water. Add 75.0 ml. of redistilled piperidine, stopper the flask, and swirl under a stream of cold water until cool. Add a solution of 20 g. of anhydrous sodium sulfite in 150 ml. of water and dilute to 500 ml. Store in a tightly stoppered bottle with a polyethylene-lined screw cap.

Morin, 0.0075%.—Dissolve 7.50 mg. of pure anhydrous morin in 40 ml. of 95% ethyl alcohol, and dilute to 100 ml. with water. Analytical grade morin of excellent quality is available from Dr. Theodor Schuchardt, Munich, Germany, and from Fluka AG, Buchs SG, Switzerland.

Standard Beryllium Solution.—Dissolve 0.1964 g. of beryllium sulfate tetrahydrate in water, add 10 ml. of 72% perchloric acid, and dilute to 1 liter. Dilute 5.00 ml. of the stock solution and 1 ml. of 72% perchloric acid to 1 liter. One ml. contains 0.0500 μg. of beryllium.

Procedure.[27]—Dissolve 0.5 g. of a sample such as kaolin in a potassium fluoride fusion, transpose to a mixed sodium-potassium pyrosulfate fusion and dissolve the cake in dilute hydrochloric acid.[28] Boil to hydrolyze any pyrophosphates present, and determine the beryllium content as follows.

Transfer to a 50-ml. volumetric flask, dilute to the mark, and mix. To a 1-ml. aliquot, add 3.0 ml. of sodium hydroxide-DTPA-TEA solution and 3 drops of 0.01% quinine solution in 1% perchloric acid. Neutralize by adding 72% perchloric acid dropwise until a brilliant blue fluorescence is produced under ultraviolet light. Add 1 drop excess perchloric acid and roll the solution gently around the sides to redissolve all beryllium hydroxide. Transfer the solution to a 25-ml., glass-stoppered volumetric flask and add 1 *N* sodium hydroxide until the fluorescence is extinguished.

Add 5.00 ml. of piperidine buffer, mix well, and rinse down the sides of the flask with water. Add 1.00 ml. of morin, mix, bring to room temperature, and dilute to the mark. Stopper, mix well, and place in a constant-temperature bath (adjusted within 2°C. of room temperature) for 20 minutes before measuring the fluorescence at 500 mμ.

With each group of samples, prepare and measure a blank and a beryllium standard, using 5 ml. of water and 5 ml. of the 0.05 μg./ml. solution of beryllium, respectively.

[27] Sill, C. W., Willis, C. P., Flygare, J. K., Anal. Chem., **33**, 1671, 1961; reprinted with permission.

[28] For details, see Sill, C. W., Anal. Chem., **33**, 1684, 1961.

For minerals of high beryllium content, such as beryl, use a 0.1-g. sample and a 1/10,000 aliquot instead of a 1/50 aliquot.

The original paper also gives detailed procedures for the determination of beryllium in air dusts, copper alloys, monazite sands or other rare earth materials, and metallic aluminum, uranium, zirconium, or thorium.

DETERMINATION OF RIBOFLAVIN IN ANIMAL TISSUES

The fluorometric determination of riboflavin is described in Volume IIB of the 6th edition of Standard Methods of Chemical Analysis, 1963, pp. 2362–2366, as well as in the A.O.A.C. Official Methods.[29]

An improved procedure[30] with detailed discussions has become available recently for the determination of total flavins including flavin adenine dinucleotide and flavin mononucleotide. One advantage of the procedure is the improved specificity for flavins, achieved by photolytic conversion to lumiflavin, which is then separated from interfering fluorescent substances by means of a chloroform extraction.

DETERMINATION OF ZIRCONIUM

This procedure,[31] which uses flavonol as the fluorogenic reagent, is given on p. 1278 of Vol. I of Standard Methods of Chemical Analysis, 6th edition, 1962.

DETERMINATION OF URANIUM

For uranium, the fluorescence intensity is measured not in a liquid solution, but instead in a solid disc resulting from a sodium fluoride fusion. This is described on p. 1201 of Vol. I of Standard Methods of Chemical Analysis, 6th edition, 1962. A variety of procedures to fit individual circumstances is available in the original collection of papers by Grimaldi and associates.[32]

APPLICATIONS IN THE ANALYSIS OF SPECIAL MATERIALS

Fluorometric methods have been reported elsewhere in Volumes II and III of Standard Methods of Chemical Analysis. These are:

1. Chapter 47, Volume III, Instrumental Methods in Clinical Medicine.
   a. Corticosteroids
   b. Catecholamines
   c. Estrogens
   d. Serotonin
2. Chapter 50, Volume III, Foods.
   a. Amprolium
   b. Riboflavin
   c. Thiamine
3. Chapter 59, Volume III, Rubber and Rubber Products.
   a. Identification of antioxidants
4. Chapter 47, Volume IIB, Vitamins.
   a. Folic acid, page 2382.

[29] Official Methods of Analysis, Association of Official Agricultural Chemists, Washington 4, D. C., pp. 658–660, 1960.

[30] Yagi, K., in Methods of Biochemical Analysis, D. Glick, Ed., Vol. X, Interscience Publishers, New York, pp. 319–355, 1962.

[31] Alford, W. C., Shapiro, L., White, C. E., Anal. Chem., **23**, 1149, 1951.

[32] Geological Survey Bulletin 1006, Washington, D. C., 1954.

b. Thiamine, pages 2359, 2361.
c. Vitamin B_2, pages 2363, 2365.

PHOSPHORIMETRY

Phosphorimetry is closely related to fluorometry. As a method of chemical analysis, phosphorimetry is based on the nature and intensity of the phosphorescent light emitted by an appropriately excited molecule. As mentioned in the Theoretical Background section of this chapter, phosphorescence is a delayed luminescence, usually of weaker intensity and longer wavelength than the fluorescence of the same molecule.

The general technique is to measure the emission intensity at the temperature of liquid nitrogen, in a rigid glass formed by solidification of a solution of the material in a suitable solvent. A useful solvent is EPA, which is a mixture of ethyl ether, isopentane, and ethyl alcohol in a volume ratio of 5:5:2. The phosphorescence is observed at right angles to the excitation, through a rotating slit, motor-driven at a speed which can be varied for the different phosphorescence lifetimes.

Lifetime, quantum yield, and excitation and emission peaks are characteristic properties of each phosphorescence, which may be used for either identification or the analysis of mixtures. Mixtures of acetophenone and benzophenone have been analyzed successfully by phosphorimetry, taking advantage of the different lifetimes of 0.008 second and 0.006 second, respectively.[33] In the same paper, a mixture of diphenylamine and triphenylamine was analyzed phosphorimetrically, through the use of selective excitation in the vicinity of 325 mμ.

An example of a practical phosphorimetric method is the analysis of aspirin in blood serum or plasma.[34] The aspirin in 0.4 ml. of serum is extracted into chloroform, the chloroform is evaporated, and the residue is dissolved in EPA. The solution is placed in a quartz sample tube, and the phosphorescence intensity at 410 mμ is measured after cooling to 77°K., using white light for excitation. For the concentration range of 1 to 100 mg. aspirin per 100 ml. of serum, the analysis can be performed in less than 10 minutes with good accuracy and reproducibility. No serious interference is given by the normal constituents of serum or plasma.

SELECTED BIBLIOGRAPHY

1. Bowen, E. J., and Wokes, F., Fluorescence of Solutions, Longmans Green and Co., New York, 1953.
2. Danckwortt, P. W., and Eisenbrand, J., Lumineszenz-Analyse in Filtrierten Ultravioletten Licht, 6th edition, Akademische Verlagsgesellschaft, Guest and Partig, Leipzig, Germany, 1956.
3. Foster, T., Fluoreszenz Organischer Verbindungen, Vandenhoeck and Ruprecht Verlagsbuchhandlung, Gottingen, Germany, 1951.
4. Nairn, R. C., Fluorescent Protein Tracing, Wilkins & Williams, Baltimore, 1962.
5. Parker, C. A., and Rees, W. T., Fluorescence Spectrometry; a Review, Analyst, **87,** 83, 1962.
6. Pringsheim, Peter, Fluorescence and Phosphorescence, Interscience Publishers, New York, 1949.
7. Radley, J. A., and Grant, J., Fluorescence Analysis in Ultraviolet Light, 4th Ed., D. Van Nostrand Company, Princeton, 1954.
8. Undenfriend, S., Fluorescence Assay in Biology and Medicine, Academic Press, New York, 1962.
9. Weissler, A., and White, C. E., Handbook of Analytical Chemistry, L. Meites, Ed., Chapter 6, pp. 176–196, McGraw-Hill, New York, 1963.

[33] Keirs, R. J., Britt, R. D., Jr., and Wentworth, W. E., Anal. Chem., **29,** 202, 1959.
[34] Winefordner, J. D., and Latz, H. W., Anal. Chem., **35,** 1517, 1963.

10. White, C. E., Chapter VII in Trace Analysis, Yoe, J. H., and Koch, H. J., Eds., John Wiley and Sons, New York, 1957.
11. Reviews of Fluorometric Analysis, White, C. E., Ind. Eng. Chem., Anal. Ed., **11,** 63, 1939; Anal. Chem., **21,** 104, 1949; **22,** 69, 1950; **24,** 85, 1952; **26,** 129, 1954; **28,** 621, 1956; **30,** 729, 1958; **32,** 47R, 1960; White, C. E., and Weissler, A., Anal. Chem., **34,** 81R, 1962; **36,** 116R, 1964.

Chapter **6**

ATOMIC ABSORPTION SPECTROMETRY

By A. Walsh and J. B. Willis
C.S.I.R.O. Division of Chemical Physics
Melbourne, Australia

PRINCIPLES

Chemical analysis by atomic absorption spectrometry involves converting the sample, at least partially, into an atomic vapor and measuring the absorption of this atomic vapor at a selected wavelength which is characteristic for each individual element.[1] The measured absorbance is proportional to concentration, and analyses are made by comparing this absorbance with that given under the same experimental conditions by reference samples of known composition.

Although several methods of vaporizing solids directly are known,[2,3,4] almost all analytical applications of the atomic absorption method at the present time involve spraying a solution of the sample into a flame. For this reason the technique is sometimes referred to as "absorption flame photometry." With the types of flame commonly used, the atomic absorption lines are so narrow (usually less than 0.05 A) that it is extremely difficult to design a monochromator to isolate a sufficiently narrow band from the spectrum of a light source emitting a continuum. For such a technique to be satisfactory the resolution of the monochromator would have to be of the order of 0.01 A, and this cannot be achieved with any simple monochromator. Assuming the availability of a monochromator of this resolution, it would be necessary to use a scanning technique since it would be scarcely feasible to measure peak absorption at a fixed wavelength setting adjusted to an accuracy of 0.01 A. All commercially available atomic absorption spectrophotometers overcome this difficulty by using light sources which emit atomic spectral lines of the element to be determined under conditions which ensure that the lines in the spectrum are narrow, compared with the absorption line to be measured. With this arrangement peak absorptions can be measured, and the monochromator is only required to isolate the line to be measured from all other lines in the spectrum of the light source. Figure 6-1 illustrates the way in which this peak absorption is carried out, and Fig. 6-2 shows the spectrum of a magnesium light source on which is marked the spectral line which is normally used in chemical analysis. It must be noted that of the large number of lines emitted by any light source, only a small number show any appreciable absorption.

Recent work has led to the development of resonance detectors which permit the

[1] Walsh, A., Spectrochim. Acta, **7,** 108, 1955; Alkemade, C. T. J., and Milatz, J. M. W., Appl. Sci. Research, **B4,** 289, 1955.
[2] Gatehouse, B. M., and Walsh, A., Spectrochim. Acta, **16,** 602, 1960.
[3] Goleb, J. A., and Brody, J. K., Anal. Chim. Acta, **28,** 457, 1963.
[4] L'vov, B. V., Spectrochim. Acta, **17,** 761, 1961.

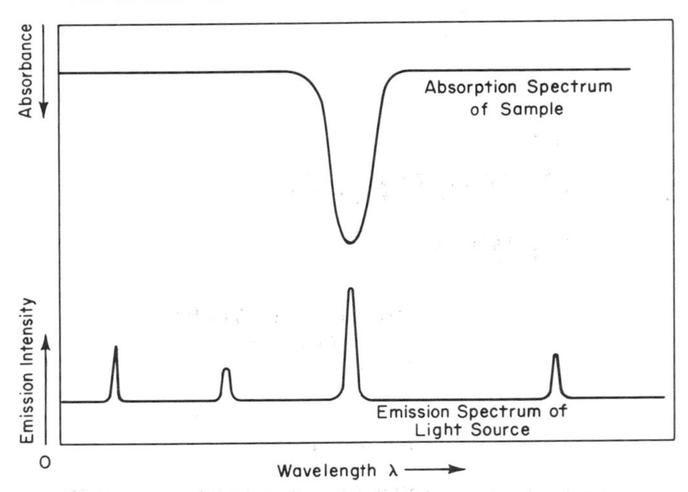

Fig. 6-1. Lines Emitted by the Light Source are Much Narrower Than the Absorption Line to be Measured.

isolation of the resonance lines of a metal, *i.e.*, those lines showing highest absorption intensity, without the need for a monochromator.[4a] Such detectors are likely to be of particular value where routine determinations are required on only one or two metals.

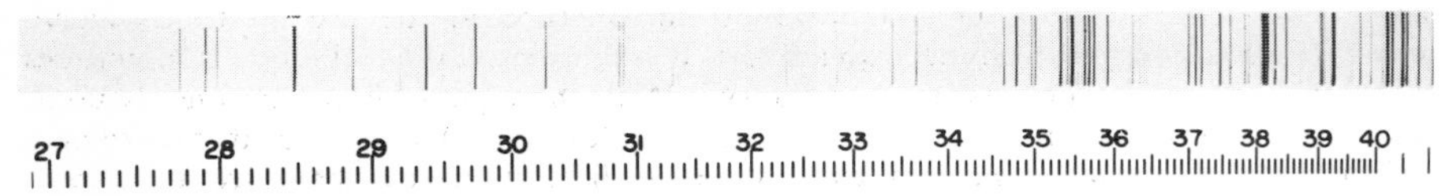

Fig. 6-2. Spectrum of Magnesium Hollow-cathode Discharge Lamp, Showing the Line at 2852A, Used in Atomic Absorption Analysis.

INSTRUMENTATION

Figure 6-3 shows schematically the mode of operation of an atomic absorption spectrophotometer, and Fig. 6-4 shows a single-beam instrument. Radiation from the light source emitting the spectrum of the element being determined is passed through a flame into which a fine spray of sample is introduced. The emerging radiation passes through a monochromator to isolate a selected spectral line of the element, and is then detected by a photocell or photomultiplier, the output of which is amplified and measured on a meter or recorder. Since the flame may be emitting appreciably at the wavelength at which the absorption measurement is to be made, it is essential to compensate for any such flame emission. The usual procedure is to modulate the power supply to the light source and use an a.c. amplifier tuned to the same frequency: thus, any radiation from the flame which is not so modulated gives no signal at the output of the amplifier. The absorbance measurement is made by measuring the ratio of the output signals of the amplifier with and without the sample solution being sprayed into the flame. It is usual to take the blank reading with the solvent being sprayed into the flame.

The various items of equipment are discussed below.

[4a] Sullivan, J. V., and Walsh, A., Spectrochim. Acta, **21,** 719, 727, 1965.

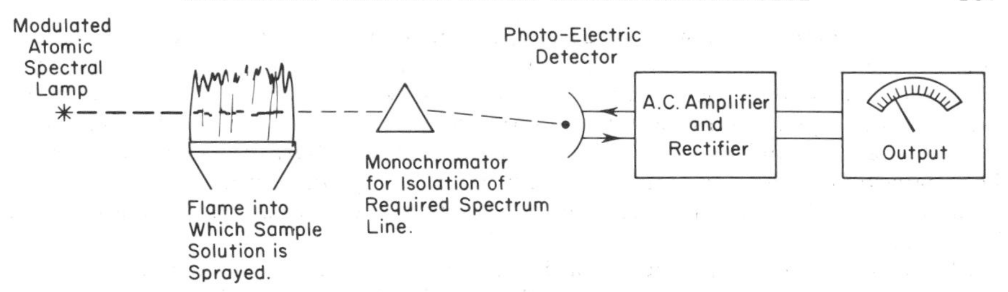

FIG. 6-3. Schematic Diagram Illustrating Mode of Operation of an Atomic Absorption Spectrophotometer.

Light Sources.—These are required to emit spectra of the elements to be determined and these spectra should have sharp lines, negligible background, and high stability. It is desirable that the light source reach equilibrium as quickly as possible. The most generally suitable light sources are hollow-cathode lamps and these are now available for all the elements which can be usefully determined by an atomic absorption spectro-

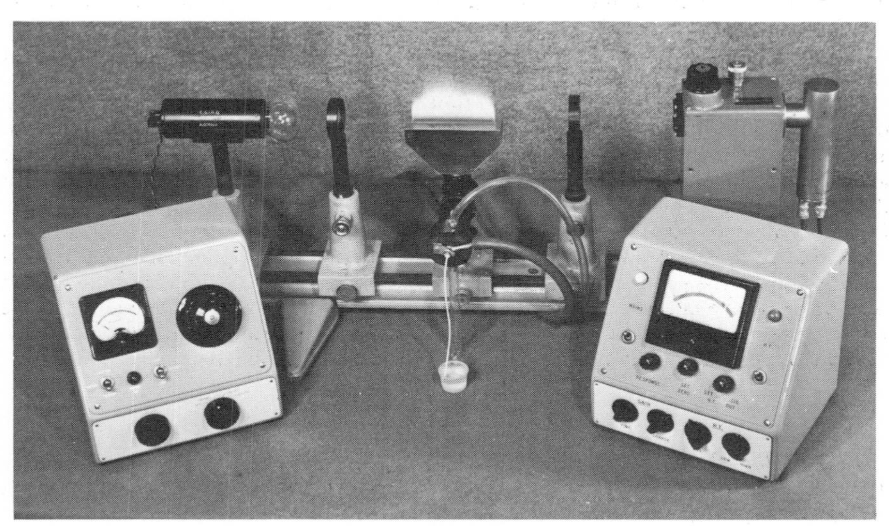

FIG. 6-4. Simple Atomic Absorption Spectrophotometer.

photometer. For the alkali metals and for thallium, mercury, cadmium, and zinc, laboratory-type discharge lamps can be used. The power supplies for these lamps should be stabilized so that the light output is independent of changes in power line voltage or frequency. For hollow-cathode lamps the modulated d.c. power supply should be capable of operating over the range 2–20 milliamperes at an output voltage of 500 volts, while for laboratory discharge lamps, the current range extends from about 0.6–0.9 amperes at 230–400 volts according to the type of lamp used. Modulation frequencies may range from 50 cps. to several kc./sec.

Flame.—Air-coal gas, air-propane, air-acetylene, and oxy-acetylene flames have been used, but the most widely useful flame is air-acetylene. Optimum flame conditions vary for different elements and it is important that the various gas supplies can be controlled and metered. Similarly, the optimum flame region to be used varies for different elements and so it is essential that the burner height can be adjusted to give maximum absorption. Most published work has used premixed flames, in which the sample is aspirated through an atomizer with compressed air, mixed with the combustible gas in a spray chamber, and then burned at a long (*ca.* 10-cm.) burner. Some work has also been carried out using direct injection burners of the type used in many emission flame photometers. It is advisable to remove the products of combustion by means of an exhaust hood over the burner.

Monochromator.—The function of the monochromator is to select a given line in the emission spectrum of the light source and isolate it from all other lines. The resolution required varies for each element, but in a general-purpose instrument a resolution of the order of 0.5 A is desirable.

Detection System.—For most elements the lines used lie in the ultraviolet or blue region of the visible spectrum; for the detection of such lines a photomultiplier is necessary. For the detection of lines in the spectra of the alkali metals which lie in the visible or near infrared region of the spectrum, red-sensitive photomultipliers are generally employed, although photoconductive or photovoltaic cells have been used in specialized instruments. The amplification of the signal from the detector is straightforward, and simple a.c. amplifiers, tuned or untuned, are used. As pointed out earlier the use of an unmodulated light source and a d.c. amplifier is not satisfactory if the flame is emitting at the wavelength at which the absorption measurement is to be made.

Single-beam and Double-beam Operation.—In single-beam operation the output of the amplifier is arranged to give full-scale deflection with no sample in the flame, and it is important that the power supply to the lamp and photomultiplier be highly regulated and that the gain of the amplifier be independent of power line variations to ensure that the conditions do not change before the sample solution is sprayed into the flame. Double-beam methods have the advantage of permitting a higher speed of operation and are not critically dependent on the stability of the power supplies. However, it must be noted that even with a double-beam system, variations in the power supply to the lamp must not be of such an extent that they may cause an appreciable change in the width of the line to be measured. Any fluctuations due to variations in the rate of production of atoms in the flame cannot be compensated by double-beam operation.

APPLICATIONS

Scope of the Method.—Atomic absorption spectrometry is applicable to the determination of some sixty metals; the only limitation on the type of sample is that it must be capable of giving a solution of the metal concerned in either an aqueous or an organic solvent. The viscosity of the solution must not be such as to cause clogging of the atomizer.

Table 6-1 shows the range of metals which can be determined with an air-coal gas, air-propane, or air-acetylene flame. Metals forming highly refractory oxides, *e.g.*, beryllium, aluminum, vanadium, titanium, tantalum, and the rare earths, cannot be determined in any of these flames, but require a highly reducing oxy-acetylene flame. Preliminary work on these metals has been reported,[5,6,7] but their routine determination by atomic absorption methods is not yet general.

Use of a flame of acetylene, burning either with oxygen-enriched air or with nitrous oxide, enables the determination of some twenty-five elements over and above those

[5] Slavin, W., and Manning, D. C., Anal. Chem., **35**, 253, 1963.
[6] Chakrabarti, C. L., Lyles, G. R., and Dowling, F. B., Anal. Chim. Acta, **29**, 489, 1963.
[7] Fassel, V. A., and Mossotti, V. G., Anal. Chem., **35**, 252, 1963.

TABLE 6-1. SENSITIVITIES FOR METALS DETERMINED BY ATOMIC ABSORPTION SPECTROMETRY

Concentrations giving one percent absorption[a] when sprayed as an aqueous solution into the 10-cm. flame of a single-beam instrument.[b]

Metal	Spectral Line A	Flame[c]	Concentration μg./ml.	Metal	Spectral Line A	Flame[c]	Concentration μg./ml.
Li	6708	C	0.02	Sn	2246	A	2
Na	5890	C	0.02	Pb	2171	C	0.4
K	7665	C	0.03	As	1937	A	1.5
Rb	7800	C	0.04	Sb	2176	C	1
Cs	8521	C	0.15	Bi	2230	C	0.4
Cu	3248	C	0.07	Cr	3579	A	0.15
Ag	3281	C	0.06	Mo	3133	A	0.7
Au	2428	C	0.3	Se[d]	1961	C	0.6
Mg	2852	A	0.008	Te	2143	C	0.3
Ca	4227	A	0.08	Mn	2795	C	0.06
Sr	4607	A	0.15	Fe	2483	A	0.1
Ba	5536	A	7	Co	2407	A	0.1
Zn	2139	C	0.02	Ni	2320	C	0.1
Cd	2288	C	0.02	Ru	3499	A	0.9
Hg	2537	C	5	Rh	3435	A	0.4
Ga	2874	A	2	Pd	2476	C	0.2
In	3040	C	0.4	Pt	2659	A	8
Tl	2768	C	0.5				

[a] For details of less sensitive lines and discussion of instrumental conditions see footnotes 11 and 20.
[b] The Techtron AA-3 instrument (Techtron Pty. Ltd., 271 Huntingdale Road, East Oakleigh, Victoria, Australia).
[c] C = air-coal gas, A = air-acetylene.
[d] Figures obtained with an experimental hollow-cathode tube with a high noise-level.

listed in Table 6-1. Table 6-2 shows sensitivities for metals determined in such a flame.[7a]

The principal fields of application to date have been:

(1) Agriculture: Soils, soil extracts, plant materials, and fertilizers[8,9] for Ca, Cu, Fe, K, Mg, Mn, Mo, Na, Sr, Zn; wines[10] for Cu, Fe, Pb; dairy products[11] for Cu.
(2) Medicine and Biology:[11,11a] Blood sera, urine, and tissues for Ca, Cd, Cu, Fe, Hg, K, Mg, Na, Ni, Pb, Zn.

[7a] Amos, M. D., and Thomas, P. E., Anal. Chim. Acta, **32,** 139, 1965; Willis, J. B., Nature, in press; Amos, M. D., and Willis, J. B., Spectrochim. Acta, in press.
[8] Allan, J. E., Analyst, **83,** 466, 1958; **86,** 530, 1961; Spectrochim. Acta, 800, 1959; **17,** 459, 1961.
[9] David, D. J., Analyst, **83,** 655, 1958; **84,** 536, 1959; **85,** 495, 1960; **86,** 730, 1961; **87,** 576, 1962.
[10] Zeeman, P. B., and Butler, L. R. P., Appl. Spec., **16,** 120, 1962.
[11] Willis, J. B., Spectrochim. Acta, **16,** 259, 273, 551, 1960; Anal. Chem., **33,** 556, 1961; **34,** 614, 1962; Australian J. Dairy Technol., **19,** 70, 1964; also in Vol. 11 of Methods of Biochemical Analysis, D. Glick, ed., Interscience Publishers, New York, 1963.
[11a] Zettner, A., and Seligson, D., Clin. Chem., **10,** 869, 1964.

TABLE 6-2. SENSITIVITIES FOR METALS REQUIRING A HIGH-TEMPERATURE FLAME[a]

Metal	Spectral Line A	Concentration, μg./ml.	Metal	Spectral Line A	Concentration, μg./ml.
Be	2349	0.02	Yb	3988	0.25
B	2498	50	Si	2516	5
Al	3093	1	Ge	2652	2.5
Y	4102	5	Ti	3643	3.5
La	3574	110	Zr	3601	15
Pr	4951	72	Hf	3073	14
Nd	4634	35	V	3184	1.5
Sm	4297	21	Nb	3349	24
Gd	3684	38	Ta	2714	11
Dy	4212	1.5	W	2551	5
Ho	4104	2	U	3585	120
Er	4008	1.5	Re	3460	12

[a] Concentrations giving one percent absorption when sprayed as an aqueous solution into a 5-cm. nitrous oxide-acetylene flame in a single-beam instrument.

(3) Geology and Mining: Ores and concentrates[12] for Ag, Co, Cu, Fe, Ni, Pb, Zn; cyanide liquors[13] for Au; rocks for Cu and Zn.[13a]
(4) Metallurgy: Iron and steel[14,15] for Co, Cr, Mg, Mn, Pb, Zn; non-ferrous metals[15] for Ag, Bi, Cd, Co, Cr, Mg, Mn, Mo, Ni, Pb, Sb, Sn, Zn; noble metals for Ag, Au, Pd, Pt.[15a]
(5) Oil Analysis: Crude oils, feedstocks, and lubricating oils[16] for Ag, Ba, Ca, Cr, Cu. Fe, Na, Ni, Pb.
(6) Coal ashes and boiler deposits[17] for Ca, Fe, K, Na, Mg, Sr.
(7) Electroplating solutions[18] for Cd, Cu, Fe, Ni, Zn.

Interferences.—Since the atomic absorption technique measures the concentration of unexcited (ground state) atoms it does not suffer from interference due to the influence of one element on the excitation potential of another. Furthermore, the use of a sharp-line source gives the system an effective resolution of about 0.01 A and avoids spectroscopic interference, common in emission flame photometry, due to the overlapping of the line to be measured with unwanted lines or bands due to other substances present. This latter property of the absorption technique is particularly valuable, for instance, in the determination of traces of magnesium, whose absorption line lies at 2852.13 A, in the presence of large amounts of sodium, which has an absorption line at 2852.83 A.

Chemical interference, however, can still occur, as in emission flame photometry, through the formation in the flame of compounds which are incompletely dissociated and atomized. Typical examples occur in the determination of calcium in the presence

[12] Rawling, B. S., Amos, M. D., and Greaves, M. C., Nature, **188,** 137, 1960; Bull. Inst. Mining and Metallurgy, No. 662, 227, 1962.
[13] Skewes, H. R., Proc. Australian Inst. Mining and Met., No. 211, 217, 1964.
[13a] Belt, C. B., Jr., Econ. Geol., **59,** 240, 1964.
[14] Belcher, C. B., *et al.*, Anal. Chim. Acta, **26,** 322, 1962; **29,** 134, 1963; **30,** 64, 483, 1964.
[15] Elwell, W. T., and Gidley, J. A. F., Atomic Absorption Spectroscopy, Pergamon Press, Oxford, 1961.
[15a] Strasheim, A., and Wessels, G. J., Appl. Spectrometry, **17,** 65, 1963.
[16] Burrows, J. A., Heerdt, J. C., and Willis, J. B., Anal. Chem., **37,** 579, 1965.
[17] Belcher, C. B., and Brooks, K. A., Anal. Chim. Acta, **29,** 202, 1963.
[18] Whittington, C. M., and Willis, J. B., Plating, **51,** 767, 1964.

of phosphorus and of magnesium in the presence of aluminum. Methods of overcoming these interferences have been developed; they depend in general on the addition to the solution being analyzed of a relatively large concentration of an element which can compete with the metal being determined for combination with the interfering element. Thus, the addition of an excess of strontium, lanthanum, or magnesium in the presence of sulfuric acid, overcomes the interference of phosphorus in the determination of calcium.

Sensitivity. Table 6-1 shows the sensitivity of the method for a number of metals in aqueous solution using a typical commercially-available single-beam instrument. In using this table to assess the possibilities of the method for a particular analysis the following points must be kept in mind:

(1) Use of a solution in a suitable organic solvent, usually an ester or a ketone, increases the sensitivity by a factor of about three.[19]

(2) The figures in Tables 6-1 and 6-2 were obtained using solutions containing only a salt of the metal being determined. If the solution to be analyzed also contains large concentrations of other substances, the viscosity and surface tension will be altered and the sensitivity will be somewhat reduced.

(3) The "limit of detection" with most single-beam instruments is usually a little lower than the concentration required to give 1 percent absorption, and can sometimes be improved by using a scale-expansion device if the stability of the light source and associated electronic equipment warrant it.

(4) Where it is desired to measure higher concentrations, the sensitivity of the equipment may be reduced by diluting the sample solution, using a less strongly absorbed line, or rotating the burner to reduce the length of the light path through the flame.

(5) The quantity of solution normally required for one reading is about 1 ml.

Precision and Accuracy.—The factors determining the precision of atomic absorption measurements are chiefly the stability of the hollow-cathode or other sharp-line source and the steadiness of the atomization of the sample solution in the flame. Use of a double-beam system minimizes the effect of fluctuations in the former, but cannot influence the latter. With a simple single-beam instrument a typical coefficient of variation would be 1–1.5 percent provided that the concentration of the sample solution is such as to produce an absorption of 40–80 percent. It will be apparent that at very low levels of absorption the accuracy attainable will be limited.

If the method has been carefully developed and possible interferences have been investigated and corrected, the results of an atomic absorption analysis over the optimum range should be correct to within about ±2 percent of the concentration of the metal being determined. Since this relative accuracy is roughly independent of the concentration of the metal in the sample, it is clear that the atomic absorption technique is better suited to the accurate determination of trace and minor constituents rather than of major components.

Advantages and Limitations.—The principal advantages of the atomic absorption technique are:

(1) It shows high sensitivity for a wide range of metals, including many which are difficult or impossible to determine by flame photometry.

(2) It is highly specific.

(3) Any one metal can normally be determined in the presence of large amounts of other substances.

(4) It is rapid and requires only small amounts of material.

(5) The small amount of pretreatment and handling of the samples normally required minimizes the risk of contamination.

[19] Allan, J. E., Spectrochim. Acta, **17**, 467, 1961.

The use of the technique is at present limited to metals. With nonmetals, which have their resonance lines in the vacuum ultraviolet (*i.e.*, below 1850 A), difficulties arise from the strong absorption of light by the oxygen in the light path and from the flame gases themselves. As mentioned earlier, metals which form highly refractory oxides require the use of highly reducing high-temperature flames.

PROCEDURE

The atomic absorption spectrophotometer is normally arranged so that the radiation from the hollow-cathode or other sharp-line source is focused by a lens to a slightly reduced image at the center of a long (10-cm.) flame into which the solution to be measured is sprayed. This image is then re-imaged by means of a second lens on to the entrance slit of the monochromator. In a double-beam instrument the light from the sharp-line source is split into two beams, one of which passes through the flame while the other, the reference beam, bypasses it. The two beams are recombined before entering the monochromator. The alignment of the optical system is usually straightforward, and in any case only needs to be carried out when the instrument is installed.

In performing an analysis, the appropriate hollow-cathode lamp or other light source is placed in position and allowed to warm up for five or ten minutes. The choice of lamp current depends on various factors; *e.g.*, (1) inherent intensity and stability of the resonance line used, (2) sensitivity of the photomultiplier detector, (3) age and quality of the source, and (4) slit-width of the monochromator. In general, where it is desired to obtain maximum sensitivity and as linear a calibration curve as possible, the minimum hollow-cathode current should be used consistent with adequate signal intensity and stability, and the maximum slit-width compatible with the complete isolation of the resonance line from any adjacent lines.

Guidance on the choice of suitable operating conditions for different analyses is usually supplied by the makers of individual instruments; a fuller discussion of the factors involved appears elsewhere.[11,20]

Most commercial instruments make provision for an air-coal gas, air-propane, or air-acetylene flame. Choice of the most suitable flame for a particular analysis depends on the metal to be determined and to some extent on the other materials present. Chemical interference, such as occurs when determining magnesium in the presence of aluminum or calcium in the presence of phosphorus, is usually less pronounced and more easily controlled in the air-acetylene flame than in the air-coal gas or air-propane flames. The latter two flames, being cooler, however, give slightly greater sensitivity for many of the heavy metals and in general are to be preferred in the determination of alkali metals.

The position and composition of the flame are adjusted to give maximum absorption while spraying a solution containing a known concentration of the metal to be determined. Since it is difficult to insure a flame which is perfectly reproducible in position and composition day after day, it is common practice to prepare a working curve for each batch of sample solutions; however, this takes only a short time, as will be seen in "Methods of Calibration."

Preparation of Samples.—The samples to be analyzed are brought into solution. For the most accurate results, it is desirable that the metal to be determined should produce an absorption of between 20 and 80 percent (*i.e.*, an absorbance of between 0.1 and 0.7).

Aqueous solutions may usually be sprayed as such or after appropriate dilution with water. Solutions in oils or other nonaqueous liquids may usually be sprayed after dilution with a solvent such as methyl isobutyl ketone.

Plant and animal tissues are normally ashed by one of the standard wet- or dry-ashing

[20] Gatehouse, B. M., and Willis, J. B., Spectrochim. Acta, **17,** 710, 1961.

techniques and a solution of the ash in hydrochloric acid is made to volume with water.

Metals and alloys are dissolved in acid or alkali, and made to volume with water.

Trace elements in aqueous solutions can be concentrated by extraction with a chelating agent into an immiscible solvent and this solution sprayed into the flame. The usual microchemical precautions against contamination must of course be observed.

Calibrating Solutions.—When the metal being determined forms a significant fraction of the whole sample being analyzed, it is frequently sufficient to make up calibrating solutions containing only this metal, usually as a simple salt dissolved in water or dilute acid. When, however, the metal to be determined occurs as a minor or trace constituent, the viscosity and efficiency of atomization may be different for the sample and calibrating solutions. In this latter case it is usually desirable to add to the calibrating solutions the appropriate concentration of the major constituent.

Where chemical interference is known to occur a suitable suppressant is added at the same concentration to both sample and calibrating solutions.

Methods of Calibration.—The most usual method of calibration is to measure three or four standard solutions containing known concentrations of the metal to be determined and covering the concentration range expected in the sample solutions. The solutions are measured in the order: standards, samples, standards, samples, standards, and the transmission values obtained for each solution are averaged and converted to absorbance. The absorbances of the standards are plotted against their concentrations and the sample concentrations are read off by interpolation. A typical calibration curve is shown in Fig. 6-5.

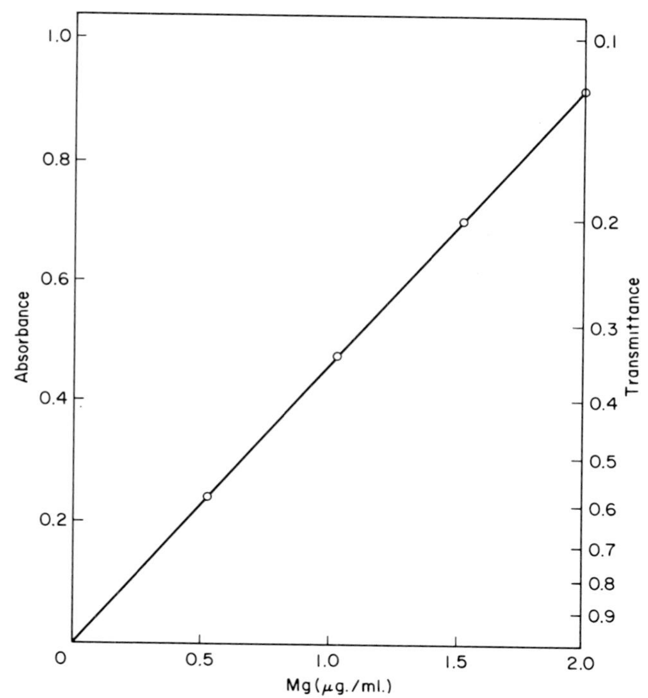

FIG. 6-5. Typical Calibration Curve for the Determination of Magnesium.

In some types of analysis it is necessary to measure as accurately as possible the differences between the concentrations of a number of solutions of approximately the same strength. This can best be done by verifying first that the absorbance-concentration curve is sensibly a straight line over the concentration range concerned, and then preparing a standard of about this concentration. The sample solutions are measured alternately with the standards and their concentrations calculated directly from the ratios of the absorbances.

Where it is not possible to suppress interferences completely the standard addition method may be used. If the absorbance-concentration curve is known to be a straight line, and if the absorbance of the sample solution of concentration x is A_1 and that of a similar solution to which a known concentration a of the metal has been added is A_2, then x can be calculated from the relation

$$x/(x + a) = A_1/A_2$$

It is advisable to check the result by measuring also the absorbance of A_3 of a similar solution with a different added concentration of metal b. If the assumption of linearity holds, the two values of x should agree, and if not, an approximate figure for x may be derived from the three measurements.

TYPICAL DETERMINATIONS BY ATOMIC ABSORPTION SPECTROMETRY

The following detailed description of six atomic absorption determinations is intended to illustrate the procedures used in several types of analyses which can be performed by this technique. In cases where the concentration of metal to be determined varies widely from sample to sample it may be necessary to alter the amount of sample taken or the degree of dilution of the resulting solution.

EXCHANGEABLE MAGNESIUM IN SOIL[21]

Procedure.—Extract a 10-g. sample of the soil with 1 *M* ammonium chloride solution, and make up to 200 ml. with this solution. Dilute a 5-ml. aliquot to 200 ml. with a 1 *M* ammonium chloride solution containing 1500 μg./ml. strontium (*i.e.*, 4.55 g. $SrCl_2 \cdot 6H_2O$ per liter).

From a stock solution containing 1.00 g. magnesium per liter, prepare calibrating solutions containing 0.0, 0.5, 1.0, and 1.5 μg./ml. magnesium in 1 *M* ammonium chloride solution containing 1500 μg./ml. strontium.

Plot the absorbance against magnesium concentration of the standards and read off the concentration of the sample solution.

NOTE.—The use of an air-acetylene flame is desirable for this analysis. The strontium chloride is added to overcome the suppression of magnesium absorption by aluminum and silicate.

CALCIUM IN BLOOD SERUM[11]

Procedure.—Pipet 0.50 ml. of serum into a 10-ml. centrifuge tube and add 4.50 ml. of a solution containing 2500 μg./ml. of strontium and 4 percent trichloroacetic acid (*i.e.*, 7.7 g. $SrCl_2 \cdot 6H_2O$ and 40 g. $CCl_3 \cdot COOH$ per liter). Stir, allow to stand 5 minutes, and centrifuge for 5 minutes.

From a stock solution of 1000 μg./ml. calcium (2.50 g. dried $CaCO_3$ dissolved in the minimum quantity of hydrochloric acid and made to 1 liter) make up calibrating solu-

[21] David, D. J., Analyst, **85**, 495, 1960.

tions containing 0.0, 5.0, 10.0 and 15.0 μg./ml. of calcium in a solution containing 2500 μg./ml. strontium and 4 percent trichloroacetic acid.

Plot the absorbance of the standards against concentration and read off the concentration of the supernatant liquid from the centrifuged serum solution.

NOTE.—The use of an air-acetylene flame is necessary for this analysis. Serum proteins, which enhance the absorption of calcium, are removed by precipitation with trichloroacetic acid. Strontium chloride overcomes the depression of calcium absorption by the phosphate in the serum.

LEAD IN URINE[22]

Procedure.—In each of two 100-ml. separatory funnels place 50 ml. of urine* and add to one 0.30 ml. of a standard solution containing 50 mg./liter of lead (as lead nitrate). Add to each 0.5 ml. of a freshly prepared 4 percent aqueous solution of ammonium pyrrolidine dithiocarbamate[23] and 2.0 ml. of methyl *n*-amyl ketone, and shake thoroughly. Allow to stand for 5–10 minutes, run off and discard the bulk of the lower layer and transfer the last 5 ml. or so, together with the upper layer and the emulsion at the interface, to 10-ml. centrifuge tubes. After centrifuging at 3500 r.p.m. for 5 minutes, to effect a partial separation of the layers, transfer the upper layers by means of Pasteur pipets to 5 ml. beakers. Add the drainings from the funnels to the centrifuge tubes, stir thoroughly, and centrifuge again. Pipet off the upper layers as before and add to the 5-ml. beakers.

Using the lead line at 2833 A and the leanest possible air-coal gas or air-acetylene flame measure the absorbances of these two extracts. Calculate the concentration of lead in the urine, x mg./liter from the measured absorbances A_1 and A_2 by the relation

$$\frac{x}{x + 0.30} = \frac{A_1}{A_2}$$

NOTES.—(1) To insure that the absorbance-concentration curve is a straight line, which is necessary for the standard addition technique, run the lead hollow-cathode lamp on a current of not more than 4 ma., and check the linearity of the curve with aqueous solutions containing 0, 25, 50, 75, and 100 μg./ml. of lead.

(2) To avoid contamination, wash all glassware in hot dilute nitric acid before use, and spray dilute nitric acid through the flame before measuring the organic extracts.

(3) If a number of specimens have to be measured it is quicker to calibrate with a set of standard solutions of lead containing 0.00, 0.30, 0.60, and 0.90 mg./liter which are brought to the pH of the samples and extracted in exactly the same way.

CHROMIUM IN STEEL[24]

Procedure.—Dissolve 1.00 g. of steel by simmering in 30 ml. of 15 percent vol./vol. phosphoric–15 percent vol./vol. sulfuric acid and adding dropwise nitric acid or aqua regia. Evaporate to fumes, fume gently for 1 minute, extract with 30 ml. of water, and digest for 5 minutes to insure solution of all soluble salts. Filter if necessary through a Whatman 541 filter paper into a 100-ml. graduated flask, and rinse the beaker and filter several times with hot 2 percent vol./vol. sulfuric acid. Allow to cool and dilute to the mark.

Prepare a series of calibration solutions by adding to 1-g. samples of spectrographically

[22] Willis, J. B., Anal. Chem., **34,** 614, 1962.

* Urine is conveniently preserved by the addition of about 1 percent by volume of glacial acetic acid, which maintains the pH at a suitable value (3-4) for extraction of the heavy metals.

[23] Malissa, H., and Schöffmann, E., Mikrochim. Acta, 187, 1955.

[24] Kinson, K., Hodges, R. J., and Belcher, C. B., Anal. Chim. Acta, **29,** 134, 1963.

pure iron 0.0, 2.5, 5.0, 7.5, and 10.0 ml. of a 500 μg./ml. chromium solution (1.414 g. dry $K_2Cr_2O_7$ in 1 liter of water), and treating as for the sample.

Using the 3579 A chromium line and a slightly rich air-acetylene flame, adjust the height of the 10-cm. burner to obtain maximum absorption. Measure the absorbance of the standards, plot against concentration, and read off the concentration of the sample solution.

NOTE.—The above method covers the range 0.0–0.5 percent chromium; for accurate measurement of steels containing 0.0–0.1 percent, a scale-expansion device is recommended.

COPPER IN USED LUBRICATING OIL[16]

Procedure.—After thoroughly mixing the oil by shaking, weigh 2.0 g. into a 10-ml. volumetric flask and dilute to volume with methyl isobutyl ketone.

From a stock solution containing 100 μg./ml. of copper (0.199 g. copper butyl phthalate in 250 ml. methyl isobutyl ketone) make up calibrating solutions containing 0.0, 2.0, 4.0, and 6.0 μg./ml. of copper in methyl isobutyl ketone containing 20 percent wt./vol. of an unused oil known to be free of copper.

Measure the absorbance of the standards, plot the absorbance-concentration graph, measure the absorbance of the sample solution, and read off its copper concentration.

NOTES.—(1) Use the leanest possible air-acetylene flame.

(2) Prolonged inhalation of the vapor of methyl isobutyl ketone may cause headaches. Kerosene may be substituted for this solvent in many oil analyses with some loss of sensitivity. Heptane is also suitable, though its use requires the introduction of extra air directly into the spray chamber to stabilize the flame.

(3) Other suitable copper standards are copper acetylacetonate and the compounds supplied by the National Bureau of Standards.[25]

SILVER IN LEAD CONCENTRATES[12,26]

Procedure.—Digest 1 g. of sample with 20 ml. of 10 *M* hydrochloric acid, add 5 ml. of 16 *M* nitric acid when reaction is complete, and evaporate to dryness. Elute the residue while still warm with 5 ml. of 5 *M* hydrochloric acid and make up to 100 ml. with 7 percent wt./vol. ammonium acetate; the final pH of the solution should be 5.0 or more. While making up the solution add 0.1 g. of potassium cyanide to insure that all the silver remains in solution.

Prepare standards containing 0, 2, 4, and 6 μg./ml. silver in the same hydrochloric acid–ammonium acetate–potassium cyanide mixture.

Using a lean air-acetylene flame measure the absorbances of the standards, plot as a function of silver concentration, measure the absorbance of the sample solution and read off its concentration.

NOTE.—Sample solutions should not be left more than a few hours in contact with potassium cyanide as at a pH of 5 the latter hydrolyzes fairly quickly.

APPLICATIONS IN THE ANALYSIS OF SPECIAL MATERIALS

A number of procedures employing atomic absorption spectrometry are discussed elsewhere in Volume III. These methods, listed according to the material analyzed, are:

1. Chapter 44, Volume III, Alloys: Nonferrous.
   a. Magnesium in nickel and nickel alloys
   b. Zinc in aluminum

[25] Analytical Standards for Trace Elements in Petroleum Products, National Bureau of Standards Monograph 54.

[26] Rawling, B. S., personal communication.

c. Zinc in copper and electrolytic copper
d. Zinc in zirconium-base alloys

2. Chapter 46, Volume III, Portland Cement.
   a. Determination of metals, including lead and zinc
3. Chapter 49, Volume III, Fertilizers.
   a. Calcium
   b. Cobalt
   c. Copper
   d. Iron
   e. Magnesium
   f. Manganese
   g. Molybdenum
   h. Zinc
4. Chapter 53, Volume III, Glass.
   a. Calcium
   b. Iron
   c. Magnesium
   d. Manganese
   e. Potassium
   f. Sodium
   g. Strontium
5. Chapter 57, Volume III, Petroleum and Petroleum Products.
   a. Determination of copper, iron, and nickel in gas oil fractions
   b. Determination of cadmium, calcium, copper, gold, iron, lead, magnesium, manganese, molybdenum, palladium, platinum, potassium, rhodium, sodium, and zinc
6. Chapter 62, Volume III, Soils.
   a. Calcium
   b. Magnesium
   c. Potassium
   d. Sodium

Chapter 7

FLAME EMISSION SPECTROMETRY

By John A. Dean
Professor of Chemistry
University of Tennessee
Knoxville, Tennessee

The basic principle of flame emission spectrometry rests on the fact that salts of metals when introduced under carefully controlled conditions into a suitable flame are vaporized and excited to emit radiations that are characteristic for each element. Correlation of the emission intensity with the concentration of that element forms the basis of quantitative evaluation.

THE FLAME SPECTROMETER

The flame spectrometer consists of these components: (1) the pressure regulators and flow meters for the fuel gases, (2) the atomizing device, (3) the flame source, (4) the optical system, (5) appropriate photosensitive detectors, and (6) the electrical circuit for measuring or recording the intensity of the radiation. Depending upon the use intended, the instrument may be a relatively simple assemblage of interference filters and a photodetector, *i.e.*, *a flame photometer*, or it may be an elaborate prism or grating monochromator, *i.e.*, *a flame spectrometer*. The former type of instrument is widely used for the determination of sodium and potassium, and sometimes calcium, in waters, cement, glass, ash, and slags and in agronomic, biological, and clinical materials. However, to realize the full potentialities of flame emission methods a flame spectrometer is needed. An optical schematic of a flame spectrometer is shown in Fig. 7-1.

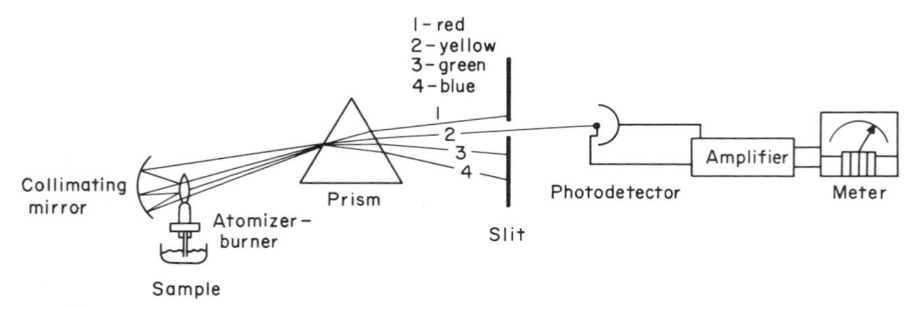

FIG. 7-1. Schematic Diagram of a Flame Spectrometer. (Reproduced from Willard, Merritt, and Dean, Instrumental Methods of Analysis, 4th Ed., D. Van Nostrand Co., Princeton, N. J., 1965.)

COMPONENTS

Pressure Regulators and Flow Meters.—In order to achieve a steady emission reading, it is imperative that the gas pressures and gas flows be maintained constant while the flame spectrometer is in use. For double-beam instruments this requirement can be relaxed somewhat. Double-diaphragm pressure regulators—a 10 lb./in.^{2} for the fuel and a 30 lb./in.^{2} gauge for the oxygen or air supply—followed by a rotameter should be installed in the lines from the gas cylinders to the burner. Usual flow rates range from 2 to 10 ft.^{3}/hr.

Atomizer and Burner.—Virtually all flame spectrometers rely on atomization to deliver a steady flow of solution to the flame. The solution is drawn through a capillary positioned either concentric with (Fig. 7-2), or at right angles to (Fig. 7-3), the annulus or capillary from which the aspirating gas (oxygen or air under pressure) enters. At the tip of the solution capillary the liquid is sheared off and dispersed into droplets by the blast of oxygen or air.

The integral atomizer-burner injects the entire spray directly into the flame. An outer annulus (Fig. 7-2) supplies the combustible gas to the flame. This type of atomizer avoids variations due to drop size and evaporation rates. Integral atomizer-burners are almost universally used with flame spectrometers and in combination with high temperature oxygen-acetylene (3000°C.) or oxygen-hydrogen (2700°C.) flames. In special cases an outer sheath of oxygen is provided to minimize entrainment of room air into the flame.

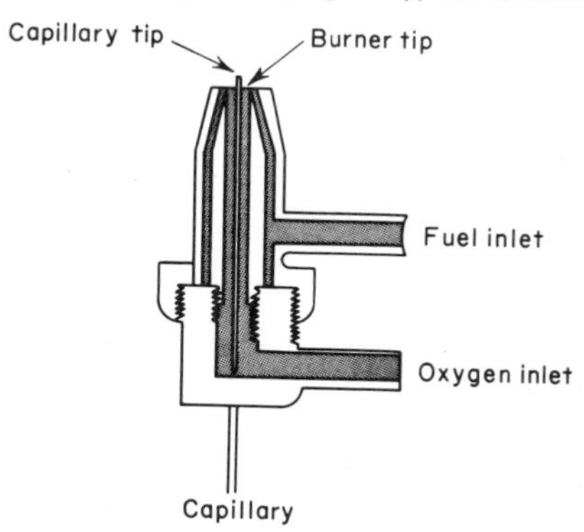

Fig. 7-2. Integral Aspirator-burner. (Reproduced from Willard, Merritt, and Dean, Instrumental Methods of Analysis, 4th Ed., D. Van Nostrand Co., Princeton N. J., 1965.)

In the second type of atomizer, only a portion of the spray is utilized. The aerosol, which consists of both mist and a distribution of larger droplets, is fed to an enclosed expansion chamber where the larger droplets condense on the walls and only a fine, homogeneous fog reaches the burner (Fig. 7-3). The condensate flows off to the waste drain. The burner is usually the familiar Meker type in which the gas and air/sample mixture is ignited through a series of concentric holes in a stainless steel burner head. The head and venturi throat are interchangeable for alternative gases. Air-propane or air-city gas, which provide temperatures of 1900° to 2000°C., are commonly employed. Air is supplied at suitable pressures (usually 10 lb./in.^{2}) from a small compressor or from cylinders.

The Optical System.—A variety of filter instruments is available. Filters are intended primarily for analyses of sodium and potassium when these elements predominate in samples. Radiation characteristic of the analysis element is isolated by means of interference filters which possess bandwidths from 2 to 13 mμ. Absorption glass filters are rarely employed any more.

The best isolation of radiant energy can be achieved with flame spectrometers which incorporate either a prism or grating monochromator, those with prisms having variable ganged entrance and exit slits. Both these spectrometers provide a continuous selection of wavelengths with resolving power sufficient to separate completely most of the easily

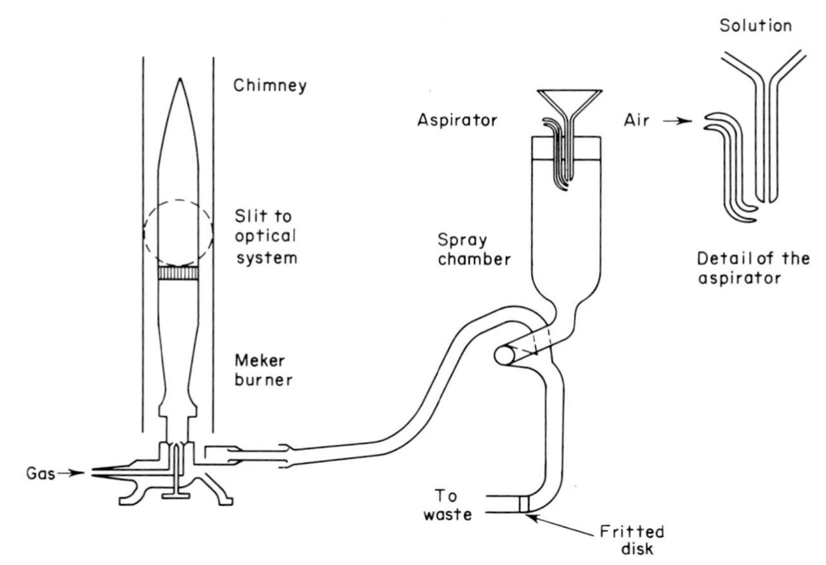

Fig. 7-3. Discharge Type of Atomizer and Burner System. (Reproduced from Willard, Merritt, and Dean, Instrumental Methods of Analysis, 4th Ed., D. Van Nostrand Co., Princeton, N. J., 1965.)

excited emission lines, and afford freedom from scattered radiation sufficient to minimize interferences. Fused silica or quartz optical components are necessary to permit measurements in the ultraviolet portion of the spectrum below 350 mμ. Figure 7-4 shows a Littrow-type mounting which is employed in a widely-used make of prism flame spectrometer, and Fig. 7-5 shows the optical schematic for 0.5-meter Ebert mounted grating

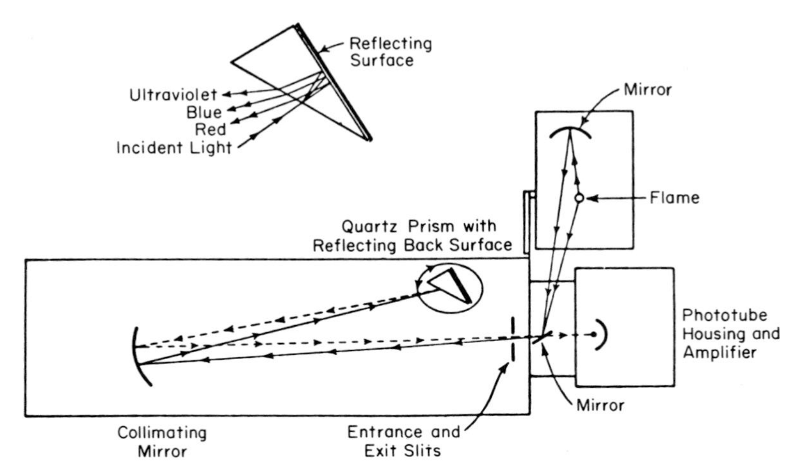

Fig. 7-4. Optical Diagram of the Beckman Model DU Flame Spectrophotometer, a Littrow-type Prism Mounting. Entrance slits are below the exit slits; both are operated by the same slit mechanism. (Courtesy Beckman Instruments, Inc.)

instrument. The latter instrument has a dispersion of 16 A/mm. For prism instruments the graph of dispersion *vs.* wavelength supplied by the manufacturer must be consulted. Large dispersion and high resolving power in monochromators will stress the importance of spectra with discrete lines, while continua and band spectra will show up more clearly with instruments of small dispersion.

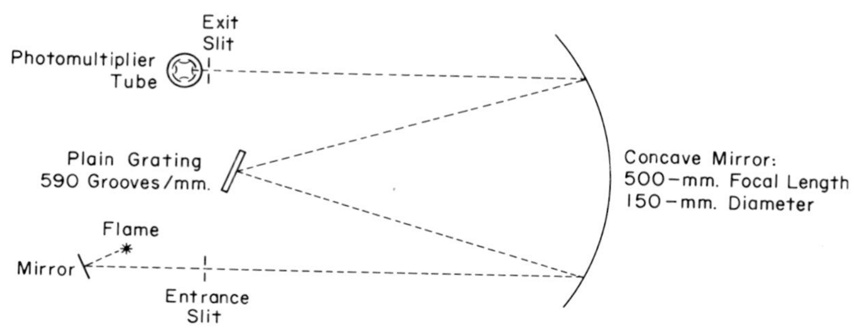

FIG. 7-5. Optical Schematic of 0.5-Meter Ebert Grating Flame.

Photosensitive Detectors.—Flame photometers and flame spectrometers employ either vacuum phototubes or photomultiplier tubes. The photomultiplier tube provides a maximum signal, and permits applying flame emission methods to systems that are weak in emission, either because of a small concentration of test element or because of difficulty in exciting any appreciable fraction of the test element. The RCA 1P28 tube is used over the range 200 to 700 mμ. The EM1 tube enjoys a more level response in the visible region, and is usable to about 800 mμ. For the infrared region between 800 and 1000 mμ, no completely satisfactory tube is currently available. The Farnsworth 16PM1, the DuMont K1292, and the RCA 1P22 are available but excessive dark current is a problem.

TYPES OF INSTRUMENTS

Flame spectrometers are essentially of two basic designs which can be designated as either single- or double-beam arrangement.

Single-beam Instruments.—A single-beam instrument contains only one set of optics. Light emitted from the center of the flame is collected by a reflector and focused by a lens of heat-resistant glass through interchangeable optical filters onto a single photodetector, or light from the burner passes into a monochromator, and radiation leaving the exit slit is focused onto the detector.

The d.c. measuring systems that have been used in evaluating signals from detectors are a multireflection galvanometer provided with a variable shunt, the potentiometric null-point system, or matching of signal e.m.f. with a bridge, or of light intensities with a variable diaphragm. Often a small opposing e.m.f. (zero suppression) is applied in opposition to the detector signal to suppress unwanted flame background radiation. A long time constant (approximately 1 sec.) is incorporated in the measuring circuit to render the meter or recorder unresponsive to sudden flashes of light in the flame. For less strongly emitting elements, or for low concentrations of any element, one or more stages of amplification is necessary before the signal is presented to the readout device. For recording purposes, the wavelength dial on the monochromator is replaced by a drive mechanism which is synchronized with the chart drive of a pen recording potentiometer.

In a.c. measuring systems, radiation leaving the exit slit of the monochromator is chopped with a rotating disc and amplified by an a.c. amplifier which is stabler than its d.c. counterpart.

Double-beam Instruments.—In double-beam instruments a second light path is provided for the light emitted by the internal standard element which is added in a fixed amount to each test solution and calibration standard. The signal of one detector opposes that of the other, through a suitable indicating device, to provide a ratio method of comparing the light intensities between the internal standard and analysis element, as shown in Fig. 7-6. By means of a potentiometer (*P*-1), the opposing photoelectric currents are

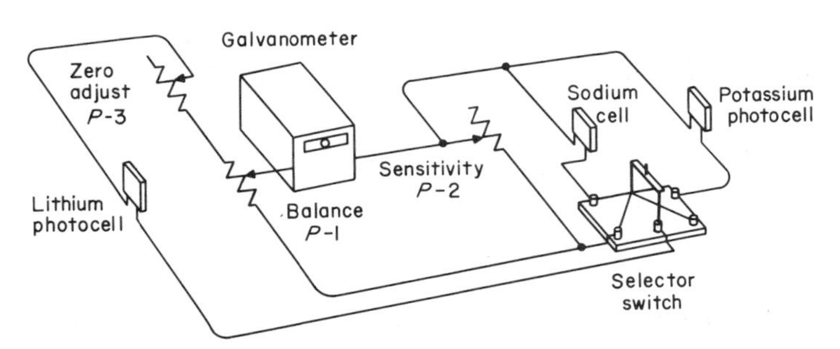

Fig. 7-6. Circuit Diagram for Double-beam Flame Photometer. *P*-1 is a precision 10,000-ohm potentiometer; *P*-2 is a 10,000-ohm potentiometer; *P*-3 is a 500-ohm potentiometer; barrier-layer photocells. (Reproduced from Willard, Merritt, and Dean, Instrumental Methods of Analysis, 4th Ed., D. Van Nostrand Co., Princeton, N. J., 1965.)

balanced. The readings of the balancing potentiometer are compared directly with a calibration curve of balance readings *vs.* element concentrations. Sensitivity adjustments are made with *P*-2 by shunting current generated by the measuring photocell. In filter flame photometers, light usually leaves the flame through two apertures on different sides of the flame and thence through the respective optical filters and onto the detectors.

FLAME PHOTOMETRY PRINCIPLES

Metallic Spectra.—When an aerosol is uniformly delivered into a flame, the following sequence of events occurs in rapid succession.

1. The water, or other solvent, is vaporized, leaving minute particles of dry salt.
2. At the high temperature of the flame, the dry salt is vaporized, and part or all of the gaseous molecules are progressively dissociated to give neutral atoms which are the potentially emitting species.
3. Some of the free metal atoms unite with other radicals or atoms that are present in the flame gases or are introduced into the flame concomitantly with the test element.
4. The vapors of the neutral metal atoms, or of molecules containing the metal atom, are then excited by the thermal energy of the flame, or by a chemiexcitation mechanism. Ionization and excitation of the ionized atoms may occur to some degree.
5. From the excited levels of the atom, or molecule, or ion, a reversion takes place to the ground electronic state—partly by impacts with other species, partly spontaneously by emission of characteristic radiation.

In neutral-atom spectra, the emission of radiation occurs as discrete lines when an excited electron from the upper energy levels of the neutral atom falls back into a lower energy level or the ground state of the atom. In a flame most of the lines emitted are from the neutral atom, but for the alkaline earth metals, emission lines arising from singly ionized atoms are also observed, particularly in high-temperature flames. Band spectra arise from electronic transitions involving molecules. Molecules possess energy of internal vibration (and rotation) as well as electronic excitation levels and, for each electronic transition, there will be a whole suite of vibrational levels involved. This causes the emitted radiation to be spread over a portion of the spectrum, rather than being concentrated in discrete lines. Often the vibrational contribution leads to asymmetrical bands with sharp edges or heads on one side and degraded on the other side.

Flame Background.—The spectrum (Fig. 7-7) associated with the flame of a given fuel is very dependent on flame conditions, principally the fuel-oxygen ratio and the

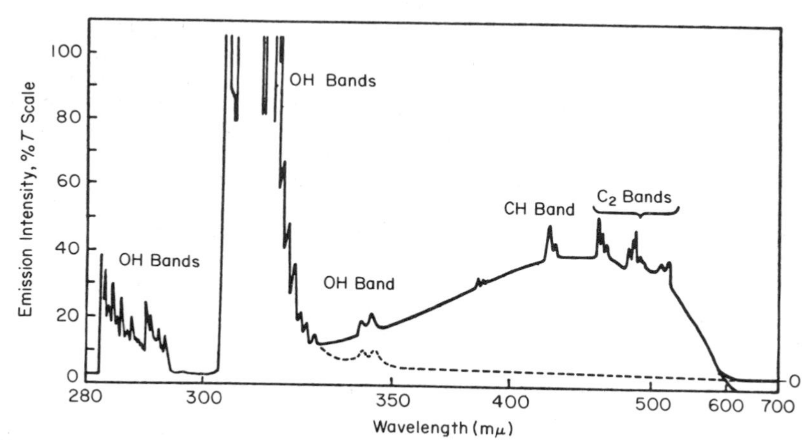

Fig. 7-7. Flame Background Spectrum of an Acetylene-oxygen Flame (*upper*) and a Hydrogen-oxygen Flame (*lower*).

temperature. The hydrogen flame gives the best combination of signal-to-background. Prominent OH band structures occur between 280 and 295 mμ, 306 and 320 mμ, and 340 and 348 mμ. Between 800 and 1250 mμ there is a broad emission that is due to the spectrum of water, one of the products of combustion.

The acetylene flame shows principally the OH band spectrum and the continuum of dissociating CO molecules. Superimposed on this background may be seen the faint bands due to the CH radical at 431.5 and 438.4 mμ, and several heads of diatomic carbon, C_2, in the green. The CH, C_2, and other hydrocarbon flame bands become stronger when employing fuel-rich flames and when viewing the reaction zone of flames.

Mavrodineanu[1,2] has ably reviewed the subject of flame characteristics and emission.

Variation of Emission Intensity Within the Flame.—The intensity of spectral lines varies in different parts of the flame. For this reason adjustable burner mounts are desirable, as the region of maximum intensity is often sharply localized.[3]

Lines of a number of elements (molybdenum, niobium, rhenium, tantalum, titanium, tungsten, and vanadium) that are absent or very weak in the plume of a stoichiometric oxygen-gas flame appear in unusual strength in the spectrum of a rich acetylene-oxygen

[1] Mavrodineanu, R., Spectrochim. Acta, **17**, 1016, 1961.

[2] Mavrodineanu, R., Colloquium Spectroscopicum Internationale, VIII, Sauerlander, Aarau (Switzerland), 1959, p. 15 of Part III.

[3] Dean, J. A., and Adkins, J. E., unpublished studies.

flame when the analyte is dissolved in a hydrocarbon solvent.[4,5,6] Fuel-rich flames[7] provide an environment more favorable for the existence of free atoms of those elements which have a strong predilection to form stable monoxide molecules in ordinary flames.

The spectrum of the inner cone and reaction zone of hydrocarbon flames provides another rich source of lines whose intensity far exceeds that expected from purely thermal excitation. Lines are primarily from elements of high excitation potential and high ionization potential; they include antimony, arsenic, bismuth, boron, cobalt, mercury, platinum, selenium, tellurium, tin, and zinc from oxygen-acetylene-ketone flames[3,8,9] or oxygen-hydrogen-naphtha flames.[10]

Chemiexcitation processes have been discussed by Gilbert.[11]

Organic Solvents.—The emission intensity is enhanced significantly when elements are aspirated into the flame from an organic solution instead of an aqueous solution.[12,13] Increases in emission intensity ranging from three- to sevenfold are usual, although significantly larger increases are found for Group IIIB elements. The degree of enhancing action is dependent somewhat upon the atomizing system employed. Combinations of organic solvents often provide greater enhancement and advantages in maintaining the sample ingredients in solution.

More spectacular enhancements are found for elements that are aspirated into a flame from essentially a nonaqueous solvent.[12,13] Liquid-liquid extraction techniques can be exploited to accomplish analytical separations, and then the organic phase can be aspirated directly into the flame. Rather specific extractants are useful for isolating one metal from other elements in the sample, among which may be interferences. Numerous possibilities exist for the simultaneous extraction and successive determination of several elements in a sample matrix.[14]

APPLICATIONS

In Table 7-1 are listed the wavelength and useful emission sensitivity of a representative group of lines and bands. Here, useful emission sensitivity is that concentration of analyte for which the mean net signal exceeds the mean background by the root mean square of the variability of the signal (essentially $\sqrt{2}$ times the fluctuation of either, and which includes the instrument and flame noise).[15] Ideally, signals will exhibit a fluctuation of 0.2 to 0.5 percent. The limit of detectability is considered to be twice the useful emission sensitivity.

Errors in manipulation, instrumental errors, and other accidental errors limit the precision of a determination. A standard deviation of about 2 percent should be achievable for most elements.

[4] D'Silva, A. P., Kniseley, R. N., and Fassel, V. A., Anal. Chem., **36,** 532, 1964.
[5] Fassel, V. A., Curry, R. H., and Kniseley, R. N., Spectrochim. Acta, **18,** 1127, 1962.
[6] Fassel, V. A., Myers, R. B., and Kniseley, R. N., Spectrochim. Acta, **19,** 1194, 1963.
[7] Knutson, K. E., "Flame Photometric Determination of Magnesium in Plant Material," Analyst, **82,** 241–254, 1957.
[8] Dean, J. A., and Simms, J. C., Anal. Chem., **35,** 699, 1963.
[9] Dean, J. A., and Carnes, W. J., Analyst, **87,** 743, 1962.
[10] Buell, B. E., Anal. Chem., **34,** 635, 1962; **35,** 372, 1963.
[11] Gilbert, P. T., Jr., Proceedings of the Xth Colloquium Spectroscopicum Internationale, Spartan Books, Washington, 1963, p. 171.
[12] Dean, J. A., "Use of Organic Solvents in Flame Photometry," Am. Soc. Testing Materials, Spec. Tech. Publ. 238, 43–54, 1958.
[13] Dean, J. A., Flame Photometry, McGraw-Hill, New York, 1960, Chapter 5.
[14] Dean, J. A., and Cain, C., "Flame Spectrophotometric Determination of Copper, Nickel and Manganese in Aluminum-base Alloys," Anal. Chem., **29,** 530–532, 1957.
[15] Alkemade, C. Th. J., Ph.D. thesis, University of Utrecht, 1954.

TABLE 7-1. FLAME SPECTRA OF THE ELEMENTS

Element	Wavelength, mμ	Type of Emission[a]	Type of Flame[a]	Emission Sensitivity, μg., ml.$^{-1}$ (%T)$^{-1}$
Aluminum	396.2	L	OA*n*	0.5
	484	B	OA*n*	0.5
Antimony	252.8	L	OA*nr*	1.0
Arsenic	235.0	L	OA*nr*	2.2
Barium	455.5	I	OH	3
	553.6	L	OH	1
Bismuth	223.1	L	OA*nr*	6.4
Boron	249.8	L	OA*nr*	7
	518	B	OA	3
Cadmium	326.1	L	AH	0.5
Calcium	422.7	L	OA	0.07
	554	B	OA	0.16
	622	B	OA	0.6
Cesium	455.5	L	OH	2.0
	852	L	OH	0.5
Chromium	425.4	L	OA	5.0
Cobalt	242.5	L	OA*nr*	1.7
	353.0	L	OA	4.0
Copper	324.7	L	OA	0.6
Gallium	417.2	L	OA	0.5
Indium	451.1	L	OH	0.07
Iron	372.0	L	OA	2.5
	386.0	L	OA	2.7
Lanthanum	442	B	OA	0.7
	741	B	OA	4.5
Lead	405.8	L	OA	14
Lithium	670.8	L	OA	0.067
Magnesium	285.2	L	OA	1.0
	383	B	OA	1.6
Manganese	403.3	L	OA	0.1
Mercury	253.6	L	OA*nr*	2.5
Molybdenum	379.8	L	OA*nr*	0.5
Neodymium	555	B	OH*n*	0.2
	702	B	OH*n*	1.0
Nickel	352.4	L	OA	1.6
Niobium	405.9	L	OA*nr*	12
Palladium	363.5	L	OH*n*	0.1
Phosphorus	253	B	OH*n*	1.0
Platinum	265.9	L	OA*nr*	15
Potassium	404.4	L	OH	1.7
	767	L	OH	0.02
Rhenium	346.1	L	OA*nr*	3
Rhodium	369.2	L	OH*n*	0.7
Rubidium	780.0	L	OH	0.6
Ruthenium	372.8	L	OA	0.3
Scandium	604	B	OH*n*	0.012

TABLE 7-1 (cont.)

Element	Wavelength, $m\mu$	Type of Emission[a]	Type of Flame[a]	Emission Sensitivity, $\mu g.$, $ml.^{-1}$ $(\%T)^{-1}$
Silicon.	251.6	L	OH*n*	4.5
Silver.	328.0	L	OH	1.0
	338.3	L	OH	0.6
Sodium.	590.0	L	OH	0.001
Strontium.	460.7	L	OA	0.06
Tellurium.	238.6	L	OA*nr*	2.0
Thallium.	377.6	L	OH	0.6
Tin.	243.0	L	OA*nr*	1.6
Titanium.	399.9	L	OA*nr*	5
Vanadium.	437.9	L	OA*nr*	3
Yttrium.	597	B	OA*n*	0.2
Zinc.	213.9	L	OA*nr*	77

[a] The symbols used in this table and their meanings are as follows:
B = molecular band emission;
I = ionic-line emission;
L = atomic-line emission;
AH = air-hydrogen flame;
OA = oxygen-acetylene flame;
OH = oxygen-hydrogen flame;
n = organic solvent (usually methyl isobutyl ketone); and
r = reaction zone of fuel-rich flame.

Selection of Optimal Working Conditions.—There are many operational variables that affect the effective light flux that actually reaches the photodetector.[16] With filter photometers many of these variables are fixed, which simplifies the operation of the instrument. However, the more versatile flame spectrometers allow the operator to select the optimal working conditions for each problem.

A choice has to be made of the best wavelength from among the usable wavelengths of spectral emission lines or bands (Table 7-1). Measurements should be conducted with varying oxygen and fuel flows (not merely different pressures) to ascertain the optimum ratio of oxygen to fuel. Lacking specific information, suitable flows are found experimentally by scanning the emission line and adjacent background, adjusting the fuel and oxygen flows independently, until maximum line emission, associated with a steady background, is obtained. The region of maximum emission intensity in the flame should be ascertained.

The choice of mechanical slit width (or bandwidth of a filter) affects the ratio of signal-to-background and also the interference ratio of two closely spaced emission lines. Of course, the net emission of an analysis line, which is the line or band emission diminished by the background, must be sufficiently large to be distinguishable from the background alone (limit of detectability) and to provide adequate sensitivity in the determination of the test element. On direct-reading instruments the zero-suppression circuit will depress the background reading to any desired position on the reading scale.

Flame Background.—The emission reading of a spectral line and band always includes any contribution from the flame and sample matrix. When the flame background

[16] Alkemade, C. Th. J., Proceedings of the Xth Colloquium Spectroscopicum Internationale, Spartan Books, Washington, 1963, p. 143.

results solely from the flame gases, it may be measured by aspirating the pure solvent into the flame and subtracting the resultant emission reading from subsequent sample readings. Alternatively, the flame spectrometer may be adjusted to give a reading of zero while the solvent is being aspirated. The contribution of matrix elements can be eliminated by the use of a synthetic blank but, unless routine samples are being handled, this begs the question. With instruments that provide a choice of contiguous narrow bands of radiant energy, the background radiation is measured directly on the sample itself. First, the line-plus-background intensity is measured at the peak of the line or the crest of the band system. Next, the wavelength dial is rotated until the emission readings decrease to the background off to one side or the other of the emission line or band system. The background reading is then subtracted from the line-plus-background reading. When a recorder is employed, the background can be estimated by means of a line drawn across the base of the emission line or band system—*the base-line method.*

Interferences.—The term interference is intended to cover all types of difficulties which affect the flame emission of a test element—these include spectroscopic interferences and interferences that arise from variations in the physical properties of the test solution.[16]

Spectral interference is especially prevalent when filters are used to isolate the desired radiant energy. With monochromators, interference is much less. It may be caused by adjacent line emissions when the analysis element and the interferent have nearly the same wavelength. If the interference cannot be obviated by increased resolution, the difficulty must be overcome by selecting other spectral lines where mutual interference does not occur, or by prior removal of one element.

Ionization occurs to a measurable extent with elements having ionization potentials of about 6 eV., and lower, particularly when their concentration is low. It becomes a serious problem with the higher-temperature flames. Incorporation of a second easily ionizable element into sample and standards (*radiation buffer*) is mandatory. Ionization is minimized when the emission is observed close to the outer boundary of the blue zone of the inner cone where there is a relatively high concentration of flame ions. Ionization of neutral atoms causes the curve of intensity *versus* concentration to be concave upward at low concentrations. However, the addition (or presence) of a second ionizable element will repress the ionization of the test element and, subsequently, straighten the working curve—the *radiation-buffer technique.*

In general, the emission of elements is lowered when relatively large amounts of acids and their salts are introduced into the flame concomitantly. Exceptionally marked interference with the emission of magnesium and the alkaline earth elements occurs in the presence of phosphate, aluminum, sulfate, and other similar oxy-anions.[17] In fact, over limited intervals of concentration, the depression is linear and forms the basis for indirect determination of the depressant in the presence of a standard amount of calcium (or magnesium).[18] Chemical interference arises from formation of condensed phases in the flame, composed generally of involatile compounds which are difficult to volatilize and dissociate into free metal atoms. The use of releasing agents or protective chelating agents has been recommended by a number of workers.[19,20] Two routes are feasible: (1) Addition of a competing cation which preferentially combines with the interferent, or, simply by mass action, denies the interferent access to the test element. An example is the addition of a large concentration of strontium or lanthanum to free calcium from the de-

[17] Alkemade, C. Th. J., and Jeuken, M. E. J., "Influence of Aluminum upon Calcium Emission," Z. anal. Chem., **158,** 401–409, 1957.

[18] Dippel, W. A., Bricker, C. E., and Furman, N. H., "Flame Photometric Determination of Phosphate," Anal. Chem., **26,** 553–556, 1954.

[19] Dinnin, J. I., Anal. Chem., **32,** 1475, 1960.

[20] West, A. C., and Cooke, W. D., Anal. Chem, **32,** 1471, 1960.

pressant action of phosphate.[21] (2) Addition of a competing anion, such as EDTA, which preferentially complexes calcium in the presence of phosphate, and yet which is promptly decomposed by the flame. Addition of 10 percent by volume of glycerol as a releasing agent often overcomes the inhibition effect of phosphate and sulfate on strontium and calcium.[22] Control of hydrogen ion concentration is important, and a complete release is accomplished only when the pH is adjusted between 1 and 2.

Various solution properties affect the observed emission intensities, particularly in the case of an atomizer with a condensing chamber. Vapor pressure and surface tension influence droplet size. Added salts and acids hinder the evaporation of solvent; larger droplets result in a diminished quantity of aerosol reaching the burner. A high concentration of lithium chloride is often added to sample and standards to minimize the effect of variable concentrations of salts and acids. A nonionic surfactant, added in small amounts, minimizes changes in surface tension, which influences the particle size of aerosol droplets. Viscosity, through its effect upon aspiration rate, also influences the rate at which aerosol reaches the flame. Of course, samples and standards must be treated alike.

EVALUATION METHODS

The selection of standards is of primary importance. Generally, a set of concentrated stock solutions, each containing, for example, 1000 μg./ml. of a single element are prepared from pure salts. From them, dilutions to any desired concentration are made as needed. For storage it is advisable to emply bottles of polyethylene or of resistant-glass composition. Care must be exercised in the handling of diluted samples and standards—in particular, solutions of sodium, potassium, and calcium—to avoid contact with the operator's hands, losses from adsorption on the surface of the storage container, and contamination from soap powder, smoke, and dust particles in the air and detached from the floor or clothes.

***Emission Intensity* vs. *Concentration*.**—When interferences are absent, the procedure for calibrating the flame photometer for a given metal is as follows:

With the flame burning properly and the correct filter in place, or the monochromator set at the correct wavelength, deionized water is introduced into the atomizer and the background emission is recorded or zero suppression controls are adjusted to bring the instrument reading to zero. Next, the most concentrated comparison standard is introduced and the sensitivity adjusted so that the maximum scale reading (or any predetermined reading) is attained. The zero reading is rechecked and any necessary adjustments are made. These two steps are repeated until duplicate readings are within one scale division out of 100 total divisions. Then several standards of lower concentration are introduced in turn and the respective readings noted.

The instrument readings, plotted on the axis of ordinates, *vs.* the concentrations in micrograms per milliliter, plotted on the axis of abscissas, produce the calibration (or analytical) curve. On nonlinear portions of the curve, interpolation within limited portions of the curve suffices. Standards should always bracket the sample closely.

When interferences are encountered, it is necessary to use standard solutions containing all the important constituents of the specimen in exactly equivalent amounts. If this step is insufficient or not feasible, self-compensating methods of evaluation must be employed or prior chemical separation made. However, when all the constituents in the

[21] Yofe, J., and Finkelstein, R., "Elimination of Anionic Interferences in Flame Photometric Determination of Calcium in the Presence of Phosphate and Sulfate," Anal. Chim. Acta, **19,** 166, 1958.

[22] Rains, T. C., Zittel, H. E., and Ferguson, M., Anal. Chem., **34,** 778, 1962.

unknown are exactly reproduced in the comparison standards, no other evaluation method is capable of providing such freedom from disturbing influences.

Standard-addition Method.– In the method of standard addition, net emission readings are obtained on two solutions, solution A containing an aliquot of the unknown solution, and solution B containing the same quantity of unknown solution plus a measured amount of a standard solution of the element. The quantity of test element in each of these solutions is then determined from its measured emission intensity and the standard calibration curve. Subtracting the quantity of unknown found in solution A from that found in solution B yields an amount of test element equal to that added when there is no depression or enhancement. When one of these effects is present, however, the quantity of the test element found by subtraction is greater or less than that added. In such cases, the true metal content of solution A is found by multiplying the observed metal content by a factor which corrects for the interference. This factor is found by dividing the quantity of metal added to solution B by the amount of metal found by subtracting the observed metal content of solution B from that of solution A.

The concentration of an unknown is found from the following relationships:

$$(L_1 - H)_A = kX_{\text{found}}$$
$$(L_2 - H)_B = k(X + S)$$
$$L_2 - L_1 = kS_{\text{found}}$$

$$X_{\text{found}} \frac{S_{\text{added}}}{S_{\text{found}}} = X_{\text{actually present}}$$

where L_1 = emission reading of unknown (solution A);
L_2 = emission reading after addition of standard (solution B);
H = background reading;
S = amount of standard added (considering any dilution factor); and
X = concentration of unknown.

Improved results can be obtained by employing a series of standard additions.[23] Normally additions which are equal to, twice, or one-half the original amount are optimum (Fig. 7-8). The resulting net emissions are plotted against the concentration of the increments of the standard solutions that were added to the unknown. The extrapolated line intersecting the response axis indicates the emission of the test element in the unknown sample. Typical emission readings for strontium in sea water are given in Table 7-2, third column. For comparison, "normal" readings obtained with pure strontium solutions equal to the added increments of strontium "spike" are given in the first column.

The method of standard addition is well established as an evaluation method. By its use, a number of radiation interferences can be overcome; it is particularly suited for residual matrix effects and in trace analysis. However, limitations exist which must be recognized. The calibration curve must be linear over the range of concentrations employed and it must pass through the origin. Proper correction for background radiation must be made on both the sample and the sample plus added standard solution. Ionization effects must be stabilized by means of a radiation buffer. It is desirable that all the solutions be diluted to the same final volume for then any interference substance will be

[23] Chow, T. J., and Thompson, T. G., "Flame Photometric Determination of Strontium in Sea Water," Anal. Chem., **27**, 18–21, 1955.

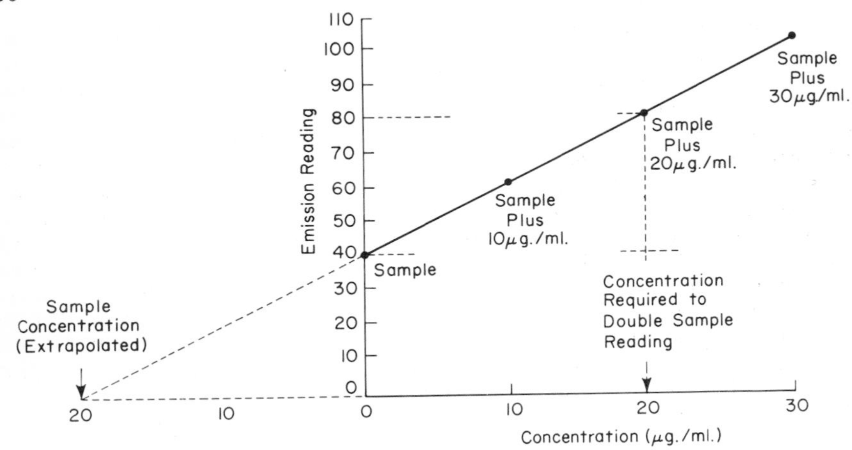

FIG. 7-8. Graphical Representation of Standard-addition Method.

present at the same concentration in all solutions and will affect equally the radiation from the test element either originally present or added as the standard increment.

Internal-standard Method.—A fixed quantity of internal-standard element is added to samples and standards alike. Upon excitation, radiant energy emitted by the standard

TABLE 7-2. EVALUATION BY METHOD OF STANDARD-ADDITION[a]

Meter Readings, Strontium Standards	Strontium, μg. per ml., Present or Added	Meter Readings, Sea Water Sample
0	0	18
16.0	2.62	24
32.5	5.24	30
47.1	7.86	36
63.7	10.50	42
79.2	13.10	48

[a] The net emission readings are given for a series of pure strontium standards and for a series of solutions containing equal volumes of sea water and added standard solution of strontium. Sample contained 7.86 μg. of strontium per milliliter.

and by the test element is measured simultaneously by dual detectors or by scanning successively the two emission lines. The ratio of the emission intensity of the analysis line to that of the internal-standard line is plotted against the concentration of the analysis element on double log paper to prepare the calibration curve for a series of standards. The intensity of each line is corrected for the background radiation in which it lies. The plot of log (emission ratio) *vs.* log (concentration of test element) will give a straight line whose slope ideally is 45° over limited concentration intervals. On most double-beam instruments, the ratio is given by the reading of the balancing potentiometer. Calibration curves on linear coordinate paper suffice.

The choice of a suitable element and spectral line as an internal standard is rather limited in flame photometry because of the small number of lines excited. Lithium is frequently used, particularly when analyzing for sodium, potassium, and sometimes calcium. The characteristics of lithium, in respect to excitation and ionization potentials and the influence of anions on its emission in air-gas flames, are almost identical with those of sodium, with some variation in respect to potassium and considerable deviation for calcium. The method is most effective when the content of the reference element is of the same order of magnitude in emission intensity as the test element. In any event, for dual-beam instruments, the concentration of the internal standard should be adequate so that, when the current produced by the internal-standard photocell is fully amplified, it will exactly balance the current output from the photocell that is measuring the test element.

When light-intensity ratios rather than absolute light intensities are measured, disturbing effects due to variation in spray rates, changes in droplet size, variations in viscosity and surface tension, and fluctuations in pressure of the fuel gases are greatly minimized. The technique possesses particular merit with atomizers in series with a condensing chamber. However, unsuspected errors may arise. If the test sample were to contain some of the reference element, a corresponding error would result. More serious is the fact that the emissivity of the standard and analysis lines is usually influenced differently with respect to ionization and excitation and by variations in flame temperature. Seldom will an interferent affect the internal-standard and test elements in precisely the same manner, although the effect is often similar among members of a family in the Periodic Table of elements. Changes in background radiation must also be considered for instruments that provide no means for independent measurement. The presence of other radiating species, including the added reference element, may increase the background more at one wavelength than at the other.

SPECIAL APPLICATIONS

Determinations of sodium and potassium constitute the majority of published applications. However, the flame is a suitable emission source for at least 45 elements, which may be grouped as follows:[24]

(1) Elements rather commonly determined: aluminum, barium, boron, calcium, cesium, chromium, copper, iron, lead, lithium, magnesium, manganese, potassium, rubidium, sodium, strontium. The flame method is virtually indispensable for the determination of cesium and rubidium.
(2) Elements easily determined but more or less neglected: antimony, arsenic, bismuth, cadmium, cobalt, gallium, indium, lanthanum, nickel, palladium, rare earths (except cerium), rhodium, ruthenium, scandium, silver, tellurium, thallium, tin, and yttrium.
(3) Elements with distinctive but less sensitive flame spectra: beryllium, germanium, gold, mercury, molybdenum, niobium, rhenium, selenium, silicon, titanium, tungsten.
(4) Elements determined by indirect means:[18,25] bromine, chlorine, fluorine, iodine (although bromine, chlorine, and fluorine can be determined by their metallic halide spectra), phosphorus, and silicon.

As a guide to the applications of flame emission spectrometry, methods for constituents in various types of sample materials will be outlined in the following sections. Detailed procedures will be found in the references cited. A thorough discussion for the elements, which includes the spectrum excited to emission, optimum excitation con-

[24] Gilbert, P. T., Jr., "Less Familiar Elements," in G. L. Clark, Ed., The Encyclopedia of Spectroscopy, Reinhold, New York, 1960.
[25] Menis, O., House, H. P., and Rains, T. C., "Indirect Flame Photometric Method for Determination of Halides," Anal. Chem., **29**, 76–78, 1957.

ditions, and spectral and radiation interferences from other cations and anions, is available and should be consulted.[26]

Waters.—Waters ordinarily contain calcium, iron, magnesium, silicon, sodium, and sometimes aluminum and potassium in the form of bicarbonates, chlorides, hydroxides, nitrates, and sulfates. In addition, sea water contains small amounts of nickel and strontium. Industrial wastes usually contain elements peculiar to the plant operation.

The main problem in the analysis of fresh waters by flame spectrometry is the very low concentration of most of the components. A prior concentration step is usually required. Often the cations are isolated by means of cation-exchange resins and then eluted with 0.2 *N* hydrochloric acid. Trace amounts of cesium have been adsorbed upon ammonium 12-molybdophosphate with aluminum(III) as flocculant, after which the solids are dissolved in sodium hydroxide, the cesium is extracted with hexone–cyclohexane solution of sodium tetraphenylboron, and the extract is burned.[27] To avoid mutual interferences, particularly among the constituents of sea water, the method of standard addition is recommended for the determination of calcium and strontium.

The analysis of water-formed deposits differs only in that a solution must first be prepared, not always a simple procedure. After ignition at 700° to remove organic matter, the sample is digested with hydrochloric acid (and hydrofluoric acid if necessary), and the silica removed. The filtrate, 0.6 *N* in hydrochloric acid, is diluted to volume and aliquots taken for individual determinations.

Glasses.—The sodium and potassium content in a glass melt largely determines its behavior in further processing as well as the quality of finished products. Rapid methods of analysis are a requisite, flame methods offer virtually the only possibility.[28,29]

Glass powder, ground with an emery disc and passing a 100-mesh screen, is easily soluble in perchloric acid (or sulfuric acid) plus hydrofluoric acid. After evaporation to fumes of perchloric acid, the residue is taken up in water and diluted to volume. The mutual interference of sodium and potassium can be buffered by addition of barium chloride.[30]

Methods for magnesium and the alkaline earth elements provide for the removal of aluminum and other interfering elements plus the use of synthetic standards in conjunction with radiation buffers.[31]

Aluminum can be determined by extraction with cupferron or TTA,[32] and boron can be extracted as a tetraalkylboron tetrafluoride complex.[33]

Cement.—Because the quality of cement is affected by certain elements, rapid methods of analysis are needed for control purposes during production as well as for screening raw materials. In the ASTM procedure for Na_2O and K_2O, the cement samples are compared against a series of standards containing 630 μg./ml. of CaO in 5:95 hydro-

[26] Dean, J. A., Flame Photometry, McGraw-Hill, New York, 1960.

[27] Feldman, C., and Rains, T. C., Anal. Chem., **36,** 405, 1964.

[28] Williams, J. P., and Adams, P. B., "Flame Spectrophotometric Analysis of Glasses and Ores: I. Lithium, Sodium, Potassium, Rubidium and Cesium," J. Am. Ceram. Soc., **37,** 306–311, 1954.

[29] Williams, J. P., and Adams, P. B., "Flame Spectrophotometric Analysis of Glasses and Ores: II. Calcium, Magnesium and Barium Including the Alkalies," J. Am. Ceram. Soc., **39,** 351–357, 1956.

[30] Hegemann, F., Kostyra, H., and Pfab, B., "Flame Photometric Determination of Sodium and Potassium with a Buffering Solution of Barium Chloride," Glastech. Ber., **30,** 14–17, 1957.

[31] Roy, N., "Flame Photometric Determination of Sodium, Potassium, Calcium, Magnesium and Manganese in Glass Materials," Anal. Chem., **28,** 34–39, 1956.

[32] Eshelman, H. C., Dean, J. A., Menis, O., and Rains, T. C., Anal. Chem., **31,** 183, 1959.

[33] Maeck, W. J., Kussy, M. E., Ginther, B. E., Wheeler, G. V., and Rein, J. E., Anal. Chem., **35,** 62, 1963.

chloric acid for the determination of sodium and potassium[34,35] (and can be extended to manganese[36,37] and lithium).[38] A mixed series of standards, also containing the same quantities of calcium oxide and hydrochloric acid is used to prepare the working curves. The internal-standard method is inapplicable since lithium is often a constituent of cements. In contrast with most other methods, flame spectrometry permits the separate determination of lithium along with the other alkali metals.

For the determination of magnesium[39] and strontium,[40] compensatory standards are necessary to eliminate the effects of sulfate, silica, aluminum, and calcium.

Agronomic Materials.—Flame emission spectrometry has changed the analysis pattern for workers in agronomy. Determinations of sodium and potassium are made rapidly and accurately.

The procedure of the Association of Official Agricultural Chemists for the analysis of exchangeable cations in soils requires the extraction and leaching of a 10-g. soil sample with 250 ml. of 1 *N* ammonium acetate solution (with inclusion of 0.06 *N* ammonium oxalate when calcium is to be eliminated). Standards are also prepared in 1 *N* acetate solution. Leaching with neutral 1 *N* ammonium acetate solution is sufficient for non-calcareous soils in the determination of potassium, but the method is unsuited for calcareous soils unless calcium is removed with oxalate. Very little aluminum, which would interfere seriously in the determination of calcium and strontium, is brought into solution.

Plant materials can be treated as described for soils, or they can be ashed by procedures described under biological fluids. Simple extraction of freshly homogenized material with hot water usually suffices for comparative values (although oil-bearing substances cannot be handled in this manner).

Potassium in potash fertilizers is quickly determined simply by dissolving a 1-g. sample in water and diluting to 250 ml. In mixed fertilizers, undesired phosphate and sulfate ions are removed by anion-exchange resins.[41]

Calcium and magnesium are also determinable after preliminary separation of interferents. In addition, the determination of several trace elements is also possible; usually, the trace elements must be concentrated and separated from interferences.[42] One method involves an 8-quinolinol differential pH precipitation to separate copper, iron, and manganese from matrix elements.[43]

Biological Fluids and Tissues.—In biological and medical sample material, the rela-

[34] Diamond, J. J., and Bean, L., "Use of the Beckman and Perkin-Elmer Flame Photometers for the Determination of Alkalies in Portland Cement," Am. Soc. Testing Materials, Spec. Tech. Pub. 116, 28–32, 1951.

[35] Ford, C. L., "Determination of Sodium and Potassium Oxide by Flame Photometry in Portland Cement Raw Materials and Similar Silicates," Anal. Chem., **26**, 1578–1581, 1954.

[36] Diamond, J. J., "Flame Photometric Determination of Manganese in Cement," Anal. Chem., **28**, 328–329, 1956.

[37] Ford, C. L., "The Successive Determination of Manganese, Sodium, and Potassium in Cement by Flame Photometry," Am. Soc. Testing Materials Bull. 233, 57–63, 1958.

[38] McCoy, W. J., and Christiansen, G. G., "The Determination of Lithium Oxide in Portland Cement by Flame Photometer," Am. Soc. Testing Materials, Spec. Tech. Pub. 116, 44–51, 1951.

[39] Wilson, T. C., and Krotinger, N. J., "Flame Photometric Determination of Magnesium Oxide in Portland Cement," Am. Soc. Testing Materials Bull. 189, 56–58, 1963.

[40] Diamond, J. J., "Flame Photometric Determination of Strontium in Portland Cement," Anal. Chem., **27**, 913–915, 1955.

[41] Gehrke, C. W., Affsprung, H. W., and Wood, E. L., "Flame Photometric Determination of Potassium with Ion Exchange Separation of Interfering Anions," J. Agr. Food Chem., **3**, 48–50, 1955.

[42] Schrenk, W. G., and Johnson, R., Anal. Chem., **33**, 1799, 1961.

[43] Berneking, A. D., and Schrenk, W. G., "Flame Photometric Determination of Manganese, Iron and Copper in Plant Material," J. Agr. Food Chem., **5**, 742–744, 1957.

tive concentrations of the elements vary only within moderate limits. As a consequence, precision must be at least ±1 percent, or better, if an analysis is to possess clinical significance.[44] Because the speed and sensitivity of flame spectrometry is ideally suited for problems in biology and medicine, a vast literature has developed which describes the determination of sodium and potassium. Data on the concentration of these elements can be obtained in a matter of minutes, when the results are yet of practical value, and on very small quantities of material, since the consumption of sample material is generally much less than in chemical micromethods. Flame spectrometry often provides the first insight into the incidence of pathological disturbances.

In general, biological fluids can be directly atomized and analyzed for sodium after appropriate dilution and without additional treatment, unless the interference of protein, sugars, etc. must be avoided. Owing to the dominance of sodium in most body fluids, interferences are minimal. Cool air-gas flames are preferable. Dilutions should be such that the final sodium concentration lies on the linear part of the working curve, usually from 0.1 to 10 μg./ml.

The determination of potassium is also relatively simple. Cool air-gas flames are preferable to minimize ionization. Since most biological fluids contain less potassium than sodium, several series of potassium standards are prepared with a fixed amount of sodium in each series as parameter. Readings on both elements are then taken. The working curve for potassium corresponding to the content of sodium found is then used for the estimation of potassium. Interpolation between adjacent working curves is permissible.

Tissues, bones, and feces require a preliminary ashing. Dry ashing is usually done in an electric muffle furnace at 550°C. Heating should be gradual and the sample maintained at 550° until a grey ash is obtained. Upon cooling, the ash is treated with an excess of 12 *M* hydrochloric acid, and the excess is then removed by careful heating. The residue is reheated to 550°C. until the powder is white; if necessary, a treatment with 15 *M* nitric acid as oxidant is employed, followed by drying and heating again. After cooling, the ash is dissolved in the minimum amount of 12 *M* hydrochloric acid, and the solution is diluted quantitatively with appropriate solvent. Suspended particles are removed by centrifugation, never by filtration. Only platinum or quartz dishes and stirring rods may be used.

Wet ashing is accomplished by treating the sample with 15 *M* nitric acid—equal volumes for liquids, and 5 to 10 parts for solids—and digestion on a hot plate until the evolution of brown fumes has ceased. The digestion is repeated until the residue is no longer dark. The residue is then dissolved as for dry ashing.

The determination of calcium is fraught with difficulties, partly because the mode of bonding of calcium to protein is very complex and variable. To maintain the advantage of speed, inherent in flame work, a simple rapid method is desirable wherein no removal of protein, nor ashing, nor prior separation of calcium is envisaged. A hot oxygen-acetylene flame and the calcium line at 423 mμ is then best. Suitable releasing agents and, perhaps, dilution of the sample with organic solvent, will need to be employed. Standards must simulate the particular fluid closely through adding such substances as gelatine, albumen, sugars, and urea.

Petroleum Products.—Tetraethyllead (TEL)[45] and manganese[46] in gasoline stocks can be determined with speed and accuracy.

[44] Herrmann, R., and Alkemade, C. Th. J., Flammenphotometrie, 2nd Ed., Springer-Verlag, Berlin, 1961.

[45] Gilbert, P. T., "Determination of Tetraethyllead in Gasoline by Flame Photometry," Am. Soc. Testing Materials, Spec. Tech. Pub. 116, 77–91, 1951.

[46] Smith, G. W., and Palmby, A. K., "Flame Photometric Determination of Lead and Manganese in Gasoline," Anal. Chem., **31,** 1798–1802, 1959.

In handling gasoline samples, speed is essential if evaporation losses are to be avoided. Special sample-cup covers and small-bore capillary integral-aspirator burners are used. The proper oxygen-hydrogen flame will be only 0.5 inch in height without gasoline, and will expand to normal size when gasoline is sprayed into the flame. Samples are diluted with isooctane to a range of 0.5 to 3.0 ml. of TEL per gallon and, for manganese, in the range of 0.02 to 0.1 g. per gallon. Lead or manganese naphthenate are used as standards. The standard addition method is used for lead. The manganese samples can be compared against a standard calibration curve if the sample dilution is at least twentyfold to overcome the effects of variations in gasoline base stocks.

Metal additives in lubricating oils are determined by diluting a weighed amount of the unknown sample with an organic solvent and atomizing the mixture. A solvent mixture of 1:1 cleaners naphtha (or benzene)-isopropyl alcohol is satisfactory for the determination of boron,[47] and of lithium, potassium, calcium, strontium, and barium.[48] Standards are metal naphthenates.

Metallurgical Products.—Applications of flame emission spectrometry to the analysis of metallurgical products are not as widespread as the utility of the technique warrants, especially in production and control laboratories having no spectrographic facilities. Methods have been reviewed.[49]

The alkali and alkaline earth metals are determined in a variety of metallurgical materials, catalysts, alloys, and "high purity" metals. Sometimes the bulk of the matrix metal is removed beforehand, as, for example, the preliminary extraction of iron by ether (or methyl isobutyl ketone) prior to the determination of lithium and sodium in cast iron and nodular iron[50] or the sublimation of tungsten prior to the determination of sodium and potassium.[51] To compensate for the suppression (or enhancement) of metallic emission by some matrix elements, the standard-addition method is desirable and rapid for infrequent analyses. For routine work the metallic emission is compared with emissions from standards prepared from the pure bulk metal or synthetic matrices. By these methods, sodium has been determined in aluminum,[52] aluminum alloys,[53] and lithium. Potassium in bulk metals has been determined in a similar manner. Traces of lithium, sodium, potassium, and calcium are determined in high purity phosphorus, arsenic or antimony, following removal of the matrix by treatment with chlorine and distillation in vacuo.[54] Methods have been described for lithium in Mg-Li-Al alloys[53,55,56] and for traces of lithium in aluminum metal.[57]

[47] Buell, B. E., "A Direct Flame Photometric Determination of Boron in Organic Compounds," Anal. Chem., **30,** 1514–1517, 1958.

[48] Conrad, A. L., and Johnson, W. C., "Flame Photometer Techniques for Determining Typical Additives in Petroleum Oils," Anal. Chem., **22,** 1530–1533, 1950.

[49] Dean, J. A., Analyst, **85,** 621, 1960.

[50] Kuemmel, D. F., and Karl, H. L., "Flame Photometric Determination of Alkali and Alkaline Earth Elements in Cast Iron," Anal. Chem., **26,** 386–391, 1954.

[51] Hegedus, A. J., Neugebauer, J., and Dvorsky, M., "Microdetermination of Traces of Sodium, Potassium and Calcium in Wolfram Metal and Wolfram Oxides with a Flame Photometer," Mikrochim. Acta, 282–293, 1959.

[52] Ikeda, S., "Flame Spectrophotometric Analysis: I. Determination of Micro-amounts of Sodium in Aluminum Metal," Sci. Repts. Research Insts., Tohoku Univ., Ser. A, **7,** 29–34, 1955.

[53] Hourigan, H. F., and Robinson, J. W., "Determination of Sodium in Aluminum-copper Alloys with Flame Photometer," Anal. Chim. Acta, **16,** 161–164, 1957.

[54] Neeb, K. H., Z. anal. Chem., **200,** 278, 1963.

[55] Robinson, A. M., and Overston, T. C. J., "Lithium in Magnesium-Lithium Alloys by Internal Standard Flame Photometry," Analyst, **79,** 47–50, 1954.

[56] Strange, E. E., "Determination of Lithium in a Magnesium Alloy by the Flame Photometer," Anal. Chem., **25,** 650–651, 1953.

[57] Pilgrim, W. E., and Ford, W. R., Anal. Chem., **35,** 1735, 1963.

Among the other elements, copper can be determined directly in nonferrous alloys,[58] as can also be silver.[59] However, prior separation is required for steel and iron samples.[60] In this connection solvent extraction provides a powerful and useful technique. After the extraction step, the organic phase is aspirated directly into the flame. The technique provides great sensitivity and selectivity; simultaneous extraction followed by successive scans of pertinent lines of several elements in a sample is quite feasible. Methods have been described for copper, manganese, and iron in aluminum alloys,[14] and for iron, cobalt, nickel, and vanadium.[61] In each case diethyldithiocarbamate was the extractant.

Aluminum can be removed as its cupferrate (pH 2.5 to 4.5) or 2-thenoyltrifluoroacetonate (TTA) complex (pH 5–6) into methyl isobutyl ketone and its flame emission measured with excellent sensitivity.[32] By contrast with colorimetry, interfering color-bodies from similar chemical entities need not be removed. In a similar manner, chromium(VI) has been selectively extracted from many types of steel and aluminum alloys with methyl isobutyl ketone from an aqueous solution *M* in hydrochloric acid.[62] Although copper cannot be determined directly in ferrous alloys, extraction of copper as its diethyldithiocarbamate from aluminum alloys[14] or as its salicylaldoximate[60] from solutions of ferrous alloys masked with citrate (pH 3) provides a method which is free from interferences. A single extraction of iron with methyl isobutyl ketone from a solution 6 *M* in hydrochloric acid is sufficient for its determination in nonferrous alloys[63] and cobalt mattes.[64]

In nickel-plating baths boron can be determined after addition of sufficient methanol to bring the alcohol concentration to 50 percent.[65] Boron can be also extracted as the tetrabutylboron tetrafluoride ion association complex in methyl isobutyl ketone.[33] Either the fluctuation bands[66] or the atomic line[3] offers adequate sensitivity.

The determination of a number of less common elements should be attractive although no detailed methods have been reported in most instances. Ruthenium, rhodium, and palladium have sensitive and line-rich spectra. All the rare earth elements (except cerium and praseodymium)[67] plus lanthanum,[68] scandium, and yttrium[69] have intense band spectra, and, in fuel-rich oxygen-acetylene flames, the rare earths (except cerium) emit characteristic line spectra.[4] Following extraction from 5 *M* hydrochloric acid by methyl isobutyl ketone, or as the diethyldithiocarbamate at pH 4 in the presence of EDTA, tellurium can be determined.[8] Few elements interfere with the determination of gallium, indium, and thallium, and all interferences can be eliminated by using an ether-extraction step before flame photometry.[70]

[58] Dean, J. A., "Flame Spectrophotometric Determination of Copper in Nonferrous Alloys," Anal. Chem., **27,** 1224–1229, 1955.
[59] Dean, J. A., and Stubblefield, C. B., Anal. Chem., **33,** 382, 1961.
[60] Dean, J. A., and Lady, J. H., "Flame Spectrophotometric Determination of Copper in Ferrous Alloys," Anal. Chem., **28,** 1887–1889, 1956.
[61] Schöffman, E., and Malissa, H., Mikrochim. Acta, 319, 1961.
[62] Bryan, H. A., and Dean, J. A., "Extraction and Flame Spectrophotometric Determination of Chromium," Anal. Chem., **29,** 1289–1291, 1957.
[63] Menis, O., and Rains, T. C., Anal. Chem., **32,** 1837, 1961.
[64] Galloway, N. McN., Analyst, **84,** 505, 1959.
[65] Fornwalt, D. E., "A Flame Spectrophotometric Method for the Determination of Nickel and Boron in Plating Solutions," Anal. Chim. Acta, **17,** 597–602, 1957.
[66] Dean, J. A., and Thompson, C., "Flame Photometric Study of Boron," Anal. Chem., **27,** 42–46, 1955.
[67] Rains, T. C., House, H. P., and Menis, O., Anal. Chim. Acta, **22,** 315, 1960.
[68] Menis, O., Rains, T. C., and Dean, J. A., "Extraction and Flame Spectrophotometric Determination of Lanthanum," Anal. Chem., **31,** 187–191, 1959.
[69] Carnes, W. J., and Dean, J. A., Anal. Chem., **33,** 1961, 1961.
[70] Bode, H., and Fabian, H., Z. anal. Chem., **170,** 387, 1959.

PROCEDURES

DETERMINATION OF SODIUM, MANGANESE, AND POTASSIUM IN CEMENT
(and Acid-soluble Limestones)[71]

Reagents.—Prepare an alkali-manganese stock solution containing 1000 μg. per ml. each of Na_2O, K_2O, and Mn_2O_3 by dissolving in water 1.8858 g. NaCl, 1.5838 g. KCl, and 2.1412 g. $MnSO_4 \cdot H_2O$ (dried at 105°C. for 4 hrs.) and dilute to 1 liter.

Prepare a lime-acid stock solution containing 6300 μg. of CaO per ml., in approximately 1 *M* hydrochloric acid, by adding 100 ml. of hydrochloric acid to 11.244 g. of $CaCO_3$ suspended in 300 ml. of water; after CO_2 is released, dilute to a 1-liter volume.

Procedure.—Place 1.000 g. of the sample, ground to pass a 100-mesh screen, in a 250-ml. beaker, and disperse with 20 ml. of water, swirling the beaker. While still swirling, add 5 ml. of hydrochloric acid all at once. Break up any lumps of cement remaining undispersed with a rubber policeman. Dilute immediately with 25 ml. of water, using the water to rinse the policeman. Bring to just short of boiling on a hot plate. Digest for 15 minutes and filter through medium-texture paper into a calibrated 100 ml. volumetric flask. Wash the beaker and paper thoroughly with water. Cool the contents of the flask to room temperature, dilute to 100 ml., and mix the solution thoroughly. Aspirate the solution and measure the sodium at 590 mμ, the manganese at 403.3 mμ, and the potassium at 767 mμ. For manganese, the spectral band width must not exceed 0.3 mμ due to the potassium line at 404.4 mμ.

For sodium, potassium, and manganese, a single set of standard solutions, containing from 0 to 100 μg. per ml. of each element, expressed as Na_2O, K_2O, and Mn_2O_3 and 630 μg. per ml. of CaO, is prepared by measuring 0, 10, 25, 50, 75, and 100 ml. of manganese-alkali stock solution into 1-liter volumetric flasks, adding 100 ml. of lime-acid stock solution, and diluting to the mark with deionized water. No appreciable error is introduced in the analyses by the normal variation in the amount of calcium in cement when 630 μg. of CaO per ml. is incorporated in the standards. For limestone samples, the amount of lime-acid solution may have to be modified.

DETERMINATION OF COPPER IN ALUMINUM- AND ZINC-BASE ALLOYS[72]

Reagents.—Prepare a stock solution of copper containing 1000 μg. per ml. by dissolving 3.942 g. fresh crystals of $CuSO_4 \cdot 5H_2O$ in deionized water by diluting to 1 liter. Weaker standards are prepared by appropriate dilution.

Procedure.—Weigh samples containing from 2 to 10 mg. of copper into 150-ml. beakers. Dissolve in the minimum amount of 6 *N* perchloric acid or 8 *N* nitric acid. Heat to action and simmer until all the sample is dissolved. Evaporate nearly to dryness to remove excess acid. Add 25 ml. of deionized water and transfer to a 100-ml. volumetric flask. Dilute to the mark with deionized water. Final concentrations will range from 20 to 100 μg. of copper per ml. Atomize the solution into an oxygen-fuel flame, and record the emission intensity.

Bracket the unknown with a series of standards. Measure the atomic line of copper at 324.7 mμ and the background at 325.0 mμ. Use a slit width of 0.030 mm. (spectral band width 0.15 mμ). The background readings are subtracted from the unknown and standard readings to obtain net emission readings, which are averaged for each sample.

[71] Adapted, with permission, from C. L. Ford, ASTM Bull, **233,** 57, 1958.

[72] Reprinted, with adaptations, from Anal. Chem., **27,** 1224, 1955. Copyright 1955 by the American Chemical Society and reprinted by permission of the copyright owner.

Self-absorption of the copper line precludes the use of the serial method of standard addition.

DETERMINATION OF ALUMINUM IN MAGNESIUM-BASE ALLOYS[73]

Reagents.—Prepare a stock solution of aluminum containing 100 μg. per ml. by dissolving 0.100 g. of aluminum wire in the minimum amount of hydrochloric acid, and dilute to 1 liter with 0.1 *M* acid.

Procedure.—Weigh samples containing 0.5 to 4.0 mg. of aluminum into 150-ml. beakers. Dissolve the sample in the minimum amount of 1 *N* sulfuric acid. Transfer the solution to a 100-ml. volumetric flask and dilute to the mark. Transfer an aliquot that contains between 100 to 400 μg. of aluminum to a small beaker and adjust the pH between 2.5 and 4.5 with 1 *M* ammonium acetate solution. Transfer this solution quantitatively to an extraction funnel. Adjust the volume to approximately 30 ml. and add 3 ml. of a 0.1 *M* solution of *N*-nitrosophenylhydroxylamine (cupferron). Add exactly 10.0 ml. of methyl isobutyl ketone, and shake until any precipitate which may have formed in the aqueous phase has disappeared, then shake for an additional 2 minutes. Allow the phases to separate, and transfer the ketone layer to a small beaker. Aspirate the organic phase into the flame.

Measure the emission intensity of the atomic line or the oxide band head and the appropriate flame background at the following wavelengths:

Emitting Species	Wavelength, mμ	Background, mμ
Al	396.2	395
AlO	484	482

To obtain the net emission intensity, subtract the flame background emission from the total emission intensity of the aluminum line or the aluminum oxide band. Bracket the sample with standard solutions which contain from 5 to 40 μg. of aluminum per ml., and treated as described for the sample solution.

DETERMINATION OF IRON IN NONFERROUS ALLOYS[74]

Reagents.—Prepare a stock solution of iron containing 1000 μg. per ml. by dissolving 1.000 g. of iron wire in 11 ml. of 6 *M* hydrochloric acid and diluting to volume with deionized water. Dilute with approximately 25 ml. of deionized water. Add 5 ml. of concentrated nitric acid, and boil for 10 minutes. Cool and dilute to 1 liter with deionized water.

Procedure.—Weigh samples containing 0.1 to 0.4 mg. of iron into 150-ml. beakers. Dissolve with 20 ml. of 6 *M* hydrochloric acid plus a few drops of nitric acid. Transfer the solutions to 50-ml. volumetric flasks and dilute to calibrated volume with 6 *M* hydrochloric acid. For tin-base alloys, add 20 ml. of sulfuric acid, boil, and volatilize the tin as $SnBr_4$ by the repeated addition of hydrobromic acid. Transfer the sample to a 50-ml. volumetric flask and dilute to the mark with 6 *M* hydrochloric acid.

Transfer aliquots of the sample solutions which contain from 20 to 80 μg. of iron to 30-ml. separatory funnels. Dilute to 10 ml. with 6 *M* hydrochloric acid. Add exactly 10.0 ml. of methyl isobutyl ketone (or *n*-amyl acetate) and equilibrate for 2 minutes at the rate of 30 inversions per minute. After the phases have separated, transfer the organic phase to a small beaker and aspirate it into an oxygen-fuel flame.

[73] Reprinted, with adaptations, from Anal. Chem., **31,** 183, 1959. Copyright 1959 by the American Chemical Society and reprinted by permission of the copyright owner.

[74] Reprinted, with adaptations, from Anal. Chem., **32,** 1837, 1960. Copyright 1955 by the American Chemical Society and reprinted by permission of the copyright owner.

Measure the emission intensity of the atomic iron line at 372 mμ and the background at 368 mμ. To obtain the net emission intensity, subtract the flame background measurement from the total emission intensity of the iron line. Compare with a calibration curve prepared as follows: Transfer 1-, 2-, 3-, 4-, and 5-ml. aliquots of a standard solution of iron (20 μg. per ml.) to 30-ml. separatory funnels. Add 5 ml. of hydrochloric acid and dilute to 10 ml. with water. Add exactly 10.0 ml. of methyl isobutyl ketone to each solution and proceed as described for the sample solutions.

APPLICATIONS IN THE ANALYSIS OF SPECIAL MATERIALS

The applications of flame emission spectrometry in the analysis of special materials listed elsewhere in Standard Methods of Chemical Analysis are as follows:

1. Chapter 44, Volume III, Alloys: Nonferrous.
   a. Copper in aluminum-, tin-, and zinc-base alloys
   b. Copper in copper-rich alloys
   c. Indium in magnesium-base alloys
   d. Silver in magnesium-base alloys
2. Chapter 46, Volume III, Portland Cement.
   a. Magnesium
   b. Manganese
   c. Potassium
   d. Sodium
   e. Also aluminum, barium, calcium, iron, lithium, and strontium.
   Chapter 29, Volume IIA, Portland Cement.
   a. Potassium and sodium, page 1063.
3. Chapter 47, Volume III, Instrumental Methods in Clinical Medicine.
   a. Potassium and sodium
4. Chapter 32, Volume IIB, Explosives and Propellants.
   a. Calcium, pages 1377, 1398.
   b. Potassium, pages 1376, 1398.
   c. Sodium, pages 1377, 1398, 1400.
5. Chapter 48, Volume III, Natural Fats.
   a. Determination of soaps in oils
6. Chapter 49, Volume III, Fertilizers.
   a. Potassium (also Chapter 34, Volume IIB, pages 1501, 1503)
7. Chapter 53, Volume III, Glass.
   a. Alkali metals
   b. Alkaline earths
   c. Aluminum
   d. Iron
   e. Manganese
8. Chapter 54, Volume III, Paint, Varnish, and Lacquer.
   a. Alkali metals
   b. Metals in vehicles
   c. Metal content of paint driers
   Chapter 37, Volume IIB, Paint, Varnish, and Lacquer.
   a. Determination of inorganic pigments in paint, page 1685.
9. Chapter 61, Volume III, Soaps and Synthetic Detergents.
   a. Potassium and sodium in soaps and syndets
10. Chapter 62, Volume III, Soils.
    a. Calcium

   b. Magnesium
   c. Potassium
   d. Sodium
11. Chapter 48, Volume IIB, Water Analysis.
   a. Lithium, page 2438.
   b. Potassium, page 2470.
   c. Sodium, page 2478.
   d. Strontium, page 2481.

SELECTED BIBLIOGRAPHY

Dean, J. A., Flame Photometry, McGraw-Hill, New York, 1960.

Herrmann, R., and Alkemade, C. Th. J., Flammenphotometrie, 2nd Ed., Springer-Verlag, Berlin, 1960. English translation by P. T. Gilbert, Jr., Chemical Analysis, Vol. 14, Interscience, New York, 1963.

Mavrodineanu, R., and Boiteux, H., Flame Emission Spectroscopy, John Wiley and Sons, New York, 1964.

Chapter 8

EMISSION SPECTROMETRY

By Richard N. Kniseley
Institute for Atomic Research
Iowa State University
Ames, Iowa

INTRODUCTION

Analytical emission spectrometric methods utilize the characteristic radiation produced when materials are introduced into thermal or electrical sources. These sources excite the atoms or molecules to energy levels above the ground state; as they return to lower energy states, the characteristic radiation is emitted in the form of discrete wavelengths of light called spectral lines. The wavelength of a spectral line is inversely proportional to the energy difference between the initial and final energy levels involved in the transition. Since no two elements have identical energy level schemes, no two will have identical spectra. In the case of a compound or alloy, the spectrum emitted will be a composite of the individual spectra of the elements in the specimen.

The emitted light is analyzed by a spectrometer which sorts out and records the spectral lines according to their wavelength. Qualitative spectrometric analyses are performed by identifying these lines using available tables and charts. Quantitative analysis is based on the fact that the intensity of a line emitted by an atom or molecule is a function of the concentration of that atom or molecule in the emitting source.

In theory analytical emission spectrometry is applicable to all elements, but, using standard techniques, only the metals and metalloids can readily be detected. However, in several instances, specialized techniques have been devised for the determination of the nonmetals and the permanent gases. The ultimate limit of detection is a function of many factors, including the element determined, the nature of the sample involved, and the specific equipment used. In many instances these detection limits may be as low as a few parts per million. In ideal cases, especially when special techniques are used, the detection limits may lie in the part per billion range. Even under the most adverse conditions a detection limit of a fraction of a percent can usually be easily achieved. These detection limits require only a few milligrams of sample. For these reasons spectrometric techniques find a wide field of application in trace analysis.

Unlike classical analytical procedures, which are usually less precise at lower concentration levels, spectrometric methods tend to show a uniform precision over most of the applicable concentration range. In general, it is found that the precision of spectrometric analysis is superior to classical chemical methods at very low concentration levels, about equal at concentrations near 1 percent, and inferior at higher concentration levels. This statement must of course be modified, depending on the nature of the problem and the amount of sample available for the analysis. Under ideal conditions a precision of ± 1 percent of the amount present can be attained using spectrochemical procedures. Usually, however, this degree of precision cannot be achieved and values of ± 5–10 percent are more typical of the average analytical method.

Despite its relatively poor precision at higher concentration levels, spectrometric techniques have found a wide area of application in major constituent work. This is largely due to the rapidity and selectivity of the analyses. In many instances analyses requiring several hours or days by conventional chemical techniques can be performed in a matter of minutes using spectrometric techniques. This is especially important in the metals industries where melts must be held until analysis can be performed. Spectrometric techniques are also applicable to analyses which cannot be accurately performed by classical chemical methods because of difficulties with separations or because of the insensitivity of the chemical method. Examples of these areas include the analysis of hafnium-zirconium, niobium-tantalum, and rare earth element mixtures. Likewise, spectrometric techniques are used extensively for the determination of isotope ratios.

With the exception of qualitative and semiquantitative analyses, a specific spectrometric method must usually be developed for each general analytical problem. Since spectrometric methods are not absolute, they must be carefully standardized against synthetic or chemically analyzed standards. Also, this calibration is usually dependent on the general composition and past history of the sample. Thus, when the sample type or composition changes greatly, modification or complete revision of a method may be necessary. The development of a good spectrometric method requires very careful selection of optimum operating parameters for the equipment. In addition standards must be carefully selected or prepared to correspond as closely as possible both chemically and physically to the samples to be analyzed.

Units.—The basic unit of spectroscopic wavelength is the Angstrom unit (A) which is equal to 10^{-10} meter. However, because of the extreme accuracy of spectroscopic wavelength measurements, the standard meter as well as the Angstrom unit is now defined on the basis of the krypton-86 line at 6057.8021 A. Spectral lines are also referred to in terms of their wavenumber (ν). The wavenumber of a line is equal to the reciprocal of the wavelength in centimeters, and is directly related to the energy involved in the transition producing the line emission. The following relationships are of importance in spectrometric work:

1 Angstrom unit (A) = 1×10^{-10} meters = 1/6057.8021 of the wavelength orange red line of Kr-86;
1 millimicron (mμ) = 10 A = 10^{-9} meters;
1 micron (μ) = 1000 mμ = 10^{-6} meters;
1 cm.$^{-1}$ = 1/wavelength in centimeters.

In some literature the wavenumber of a line is given as Kayser (K) units, one Kayser unit being equal to 1 cm.$^{-1}$. This unit is no longer a recommended usage, and the unit for wavenumber is commonly called a "reciprocal centimeter."

APPARATUS

A considerable amount of equipment is necessary for an emission spectrometric laboratory. In general this equipment can be classified into three general areas: (1) optical, consisting of the spectrometer and associated optics; (2) excitation, consisting of the source unit and accessories for sample excitation; and (3) data processing, including the photographic plate processing, intensity measuring, and calculating equipment.

OPTICAL

SPECTROMETERS

Rating of Spectrometers.—Spectrometers are rated on the basis of several characteristics related to their ability to separate and record distinct spectral lines. The most important of these characteristics are defined below.

Resolution.—Resolution is defined as the ability of the spectrometer to separate two spectral lines which have a very small wavelength separation. This is defined as a dimensionless number, $\lambda/\Delta\lambda$, in which λ is the average wavelength and $\Delta\lambda$ is the wavelength separation of two lines which are just distinguishable as two. Resolution is not a simple quantity to define accurately, and the working resolution is a function of many factors.[1]

Dispersion.—Dispersion is specified in several different ways but in emission spectrometric analysis it has become common practice to specify the reciprocal linear dispersion $\Delta\lambda/\Delta d$. This is usually expressed as A/mm. and is obtained by measuring the wavelength separation of two lines in A and dividing by the linear separation of these lines on the photographic plate or focal plane of the instrument. Dispersion and resolution are interrelated and the overall ability of a spectrometer to separate lines depends upon adequate resolution and dispersion.

Speed.—The speed of a spectrometer is difficult to define in general terms. It is basically related to the minimum level of illumination at the entrance slit required to produce a detectable response at the detector. In general the relative speeds of two spectrometers will be inversely proportional to the squares of their effective *f*/numbers, where the *f*/number is defined as the focal length divided by the effective diameter of the limiting aperture in the system. In systems utilizing photoelectric detection the light gathering power or flux transmitting power becomes the important factor.[1]

Classification of Spectrometers.—Spectrometers are classified in accordance with the dispersive element used, the optical mounting of the dispersive element, and the manner in which the spectra are recorded. The common dispersive elements are the prism and the diffraction grating. These may be mounted in many optical arrangements but only a few are in common use. The principal methods of recording the spectra are photographic and photoelectric. Through common usage the photoelectric instruments are commonly referred to as direct reading instruments. Although prism instruments have been widely used in the past, the development of high quality gratings at a reasonable cost has led to the almost universal current use of grating instruments in the field of emission spectrometry. Therefore, prism instruments will be discussed only briefly.

The Prism Spectrometer.—The prism spectrometer utilizes the optical principles of refraction and dispersion to separate light into its component wavelengths. The basic instrument consists of an entrance slit, a collimating lens which provides a parallel beam of light through the prism, and a second lens to focus the spectral lines onto the focal plane of the instrument. The most common prism mounting used today for emission spectrometry is the Littrow arrangement. In this optical arrangement a mirror is placed behind the prism (usually a 30°-60°-90° prism) so that the light passes through the prism twice and the same lens is used for both collimation and focusing. Relatively low dispersion and poor resolution at higher wavelengths coupled with nonlinear dispersion has made prism instruments rather undesirable.

The Grating Spectrometer.—In contrast to the prism spectrometer, grating instruments are capable of providing a high, constant resolving power and dispersion. Diffraction gratings are produced by ruling a large number of narrow lines on a special aluminum-coated glass blank. For normal emission spectrometers the spacing must be very fine, usually of the order of 5000 to 30,000 grooves per inch. In recent years replicating techniques have been perfected and replica gratings made from superior master gratings are commonly used. Modern gratings are "blazed" to concentrate the radiation into a desired wavelength region. In most instances a good grating will have a high intensity over the wavelength region from $\frac{2}{3}$ to $1\frac{1}{2}$ times the wavelength of the blaze

[1] Jarrell, R. F., "Optical Qualities of Spectroscopic Instruments," in Encyclopedia of Spectroscopy, G. R. Clark, Ed., Reinhold Publishing Corp., New York, 1960.

maximum. One must emphasize that the blaze of a grating is primarily a matter of angles; thus, a grating is blazed for all the various wavelengths in all of the orders corresponding to a specific angle with respect to the grating normal.

The theory of diffraction gratings has been discussed by numerous authors.[2,3] Using this theory the basic grating equation can be written as

$$n\lambda = d(\sin \theta \pm \sin \phi)$$

where n is the order of diffraction, λ is the wavelength of interest, d is the distance between corresponding points on adjacent grating rulings, θ is the angle of incidence, and ϕ is the angle of diffraction. Figure 8-1 illustrates diffraction from a grating and

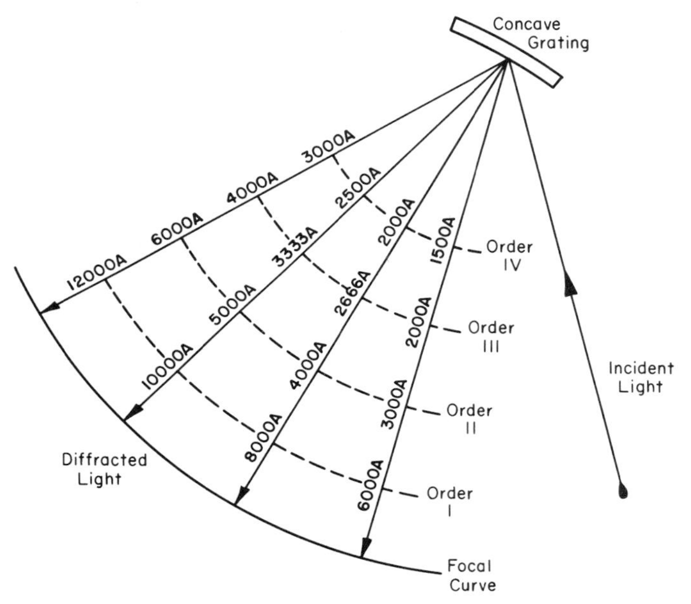

FIG. 8-1. Diffraction of Light by a Concave Grating and the Occurrence of Orders of Diffraction. (Courtesy Baird-Atomic, Inc.)

also the occurrence of orders of diffraction. It is important to realize that due to the existence of these orders, several wavelengths will occur at a given diffraction angle. The use of optical filters in conjunction with a photographic plate of proper wavelength sensitivity will usually allow the elimination of the undesired wavelengths. Both resolution and dispersion increase with increasing order of diffraction, and often the use of higher orders is desirable, especially where complex spectra are involved.

Gratings are ruled on both concave and plane blanks. The concave grating has focusing properties and thus has the advantage that a spectrometer can be built which has only a single optical element. These single-element spectrometers are based on a Rowland Circle arrangement. The Rowland Circle corresponds to a circle having a radius equal to $\frac{1}{2}$ the radius of curvature of the grating and represents the focal curve

[2] Sawyer, R. A., Experimental Spectroscopy, 2nd Ed., Prentice-Hall, New York, 1951.
[3] Jenkins, F. A., and White, H. E., Fundamentals of Optics, McGraw-Hill, New York, 1950.

of the grating. Thus, if the circle is constructed such that the center of the grating is tangent to it and the entrance slit is located on it, then all points on the circle are in focus. The concave grating mounts are, however, generally astigmatic, not readily used in high orders, and often have complex wavelength adjustments. These difficulties have led to the development of plane grating spectrometers which circumvent these difficulties to a large degree.

Three typical concave grating mountings are illustrated in Fig. 8-2. The Eagle mount has the advantages of compactness and relatively low astigmatism as compared with

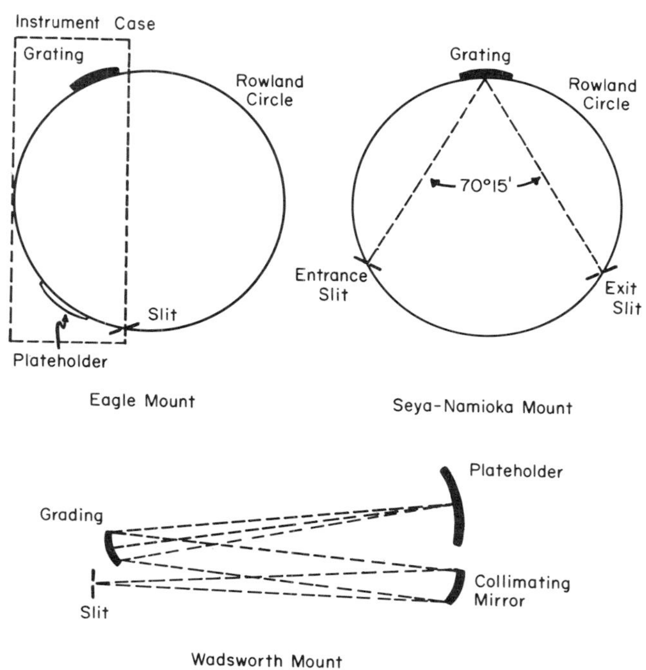

FIG. 8-2. Three Typical Concave Grating Mountings.

other Rowland Circle mounts. The Seya-Namioka has the advantage that only a slight defocusing occurs for a relatively large grating rotation and thus wavelength adjustment is simplified. This mounting is popular for vacuum ultraviolet scanning monochromators. The Wadsworth mount is different in that the individual elements are not placed on the Rowland Circle. The introduction of a collimating mirror causes the grating to be illuminated with parallel light and stigmatic images are produced.

In the field of large spectrometers almost all modern instruments are modifications of the Ebert mounting. Optical diagrams of two of these mountings are illustrated in Fig. 8-3. The Ebert-type mountings utilize a plane grating for dispersion in conjunction with concave mirrors for collimation and focusing of the spectrum. The use of a plane grating simplifies the problem of grating production and replication as well as providing easier accessibility to higher orders. It is well to note that in practice it is difficult to achieve good focus over an extended length on the focal plane, and Ebert spectrometers often show a slight loss of focus at the extremes of the plateholder.

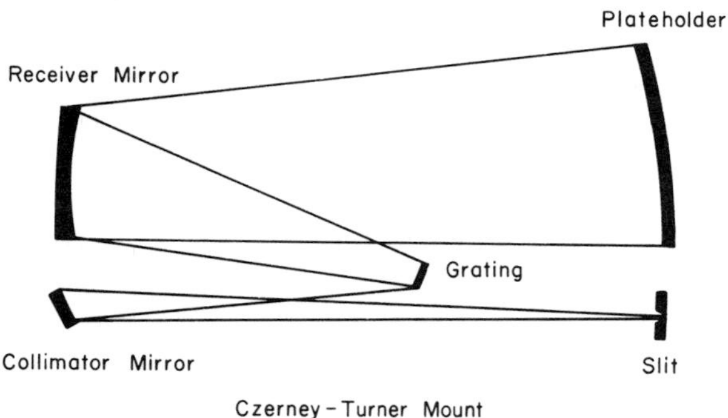

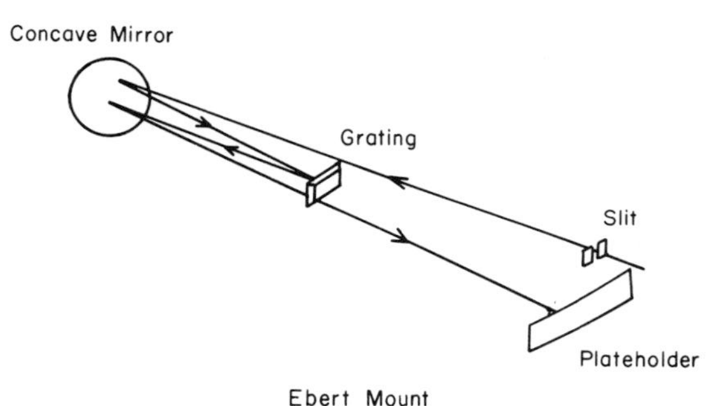

FIG. 8-3. Two Typical Plane Grating Mountings.

ILLUMINATION SYSTEMS

A system of one or more lenses is usually placed between the source and the spectrometer slit to maximize the light input to the spectrometer and provide uniform slit illumination. In some instances a lens system is also used to select light from specific portions of the source. Other optical elements such as diaphragms and filters are often used as components of the illumination system.

The simplest illumination systems utilize only one spherical lens. If the lens is placed to focus an image of the source onto the slit, maximum light input into the spectrograph is achieved as long as the image is larger than the slit dimensions. In stigmatic spectrographs, this allows the study of the distribution of intensities from different portions of the source, since the spectral lines will exhibit the same intensity variations as those present in the source image.

However, in quantitative analysis, uniform slit illumination is usually desired in order that the intensities along the lines will be constant. A simple single-lens system for achieving this utilizes a spherical lens at the slit to form an image of the source at the collimator. In this manner each point in the source equally illuminates every point on the slit, giving rise to uniform spectral lines. The focal length of the lens must be chosen such that the image of the source is equal to or greater than the aperture at the dispersing element in order to provide maximum intensity of the spectra.

Usually the dispersing element is greater in width than in height, whereas the converse is true for most sources. Failure to fill the full width of the dispersing element will cause a serious loss in resolving power as well as intensity loss. Since it is difficult to fill such an aperture using a spherical lens system, a crossed cylindrical lens system is often used. The cylindrical lenses are arranged to form an image with greater magnification in the horizontal plane than in the vertical plane, and thus expand the width of the source image to fill the aperture.

It is important to prevent light from the electrodes from reaching the focal plane since the continuum from these hot electrodes would contribute to the spectral background. In order to accomplish this, the electrodes must be diaphragmed off at some image plane. In the case where an image of the source is formed on the collimator or slit, the electrode diaphragming can be accomplished here. In other systems an intermediate image is formed outside the spectrograph, the electrodes are diaphragmed off, and the normal illumination system is then used with the intermediate image acting as the source.

Normally the lenses used in the illumination systems are simple lenses (not achromatic), and the adjustments are made in the visible region where the images can be easily observed. Thus, some adjustments may be necessary as the wavelength is changed, although a compromise position can usually be found where a wide range of wavelengths can be covered without adjustment. Also, the lenses used must have a diameter sufficient to accept the entire solid angle of the spectrograph; otherwise vignetting will occur and illumination difficulties will be experienced.

The other normal components of the external optical system include the excitation stand and the intensity controlling devices. These will be discussed in later sections. The exact arrangement of the illuminating system depends on the specific spectrograph being used; usually, the manufacturer's literature will provide details on recommended systems.

EXCITATION SOURCES

The selection of the proper excitation source is of prime importance in the development of any spectroscopic method. If the proper source is not chosen the result may be poor accuracy, poor precision, and, perhaps, the inability to excite the elements of interest. Under ideal situations the excitation source should:

1. excite lines of all the elements of interest;
2. provide constant excitation conditions over a period of time corresponding to the sample excitation time;
3. provide reproducible excitation conditions from sample to sample;
4. provide sufficient line intensity to achieve the required detection limit;
5. provide a low spectral background; and
6. provide uniform and reproducible sample vaporization.

In most instances no one source is capable of fulfilling all these requirements; compromises must be made. When settling upon compromises, care must be taken to optimize the characteristics most important to the specific method. For example, detection limits are principally dependent on the line to spectral background ratio (signal to noise), and, thus, the detection of very low concentrations requires a source which produces a high line intensity and a low background. For precise quantitative measurements at higher concentration levels, however, the uniformity and reproducibility of excitation and vaporization are the most important factors.

The most common sources in analytical emission spectrometry are the flame, the arc, and the spark. In addition to these, special sources such as plasma jets, microwave discharges, and hollow cathode discharges are sometimes used for special analytical problems.

Flames.—In general, flames are sources of low excitation energy and are used primarily for the determination of the metallic elements. The energy available is insufficient for the excitation of the nonmetals, and application in this area has been through the use of molecular band spectra. The methods of sample injection into flames essentially limit the application of this source to solutions or to samples which can be readily dissolved. Flames are inexpensive but stable and reproducible sources which are capable of handling many analytical problems. A complete discussion on flames may be found in Chapter 7.

Arc Discharges.—As an emission spectrometric source, the direct current arc is a low voltage d.c. discharge with a current of about 1 to 50 amperes between two electrodes spaced 1 to 15 mm. apart. Once initiated, the d.c. arc is self-sustaining and provides a continuous light output. The source is simple, requiring only a direct current source of 100 or more volts and a series ballast resistance. The ballast is required because the voltage-current relationship for an arc is not ohmic and in some regions the voltage-current curve may have a negative slope. Thus, the current may increase without limit unless a ballast resistor is placed in series with the gap. Usually the ballast resistor is adjustable so that the arc current may be varied. Many commercial units utilize a rectifier power supply, a saturable reactor for current control, and a special regulator circuit to insure a constant arc current.

The d.c. arc is capable of detecting very low concentrations of most metals and, for this reason, is widely used for qualitative analysis as well as for the quantitative determination of trace elements. Wider application of the arc has been limited by its erratic behavior and generally poor reproducibility. In addition, since the sample is introduced into the discharge by a thermal process, selective vaporization of the sample constituents often poses problems. Some extension of the usefulness of the d.c. arc has resulted from some of the newer techniques. These include gas sheathing techniques, inert atmosphere excitation, and low pressure stabilization.

Two types of a.c. arcs have been used as spectrochemical sources. The so-called "self-igniting" a.c. arc consists of a transformer providing several thousand volts output and a ballast resistance or inductance. The discharge is initiated by narrowing the electrode gap down to less than 1 mm. Once initiated, the arc will continue until the gap voltage drops below the sustaining voltage and will re-ignite, with opposite polarity, on the next half-cycle of the line voltage. The "self-sustaining" a.c. arc operates in the same manner except that a lower voltage and higher current ($\sim$300 volts and 8 or more amperes) are used. The higher current heats the electrodes to a high temperature, and the thermionic emission from the cathode allows the gap to be broken down during each half-cycle in spite of the relatively low impressed voltage. In theory the re-ignition of an arc, twice each cycle and with alternating polarity, should minimize arc wandering and provide more uniform vaporization of the sample. In practice, these arcs have not found wide acceptance, and only a few references to their actual use are found in the literature.

Spark Discharges.—The spark source provides a means of exciting higher energy levels in atoms as well as the spectra of ions. Basically, a spark is produced by placing a voltage of 10,000 to 30,000 volts across the electrodes of the analytical gap. Under these conditions the discharge is self-igniting. For spectroscopic purposes it is desirable to have a high discharge current which can be controlled, and, for this reason, a condenser discharge is most often used for analytical purposes.

A basic spark circuit is illustrated in Fig. 8-4. The condenser is charged from the secondary winding of the high voltage transformer. The condenser continues to charge until the voltage at which the analytical gap begins to conduct is reached, and at that point the discharge commences. The energy stored in the condenser flows through the analytical gap, producing instantaneous currents of several hundred amperes. This high current pulse will essentially explode material from the electrodes into the spark gap where the atoms are excited by collision with the high energy electrons. If the discharge is properly damped by the series resistor, the discharge will cease and the gap will

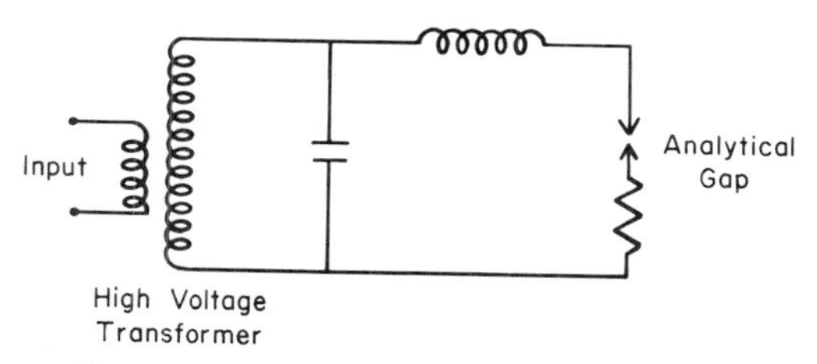

FIG. 8-4. A Basic Spark Discharge Circuit.

become nonconducting before the next half-cycle of the line voltage. As the voltage increases during the next half-cycle, the condenser will again charge, and the discharge will repeat itself each half-cycle. In general the initial current and the rate of energy dissipation in the spark gap increases with increasing condenser capacity and thus higher atomic energy levels are excited.

The simple spark circuit as described above is seldom used in spectroscopic analysis since it does not provide the uniform and reproducible results desired in quantitative spectrochemical analysis. This variability is related to variations in the duration of the discharge and in the breakdown voltage as a result of changes in the characteristics of the analytical gap. As a result "controlled" spark sources have been developed to circumvent these difficulties. For the most part stabilization of the discharge is based on the use of an auxiliary spark gap, having uniform characteristics, which is used to control the discharge. Figure 8-5 illustrates two sources of this type. In both cases an auxiliary discharge gap is connected in series with the analytical gap. In the Feussner type, this auxiliary gap is closed by a rotating electrode which is driven by a synchronous motor. Thus, the discharge across the analytical gap occurs only during the brief interval during which the auxiliary gap is shorted. The uniformity of the auxiliary gap is usually maintained by illuminating it with ultraviolet light from a mercury vapor lamp, thus insuring a constant ion concentration within the gap.

The second source illustrated in Fig. 8-5 utilizes a fixed auxiliary gap for control. A high velocity stream of air is blown across this gap to deionize it quickly at the end of a discharge. In this way the conductance of the auxiliary gap is always higher than that of the analytical gap, and the discharges can occur only during the period when the voltage exceeds the breakdown voltage of this auxiliary gap. The rapid quenching of the spark by the air blast permits several individual discharges to occur during each half-cycle of the voltage until the peak voltage becomes too low for breakdown. In ordinary commercial units the number of breakdowns per half-cycle can be varied from approximately 1 to 10 by changing the discharge parameters. Usually the conditions in the auxiliary gap are maintained more uniform by using a mercury vapor lamp to provide uniform ionization in the interelectrode space.

A third type of excitation source described by Hasler *et al.*,[4] is a highly versatile unit called a "Multisource." This unit provides a variety of discharges similar to conventional arcs and sparks as well as discharges of an intermediate nature. As diagrammed in

[4] Hasler, M. A., and Dietert, H. W., J. Opt. Soc. Am., **33**, 218, 1943.

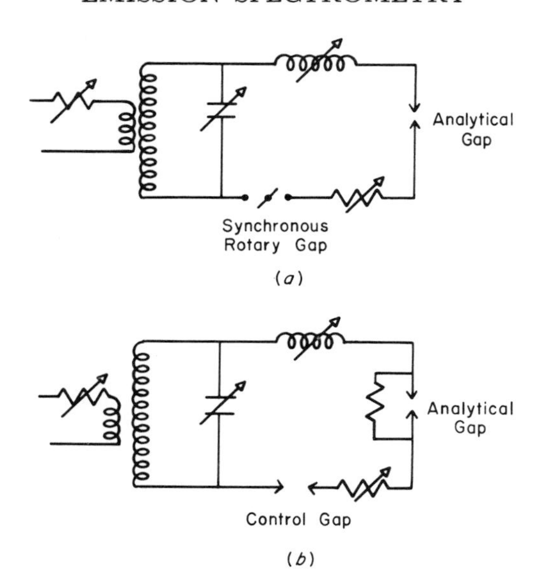

FIG. 8-5. Basic Circuits for Two Types of Controlled Spark Sources.

Fig. 8-6, the unit consists of a 1000-volt transformer, which charges a variable capacitance placed in parallel with the analytical gap. The power circuit also contains a variable inductance and resistance in series with the analytical gap. The discharge is initiated by a low power 25,000-volt ignitor circuit connected across the analytical gap and controlled by the synchronous interrupter. By proper synchronization of the ignitor, the unit will charge the condenser during one half-cycle and the condenser will discharge during the next half-cycle, thus producing one discharge for every cycle of the input current. Because a relatively low voltage is used, larger capacitances are feasible and very high instantaneous currents can be obtained. Likewise, variation in the resistance can produce short duration "spark-like" discharges as well as long duration "arc-like" discharges.

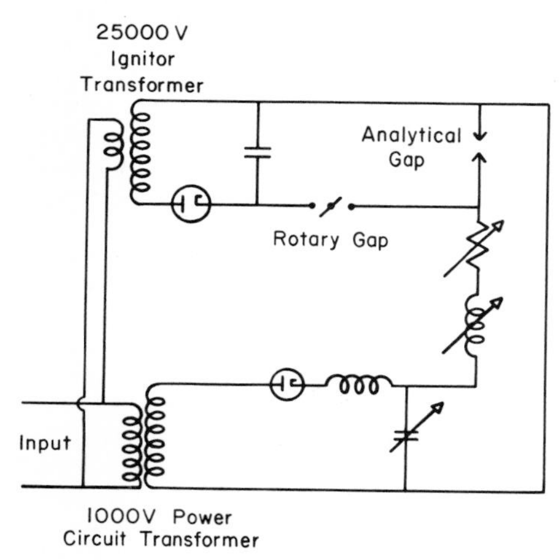

FIG. 8-6. Basic Circuit for a Multisource Source Unit.

In recent years there has been a trend toward the use of electronically controlled spark sources. The general discharge circuit used in these units is similar to that used in the "Multisource" except that the ignitor pulse is controlled by a thyratron circuit instead of a rotary gap. This thyratron is triggered by an electronic timing circuit which allows the ignition frequency to be varied from ~120 breakdowns/sec. to ~1 breakdown/sec. These electronically controlled units produce discharges similar to those of the "Multisource" unit. In addition the use of electronic discharge control is desirable when time resolution techniques are used.[5]

The modern commercial spectroscopic source unit usually combines two or more of the above types of sources into one unit. The basic unit will usually combine a spark and a d.c. arc unit. More elaborate units will offer a wider selection of sources and discharge conditions. Some units also provide hybrid discharges such as spark-ignited pulsating arcs. These intermittent arcs consist of a low voltage a.c. or half-wave rectified d.c. source connected in parallel with a spark source across the analytical gap. At or near the maximum of each voltage pulse, the arc is ignited by a condensed spark discharge. The discharge is then extinguished as the arc voltage drops below the sustaining voltage, and re-ignited by the spark during the next cycle. Hybrid sources of this type have not as yet been extensively used, but they may find greater application in the future, especially for analyses which present special problems in the area of excitation.

In addition to the source parameters, the discharge characteristics and vaporization processes are greatly dependent on the atmosphere within the discharge gap. For this reason work has been done on the use of controlled atmosphere excitation. Perhaps the greatest amount of work in this area has been concerned with the analysis of metals. The work of Majkowski and Schreiber[6] and of Kemp[7] has shown that the accuracy and reproducibility of analyses can be greatly improved for alloys of varying composition by utilizing controlled atmosphere excitation. Likewise, Fassel and his co-workers,[8] have made extensive use of inert atmosphere excitation for the determination of gases in metals. Basically, controlled atmosphere excitation involves replacement of the air in the vicinity of the analytical gap with another gas or gas mixture. This may be accomplished by many different schemes, some as simple as a stream of gas surrounding the gap and others as elaborate as using a special vacuum-tight chamber which allows the air to be pumped out and another atmosphere admitted. The latter type offers the advantage of almost complete removal of atmospheric constituents, as well as the ability to vary the pressure in the analytical gap. The flow systems usually do not completely remove all atmospheric constituents, but complete removal is often unnecessary, and in such cases the simplicity of this system dictates its use.

In addition to modifying the excitation characteristics, the use of controlled atmosphere systems provides a means of reducing the spectral background by eliminating many of the molecular species which contribute greatly to this background. This is especially true if the spectral lines of interest lie in the region of the cyanogen bands which emit strongly when carbon electrodes are used in an atmosphere containing nitrogen.

Gaseous Discharge Tubes.—Although the term discharge tube covers a wide range of sources, it normally applies to discharges in gases at low pressures. The discharge tubes most commonly used in analytical spectroscopy are the "hollow cathode tube" and the high-frequency, electrodeless discharge tube.

A hollow cathode discharge tube is a small sealed chamber containing a cathode in the form of a small metal tube or hollowed-out metal rod. The material to be excited is either placed inside the cathode or the cathode is made from the sample itself. The tube is normally evacuated and then filled with a rare gas to pressure of a few Torr. If the pressure is properly adjusted, the discharge will be confined within the cathode,

[5] Laqua, K., and Hagenah, W., in Lippincott, E. R., and Margoshes, M., Eds., Proceedings of the Xth Colloquium Spectroscopicum Internationale, Spartan Books, Washington, 1962.

[6] Majkowski, R. F., and Schreiber, T. P., Spectrochim. Acta, **16,** 1200, 1960.

[7] Kemp, J. W., in "Symposium on Spectroscopic Excitation," ASTM Spec. Tech. Publ. 209, 1960.

[8] Fassel, V. A., Gordon, W. A., Jasinski, R. J., and Evens, F. M., Rev. universelle mines, **9,** 278, 1959.

and the material in the cathode will be vaporized and excited. The hollow cathode produces very narrow spectral lines and is very useful for high resolution work such as isotope analysis. In addition it has the advantages of high sensitivity, reuse of the sample, and containment of toxic and radioactive materials.

Electrical discharges can also be maintained in discharge tubes without electrodes by using excitation from a high frequency electrical field. The discharge tube containing the sample is placed in a coil carrying a high frequency current or in a tuned cavity connected to a microwave generator. The character of the discharge can be varied by adjusting the strength and frequency of the exciting field and by varying the gas pressure. The utilization of this source is limited to gases and to samples which can be vaporized at the relatively low temperatures (800°–1000°) to which these tubes are restricted. Although this source shows high sensitivities for trace impurities, especially in rare gas atmospheres, it has not found wide usage for analytical purposes due to the strong interelement effects which are usually observed.

EXCITATION STANDS

Some arrangement is necessary to hold the electrodes on the optic axis of the spectrograph, as well as to make electrical contact with the electrodes. This function is performed by the excitation stand. The excitation stand also affords the operator protection from electrical shock, and from the ultraviolet radiation emitted from the discharge. An exhaust system is provided to remove the vapors produced in the discharge.

The electrode clamps are made from a corrosion-resistant material, and they usually have provision for water cooling. A mechanism attached to the clamps provides both horizontal and vertical movement of the electrodes so that proper positioning on the optical axis can be maintained. Most excitation stands also provide an optical projection system to aid in electrode alignment. Accessory equipment includes Petry stands for holding large metal samples and an interlock system on the door which turns off the source unit when the door is opened.

SAMPLE HANDLING AND PREPARATION

ELECTRODES

Graphite, almost exclusively, is used as an electrode material for emission spectrometry. Carbon is utilized in a few cases, and there are indications that some increased sensitivity can be realized. However, due to its higher cost and difficulty in machining, carbon has not found general acceptance. Several other metals, such as copper and silver, have also been used as electrode materials, but again their use has been restricted to special problems.

Graphite can be obtained in several grades based on its purity, density, and porosity. It is available in both rod and powder form, rod diameters of $\frac{1}{4}$ in. and $\frac{1}{8}$ in. being most commonly used. These rods may readily be machined to the shape needed. However, preformed electrodes, shaped and purified after machining, are available from manufacturers, and these are generally used by spectroscopists.

The simplest form of electrode for powders is a simple cavity drilled into a graphite rod. An electrode of this type has limited use, however, and more elaborate forms are ordinarily used. A variety of electrode designs have been proposed for d.c. arc work. The design variations are primarily concerned with controlling sample vaporization and stabilizing the discharge. Although many designs have been proposed, a recommended group of electrode designs has been published by the American Society for

Testing and Materials,[9] and these should serve almost all the needs of the analyst.

Special electrodes have also been designed for solution analyses. Of these the rotating disc, vacuum cup, and porous cup are most widely used. The "platrode" or rotating platform electrode is useful for viscous samples such as oils and lubricants.

SAMPLE PREPARATION

Since very small samples are ordinarily used in spectrochemical analysis, it is often difficult to obtain a sample that is representative. The problem of sampling must, therefore, be carefully considered. Likewise, extreme care must be taken to insure that the sample does not become contaminated. Since 10- to 50-mg. sample sizes are common in spectrochemical analysis, a very small amount of contaminate can introduce serious error.

The samples ordinarily used for spectrochemical analysis can be divided into the three general classes: powders, bulk metal specimens, and solutions. Gases are sometimes analyzed by emission spectrometry, but as this is a specialized area, it will not be covered here. Although samples are often run in the form in which they are submitted, convenience sometimes requires changing the form of the sample in order to eliminate problems resulting from the variations in the previous sample history, or to make the sample conform to a previously developed method.

Powders.—Powders, a common sample form, are extensively used for both qualitative and quantitative analysis. The powdered sample is ordinarily reduced to a fairly uniform particle size (~100 mesh) by grinding. Powdered graphite (~100 mesh) is often mixed with the sample to assure conductivity and to improve the stability of the discharge. In the case of d.c. arc method, the powdered mixture is usually placed directly into the crater of the electrode and arced. However, when spark discharges are used, a powdered sample may be "thrown out" of the electrode crater by the impinging spark streamers. For this reason pelletized samples are used when powders are analyzed by spark methods. The sample preparation for pelletized samples involves grinding the sample with a special pelletizing graphite and subsequently pressing the sample into a pellet (~$\frac{1}{4}$ in. diameter) using a hydraulic press designed for this purpose. In some cases a Parr hand press can be used to press the sample-graphite mixture into an electrode crater but this method is not always satisfactory.

Fusion is another technique used for the quantitative analysis of powders, particularly where large variations in the previous sample history or in the matrix composition are encountered. An example of this technique is the work of Tingle and Matocha,[10] in which the sample is fused with a mixture of boric oxide and lithium carbonate. The resulting fused bead is ground, mixed with graphite powder, and formed into a pellet. The pellet is then vaporized and excited, using a spark discharge, and the concentrations are determined by direct reading techniques. The major disadvantage of the fusion technique is that it usually requires considerable dilution of the sample, resulting in a decrease in the sensitivities of detection.

Metals.—Casting is the common method of forming metal samples for analysis, particularly in the metal industries. The standard casting is a disc of 1$\frac{1}{4}$ in. in diameter recommended by the National Bureau of Standards. Before analysis the disc is usually surfaced using a lath or other metal surfacing equipment. Care must be taken to provide a flat sparking surface and to prevent contamination during preparation. Metal samples of this type are ordinarily analyzed by a spark method using a special Petry stand

[9] ASTM Committee E-2, Methods for Emission Spectrochemical Analysis, Amer. Soc. for Testing and Materials, Philadelphia, 1964.

[10] Tingle, W. H., and Matocha, C. K., Anal. Chem., **30,** 495, 1958.

attachment in the excitation stand to hold the sample disc. Problems arise in the spark analysis of metal samples, and several investigations have been conducted on the improvement of these methods with particular emphasis on the use of different atmospheres for excitation.[6,7]

Samples of metal are also cast in the form of rods ($\frac{1}{4}$ in. or $\frac{1}{2}$ in. in diameter); these are used in pairs as the electrodes in a discharge. Spark excitation is most common, but arcs may be used if the metal can withstand the heat produced by the arc.

Small metal samples can be handled in a variety of ways. For qualitative analysis they can be introduced directly into an electrode cavity. In case the sample is too large for this, filings or turnings may be used. Metals may also be converted into powders by physical or chemical conversion or into solutions by dissolution in a suitable solvent. The latter method is often used for quantitative analysis for reasons discussed below.

Solutions.—The use of solutions offers a simple and convenient means of eliminating the previous history of samples, as well as simplifying the standard preparation procedure. There are several methods available for handling solution samples, most of them utilizing a spark for sample introduction. Of these methods the ones most commonly used are the rotating disc, the vacuum cup electrode, and the plasma jet. The rotating disc method makes use of a wheel-shaped graphite electrode which is turned slowly in the vertical plane by a small motor (Fig. 8-7). A solution is placed in a reservoir below

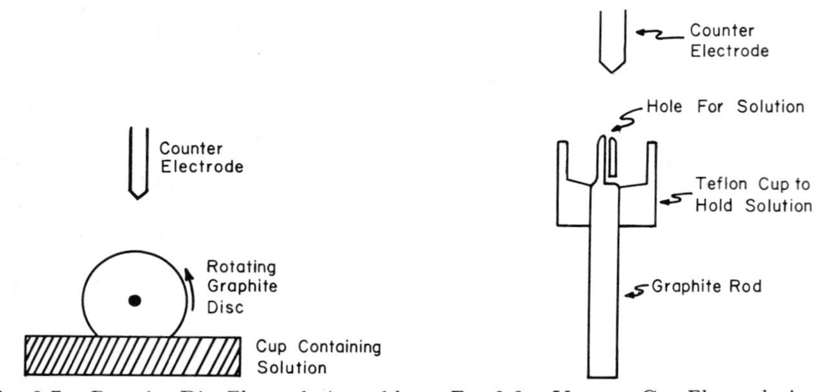

FIG. 8-7. Rotating Disc Electrode Assembly. FIG. 8-8. Vacuum Cup Electrode Assembly.

the electrode and a spark discharge is struck to the upper rim of the electrode. The disc dips into the solution and, as it rotates, carries the solution into the discharge zone. The vacuum cup electrode is shown in Fig. 8-8. A solution is placed in the reservoir and a spark discharge is struck to the tip of the electrode. The low pressure created by the spark discharge sprays the solution into the discharge zone. A plasma jet is a specialized discharge which is described in the literature.[11] The portion of the discharge used is the plasma "flame" which issues from this source. A carrier gas (usually argon) is used to drive a conventional pneumatic atomizer which sprays the solution into the plasma zone.

Solution techniques are often somewhat less sensitive than other methods since the samples are diluted by the solvent. The possibility of contamination from reagent must be considered, as well as the problems involved in the storage of dilute solutions, during which time concentration changes resulting from adsorption on container walls, evaporation of solvent, and contamination may occur.

[11] Margoshes, M., and Scribner, B. F., Spectrochim. Acta, **15**, 138, 1959.

The various techniques for handling solutions and the advantages and disadvantages of each have been discussed in the literature.[12]

SAMPLE POLARITY

In unidirectional discharges the sample polarity is important to proper sample vaporization. In arc discharges the anode is the hotter electrode and the sample electrode is usually used as the positive electrode in order to increase the vaporization rate, as well as to insure vaporization of the refractory constituents. In some cases, however, the sample electrode is used as the cathode and the discharge is observed in the region very near the cathode. This so-called "cathode layer excitation" can often produce a significant increase in the sensitivity of detection and thus is useful in trace analysis.

In spark discharges the vaporization is primarily one of "sputtering" by positive ions. In this case the sample should be in the cathode position in order to provide a suitable vaporization rate. Since many spark discharges are bidirectional (not rectified) the use of two sample electrodes will often provide increased sensitivity since proper vaporization will continually occur as the discharge changes polarity.

QUALITATIVE ANALYSIS

The greatest advantages of emission are the ease, speed, and accuracy of performing qualitative analyses. Spectrographic qualitative analyses are completely objective since both expected and unexpected elements are detected at high sensitivity with the same ease and certainty. Likewise, this technique is directly applicable to substances which are difficult to handle chemically such as slag, glasses, ores, etc.

The principle upon which qualitative analysis is based is the established fact that each chemical element emits a unique and characteristic set of spectral lines when the constituents of the sample are excited in flames, arc, sparks, or glow discharges. For general qualitative analysis the use of a d.c. carbon arc discharge has the advantages of convenience, high sensitivity, and general applicability. The high sensitivity arises largely from the greater quantity of sample which this source introduces into the discharge zone. The convenience and general applicability stem from the wide range of sample form and type which may be examined directly with a minimum of sample preparation. It is necessary only to introduce the sample into the cavity of the graphite supporting electrode which forms the anode of the arc discharge. Thus filings, shavings, fragments of rocks, powders, solution residues, and ashes may all be handled by a uniform procedure. The temperatures achieved in the anode receptacle are high enough to vaporize the most refractory samples. However, it is essential that the sample be completely volatilized, lest these very refractory constituents escape detection.

If it were necessary for the analyst to identify each line in the spectrum of an unknown sample, the analysis would be extremely tedious. Fortunately, the identification of only a few of the most persistent or intense lines of each element is all that is necessary to establish the presence of an element beyond all reasonable doubt. Similarly, the absence of these same lines indicates that these elements do not occur in the sample. Table 8-1 gives a list of the more sensitive lines of the elements along with their relative intensities. In general, the most intense lines are most useful for qualitative analysis but the analyst must always be cognizant of the danger of interferences arising from other lines in the spectrum. For this reason wavelength tables are used to check for possible line interferences. The most useful of these wavelength tables are those compiled by Meggers,

[12] Zink, T. H., "Spectrochemical Analysis of Solutions" in G. L. Clark, Ed., Encyclopedia of Spectroscopy, Reinhold Publishing Co., New York, 1960.

TABLE 8-1. SENSITIVE ARC LINES OF THE ELEMENTS BETWEEN 2000–10,000 A*
(Most Sensitive Line for Each Element is Listed First)

Element	*Wavelength (A)*
Aluminum	3961.53
	3944.03
	3092.71
Arsenic	2288.12
	2349.84
	2456.53
Barium	5535.55
	5777.66
	5519.12
Beryllium	2348.61
	3321.34
	3321.01/.09
Bismuth	3067.72
	2897.98
Boron	2497.73
	2496.78
Cadmium	2288.02
	3261.06
	3466.20
Calcium	4226.73
	3968.47
	3933.67
Cesium	8521.10
	8943.50
	4593.18
Chromium	4254.35
	4274.80
	4289.72
Cobalt	3453.51
	3405.12
Copper	3247.54
	3273.96
Gallium	4172.06
	4032.98
	2943.64
Germanium	2651.18
	3269.49
	3039.06
Gold	2427.95
	2675.95
Indium	4511.32
	3256.09
Iridium	2543.97
	3133.32
	3220.78
Iron	3581.20
	3719.94
	3020.64
Lanthanum	3947.11
	3988.52
	4333.73
Lead	4057.82
	3683.47
	2833.07
Lithium	6707.84
	6103.64
	4602.86
Magnesium	2852.13
	3838.26
	5183.62
Manganese	4030.76
	2576.104
	4033.073
Mercury	4358.35
	2536.52
Molybdenum	3798.25
	3902.96
	3107.35
Nickel	3414.765
	3492.96
	3524.54
Niobium	4058.94
	4079.73
Osmium	2909.06
	3058.66
Palladium	3404.58
	3421.24
Phosphorus	2535.65
	2553.28
	2554.93
Platinum	2659.45
	3064.71
Potassium	7664.91
	7698.98
	4047.20
Rhenium	3460.47
	4889.17
Rhodium	3434.89
	3692.36
Rubidium	7800.23
	7947.60
	4215.56

TABLE 8-1 (cont.)

Element	*Wavelength (A)*	*Element*	*Wavelength (A)*
Ruthenium	3436.74	Tin	3175.02
	3498.94		2839.99
Scandium	4246.83		3262.33
	4023.69	Titanium	4981.73
	3911.81		3361.21
Silicon	2881.58		3349.88
	2516.12	Tungsten	4302.108
Silver	3280.68		4294.61
	3382.89		4008.75
Sodium	5889.95	Uranium	4244.37
	5895.92		4241.67
	3302.32	Vanadium	4379.24
Strontium	4607.33		3185.40
	4077.71	Yttrium	3710.29
Tantalum	2714.67		3242.28
	3311.16		4374.94
Tellurium	2142.75	Zinc	2138.56
	2383.25		3345.02
	2385.76		4810.53
Thallium	5350.46	Zirconium	4687.80
	3775.72		3438.23
	3519.24		3391.98
Thorium	4019.14		
	2837.30		

* Data from Ahrens, L. H., and Taylor, S. R., Spectrochemical Analysis, 2nd Ed., Addison-Wesley, Reading, Mass., 1961.

Corliss, and Scribner.[13] Ordinarily the spectrographs used for qualitative analysis are capable of resolving lines which lie within a few tenths of an Angstrom unit, and thus one need only be concerned with those interfering lines which are this near to the line in question.

The usual method of qualitative analysis utilizes the juxtaposition of two standard spectra with the spectrum of the sample. The two standard spectra used are those of an iron arc and a mixture which will produce the most persistent lines of the elements. The latter is a standard mixture of approximately 70 elements in the proper proportion, such that it provides a spectrum which contains only about the 5 most persistent lines of each element. This mixture is commonly called Principal Line Powder (PLP). These standard mixtures are available commercially.

The spectra are ordinarily exposed in juxtaposition using a Hartman diaphragm. This diaphragm is a metal slide which has a series of staggered openings and is placed at the slit of a stigmatic spectrograph or at the secondary focus of an astigmatic spectrograph. Movement of this slide brings these openings, in turn, over adjacent portions of the slit length. Movement of the plate holder is then not necessary, and, in this manner, spectrograms can be exposed in precise juxtaposition. This provides an excellent method of determining the presence or absence of a particular line.

[13] Meggers, W. F., Corliss, G. H., and Scribner, B. F., Tables of Spectral Line Intensities: Part I, Arranged by Elements; Part II, Arranged by Wavelengths, U. S. Government Printing Office, Washington, 1961.

QUANTITATIVE ANALYSIS

The fundamental assumption in quantitative analysis is that the intensity of a line emitted within an excitation source is directly proportional to the concentration of the atoms of the emitter which are present in the discharge. Thus,

$$I = KC$$

or

$$\log I = \log K + \log C$$

where I is the measured intensity, C is the concentration and K is a proportionality constant. This assumes that the measured intensity is proportional to the emitted intensity and that the concentrations of atoms in the sample are directly related to the concentrations of atoms in the discharge column. If the logarithm of the concentration is plotted against the logarithm of the intensity, a straight line should result, and this graph is referred to as an analytical curve. Curves of unit slope usually result. However, the presence of background, self-absorption, or residual impurity in the standards cause deviations from linearity. While methods can be developed using a comparison of the line intensities of standards and samples, these methods usually exhibit very poor precision and are relegated to the area of so-called semiquantitative analysis. In most instances quantitative analyses are based on the internal standard principle.

The internal standard method is based on the measurement of the intensity ratio of a line of the element to be determined relative to a line of another element present in a constant amount. If the internal standard line is properly chosen, its intensity will vary in consort with the intensity of the analytical line, thus providing automatic correction for variations in excitation, optical alignment, and exposure, and some correction for variations in the response of the photographic emulsion. The internal standard may be either an element present as a major constituent of essentially constant concentration, or as an element which is added to the specimen in a constant amount.

In selecting an element and a line for use as an internal standard, the following criteria should be considered:

1. the internal standard element should be present in a constant concentration;
2. if an added element is used as an internal standard, the added element should be present in a negligibly small concentration in the samples;
3. if an added internal standard is used, it should have very high purity with respect to the elements sought;
4. the internal standard and analysis elements should have similar volatilization rates;
5. the internal standard and analysis lines should be roughly the same wavelength in order to reduce errors in photographic photometry;
6. the internal standard and analysis lines should have similar excitation potentials;
7. the internal standard line should be free from self-absorption; and
8. the concentration of the internal standard element should be adjusted or else the line should have an intensity such that the intensity ratio of the analysis line to the internal standard line is approximately 1, thus minimizing errors in calculating intensity ratios.

It is, of course, seldom possible to fulfill all of these requirements and, thus, compromises must be made. Usually these can be made without too much difficulty and satisfactory internal standardization can be achieved.

The selection of the analytical line is usually accomplished by first exposing spectra of the matrix and the impurity elements. By identifying the lines of the impurity elements which are likely to show up with sufficient intensity for the actual analysis, it is then possible to select those lines which are free from spectral interference. The more sensitive lines can be selected by reference to one of the wavelength tables. Likewise the wavelength tables should be consulted for other possible spectral interference from elements likely to be present in the samples. The final selection of the analytical and internal standard lines is then based on the behavior of the tentatively selected lines when exposing a series of standards with varying concentrations of impurities. The best lines will provide:

1. analytical data over the desired concentration range;
2. a straight analytical curve with a slope near 1; and
3. reproducible intensity ratios over a reasonable period of time.

INTENSITY MEASUREMENTS

In any type of quantitative analysis it is necessary to measure the intensity of spectral lines. This may be accomplished photoelectrically or, if photographic techniques are used, by measuring the blackness of the lines on the photographic emulsion. In photoelectric instruments the intensity readout system is usually integral to the system and no additional equipment is necessary. In photographic readout, however, a densitometer or microphotometer is necessary in order to measure the line blackness of the emulsion. In addition, some type of graphical calculating equipment is convenient for the conversion of line blackness to original line intensity.

PHOTOGRAPHIC DENSITOMETRY

The densitometer used for spectroscopic work is ordinarily both a plate projection system and a photoelectric measuring system which is capable of selecting and measuring an individual spectral line. The projection system displays an enlarged image of a select portion of the plate on a viewing screen. A narrow slit either at the plate or at the focal plane selects the individual line of interest and the light passing through this slit is measured by a photosensitive detector. The instrument is arranged so that a spectral line can be scanned slowly across this slit and the intensity of the light passing through the spectral line can be measured relative to the incident intensity. In order to measure line blackness conveniently and accurately, the densitometer should fulfill several requirements:

1. lines to be measured must be easily found and identified;
2. a rapid motion should be provided in order to move the lines of interest and then a slow and steady scan should be provided for the measuring scan;
3. a means of aligning the slit parallel to the line should be provided;
4. the detection circuit should be sensitive and have a short response time; and
5. stray light should be low.

The majority of microphotometers uses the deflection type of intensity readout, *i.e.*, the variation in intensity as received by the photocell is read directly by means of a galvanometer or meter, or is recorded automatically on a strip chart recorder.

A microphotometer provides data on the percent transmission of the spectra line image, and this must be related to the intensity of the light producing this line. Since the photographic emulsion does not respond linearly to the light intensity producing the exposure, these percent transmission data are not directly related to line intensities. Likewise the response of photographic emulsions to various incident light intensities varies with wavelength, temperature, nature of the emulsion, development procedure, and exposure conditions. Thus, the blackening of the photographic image depends on so many factors that it is necessary to calibrate empirically the response of the photographic plate or film under the same experimental conditions used for the analytical method.

As discussed below, in the section on analytical curves, *intensity ratios* are related to concentration during the standardizing procedure. This procedure eliminates the need for measuring absolute intensities since relative intensity data provide identical results when ratios are taken. This then simplifies the calibration problem, since it is merely necessary to measure the transmittance of the developed plate after exposure to a set of light signals of known relative intensity. The log percent transmission is then plotted against the log of the relative exposure (the product of line intensity and time), giving rise to the emulsion calibration curve. In order to provide a more linear relationship, the Seidel function $\left[\log\left(\frac{100}{\%\ T} - 1\right)\right]$ is often used in place of log $\%\ T$. A typical emulsion calibration curve is shown in Fig. 8-9.

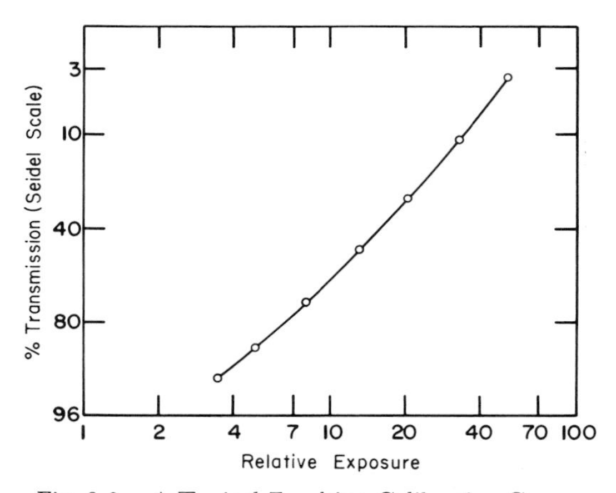

Fig. 8-9. A Typical Emulsion Calibration Curve.

There are two commonly used methods of providing a graded series of relative exposures on an emulsion. The "intensity-scale" method is based on placing a graded neutral step filter at the stigmatic position of the spectrograph or immediately in front of the photographic plate. This filter allows definite fractions of the total incident radiation to pass through each of its steps. If the spectrum from a line source is photographed through this filter, each spectral line will show a step-wise gradation in $\%\ T$ along its length. If the relative transmittance of the steps of the filter are known, this information can be combined to produce an emulsion calibration curve.

The "time-scale" method is based on placing a rotating step-sector (Fig. 8-10) at the stigmatic position of the spectrograph, and exposing a spectrum of a line source through this sector. In this case the exposure times are proportional to the angular openings of the various sector "steps."

The description of the above methods does not provide a means of combining data from several different lines in order to cover a wide range of exposure level. For this reason, as well as problems involved with the uniformity of vertical slit illumination, the "two-step preliminary curve method" has been developed. In this method two adjacent steps on the exposure are selected. Thus there will be a "lighter" step and a "darker" step in each pair. Pairs of % T readings for these two steps are made using a large number of different spectral lines. Using coordinate paper, the % T of the weaker step is plotted on the ordinate against the % T darker step. Thus the data from all of the spectral lines are combined to form the preliminary curve similar to the one shown in Fig. 8-11. In order to construct the emulsion calibration curve, a point on the ordinate

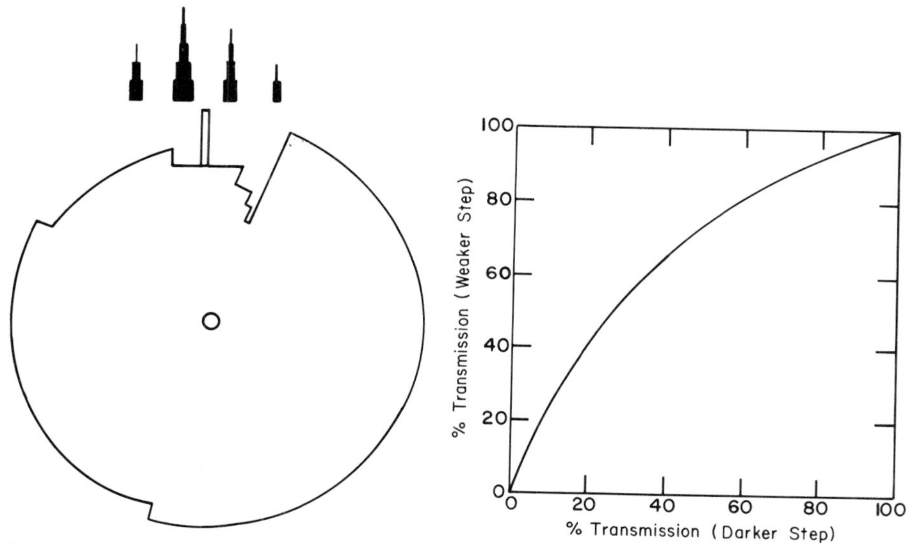

FIG. 8-10. A Rotating Step Sector with a Schematic Representation of Sectored Lines Shown Above.

FIG. 8-11. A Two-step Preliminary Curve for Emulsion Calibration.

at a high % T (*e.g.*, 97% T) is arbitrarily selected. The corresponding % T value for the darker component is then read from the abscissa. This value is recorded and transferred to the ordinate. Again the corresponding % T value is read from the abscissa and recorded. This process is continued until the entire % T scale has been covered. This results in a series of % T values which represent the values produced by a step-wise variation in intensity in accordance with the "step-ratio" of the intensity reducer used. The log % T values, starting with the highest value, are plotted on the ordinate, while the value of the abscissa is sequentially increased by a value equal to the log of the "step-ratio," thus producing an emulsion calibration curve.

An intensity ratio between two lines can be calculated using the calibration curve by merely reading the relative intensities corresponding to the % T readings and ratioing the two intensity values. In practice it is often necessary to measure and correct the relative intensity values for spectral background in the neighborhood of the spectral lines. This is best accomplished by measuring the % T of the background adjacent to the line, converting this to a relative intensity reading, and subtracting this from the relative intensity of the line. This should be done for both lines before the intensity ratio is calculated.

A more detailed procedure for photographic photometry has been published by the American Society for Testing and Materials.[8]

PHOTOELECTRIC READOUT SYSTEMS

Spectrometric readout systems must integrate the line intensities over a period of time in order to average the fluctuations in the emission source. A photographic plate by its very nature provides this signal integration, but this is not true of photomultipliers which are the most common detectors for direct-reading applications. In photoelectric instruments this integration is normally achieved by use of a capacitor for signal storage. At the end of the exposure time the charge on the capacitor, which is proportional to the line intensity, is measured by some suitable electronic circuit. Several methods of presentation of the readout signal are used including dials, meters, counters, and strip chart recorders.

Most direct-reading instruments are equipped with several photomultipliers in order to readout several lines simultaneously. Calibration of the instrument, using suitable standards, is necessary, but once calibrated, the integrated signals are directly related to concentration. The utilization of direct-reading techniques usually provides a definite improvement in precision and a decrease in time for analysis. However, these are achieved at a sacrifice of versatility, since only the lines selected by the phototubes can be measured, and, thus, the information that can be obtained from a sample is limited by the number and positions of these phototubes.

STANDARDS

It is a well established fact that the chemical composition and physical properties of a sample have a pronounced effect on the intensity of a spectral line emitted by an element at a given concentration level. For this reason it is essential that the basic chemical composition and physical nature of the standards be very similar to those of the samples. Unless this is true, systematic errors may be introduced into analysis and may go undetected. These changes in intensity result from several different effects, the most important being: volatilization effects; changes in excitation energy in the discharge column; and chemical reactions in the electrodes and the discharge column.

Volatilization effects are very important and are the source of many errors, particularly in arc methods. Since the process of vaporization in the arc discharge is thermal in nature, the concentration of a given element in the discharge will vary with time depending on its boiling point relative to that of the other sample components. This vaporization behavior will, of course, depend on the chemical form of the element in the sample; changes in the chemical form will produce changes in the vaporization characteristics.

In most spark-type discharges the vaporization process is principally that of sputtering; selective vaporization effects are often less pronounced. Even in spark discharges, however, these effects may not be negligible, and concentration changes on sparked metal surfaces are well known.

Volatilization behavior is also a function of the physical properties of a sample. For example, changes in the grain structure of a metal can produce large changes in the vaporization process when using spark excitation. Likewise, the grain size of powdered samples can have a direct influence on the rate of vaporization, and should, therefore, be held constant.

Even though the electrical parameters of a discharge source can be controlled, variations in the excitation energy in the analytical gap can be produced by variation in the composition of the sample. The excitation energy available in the analytical gap is a function of the excitation and ionization characteristic of the plasma components. This plasma concentration is in turn governed, to a large extent, by the composition and vaporization behavior of the sample. Thus, varying amounts of an easily ionizable element, such as sodium, in the sample can cause variations in the available excitation energy and, consequently, variations in line intensities will result. Even small changes in the sample composition can produce measurable variations in line intensities.

The high temperatures present at the electrodes and within the discharge zone are conducive to chemical reaction. At the electrodes, for example, compounds such as oxides, nitrides, and carbides may form and thereby cause large changes in vaporization behavior. Likewise, reactions occur in the discharge zone which may "tie up" free atoms in a molecular form and thereby decrease the intensity of atomic lines. Examples of this include the formation of AlO in arc discharges in air and the formation of BaF in arc discharges where both Ba and F are present in the sample. In addition introduction of molecular species into the discharge zone may influence the effective excitation energy, since they often lower the gap energy due to their frequently low excitation, ionization, and dissociation energies.

The above is only a brief discussion of some of the more important factors which relate to the necessity for having close similarity between the standards and the samples. More complete discussion can be found in the literature.[14]

ANALYTICAL CURVES

As mentioned above, under ideal conditions, a plot of the line intensity *vs.* the concentration should yield a straight line passing through the origin. Likewise, a plot of the ratio of the intensity of the analytical line to that of the internal standard line (I_a/I_s) should yield a similar curve. If background is present under the lines, the intensity of the background (I_b) is added to that of the lines, and the equation relating intensity ratio to concentration assumes the form:

$$\frac{I_a + I_b}{I_s + I_b} = KC$$

Plotted on coordinate paper, this will yield a straight line which does not pass through the origin.

A similar situation exists if standards are prepared from a contaminated base material. In this case the residual impurity will contribute a constant intensity I_r to the intensity of the analytical line and the following equation results:

$$\frac{I_a + I_r}{I_s} = KC$$

A plot of this equation also yields a straight line which does not pass through the origin. A correction must be made for this residual before an accurate analytical curve can be obtained. The first step in correcting for residual impurities is making an accurate correction for background. After the background correction is made, the displacement from the origin of the curve obtained by plotting I_a/I_s *vs.* C is due to residual. A curve is then drawn parallel to the original curve such that the new curve passes through the origin. The displacement between these two curves along the concentration axis corresponds to the residual correction, and this value is added to the concentration value for each individual standard.

In practice, self-absorption often affects the measured line intensities, and in this case the relationship between intensity ratio and concentration often follows the equation

[14] Ahrens, L. H., and Taylor, S. R., Spectrochemical Analysis, 2nd Ed., Addison-Wesley, Reading, Mass., 1961.

$$\frac{I_a}{I_s} = KC^b$$

or

$$\log \frac{I_a}{I_s} = \log K + b \log C$$

The curve for the latter form of this equation is a straight line.

Since all of the general equations for the relationship between intensity and concentration yield a linear curve on a log-log plot, the analytical curves are commonly constructed by plotting log concentration *vs.* log intensity ratio. A typical curve is

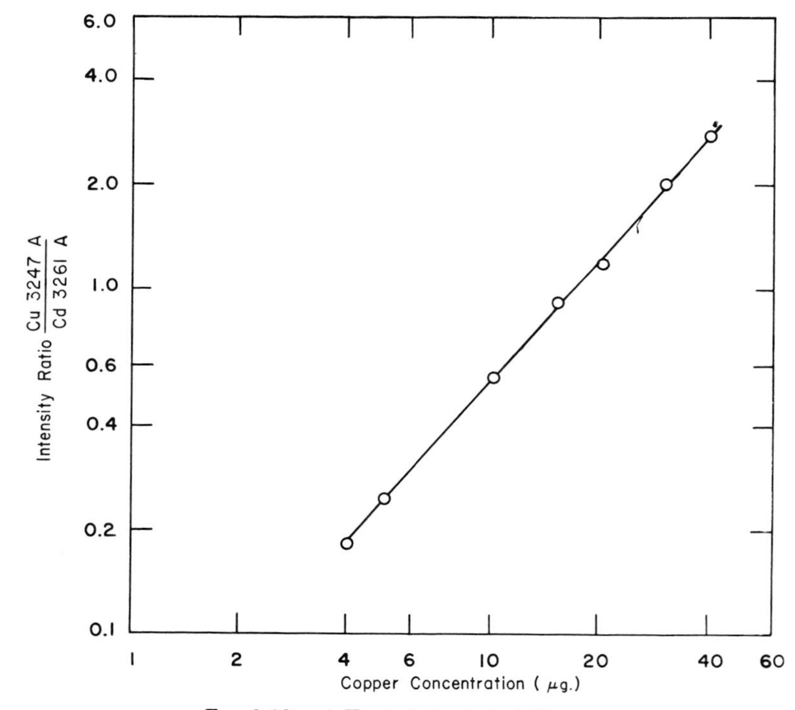

FIG. 8-12. A Typical Analytical Curve.

shown in Fig. 8-12. It is important that the intensity ratio be corrected for background and that the concentration value be corrected for residual as described above.

SEMIQUANTITATIVE ANALYSIS

At times it is desirable to obtain analyses on materials for which no standards are available, and for which it is not worthwhile to prepare suitable standards. In order to handle these samples, general semiquantitative methods are often developed. These methods permit handling a wide variety of samples but at a sacrifice in accuracy and precision.

The simplest approach to a method of this type is the d.c. arc excitation of a weighed sample under carefully controlled conditions. The net line intensity or the line to background ratio is measured and related to concentration through standard mixtures run under the same conditions.

More popular techniques utilize dilution of the sample with a standard material in order to provide a common matrix for every sample. Commonly graphite, germanium dioxide, and alkali metal salts are used as diluents. A general set of standards is prepared using the same matrix material. Combinations of the above materials have also been used. In some cases fusion techniques have proven valuable for semiquantitative analysis as mentioned above in the section on sample handling.

APPLICATIONS IN THE ANALYSIS OF SPECIAL MATERIALS

A number of methods using emission spectrometry have been applied to the analysis of special materials, and are considered elsewhere in Standard Methods of Chemical Analysis. These methods, listed under the type of material analyzed, are as follows:

1. Chapter 22, Volume IIA, Commercial Acids and Bases.
   a. Impurities in fluoboric acid, page 576.
   b. Impurities in nitric acid, page 565.
   c. Impurities in sodium hydroxide, page 607.
   d. Impurities in sulfuric acid, page 552.
2. Chapter 42, Volume III, Air Pollutants.
   a. Metals in air
3. Chapter 43, Volume III, Alloys: Iron, Steel, Ferro-alloys, and Related Products.
   a. Determination of metals in iron, steel, ores, and refractories
4. Chapter 44, Volume III, Alloys: Nonferrous.
   a. Determination of metals
   b. Analysis of aluminum and aluminum-base alloys
   c. Trace elements in nonferrous metals and alloys
   d. Hydrogen, nitrogen, and oxygen in nonferrous metals and alloys
   e. Analysis of tantalum and tantalum oxide
5. Chapter 46, Volume III, Portland Cement.
   a. Determination of elements
6. Chapter 48, Volume III, Natural Fats.
   a. Copper in fats and oils
   b. Iron in fats and oils
7. Chapter 54, Volume III, Paint, Varnish, and Lacquer.
   a. Determination of low amounts of aluminum, boron, lithium, magnesium, silicon, sodium, and trace elements in pure pigments
   b. Analysis of titanium dioxide and zinc oxide

   Chapter 37, Volume IIB, Paint, Varnish, and Lacquer.
   a. Determination of inorganic pigments in paints, page 1685.
8. Chapter 41, Volume IIB, Plastics.
   a. Determination of metallic impurities in plastics, page 2048.
9. Chapter 60, Volume III, Semiconductors.
   a. Determination of impurities in semiconductors and semiconductor materials
10. Chapter 62, Volume III, Soils.
    a. Determination of trace constituents
11. Chapter 63, Volume III, Water Analysis.
    a. Silver in water

SELECTED BIBLIOGRAPHY

BOOKS

General

Ahrens, L. H., and Taylor, S. R., Spectrochemical Analysis, 2nd Ed., Addison-Wesley, Reading, Mass., 1961. A treatise on d.c. arc analysis of geological and related materials.
Nachtreib, N. H., Principles and Practice of Spectrochemical Analysis, McGraw-Hill, New York, 1950. A general textbook.
Sawyer, R. A., Experimental Spectroscopy, 2nd Ed., Prentice-Hall, New York, 1951. A general textbook with particular emphasis on optical instrumentation.
Twyman, F., Metal Spectroscopy, Charles Griffin, Ltd., London, 1951. A general textbook.
Harrison, G. R., Lord, R. C., and Loofbourow, J. R., Practical Spectroscopy, Prentice-Hall, New York, 1948. A general textbook covering emission and absorption spectrometry.
Clark, G. L., Ed., Encyclopedia of Spectroscopy, Reinhold Publishing, New York, 1960. Contains articles on emission spectrometry as well as other fields of spectroscopy.
Scribner, B. F., and Margoshes, M., "Emission Spectroscopy," in Treatise on Analytical Chemistry, Part I, Vol. 5, Optical Methods of Analysis, Kolthoff, I. M., and Elving, P. J., Eds., Interscience, New York, 1964. A general discussion of the principles of emission spectroscopy.

Atomic Structure

White, H. E., Introduction to Atomic Spectra, McGraw-Hill, New York, 1934.
Kuhn, H. G., Atomic Spectra, Academic Press, New York, 1962.
Herzberg, G., Atomic Spectra and Atomic Structure, 2nd Ed., Dover Publications, New York, 1944.

Tables

Harrison, G. R., MIT Wavelength Tables, John Wiley, New York, 1939. Approximately 100,000 lines listed according to wavelength.
Meggers, W. F., Corliss, G. H., and Scribner, B. F., Tables of Spectral Line Intensities; Part I, Arranged by Elements; Part II, Arranged by Wavelength, U. S. Government Printing Office, Washington, 1961. Approximately 39,000 lines of 70 elements listed with wavelengths and intensity data. Part I also lists energy levels involved in the transition for each line.
Gatterer, A., and Junkes, J. Atlas der Restlinien I. Spektren von 30 Chemischen Elementen; II. Spektren der Seltenen Erden; III. Spektren Seltener Metalle and Einiger Metalloide, Specola Vaticana, Vatican City. Wavelength tables and reproductions of spectra.
Gatterer, A., Grating Spectrum of Iron, Specola Vatican, Vatican City, 1951. Reproductions of the arc and spark spectra of iron with wavelengths.
Zaidel, A. N., Prokof'ev, V. K., and Raiskii, Tables of Spectrum Lines, 2nd International Ed., Pergamon Press, N. Y., 1961. Wavelength for 60 elements arranged by element and by wavelength.
Moore, C. E., Atomic Energy Levels, Vols. I, II, III, NBS Circular 467, U. S. Government Printing Office, Washington. Data on atomic energy levels of the elements.
Moore, C. E., An Ultraviolet Multiplet Table, NBS Circular 488, Sections 1–5, U. S. Government Printing Office, Washington. Term symbols and energies for upper and lower levels for the transitions producing spectral lines.
Moore, C. E., A Multiplet Table of Astrophysical Interest, N.B.S. Technical Note 36, U. S. Department of Commerce, Office of Technical Services, Washington, 1959. Term symbols and energies for upper and lower levels for the transitions producing spectral lines.
Corliss, C. H., and Bozman, W. R., Experimental Transition Probabilities for Spectral Lines of Seventy Elements, NBS Monograph 53, U. S. Government Printing Office, Washington, 1962. Transition probabilities for approximately 25,000 lines of 70 elements.

Bibliographies

Meggers, W. F., and Scribner, B. F., Index to the Literature on Spectrochemical Analysis, Part I, 1920–1939, ASTM, Philadelphia.
Scribner, B. F., and Meggers, W. F., Index to the Literature on Spectrochemical Analysis, Part II, 1940–1945; Part III, 1946–1950; Part IV, 1951–1955, ASTM, Philadelphia.
Twyman, F., Spectrochemical Abstracts, Vol. I, 1933–1937, Adam Hilger, Ltd., London.
van Someren, E. H. S., Spectrochemical Abstracts, Vol. II, 1938–1939; Vol. III, 1940–1945; Vol. IV, 1946–1951, Hilger and Watts, Ltd., London.
See also the reviews published regularly in the Reviews Issue of Analytical Chemistry.

Methods and Techniques

Ahrens, L. H., Quantitative Spectrochemical Analysis of Silicates, Pergamon Press, London, 1955.

ASTM, Committee E-2, Methods for Emission Spectrochemical Analysis, ASTM, Philadelphia, 4th Ed., 1964.

Iron and Steel Institute, Spectrographic Analysis of Low Alloy Steels, Special Report 47, Iron and Steel Institute, London, 1952.

Harvey, C. E., A Method of Semiquantitative Spectrographic Analysis, Applied Research Laboratories, Glendale, California, 1947.

Horwitz, W., Ed., Official Methods of Analysis of the AOAC, 9th Ed., Assoc. of Official Agricultural Chemists, Washington, 1960.

Michaelis, R. E., Report on Available Standard Samples and Related Materials for Spectrochemical Analysis, ASTM Special Technical Pub. 58-E, ASTM, Philadelphia, 1963.

Strock, L. W., Spectrum Analysis with the Carbon Arc Cathode Layer, Adam Hilger, Ltd, London, 1936.

NBS, Standard Materials Issued by the National Bureau of Standards, NBS Publication 241, U. S. Government Printing Office, Washington, 1962.

JOURNALS

Three journals specialize in spectroscopic publications: Spectrochimica Acta, Applied Spectroscopy, and Optika i Spektroskopiya (Optics and Spectroscopy). Journals on analytical chemistry, such as Analytical Chemistry and Analytica Chimica Acta, publish articles on spectrochemical analysis. In addition, Applied Optics and the Journal of the Optical Society of America often publish articles on this subject, particularly with reference to instruments.

Publications by equipment manufacturers often contain useful information. Notable publications in this area include the JACO Newsletter (Jarrell-Ash Co., Newtonville, Mass.), Spectrographer's Newsletter (Applied Research Laboratories, Glendale, Calif.), and the Spex Speaker (Spex Industries, Metuchen, N. J.). These publications often contain discussions of methods and techniques which are useful to the analyst.

REFERENCE TO SPECIFIC APPLICATIONS

The following references illustrate specific applications of emission spectrometry in a few selected areas. The references given are, in general, reviews or general methods which are representative of the scope of application of emission spectrometric techniques.

Biological and Clinical Chemistry

Grant, C. L., Science, **134,** 1207, 1961. Analysis of foods.

Rosan, R. C., Healy, M. K., and Mc Nary, W. F., Science, **142,** 236, 1963. Microanalysis of animal tissues.

Glick, D., Ed., Methods of Biochemical Analysis, Vol. V, Interscience, New York, 1957.

Geological Materials

Weber, J. N., Spectrochim. Acta, **17,** 669, 1961. Carbonate rock analysis.

Fassel, V. A., "Analytical Spectroscopy of the Rare-Earth Elements," in Rare Earths, F. H. Spedding and A. H. Daane, Eds., John Wiley, New York, 1961. Review of rare earth analysis.

Harvey, C. E., and Mellichamp, J. W., Anal. Chem., **33,** 1242, 1961. Determination of non-metallic elements.

Weber, R., Bull. Soc. Chim. (France), 805, 1961. Halogens in ores.

Lemicux, P. E., Appl. Spectroscopy, **16,** 36, 1962. Semiquantitative method.

McKenzie, R. M., Oertel, A. C., and Tiller, K. G., Geochim. et Cosmochim. Acta, **14,** 68, 1958. Analysis of rocks.

Isotope Analysis

Lee, T., Katz, S., and Mac Intyre, S. A., Appl. Spectroscopy, **16,** 92, 1962. Uranium isotopes.

Lee, T., and Rodgers, L. H., Appl. Spectroscopy, **15,** 3, 1961. Determination of U^{235}.

Faust, H., Z. Anal. Chem., **175,** 9, 1960. Determination of nitrogen isotopes.

Metals

Spectroscopy in the Metallurgical Industry, L. Bovey, Ed., Hilger and Watts, London, 1962.

Woodruff, J. F., and Thomas, A. H., Appl. Spectroscopy, **16,** 29, 1962. Steel analyses.

Mirkin, I. L., and Rikman, E. P., Izvest. Akad. Nauk (USSR), Sev. Fiz, **23,** 1167, 1959. Analysis of grain boundries.

Peterson, M. J., U. S. Bur. Mines, Inform. Circ. 80392, 1961. Review of methods of trace analysis.
Addink, N. W., J. Iron. Steel Inst. (London), **194,** 199, 1960. Review of methods.
Fassel, V. A., Iron Steel Inst. (London), Spec. Rept. 68, 103, 1960. Oxygen, nitrogen, and hydrogen in metals.
Rupp, R. L., Klecok, G. L., and Morrison, G. H., Anal. Chem., **32,** 931, 1960. Trace impurities in nickel.
Romand, J., and Berneron, R., Colloq. Spectros. Intern., 9th Lyons, Vol. 2, 325, 1961. Analysis for nonmetallic elements.

Miscellaneous Analyses

Myers, W. C., and Henry, W. M., Proc., Ultrapurif. Semicond. Mater., Conf., Boston, Mass., 1962, pp. 349–55. Analysis of Semiconductor materials.
Norris, J. A., and McCutchen, R. L., U. S. Atomic Energy Commission Rept., ORNL-2927, 1960. Study of solution methods.
Merrill, J. R., Honda, M., and Arnold, J. R., Anal. Chem., **32,** 1420, 1960. Trace analysis for impurities in water.
Morrison, G. H., Rupp, R. L., and Klecak, G. L., Anal. Chem., **32,** 933, 1960. Trace impurities in Silicon carbide.
McGrath, W. D., Magee, R. J., Pickering, W. F., Wilson, C. L., Talanta, **8,** 892, 1961. Analysis of gas mixtures.

Petroleum

Azcona, J. M., Appl. Spectroscopy, **16,** 71, 1962. Analysis of crude oil.
McGowan, R. J., Appl. Spectroscopy, **15,** 179, 1961. Analysis of lubricating oils.
Vaisberg, K. M., and Zinin, V. G., Zavodsk. Lab., **26,** 1123, 1960. Vanadium and nickel in petroleum.

Soils and Plant Materials

Bass, S. T., and Conner, J., J. Assoc. Offic. Agr. Chemists, **43,** 113–115, 1960. Analysis of plant materials.
Bass, S. T., and Soulati, J., J. Assoc. Offic. Agr. Chemists, **45,** 752, 1962. Solution techniques.
Mitchell, R. L., Anal. Chem., Proc. Intern. Symp., Birmingham Univ., Birmingham, England, 1962, pp. 314–19. Trace analyses.
Wang, M. S., Univ. Microfilms (Ann Arbor, Mich.), L. C. Card No. Mic. 60–250; Dissertation Abstr., **20,** 3044, 1960. Review of soil analysis.

Chapter 9

X-RAY EMISSION AND ABSORPTION

By William J. Campbell
Bureau of Mines
College Park Metallurgy Research Center
U. S. Department of the Interior
College Park, Maryland

INTRODUCTION

X-rays are generated by bombarding matter with either high energy electrons or x-ray photons. According to the Bohr model of the atom, the electrons are arranged in discrete orbits, K, L, M . . . shells around the nucleus. When the atom is ionized by the incident radiation, an electron from one of the inner shells, K, L, or M, is ejected from the atom. This vacancy is immediately filled by an electron from a lower energy shell, thus creating a new ionization level in the atom. Thus, by a series of transitions, $L \rightarrow K$, $M \rightarrow L$, $N \rightarrow M$, each new vacancy is filled until the excited atom returns to its ground state.

If radiationless transitions are neglected, each electronic transition results in a characteristic x-ray spectral line whose energy, $h\nu$, is equal to the difference between the binding energies of the two electrons. The x-ray spectral lines are designated by symbols such as $K\alpha$, $K\beta$, $I\alpha$, and $M\alpha$ in which the prefix K, L, or M indicates that the lines originate by removal of K, L, and M shell electrons, respectively (see Fig. 9-1). Because there is a limited number of possible inner shell transitions, the resultant x-ray spectrum is much simpler than the complex optical spectrum which originates from removal of valence electrons. In addition, both the intensity and wavelength of x-rays resulting from inner shell transitions are essentially independent of the chemical and physical state of the ionized element.

A linear relationship exists between the reciprocal values of wavelength for each transition series and the square of the atomic number, Z, of the excited element:

$$\frac{1}{\lambda} = K(Z - 1)^2 \tag{1}$$

This equation, known as Moseley's Law, is the basis for x-ray spectrochemical analysis. Qualitative analyses are achieved by comparing the measured x-ray wavelengths to tables of characteristic wavelengths of each element. For convenience the wavelength tables are expressed in degrees 2θ for each of the analyzer crystals used in x-ray spectrography. The wavelengths of the diffracted x-rays are related to the interplanar spacing of the analyzer crystal by the Bragg equation:

$$n\lambda = 2d \sin \theta \tag{2}$$

where n = order of reflection,
λ = wavelength of incident radiation, A,
d = interplanar spacing, A; and
θ = angle between incident radiation and reflecting plane.

Quantitative values are obtained by relating accurately measured intensities to concentration by means of graphical or arithmetical procedures.

The x-ray absorption process can also be used to provide qualitative and quantitative analysis. There are two principal types of x-ray absorption. The first type is photoelectric,

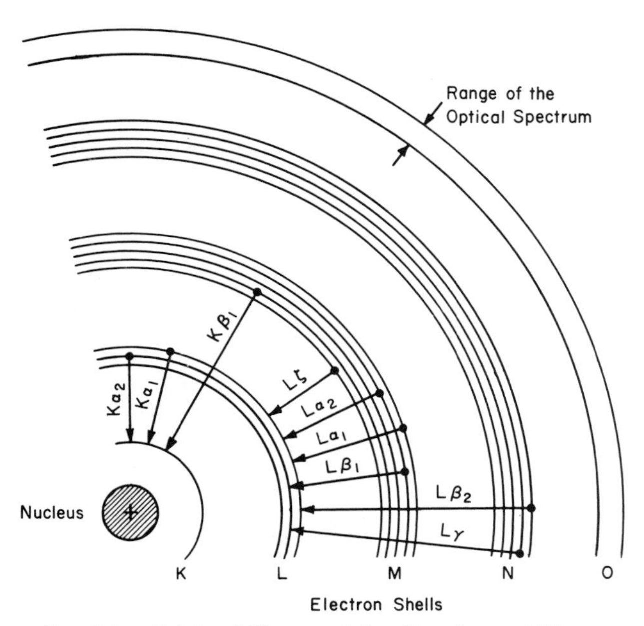

FIG. 9-1. Origin of Characteristic x-Ray Spectral Lines.

whereby all the energy of the incident x-ray quantum is transferred into kinetic energy of the photoelectron, thus resulting in emission of characteristic x-rays. The second type is scattering, whereby the incident x-ray intensity is decreased due to scattering. The linear absorption coefficient μ for an element is equal to the sum of the photoelectric absorption τ and the scattering coefficient σ. The photoelectric coefficients predominate except for low values of Z and high values of λ. By application of Beer's Law, x-ray transmission can be used to determine either composition or thickness:

$$\frac{I}{I_0} = e^{-\frac{\mu}{\rho}\cdot\rho\cdot X} \tag{3}$$

where ρ = density, g./cm.^{3}, and
X = thickness, cm.

Values for μ/ρ, the mass absorption coefficient, are listed in standard reference tables.

As a first approximation μ/ρ is proportional to $Z^4\lambda^3$ up to the K or L absorption edge; thus the absorption coefficient is both compositional and wavelength dependent (see Fig. 9-2). Polychromatic radiation is used for thickness gauging by employing standards and unknowns similar in composition. This technique offers the advantages of simple instrumentation and fast response because of the intense x-ray flux. Absorption edge absorptiometry is used for elemental determination for samples of variable composition.

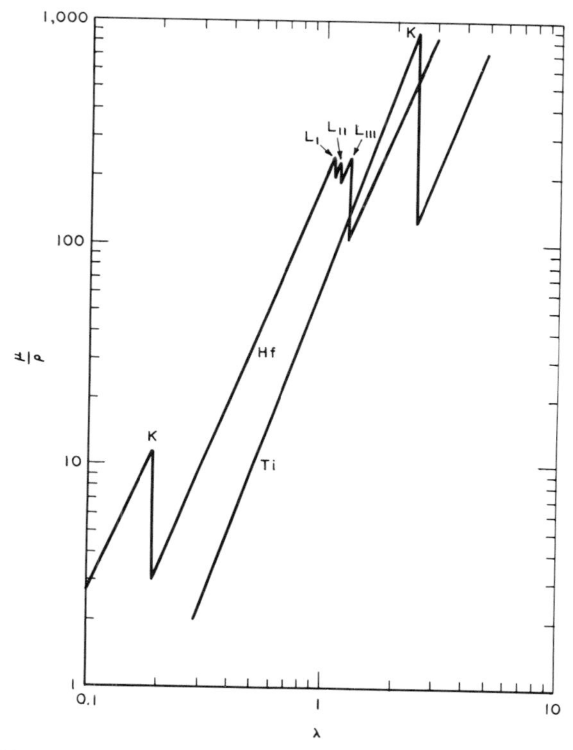

FIG. 9-2. Mass Absorption Coefficient as a Function of Atomic Number and Wavelength.

INSTRUMENTATION

The x-ray spectrometer-absorptiometer consists of a high intensity x-ray tube and its stabilized high voltage power supply, a sample chamber, a goniometer with collimator and analyzer crystal, and a detector with its associated electronics, which include a power supply, scaler-ratemeter, linear amplifier, single-channel pulse-amplitude discriminator, and strip-chart recorder. An arrangement which is suitable for fluorescent x-ray spectrography and both monochromatic and polychromatic absorptiometry is shown in Fig. 9-3. For emission analysis the absorption cell is replaced by a parallel-plate collimator. In monochromatic absorptiometry the secondary emitter is an element that has a strong characteristic spectral line of the desired wavelength. If absorption edge techniques are employed, then a secondary emitter will be selected that has strong spectral lines on both sides of the absorption edge. Polychromatic absorptiometry is accomplished by removing the secondary emitter and passing the output of the x-ray tube directly through a sample to the detector.

In both emission and absorption the x-rays must be transmitted from the x-ray tube target to the counting volume of the detector. Applications that use x-rays of wavelengths longer than 3 A require that the air path from the x-ray tube to the detector be replaced by a helium or vacuum path. Low energy x-rays, longer than 3 A, are readily absorbed in air.

Excitation.—The x-ray spectrum resulting from electron bombardment consists of a broad band of wavelengths (continuum) and several sharp characteristic spectral lines

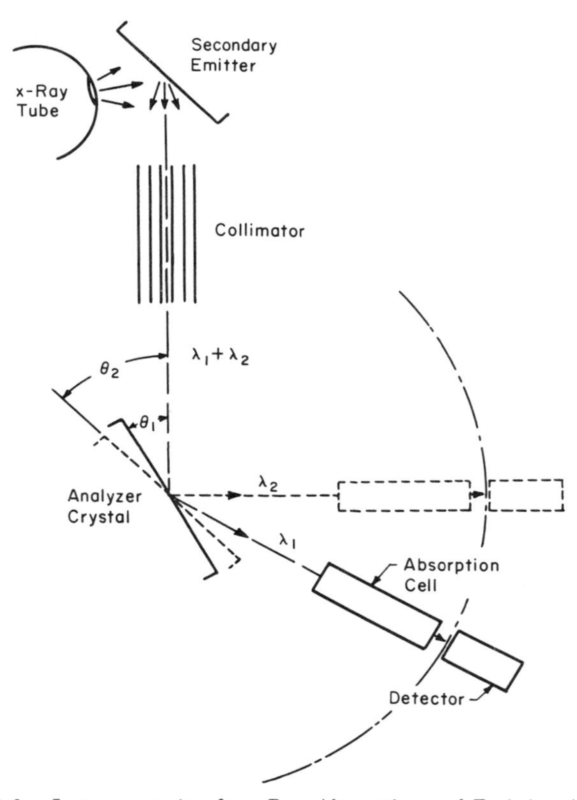

Fig. 9-3. Instrumentation for x-Ray Absorption and Emission Analysis.

(see Fig. 9-4). The wavelength distribution in the continuum is related to the atomic number of the target element and the applied voltage as given by the following equation:

$$I(\lambda) = KZi\left(\frac{\lambda}{\lambda_0} - 1\right)\frac{1}{\lambda^2}\,d\lambda \tag{4}$$

where i = x-ray tube current, and

$$\lambda_0 = \frac{12.4}{\text{kv}}, \text{ in A.}$$

Summation of $I(\lambda)$ over all wavelengths shows that the integrated intensity of the continuum is proportional to Z, V^2, and i.

$$I = K_2 iZV^2 \tag{5}$$

The voltage required to produce the characteristic lines of each series increases with increasing atomic number. Minimum voltages for excitation of the *K* series range from 1.3 kilovolts for magnesium to 39 kilovolts for lanthanum; *L* series minimum voltages range from approximately 3 kilovolts for molybdenum to 20 kilovolts for uranium. The

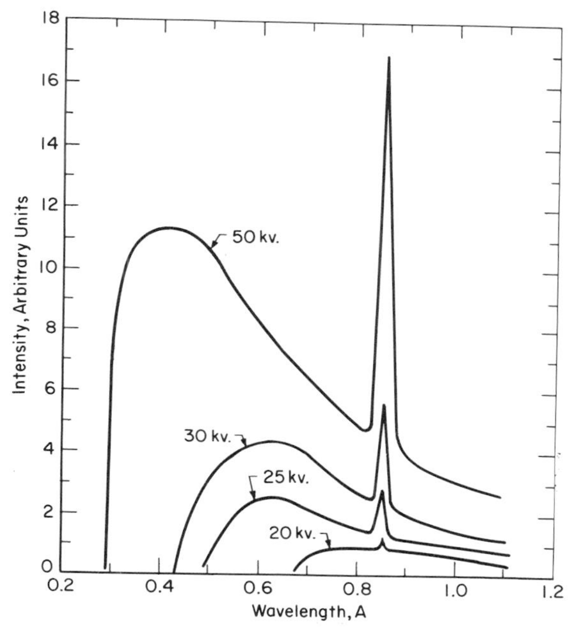

FIG. 9-4. Variation in x-Ray Distribution with Voltage for a Molybdenum Target.

intensity of the characteristic lines is related to applied voltage by the following expression:

$$I = Ki(V - V_0)^n \tag{6}$$

The value of n (ranges between 1 and 2) depends on the atomic number of the element and the ratio of the applied voltage V, to the critical voltage V_0.

An important factor to be considered is the relative excitation by the continuum as compared to that by the characteristic spectral lines. Although the number of characteristic photons is small compared to the continuum, the characteristic lines are an important source of excitation. Effective secondary x-ray production is related to the limiting depth beyond which the fluorescent x-rays cannot escape from the sample. This depth is a function of the linear absorption coefficient of the sample for the incident and fluorescent x-rays. Radiation that is absorbed near the surface has been proven to be the most effective source of secondary x-rays; for example, characteristic spectral lines that lie close to, but on the short wavelength side of, the critical absorption edge of the element being determined.

X-ray spectrographic tubes are operated at voltages up to 60 kilovolts. This voltage is adequate to excite efficiently the *K*-series spectra of all elements up to atomic number 50, and the *L* series lines for all higher atomic number elements. X-ray tubes and power supplies for 75 and 100 kilovolt operation are commercially available; however, their usefulness is limited by the lack of suitable crystals that provide both good dispersive power and high reflectivity for high energy x-ray photons.

All commercially available power supplies have voltage and current stabilization of ± 0.1 percent or better. A highly stabilized source of x-rays is essential for achieving the high precision inherent in x-ray analysis. Most efficient operation is achieved when the applied voltage is at least two to three times the critical voltage. Constant potential power supplies are more efficient than full-wave rectification, particularly in the high energy x-ray region where the critical excitation voltage exceeds 30 kilovolts.

X-ray tube targets of high atomic number elements such as tungsten, platinum, or gold are preferred for most applications because the intensity of the continuum is proportional to Z. For optimum results a target is selected whose characteristic lines do not overlap the analytical lines of interest. Commercially available thin-window chromium target tubes are an efficient source of excitation for the Period 3 elements. In the very long wavelength region the most significant gains in improved excitation have been in the development of experimental low voltage-high current demountable x-ray tubes with very thin windows. These demountable tubes, when coupled with vacuum spectrometers, make possible the measurement of x-ray emission lines from elements, atomic numbers 5 to 12.

Excitation of secondary x-rays (fluorescence) is a continuum-less process; however, some of the primary x-rays are scattered by the sample into the x-ray spectrometer optical system. Under optimum conditions line-to-background ratios of several thousand to one can be achieved by the secondary excitation process.

Dispersion.—There are two principal types of x-ray spectrometric optical systems, nonfocusing (flat crystal) and focusing (curved crystal). In flat crystal optics the x-ray beam is collimated by a series of parallel plates (see Fig. 9-3) where the beam divergence is limited by the spacing and length of the plates. Maximum resolution and peak-to-background are achieved by using dual collimators, one between the sample and crystal, and the other between the crystal and detector. However, a one-collimator system is preferred for general analysis because the maintenance of spectrometer alignment is critical for two-collimator optics.

In curved-crystal optics either a small sample area is excited through a pinhole collimator (x-ray microprobes), or the entire sample is irradiated and a slit image of the sample acts as the effective source of secondary x-rays (see Fig. 9-5). A cylindrical concave crystal focuses the diffracted x-rays onto a circle having a radius equal to half the radius of curvature of the crystal lamina. The crystal is bent to a radius $2R$, then ground to the radius R of the focusing circle. The x-ray source, crystal surface, and detector slit lie on the focusing circle. This principle is analogous to that of the Rowland Circle used in optical spectrography.

Focusing and nonfocusing optics give essentially the same intensity for large samples, whereas for microsamples, focusing optics are at least an order of magnitude stronger in intensity. Nonfocusing optics require a large detector window to view the area of the collimator opening effectively. These large windows are a problem in the long wavelength region where very thin plastic films must be used. Here, the narrow slit windows of focusing optics are a distinct advantage.

Analyzer crystals must have $2d$ spacing values that will satisfy the Bragg equation without exceeding the maximum 2θ angle, which is approximately $150°2\theta$ for most commercial goniometers. Maximum intensity is achieved with crystals having a slightly mosaic structure and a diffracting layer free of gross distortion due to cleavage or polishing. In addition, the crystal should not be composed of elements whose character-

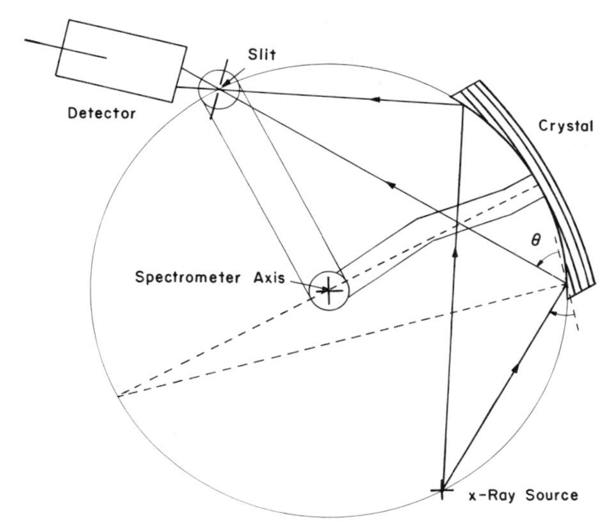

FIG. 9-5. Curved-crystal x-Ray Optics.

istic lines would result in a high background. In certain applications it is desirable to employ crystals for which the even-ordered reflections are weak or absent.

The dispersion of x-rays is inversely related to the *d*-spacing and to the Bragg angle:

$$\frac{d\theta}{d\lambda} = \frac{n}{2d \cos \theta} \tag{7}$$

Therefore crystals of low *d*-spacing are used to achieve dispersion of overlapping x-ray spectral lines. Characteristics of the more important analyzer crystals are summarized in Table 9-1.

TABLE 9-1. PROPERTIES OF ANALYZER CRYSTALS

Analyzer Crystal	Reflecting Plane (*hkl*)	2*d*, A.	Comments
Topaz	303	2.71	Special applications where high resolution is required
Lithium fluoride	200	4.03	Optimum crystal for all $\lambda < 3$ A
Silicon	111	6.27	Suppresses even-ordered reflections
PET	002	8.74	Optimum for atomic numbers 13 to 17
Gypsum	020	15.12	Used in curved crystal optics for several low atomic number elements
Mica	002	19.8	Used primarily in curved crystal optics for long wavelength x-rays
KAP	002	26.63	Used primarily in flat crystal optics for atomic numbers 6 to 12
Barium stearate		100.	Used with curved or flat crystal optics for wavelengths greater than 20 A

Detection.—There are three types of detectors used in x-ray absorption and emission analysis: Geiger, proportional, and scintillation detectors. Modern Geiger tubes have a sufficiently large volume sensitivity to allow efficient use of nonfocusing optics. Geiger tubes are simple to operate and do not require highly stabilized electronic circuitry. A third advantage is that physical discrimination against undesired x-rays can be achieved by selecting the appropriate counting gas mixture. This physical discrimination is especially useful in process control instrumentation in which the simplest effective mode of operation is desired. However, there are two principal deterrents to the wide application of Geiger tubes. Their dead time is 200 to 300 microseconds; thus, the counting loss (nonlinear response) is significant even at moderate x-ray intensities. Also, electronic discrimination is excluded since the output pulse voltage is independent of the energy of the incident radiation.

Proportional detectors use the same counting gas mixtures as Geiger detectors; thus, their spectral sensitivities are similar. Proportional detectors offer the advantages of high counting rates, dead time of <1 microsecond, and output pulse voltages that are proportional to the energy of the incident x-ray photon. Flow-proportional detectors are used for x-rays of wavelengths longer than 2 A. The windows of these detectors are very thin organic films of mylar, formvar, or nitrocellulose, all of which have a high transmission coefficient for long wavelength x-rays. Since these windows are somewhat porous, the counting gas must be constantly replenished by being passed in a continuous stream through the detector.

The most generally useful detector is the scintillation counter, which incorporates a very low dead time, <1 microsecond, and high spectral response for x-rays of wavelengths less than 2 A. Since the output pulse voltage is proportional to the energy of the incident x-ray photon, electronic pulse-amplitude discrimination can be used to reject continuous and characteristic x-rays whose energies are sufficiently different from those of the spectral lines being counted. The resolving power of the scintillation counter is approximately one-half that of the proportional detector. However, a high degree of energy resolution is not generally required in x-ray analysis, since the discrimination is against multi-ordered radiations whose energies are multiple integer values of the desired radiation.

Rules for selecting the optimum detector for a specific application are as follows:

Detector	*Application*
Geiger	Routine control analysis where low counting rates and physical discrimination are adequate
Flow-proportional	Determination of all elements, atomic number 24 or below
Proportional	Unique applications where the maximum resolution of a detector is required
Scintillation	Determination of all elements, atomic number 25 and above

Samples.—Samples for x-ray absorption and emission analysis can be in any physical form: solid, liquid, or gas. Thick solid samples are not amenable to absorption analysis since the low energy x-rays, 5 to 50 kev., have very limited penetration power.

The flux of the incident primary x-ray beam is inversely proportional to $\frac{1}{d^2}$ where d is the distance from the target to the sample. Because of the small values of d used in emission analysis, approximately one inch, there must be provision for accurately positioning the sample. With care the coefficient of variation due to sample positioning can be reduced to the order of ± 0.1 percent.

The types of solid samples submitted for emission analysis include metallurgical specimens, briquetted powders and borax discs. Since only the surface layers contribute to the secondary x-ray beam, the surface must be smooth, clean, and representative of the overall sample. Rotation of the sample during analysis minimizes variations in intensity due to preferential polishing and localized inhomogenieties. The x-ray intensity is dependent on surface smoothness, therefore, both standard and unknown must be subjected to the same surface treatment. Surface preparation is more critical in the long wavelength region because of the decreased penetration power of the low energy x-rays.

Solution samples for either emission or absorption analysis are held in plastic or metallic containers having thin mylar windows that are transparent to x-rays. The most convenient procedure is to use cup-like containers with $\frac{1}{4}$- or 1-mil mylar windows. In absorptiometry the optimum length of the sample cell is a function of the transmission characteristics of the x-rays and the concentration of the element being determined.

Samples in the gaseous or vapor state require sample cells that have x-ray transparent windows that can withstand high pressure differentials. Also, some type of pressure regulation must be used since the number of atoms in the x-ray beam is pressure dependent.

EMISSION ANALYSIS

The major problem in most instrumental methods of analysis is the correlation of measured intensity to calculated concentration, and emission analysis is no exception. In x-ray spectrography the intensity from an infinitely thick sample is related to concentration by the following expression:

$$I_A = \frac{KW_A}{\mu_1 + \mu_2} \tag{8}$$

where K = an empirical constant,
W_A = weight fraction of element A,
μ_1 = linear absorption coefficient of sample for incident radiation, and
μ_2 = linear absorption coefficient of sample for secondary radiation.

The value of μ for any wavelength, λ, is equal to the summation of the linear absorption coefficient of each element times its weight fraction

$$\mu_{\text{sample}} = \sum^{i} \mu_i W_i \tag{9}$$

Inspection of Eqs. 8 and 9 shows that the intensity of a spectral line is dependent on both the concentration of the element being determined and the overall sample composition. For example, the intensity from 10-weight-percent iron in tungsten is a factor of 2 to 3 lower than the intensity from 10-weight-percent iron in silicon. This compositional dependence, or matrix effect, is the principal obstacle to achieving quantitative values.

There are five general procedures that are used to eliminate or correct for the matrix dependence: comparison standards, internal standards, addition standardization, dilution techniques, and preparation of thin films. Principles and applications of each technique are briefly summarized. One essential requirement of both samples and unknowns in the first four procedures is homogeneity on a one-to-ten-micron scale; this distance is inversely related to the wavelength of the x-rays of interest. A high degree of homogeneity is critical because of the low penetration of the x-ray photons used in emission analysis.

Method I: Comparison Standards.—The most widely used method in emission analysis is the comparison of intensities from unknowns with those from standards of similar composition. This approach is, therefore, limited to samples for which the analyst has knowledge of history and probable composition. Use of comparison standards is the basis for control analyses in the chemical, metallurgical, and petroleum industries. Intensity can be related to concentration by three methods: linear ratioing, graphical, and mathematical, the latter uses correction terms for enhancement and absorption.

When the unknowns and standards are very close in composition, a simple ratio of $\frac{I_\mu}{I_s} = \frac{C_\mu}{C_s}$ is adequate, the subscripts μ and s refer to unknowns and standards respectively. Applications in which the unknowns vary over a wide range of composition necessitate the use of graphical and mathematical correction techniques. Graphical methods are used extensively for binary and ternary systems, *e.g.*, the ternary mixture Nb_2O_5, Ta_2O_5, and TiO_2. Calibration curves are prepared by measuring the spectral line intensity from samples of known composition. The present trend in industrial process control is to use simultaneous equations having corrective factors for enhancement and absorption. This mathematical approach is now practical, due to the wide availability of small laboratory computers. Several manufacturers of x-ray emission equipment are providing computer facilities as part of their process control instrumentation.

Method II: Internal Standard.—Internal standardization is the addition to the sample of a reference element whose characteristic radiation will be excited and absorbed in the same manner as the characteristic radiation of the element being determined. The effects of the matrix on the relative intensities of the reference and analytical lines can be grouped into three general classes:

(a) the matrix has a higher absorption for the longer wavelength line;
(b) an element has an absorption edge between the lines; and
(c) emission lines from the matrix preferentially excite the lower atomic number of the two elements.

These sample classes are shown in Fig. 9-6 where the matrix is considered as the third element. If the matrix "element" emits lines L_1 or L_3 or has absorption edges E_1 or E_3,

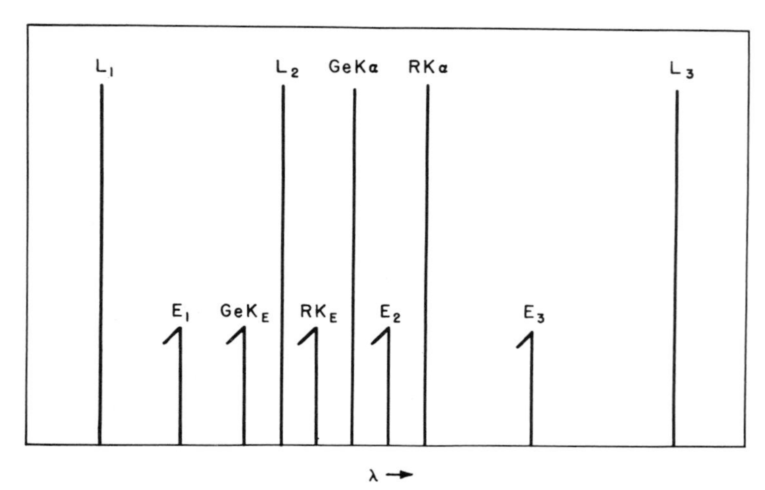

FIG. 9-6. Characteristic Lines and Absorption Edges.

then the sample belongs in Class A. An example of Class B is a matrix having a strong absorption edge at E_2 so that $SK\alpha$ is preferentially absorbed. If the matrix emits strong spectral lines of wavelength L_2, then reference element R is preferentially excited, thus creating a Class C sample.

When using internal standards the analyst must select a reference element that will result in a Class A sample. Class B and C samples are to be avoided; otherwise, the characteristic x-rays of the element being determined and the reference element are no longer affected in the same manner.

The percentage of the element being determined is calculated from the following equation:

Weight percent $X =$

$$\text{weight percent reference} \cdot \text{dilution factor} \cdot \frac{I_R}{I_A} \text{ (standard)} \cdot \frac{I_A}{I_R} \text{ unknown} \qquad (10)$$

where weight percent reference $= \dfrac{\text{weight of reference element added}}{\text{weight of sample + weight of reference material}}$,

dilution factor $= \dfrac{\text{weight of sample + weight of reference material}}{\text{weight of sample}}$,

$\dfrac{I_R}{I_A} =$ intensity ratio of $\dfrac{\text{reference element}}{\text{element being determined}}$ for a sample containing a 1:1 ratio of the two elements, and

$\dfrac{I_A}{I_R} =$ intensity ratio of $\dfrac{\text{element being determined}}{\text{reference element}}$ on sample being analyzed.

Method III: Addition Technique.—This method assumes a linear relationship between line intensity and concentration over a limited concentration range. Hence, addition techniques are used primarily for the determination of trace and minor constituents, as the linear relationship is valid in this concentration range. It is an essential requirement that the reference material be intimately mixed with the sample. Various procedures have been used to achieve this mixing, such as grinding the mixture together with an abrasive such as silicon carbide, forming pastes or slurries, and fusing by means of borax, carbonate, or pyrosulfate flux.

The analysis is accomplished by measuring the intensity of a characteristic spectral line of the element before and after addition of a known amount of the element to the sample. Using the ratio of intensities which are corrected for background, the percentage of the element in the sample is calculated from the following equation:

$$X = \frac{(I_x/I_{x'+y})y}{1 - (I_x/I_{x'+y})D} \qquad (11)$$

where
X = percentage of element in original sample,
I_x = intensity of characteristic line before addition,
$I_{x'+y}$ = intensity of characteristic line after addition,
y = percentage of element in reference material, *e.g.*, $\dfrac{Ge}{GeO_2} \times 100$, and
D = weight of sample/weight of sample + weight of reference material added.

Method IV: Dilution.—One of the major advances in x-ray analysis was the development of dilution techniques. Examination of Eq. (12) reveals that all dilute solutions have approximately the same absorption coefficient, that of the solvent, since with sufficient dilution the small weight fraction of the solute makes its contribution negligible:

$$\frac{\text{Limit } \mu_{\text{sample}}}{C_A \rightarrow o} = \mu_{\text{solvent}} \tag{12}$$

where C_A is the concentration of sample after dilution.

As a result of dilution, the element or elements being determined are present as minor constituents so that the intensity to concentration relationship is linear and matrix effects are minimized.

Dilution may be achieved by dissolution with an inorganic or organic solvent, or by fusion with a flux of borax, carbonate, or pyrosulfate. Another approach is to add a heavy absorber plus flux; this combination minimizes the absorption contribution of the original sample. Dilution, with or without a heavy absorber, has been used successfully on a wide variety of materials.

Method V: Thin Films.—Matrix (interelement) effects are low or negligible in thin film type samples because neither the primary nor the secondary x-rays are strongly absorbed by the sample. Thus the intensity of the secondary x-rays are directly proportional to the amount of the element present, matrix effects are minimized by this technique. Because standards and unknowns are prepared in a similar manner, linear comparison of intensities is valid.

Generally this method involves the chemical or physical separation of the desired elements from the host compound. The elements being determined are collected by ion exchange, solvent extraction, or precipitation, in a physical form suitable for x-ray analysis. For example, metallic ions may be collected on a cation ion-exchange resin-loaded paper which also serves as the supporting media for presentation in the x-ray spectrograph. Since the sensitivity for elements isolated from the host compound is 0.01 to 10 μg., analysis of trace elements is possible by means of this preconcentration approach.

ABSORPTION ANALYSIS

Absorptiometry can be divided into three classes: polychromatic, monochromatic, and differential absorption across an absorption edge. Because absorption of polychromatic radiation is not specific for any element, this technique is limited to samples for which the composition is qualitatively known and which the matrix changes only slightly from sample to sample. Thus polychromatic x-rays cannot be used to identify elements or to obtain quantitative values for samples of unknown composition. The utility of polychromatic x-rays lies in their ability to distinguish differences in ultimate composition and in thickness. Their advantage for control analysis lies in the extremely high beam intensity which permits instantaneous observation and feedback for control purposes.

Simple monochromatic x-ray absorptiometry yields information similar to polychromatic radiation, but the former offers greater flexibility and ease in interpretation of data. Monochromatic x-rays can be achieved by Bragg diffraction, selective filtration of polychromatic radiation, use of characteristic lines that predominate over background, and as products of radioactive isotopes.

Quantitative values are obtained by measuring the transmitted intensity of a selected x-ray wavelength through samples and unknowns that are similar in composition. A good example is the determination of sulfur in a hydrocarbon in which Fe^{55} (MnK radiation) is used as the source of monochromatic radiation. The mass absorption coefficient of the sample is equal to:

$$\left(\frac{\mu}{\rho}\right)_{\text{sample}} = \left[\left(\frac{\mu}{\rho}\right)_C W_C + \left(\frac{\mu}{\rho}\right)_H W_H + \left(\frac{\mu}{\rho}\right)_S W_S\right] \tag{13}$$

Equation (13) can be expressed in a simpler form, since the carbon to hydrogen ratio does not vary with the variable sulfur content:

$$\left(\frac{\mu}{\rho}\right)_{\text{sample}} = \left(\frac{\mu}{\rho}\right)_{\text{matrix}} (1 - X) + \left(\frac{\mu}{\rho}\right)_S Y \tag{14}$$

where X = weight fraction of sulfur.

Thus a linear plot of $\log_e \frac{I}{I_0}$ versus concentration of sulfur is obtained where the slope is related to the difference in the mass absorption coefficient of sulfur as compared to the matrix.

Absorption edge analysis is based on the large change in the mass absorption coefficient across the absorption edge. The absolute difference is more important than the absorption jump ratio (the ratio of absorption coefficient on either side of the absorption edge). Thus the L_{111} edge gives greater analytical sensitivity than the K edge, even though the K jump ratios are a factor of 2 or more larger than the L_{111} jump ratios. The large difference at the L_{111} edge is a result of the much larger values of the absorption coefficient since μ/ρ is proportional to λ^3.

The absorption edge method uses two x-ray spectral lines one below, λ_1, and the other above, λ_2, the absorption edge (see Fig. 9-7 in which λ_1 and λ_2 are $SrK\alpha$ and $BrK\beta_1$ respectively). The following relation is derived from the fundamental absorption law:

$$\frac{I_{\lambda_1}}{I_{\lambda_2}} = \frac{I_{\lambda_1}^0}{I_{\lambda_2}^0} e^{-[AW_A + BW_M]\rho 1} \tag{15}$$

where $A = \left[{}_{\lambda_1}\left(\frac{\mu}{\rho}\right)_A - {}_{\lambda_2}\left(\frac{\mu}{\rho}\right)_A\right]$,

$B = \left[{}_{\lambda_1}\left(\frac{\mu}{\rho}\right)_M - {}_{\lambda_2}\left(\frac{\mu}{\rho}\right)_M\right]$,

W_A = weight fraction of the element being determined, and
W_M = weight fraction of matrix = $100 - W_A$.

Equation (16) can be considered as two independent terms:

$$\frac{I_{\lambda_1}}{I_{\lambda_2}} = \frac{I_{\lambda_1}^0}{I_{\lambda_2}^0} e^{-B\rho 1 W_M} \cdot e^{-A\rho 1 W_A} = Ke^{-A\rho 1 W_A} \tag{16}$$

where $K = \frac{I_{\lambda_1}^0}{I_{\lambda_2}^0} e^{-B\rho 1 W_M}$.

where the slope of the curve (analytical sensitivity) is equal to $A\rho 1$. The sensitivity can be increased by use of long path lengths, but there is a practical working limit due to reduction in intensity.

Application of this procedure is demonstrated by the determination of bromine in a hydrocarbon matrix (see Fig. 9-8). The samples were a series of successive dilutions of ethylene dibromide in xylene. The secondary emitter was composed of NaBr and $SrCO_3$.

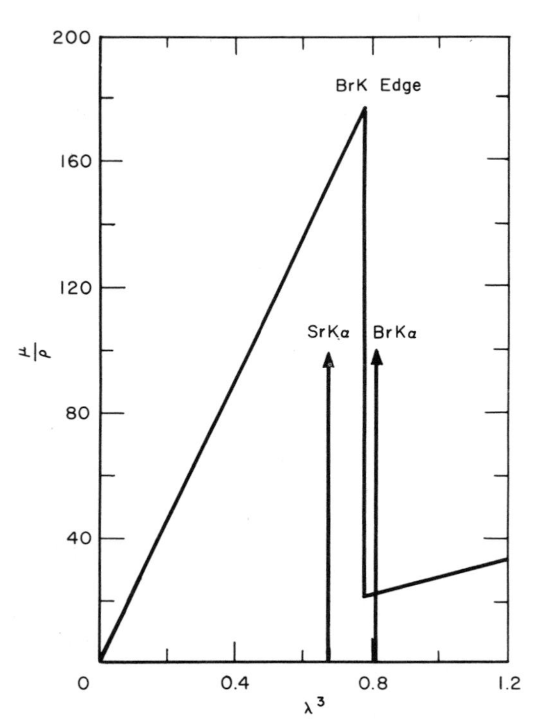

FIG. 9-7. Differential Absorption Edge Analysis of Bromine Using SrKα and BrKβ_1 Radiation.

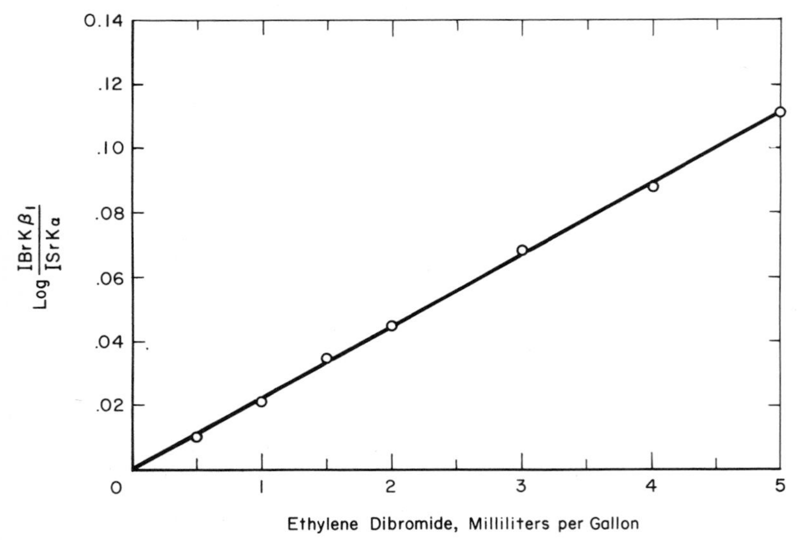

FIG. 9-8. Calibration Curve for Differential Absorption Edge Analysis of Bromine.

LIMITATIONS AND APPLICATIONS

X-ray methods are nondestructive; therefore, the samples can be used for other tests and the standards may be retained indefinitely. X-ray analysis can be applied to amorphous or crystalline samples in any physical state of subdivision. Electrical and mechanical properties of the sample are not a consideration.

The accuracy of the analysis depends on the surface preparation, reliability of standards, stability of the x-ray tube output, and the number of x-ray photons counted. At the one percent concentration level the line intensity and line-to-background ratio is sufficiently high that the counting error can be reduced to less than one percent for counting times of one minute. Instrumental and sample variables can also be reduced to less than one percent by use of carefully standardized techniques and modern instrumentation in good condition.

X-ray absorption is not as versatile as emission for general elemental analysis. Emission has the advantages of spectral line specificity, sensitivity of one to two orders of magnitude greater than absorption, and applicability to a wide range of elements without changing any instrumental parameter other than the Bragg angle. X-ray emission methods are applicable to all elements, from atomic number 11 to 92. However, there are many practical and theoretical limitations to be overcome before quantitative results for low atomic number elements become routine. A unique advantage of the absorption edge method over emission is the elimination of the matrix effect which is inherent in emission analysis. Also the concentration can be calculated from absorption edge measurements without recourse to the use of standards.

The lower limit of detection by emission techniques is a function of the peak-to-background ratio and the number of photons counted. For ten-minute counting times, detection limits vary from several parts per million in favorable samples to 1000 parts per million for the less sensitive elements. By employing a chemical or physical preconcentration, the limit of detection can be reduced by one to two orders of magnitude since isolated microgram amounts of all elements, atomic number 12 and above, give readily measurable intensities.

Emission x-ray methods are used worldwide for research and for control analysis of major, minor, and trace elements. This increasing interest in emission methods results from the wide applicability of x-rays for rapid quantitative analysis. These methods have been used in such diversified analytical problems as iron in blood, lead in gasoline, calcium in cement, titanium in paper products, chromium in glass, and selenium in plant material.

Absorption methods for control analysis, using radioactive isotopes as the x-ray source, are increasing in popularity because of their low cost and high reliability. Both emission and absorption are used extensively for on-stream control in the plating industry. The x-ray signal is used in conjunction with feedback circuits to alter the plating variables. The most recent development in emission applications has been the on-stream process control of metallurgical systems. For example, addition of flotation reagents to a sphalerite concentrate is controlled by on-stream analysis of heads, concentrates, and tailings.

Most of the commercial x-ray spectrographs have attachments for achieving analyses of selected microareas. The use of special collimating systems permits the selection and analysis of areas as small as 25 to 50 microns in diameter for concentrations ranging from 0.1 to 100 percent.

A number of methods based on x-ray spectrometry have been used in the analysis of special materials. Those described elsewhere in Standard Methods of Chemical Analysis are as follows:

1. Chapter 43, Volume III, Alloys: Iron, Steel, Ferro-alloys, and Related Products.
   a. Analysis of pig iron
   b. Analysis of slags and sinters
   c. Analysis of steel
   d. Analysis of highly alloyed and heat-resistant steels
   e. Determination of thickness of tin coating on steel
2. Chapter 44, Volume III, Alloys: Nonferrous.
   a. Determination of copper diffusion in titanium
   b. Analysis of hafnium-zirconium alloys
   c. Mercury in zinc
   d. Uranium in copper
3. Chapter 46, Volume III, Portland Cement.
   a. Determination of aluminum, calcium, iron, magnesium, manganese, potassium, silicon, and sulfur
4. Chapter 49, Volume III, Fertilizers.
   a. Possible use is discussed
5. Chapter 53, Volume III, Glass.
   a. General classification of soda-lime-silicate glasses
   b. Aluminum
   c. Antimony
   d. Arsenic
   e. Barium and titanium
   f. Calcium
   g. Chlorine
   h. Chromium
   i. Cobalt
   j. Copper
   k. Iron
   l. Magnesium
   m. Manganese
   n. Nickel
   o. Phosphorus
   p. Potassium
   q. Selenium
   r. Silicon
   s. Sodium
   t. Strontium
   u. Sulfur
   v. Zinc
   w. Zirconium
6. Chapter 54, Volume III, Paint, Varnish, and Lacquer.
   a. Determination of drier or catalyst metals
   b. Quantitative pigment analysis
   c. To determine level of metal treatments, as zinc phosphate on steel for galvanized iron, chromium and phosphate treatment on aluminum, and thickness on tin plate stock.
7. Chapter 57, Volume III, Petroleum and Petroleum Products.
   a. Barium, calcium, and zinc in new and used oils
   b. Cobalt, iron, and zinc in organic matrices
   c. Halogens in petroleum hydrocarbons
   d. Trace amounts of iron, nickel, and vanadium on catalysts
   e. Sulfur in petroleum hydrocarbons

The following x-ray fluorescence methods have been included:

1. Chapter 37, Volume IIB, Paint, Varnish, and Lacquer.
   a. Inorganic pigments in paints, page 1685.
2. Chapter 58, Volume III, Plastics.
   a. Determination of elements with atomic number of 11 or greater
   b. Zinc stearate as surface additive on polymers

SELECTED BIBLIOGRAPHY

Textbooks

Birks, L. S., X-Ray Spectrochemical Analysis, Interscience Publishers, New York, 1959.

Compton, A. H., and Allison, S. K., X-Rays in Theory and Experiment, 2nd Ed., D. Van Nostrand, Princeton, New Jersey, 1935.

Liebhafsky, H. A., Pfeiffer, H. G., Winslow, E. H., and Zemany, P. D., X-Ray Absorption and Emission in Analytical Chemistry, John Wiley, New York, 1960.

Smith, R. W., Ed., Symposium on X-Ray and Electron Probe Analysis, ASTM Spec. Tech. Pub., 349, American Society for Testing and Materials, Philadelphia, 1963.

Reviews

Campbell, W. J., and Brown, J. D., "X-Ray Absorption and Emission," Anal. Chem., **36**, 312R–328R, 1964.

Liebhafsky, H. A., Winslow, E. H., and Pfeiffer, H. G., "X-Ray Absorption and Emission," Anal. Chem., **34**, 282R–292R, 1962.

Tables

Sagel, K., Tabellen zur Rontgen—Emissions und Absorptions—Analyse, Springer-Verlag, Berlin, 1959.

X-Ray Wavelengths for Spectrometer, Cat. No. A4961DA, General Electric Co., Milwaukee, Wisconsin, 1959.

Chapter 10

ELECTRON PROBE X-RAY MICROANALYZER

By E. J. Brooks
Analytical Chemistry Branch
Metallurgy Division
U. S. Naval Research Laboratory
Washington, D. C.

The electron probe x-ray microanalyzer is used to excite and measure the characteristic x-ray spectra of material in a micron diameter area of a sample. This is a recent development in the field of x-ray spectroscopy to extend the method to samples approaching only 10^{-12} grams in weight.

This capability is both a product of, and a necessity for, continuing fundamental research into the nature of materials. The concurrently increased demand on the analytical chemist for improved detection, precision, and accuracy of materials analysis necessitates integrating many disciplines into the whole field of analytical chemistry. While other methods are more sensitive for determining the average trace composition even on small samples, the special ability of the "probe" to provide analyses in small areas is providing valuable and, indeed, unique information on such factors as the influence of impurities and additives in materials of the ultra-trace concentration level, and on the mechanisms of inter-metallic diffusion, segregation, precipitation, and corrosion. These are all factors which must be understood and evaluated to continue development of the new sophisticated metallurgical and solid state materials required in the current advancing technology. Significant applications have also been made in geological, biological and meteoritic sciences to trace and understand origins of deposits and bodies and their formation mechanisms. An indication of the value and extent of the practical probe applications is the increase in probe population from about 5 instruments in 1957 to some 200 instruments now operating in the industrial and research laboratories of this country and abroad.

INSTRUMENT DESCRIPTION

The instruments in use now are generally the same in basic concept.[1–9] Each has an electron optics system which generates and focuses an electron beam to bombard a

[1] Hillier, J., U. S. Patent 2,418,029, 1947.
[2] Castaing, R., and Guinier, A., Electron Microscope, Proc., Delft. Conf., 1949.
[3] Castaing, R., Thesis, University of Paris, 1951.
[4] Cosslett, V. E., and Duncumb, P., Nature, **177,** 1172, 1956.
[5] Birks, L. S., and Brooks, E. J., Rev. Sci. Instr., **28,** 709, 1957.
[6] Fisher, R. M., and Schwartz, J. E., Proc. 5th Conf. Ind. Appl. X-ray Anal., Denver.
[7] Wittry, D. G., Thesis, California Institute of Technology, 1957.
[8] Schwartz, C. S., and Austin, A. E., J. Appl. Phys., **28,** 1368, 1957.
[9] Haine, M. E., and Mulvey, T., J. Sci. Instr., **36,** 350, 1959.

specimen and excite the x-ray spectra of the elements present in a specimen, and each incorporates an electronic x-ray optics measuring system to relate emitted x-ray intensity to the elemental composition. The geometrical arrangement of the components of a particular probe reflects the design fabrication compromises which are accepted in order to extend the range of measurable elements, to improve analytical accuracy, to accommodate particular specimen sizes, or to facilitate adaption to special problems.

Electron Optics.—The beam is generated in the electron gun.[10] A 0.004-inch diameter tungsten wire filament bent to a "V" is heated to emit electrons from the tip. A 5- to 40-thousand volt negative potential on the filament accelerates the emitted electrons toward the grounded anode's aperture. An initial improvement to this basic gun design is the inclusion of an apertured grid cap over the filament. With this cap biased negatively by several hundred volts, the electron beam is focused to a small (about 50-micron) crossover, or focus, of uniform density, just before emerging from the anode aperture. This focus serves as the object source used in the calculations to determine the parameters and geometry of the focusing lenses.

The electron beam, after emerging from the gun, is directed through the bores of the focusing magnetic lenses. As the electrons pass through the magnetic field of the first lens, their straight flight path is altered to a spiral trajectory converging to a focus, which will be somewhat smaller than the 50-micron source. This latter focus is further demagnified by a second lens. Ideally, the final focus should be about 0.5 micron in diameter. Lenses are not perfect, however, and aberrations limit the smallest final focus to about 1.5- to 2-micron diameter for practical excitation sources. Magnetic lenses are used almost exclusively, because their design and fabrication are somewhat simpler than electrostatic lenses. In addition, the necessary magnetic fields are readily produced by selecting the number of coil windings and the coil current. The coil current is a conveniently adjustable parameter for changing the beam intensity and final focus during the probe's operation.

The simplest magnetic lenses are coils of wire wound in many layers on a nonmagnetic spool. However, for efficient use as a focusing lens, an iron spool is used and the coil is completely surrounded with iron, except for a short brass section brazed into the spool cylinder. This break in the iron casing concentrates the magnetic field at the brass section of the lens bore. This concentration is further confined to a short central section of the lens bore by sliding well-machined iron cylinders with centrally-protruding iron sections into the bore. These centrally-protruding sections form the pole faces for the lens and determine the symmetry of the magnetic field.[11] They require exceptionally careful and fine machining, otherwise complicated field compensators must be included to correct the lens aberrations.

Liebman[12] has investigated the complex parameters of the magnetic lens and has reduced to near engineering-type data the intereffects of the field strength; number of windings; coil currents; pole piece configuration, gap and bore; magnetic saturation; chromatic and spherical aberration; and the focal length.

Component Arrangements.—Several general types of the probe are shown schematically in the first figure. The arrangement sketched in Fig. 10-1a is perhaps the simplest. The dashed line outlines the electron beam, although the beam size relative to the components is exaggerated. The gun and lenses are of simple geometry. Not shown are the short cylindrical spacers between the gun and the first lens and between the two lenses. These spacers hold the translation screws, fluorescent screens and viewing ports for aligning the gun and the lenses. Small diameter grooves are cut into the spacers to hold

[10] Haine, M. E., Einstein, P. A., and Borcherds, P. H., Brit. J. Appl. Phys., **9**, 482, 1958.
[11] Mulvey, T., Proc. Phys. Soc. B, **66**, 441, 1953.
[12] Liebman, G., Proc. Phys. Soc. B, **68**, 737, 1955.

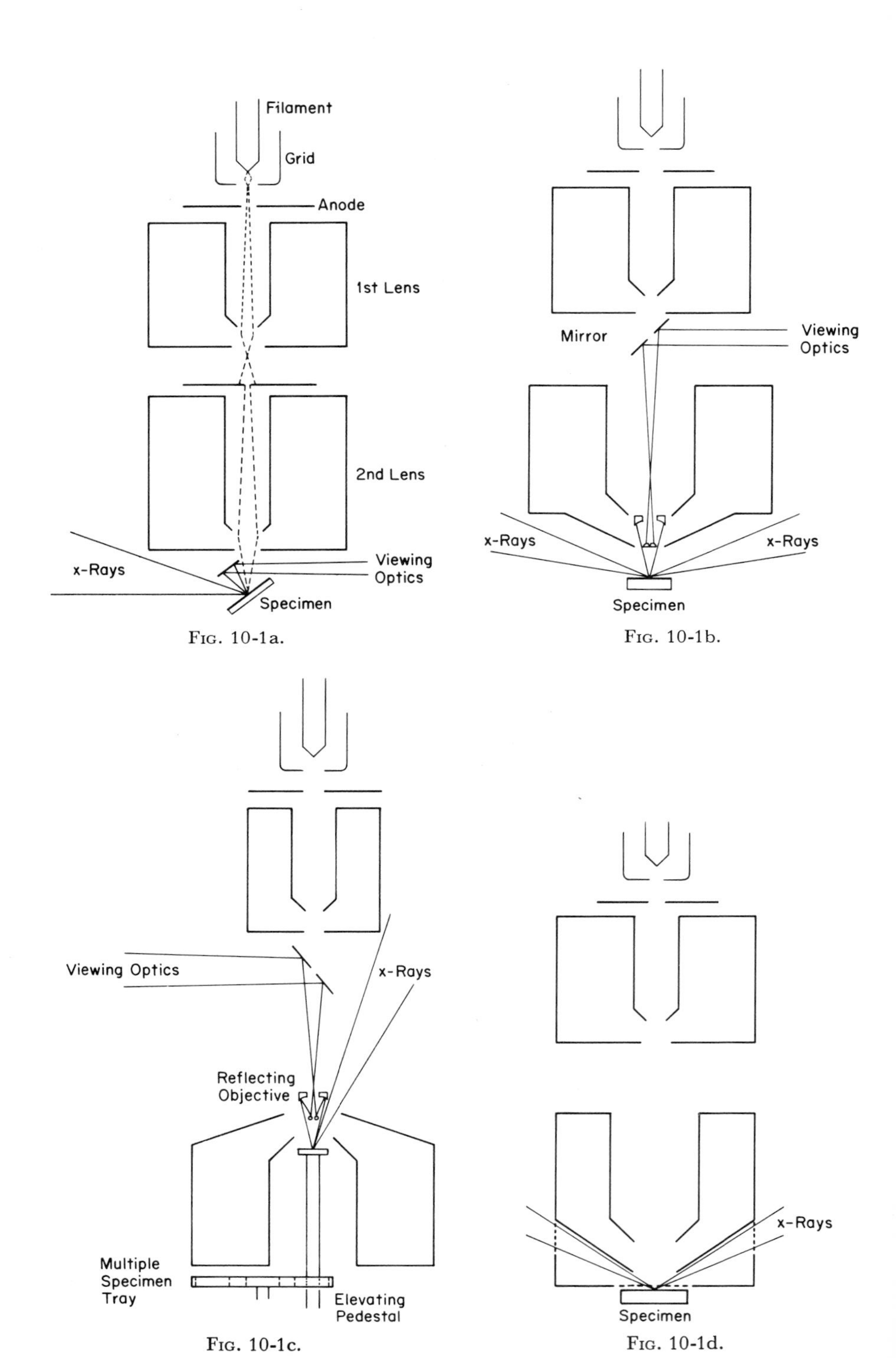

FIG. 10-1a.

FIG. 10-1b.

FIG. 10-1c.

FIG. 10-1d.

the vacuum-type "O" rings. The matching surfaces of the gun and lenses then need only be machined flat to complete the vacuum seal, as the components are stacked one on the other. The volume to be evacuated is kept to a minimum and includes just the gun, the small bore of lenses and the specimen chamber. This small system requires only a 2-inch bore oil diffusion pump and mechanical pump to evacuate the probe and maintain 10^{-5} mm. pressure. The extent of the sample tilt is considered in the design and selected for low or medium x-ray take-off angles. A wide x-ray window will allow a large portion of the emitted x-rays to escape from the specimen chamber so that several x-ray optics analyzing systems may be set up around the probe.

In Fig. 10-1b, although the second lens is of a more complicated geometry, it provides the means for incorporating a reflecting light objective to improve the visual observation of the specimen during operation. With suitable windows a larger portion of the emitted x-rays escape the chamber for measurement. The lower range of x-ray take-off angles is inherent in this design, but the electrons strike perpendicular to the sample surface. The vacuum volume is not significantly larger.

Figure 10-1c is a very similar instrument, except that the second lens is inverted. With this arrangement, larger x-ray take-off angles are used, increasing the sensitivity for lighter elements. A multiple-specimen tray and an elevated pedestal are used to load and analyze some eight specimens with one vacuum let down.

Figure 10-1d is a sketch of an interesting variation. The electron beam emerges from the vacuum, through a tiny aperture in a mica disc, to strike the specimen. The specimen must, of course, be very close to the mica. Since they have no escape path the emitted x-rays are transmitted back through the mica into the vacuum and emerge again through a second window to be measured. Since the aperture is small, larger capacity vacuum pumps must be used to overcome the pinhole "leak" and maintain sufficient vacuum. The advantage of this arrangement is that small areas of very large specimens which cannot be sectioned or sampled, for one reason or another, may be examined by the probe.

Specimen Chamber.—Specimen chamber designs vary depending on the contemplated sample size; the mechanisms necessary to position selected areas of the specimen under the beam; the x-ray windows' orientation, which is dictated by the geometry of the x-ray analyzing optics; the light optics system for observing the specimen during analysis; and the sample loading gate.

X-Ray Optics.—The emitted x-ray spectra are analyzed with two general classes of conventional x-ray spectrometer, (a) the dispersive spectrometer, which employs an analyzing crystal to separate characteristic wavelengths from the emitted spectra for identification and measurement of the elements, and (b) the nondispersive spectrometer, which uses an energy-sensitive detector to convert impinging x-ray quanta to voltage pulses and electronic circuits to separate characteristic pulse amplitudes for identification and measurement of the elements.

The conventional x-ray spectrometer[12a,13] employs a collimator to limit the incident beam, a flat single crystal to analyze the beam, and a detector to measure the intensity of diffracted wavelengths. These components are arranged so that the angle of the incident beam with the crystal, *i.e.*, the Bragg angle, is the same as the angle of the detector with the crystal. As the crystal rotates in the spectrometer, changing the Bragg angle, the detector rotates at twice this angular rate to keep the same angle between it and the crystal. This satisfies the fundamental Bragg diffraction relationship[14] that at each inci-

[12a] Friedman, H., and Birks, L. S., Proc. Sci. Instr., **19**, 323, 1948.
[13] Birks, L. S., X-ray Spectrochemical Analysis, in Elving, P. J., and Kolthoff, I. M., Eds., Chemical Analysis, Vol. XVII, Interscience Publishers, New York, 1963.
[14] Bragg, W. L., Ed., The Crystalline State, Bell, London, 1933.

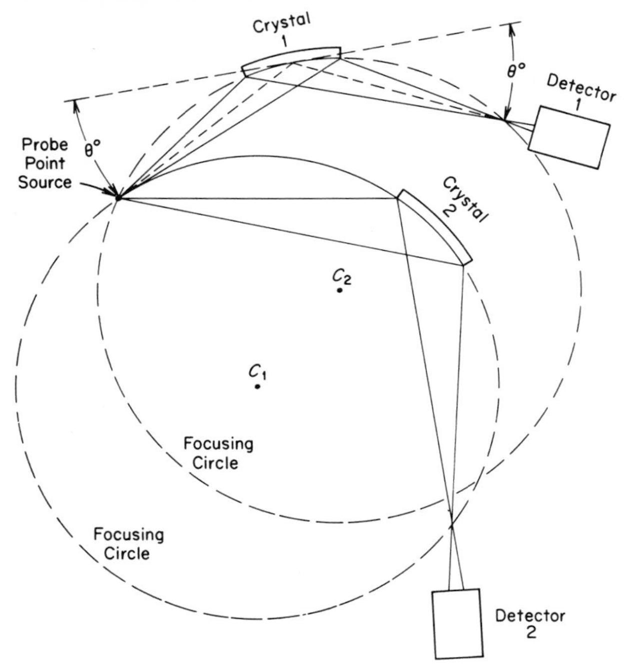

Fig. 10-2a.

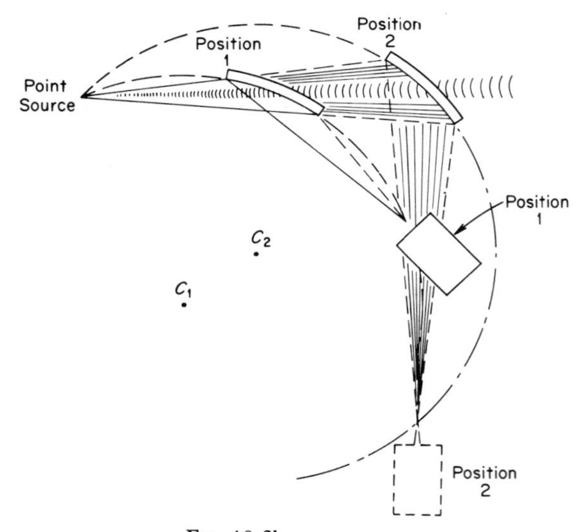

Fig. 10-2b.

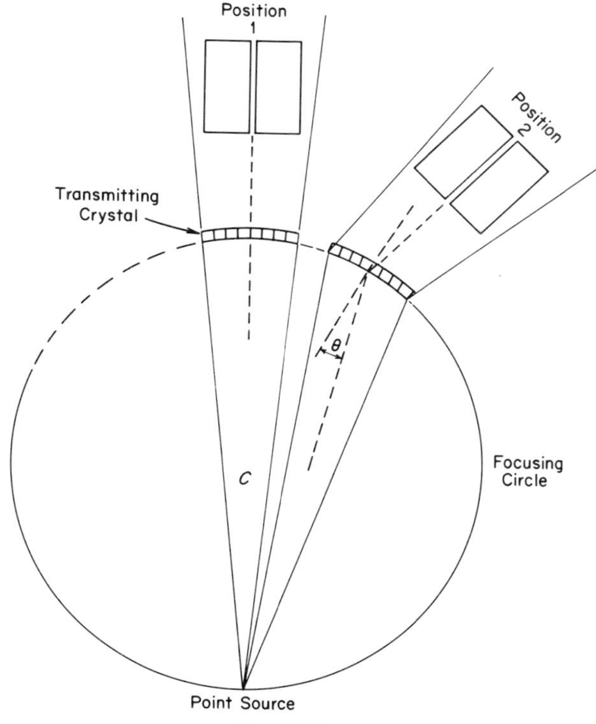

FIG. 10-2c.

dent angle only one wavelength out of the heterogeneous incident beam will be diffracted toward the detector. This relationship is expressed in the equation $n\lambda = 2d \sin \theta$; n is the order, λ the wavelength, d the atomic plane spacing and θ the Bragg angle. To improve the sensitivity of the flat crystal spectrometer when the x-ray source is small, as in the probe, a plastically or elastically bent crystal[13,15] is employed. A diverging x-ray beam from a small source is diffracted into a line focus by such a curved crystal. The curved crystal optics[16] require that the x-ray point source, the curved crystal, and the detector must be located on a focusing circle.

The central ray from the point source to the crystal, and the crystal plane tangent to the focusing circle, determine the Bragg angle. The detector must move along the focusing circle in order to make the same angle with the crystal. Practically, this is accomplished[17] easily by mounting the crystal and detector on radius arms from the center of the circle. Rotating these arms, again at a 2 to 1 angular rate, slides the crystal and detector along the focusing circle, changing the Bragg angle and always keeping the detector at the corresponding diffracted angle. Many probes incorporate a spectrometer for analyzing unknown specimens by scanning the Bragg angle continuously. More frequently, simultaneous measurement of several elements is necessary, and most probes offer x-ray optics which allow at least two elements to be measured. In Fig. 10-2 several

[15] Birks, L. S., and Seal, R. T., J. Appl. Phys., **28**, 541, 1957.
[16] Johannson, Naturwissenschaften, **20**, 758, 1932.
[17] Birks, L. S., Brooks, E. J., and Gourlay, G. W., Rev. Sci. Instr., **29**, 425, 1958.

arrays of crystal and detector are sketched. The first shows $crystal_1$ and $detector_1$ located on a focusing circle centered at C_1 to measure λ_1 and another $crystal_2$ with $detector_2$ located on a focusing circle centered at C_2 to measure λ_2. These are not necessarily spectrometers but the crystal and detector combination are oriented properly so that each measures a given wavelength. As many as four such arrays may be laid out on a table around the specimen chamber.

Figure 10-2b is a sketch of a spectrometer arrangement in which the crystal is moved away from the source and rotated at the same time.[18] In position 1 the crystal and detector are located on the focusing circle centered at C_1. In moving to position 2 the crystal has been moved away from the source and rotated to a new Bragg angle, requiring the detector and focusing circle center to move to position 2. The proper location for the detector in successive positions, as the crystal is moved and rotated, is a compound curve and requires an accurate camming arrangement. Each wavelength in this arrangement is measured separately, but with the same x-ray take-off angle from the specimen. At low Bragg angles the reflecting crystal must be moved in close to the source, thus intercepting a smaller portion of the emitted beam. Also the difficulty in shielding the detectors from the direct beam at low Bragg angles is greatly increased. To overcome this difficulty, thin bent transmitting crystals[19,20] are used. The third sketch shows this arrangement. Position 1 is the zero Bragg angle position. As the crystal moves along the focusing circle centered at C_1, the crystal planes and x-rays come into successive Bragg angle positions. Then rotating the detector about the crystal to the same angle completes the diffraction requirements. Such arrangements, with thin crystals on the order of 1 mm., will significantly increase the sensitivity for elements in the range from molybdenum to tin. The radius of bending for the crystal, the crystal spacing, and the detectors are selected to provide optimum sensitivity for the particular elements of interest. The x-ray optics should be enclosed in a chamber and evacuated or filled with helium to permit the lighter elements from titanium to sodium to be determined.

The vertical angle of divergence from the source to the crystal is continued to the line focus so that it may be as high as 3 inches. Some x-ray optics arrangements double-up detectors and stack them vertically to intercept more of the useful beam.

The second general approach to x-ray spectra analysis is nondispersive electronic spectroscopy.[21] The "spectrometer" in this system has no moving parts. The heterogeneous emitted x-ray beam is incident on an energy-sensitive detector such as a scintillation counter or a gas proportional counter.[22,23,24] These counters convert the x-ray beam to voltage pulses proportional to the energy of the incident x-ray quanta. This voltage pulse spectrum is scanned electronically by Pulse Height Analyzer circuits in terms of the individual pulse voltage in order to relate characteristic energies to the identification of the elements and the counting rates to the amounts present.

In addition to the x-rays produced, the back scattered electrons and specimen currents may be used for analytical data.

An early facility[25] which recently has become almost standard on probes presents a cathode ray tube display of the specimen surface. This is done by introducing deflection plates into the beam column to sweep the beam over a rectangular area on the sample.

[18] Kemp, J. W., Hasler, M. F., Jones, J. L., and Zeitz, L., Spectrochim. Acta, **7**, 141, 1955.
[19] Cauchois, Y., J. Phys. Radium, **3**, 320, 1932.
[20] Brissey, R. M., Anal. Chem., **24**, 1034, 1952.
[21] Connally, R. E., and Laboenf, M. B., Anal. Chem., **27**, 1095, 1953.
[22] Friedman, H., Birks, L. S., and Brooks, E. J., Am. Soc. Testing Materials, Spec. Tech. Publ. #157, 3, 1954.
[23] Parrish, W., and Kohler, T. R., Rev. Sci. Instr., **27**, 795, 1956.
[24] Hendee, C. F., and Fine, S., Phys. Rev., **95**, 281, 1954.
[25] Cosslett, V. E., and Duncumb, P., Proc. Stockholm Conf. Electron Microscopy, 1956 (Pub. 1957).

Synchronized with this sweep is the beam of a cathode ray tube. The output signals, whether x-rays, specimen current, or back scattered electrons, are used to modulate the brightness of the cathode ray tube beam. This results in a television-type presentation of the elemental distribution in the sample surface. The size of the raster sweep may be as large as 200–300 microns square. As an extension to this display, multichannel analyzers[26] are being used as scalers to accumulate the same information point by point and to print out a quantitative topograph of the specimen surface in terms of element concentration.

ANALYTICAL INFORMATION

Analytical information is derived from the dependence of x-ray intensity on the amount of the element present. In some analyses this relationship is a linear function, at least to a first approximation, and only one standard reference sample is necessary. In many problems a series of a few standards may be sufficient to establish a calibration curve. However, since these situations do not always suffice, and to provide better accuracy or fill the concentration regions not covered by standards, methods of concentration calculations designed to consider factors of x-ray excitation and measurement have been devised in recent years.[27,28,29] Overall quantitative analysis with the probe is good to about 3 percent of the amount present. It is interesting to keep in mind that this analysis is performed on an amount of about 10^{-13} grams.

In a probe the excitation of x-rays depends on a number of factors: (1) the number of electrons absorbed, which is a function of the atomic number and the atomic weight; (2) the number of electrons back-scattered without energy loss, since they do not contribute to x-ray excitation; (3) the penetration of electrons, which is dependent on (a) the angle of incidence (this becomes a design factor in determining the tilt of the specimen), and (b) the electron accelerating potential; (4) the x-ray spectrum of the matrix which contributes to the excitation of characteristic x-rays emitted by other elements of the matrix which are of sufficient energy; (5) the absorption of emitted characteristic x-rays by elements of the matrix; (6) and the emergence angle at which the x-rays escape from the sample toward the crystal analyzers. The measurement of these factors, the extent of their influence in particular combinations of compositions, and the reliability of preciseness of constants are still being investigated and evaluated.

Sample Preparation.—The take-off angle and matrix factors mentioned above can be affected by the sample preparation. Samples are given a good flat metallurgical polish (to keep the same path length for emergent x-rays from all points on the surface), and perhaps a light etch to bring out surface features for orientation or examination. If the sample is electrically nonconducting it must be coated with a thin layer of conducting material, usually by evaporation.

Extraction techniques are employed to lift out small segregates or inclusions for separate analysis, to eliminate absorption or excitation influence from the matrix material. If the sample can be etched heavily, but gently, a polished surface of soft aluminum can be pressed onto the sample to imbed the loosened particles in their original orientation. This gives a mirror image of the surface, and holds the particles in a flat, noninterfering matrix. The extraction techniques used by the electron microscopist are suitable in many instances, also.

[26] Birks, L. S., and Batt, A. P., Anal. Chem., **35,** 778, 1963.
[27] Castaing, R., and Descamps, J., J. Phys. and Rad., **16,** 304, 1955.
[28] Birks, L. S., Electron Probe Microanalysis, Interscience Publishers, New York, 1963.
[29] Zeibold, T. O., and Ogilvie, R. E., Anal. Chem., **36,** 322, 1964.

APPLICATIONS

The literature contains many papers on interesting and varied applications of the probe.

The probe provides a unique analysis in that it can pinpoint such small areas of a sample for study. Several elements are analyzed simultaneously to eliminate any question of exact repositioning of the sample and that the composition was indeed achieved on the same small area for each element.

A case in point was the examination of stainless steel tubing corroded by a heat exchange medium of air-contaminated lithium.[30] In this study a stainless steel tubing was purposely corroded with air-contaminated lithium at 1500°F. At the end of the experiment the tubes were cooled rapidly to freeze the material conditions existing at 1500°F. Microscopic examination revealed the general type of corrosive action and the physical appearance of the metallic mass transfer deposit. Specimens of the mass transfer deposit and specimens of cross sections of the tube container were prepared for x-ray microanalysis. The inner surface of the container was heavily plated with silver so that the edges of the specimen would not be rounded over during the normal metallographic mounting and polishing techniques. Analysis of the mass transfer material by the probe showed the mass transfer deposits to be homogeneous in iron and nickel. Examination of the container cross sections showed that chromium had been selectively leached from the steel. Figure 10-3 is a micrograph of the surface of a container cross section. The area A (generally on the left) is the plated silver and B is the container surface. The inner cylindrical surface of the container is perpendicular to the page. The arrow points to the contamination trace left by the beam as the sample was translated from silver to steel. Figure 10-4 shows the results of the analysis in percent composition of Fe-Ni-Cr *vs.* distance from the corroded surface. Clearly, the chromium has been preferentially leached out of the steel to a depth of some 8 microns from the surface. The three elements were measured simultaneously while the sample was translated. The irregular inner surface of the corroded tubing would preclude other methods of analysis and, except for simultaneous measurement, make suspect the exact position of analysis for each element being measured.

The literature contains many other accounts of probe applications to metallurgical problems, probably because metal specimens are easily prepared, electrically conducting, and reference standards, at least the pure elements, are usually available. Among the accounts is one on the analysis of precipitates in Inconel-X[31] which again points out the value of simultaneous analysis of several elements. Some of the precipitates examined were only 3 microns wide and had a central core only 1 micron wide. Analyses in the probe for niobium (columbium) and titanium simultaneously revealed that the center core was 50 percent titanium with no niobium and the edges were 40 to 50 percent niobium with no titanium.

The probe has also been used to measure the diffusion of one element along the grain boundaries of another matrix.[32] The diffusion of zinc vapor into the grain boundaries of a copper matrix was traced some 100 microns farther along the boundary than could be otherwise determined. Concentration contours across and along the grain boundary were mapped from 0.5 percent to 21 percent zinc.

Thin metallic films have been examined to determine the thickness and homogeneity

[30] Seebold, R. E., Birks, L. S., and Brooks, E. J., Corrosion, **16,** 468, 1960.
[31] Birks, L. S., and Brooks, E. J., Am. Soc. Testing Materials, Spec. Tech. Publ. #245, 1958.
[32] Achter, M. R., Birks, L. S., and Brooks, E. J., J. Appl. Phys., **30,** 1875, Nov. 1959.

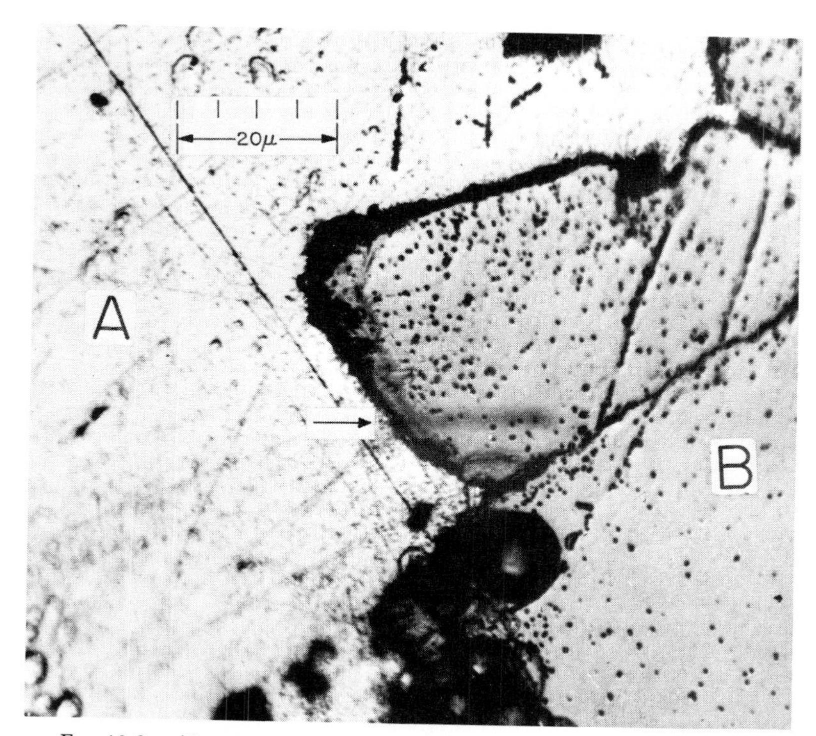

FIG. 10-3. (Reprinted with permission from Corrosion, **16,** 141, 1960.)

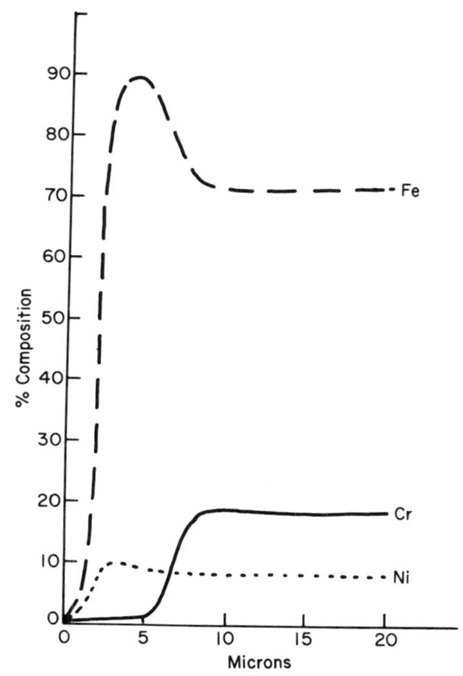

FIG. 10-4. (Reprinted with permission from Corrosion, **16,** 141, 1960.)

of the deposit.[33,34,35] Solid state devices and complete integrated circuits have been examined in the probe. Corrosion products, and material splattered during fabrication have been discovered by these analyses.[36–40]

The composition of minute inclusions in minerals has been determined by probe analysis.[41] In one case polarized light microscopy had to be used to locate and map the position of narrow birefringent grains. Results of the probe analysis suggested that the particular grains were not sphalerite, but an unknown sulfide.

Analysis of biological tissue has been reported. The concentration of calcium was measured from the calcified edge of the epiphyseal plate through the calcification and maturation zones.[42] The analysis for copper in Descemet's membrane from the eye cornea of deceased patients who had Wilson's disease, revealed the concentration level and nature of the copper deposited there.[43]

The cases cited represent only the scope of current applications of the probe to minute area analysis. Certainly the information presented in this chapter is cursory. Much more detail is contained in the literature, which is particularly well referenced in the April Review Issues of Analytical Chemistry and catalogued in an invaluable and extensive bibliography compiled by Dr. Kurt Heinrich at the National Bureau of Standards. Several recent texts, by Birks[44,45] and Liebhafsky,[46] which cover the companion subjects of x-ray spectroscopy and the electron probe extensively, along with chapters in several standard works by Clark[47] and Wittry[48] will prove indispensable to newcomers to the field.

The use of the electron probe microanalyzer for phase identification in a niobium-zinc alloy is described in Chapter 44 on nonferrous alloys. In Chapter 53, on the analysis of glass, the following methods are discussed: (a) the study of diffusion profiles at glass-glass or glass-metal seals; (b) analysis of the dielectric material in electronic microcircuits; (c) investigation of surface volatilization phenomena; and (d) the analysis of stones and cords to determine their origin.

SUMMARY

The electron probe x-ray microanalyzer is being used to analyze small samples and small areas of samples. The elemental composition distribution determined with the

[33] Sweeney, W. E., Jr., Seebold, R. E., and Birks, L. S., J. Appl. Phys., **31,** 1061, 1960.
[34] Ichinokawa, T., and Yamada, Y., J. Phys. Soc. Japan, **18,** 1223, 1963.
[35] Hutchins, G. A., Abstract 213, Electrochemical Society, 120th Meeting, Washington, D. C., October, 1964.
[36] Everhart, T. E., Abstract #234, Electrochemical Society, 120 Meeting, Washington, D. C., Oct. 1964.
[37] Lublin, P., and Lutkowski, W. J., Abstract #235, *Ibid.*
[38] Kyser, D. F., and Wittry, D. B., Abstract #236, *Ibid.*
[39] Ramsey, J. N., and Weinstein, P., Abstract #237, *Ibid.*
[40] Mealey, C. C., and Laakso, C. W., Abstract #238, *Ibid.*
[41] Birks, L. S., Brooks, E. J., Adler, I., and Milton, C., Amer. Mineralogist, **44,** 974, 1959.
[42] Brooks, E. J., Tousimis, A. J., and Birks, L. S., J. Ultrastruct. Res., **7,** 560, 1962.
[43] Tousimis, A. J., ISA Proceedings, **8,** 53, 1962.
[44] Birks, L. S., Electron Probe Microanalysis, in Elving, P. J., and Kolthoff, I. M., Eds., Chemical Analysis, Vol. XVII, Interscience Publishers, New York, 1963.
[45] Birks, L. S., X-Ray Spectrochemical Analysis, in Elving, P. J., and Kolthoff, I. M., Eds., Chemical Analysis, Vol. XI, Interscience Publishers, New York, 1959.
[46] Liebhafsky, H. A., Pfeiffer, H. G., Winslow, E. H., and Zemany, P. D., X-Ray Absorption and Emission in Analytical Chemistry, John Wiley and Sons, New York, 1960.
[47] Clark, G. L., Ed., X-ray Emission Spectrometry, Encyclopedia of Spectroscopy, Reinhold Publishing Corp., New York, 1960.
[48] Wittry, D. B., X-ray Microanalysis by Means of Electron Probes, in Elving, P. J., and Kolthoff, I. M., Eds., Treatise on Analytical Chemistry, Part I, Vol. 5, Interscience Publishers, New York, 1964.

probe is essential information in many research fields. This information is providing a better understanding of the dependence of the properties of metals on composition and formation mechanisms. The probe has also contributed to a deeper insight into the evolution of geological and meteoritic materials.

Chapter 11

X-RAY DIFFRACTION

By C. M. Mitchell
Department of Mines and Technical Surveys,
Ottawa, Canada

Introduction.—The application of x-ray diffraction methods to chemical analysis is primarily in the identification of compounds present from their diffraction patterns, and the determination of the relative concentrations by the intensities of pattern lines.

However, the x-ray diffraction pattern of a crystal structure contains sufficient information to determine both the dimensions of the unit cell of the crystal lattice and the atomic arrangement within the cell. Measurement of structure changes, particularly of unit cell dimensions, can be used in certain analytical problems.

Qualitative identification of structures can be made by comparison of the interplanar spacing values of the specimen pattern with an index of standard patterns. This procedure can be carried out with relatively simple apparatus. The detectable concentration in the presence of the continuous x-ray background is of the order of 5 percent. The use of a crystal monochromator to eliminate the continuous component of the background in the x-ray beam will increase the sensitivity, giving a detectable concentration limit of the order of 1 percent.

Quantitative analysis is carried out by comparing the intensity of a chosen diffraction line in a compound to the intensity of the same line in a standard mixture. The sensitivity of the determination depends directly on the accuracy of intensity measurement and is highest in the proportional counter or scintillation detector diffractometer where an accuracy of ± 1 percent can be achieved at high concentrations. Correction must be made for absorption effects in both specimen and standard. The success of this method depends on obtaining a truly randomly oriented sample. In certain materials preferred orientation occurs readily, and while this can be detected, eliminating the effect can require special procedures in specimen preparation.

Unit cell parameters can be measured to high accuracy, changes of 1:50,000 being detectable with normally available equipment and this provides a method of determining the constitution of compounds in which there has been partial isomorphous replacement of one or more atoms in the unit cell, as in solid solutions of metals or inorganic compounds. While graphical methods of eliminating instrumental aberrations in unit cell determination can be used, the determination can be facilitated by the use of computer programs for error extraction and least squares refinement.

EXPERIMENTAL METHOD

Production and Detection of X-Rays.—The diffraction of x-rays by the crystal lattice occurs over a wide angular range when the wavelength of the x-rays is of the order of the spacing between planes of atoms. X-rays with a narrow wavelength spread, in a region suitable for diffraction analysis, are obtained in the K spectra of the light metals, chromium, cobalt, copper, iron, manganese, molybdenum, and nickel which cover the range from 0.7 A to 2.2 A. The spectra are obtained by bombarding a target of the element with electrons of energies between 25 kv. and 50 kv. The x-rays in this wavelength region are readily absorbed, and special windows of beryllium or mica are used on ports of x-ray tubes and detectors.

The K spectrum contains three strong lines α_1, α_2 and β, of which the α_1 and α_2 form a doublet with a narrow wavelength separation. The x-rays can be detected by film, industrial or medical, x-ray film of the highest speed being normally used. They can also be detected by a Geiger or proportional counter, and by a scintillation counter of the cadmium iodide type.

In the diffraction pattern, the patterns due to the three characteristic lines are superimposed. The K_β radiation can be eliminated using a thin foil filter, usually of the element of next lower atomic number to that of target element. The incident x-ray beam can also excite fluorescent K or L radiation from certain elements in the specimen, where the fluorescent radiation is of higher wavelength, and this can obscure the pattern. This radiation can be eliminated by change of characteristic radiation to a longer wavelength, or where it is beyond the 2.0 A limit, by the use of thin aluminum or cellulose filters at the detector.

The wavelengths of the characteristic x-rays are given for the standard target materials in the International Tables of Crystallography[1] and a re-evaluation of the complete spectra of all the elements has recently been made by Bearden.[2] In accurate parameter measurements, if wavelength values are taken from other sources, care must be taken to ensure that the values given are quoted in Angstrom units and not in the older KX units which are larger by a factor of 1.00202. Similarly, in abstracting unit cell parameter data, the wavelength used in the determination should be checked.

Diffraction of X-Rays.—A monochromatic beam of x-rays, of wavelength λ, incident on a crystal, will be diffracted by sets of planes of high atomic concentration when the relation of the interplanar spacing d to the angle θ between x-ray beam and the plane set fulfils the Bragg relation

$$d = \frac{\lambda}{2 \sin \theta} \tag{1}$$

The diffracted beam will lie in a plane defined by the incident x-ray beam and the diffracting plane normal. If the x-ray beam is diffracted by a fine powder, made up of small crystallites, diffraction will occur for all crystallites whose planes of spacing d make an angle θ to the incident beam, and the diffracted beam will lie on a cone of semi apex angle 2θ. The minimum interplanar spacing giving a diffraction is at $d = \lambda/2$, $\theta = 90°$.

X-Ray Powder Cameras.—X-ray cameras for powder diffraction are of two main types, the Seeman-Bohlin focusing camera[3] in which the specimen is mounted coincident with the surface of a cylindrical film, and the Debye-Scherrer design[4] in which a cylindrical specimen is set on the axis of the film cylinder.

In the focusing type a divergent beam of x-rays enters the camera through a narrow slit, with the axis of the incident beam perpendicular to the axis of the film cylinder. The diffracted x-ray at a given Bragg angle θ will converge to a focus at the film cylinder, along the axis formed by the intersection between the film and the plane of incidence. In Fig. 11-1*a* an asymmetric arrangement of the specimen is shown, and in Fig. 11-1*b*

[1] International Tables of Crystallography, Vol. 3, Kynoch, Birmingham, 1962, p. 59.

[2] Bearden, J. A., X-ray Wavelengths, Atomic Energy Commission, Division of Technical Information, NYO-10586, Oak Ridge, Tenn., 1964.

[3] Seeman, H., Ann. Physik, **59**, 455, 1919; and Bohlin, H., Ann. Physik, **61**, 421, 1920.

[4] Debye, P., and Scherrer, P., Physik. Z., **17**, 277, 1916.

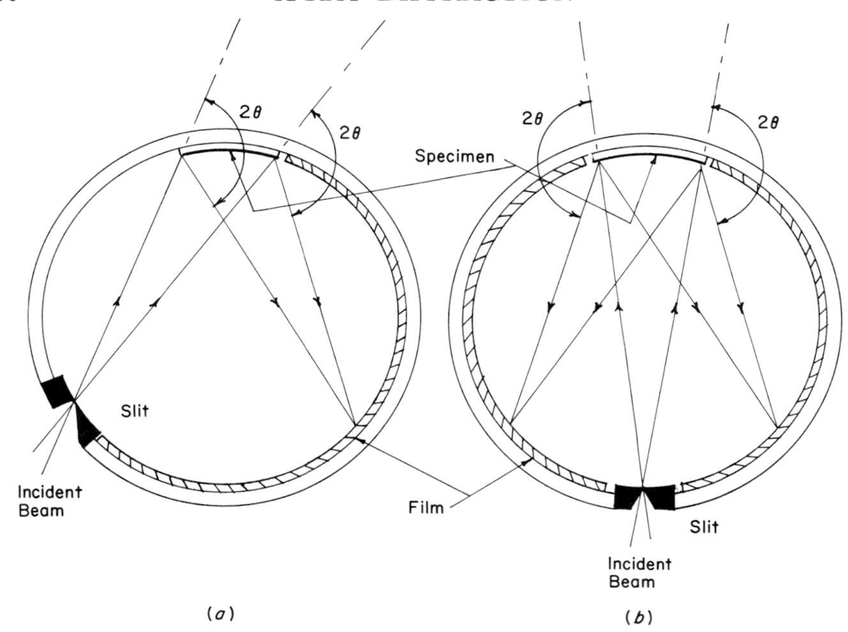

FIG. 11-1. x-Ray Powder Diffraction Cameras of the Seeman-Bohlin Focusing Type: *a*, Asymmetric Arrangement; *b*, Symmetric Arrangement for Measurement at High 2θ.

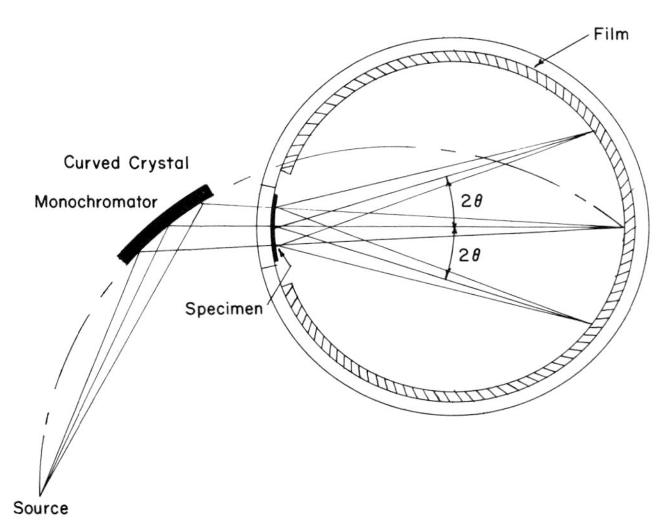

FIG. 11-2. Guinier Camera Using a Curved Single Crystal Monochromator and a Thin Transmission Powder Specimen Curved to Lie on the Film Cylinder. The diffracted x-rays focus along the film axis.

a symmetric arrangement in which the diffraction pattern is limited to $2\theta > 90°$. The symmetric arrangement is normally used in accurate lattice parameter measurement.

A focusing camera employing a monochromator is shown in Fig. 11-2. This design is due to Guinier[5] and provides a pattern of low background intensity suitable for determining trace constituents. The diffraction is limited to $2\theta < 90°$.

In the Debye-Scherrer camera in Fig. 11-3 a thin cylindrical specimen is set on the

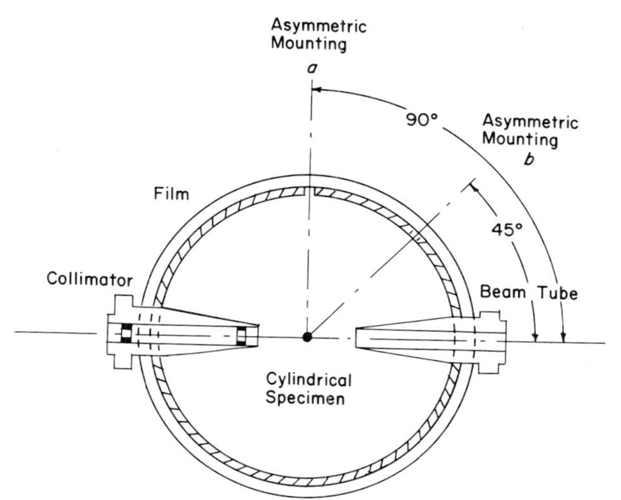

FIG. 11-3. The Debye Scherrer Circular Powder Camera Which Uses a Thin Cylindrical Powder Specimen Set on the Axis of the Film Cylinder. Asymmetric film mounting for self calibration of the film is illustrated; *a*, for patterns over the full range $0 < 2\theta < 180°$; *b*, for patterns having $2\theta < 90°$.

film cylinder axis and can be rotated to increase the number of diffracting particles. The camera is not focusing, and for specimens of low absorption the limiting line width is equal to the specimen diameter. For specimens of high absorption a virtual focus is obtained. The absorption effect is large in this design and must be corrected in accurate interplanar spacing measurement. The diffraction pattern is registered over the range $0 < 2\theta < 180°$. The film is shown with the asymmetric mounting designed by Levins and Straumanis,[6] which makes the film self-calibrating and corrects for uniform film shrinkage. In Fig. 11-3*a* the film is divided at $2\theta = 90°$ and in Fig. 11-3*b* at $2\theta = 45°$. The latter is to provide calibration when the pattern is limited to low angles, $2\theta < 90°$.

The Bragg angle can be determined by measuring the arc length along the central axis of the unrolled cylinder, either from a fiducial mark of known Bragg angle, or using both intercepts of the diffraction cone with the film cylinder axis. The relation for the full arc subtended by the diffraction cone is

$$\theta = \frac{S}{D} \cdot \frac{90}{\pi} \tag{2}$$

[5] Guinier, A., Comptes rendus, **204,** 1115, 1937; and X-ray Crystallographic Technology, Hilger and Watts, London, 1952.

[6] Straumanis, M., and Levins, A., Die Prazisions Bestimmung von Gitterkonstanten Noch dei asymetrischen Methode, Edwards Brothers, Ann Arbor, 1948.

where S = arc length, and
D = camera diameter.

Film shrinkage during processing is equivalent to a reduction of the effective camera diameter and can be corrected in the asymmetric mounting using the relation

$$\theta = \frac{S}{S_c} \cdot 45° \quad (3)$$

where S_c = arc length between centers of the diffraction cones for

$$\theta < 45° \quad \text{and} \quad \theta > 45°.$$

Direct reading scales for a range of S_c values are provided for Debye-Scherrer cameras[7] in standard diameters of 57.3, 114.59 and 171.89 mm, and give d values of lines for a given characteristic wavelength.

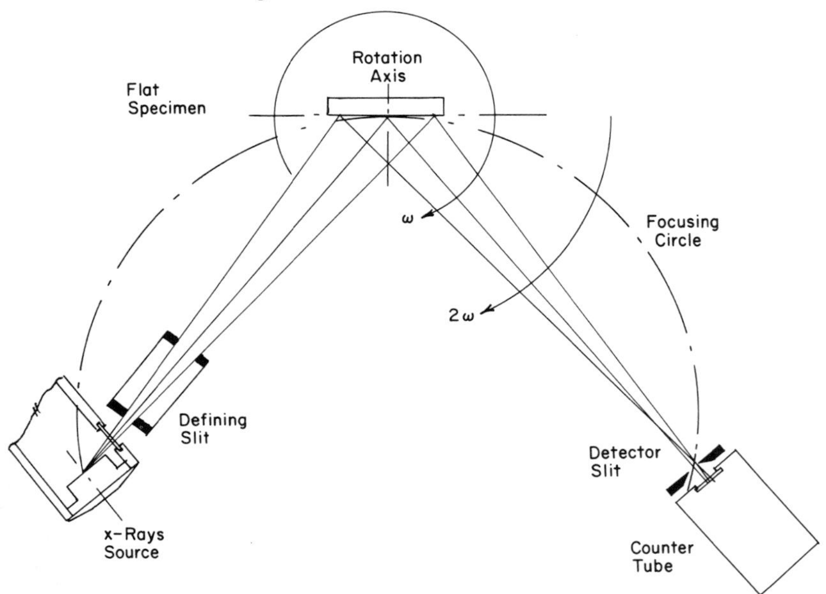

Fig. 11-4. Diffractometer Using a Flat Powder Specimen with the Bragg-Brentano Parafocusing Geometry. The x-ray tube is set with its focal spot on the focusing circle in the standard arrangement to provide maximum intensity.

For accurate interplanar spacing measurement the line centers must be accurately determined either by microphotometer or by optical comparator, and the instrumental aberrations and specimen absorption corrected by the methods described in the section on Methods of Accurate Lattice Parameter Measurement. A linear measuring instrument having an accuracy of ±0.005 mm. over the full film length in position determination, is adequate for precision measurement.

X-Ray Diffractometer.—The x-ray diffractometers for powder diffraction, using standard photon counters have a common design geometry (Fig. 11-4). The design is

[7] Scales for Cylindrical Cameras Supplied by Nies, N. P., 969 Skyline Drive, Laguna Beach, Calif.

due to Bragg and Brentano[8] in which the specimen mount and the detector have a common rotation axis, the specimen mount being geared to twin at one half the angular velocity of the detector. For high intensity the focal spot of the x-ray tube is viewed directly without a defining slit, the line source of the x-ray tube and the detector slit being set at equal distances from the rotation axis. A flat powder specimen is set on the axis at equal inclination to the incident beam and detector slit axes. The specimen is then tangent to a circle passing through the source rotation axis and detector slit, providing approximate focusing. Complete focusing could be obtained in this design only with a specimen of continuously changing curvature.

Soller slits made of stacks of equally spaced foils parallel to the incident plane are used to reduce vertical divergence of the incident and diffracted beams. Accuracy of angular measurement in commercial instruments is between $\pm.01°$ and $\pm.003°$ of 2θ.

The instrument can be adapted to single crystal measurement using a goniostat,[9] which provides two angular rotations for the specimen. In certain diffractometers an additional rotation is provided by permitting the specimen mount to be rotated relative to the detector.

IDENTIFICATION OF STRUCTURES FROM POWDER DIFFRACTION PATTERNS

ASTM Index.—The identification of a structure from its powder diffraction pattern is normally made using an index of standard patterns. A comprehensive index based on the Hanawalt system[10] is published in card form by the American Society for Testing and Materials,[11] and at present includes the patterns of approximately 12,000 compounds.

Under the Hanawalt system each powder pattern is characterized by the interplanar spacings d_i and the relative intensities I_i of the three strongest lines in the pattern. The complete list of interplanar spacings, their relative intensities and where known, the indexes of the crystallographic planes are given together with the unit cell parameters and physical constants of the compound. An index book[12] arranged in order of the magnitude of the interplanar spacings, using each line in turn as the primary index, together with the names and chemical formulas of the compounds and the card index number is used to identify the possible compounds. The cards for these compounds can then be checked against the complete pattern on the index card. A cross index of the compounds arranged alphabetically is also provided which gives the three strongest lines and their relative intensities and the pattern index number.

An alternative method, the FINK index,[13] has recently been provided for the same ASTM card file. The listing for the FINK index contains the interplanar spacing values of the first eight strong lines in the pattern. The listing contains multiple entries for each compound, the first six strong lines being brought into the primary index position in turn. The lines of higher spacing are listed following the last value in the original sequence. This listing is designed to overcome the intensity variation produced by preferred orientation in the sample, in both x-ray and in electron diffraction.

[8] Brentano, J. C. M., J. App. Phys., **17,** 420, 1946.

[9] Hanawalt, J. D., and Rinn, H. W., Ind. Eng. Chem., Anal. Ed., **8,** 244, 1936.

[10] Hanawalt, J. D., Rinn, H. W., and Frevel, L. K., Ind. Eng. Chem., Anal. Ed., **10,** 457, 1938.

[11] ASTM Card File supplied by the American Society for Testing and Materials, 1916 Race Street, Philadelphia 3, Pa.

[12] Index to the Powder Diffraction File, ASTM Special Technical Publication 48-M2, American Society for Testing and Materials, Philadelphia, 1963.

[13] FINK, Inorganic Index to the Powder Diffraction File, ASTM Special Technical Publication 48-M2, American Society for Testing and Materials, Philadelphia, 1963.

An additional aid to identification is the Matthews co-ordinate index which can also be used with the ASTM card file. This is a set of cards which can be stacked to build up a description of the compound using such factors as the knowledge of elements present or not present and physical properties of the material such as color and density in addition to interplanar spacing values. The Matthews index cross references "co-ordinate addresses" obtained by the composite description to the ASTM card file.

Cases will be encountered of compounds whose structure including unit cell parameters and atomic positions is given in the literature, but whose pattern is not included in the ASTM index. For these cases crystallographic programs are available for the computation of interplanar spacings and intensities of lines in the powder pattern. Programs suitable for particular computer installations can be found in the International Union of Crystallography World List.

Compound Identification by Unit Cell Determination.—An alternative approach to the data file method is to determine the unit cell parameters of the individual components of the specimen. Where small single crystals of the unknown compound are available J. D. H. Donnay and G. Donnay[14] suggest that the single crystal diffraction pattern be analyzed to obtain the unit cell. This can be carried out using either the Weissenberg Method[15], the Buerger precession method[16] or a combination of these. The Donnays have prepared a comprehensive determinative table[14] to enable a compound to be identified from the unit cell symmetry and dimensions.

It is possible also to determine the unit cell from the interplanar spacing values of the powder diffraction pattern. This procedure has normally been applied in unit cell determination on the isolated patterns of compounds of known constitution. It is possible, however, to index the pattern and determine the unit cell of a constituent in a mixture. Graphical methods of indexing cubic, tetragonal and hexagonal patterns have been developed by Bunn[17] which involve only one variable parameter. The charts used in this method must be drawn to a very large scale to be effective.

A system for pattern indexing of structures of general symmetry has been developed by Ito[18] and applied to the determination of a large number of unit cells by de Wolff.[19] This method depends on accurate interplanar spacing measurement and a careful evaluation of errors is necessary to eliminate false unit cell determinations. An alternate method applicable to cells having orthogonal parameters has been developed by Hesse.[20] This procedure is also dependent on accurate interplanar spacing measurement. A computer program combining these methods has recently been described by Scatturin.[21]

QUANTITATIVE ANALYSIS

Introduction.—The relative intensity of the diffraction pattern of a component in a mixture varies directly as the concentration and inversely as the mean absorption coefficient of the mixture.

For a mixture of compounds having the same absorption coefficients, as in the case of polymorphism, a linear relation between line intensity and concentration exists.

[14] Crystal Data Determinative Tables, Donnay, J. D. H., and Donnay, G., Second Edition, ACA Monograph 5, American Crystallographic Association, 1963.
[15] Buerger, M. J., Elementary Crystallography, John Wiley and Sons, New York, 1956.
[16] Buerger, M. J., The Precession Method in X-ray Crystallography, John Wiley and Sons, New York, 1964.
[17] Bunn, C. W., Chemical Crystallography, Oxford University Press, London, 1945.
[18] Ito, T., X-ray Studies of Polymorphism, Maruzen, Tokyo, 1950.
[19] de Wolff, P. M., Acta Cryst., **14,** 579, 1961.
[20] Hesse, R., Acta Cryst., **1,** 200, 1948.
[21] Scatturin, V., Abstract Sl. 14 International Union of Crystallography 6th Congress, Rome, Italy, 1963.

In general, since the mass absorption coefficient of an element increases rapidly with atomic number, the absorption effect can be large. The relative line intensity will be increased when the compound has a higher absorption coefficient than the mean absorption coefficient of the specimen. The absorption effect was first treated by Alexander and Klug.[22]

Quantitative analysis can be carried out using either the counter diffractometer or any of the photographic cameras. The counter detector has the advantage that a direct reading is obtained, and that the counter response curve is linear up to high counting rates. In the photographic method a microphotometer must be used and in precise work the intensity *vs.* density characteristic of the film must be determined using a calibrating wedge or stepped sector.

The peak intensity of a powder diffraction line varies with the line width, and broadening can occur due to fine particle size or residual lattice strain in the specimen. To eliminate the variations in intensity ratio due to differences of this type the total intensity of the diffraction line must be used, and this obtained by scanning at a uniform rate or step counting in equal intervals across the diffraction line.

The measured intensity also depends on the number of crystallites oriented in the diffraction position and care in specimen preparation is needed to ensure random orientation.

The experimental procedures for counter and photographic methods have been reviewed in detail by Klug and Alexander.[23] A comprehensive series of articles on powder diffraction, and particularly on photographic techniques is given by Peiser *et al.*[24]

Quantitative Analysis of a Mixture of N Compounds.—Alexander and Klug[22] have derived relations for the analysis of binary mixtures and for the determination of a desired component in a mixture using an internal standard. A general statement of the problem of a multi-component mixture has been given by Black[25] based on the relative intensities of reference lines in the mixture and in the pure compounds. Black's treatment is given here, and has been modified to include the use of standard samples made up of mixtures of the components. This will permit standard specimens to be made which are closely equivalent to the unknown in the mean absorption coefficient and the intensities of the reference lines, with a consequent increase in accuracy of the analysis. The specimen contains N compounds, the volume fraction of the ith component being f_i and I_i the integrated intensity of the reference lines of this component

$$I_i = K_i \frac{f_i}{\mu} \tag{4}$$

K_i is a constant characteristic of the reflection used for component i, the incident wavelength, and the geometry of the apparatus, and directly proportional to the intensity of the incident beam. Mu (μ) is the mean linear absorption coefficient of the specimen for the diffracted wavelength.

The integrated intensity I_i is obtained by scanning at a uniform angular velocity across the full angular width of the reflection. The use of the peak intensity ratio in this analysis can lead to errors due to difference in diffraction line width between the specimen and reference standard due to difference in particle size and residual lattice strain.

The relation can be expressed in terms of the mass fraction x_i as

[22] Alexander, L., and Klug, H. P., Anal. Chem., **20**, 886, 1948.
[23] Klug, H. P., and Alexander, L. E., X-ray Diffraction Procedures for Polycrystalline and Amorphous Materials, John Wiley and Sons, New York, 1954.
[24] Peiser, H. S., Rooksby, H. P., and Wilson, A. J. C., X-ray Diffraction by Polycrystalline Materials, The Institute of Physics, London, 1955.
[25] Black, R. H., Norelco Reporter, **10**, No. 1, 14, 1963.

$$I_i = \frac{K_i x_i}{\rho_i \cdot \mu_m} \tag{5}$$

ρ_i = density of component i

μ_m is the mean mass absorption coefficient of the specimen and is given by the relation

$$\mu_m = \Sigma\, \mu_m{}^i \cdot x_i \tag{6}$$

where $\mu_m{}^i$ is the mass absorption coefficient of the compound i.

The mass absorption coefficient of a compound is determined from the mass absorption coefficients of its constituent elements by a similar relation

$$\mu_m{}^i = \sum_e g_e \mu_m{}^e \tag{7}$$

where g_e is the mass fraction of the element e in the compound and $\mu_m{}^e$ is its mass absorption coefficient. A comprehensive table of the mass absorption coefficients for the elements, for the range of wavelengths used in diffraction, is given in the International Tables for X-ray Crystallography Vol. III.[26]

In theory it is possible to compute the constant K_i for the compound from a knowledge of the atomic arrangement in the lattice, the temperature factor, the spectrometer geometry and the incident beam intensity. In practice, however, the factor K_i is eliminated by obtaining the ratio of the integrated intensities of the reference line in the unknown and standard specimens.

The ratio r_i of the intensity in the specimen to that of the standard

$$r_i = \frac{I_i}{I_i^s} = \frac{x_i}{x_s{}^i} \cdot \frac{\mu_m{}^s}{\mu_m} \tag{8}$$

The unknowns x_i and μ_m of the specimen are obtained as

$$\frac{x_i}{\mu_m} = r_i \cdot \frac{x_i^s}{\mu_m{}^s} \tag{9}$$

Two auxiliary equations are obtained. The first from the condition that, where the intensity ratios of all component compounds are obtained, the sum of the mass fractions is unity.

$$\Sigma\, x_i = 1 \tag{10}$$

The second is the relation for the mean mass absorption coefficient of the specimen

$$\mu_m = \Sigma\, x_i \mu_m{}^i \tag{11}$$

There are $N + 2$ possible equations in the $N + 1$ unknown weight fractions.

It is therefore possible to determine the constitution with the measurement of one less ratio than the total number of unknowns, provided that the mass absorption coefficient of the residual compound is known.

Binary Mixtures.—In the case of a binary mixture, one ratio is sufficient

$$x_1 = \frac{r_1 \cdot x_1{}^s}{\mu_m{}^s} \cdot \mu_m \tag{12}$$

The mean absorption coefficient of the specimen

[26] International Tables for X-ray Crystallography, Vol. 3, Kynoch, Birmingham, 1962, p. 175.

$$\mu_m = x_1\mu_m^{(1)} + (1 - x_1)\mu_m^{(2)} \tag{13}$$

Combining these the binary relation is obtained

$$x_1 = \frac{\mu_m^{(2)} \cdot r_1 x_1^s}{\mu_m^s + (\mu_m^{(2)} - \mu_m^{(1)}) r_1 x_1^s} \tag{14}$$

This relation has been tested by Klug and Alexander[23] using quartz-beryllium, quartz-cristobalite and quartz-potassium chloride mixtures. The quartz-α cristobalite mixture provided a test of the binary relation where the components have equal mass absorption coefficients. Close agreement between the above relation and the known constitution of the mixtures was obtained.

Internal Standard Method.—Klug and Alexander[23] have used an internal standard method similar to that used in emission spectroscopy to analyze for components in an unknown matrix. Standard material is added to obtain a specimen with a known weight fraction x_p of the added constituent p. The new weight fraction of a component i

$$x_i' = x_i(1 - x_p) \tag{15}$$

The ratio of intensities between the standard and constituent i gives the new weight fraction

$$x_i' = \frac{I_i}{I_p} \cdot \frac{\rho_i}{\rho_p} \cdot \frac{K_p}{K_i} \cdot x_p \tag{16}$$

The ratio of the constants of diffraction can be measured by obtaining the same line intensities from a standard specimen containing both constituents

$$\frac{K_p}{K_i} = \frac{I_p^s}{I_i^s} \cdot \frac{x_i^s}{x_p^s} \cdot \frac{\rho_p}{\rho_i} \tag{17}$$

where, as before the superscript s indicates measurements on a standard specimen.

The internal standard method has the disadvantage of dilution of the specimen which decreases the line intensities of the required constituents, and it increases the probability of pattern overlap. These can be overcome by using a standard of high symmetry, having few pattern lines, and of low absorption to minimize the intensity loss in the specimen pattern. The choice of an internal standard having particles of an essentially spherical or random shape can be used to minimize preferred orientation in a specimen. One example of a suitable standard is magnesium oxide, (MgO), which in addition to having spherical particles is of low absorption and has a simple pattern.

Combined Diffraction–Absorption Technique.—An alternative procedure is to determine the mean absorption coefficient of the specimen, by the x-ray absorption technique, in addition to the determination of diffraction line intensity ratios. This permits Eq. 12 to be used directly to give the weight fractions

$$x_i = \frac{r_i x_i^s}{\mu_m^s} \cdot \mu_m \tag{12}$$

This method has been treated by Leroux, Lennox and Kay.[27] A variation on this method, in which the absorption coefficient is determined for a thin specimen by measuring the intensity of x-rays diffracted by an underlying standard has been described by Williams.[28]

[27] Leroux, J., Lennox, D. H., and Kay, K., Anal. Chem., **25,** 740, 1953.
[28] Williams, P. P., Anal. Chem., **31,** 1842, 1959.

Relative Concentration of Compounds in a Matrix.—The relations for weight fraction determination can be used, without reference to specimen absorption, to determine the relative concentrations of several compounds in a matrix. In this case the sum of the relative weight fractions is taken as unity. The mean absorption coefficient becomes an undetermined constant. This treatment can also be used for a specimen in which an undetermined amount of amorphous diluent is added.

Preferred Orientation.—The intensity ratio method is based on the assumption that a random orientation of crystallites exists. In solid specimens preferred orientation can be introduced by temperature gradients during cooling and by almost every forming method, including rolling and extrusion. In the case of powders it can be introduced during specimen preparation by pressure or flow where the particles do not have spherical or random shape.

The effect can be detected for any component by measuring the intensity ratios, between specimen and standard, for two or more lines whose Miller indexes are not related by an order factor, that is, planes which do not have the same orientation in the specimen. If the ratios do not agree within the standard deviation, preferred orientation is the most likely cause.

The effect has been examined extensively by Birks,[29] and he obtained a very great reduction in preferred orientation by reducing crystallite size by grinding. This has the advantage that it also reduces intensity variation due to extinction effects which occur in large crystallites.

The reduction in preferred orientation using a powder of spherical or randomly shaped crystallites as an internal standard or as a diluent has also been cited.

ANALYSIS OF SOLID SOLUTIONS BY LATTICE PARAMETER MEASUREMENT

Solid Solutions.—The unit cell dimensions can be measured with high accuracy, of between 1:20,000 and 1:50,000, with normally available equipment including the Debye-Scherrer and symmetrical focusing cameras, and the standard counter diffractometer. The change in unit cell parameters with constitution can therefore be used as a sensitive method of analysis of a compound.

Vegard[30] observed that a nearly linear change in lattice parameter with solute concentration occurred in binary solid solutions of metals. A similar change occurs in solid solutions of inorganic compounds where the solution is formed by partial isomorphous replacement of one or more atoms in the unit cell by solute atoms. Departures from linearity occur but Vegard's "law" is obeyed with reasonable accuracy for a large number of solid solutions.

Examples of compounds where isomorphous replacement occurs on one lattice site and double oxides of the type $(Na,K)NbO_3$;[31] and spinels of the form $(Ni,Mn)_{1.5}FeTi_{0.5}O_4$, and $Ni(Fe,Al)_2O_4$. The lattice parameter changes over the full solid solution range have been determined for these compounds.[32] To use the lattice parameter alone in analysis of a compound of this type it must be established that the stochiometric formula is followed.

In the general analytical case knowledge of the lattice parameter changes over the phase field will enable the range of possible constitutions to be mapped by unit cell determination.

[29] Birks, L. S., Naval Research Laboratory, Washington, Report H2517, 1945.
[30] Vegard, L., Z. Krist., **67**, 239, 1928.
[31] Structure Reports Vol. 18, p. 428.
[32] Structure Reports Vol. 18, p 453.

The lattice parameter changes for a number of inorganic solid solutions are given in Structure Reports[33] and in the case of metals the lattice parameter for a large number of systems has been collected by Pearson.[34] The accuracy to which the solute concentration can be determined depends directly on the slope of the lattice parameter *vs.* concentration curve. The rate of parameter change and the accuracy of analysis for a group of binary aluminum alloys is given in Table 11-1. Concentrations can be measured to

TABLE 11-1. ALUMINUM ALLOYS

Solute	δ (*a/a Per Atomic Percent*)	*Analysis Accuracy,*[a] (*Atomic Percent*)
Thorium	935×10^{-5}	0.002
Cadmium	576×10^{-5}	0.0035
Magnesium	104×10^{-5}	0.019
Germanium	52×10^{-5}	0.039
Silver	3.5×10^{-5}	0.6
Lithium	-9.2×10^{-5}	0.22
Zinc	-14.9×10^{-5}	0.13
Silicon	-40.5×10^{-5}	0.05
Cadmium	-74.8×10^{-5}	0.027
Copper	-85×10^{-5}	0.024
Manganese	-151×10^{-5}	0.013
Chromium	-182×10^{-5}	0.011

[a] Accuracy based on lattice parameter measurement to a/a = ±1:50,000.

±0.01 atomic percent in the most favorable cases and to 0.1 atomic percent in normal alloys. This compares favorably with the accuracy obtainable by emission methods.

Methods of Accurate Lattice Parameter Measurement.—The precision determination of lattice parameters involves the extraction of instrumental aberrations. These are systematic functions of the Bragg Angle, and it was shown by Bradley and Jay[35] that most of these tend to zero in the back reflection region where 2θ approaches 180°. Measurement of diffraction lines in this region can yield highly accurate interplanar spacing values. The residual systematic error can be removed by plotting the unit cell parameter values against a suitable function of θ, or by computing the systematic error and carrying out a least squares refinement.

The diffraction cameras normally used for precision determination are the symmetric back reflection camera which records diffraction lines for $90° < 2\theta < 180°$ and the Debye-Scherrer Circular camera.

The instrumental aberrations in the cameras and the diffractometer are introduced by beam divergence, specimen absorption, and alignment errors, particularly errors produced by displacement of the specimen. These have been summarized for both camera and diffractometer in the International Tables of Crystallography.[36]

In the symmetrical focusing camera the major errors expressed in $\phi = \pi/2 - \theta$ are the absorption which varies as $\tan^2 \phi$ and the specimen displacement and vertical divergence which have the form $\tan^2 \phi \tan \phi$. Extrapolation to $\phi = 0°$ of a plot of lattice parameter against the function $\phi \tan \phi$ is recommended, and this function is tabulated.[36]

[33] Structure Reports, Vol. 8–18, A. J. C. Wilson, Ed., Oosthoek's Vitgevers M.I.J., Utrecht, 1956–1964.

[34] Pearson, W., Handbook of Lattice Spacings and Structures of Metals and Alloys, Pergamon, New York, 1958.

[35] Bradley, A. J., and Jay, A. H., Proc. Phys. Soc., **44**, 563, 1932.

[36] International Tables for Crystallography, Vol. 2, Sec. 4.7.4, p. 228.

In the Debye-Scherrer camera the eccentricity correction can be reduced to the eccentricity of the mounting shaft when the specimen is rotated. The major aberration is due to absorption. The absorption effect was investigated by Taylor[37] who derived an extrapolation function

$$\frac{1}{2}\left(\frac{\cos^2\theta}{\sin\theta} + \frac{\cos^2\theta}{\theta}\right) \tag{18}$$

This relation was tested and tabulated by Nelson and Riley.[36,38]

An analytic treatment for absorption by cylindrical specimens was carried out by B. E. Warren[39] and has the advantage that, for highly absorbing specimens the absorption error can be directly determined. A further correction for specimens of intermediate absorption has been derived by Mitchell.[40]

The diffractometer has approximate focusing, and systematic errors are small except for specimens of low absorption, where they can be reduced using thin specimens. The systematic errors have been derived by Wilson[41] and by Pike and Wilson[42] and tested extensively by Ladell *et al.*[43]

The major problem is to obtain a precise alignment to eliminate zero error and specimen displacement from the rotation axis. In the majority of diffractometers the detector is restricted to rotation on one side of the axis and alignment must be performed using the incident beam. In one design, produced by Siemens, the detector can scan past the $2\theta = 0°$ position and the specimen can be rotated through 180° so that the diffraction line can be measured on both sides of the incident axis, and correction made for zero error.

The systematic error displacement relations derived by Wilson are based on determination of the centroid position of the measured diffraction line. The displacement of the diffraction line centroid due to instrumental aberrations has been shown[42] to be the sum of the centroid displacements of the individual systematic errors. The wavelength used must be that of the centroid of the characteristic line.

Recent investigations have shown that the displacement of the chord centers[44] in regions of approximately linear slope is equal to the centroid displacement for small aberrations, and these centers can be used for interplanar spacing determinations.[45] The chord centers can be obtained rapidly with high accuracy and are relatively independent of interference from neighboring lines. The wavelength value used in the determination must be that of the corresponding chord center of the characteristic line. The standard wavelength values quoted by Bearden are the extrapolation of the chord centers to maximum intensity.

Computer programs for systematic error extraction and least squares refinement based on the systematic error relations, are available, and considerably simplify the precision determination, particularly for noncubic structures.[46,47]

[37] Taylor, A., and Sinclair, H., Proc. Phys. Soc., **57**, 126, 1945.
[38] Nelson, J. B., and Riley, D. P., Proc. Phys. Soc., **57**, 60, 1945.
[39] Warren, B. E., J. App. Phys., **16**, 614, 1945.
[40] Mitchell, C. M., Code 12, Acta Cryst., **13**, 838, 1960.
[41] Wilson, A. J. C., Rev. Sci. Inst., **20**, 831, 1950; J. Sci. Inst., **27**, 321, 1950.
[42] Pike, E. R., and Wilson, A. J. C., Brit. J. App. Phys., **10**, 57, 1959.
[43] Ladell, J., Parrish, W., and Taylor, J., Acta Cryst., **12**, 253, 1959.
[44] Mitchell, C. M., Abstracts, 17th Pittsburgh Diffraction Conference, Mellon Institute, 1959.
[45] Mitchell, C. M., Abstracts, A.C.A. Meeting, Montana State College, Bozeman, 1964.
[46] Mitchell, C. M., and Milliken, K. S., Mines Branch Research Reports R80 and R81, Department of Mines and Technical Surveys, Ottawa, Canada.
[47] Mueller, M. H., and Heaton, L., Argonne National Laboratory, Argonne, Ill.

APPLICATIONS IN THE ANALYSIS OF SPECIAL MATERIALS

X-ray diffraction methods have been used in the analysis of a number of special materials. Those methods described elsewhere in Standard Methods of Chemical Analysis are the following.

1. Chapter 46, Volume III, Portland Cement.
   a. The possibilities of this technique in the analysis of Portland Cement are considered
2. Chapter 48, Volume III, Natural Fats.
   a. Characterization of crystal forms in fat analysis
3. Chapter 54, Volume III, Paint, Varnish, and Lacquer.
   a. Determination of anatase titanium dioxide in rutile titanium dioxide pigments
   b. Quality control of polycrystalline raw materials and for pigmented finished products
   c. Determination of particle size of pigments

   Chapter 37, Volume IIB, Paint, Varnish, and Lacquer.
   a. Identification and determination of organic and inorganic pigments, page 1685.
4. Chapter 58, Volume III, Plastics.
   a. Estimation of crystallinity in polymers
   b. Estimation of crystallinity in polyethylene
5. Chapter 59, Volume III, Rubber and Rubber Products.
   a. Identification of amines in rubber analysis
   b. Identification of antioxidants
   c. Identification of magnesium carbonate and magnesium oxide in rubber analysis
   d. Determination of zinc oxide filler in rubber
6. Chapter 61, Volume III, Soaps and Synthetic Detergents.
   a. Identification of water-insoluble materials in soap and syndet products
7. Chapter 64, Volume III, Determination of Water.
   a. Determination of water in crystalline substances

Chapter 12

CHEMICAL MICROSCOPY

By Harold F. Schaeffer
Professor of Chemistry
Westminster College
Fulton, Missouri

INTRODUCTION

In this brief survey of chemical microscopy, the various advantages of microscopic methods are presented by outlining specific procedures for a few representative applications in several selected categories. Although, as one naturally infers, microscopic methods are especially suited for analytical problems in which only minute samples are available, such methods may sometimes be preferred even when unlimited quantities of the sample are at hand. Small samples should require only small amounts of reagents. This fact renders it feasible to employ reagents which are too costly in the amounts required in a procedure carried out on the usual macroscale. In some instances considerable economies may be effected through the elimination of costly conventional apparatus. Work with highly combustible or explosive material may become quite safe when employed on the microscopic scale; and whenever a procedure involves reactions which liberate toxic, corrosive, or malodorous fumes, methods which require only microquantities become advantageous, indeed. Frequently the microprocedures save time; in certain instances they offer the sole, or at least, the preferred, means for solving a given problem (How else, for example, could one *conveniently* determine whether a certain powdered specimen contains sodium chloride and potassium nitrate, or sodium nitrate and potassium chloride?). It is also worth mentioning that, where the utmost in precision is not required, certain quantitative determinations may be carried out without losing any time weighing the original sample or the component sought.

QUALITATIVE ANALYSIS

GENERAL REMARKS

In the following procedures there will be repeated occasions to employ *micro pipets* for transferring reagents or sample solutions to the object slides. It will be understood that these pipets are merely ordinary 100-mm. melting point capillaries. These are sufficiently inexpensive to be disposable, and yet they are quite efficient. They quickly take up solutions by capillary action, and with a bit of care they consistently deliver a 0.033-ml. drop. Should the nature of the sample demand the use of smaller portions, it is possible to adopt a more elegant technique in which calibated wire loops replace the capillaries.[1]

When performing a test with which the analyst is not familiar, it is generally advisable to run a control on a known sample. Throughout this chapter, in stating sensitivi-

[1] Benedetti-Pichler, A. A., Microtechnique of Inorganic Analysis, John Wiley, New York, 1942.

ties for the various tests, there has been an attempt to be realistic, rather than to cite values which represent the ultimate limits attainable under ideal conditions. It should be recalled that sensitivities of the chemical tests performed under the microscope can be greatly influenced by variations in laboratory temperatures, relative humidity, presence of air currents, and other local conditions.

On occasion the analyst may be confronted with metallic objects and certain other solid specimens which are not to be marred, defaced, or destroyed (jewelry, ancient coins, antiques, art objects). In such instances it is frequently feasible to procure an adequate analytical sample by rubbing a ground-glass slide against some inconspicuous area of the specimen. (Microslides which have a one-inch etched square at one end are regularly available from supply houses.) The mark left on the ground glass can then be brought into solution by using a few drops of solvent or reagent, with or without warming, depending upon the nature of the substance involved.

INORGANIC ANALYSIS: TESTS FOR CATIONS

THE ALKALI GROUP

Sodium.—A frequent problem confronting the analyst is to determine whether the cation in a given substance is sodium or potassium. While adherents of the platinum-wire flame tests can claim very high sensitivity, the method does have its disadvantages. However, the well known reaction for identifying sodium ion with zinc uranyl acetate reagent can readily be applied in chemical microscopy. The reagent in this case is a saturated solution of the salt zinc uranyl acetate, $Zn(C_2H_3O_2)_2 \cdot UO_2(C_2H_3O_2)_2$, in 1:3 acetic acid. Using a melting-point capillary as a pipet, a droplet of solution to be tested is applied to the center of a clean slide. The drop is then evaporated just to dryness by placing the slide on a waterbath or on a small hot plate operating at about 100°C. After the slide has cooled to room temperature, a drop of the reagent solution is caused to flow across the sample residue. The presence of sodium ion causes the separation of characteristic crystals of sodium zinc uranyl acetate, $NaC_2H_3O_2 \cdot Zn(C_2H_3O_2)_2 \cdot 2UO_2(C_2H_3O_2)_2 \cdot xH_2O$. The crystals are monoclinic twins, some of which may resemble octahedra.[2] Lithium should be absent, since it forms a similar crystalline triple acetate. Other members of the alkali group offer no interference, but phosphate and carbonate ions should be absent. Good positive tests for sodium ion are obtained with a residue containing less than 4 μg. of the element.

Ammonium.—To perform the test for the ammonium ion, one may use a drop of the original sample solution, or, if available material is very limited, he may use the mixture left on the slide after the foregoing sodium test. One can salvage this mixture by rinsing into a small crucible with one or two drops of water. One or two drops of 6 *M* sodium hydroxide solution are added to the crucible contents, and the crucible is promptly covered with a slide bearing a hanging drop of 5 percent chloroplatinic acid solution. If sufficient sodium hydroxide has been added to render the reaction mixture alkaline, any ammonium ion will be released as ammonia gas, which will react with the chloroplatinic acid to form the insoluble ammonium chloroplatinate, $(NH_4)_2[PtCl_6]$.[3] When the slide is placed under the microscope, the latter compound appears as beautiful yellow octahedra. As little as 0.5 μg. may be detected. Instead of using a conventional microslide for suspending the hanging drop of reagent, a petrographic half-slide may be found more convenient. This will decrease the risk of upsetting. Slight warming of the reaction crucible, especially with low ammonium concentrations, will hasten the evolution of ammonia.

[2] Feilstein and Ward, Analyst, **56,** 245, 1931.

[3] Benedetti-Pichler, A. A., Microtechnique of Inorganic Analysis, John Wiley, New York, 1942, p. 93.

Potassium.—Potassium, in the absence of ammonium ion, can be detected by a concentrated solution of chloroplatinic acid. When a drop of reagent is allowed to flow into a test drop on an object slide, the presence of potassium causes the gradual appearance of octahedra of potassium chloroplatinate. Their appearance is similar to that of the crystals formed in the test for ammonium ion.[4] Approximately 0.5 μg. can be detected. Cesium, rubidium, and thallium should be absent, or if present, should be in very low concentration to prevent interference. Should it be necessary to work with a test drop containing ammonium ion, this can be eliminated by evaporating to dryness on platinum foil, then heating the residue carefully just at dull redness, until the ammonia has been expelled. The final residue is dissolved in a drop of water, transferred to a slide, then tested as described above.

ZINC, CADMIUM, COPPER, COBALT

Zinc.—A very interesting, as well as useful, reagent in chemical microscopy is potassium mercuric thiocyanate, $K_2[Hg(SCN)_4]$. Under favorable conditions this salt reacts with several cations to form insoluble double salts which separate as characteristic crystals.[5] When a drop of nearly saturated potassium mercuric thiocyanate solution is applied to a dilute test drop containing the zinc ion, there is a prompt separation of zinc mercuric thiocyanate, $Zn(SCN)_2 \cdot Hg(SCN)_2$, in the form of feathery crosses, daggers, and related forms, which are characteristic. This has been claimed to be one of the most sensitive microtests for zinc. As little as 1.3 μg. can be detected in a test drop containing 1 part zinc ion in 25,000. If the sample contains more than a trace of strong acid, a small amount of ammonium or sodium acetate should be added.

Cadmium.—In the presence of cadmium ion potassium mercuric thiocyanate causes more slowly the separation of orthorhombic prisms, typical of the cadmium compound. When the reagent is added to a test solution which contains both zinc and cadmium, the crystalline form of the product may be considerably modified. The presence of a small quantity of cadmium with much zinc results in the loss of the feathery appearance which is so typical of the latter metal. With conditions reversed, *i.e.*, a small quantity of zinc in the presence of much cadmium, the zinc may go undetected. Preferably, tests for these two ions should be on samples from which one of the ions has been removed.

Copper.—Most attractive crystals of the copper salt, $Cu(SCN)_2 \cdot Hg(SCN)_2 \cdot H_2O$, are formed by the reaction of potassium mercuric thiocyanate solution with a solution containing copper(II) ions. The crystals separate as greenish-yellow, mossy dendrites and radiates, as well as individual pointed prisms and boat-shaped structures. The individual crystals seem to exhibit parallel extinction between crossed Nicol prisms, but they do not show bright polarization colors. At a copper concentration of 1 part in 20,000, less than 2 μg. of the metal can be detected or identified by the separation of characteristic crystals within approximately two minutes. Incidentally, if there is any doubt concerning the acidity of the test drop, the addition of the powdered sodium acetate may be deferred until after the addition of the reagent. In the event that no crystals separate within a few minutes, the addition of sodium acetate then may favor their formation. Under appropriate conditions the cobalt ion also causes the formation of groups of beautiful, deep blue prisms of its double salt. However, if the solution is dilute, these crystals may not separate until partial evaporation of the preparation has occurred. It might be mentioned in passing that auric chloride solutions react to yield fine orange-red crystals and mossy dendrites resembling the form of those obtained in the test for copper. At a concentration of 1 part per 1000, 30 μg. of gold will yield a good

[4] Chamot, Emile Monin, and Mason, Clyde Walter, Handbook of Chemical Microscopy, Vol. II, 2nd. Ed., John Wiley, New York, 1940, p. 65.
[5] *Ibid.*, pp. 136–144.

test. In all the foregoing tests with potassium mercuric thiocyanate, any appreciable concentrations of lead, manganese, silver, nickel, and iron should be avoided.

Copper–Cobalt Mixtures.—A reagent which is useful for detecting ions of both copper and cobalt in the same sample is prepared from isoquinoline and ammonium thiocyanate.[6] Since the actual reagent solution should not be kept very long, there should be two stock solutions. One of these is merely a 1 *M* aqueous solution of ammonium thiocyanate; the other is prepared by dissolving 13 g. of isoquinoline in sufficient 1 *M* hydrochloric acid to yield 100 ml. of solution. The final reagent is obtained by mixing equal volumes of the two stock solutions a short time before using. The individual stock solutions seem to be stable indefinitely.

When a drop of the mixed reagent is caused to flow into a test drop containing cobalt chloride or cobalt acetate, droplets of a rich blue, oil-like liquid begin to separate; gradually these are replaced by beautiful blue crystals of the derivative having the composition $[Co(C_9H_7N)_2](CNS)_2$. The crystals appear as individual prisms of a deep blue color peculiar to the cobalt compound. At a concentration of 1 part cobalt in 4000, the test will readily detect 8 μg. of the metal. The presence of sulfate ion appears to reduce the sensitivity somewhat. With the same reagent the copper(II) ion causes the separation of small characteristic thin leaves or plates of a yellow-green color. Whether present as acetate, chloride, or sulfate, the copper(II) ion can be readily detected when it represents as little as 1 part in 15,000. An advantage of the thiocyanate-isoquinoline reagent is its facility in revealing both copper and cobalt when both are present in the same sample, even in the presence of nickel. (If the liquid surrounding the cobalt-copper precipitate is transferred to another slide, with a drop of water if necessary, it can be used in the test for nickel to be described later.)

In the absence of copper and cobalt, the thiocyanate-isoquinoline reagent also serves to detect zinc, which yields characteristic colorless needles and clusters. The sensitivity is comparable with that of the copper test, namely, as little as 2 μg. in a microtest drop, when present as the acetate. At a concentration of 1 part per 1000, cadmium likewise yields a test in the form of colorless prisms, singly or as X's.

NICKEL

When present as its complex hexammine ion, nickel is readily identified by means of a 1 percent solution of dimethylglyoxime in 95 percent ethanol,[7,8] as observed by Tschugaeff early in the present century. More recently Kirschner and Korenman showed that the compound could also be applied as an effective microchemical reagent.[9,10,11,12] If the test solution contains nickel nitrate, a drop is placed on a clean slide, which is then inverted over a small beaker or other small vessel containing concentrated ammonium hydroxide. Unless the original sample solution was too acidic, a 1-minute exposure should suffice to convert any of the nickel ion into its hexammine complex. Should there be a precipitate of hydroxides of other metals during the ammonia treatment, the clear solution should be transferred to another slide. When a drop of dimethylglyoxime reagent is then added to the alkaline test drop just prepared, the nickel will be revealed by the separation of very small red-, or magenta-colored needles, individually or in clusters. A mere fraction of a microgram of nickel yields a positive

[6] Schaeffer, Harold F., Anal. Chem., **23,** 1674–5, 1951.
[7] Tschugaeff, L., Compt. rend., **145,** 675–681, 1907.
[8] Tschugaeff, L., Ber., **38,** 2520, 1905.
[9] Kirschner, F., Mikrochemie, **1,** 88, 1923.
[10] Korenman, I. M., Mikrochemie, **21,** 17020, 1936.
[11] Korenman, I. M., Zavodscaya Lab., **6,** 308–311, 1937.
[12] Korenman, I. M., *Ibid.*, **7,** 428–429, 1938.

test. If a solution has been tested for copper and cobalt by means of the thiocyanate-isoquinoline reagent discussed earlier, a test for nickel can be performed on the solution which surrounds the precipitate. For this purpose the clear solution is transferred to a clean slide. After inverting the slide over a container of ammonium hydroxide long enough to insure alkalinity in the hanging-drop, the slide is turned right-side-up and the reaction with dimethylglyoxime is carried out as described previously.

GOLD AND THE PLATINUM METALS

Gold.—As a microtest for gold in very dilute solutions (present as chlorauric acid, for example) it has been suggested that a drop of the sample be treated with a drop of reagent consisting of 2 parts of saturated aqueous picric acid and 1 part of 10 percent ammonium hydroxide.[13] This reaction is said to be capable of detecting as little as 0.2 μg. gold, but certain other metals, including copper and palladium, for example, also react, yielding similar crystals. An alternative method[14] employs a 0.4 *M* solution of isoquinoline in 1 *M* hydrochloric acid. The metal should be present as the chloride in 1 *M* hydrochloric acid. When a drop of this reagent is added to a test drop containing gold, the metal combines to yield characteristic pale-yellow needles. At a concentration of 1 part in 5000 the test will reveal the presence of 6.5 μg. of gold. Platinum, ruthenium, and iridium should be absent, although none of these would be mistaken for gold; each yields its own typical crystalline derivative. If necessary, any possible gold in the acid test solution can be isolated from the other metals by extracting with ethyl acetate. Drops of the extract are then carefully evaporated on a clean slide, and the resulting residue is dissolved by adding a drop of 1 *M* hydrochloric acid, after which the test is performed as described above. In the absence of other members of the group, the isoquinoline reagent may serve to detect ruthenium when present as the trichloride in 1 *M* hydrochloric acid. As little as 5 μg. can be identified by the gradual appearance of thin, amber-colored, lath-shaped crystals.

Palladium.—A convenient reagent for palladium is a 0.5 *M* solution of 2-cyanopyridine in 2 *M* hydrochloric acid.[15] The metal should be in solution as palladium(II) chloride in 1 *M* hydrochloric acid. A drop of reagent added to a test drop on a microslide will reveal palladium by the separation of diamond-shaped crystals, together with formations which resemble serrated daggers. With a palladium concentration of 1 part in 7500, a distinct positive test for 4–5 μg. of palladium is obtained in approximately 1 minute. Under the conditions indicated, no other member of the platinum group yields a crystalline product with 2-cyanopyridine. An alternative method suggested by Korenman is more sensitive but less convenient.[16] The reagent consists of a saturated solution of dimethylglyoxime in a solvent prepared by mixing 2.5 ml. glacial acetic acid with 97.5 ml. of 50 percent ethanol. On a clean slide one drop of the test solution is evaporated to dryness by warming gently. After the slide cools, a drop of reagent solution is caused to flow across the dry residue, whereupon the presence of palladium is indicated by the formation of small, thin, yellow needles. It is claimed that under favorable conditions, as little as 0.3 μg. of palladium can be detected.

Osmium.—Whether in the form of potassium osmate, K_2OsO_4, or osmium tetroxide (also called osmic acid), osmium can be detected on the microscale by means of 1,2,3,4-tetrahydro-6-methoxyquinoline.[17] The reagent is made up as a 3 percent solution of

[13] Korenman, I. M., Pharm. Zentralhalle, **72,** 225–226, 1931.
[14] Schaeffer, Harold F., Anal. Chem., **31,** 1111, 1959.
[15] Schaeffer, Harold F., in N. D. Cheronis, Ed., Proceedings of the International Symposium on Microchemical Techniques, Pennsylvania State University, 1961, Interscience Publishers, New York, 1962.
[16] Korenman, I. M., J. Appl. Chem. (U.S.S.R.), **13,** 1523–1524, 1940.
[17] Schaeffer, Harold F., Anal. Chem., **31,** 1112, 1959.

the organic base in 2 *M* hydrochloric acid. Although not completely stable, the solution yields satisfactory results for at least a month. To determine the presence of osmium, one drop of test solution is added to a drop of reagent on an object slide. After the preparation assumes a dark green color, it is examined under a magnification of 50–100 diameters. A positive test is indicated by the appearance of characteristic crystals resembling feathery V's, X's, and daggers. Small concentrations of copper or iridium apparently do not inhibit the separation of the osmium derivative; however, gold, platinum, and ruthenium should be absent. The presence of 15 μg. of osmium yields a positive test within 10 minutes. If interfering metals are present, the osmium tetroxide is easily removed because of its high volatility. To bring about this isolation of the osmium, a slide bearing a hanging drop of reagent is placed over a microcrucible containing one or two drops of the test solution. With a sample containing 20 μg. of the osmium, sufficient vapor generally reaches the hanging drop to form a positive test within 10 minutes.

Platinum.—A very satisfactory reagent for the microscopic detection of platinum in relatively low concentrations is 4-bromoisoquinoline, in the form of a 0.4 *M* solution in 1 *M* hydrochloric acid.[18] The solution retains its efficacy over a 2-month period. The sample to be tested is brought into solution as chloroplatinic acid in 1 *M* hydrochloric acid. When a microdrop of reagent is applied to a similar test drop on a slide, the presence of platinum is indicated by the gradual separation of long, branched needles having a yellow color. At a platinum concentration of 1 part in 75,000 as little as 0.5 μg. of the metal can be identified in an uncovered preparation within 2–2.5 minutes, even if the test solution is also 0.125 *M* in respect to the copper(II) ion. Other members of the platinum group, as well as gold, should be absent. If no other members of the group are present the bromoisoquinoline reagent can be used for the detection of iridium. As little as 5 μg. of iridium, as the tetrachloride in 1 *M* hydrochloric acid, will react to form comparatively small lenticular crystals of a bright yellow color. These crystals may occur singly or in small clusters.

URANIUM

Uranium can readily be detected or identified by an adaptation of the zinc uranyl acetate test for sodium, which was discussed earlier. Any uranium in the sample should be in the form of uranyl acetate or nitrate. In case of doubt, the material may be evaporated to near dryness on the slide, then dissolved in dilute nitric acid. The resulting solution is evaporated, and the new residue is taken up in very dilute acetic acid. Toward one end of the slide a little solid sodium acetate and twice its bulk of zinc acetate are dissolved in 1 or 2 drops of 1:3 acetic acid by stirring with a thin glass thread. After this mixture has been carefully evaporated to obtain a uniform film of the reagent, the test drop, acidified with acetic acid, is placed nearby. By means of a glass thread the test drop is then caused to flow across the reagent film. The presence of uranium will be indicated by the separation of two main types of crystals; there will be some highly refractive tetrahedra of sodium uranyl acetate, along with some of the octahedra-like crystals of the triple salt previously described in connection with the test for sodium.

ANION ANALYSIS

HALIDES

Chloride.—If the addition of silver nitrate solution to a test drop results in the formation of a white precipitate which is insoluble in nitric acid, there is a possibility of

[18] Schaeffer, Harold F., Anal. Chem., **36**, 169, 1964.

chloride, iodide, bromide, cyanide, bromate, thiocyanate, or certain other ions. Should chloride be present it may be confirmed by converting into chromyl chloride. On the reaction slide a small quantity of powdered potassium dichromate is added to a test drop, and the mixture is then carefully evaporated to dryness. A small drop of concentrated sulfuric acid is added to the dried residue and a glass ring (approximately 18 mm. in diameter by 7 mm. in height) is placed around the mixture. (If a glass ring is not available the reaction may be carried out in a microcrucible.) After placing a slide with a hanging drop of water over the ring, the assembly is set aside for about 10 minutes. During this time any chloride ion in the original drop should react with the sulfuric acid to yield chromyl chloride, which, in turn, yields hydrochloric and chromic acids when absorbed in the hanging drop of water. After turning the slide over, it is carefully heated over the *small* flame of a good microburner until the drop has been evaporated *ust* to dryness. This procedure should expel the hydrogen chloride and leave a thin film of chromic acid. The latter is then identified by covering with a small drop of water and adding a very small grain of silver nitrate. A reddish precipitate of silver chromate constitutes a positive test.

Bromide.—Bromide ion can be detected by the separation of a crystalline bromoderivative of an aromatic amine, such as aniline or *m*-phenylenediamine.[19] On an object slide a drop of the solution to be investigated is rendered strongly acidic by the addition of 1:4 sulfuric acid. After placing a glass ring around the solution, a pinch of powdered potassium dichromate is added; promptly a half-slide bearing a hanging drop of *m*-phenylenediamine hydrochloride solution is placed on top of the glass ring. In the presence of bromide ion, the mixture releases bromine, which in turn reacts to produce small highly refractive needles of 2,4,6-tribromophenylenediamine. These crystals, which exhibit parallel extinction, develop best if the evolution of the bromine is slow. For optimum results the phenylenediamine solution should be relatively dilute (only about $\frac{1}{20}$ saturated), and should contain a trace of sulfuric acid. The test readily reveals less than 1 μg. of bromide ion. If no crystals appear after 10 minutes, it may be advisable to warm the reaction slide (or microcrucible) slightly.

Iodide.—In testing for iodide ion, a drop of sample is acidified with sulfuric acid or acetic acid, and a few grains of starch are added, followed by a granule of potassium nitrite or sodium nitrite. The presence of iodide in the original sample results in the liberation of elementary iodine, which then produces the familiar blue color with the starch. The color may range from a very faint blue to almost black, depending upon the amount of iodine released. Less than 1 μg. of iodide is required to give a test.

Fluoride.—Even in concentrated solutions certain anions do not react with silver nitrate to yield precipitates. These include fluoride, nitrate, chlorate, and perchlorate, among others. If there is any reason to suspect fluoride, it may be identified by converting it into crystalline sodium fluosilicate. A small quantity of the solid sample to be tested is dropped into a 5-ml. microbeaker, along with a few grains of crushed quartz, fluorine-free sand, or glass. After adding 1 or 2 drops of concentrated sulfuric acid the beaker is promptly covered with a half-slide bearing a hanging drop of water. In the absence of any apparent action, the beaker should be warmed briefly. The presence of fluoride should cause the formation of silicon tetrafluoride, which is absorbed by the water and hydrolyzed to yield fluosilicic acid and silicic acid. The latter, being insoluble, separates out as a precipitate which can be observed when the slide is turned over for examination under the microscope. Further confirmation is readily obtained by adding a few grains of sodium chloride to the center of the preparation on the slide. This results in the formation of the slightly soluble sodium fluosilicate, which separates in

[19] Mason, Clyde W., Mikrochemie, **4**, 145–148, 1926.

the form of small six-pointed stars and hexagonal plates. Approximately 0.25 mg. of fluorine will yield a positive test.

OTHER COMMON IONS

Chlorate.—Since chlorates as a group are rather soluble salts, the chlorate ion must be converted into some other radical for isolation and identification. Various reducing agents may transform chlor*ate* into chlor*ide*, which can be detected by any one of several methods. A satisfactory procedure is the following: a drop of test solution hanging from a slide is placed over a small crucible containing acetic acid to which some solid potassium sulfite (or sodium sulfite) has been added. The sulfur dioxide which is evolved is absorbed in the test drop where it reduces any chlorate ion present to chloride. The slide is turned over and carefully heated to evaporate the preparation barely to dryness. This should leave a residue containing only the chloride. The presence of chloride may be confirmed according to the previously described test, or according to the following procedure: the residue is dissolved in a droplet of water *in situ*, and a drop of silver nitrate solution is caused to flow in. A white precipitate indicates chloride ion was present, which in turn shows that the original sample contained chlorate. A drop containing 12–15 μg. of chlorate should yield a positive test.

Perchlorate.—Perchlorate ion can be identified in an aqueous test drop by applying, or sliding in, a fragment of strychnine sulfate, which should cause the separation of colorless rectangular lath-shaped crystals, some of which are grouped in paralell clusters. Between crossed Nicols, the individual crystals exhibit parallel extinction. A positive test may be obtained with a drop containing as little as about 8 μg.

Nitrate.—Not only does nitrate ion fail to yield a precipitate with silver nitrate; it likewise fails to form a precipitate with lead acetate or barium acetate. A satisfactory microreagent consists of a solution of nitron in 30 percent acetic acid.[20] A drop of this reagent, when caused to flow into a test drop containing nitrate, brings about a prompt separation of long, slender, acicular crystals, most of which are grouped together in the form of sheaves. Eventually there may also be a formation of laths, which exhibit parallel extinction. Iodide and bicarbonate radicals should be absent, as they may react if not sufficiently dilute. Should there be any doubt regarding the reason for the precipitate, slight warming of the slide will cause any product due to iodide or bicarbonate ion to quickly dissolve.

Cyanide.—Cyanides react with a silver nitrate solution to yield a copious white precipitate, which is insoluble in concentrated nitric acid. Unfortunately this precipitate generally consists of very fine particles, rather than well-defined, distinct crystals characteristic of silver cyanide. However, this precipitate, or some of the original solid sample, may be tested for cyanide ion by the following procedure: a small quantity of the solid is placed in a small crucible (or a 5-ml. beaker) with 2 or 3 drops of dilute sulfuric acid, and the reaction vessel is immediately covered with a slide bearing a small hanging drop of 5 percent silver nitrate solution. After warming gently at approximately 60°C. for a minute the assembly is set aside to permit any hydrogen cyanide fumes evolved to react with the silver nitrate. After several minutes the slide is searched for any crystals produced, using the 8-mm. objective and a 10× ocular. A positive test for cyanide is the separation of rather squat, colorless prisms which are comparatively small and highly refractive. Some crystals may appear as V's, as prisms with cleft ends, or even in the form of sheaves of slender needles. Upon draining off the bulk of the mother liquor the crystals should not dissolve when a drop of dilute nitric acid is added.

[20] Schaeffer, Harold F., Microscopy for Chemists, D. Van Nostrand, Princeton, N. J., 1953, p. 233.

In the event that no crystals are found in the silver nitrate drop, it may be advisable to replace the slide over the reaction vessel and heat for an additional period. If the original mixture is heated too strongly, the hydrogen cyanide may be evolved so rapidly that the resulting silver cyanide crystals will be too small and too poorly formed to be characteristic. In view of the fact that ordinary cyanides are not the sole compounds which can release hydrogen cyanide when heated with dilute sulfuric acid, it is important that the test sample be free from various complex ions, such as ferrocyanide.

It is, of course, quite feasible to carry out the test on liquid samples. Under favorable circumstances a single drop may suffice for the test. Since some aqueous solutions of cyanide hydrolyze sufficiently well without the addition of other reagents, it may be desirable first to determine whether the hanging drop of silver nitrate yields a crystalline precipitate without the use of acid, and without warming. If after 5 minutes no positive test results, one may warm the preparation and examine the hanging drop again. If this fails, one can make a third trial, using 1 or 2 drops of the dilute sulfuric acid. Working with 1 drop of sodium cyanide solution containing 1 part cyanide ion per 15,000, this procedure can readily reveal 2.3 μg. of cyanide without the use of acid.[21]

Sulfate.—Sulfate ion may be detected by precipitating with barium chloride or acetate, but the particles are actually too fine for identification purposes. If a granule of lead acetate is moved into a test drop containing sulfate, there is a prompt formation of a white granular precipitate. Upon standing for only a short time, the granular material gradually changes into rather small dendrites and aggregates of squat rhombic crystals. These dissolve in nitric acid only very slightly. As little as 6 μg. of sulfate ion can be detected by this method.

Phosphate.—Soluble orthophosphates react with silver nitrate to form a heavy, pale-yellow precipitate, which eventually yields small stars, crosses, clusters of fine needles, and other forms. These crystals are soluble in nitric acid. If the amount of sample is limited, the nitric acid solution should be evaporated to dryness on the slide and used as follows: "magnesia mixture" is prepared by adding a crystal of magnesium acetate and twice as much ammonium chloride to a drop of water on a slide; finally a drop of ammonium hydroxide is added. This mixture is next transferred to the residue from the nitric acid solution mentioned above. Upon warming the preparation gently, the presence of the orthophosphate ion is revealed by the separation of fair-sized feathery stars of magnesium ammonium phosphate. There may also be some prismatic forms after a time. Arsenates should be absent because they cause the separation of crystals which are identical in appearance to those formed in the presence of phosphate. However, confusion of the two with each other is avoided by recalling that, with silver nitrate, the arsenates form a dark red precipitate, instead of the yellow one formed by phosphate. If sufficient sample is at hand the test can be performed by introducing a particle of solid test sample into the drop of magnesia mixture, instead of using the evaporated residue mentioned above.

Arsenate.—The arsenate ion is readily identified by the separation of characteristic crystals of magnesium ammonium arsenate, $MgNH_4AsO_4 \cdot 6H_2O$. Phosphate must be absent because it yields similar crystals. The sample to be tested should be in an approximately 2 *M* nitric acid solution. If necessary, it is feasible to evaporate a test drop on an object slide and then add a drop of 2 *M* acid to dissolve the residue. The slide bearing the small test drop is carefully inverted over a small beaker of concentrated ammonium hydroxide for several minutes. (It is important that the hanging drop absorb plenty of ammonia.) After turning the slide right side up, a very small grain (0.5 mm. across) of magnesium acetate is added to the test drop. In the presence of arsenate there may be an immediate separation of clusters of colorless feathery dendrites of magnesium am-

[21] Based on results in the author's laboratory.

monium arsenate[22,23] comparable with the magnesium ammonium phosphate obtained in the orthophosphate test described above. The crystalline forms are identical. If the rate of crystal formation is slow, the product will generally include some feathery X's. With a solution having an arsenic concentration of 0.3 mg. per ml., 5 μg. can be identified.

Arsenite. Distinction between arsenite and arsenate is readily accomplished by means of an ammoniacal silver nitrate solution. When a drop of this reagent is applied to an acid-free test drop containing an arsenite, there is a prompt separation of a yellow granular precipitate of silver arsenite. Gradually this precipitate changes over into thin rods or long slender prisms. Upon longer standing, the latter are oxidized to dark crystals of silver arsenate. When an ammoniacal silver nitrate solution is added to an acid-free test drop containing arsen*ate*, there will be a reddish brown, or deep red precipitate of crystalline plates, dendrites, or related forms of silver arsenate. This reaction is not likely to be confused with the behavior of arsenite. However, since the silver arsenate bears some visual resemblance to silver chromate it is important that the test solution be free from chromate ion.

ORGANIC ANIONS

Acetate.—When a dilute solution of an acetate is treated with barium chloride no precipitate is formed; however, the addition of a drop of silver nitrate solution to a neutral test drop containing acetate ion results in the formation of a white precipitate, which under the microscope is seen to consist of colorless, irregular prisms, and scale-like crystals. Eventually thin plates develop, some of which become elongated hexagonal plates which exhibit parallel extinction. The silver acetate crystals are soluble in nitric acid. A more sensitive test depends upon the formation of yellow tetrahedra of sodium uranyl acetate.[24] The reagent is a solution containing sodium formate and uranyl formate in high concentration. The test drop should be free from any ammonium ion, as well as free from acids. A drop of the reagent is added to the test drop on a slide. In the presence of less than 5 μg. of acetate ion, the characteristic tetrahedra of sodium uranyl acetate will separate. Uranyl nitrate may be substituted for the formate, but only at some sacrifice in sensitivity.

Propionate.—The reagent for the detection of propionate ion consists of a saturated solution of mercury(I) nitrate, acidified with nitric acid to prevent decomposition. A drop of this reagent is placed adjacent to the test drop on a slide. When the reagent is caused to flow into the sample, the presence of propionate ion results in the prompt separation of long, colorless crystals which are characteristic for this ion.[25]

n-*Butyrate.*—Under appropriate conditions when treated with the above reagent the *n*-butyrate ion yields microcrystals which are sufficiently characteristic for identification. If the original sample is in the form of an acidic solution, a test solution should be prepared according to the following procedure: the solution is neutralized with sodium carbonate, placed in appropriate microapparatus to distil to dryness *in vacuo*. After acidifying the residue with concentrated phosphoric acid, any liberated acids are removed by resorting to another vacuum distillation. The receiver should be surrounded by a cooling mixture consisting of 33 parts of fine salt, to 10 parts of finely shaved ice. (This mixture may attain a temperature of −21°.) One or two drops of the sample are withdrawn from the slushy distillate by inserting a glass capillary or a Wintrobe pipet. After transferring this material to a slide, it is treated with a drop of 5 percent sodium

[22] Schoorl, N., Z. anal. Chem., **47**, 367, 1908.
[23] Behrens, H., Manual of Microchemical Analysis, Macmillan and Co., New York, 1894.
[24] Kruger and Tschirch, Mikrochemie, **7**, 318, 1929.
[25] Musicant, Louis, and Kaszuba, Frank J., J. Am. Chem. Soc., **61**, 2974, 1939.

carbonate solution. The mixture is evaporated just to dryness, and the resulting residue is dissolved in a drop of water. The original sample must be free of formic acid, but acetic acid can be tolerated because it will be frozen out in the distillate. Less than 0.1 mg. in the final test drop will yield a positive result with the mercury(I) nitrate reagent.

ORGANIC ANALYSES

INTRODUCTION

Preliminary Examination.—Before starting on the more specific tests which can be performed under the microscope, it may be well to refer to several of the general reactions which are of use in a preliminary probe, as well as to comment briefly on certain of the physical constants which are the bases for some of the identifications.

Information regarding solubilities, or gas evolution when a sample is subjected to various reagents, can be obtained by using only a few grains of solid sample. To a drop of liquid reagent on a slide, a quantity of sample equivalent to one or two grains of sugar is added. Under comparatively low magnification (*i.e.*, 24- or 32-mm. objective and 5× ocular), one can determine whether the substance remains unchanged, and is, therefore, insoluble, or whether it disappears by going into solution. At the same time the observer can also make a rough quantitative estimate of the solubility. Any gas evolution during the process is revealed by the appearance of bubbles, while the formation of any insoluble liquid is manifested by the appearance of globules in the original liquid medium. Frequently it is highly rewarding to examine solid samples under the microscope in order to determine homogeneity and other properties. If the substance is granular or powdered, one may be able to determine the presence of two or more varieties which exhibit different colors or different shapes. When examined between crossed Nicol prisms (or Polaroids), one may distinguish among isotropic particles, particles which show parallel extinction, and those which exhibit oblique extinction. It may sometimes be useful to know whether particles exhibit brilliant polarization colors or only low order grays and white. Frequently it may be worthwhile to isolate certain components from a heterogeneous mixture by using a needle.

In some solid samples the presence of different components is evident from solubility behavior; part of a sample may go into solution while the remainder is unaffected. In other cases the separation of a mixture may be effected by sublimation (as, for example, isomeric forms of hexachlorobenzene). On a microscale this may be carried out by covering the sample in a microcrucible with a slide (or, better, a half-slide); the crucible is then cautiously heated with the very small flame of a microburner. (Special clamps are available for holding the slide and crucible together while heating.) Microscopic examination of both the sublimate and the residue may offer important new clues. A simple preliminary check may be conducted by placing solid sample a short distance from one end of a slide, then covering with an inverted 1-in. watch glass, and slowly heating over a microflame.

Adaptation of Macroprocedures.— Many of the general reactions originally devised for macromethods can be modified for use under the microscope. Fehling's test, for example, can be carried out with a very small sample. A single drop of test solution is taken up by applying it to the torn edge of a bit of filter paper. This is then placed on an object slide, and covered with a drop of Fehling's reagent. Heating may be carried out on a microscope hot stage operating at 100°C., on a separate heating block, on a small hot plate, or on a waterbath. If not visible to the unaided eye, any red copper oxide resulting from the test can be detected along the edge of the filter paper by examination under the microscope.[26] The Tollens silver mirror test is modified in a similar way. A drop of sample is applied to the edge of filter paper, as above, and the paper is then covered with a drop of the ammoniacal silver nitrate reagent. Instead of yielding a silver mirror as obtained in the macroprocedure, a positive test here is indicated by the microscopic dark particles of silver deposited on the paper fibers. The phenylosazone test may be carried out as described for the 2,4-dinitrophenylhydrazones, under sugars (page 232), or by a variation described elsewhere.[27] The sodium bisulfite addition reaction with aldehydes can be carried out by placing a small drop of liquid sample beside a drop of reagent (*i.e.*, saturated aqueous sodium bisulfite). If no precipitate separates when the two drops are joined by means of a glass thread, one should place a finger against the bottom of the slide to determine whether it is becoming warm (as a result of chemical action). If so, then the slide is laid on a cooling block or other cold surface, to dissipate any heat of reaction. This may cause any addition product to separate out. If the sample is not a liquid, an ether solution may be used for testing.

Optical Properties.—Concerning optical properties which are mentioned in some of the following procedures, a brief explanation may be in order. When the *analyzer* of a polarizing microscope is turned at right angles to the *polarizer* (which is located below the stage) no light passes through the objective; the field appears dark to the observer. Certain substances under the objective cannot be seen under these conditions if they are *isotropic*, or belong to the cubic system, because they have no effect on plane-polarized light. However, substances belonging to other crystal systems affect polarized light. They are known as *anisotropic* crystals. A crystal of this type (for example, picric acid) may be seen unless it is lying in its extinction position. Let us suppose such a crystal is in view when the polarizer and analyzer are crossed, and that it is perfectly centered in the field of view. If the specimen is now rotated about the center of the field it will eventually reach a position in which it becomes invisible. The crystal has now reached its extinction position. Should extinction occur when the crystal lies parallel to the vibration direction of the polarizer or analyzer, it is said to exhibit *parallel extinction*. If extinction occurs when a crystal lies in some other position in respect to the polarizer and analyzer, it exhibits *oblique extinction*. Another term, *symmetrical extinction*, may be applied to certain symmetrical forms, such as diamond-shaped, if extinction occurs when the crystal is so oriented that an axis joining opposite corners of the face of the diamond is parallel with the plane of vibration of the polarizer (or analyzer). If a crystal is moved from its extinction position, it becomes visible again, but if rotated through an angle of 90°, extinction will be re-established. When a crystal lies in its extinction position, the angle subtended between the crystal axis and the vibration direction of the polarizer (or analyzer) is its extinction angle, expressed in degrees of a circle. For more detailed explanations other sources should be consulted.[28,29,30]

With the polarizing microscope, specimens can be examined in a bright field of plane-polarized light if the analyzer is swung out of the optical path. When viewed in this way many crystalline substances change color as they are rotated into different positions. They are said to be *pleochröic;* if only two colors are involved the crystals are *dichröic*. The colors involved in the pleochröism of a given substance are characteristic.

[26] Garner, W., Industrial Chemist, **5**, 58, 1928.

[27] Schaeffer, Harold F., J. Chem. Educ., **25**, 20, 1948.

[28] Schaeffer, Harold F., Microscopy for Chemists, D. Van Nostrand, Princeton, N. J., 1953, Chapter VII.

[29] Chamot, Emile Monin, and Mason, Clyde Walter, Handbook of Chemical Microscopy, Vol. I, 3rd Ed., John Wiley, New York, 1958.

[30] Hartshorne, N. H., and Stuart, A., Crystals and the Polarizing Microscope, 3rd Ed., Edward Arnold Ltd., London, 1960.

Thermal Properties.—Generally pure crystalline solids possess very definite melting points, which are frequently of help in identifying an unknown sample. In some instances, however, this is not a convenient method for distinguishing among several substances because their melting points may lie too close together; some compounds have a tendency to decompose before attaining the melting point. An interesting situation is presented by acetamide and propionamide. Each has a micromelting point of 80°C., whereas one ordinarily expects some difference between the melting points of different members of an homologous series. We have here a good example of the advantage offered by the determination of a mixed fusion or eutectic temperature. If a small quantity of benzil is crushed or ground up with a similar quantity of the solid unknown, the analyst can determine, on the microscope hot stage, the temperature at which the mixture begins to melt. In this instance, if the unknown amide was acetamide, the temperature of this fusion will be 77°C., but if the unknown was propionamide, the melting will begin at 71°C. Ludwig and Adelheid Kofler have made an extensive study of the application of eutectic temperatures of binary mixtures in the identification of organic compounds, and, as a result, have published values for more than a thousand compounds. For greater detail, the work of the Koflers[31] or that of McCrone,[32] which is in English, should be consulted.

Refractive Index of the Melt.—Another useful constant for the characterization of an organic unknown is the refractive index of molten sample at a known temperature. Certain supply houses (such as Arthur H. Thomas Co., or William J. Hacker & Co.) can provide sets of standard refractive index powders for use in this work. In brief, a given solid unknown is slowly heated on a microscope hot stage in the presence of particles of a solid refractive index standard. If the refractive index of the molten sample differs from that of the glass standard, the particles of the glass standard will be surrounded by a Becke line, or halo; the standard is practically invisible, however, when the index of the melt matches that of the standard. The Becke line disappears. The object in this procedure is to measure the temperature at which the refractive index of the sample matches that of the standard. More details on the procedure, as well as tables of numerical data for use in identifications, are found in the works of the Koflers, and of McCrone mentioned above. A brief discussion of the Becke line method for determining refractive index is also found in *Microscopy for Chemists.*[28]

ALCOHOLS

Phenylurethane Derivatives.—Phenylurethanes have been widely employed as derivatives to aid in the identification of alcohols because of their melting points. A serious disadvantage lies in the fact that the melting points of the derivatives of some alcohols lie so close together; in some cases, they are actually duplicated. However, a very small quantity of a purified urethane derivative of a specific alcohol can well serve for the determination of several optical properties, including refractive index. It has been found that such data can serve to identify many alcohols.[33] The phenylurethanes are prepared by mixing a slight excess of a primary or secondary alcohol with phenylisocyanate. In certain instances it is necessary to warm the mixture to bring about the reaction. The resulting product is recrystallized from petroleum ether. If the identity of the original

[31] Kofler, Ludwig, and Kofler, Adelheid, Thermo-Mikro-Methoden zur Kennzeichnung organischer Stoff und Stoffgemische, Universitaetsverlag Wagner, Innsbruck, 1954.

[32] McCrone, Walter C., Fusion Methods in Chemical Microscopy, Interscience Publishers, New York, 1957.

[33] Dewey, Bartlett T., and Witt, Norman F., Ind. Eng. Chem., Anal. Ed., **12,** 459, 1940, and **14,** 648, 1942.

alcohol is suspected, the phenylurethane crystals are suspended in an appropriate immersion liquid to determine the beta refractive index (otherwise some preliminary probing is in order). A crystal is rotated to extinction position with the long axis more nearly parallel with the 6 o'clock-12 o'clock direction of the polarizing microscope, or, more specifically, parallel with the vibration direction of the polarizer. To confirm, the alpha or gamma index is also determined, having the long axis of the crystal more nearly perpendicular to the vibration direction of the polarizer. Although the presence of diphenylurea (due to moisture in the reactants) would ruin a melting point determination, it does not hamper the identification of the alcohol by optical properties, because it, too, can be identified in the mixture. Since the phenylurethanes are soluble in some immersion oils, it is necessary to have an appropriate series prepared from glycerol and water, and solutions of potassium mercuric iodide in glycerol. Some of the optical constants for a number of alcohols are given in Table 12-1.

Iodoform Reaction.—Although the iodoform reaction is not specific for ethanol, in the absence of certain interfering groups the test constitutes a convenient means for detecting the alcohol in dilute solutions. It will, of course, also be positive in the presence of acetone and other compounds containing the CH_3—CO— group. The reaction cell is a concavity slide having a depression measuring approximately 15 mm. in diameter and 2.0 mm. in depth (A. H. Thomas, #7046 or 7044). Two drops of liquid sample are introduced into the cell by means of a capillary pipet, and a pinch of anhydrous sodium carbonate is added. The exact quantity is not critical, but it should correspond to the bulk of a couple of sesame seeds. After rotating the slide to disperse the carbonate, add 2 drops of 0.2 *M* potassium iodide solution, which is also 0.2 *M* in respect to iodine. An ordinary microscope slide is laid across the reaction cell in such a way as to leave a very small opening to serve as a vent. The entire assembly is then placed on a small hot plate operating at 95–100°C., for about 3 minutes. The assembly is transferred to a metal cooling block for several minutes, after which the cooled cover slide is removed, turned over, and examined under a 16-mm. objective and a 5× or 10× ocular. A positive test is indicated by the presence of microscopic iodoform crystals in the form of yellow six-pointed stars or thin hexagonal plates. Regardless of imperfections, the crystals can be recognized as members of the hexagonal system. In case none of the iodoform has sublimed to the cover slide, the crystals can be found in the residual mixture left in the reaction cell. Positive tests can be obtained with aqueous solutions containing no more than 2 percent ethanol (approximately 1.5 mg.) or its equivalent.[34]

AMINES

Aliphatic Amines.—A number of aliphatic primary amines can be identified by noting the optical properties, especially refractive indexes, of their nitrobarbiturates.[35] These are easily prepared in hot aqueous solutions of reagent and the corresponding amines.[36] For analytical purposes, approximately equivalent quantities of nitrobarbituric acid and amine are brought together in the minimum volume of boiling water. As the solution is allowed to cool the crystalline amine nitrobarbiturate separates out, because the solubility of these salts decreases considerably with the drop in temperature. Recrystallization from hot water affords a convenient means of purification. Most of the salts separate out as thin flattened crystals. Most of the compounds give two true refractive indexes in their most frequently observed orientations. The refractive indexes are

[34] Schaeffer, Harold F., J. Chem. Educ., **19**, 15, 1942.
[35] Plein, Elmer M., and Dewey, Bartlett T., Ind. Eng. Chem., Anal. Ed., **15**, 534, 1943.
[36] Redeman, C. E., and Niemann, Carl, J. Am. Chem. Soc., **62**, 590, 1940.

TABLE 12-1. OPTICAL PROPERTIES OF PHENYLURETHANES DERIVED FROM PRIMARY AND SECONDARY ALCOHOLS[a]

Alcohol[b]	Melting Point, °C.	Extinction Angle,°	Optic Sign	Refractive Indexes		
				Alpha	Beta	Gamma
Methyl	47	16	+	1.542	1.590	1.667
Ethyl	52	20	−	1.516	1.580	1.618
n-Propyl	50	33	−	1.525	1.596	1.641
n-Butyl	57	31	−	1.507	1.592	1.655
n-Amyl	45	45	−	1.464	1.598	1.693
n-Hexyl	40	40	−	1.465	1.589	1.670
n-Heptyl	65	44	+	1.502	1.553	1.615
n-Octyl	74	16	−	...	1.559	1.627
n-Nonyl	60	36	−	1.472	1.570	1.613
n-Decyl	61	6	−	...	1.536	1.605
Benzyl	77	11	+	1.570	1.587	1.679
Phenylethyl	78	28	+	1.596	1.629	1.681
Allyl	67	25	−	1.507	1.586	1.659
Isoamyl	55	10	−	1.482	1.560	1.626
Borneol	138	30	−	...	1.561	1.621
Isobutyl	82	18	−	1.481	1.572	1.656
Cetyl	76	5	−	...	1.541	1.610
Cinnamyl	89	10	+	1.530	1.589	>1.718
Cyclohexyl	83	32	+	1.487	1.632	>1.775
Diethylcarbinol	48	45	−	1.499	1.568	1.616
Ethyleneglycol	148	7	−	...	1.625	>1.718
Furfuryl	44	15	+	1.519	1.599	>1.718
Menthol	111	5	+	1.558	1.573	1.597
Myristyl	71	12	−	1.542	1.573	1.577
Isopropyl	88	10	−	1.510	1.573	1.616
Terpineol	112	34	−	1.511	1.607	>1.718
Tetrahydrofurfuryl	58	43	+	1.570	1.608	...
Diphenylurea	235	40	+	1.583	1.621	>1.703

[a] Data are condensed and adapted from tables by Dewey and Witt.[33]
[b] All the above phenylurethanes were monoclinic, biaxial.

determined by immersion methods, using appropriate liquids.[37,38] The presence of some unchanged nitrobarbituric acid in the crystallized product causes no serious problem, as it is readily distinguished from the amine salts. A number of amines can be identified from the data in Table 12-2.

[37] Hartshorne, N. H., and Stuart, A., Crystals and the Polarizing Microscope, 3rd Ed., Edward Arnold, Ltd., London, 1960, Chapter VII.
[38] Wahlstrom, Ernest E., Optical Crystallography, 3rd Ed., John Wiley, New York, 1960, pp. 238 *et seq.*

TABLE 12-2. PRIMARY ALIPHATIC AMINE NITROBARBITURATES[a,b]

Parent Amine	Habit	Optical Orientation	Extinction Angle,° [c]	Refractive Indexes[b]	
Benzylamine	Tabular	Optic Normal	//	1.448	>1.785
Cyclohexyl	Acicular	Obtuse	//	1.483	1.648
n-Butyl	Tabular	Inclined Obtuse	//	variable	1.704
isobutyl	Foliated	Obtuse	14	1.470	1.706
Hydrazine	Columnar	Obtuse	24	1.458	1.748
Hydroxylamine	Tabular	Optic Normal	25	1.487	1.763
Methyl	Lamellar	Inclined Obtuse	//	variable	1.696
n-Propyl	Lamellar	Optic Normal	//	1.606	1.701
isopropyl	Tabular	Inclined Obtuse	43	variable	1.701
Nitrobarbituric acid	Tabular	Obtuse	//	1.388	1.684

[a] Apparent properties from most frequently observed orientation.
[b] More complete data, including the alpha, beta, and gamma indexes, along with actual diagrams of the crystals, are included in Plein and Dewey's original paper.[35]
[c] All extinction angles above are measured in the acute angle Beta; // = Parallel extinction.

Aromatic Amines.—With very slight change in the procedure, nitrobarbiturate derivatives of primary aromatic amines may also serve for identification purposes.[39] The amine under investigation is dissolved in hydrochloric or acetic acid. The resulting solution is then added to a hot aqueous solution of an equivalent quantity of nitrobarbituric acid. The derivative may precipitate immediately, or upon cooling of the mixture. If there should be an excess of reagent, no harm is done because it will generally remain in solution; its solubility is greater than that of the amine salts. Before obtaining optical measurements, the salts should be recrystallized from hot water. Observations should be made using freshly prepared material, since there may otherwise be a loss of water of crystallization. In general, the crystals are so flattened that, when suspended in an immersion liquid, practically all assume the same, or very nearly the same, orientation. This is a convenient method for distinguishing among some isomeric forms, or for detecting contamination of a given amine by an isomer; mixtures of the nitrobarbiturates prepared from isomeric amine mixtures exhibit the properties characteristic of the individual components. Data which facilitate the identification of various aromatic amines are given in Table 12-3.

AMIDES

Urea.—Among amides the detection and identification of urea is of special interest in connection with various food products because of its association with urine. Its presence on a food container, for example, may indicate that rodents infest the area concerned. A very useful reagent for detecting urea is xanthydrol:

O
C
H OH

[39] Dewey, Bartlett T., and Plein, Elmer M., Ind. Eng. Chem., Anal. Ed., **18**, 515, 1946.

TABLE 12-3. PRIMARY AROMATIC AMINE NITROBARBITURATES[a,b]

Parent Amine	Habit	Optical Orientation	Extinction Angle,° [c]	Refractive Indexes	
Benzidine	Laths	Inclined Optic Axis	30	Variable	1.690
o-Bromoaniline	Tabular	Optic Axis	Variable	Variable	1.647
m-Bromoaniline	Tabular	Inclined Obtuse	// Variable	Variable	Variable
p-Bromoaniline					
(rectangular)	Tabular	Inclined Acute	//	Variable	1.749
(diamond-shaped)	Tabular	Acute	21	1.597	1.688
o-Chloroaniline	Tabular	Inclined Optic Axis	//	Variable	1.657
m-Chloroaniline	Tabular	Acute	//	1.777	>1.785
p-Chloroaniline	Tabular	Acute	22	1.575	1.670
o-Phenylenediamine	Laths	Inclined Obtuse	6	1.470	1.756
m-Phenylenediamine	Lamellar	Inclined Obtuse	7	Variable	1.694
p-Phenylenediamine	Tabular	Obtuse	25	1.501	1.716
o-Toluidine	Tabular	Inclined Optic Axis	Variable	Variable	1.632
m-Toluidine	Tabular	Inclined Optic Axis	Variable	Variable	Variable
p-Toluidine	Tabular	Acute	24	1.670	1.680
Aniline					
(monoclinic)	Tabular	Inclined Obtuse	//	1.535	1.671
(orthorhombic)	Tabular	Obtuse	//	1.447	1.738
p-Iodoaniline	Tabular	Inclined Acute	//	Variable	1.751
o-Nitroaniline	Tabular	Inclined Optic Axis	//	Variable	1.714
m-Nitroaniline					
(from ethanol)	Lath-shaped	Acute	//	1.750	>1.785
p-Nitroaniline	Tabular	Inclined Optic Normal	17	1.626	>1.785
α-Naphthylamine					
(monoclinic)	Lamellar	Acute	14	1.635	1.684
(triclinic)	Tabular	Inclined Obtuse	Variable	Variable	>1.785
β-Naphthylamine	Tabular	Obtuse	//	1.483	1.758

[a] Apparent properties from most commonly observed orientation.
[b] For diagrams of 43 amine barbiturates, and a table listing their alpha, beta, and gamma refractive indexes, as well as other optical data, the reader should consult Dewey and Plein's original paper.[39]
[c] Extinction angles were measured between the long direction of a crystal in its particular orientation and the position of nearest extinction.

Two moles of the compound react with urea to form dixanthyl urea and two moles of water.[40] When various foods, containers, shelves, or other equipment, are suspected of contamination, they may be examined with ultraviolet light. The areas bearing urine stains will show up with a green fluorescence, although this alone is not positive proof. Such areas should be leached, rinsed, or extracted with water, depending upon the nature of the material and its structure. The clear water extract is evaporated to dryness, and the resulting residue is dissolved in the minimum volume of 2:1 acetic acid. A drop of this test solution is placed on an object slide, and a small quantity of xanthydrol is stirred in with a glass thread. The presence of urea will be manifest by the rapid formation of crystals of dixanthyl urea.[41] The nature of the crystals may vary, depending upon the concentration of the urea in the test solution. Most generally they will appear as clusters of narrow feather-like blades; they may also assume the form of straight needles, in sheaves or clusters, principally near the evaporating edge of the preparation. When examined through a first order red plate, the crystals exhibit negative birefringence. As little as 4 μg. of fresh urine solids in the test drop can be identified. Because of the source of the samples, the foregoing procedure reveals the presence of urea; however, the formation of a crystalline product with xanthydrol is not in itself a specific test for urea under uncontrolled conditions. The reagent forms derivatives with many other amides.

Other Amides.—Amides in general may be identified by taking advantage of several properties, including the micromelting points of their xanthyl derivatives.[42,43] Since some amides may not react as readily as urea, the following procedure is suggested: the reagent is prepared by dissolving 0.5 g. of xanthydrol in a mixture containing 5 ml. of ethanol, 2 ml. of glacial acetic acid, and 3 ml. of water. After thorough mixing, the preparation is centrifuged, set aside overnight, then decanted to obtain the clear liquid for use. Preparation of the xanthyl derivatives is carried out on a microculture slide having a 3-mm. depression (A. H. Thomas, #7044). A small quantity of sample containing the equivalent of 2 or 2.5 mg. of amide is placed in the depression of the slide, then covered with a drop of xanthydrol reagent. After the liquid has spread over the bottom, a thin ring of mineral oil is drawn around the rim of the well, after which a coverglass is pressed into place. After several minutes the preparation is examined under a 16-mm. objective and a 5× or 10× ocular. Should no crystalline product appear within 10 minutes, the slide may be placed on a waterbath for about 5 minutes. At the end of that time it may be necessary to set aside the entire assembly for about 12 hours. Ordinarily this is required only with rather low concentrations. To prepare the resulting crystalline derivative for the micromelting point determination, the product should be removed from the mother liquor, recrystallized from 65 percent aqueous dioxane, and dried in an oven at 80°C. for about 10 minutes. With a Kofler hot stage, a melting point determination can be carried out with a minimum amount of material. Melting points of several derivatives, as reported by Phillips and Pitt, are given in Table 12-4. Further corroboration of the identity of an amine may also be obtained by determining the eutectic temperature of a mixture of amide with another substance, or by obtaining the refractive index of the molten sample by Kofler's glass powder method.

[40] Schaeffer, Harold F., Microscopy for Chemists, D. Van Nostrand, Princeton, N. J., 1953, pp. 150–244.
[41] Food and Drug Technical Bulletin No. 1., U. S. Department of Health, Education and Welfare, 1960, p. 206.
[42] Phillips, R. F., and Pitt, Burnett M., J. Am. Chem. Soc., **65**, 1305, 1943.
[43] Adriani, W., Rec. trav. chim., **35**, 180, 1915.

TABLE 12-4.[a]

Amide	M.P., °C.	M.P. of Derivative, °C.	Eutectic Temperature, °C.	n of Glass	Temperature, °C.
Acetamide......	80	238–240	Benzil 77	1.4339	58
Propionamide...	80	210–211	Benzil 71	>1.4339	
n-Butyramide....	116	185–187			
isobutyramide...	129	210–211			
Acetanilide......	115	194–195	Benzil 78	1.5301	109–118
Benzamide......	128	222.5–223.5	Acetanilide 82	1.5400	130
Succinimide.....	126	245–247	Acetanilide 87	1.4840	102–104
Phthalamide[b]....	220	176–177	Salophen 177	Sublimes	

[a] Melting temperatures of xanthyl derivatives are according to Phillips and Pitt;[42] eutectic temperatures and refractive index data are from Kofler and Kofler.[31]
[b] Phthalamide, with melting point of 220°C., was the only substance examined which had a higher melting point than its xanthyl derivative.

SUGAR

Precipitation of Pure Sugars.—Sugars which have been isolated in comparatively pure form (by chromatography, for example) may be identified microscopically by the crystal habits when the substances are precipitated from solutions under controlled conditions.[44,45] Quense and Dehn recommend acetone, alcohol, acetonitrile, and 1,4-dioxane as precipitating agents.[46] In each instance sufficient precipitating agent is added slowly to a few drops of a saturated aqueous solution of the unknown. Generally the system becomes opalescent before crystallization sets in, so that crystal growth can be observed as it occurs in a drop under the microscope. It is important that the original aqueous solution be completely saturated in respect to the sugar, otherwise crystallization may fail to occur when the organic liquid is added. To identify a given sample, the crystals are compared with photomicrographs of known specimens precipitated by the same method. Determination of extinction angles yields additional information from which to draw conclusions. Excellent procedures for further corroboration of the identity of certain sugars are based upon the determination of a eutectic temperature of the sample with a reference substance, and measurement of the refractive index of the molten sample by the glass standard immersion method.[47,48] Data for a number of sugars are given in Table 12-5.

Hydrazone Derivatives.—When the analyst is limited to solutions containing only microgram quantities of sugar, identification in certain instances is made feasible by converting into appropriate hydrazones.[49,50] The method has proven successful with D-fructose, L-fucose, D-galactose, D-mannose, and L-arabinose.

Apparatus. *Microculture slides*, 75 × 25 *mm.*—These have a cylindrical well 3 mm. deep and 15 mm. in diameter.

[44] Hudson and Yanovsky, J. Am. Chem. Soc., **39,** 1020, 1917.
[45] Wernicke, Ber., **15,** 3105, 1882.
[46] Quense, John A., and Dehn, William M., Ind. Eng. Chem., Anal. Ed., **11,** 555, 1939, and **12,** 556, 1940.
[47] Kofler and Kofler, *op. cit.*
[48] McCrone, *op. cit.*
[49] White, Lawrence M., and Secor, Geraldine E., Anal. Chem., **27,** 1016, 1955.
[50] Secor, Geraldine E., and White, Lawrence M., Anal. Chem., **27,** 1998, 1955.

TABLE 12-5. IDENTIFICATION OF SUGARS

Sugar	M.P., °C.	Extinction Angle,°	Crystal System	Eutectic Temperatures, °C.		n of Glass	Temperature of Melt, °C.
L-Arabinose	154–162	Parallel to slightly inclined	orthorhombic bisphenoidal	Phenacetin 112		1.4937	151–154
D-Fructose	100–104	//	orthorhombic bisphenoidal	Acetanilide 97	Benzil 194	1.5101	108–110
Fucose	145	// and approx. 25	orthorhombic				
Galactose	165–168 (anhyd.)	//	orthorhombic				
D-Glucose	146–148.5	//	orthorhombic bisphenoidal	Phenacetin 133	Benzanilide 145	1.5101	142–145
D-Lactose	206–216	//	monoclinic sphenoidal	Salophen 187	Dicyandiamide 163	decomposition	
Maltose	102.5 decomp.	// to slightly inclined					
D-Mannose	130–136	// to slightly inclined	orthorhombic bisphenoidal	Acetanilide 114 tr.	Phenacetin 127 tr.		
Mellitose	132–135			Acetanilide 114	Phenacetin 130	1.5299	129–131
Raffinose	132–135	//	orthorhombic bisphenoidal	Acetanilide 114	Phenacetin 130	1.5299	129–131
L-Rhamnose		//	monoclinic sphenoidal				
L-Sorbose	136–146	//	orthorhombic bisphenoidal	Phenacetin 113	Benzanilide 131		
Sucrose	185–190	// and approx. 22.5	monoclinic sphenoidal	Salophen 173	Benzanilide 163	1.5101	172–174
Xylose	143–147	approx. 6	orthorhombic bisphenoidal	Phenacetin 130	Benzanilide 140	1.500	127

5-ml. glass syringe.
5-ml. round-bottomed microbeakers.
Micropipets, 0.5-, 1.0-, and 2.0-µl. capacities.

Reagents. 2,4-*Dinitrophenylhydrazine reagent.*—This is prepared as follows: 5 ml. ethyl acetate is added to 0.1 g. of 2,4-dinitrophenylhydrazine in a small container. This is covered with a watch glass and heated on a steam bath to effect complete solution. Upon cooling, the supernatant liquid is used without filtering.

Dioxane solution.—0.3 ml. of dilute hydrochloric acid (1:9) is mixed with 9.7 ml. of analytical grade dioxane.

Pyridine, reagent grade.

Ethyl ether, anhydrous, reagent grade.

1,1-Diphenylhydrazine reagent.—This is prefaced as follows: Add 21 mg. of powdered anhydrous sodium acetate to 55 mg. of powdered 1,1-diphenylhydrazine in a weighing bottle. After thorough mixing by shaking, store it in a desiccator. Whenever it becomes sticky (because of moisture absorption), discard it.

Mineral oil, heavy.

Procedure.—The suspected sugar sample should be taken up in not more than 6 µl. of water and transferred to the center of a clean slide. The diameter of the solution on the slide should not exceed 7 mm. After permitting it to air-dry at room temperature, the residual spot is wet with the 2,4-dinitrophenylhydrazine-ethyl acetate reagent. This is accomplished by making 4 or 5 applications with the tip of a glass rod measuring 1 mm. in diameter. Using the glass syringe, the ground area around the well in the culture slide is wet with mineral oil. After placing 1 µl. of dioxane reagent in the well, the slide bearing the sample and dinitrophenylhydrazine is immediately inverted over the culture slide, having the sugar spot directly over the well. The upper slide is pressed into place to obtain an air-tight seal. Progress of the solvent diffusion may be followed under the microscope. Some dinitrophenylhydrazones form very promptly, while others may require an hour or more. The time required for first crystal formation, rate of growth, and general appearance should be noted. After completion of the reaction, the diffusion cell is opened by using a razor blade to lift off the slide. When it has dried, 1 µl. of pyridine is placed in the well and the cell is reassembled. The rate of solution of the crystals, and the appearance of any new crystal phase should be noted. Results produced by several sugars are summarized below.

Identification. D-*Fructose.*—D-Fructose forms a 2,4-dinitrophenylhydrazone-dioxane solvate, in the form of clusters of fine yellow needles with sharp tapered ends. Moderate sugar concentration may initiate crystal formation in 2–4 minutes; with 0.5 µg., formation begins within 1 hour. These crystals are very soluble in pyridine.

L-*Fucose.*—L-Fucose also forms a solvate, but the crystals are long, straight, yellow needles with blunt ends; 5 µg. may effect their appearance within an hour, but moderate concentrations may require only 15 minutes. This product is more soluble in dioxane reagent than is the product formed by fructose; it is less soluble in pyridine.

D-*Galactose.*—D-Galactose yields bright-yellow, clear, gel-like dinitrophenylhydrazone, appearing initially in small globular patches. Moderate concentrations yield the crystals in 10 minutes, but up to 1 hour may be required if only 5 µg. is present. Very insoluble in pyridine.

D-*Mannose.*—D-Mannose yields a monohydrate of the dinitrophenylhydrazone in the form of clusters of short, wide-yellow blades; 25 µg. of mannose develops the crystals in 1 hour. When the slide bearing the crystals is placed over the cell containing pyridine, the original crystals "peel off" with formation of gas bubbles.

If L-arabinose is suspected, the procedure can be modified to increase the sensitivity for this sugar. The dried sugar spot mentioned in the first procedure is wet with several applications of the 2,4-dinitrophenylhydrazine-ethyl acetate reagent as before. This time, however, 0.5–6.0 μl. of pyridine is placed in the well of the culture slide, which is immediately sealed. As little as 5 μg. of L-arabinose will show up as fine trichitic yellow needles, in clusters or in sheaves; however, it may require 16–24 hours for the test to materialize. D-Galactose reacts at moderate concentrations, but usually the product is an uncharacteristic gel. L-Fucose may form a crystalline product, but only at relatively high concentrations.

1,1-Diphenylhydrazine can be employed to isolate L-arabinose and L-fucose from other sugars through their 1,1-diphenylhydrazones.[51,52] The following test will detect as little as 10 μg. of L-fucose. As described in the other tests above, a "sugar spot" is prepared on a slide by applying the solution to be tested. The dried spot is covered with an excess of powdered 1,1-diphenylhydrazine-sodium acetate reagent. The slide is inverted, then tapped to remove surplus reagent. Any of the reagent remaining outside the sugar area on the slide should be removed with a small camel's-hair brush. One μl. of 70 percent ethanol is placed in the well of the culture slide and the cell is promptly sealed. Depending upon the sugar concentration, a white crystalline product may be formed within a few minutes, or by the end of 2–2.5 hours. The test is even more sensitive for L-arabinose, since as little as 2 μg. will respond. Unfortunately the 1,1-diphenylhydrazones of these sugars present a somewhat similar appearance, so that the results of a test must be carefully compared with the derivatives of known samples. Even in 16 hours, neither the 1,1-diphenylhydrazine-pyridine test nor the 2,4-dinitrophenylhydrazine-pyridine test will yield a visible reaction product when performed on 100-μg. samples of any of the following sugars: L-rhamnose, L-sorbose, D-xylose, D-lyxose, D-glucose, D-mannose or D-fructose.

BARBITURATES

Of all the organic poisons encountered in toxicological examinations of body tissues and fluids from autopsies, the various barbiturates are those most frequently involved.[53] They may be extracted with ether or a chloroform-ethyl acetate mixture.[54] Barbiturates form interesting crystalline derivatives in solutions containing pyridine and a copper(II) salt.[55,56] A convenient microchemical reagent is prepared by dissolving 5 g. of copper sulfate in a solvent consisting of 25 ml. of pyridine and 25 ml. of water. Samples to be tested should be dissolved in 50 percent (by volume) aqueous pyridine. If the quantities of sample are very limited, the test may be performed by placing an ordinary drop of the sample on an object slide, then adding, by means of a good micropipet, one-tenth this volume of the reagent. The presence of as little as 0.1 mg. should gradually cause the formation of a dark purple barbiturate-copper-pyridine complex, characteristic for barbiturates. If larger quantities are prepared, these products can be isolated as comparatively stable, anhydrous crystals, by filtering, then washing successively with small portions of water, ethanol, and ether; subsequently they are dried over phosphoric anhydride in a vacuum desiccator. Heating at 100°C. for up to 1 hour causes no change in color nor loss in weight. The complexes with copper-pyridine reagent can also be employed to isolate the pure barbiturates by decomposing in dilute mineral acids, such

[51] van der Haar, A. W., Anleitung zum Nachweis, zur Trennung, und Bestimmung der Monosaccharide, Gebrueder Borntraeger, Berlin, 1920.
[52] Neuberg, C., and Wohlgemuth, J., Z. physiol. Chem., **35,** 31, 1902.
[53] Umberger, C. J., and Adams, Grace, Anal. Chem., **24,** 1309, 1952.
[54] Valov, Paul, Ind. Eng. Chem., Anal. Ed., **18,** 456, 1946.
[55] Zwikker, J. J. L., Pharm. Weekblad, **68,** 975, 1931.
[56] Levi, Leo, and Hubley, Charles E., Anal. Chem., **28,** 1591, 1956.

TABLE 12-6. IDENTIFICATION OF BARBITURATES[a]

Common Name	Chemical Name	M.P. of Barbiturate (Kofler), °C.	Decomposition Range Cu-Py Complex, °C.	Eutectic Temperatures, °C.		n of Glass	Temperature, °C.
Luminal (Phenobarbital)	Phenylethyl-barbituric acid	174	235–241	Benzanilide 137	Salophen 153	1.5400	151–152
Alphenal	Allylphenyl-barbituric acid	159	218–223	Phenacetin 108	Benzanilide 130	1.5400	159–161
Dial	Diallyl-barbituric acid	174	213–217	Benzanilide 142	Salophen 156	1.4840	159–161
Rutonal	Methylphenyl-barbituric acid	226	187–191	Salophen 175	Dicyandiamide 183	1.5203	234
Amytal	Ethylisoamyl-barbituric acid (Amobarbital)	156	180–185	Phenacetin 112	Benzanilide 128	1.4584	144
Mebaral	Ethylmethylphenyl-barbituric acid	177	207–211				
Seconal	Allyl(methylbutyl)-barbituric acid	87.4–88.2[b]	177–183				
Veronal	Diethylbarbituric acid (Barbital)	190	199–204	Salophen 163	Dicyandiamide 172	1.4584	182–184
Neonal	Ethylbutyl-barbituric acid	126	179–184	Acetanilide 80	Phenacetin 99	1.4584	153
Nembutal (Pentobarbital)	Ethyl,1-methylbutyl-barbituric acid	129	160–165	Acetamide 102	Phenacetin 104	1.4683	136–138
Alurate (Aprobarbital)	Allylisopropyl-barbituric acid	142	189–193	Phenacetin 108	Benzanilide 123	1.4840	134–136
Ipral (Probarbital)	Ethylisopropyl-barbituric acid	204	188–192	Salophen 165	Dicyandiamide 180		

[a] Range of decomposition temperatures is according to Levi and Hubley.[56] All other temperatures and refractive indexes are according to Kofler & Kofler.[47]

[b] From Levi and Hubley.[56]

as 0.1 *M* hydrochloric acid. Identification of the specific barbiturate can be effected on the microscope hot-stage by determining the eutectic temperature of a binary mixture with one of the standard compounds, or by finding the temperature at which the refractive index of the molten drug matches that of a standard glass powder. These data are given in Table 12-6. Identification can be accomplished through the purified and dried purple copper-pyridine complex with the barbiturate. Although the latter do not exhibit sharp melting points, the thermal decomposition of a given barbiturate extends over a comparatively short range (*cf.* Table 12-6).

ALKALOIDS

Isolation.—If any mixture (such as food, stomach contents, or pharmaceutical preparations) is suspected of containing alkaloids, one should first extract the alkaloids and convert them into appropriate form for analysis. The treatment will depend upon the nature and condition of the sample. Some rodent poisons, for example, consist of grain seeds which have been soaked in a solution of strychnine and then dried; here, the alkaloid can be extracted by digesting in water. In some instances, the author has encountered small pockets of powdered material encased in ground meat, or even in pores in slices of cake; such material can be removed mechanically, using suitable needles. In case the alkaloid is well dispersed in a foodstuff, or in the case of stomach contents, a method recommended for toxicological purposes by Goldstone is the following.[57] A 50-g. sample in a Florence flask is macerated in 50 ml. of 80 percent ethanol. Five ml. of tartaric acid solution is added, and the mixture is refluxed on a steam bath for 1 hour. A suitable condenser is provided to distil 5 ml. of liquid, which, for our purposes, may be discarded. The residual mash is filtered, then washed well with 80 percent ethanol. After concentrating the combined filtrate and washings to 5 ml. on a steam bath, add 50 ml. of 95 percent ethanol slowly while stirring. Any solid clumps should be crushed with a glass rod. Following filtration, any solid residue is washed with more 95 percent alcohol. The combined alcoholic filtrate and washings are evaporated on the steam bath to remove the alcohol, then diluted to 25 ml. with water. After transference to a separatory funnel, the mixture is extracted with 3 25-ml. portions of ethyl ether. The combined ether extracts are washed twice with 2-ml. portions of water, and these washings are returned to the original aqueous solution. After rendering the latter distinctly alkaline to litmus by adding ammonium hydroxide, the mixture is extracted with 3 25-ml. portions of ether, followed by 2 25-ml. portions of chloroform. The combined solvent extracts are extracted with several 2-ml. portions of water, filtered through a dry paper, and then evaporated slowly on a steam bath. The final residue is taken up in 0.2 ml. of water, which may yield 5 or 6 small test droplets. Of the more common alkaloids, morphine, strychnine, codeine, atropine, cocaine, nicotine, brucine, or pilocarpine may be present.

Detection of Alkaloids.—To determine whether any alkaloid is present, three very small test drops are transferred to a well cleaned slide, leaving ample space between the drops. A small drop of Wagner's reagent (1.27 g. of iodine dissolved in an aqueous solution of 2 g. of potassium iodide, and then diluted to 100 ml.) is added to one of the test drops. A small drop of 5 percent aqueous mercury(II) chloride solution is added to the second drop without stirring. The third drop is treated with a small drop of 5 percent chloroplatinic acid solution. The three preparations are examined under a magnification of approximately 150 diameters. The appearance of a crystalline product in any of these tests indicates the presence of an alkaloid. Table 12-7 may furnish a clue to its identity.

Identification of Individual Alkaloids.—If a few particles of the solid alkaloid are available, further confirmation of its identity may be obtained by a determination of

[57] Goldstone, N. G., Anal. Chem., **21**, 781, 1949.

TABLE 12-7.

Alkaloid	Wagner's Reagent	$HgCl_2$	H_2PtCl_6	Marmé's Reagent
Atropine.....	Numerous small dark rods and triangular plates, singly or in groups	Crystals	—	—
Brucine......	Crystals	Transparent rectangular plates; some rosettes	Crystals	—
Cocaine......	—	Amorphous ppt.	Delicate feathery crystals	—
Codeine......	Heavy red-brown ppt., slowly yielding yellow blades, extending in branches; never red	Crystals	Amorphous ppt.	Silvery, circular masses, crystallizing into dark rosettes
Heroin.......	—	Crystals	Spherical clusters of golden yellow needles, around central nucleus	—
Morphine....	Heavy red-brown ppt. gradually forming shining, overlapping plates, extending in branches	Crystals	Amorphous	Silvery ppt., yielding dense masses of fine needles extending into spray of branches
Nicotine......	Crystals	Radiating transparent blades in slight excess of H_2SO_4. Feather-like blades with HCl	Crystals	—
Pilocarpine...	—	Layers of thin yellow, triangular plates	—	—
Strychnine....	Crystals	Crystals	Clusters of wedge shaped needles and single crystals	Silvery masses gradually forming rosettes

certain physical constants, such as melting point of the purified substance, eutectic temperature of a binary mixture with another solid, or the temperature at which the molten sample attains the same refractive index as that of a standard glass powder. Several such constants are given in Table 12-8.

TABLE 12-8.[a]

Alkaloid	M.P., °C.	Eutectic Temperatures, °C.		*n* of Glass	Temperature, °C.
Atropine	115–116	Benzil 82	Acetanilide 89	1.5101 1.5000	111–112 134–136
Brucine	170–178	Salophen 149	Benzanilide 127		
Cocaine	98	Benzil 62	Azobenzene 47	1.5000	103–105
Codeine (anhyd.)	156	Phenacetin 117	Benzanilide 126	1.5400	175–177
Heroin	170–172	Salophen 122	Benzanilide 135	1.5101 1.5000	168–170 189
Morphine	245–255	Salophen 156	Dicyandiamide 174		
Pilocarpine-HCl	200	Salophen 153	Dicyandiamide 101	1.5000	211–213
Strychnine[b]	280–285	Salophen 180	Dicyandiamide 201		

[a] Most of the above numerical data are after Ludwig Kofler and Adelheid Kofler, Mikromethoden zur Kennzeichnung organischer Stoffe und Stoffgemische, Universitaetsverlag Wagner, Innsbruck, 1948.
[b] Melting point is given for the hydrochloride; other data for strychnine are for the base.

In the case of morphine, one of the most sensitive tests depends upon the use of a recent modification of Marmé's reagent,[58] which results in the formation of characteristic crystals of the morphine-Marmé complex, $(C_{17}H_{19}NO_3)[CdI_2]$. The modified reagent is prepared by dissolving 7.33 g. of cadmium iodide and 13.28 g. of potassium iodide in sufficient water to yield 100 ml. of solution. For maximum sensitivity it is important to observe a definite volume ratio between reagent and aqueous test solution. For example, 0.03 μl. of the reagent is added (from a micropipet) to 0.1 μl. of the alkaloid solution (or a solution of its hydrochloride). Under favorable conditions as little as 0.1 μg. of morphine will yield typical long, thin, colorless needles, which have a tendency to form aggregates resembling sprays. In working with trace amounts, unnecessary dilution of the test solution should be avoided; constant humidity should be maintained by keeping the reaction slide under a small bell jar so that the morphine-Marmé complex can separate out before sufficient evaporation occurs to permit excess reagent to crystallize. If the alkaloid is present as the base, separation of the complex appears to proceed more rapidly.

[58] Levi, Leo, Anal. Chem., **29,** 470, 1957.

QUANTITATIVE ANALYSIS

ANALYSIS OF AN INSECTICIDE: COMPOSITION OF DDT-GAMMEXANE MIXTURES

As shown by Kartnig,[59] an insecticide in which the active ingredients consist of DDT and the gamma isomer of hexachlorocyclohexane (HCH), can be analyzed by applying Kofler's method of determining the refractive index of the molten specimen (see page 224). The first step in the procedure is the isolation of the DDT-HCH mixture from the insecticide powder. For this purpose it will be necessary to prepare a simple glass adsorption column consisting of a 22-cm. length of 10-mm. diameter tubing, somewhat constricted near the lower end in order to retain an inert porous plug of dry asbestos fiber or glass wool. Should it be necessary to use tubing of slightly smaller diameter, the

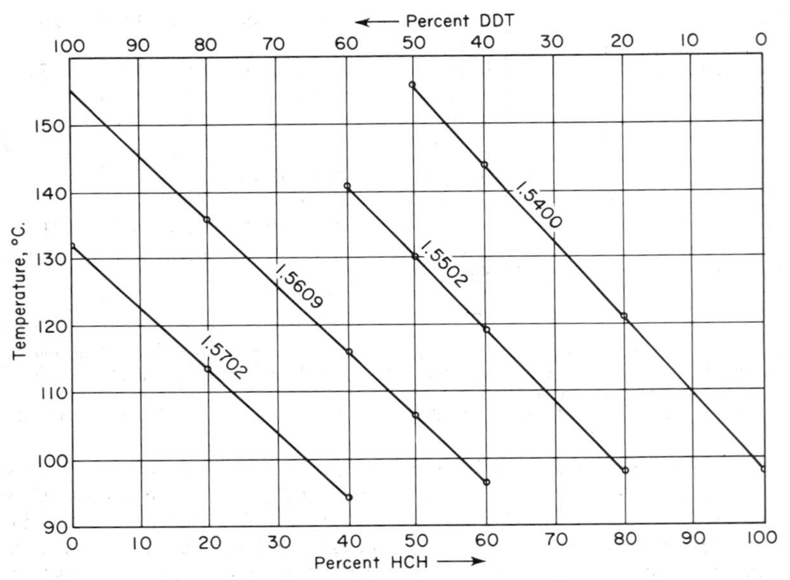

FIG. 12-1. Composition of DDD-Hexachlorocyclohexane Mixtures.

length must be varied accordingly. After introducing the glass wool or asbestos plug, the vertical tube is charged with 3–4 g. of "nonalkaline" or *neutral* alumina (*i.e.*, Camag, or Fisher Scientific Company's neutral alumina, #A-950), which adsorbs neither DDT nor HCH. Before use of the packed column, 10 ml. of *n*-hexane are allowed to flow through.

An accurately weighed 2–3-g. sample of the insecticide is mixed well with a similar weight of the neutral alumina by grinding together in a dry mortar. The mixture is carefully transferred to the prepared column, rinsing the mortar with *n*-hexane to insure complete removal of the sample. The isolation of the DDT-HCH mixture from the sample is then accomplished by extracting quantitatively with *n*-hexane, collecting the

[59] Kartnig, Thomas, Mikrochim. Acta, **1963,** 88.

eluant in a tared vessel. (Complete removal is indicated when the eluant no longer yields a positive chlorine test on copper foil.) Having completed the extraction, the solvent, which is inflammable, is expelled by evaporation *in vacuo*. The tared container and contents are then weighed, whereupon the weight of DDT-HCH mixture in the original sample can be determined by subtraction.

With an appropriate microspatula, the residue is gathered together on the bottom of the container. After covering the container with a watch glass, it is placed on a small hot plate operating at 130°C. When the residue has fused completely, it is allowed to solidify by placing the container on a metal cooling block. Finally a small portion of the solid is transferred to a half-slide, a few grains of standard refractive index powder are added, and the assembly is placed on the microscope hot stage (see page 224). A coverslip, heat baffle, and the cover are applied, and the stage is heated up in order to determine the temperature at which the refractive index of the molten sample matches that of an appropriate standard. As it is desirable to work within the 100–140°C. range, 4 refractive index standards (1.5702, 1.5609, 1.5502, and 1.5400) are required to cover the entire composition range of DDT-HCH mixtures (Fig. 12-1). Illumination should be by a sodium-vapor lamp, or another source provided with an optical filter which transmits at 590 mμ. Any variations in the procedure, including the use of different illumination for the observation of refractive index, will, of course, necessitate the preparation of other reference curves, starting with known mixtures of DDT and HCH.

For the analysis of liquid samples (*i.e.*, insecticide sprays) a weighed portion must first be subjected to evaporation to remove the dispersion medium, or solvent. This should be carried out at the lowest feasible temperature in order to minimize vaporization of active ingredients, especially in the case of samples having a relatively high HCH content. Starting with the resulting residue, the procedure parallels that just described for a powder.

ANALYSIS OF PHARMACEUTICAL PREPARATIONS

COMPOSITION OF A PROPONAL-SANDOPTAL MIXTURE

To determine the composition of a mixture of these two drugs, which are, respectively, dipropylbarbituric acid and isobutylallylbarbituric acid, a small sample of the powder is fused in contact with particles of the glass standard having a refractive index of 1.4683. According to Kofler and Baumeister,[60] a melt consisting of pure proponal should attain the refractive index of the standard at 126°C., while a pure sandoptal melt should match the standard at 150°C. (These values were obtained using the red filter supplied with the glass standard set.) For this system the temperature-composition reference curve is readily plotted, as the relationship is linear. Unfortunately the precision is only fair, as the entire composition range falls within the narrow temperature range of only 24°C.

ANTIPYRINE-PYRAMIDON

The percentage composition of mixtures of antipyrine and pyramidon can be determined by observing the temperature at which the refractive index of the molten sample matches that of the glass standard, 1.5502. For pure antipyrine this temperature is 147°C. while for pure pyramidon, the temperature is 92°C. Since the relationship between temperature change and percent composition is linear, a reference curve is readily constructed from these data. For greater accuracy, however, the reference curve should be based on measurements carried in the worker's own laboratory.

[60] Kofler, L., and Baumeister, M., Z. anal. Chem., **124,** 385, 1942.

CRITICAL SOLUTION TEMPERATURE AND QUANTITATIVE ANALYSIS

DETERMINATION OF CRITICAL SOLUTION TEMPERATURE

Among the numerical constants which can be employed in the quantitative analysis of certain systems, a very interesting one is critical solution temperature (CST) (Chapter 36). Although a binary liquid system consisting of, for example, aniline and water, or aniline and heptane, may exhibit two phases at ordinary room temperatures, only a single phase remains if the temperature is raised sufficiently. This is based on the fact that at room temperatures each member of a given pair of liquids is only very slightly soluble in the other member, whereas at a higher temperature both members are mutually soluble in all proportions. The temperature at which two given liquids become mutually soluble in all proportions is known as the consolute temperature, or the critical solution temperature (CST), and is characteristic for the binary system involved. (More exactly, this should be considered as a *maximum*, or *upper*, critical solution temperature, but we are not concerned here with a minimum critical solution temperature.) If one of the liquids in a given pair should happen to contain another substance as an impurity, the CST of the system would be altered. When performed under certain prescribed conditions the CST for the system aniline-heptane is 70°C.; in this particular instance 70°C. is known as the *aniline point* of the heptane. If the *n*-heptane contains some other paraffins as impurities, the CST, or aniline point, will have a different value. As this is a very convenient constant to measure, and as it can be used in comparing various oil products, the determination of aniline point is quite extensively employed in the petroleum industry.

Fischer and Karasek[61] have devised a means for circumventing the tedious macromethod for determining the upper CST of liquid systems by resorting to the use of the microscope hot stage. The micromethod is of special interest here not merely because it is rapid and convenient, but also because it facilitates certain quantitative analyses, using limited amounts of sample.

The Kofler stage to be used for determining the CST should be equipped with a specimen shifter (available from the William Hacker Company, Caldwell, N. J.) because some readjustment of the specimen may be required during the observations. As the sample and the "test liquid" must be confined in a capillary tube, it will be necessary to equip the shifter with an appropriate adapter. Essentially, the adapter is a 26- × 37-mm. plate of aluminum, 1.5 mm. thick, and provided with a cut-out slot measuring about 1.5 mm. across and slightly over 30 mm. in length. The slot is for the purpose of accommodating the short capillaries during observation on the hot stage.

A microdetermination of the CST is carried out as follows: one of the liquids of the pair to be investigated is brought into contact with the tip of a clean, dry, capillary (0.3 mm.–0.9 mm. in diameter and 25–30 mm. long) so that a small quantity, possibly 1 drop, enters the tube. The capillary is then applied to the second liquid, so that a similar volume of this one enters the tube. By inclining the capillary, one allows the combined sample to move up a distance of 5–7 mm., so that both ends can be sealed in a small, but hot, microflame. As the liquids are mutually immiscible, or nearly so, at room temperature, a meniscus will be formed between them. The capillary is laid in the slotted adapter of the specimen shifter, the heat baffle is laid on the stage, and the stage is covered just as for a melting point determination.

After focusing on the meniscus marking the boundary between the two liquids, one allows the stage to warm up. To keep the meniscus within the field of view during the

[61] Fischer, R., and Karasek, G., Mikrochemie v. Mikrochim. Acta, **33**, 316, 1948.

heating, it may be necessary to shift the position of the capillary. Ultimately the meniscus disappears, thereby indicating that there is only a single phase in the tube. After recording the temperature at which the meniscus has vanished, the current is adjusted to permit the stage to cool at a rate of 1 or 2 degrees per minute. The temperature at which the first faint image of a meniscus reappears is recorded as the CST. Actually, this should agree with the temperature at which the meniscus disappeared while the temperature was rising, but, in practice, this may not be the case. If the two temperatures are not in agreement, the temperature of the reappearance of the meniscus is taken as the correct one, in view of the fact that this phenomenon is more readily observed. The final accepted value should, of course, be the mean of several trials. Generally, if carefully carried out, good agreement of successive runs is readily obtained. When working with an entirely unfamiliar liquid pair, several exploratory trials should be made, in order to determine the optimum setting for the heater rheostat.

ANALYSIS OF CAMPHORATED OIL: DETERMINATION OF THE PERCENT OF CAMPHOR

Essentially this product is a solution of camphor in olive oil. The weight percent of camphor in a given sample can be determined by way of the CST, using various test liquids, such as diethylsulfate or acetonylacetone.[62] The CST of the binary system, olive oil-diethylsulfate is determined as described above. For this system, it is advisable to use capillary tubing having a diameter of approximately 0.7 mm. In constructing a reference curve, the temperature observed with pure olive oil in contact with diethylsulfate, would, of course, give the point corresponding to the camphor concentration of zero. The CST should also be determined for several concentrations of camphor in olive oil; solutions containing 5, 10, 15, and 20 percent by weight would be satisfactory. The reference curve is then obtained by plotting the several temperatures against the corresponding camphor concentrations. Subsequently the concentration of any other sample of camphorated oil can be determined within 20 or 30 minutes, merely by carrying out a CST determination on the sample in contact with diethylsulfate. It should be pointed out that a difference of 0.5 degree in temperature corresponds with practically 0.2 percent camphor.

The relationship between the CST's and the camphor concentrations is very nearly, but not exactly, linear. If the desired accuracy is not too great, a temperature-composition curve can be constructed from the data in Table 12-9.

TABLE 12-9.

Binary System	*CST*
Diethylsulfate/Pure Olive Oil.	73°C.
Diethylsulfate/20% Camphor in Olive Oil.	27°C.

By constructing the curve on the assumption that there is a linear relationship, the maximum deviation from the correct curve will be in the neighborhood of a temperature of 50°C., corresponding to a difference of approximately 0.07 percent in the camphor determination.

It is important to consider the purity of all compounds used in determining the data for the preparation of reference curves for analysis by way of CST. Furthermore, having prepared calibration curves for a given system, rechecking may be necessary whenever new batches of "test liquids" must be employed.

[62] Fischer, R., and Auer, H., Pharm. Zentralh., **96,** 502, 1957.

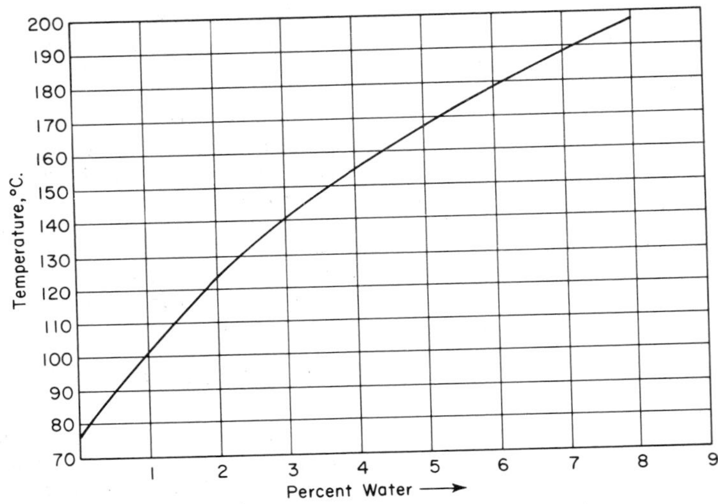

FIG. 12-2. Moisture in Glacial Acetic Acid.

ANALYSIS OF GLACIAL ACETIC ACID: DETERMINATION OF WATER CONTENT

Samples of glacial acetic acid of dubious history can readily be analyzed for moisture content by means of the CST method.[63] Using an authentic sample of pure glacial acetic, with olive oil as the test fluid, the CST should be 76°C. A sample containing as much as 7 percent water exhibits a CST of 188°C. For exact results, the analyst should prepare his own reference curve, basing it upon careful determinations of several concentrations of acid and water, carried out under the conditions of his own laboratory. As shown in Fig. 12-2, the CST-composition relationship is not linear. It is recommended that the capillaries used for the acetic acid-olive oil system should have a diameter of 0.2 mm.

AQUEOUS HYDROGEN PEROXIDE: DETERMINATION OF PEROXIDE CONTENT

As shown by Fischer and Neupauer,[64] the CST method lends itself very nicely to the determination of the percent of hydrogen peroxide in aqueous peroxide solutions containing up to 30 percent. Using pure *n*-butanol as the test fluid, pure distilled water (*i.e.*, zero percent hydrogen peroxide) has a CST of 128.5°C., while a 30 percent solution has a CST of 91.5°C. Since the temperature-composition relationship here is linear, a reference curve is readily drawn from these figures. (It is, of course, preferable to recheck with a sample of *n*-butanol available in the analyst's laboratory.)

APPLICATIONS IN THE ANALYSIS OF SPECIAL MATERIALS

The microscope has been usefully applied in the analysis of a number of special materials. Procedures described elsewhere in Standard Methods of Chemical Analysis are:

1. Chapter 36, Volume III, Critical Solution Temperatures.
   a. Characterization of organic compounds

[63] Fischer, R., Pinter, E., and Auer, H., Pharm. Zentralh, **99,** 299, 1960.
[64] Fischer, R. and Neupauer, E., Mikrochemie v. Mikrochim. Acta, **34,** 319, 1949.

   b. Analysis of liquid mixtures and solutions
   c. Characterization of complex mixtures
2. Chapter 58, Volume III, Plastics.
   a. To study crystallinity in polymers
   b. To study inclusions in polymers
   c. To study occlusions and physical characteristics of polymers
   d. To study particle-size in polymers
   e. To study polyphases in polymers
   f. To study surface characteristics of polymers
3. Chapter 59, Volume III, Rubber and Rubber Products.
   a. Dispersion analysis and other studies on rubber
   b. Dispersion of fillers in rubber
4. Chapter 63, Volume III, Water Analysis.
   a. Microelectrophoresis studies in water analysis

Chapter 13

ELECTRON MICROSCOPY

By Robert B. Fischer
California State College at Palos Verdes
Palos Verdes Peninsula, California

INTRODUCTION

The electron microscope, like any other conventional type of microscope, is an optical device for obtaining enlarged images of either small objects or small portions of larger objects. The image-forming radiation is a beam of electrons, the lenses are magnetic or electrostatic fields, and the image is made visible either by means of a fluorescent screen or photographically. The most distinctive feature of the electron microscope, as compared to conventional light microscopes, is its far better resolution. The electron microscope is applicable in many varied areas of science and technology, including several which are directly and indirectly related to analytical chemistry.

The instrumentation required for the analytically useful fields of electron diffraction, x-ray projection microscopy, and x-ray microprobe analysis are all closely related to electron microscopy. These methods are also included in this chapter.

PRINCIPLES

A definite wave nature is associated with a moving stream of electrons. The effective wavelength may be calculated from the de Broglie equation:

$$\lambda = \frac{h}{mv}$$

in which λ is the wavelength, h is Planck's constant, m is the mass of the electron, and v is its velocity. Energy relationships further indicate that

$$\text{kinetic energy} = \tfrac{1}{2}mv^2 = Ve$$

in which V is the potential difference through which the electron beam has been accelerated and e is the charge upon the electron. Combining these equations, and inserting appropriate values and units for h, m, and e, it is found that

$$\lambda = \frac{12.3}{\sqrt{V}}\,\text{A}$$

For example, the effective wavelength is 0.123 A for a 10-kilovolt electron beam and 0.039 A for a 100-kilovolt beam. Therefore, the effective wavelength of an electron beam is shorter by several orders of magnitude than the wavelength of visible light.

In order for any radiation to be useful in forming images in a microscope, there must be some means of focusing that radiation. The electron beam is not able to penetrate matter appreciably, so the path through which the beam passes must be highly evacuated. Fortunately, there are means whereby an electron beam passing through an evacuated region can be focused—by means of magnetic or electric fields. A magnetic electron lens consists of a magnetic field which is symmetrical about the axis along which the electrons travel. The field may be produced either by permanent magnets or by electromagnets or, in some instances, by a combination of both. An electric, or electrostatic, lens may be of any of several designs. One common form consists of three coaxial circular apertures, of which the outer two are at the same potential and the inner one is at a potential considerably different than the other two. The focal lengths of electron lenses are typically of the order of 1 to 5 mm., and are determined by the physical dimensions in combination with the current flow and number of turns in an electromagnetic lens or the potential difference in an electric lens.

The limiting resolution of a light microscope is set by diffraction, as indicated by the Abbe equation,

$$d = \frac{0.61\lambda}{n \sin \alpha}$$

in which d is, in effect, the resolution expressed as the closest approach between two specimen points which can be distinguished as two points, λ is the wavelength, n is the index of refraction of the medium between the object and the lens, and α is the half-aperture angle of the cone of light which is incident upon the specimen. Even with an immersion objective lens to make n as large as possible (for example: $n = 1.46$ with glycerin as the immersion medium, or 1.52 with cedarwood oil) and with $\sin \alpha$ approaching unity, the limit of resolution is about one-half of the wavelength of the light, or about 2000 A for ultraviolet light.

The resolution limit of an electron microscope, with its much shorter wavelength, is set jointly by the diffraction and the spherical aberration. The limit, insofar as spherical aberration is concerned, is represented by the equation,

$$d = kf(\alpha)^3$$

in which f is the focal length of the lens and k is a constant determined by several factors. Spherical aberration is minimized by making α small, while a large α is necessary to minimize diffraction. Therefore, a compromise half-aperture angle must be selected to achieve the optimum resolution. In light microscopy, with the much longer wavelength, this compromise is one-sided in favor of a large α. In electron microscopy, however, with the much shorter wavelength, this compromise is typically at a half-aperture angle of 10^{-2} to 10^{-3} radians. It is not possible to state an exact value for the theoretical limit of resolution of the electron microscope, because of the several factors which are of significance in the diffraction and spherical aberration effects, but the limit is of the order of 2 or 3 A.

An important by-product of the small aperture angle is the accompanying large depth of field. In some applications, this is as important as is the improved resolution.

Resolution is a necessary, but not a sufficient, requisite for visibility in an image. There must also be sufficient contrast within the image. In a light microscope, contrast arises principally from differential absorption from one portion of the specimen to another. The absorption is frequently chromatically selective. If a proper choice is made of wavelength of light, and if a color "stain" in the specimen, or a phase selective device in the microscope, is used to enhance contrast, lack of adequate contrast seldom limits the applicability of a light microscope.

In an electron microscope, the main source of image contrast is differential scattering of electrons from the various portions of the specimen, and sufficient contrast frequently is a limitation on the applicability of the instrument. Some stains have been developed to enhance contrast, usually involving a heavy metal atom, and a "shadowing" technique has proven to be useful in enhancing surface contrast. A high-voltage electron beam is more penetrating than a lower voltage beam, so the magnitude of this voltage influences the contrast.

The optical column of a typical electron microscope consists of an electron gun, a condenser lens to control the illumination of the specimen by the beam, a specimen chamber, an objective lens, and a projector lens. These several parts correspond directly in function to the portions of the optical column of a light microscope. The electron gun consists of a hot cathode and anode. The condenser lens may be a single magnetic or electrostatic field, or a double condenser of two lenses may be used to provide more intense illumination of the specimen. In some of the cheaper, simpler instruments, the condenser is omitted. The objective lens is the most critical of the several lenses, because its image must withstand the entire ultimate enlargement. The limiting aperture is inserted within this lens. Single objective and single projector lenses may be used, although it is more common to use an additional lens placed between them. The image is rendered directly visible by means of a photographic screen. All instruments are designed to permit photographic recording of the image, usually by direct impact of the electron beam upon the photographic film. The electron microscope must include, in addition to the optical column, the related electrical power supplies, vacuum pumps, and controls.

A specimen must fulfill three requirements to be suitable for observation in an electron microscope; specifically, it must be: thin enough to transmit an appreciable fraction of the incident electron beam; stable in the evacuated chamber; stable upon electron bombardment. The specimen is typically mounted upon a thin (about 100 A) film of carbon or of a plastic material, such as collodion or formvar.

A specimen becomes contaminated during irradiation by the electron beam, although recent studies have resulted in techniques to render this source of difficulty less severe than heretofore. The specimen becomes heated somewhat during the bombardment in its evacuated environment. Furthermore, the beam can serve as a reducing agent, for example by changing a silver halide into metallic silver.

The electron optical system of the electron microscope is useful in several types of work, in addition to microscopy. An electron diffraction instrument consists of an electron gun, lenses to focus the beam onto the desired area or volume of the specimen, and a means of viewing the pattern. A lens may or may not be inserted between the specimen and the image plane. Most commercial electron microscopes are readily useful for electron diffraction work in addition to microscopy. The specimen for diffraction is usually inserted after the regular objective lens, in the direction the beam travels, rather than between the condenser and objective lenses as for microscopy. In addition, several commercial microscopes are designed to permit the operator to obtain an electron diffraction pattern of any selected area within the microscopic image without moving the specimen from its normal position for microscopy. The characteristic diffraction of electrons from a crystalline specimen may be described by the Bragg equation,

$$n\lambda = 2d \sin \alpha$$

The "d" values are typically of the order of tenths of an angstrom and larger, and the wavelength of the electron beam is, as already discussed, of the order of hundredths of an angstrom. Thus, the diffraction angles are small. The efficiency of the diffraction of electrons is so great that, unlike in x-ray diffraction, the pattern may be viewed directly on a fluorescent screen or recorded photographically with an exposure of a few seconds. Diffraction from gaseous specimens is possible. Because the electron beam is of very low penetrating power, electron diffraction is particularly useful in studying the surfaces of materials. For example, electron diffraction patterns are far more sensitive than x-ray patterns in determining the effects of fluoride treatment upon the surface of dental enamel.

An x-ray projection microscope is an instrument in which a sharply focused beam of electrons strikes a metal target, causing it to emit x-rays. The electron optic portion of the complete instrument may be identical to part of the optical column of an electron microscope. The specimen is placed between the point source of x-rays and a fluorescent screen or photographic film, upon which the image appears. The magnification is equal to the ratio of the distance from the source to the screen or film divided by the distance from the source to the specimen. The resolution is limited approximately to the effective diameter of the source of the x-rays, which is, in turn, determined by the sharpness of the electron beam. Resolutions as good as 1000 A have been reported. Another practical limitation of this technique is the low image intensity, resulting largely from the inefficiency of generation of the x-rays. The specimen is not necessarily mounted in an evacuated chamber, although it frequently is, so as to minimize air scatter which could adversely affect both resolution and contrast. Although x-ray projection microscopy does not yield resolution significantly better than does light microscopy, the different forms of interactions between the radiation and the specimen can cause distinctive and useful contrast variations.

The x-ray microprobe analyzer is an instrument in which a beam of electrons is sharply focused upon the surface of the specimen, causing it to emit x-rays which are analyzed spectrally or energetically by a crystal spectrometer or proportional counter. This technique is a microextension of conventional x-ray fluorescence analysis. Both qualitative and quantitative analysis of the elements of which the specimen is compared can be obtained by this technique. The electron optical portion of the instrument is similar to that of an electron microscope, although completely separate instruments are preferably designed and constructed for the two purposes.

INSTRUMENTATION

The first electron microscope was built in the early 1930's. By 1940, commercially-available electron microscopes had resolution much better than that of the light microscope. Since the early 1940's, developments in instrumentation and in application have come rapidly. Several instruments are now available with which it is possible to approximate the theoretical limit of resolution, and other models are marketed for less critical work. All of the better instruments include compensation for astigmatism in the objective lens. Some instruments provide attachments for heating and cooling the specimen and for subjecting it to tension during the observation. Almost all provide for some electron diffraction work as well as for electron microscopy. Some instruments provide special focusing aids, and a variety of photographic techniques are incorporated in different instruments.

Among the instruments which are marketed in the United States, although some are manufactured abroad, and which have a guaranteed resolution of 10 A or better, are the Radio Corporation of America Model EMU-3G, the Norelco (Philips Electronics Instruments Co.) Model EM200, the JEOL (Fisher Scientific Co.) Model JEM-6 and Model JEM-150, the Hitachi (Perkin Elmer Co.) Model HU-11, and the Siemens Elmiskop I.

Among the other models marketed in the United States which do not so closely approach the theoretical limit of resolution, but which are generally cheaper and simpler to operate and to maintain, are (in approximate order of best guaranteed resolution) the Akashi (Hardco Scientific Corp.) Model TRS-80, Hitachi Model HS-7, JEOL Model JEM-T65, Norelco Model EM-100C, Zeiss Model EM-9, Siemens Elmiskop II, Akashi Model 50 E 1, Norelco Model EM75C, Mikros Model EM-20, and JEOL Model JEM-30. Each of these models guarantees a resolution of from 12 A to 100 A, and all are useful for many applications.

Several special types of electron microscopes have also been constructed. Instruments with accelerating voltages ranging up to one million and even higher are of some interest, and one in France has been operated at 1.5 million volts. Scanning microscopes are also of some interest, as are emission microscopes, in which the specimen is the electron emitter.

The instrumentation in an electron microscope laboratory must include more than the microscope itself. Among the common auxiliary instruments are: the microtome to cut thin sections from biological tissues and other bulk objects; shadow-casting apparatus for the vacuum-evaporation of a thin metal film obliquely onto a specimen prior to observation in the electron microscope in order to enhance the contrast of its surface contours; freeze-drying apparatus to prevent collapse of three-dimensional structures upon desiccation; and various types of instrumentation for the replication of surfaces.

APPLICATIONS

Among the many areas of science and technology, in which electron microscopy is applicable, mention will be made here of a few which fall directly or indirectly within the province of analytical chemistry.

Particle size determinations can be made over the approximate range from 10 μ to the limit of resolution. The fractional uncertainty equals the resolution divided by the size, so, for example, a spherical particle 1000 A diameter could be measured, with a resolution of 20 A, within an uncertainty of about 2 percent. Individual particles are observed and measured, and all averaging or summing must be done arithmetically from measurements on numerous particles. Thus, this is a distinctive method of particle size measurement, providing information not obtainable from the common summing methods such as surface area methods.

Particle shapes may be determined to a degree of certainty directly proportional to the ratio of size to resolution. Nothing can be observed as to the actual shape of a particle right at the limit of resolution, although its presence can be clearly established. But a particle measuring 100 A, for example, can be recognized as a cube or a hexagon, if the resolution is as good as 100 $\div$ 6, or about 16 A. Furthermore, the state and form of aggregation of small particles can be observed directly.

It is often possible to use the size and shape of particles as a means of identifying them from within a limited group of possibilities. Thus, qualitative analysis is provided. Examples include the identification of asbestos fibers as amphibole or chrysotile, and of a clay mineral as kaolinite or illite. It is also possible to develop a system of chemical microscopy, using the electron microscope, somewhat similar to the common system of qualitative analysis by chemical microscopy using the light microscope.

The concentration of colloidal particles in a suspension, expressed in terms of the number of particles per unit volume, is another useful quantitative analytical determination in which the electron microscope is useful. The internal standard method is particularly applicable.

The electron microscope is indirectly useful in quantitative analysis by serving as an important tool in fundamental studies of nucleation and crystal growth.

Electron diffraction is useful both in structure determinations and in identifications based upon the characteristic diffraction patterns. Electron diffraction occupies a role distinct from that of x-ray diffraction because of the great difference in penetrating power of electrons and x-rays. The combination of electron diffraction with electron microscopy provides a very powerful analytical tool.

The x-ray projection microscope has not yet come into widespread use, but it is applicable to the study of such varied specimens as thin strips of metal, wood and paper fibers, and biological organisms.

The x-ray microprobe analyzer (Chapter 10) directly provides both quantitative and qualitative elemental analyses of matter in volumes as small as 2 cubic microns. Elements of atomic number 12 and greater may be determined, with sensitivities as low as 0.1 percent in a few instances. Typical results are quantitatively accurate within about 10 percent, occasionally as good as 1 percent

A number of methods using electron microscopy have been included in the chapter on the analysis of Rubber and Rubber Products, Chapter 59, Volume III, of Standard Methods of Chemical Analysis. These are:

a. Dispersion analysis
b. Determination of carbon black in rubber
c. Determination of the dispersion of fillers in rubber
d. Determination of latex in rubber analysis

SELECTED BIBLIOGRAPHY

1. Botty, M. C., Davies, M. C., and Felton, C. D., Anal. Chem., **36,** 173 R, 1964. This is one of the reviews published biennially in this journal, and is a detailed survey of the recent literature of electron microscopy.
2. Fischer, R. B., Applied Electron Microscopy, Indiana University Press, Bloomington, 1953.
3. Fischer, R. B., in L. Meites, Ed., Handbook of Analytical Chemistry, McGraw-Hill, New York, 1963, pp. 6-287–6-289.
4. Hall, C. E., Introduction to Electron Microscopy, McGraw-Hill, New York, 1953.
5. Hall, C. E., in C. Susskind, Ed., The Encyclopedia of Electronics, Reinhold Publishing, New York, 1962, pp. 232–236.
6. Thomas, G., Transmission Electron Microscopy of Metals, John Wiley and Sons, New York, 1962.
7. Clark, G. L., Ed., Encyclopedia of Microscopy, Reinhold Publishing, New York, 1961. Several chapters deal with various aspects of electron microscopy.
8. Norelco Reporter, issued quarterly by Philips Electronics Instruments Co., New York. Most issues contain articles on electron microscopy.
9. Scientific Instruments, issued quarterly by Radio Corp. of America, Camden, New Jersey. Most issues contain articles on electron microscopy.
10. Siegel, B. M., Ed., Modern Developments in Electron Microscopy, Academic Press, New York, 1964.

Chapter **14**

REFRACTOMETRY

By R. D. Schwartz
Shell Development Company (A Division of Shell Oil Company)
Exploration and Production Research Division
Houston, Texas

INTRODUCTION

The index of refraction of a material is the ratio of the velocity of light in a vacuum to that in the material. Refractometry is an optical instrumental analytical technique dependent upon measurement of the index of refraction. Instrumentation and procedures for refractometry have been developed and applied for analyses in the laboratory and in processing plants. The instruments, called refractometers, are accurate and convenient to use. Another factor which increases the utility of refractometry is the availability of reliable data for the refractive indexes of high-purity substances at specified temperatures and wavelengths.

The velocity of light in a material, and, therefore, the index of refraction, depends upon several physical properties of the sample. Theoretical studies have indicated that the index of refraction is related to the number, charge, and mass of vibrating particles in the material through which the light is passing. Further, it has been possible to relate refractive index to density and molecular weight for classes of compounds which have a relatively constant number of vibrating particles per unit weight. The number of vibrating particles in a compound is determined by the atoms in the structure and by the type of electronic bonding. Correlations of this sort have been particularly successful for the analysis of hydrocarbon mixtures. Some techniques which have been developed and applied in the petroleum industry will be discussed below.

It is convenient to describe the laboratory and the process-type equipment separately, although certain laboratory instruments are used in the plant, and process-type units can be utilized to monitor laboratory processes.

The refractometric procedures selected for discussion in this chapter are based upon the following three criteria. Some are applications which are typical of procedures used in school laboratories for educational purposes. Others are procedures based upon detailed investigations of correlations with other fundamental physical constants such as those developed for hydrocarbon analysis. Finally, we have included a group of references based upon a survey of the recent literature which may serve to indicate the direction of current progress in this field.

LABORATORY EQUIPMENT

The critical-angle method of refractive index measurement is utilized for most laboratory instruments. The Abbe, precision Abbe, dipping (immersion) and Pulfrich refractometers are extensively utilized in academic and industrial laboratories.

The Abbe refractometer contains a right-angled prism. The sample is placed on the hypotenuse of the prism. White light enters at grazing incidence, and upon emerging is observed with a fixed telescope. Color-compensating prisms are employed with this instrument. Direct reading of refractive index is made with a calibrated scale. For rapid analyses, or for cases where the samples are small, the Abbe is usually employed.

The precision Abbe refractometer covers a wider range of refractive index values than the Abbe and is capable of higher accuracy. Since monochromatic light is employed, color-compensating prisms are not required. The scale values observed with this instrument are converted to refractive indexes by means of conversion tables.

The dipping refractometer provides highly accurate measurements for a small range of values. The instrument is particularly suitable for testing solutions in bulk. A white source of light provides illumination by reflection from a highly polished mirror. Color-compensating prisms are provided, and conversion tables are supplied to convert the scale readings to refractive index values.

The Pulfrich refractometer contains a cell, for liquid samples, cemented to the top of a glass prism. Monochromatic light enters the prism parallel to its horizontal surface and is observed by a movable telescope. Tables are supplied to convert the angle of emergence, read on the scale, to a refractive index value.

Differential visual refractometers are sometimes used in the laboratory for highly accurate measurements which cover a very small range of values. For instance, the Phoenix Instrument Co. version of the Brice and Halwer[1] visual instrument has a limiting sensitivity of about 0.000003 and a range of 0.01 unit. Automatic refractometers which may be utilized to record small differences between a sample and a standard are also available.

PROCESS ANALYSIS EQUIPMENT

Direct measurement of refractive index as well as measurement of the difference in refractive index between a sample and a standard are useful for the analysis and control of industrial chemical processes. Sometimes automatic recording instruments are employed, and the electrical output of these devices is used to actuate controls which will alter the process variables and change the composition of the sample, or which will cause alarm systems to function.

Direct measuring process control refractometers are generally constructed so that the light beam is measured with a photomultiplier cathode. The output of this tube can then be amplified and the resulting electrical signal may be used to return the refractometer to its original balanced condition. The refractive index of the sample is proportional to the degree of correction and may be read from a dial or recorded with a potentiometric recorder.

Process instruments which are constructed to measure a small range of values can provide an accuracy comparable to that obtained with the best laboratory instruments, if adequate temperature control of the system is provided.

Differential process refractometers allow refractive index measurements of even greater sensitivity than the direct measuring devices. Further, the degree of temperature control required for their use is substantially less than for the direct refractometers. The differential type of equipment measures the difference in refractive index between a reference material and a sample from the process stream. In some equipment, white light is utilized and compensating prisms are not required since the dispersion effects are balanced. The output signal from these instruments may be recorded, and automatic closed-loop process control is readily achieved with the usual accessory devices.

[1] Brice, B. A., and Halwer, M., J. Opt. Soc. Am., **41,** 1033, 1951.

ANALYTICAL APPLICATIONS OF REFRACTOMETRY

Qualitative Analysis.—Although refractometry has been applied to the qualitative analysis of both inorganic and organic materials, in the vapor, liquid, and solid states, the most common application of the technique is for the identification of organic liquids. The Abbe type refractometer is ordinarily employed for this purpose, because it is easy to operate, requires only a drop or two of sample, and provides results sufficiently accurate.

The density of the organic liquid and its refractive index are used to calculate the molecular refractivity from the Lorenz[2]-Lorentz[3] equation:

$$M_D = \left(\frac{n^2 - 1}{n^2 + 2}\right)\left(\frac{m}{d}\right)$$

where n = refractive index, m = molecular weight, and d = density.
The measured molecular refractivity of an unknown may be compared with the theoretical molecular refractivity of various compounds, since the theoretical value is the sum of the refractivities of the atoms plus additional values for unsaturated linkages, rings, or other groups. The values for the elements, structural units and conjugation systems are readily available in textbooks and handbooks. For example, the following values for elements, and structural groups, with sodium *D* light, may be utilized to make calculations for organic compounds.

C	2.418	O carbonyl	2.211
H	1.100	O ether	1.643
F	0.95	O hydroxyl	1.525
Cl	5.967	O ester	1.64
Br	8.865	N primary aliphatic amine	2.45
I	13.900	N primary aromatic amine	3.21
Double bond	1.733	N secondary aliphatic amine	2.65
Triple bond	2.398	N secondary aromatic amine	3.59
Three-membered ring	0.71	N tertiary aliphatic amine	3.00
Four-membered ring	0.48	N tertiary aromatic amine	4.36

Values for other atoms and groups in organic liquids may be found in Smiles, The Relation between Chemical Constitution and Some Physical Properties, Longmans, Green and Co., London, 1910.

In addition to the use of the refractive index value and the calculated molecular refractivity, the dispersion of a liquid, v, is useful for characterization purposes. When the Abbe instrument is employed, the drum reading is employed together with the dispersion chart, supplied with the instrument, to calculate v from the equation:

$$v = \frac{n_D - 1}{n_F - n_C}$$

where n_D = refractive index for sodium *D* line,
n_F = refractive index for blue hydrogen line, and
n_C = refractive index for red hydrogen line.

The partial dispersion is equal to $n_F - n_C$ and this quantity may be obtained from

[2] Lorenz, L. V., Ann. Physik u. Chem., **11,** 70, 1880.
[3] Lorentz, H. A., Ann. Physik u. Chem., **9,** 641, 1880.

tables. The specific dispersion δ is calculated by dividing the partial dispersion by the density. In most cases the value is multiplied by 10^4.

$$\delta T^0C = \frac{n_F - n_C}{T^0C} \times 10^4$$

The drum readings, obtained with Abbe instruments (Z values), for various classes of compounds will vary with instruments constructed by different companies. Therefore, these values must be used with caution.

The manufacturers of various refractometers generally provide tables for use in calculating the partial dispersion. The Bausch and Lomb Optical Co. (Rochester, N. Y.) provide a Series 525 Dispersion Table for use with their "Abbe-56" refractometer. This instrument provides a direct reading of the D refractive index. Once the D index is known, the compensating prism scale reading is used to calculate dispersion from values given in the tables. The following example, taken from the Series 525 table for water at 20°C., will serve to demonstrate the calculation of $n_F - n_C$.

$$\begin{aligned}
\text{Index } n_D &= 1.3330 \\
\text{Compensator Scale Reading} &= 17.9 \\
\text{From Table I} \quad A &= 0.02444 \\
B &= 0.03117 \\
\text{From Table II} \quad C &= -0.592 \\
n_F - n_C &= A + BC \\
n_F - n_C &= 0.02444 + 0.03117\ (-0.592) \\
n_F - n_C &= 0.00599
\end{aligned}$$

Physical Separation Techniques.—Refractometry is often a convenient method to measure the separation of binary, or more complex, mixtures by adsorption, distillation, extraction, thermal diffusion, or other physical separation techniques. Thus, it may be employed to aid in the development and evaluation of these techniques in the laboratory and to follow or control a physical separation process in a plant.

Vapor-liquid equilibrium diagrams for binary solutions are determined by making equilibrium temperature measurements, during distillation, and by determining composition from refractive index measurements. These diagrams are useful in planning separation of the components by fractional distillation, and are prepared by students in most college physical chemistry laboratories. If accurate plots of refractive index as a function of mole fraction for a given binary mixture are prepared, or are available in the literature, a simple rapid refractive index measurement provides a sufficiently accurate analysis of the sample.

Rapid procedures for the determination of the separating power (number of theoretical plates) of distillation columns are based upon the use of refractive index nomographs. In this case the change in refractive index of a binary test mixture is directly related to the number of theoretical plates.

Adsorption separations of liquids by the batch or column procedures are often studied by refractometric methods. Recording refractometers which measure the refractive index of the column effluent may be utilized to actuate relays on automatic collection devices so that fractions containing pure solvent are collected separately, or discarded, from fractions containing some of the separated components. In certain cases where only one component, or one class of components, is selectively adsorbed, refractometry may be utilized for a rapid and accurate determination. The procedures mentioned in conjunction with adsorption separation are applicable with slight modification to separations performed by other techniques such as liquid-liquid partition or ion-exchange.

The Application of Refractometry to the Structural Group Analysis of Mineral Oils.—The development and quantitative study of the relationships between the physical properties of hydrocarbons and their chemical structure have been reviewed by several authors. The emphasis in this section is upon the role of refractometry in this field.

In response to the need for a proper chemical characterization of petroleum crudes, and for the analysis of fractions and products derived from petroleum, a number of analytical methods based upon the measurement of physical properties have been developed. The measurement of refractive index has been utilized in these methods because it is an accurate, simple procedure which requires only a small sample.

Lipkin and Martin[4] studied the relationship between the refractive index and the density and the temperature coefficient of density. The equation which they developed provides calculated values, for saturated hydrocarbon compounds or for fractions containing only saturated hydrocarbons, which are in good agreement with the observed values. The Lipkin and Martin equation is:

$$n = \frac{69.878d - 0.4044Ad - 0.797A + 136.566}{5.543d - 0.746A + 126.683}$$

where n = the refractive index at 20°C. for the D line of sodium, d = density at 20°C., and $A = -10^5 \times$ temperature coefficient of density.

Plots of refractive indexes *vs.* density for various types of hydrocarbons yield a series of lines of varying intercept. This refractivity intercept varies from 1.0458 for paraffins to 1.1082 for naphthalenes. Leendertse and co-workers[5] applied the refractivity intercept procedure to the analysis of lubricating oil fractions. Van Nes and Van Westen[6] concluded that the accuracy of this relationship is nearly as good as a density method based upon the Lorenz-Lorentz specific refraction and molecular weight. However, the refractivity intercept method does not require the molecular weight determination or estimation and, thus, is more rapid.

The change in refractive index with wavelength has been applied in several methods for hydrocarbon analysis. In most cases the dispersion which is calculated is the refractive index for blue light (the hydrogen F line) minus the refractive index for red light (the hydrogen C line). When this dispersion is divided by the density of the sample the specific dispersion is obtained. Dispersion values can be used for the determination of aromatic hydrocarbons in both straight-run and in cracked naphthas. Lipkin, Sankin, and Martin[7] developed a method for the determination of aromatic hydrocarbon types based upon the refractive dispersion, the molecular weight, and the number of double bonds per molecule. Later, Martin and Sankin[8] provided a procedure for determining the number of aromatic and saturated rings in aromatic hydrocarbon mixtures.

The *n-d-M* method for the ring analysis and the carbon-type analysis of mineral oils has been widely used in many laboratories. A complete discussion of this technique is given in the book by Van Nes and Van Westen.[6] The procedure is based upon an earlier method of Vlugter, Waterman, and Van Westen[9] who used the specific refraction, aniline point, and molecular weight. In the aniline point procedure, the predicted aniline point was compared with the observed value. The difference was a measure of

[4] Lipkin, M. R., and Martin, C. C., Ind. Eng. Chem., **18**, 380, 1946.

[5] Leendertse, J. J., Vlugter, J. C., Waterman, H. I., and Van Westen, H. A., Chem. Weekblad, **39**, 282, 1942.

[6] Van Nes, K., and Van Westen, H. A., Aspects of the Constitution of Mineral Oils, Elsevier, New York, 1951.

[7] Lipkin, M. R., Sankin, A., and Martin, C. C., Anal. Chem., **20**, 598, 1948.

[8] Martin, C. C., and Sankin, A., Anal. Chem., **25**, 206, 1953.

[9] Vlugter, J. C., Waterman, H. I., and Van Westen, H. A., J. Inst. Petroleum Technol., **21**, 661, 1935.

the aromatic content. Later, it was found that density may be used for this purpose.

The structural elements which are determined by the n-d-M method are

Ring content:
- R_N = number of naphthene rings per mean molecule
- R_A = number of aromatic rings per mean molecule
- R_T = number of total rings per mean molecule

Carbon distribution:
- $\% C_R$ = number of carbon atoms in rings per 100 carbon atoms
- $\% C_A$ = number of carbon atoms in aromatic rings per 100 carbon atoms
- $\% C_N$ = number of carbon atoms in naphthene rings per 100 carbon atoms
- $\% C_P$ = number of carbon atoms not in rings per 100 carbon atoms

A more recent procedure for the analysis of oil fractions is the V-n-d method of Cornelissen and Waterman.[10] This technique avoids the complicated and rather inaccurate molecular weight determination and substitutes the measurement of V (viscosity) which is easily determined with a relatively high accuracy.

Some Quantitative Aspects of Refractometry.—The measured values of refractive index, or of refractive index differences, are used for identification, for purity determination, and for the quantitative analysis of solutions. The precision and the accuracy obtainable depends upon the equipment utilized and the degree of temperature control. In many cases it is necessary to prepare accurate calibration curves for a given binary system using purified samples of the components. In some cases the relationship between concentration and refractive index is not linear and interpolation from the calibration curve will yield the most accurate results.

A typical Abbe instrument is accurate to ±0.0001 unit, and a precision Abbe to ±0.00003 unit. The dipping instruments are also accurate to ±0.00003 unit but are restricted to a total range of 0.04 for each prism. Higher sensitivities are achieved with the differential instruments but the total range available for measurement is restricted.

The tables of refractive indexes which appear in the International Critical Tables and in the various handbooks of chemistry are useful for qualitative identifications. In addition, reference to specialized texts in the chemistry of the various classes of compounds will often facilitate the development of methods when pure components are not available. A series of Standard Samples of pure hydrocarbons is available from the National Bureau of Standards, Washington, D. C. These materials have certified densities and certified refractive indexes for light of various wavelengths at 20°, 25°, and 30°C. Many other hydrocarbons of high-purity are available from the American Petroleum Institute. Preparative-scale gas chromatography, which permits the rapid separation of complex mixtures with a high degree of resolution, is a suitable technique for the preparation of milligram or gram amounts of pure components for the calibration of refractometric methods.

APPLICATIONS

The immersion refractometer is useful in determining the concentrations of aqueous and alcoholic solutions. Wagner[11] has discussed the necessary precautions for good results. These include: constancy of temperature; rinsing the prism with water of the same temperature; wiping lightly; and allowing 2 minutes before reading.

The index of refraction has also been used to determine the composition of solutions

[10] Cornelissen, J., and Waterman, H. I., Chim. und ind., **76,** 1019, 1956; Brennstaff-Chem., **37,** 404, 1956.

[11] Wagner, B., Z. angew. Chem., **33,** I, 262, 1920.

of sodium chloride and potassium chloride. This is done by using a curve obtained by plotting percentage of sodium chloride *vs.* index of refraction.[12]

The refractometer has also proved useful in physiological chemistry. It has been used to determine nonalbuminous constituents in serum, and also total globulins, insoluble globulins, albumens, and total albumen. This can be done with high accuracy.[13] The action of ferments has also been followed with the refractometer.

Refractometry is used in the analysis of natural fats as a process control test where changes in unsaturation are involved. It also provides an index of the iodine value of vegetable oils, and also a measure of the oil content of oilseed meals and other oil-bearing materials. Refractive index is also related to such characteristics as unsaturation, molecular weight, free fatty acid content, and hydroxyl content (see Chapter 48). The refractive indexes of some fats are given in Table 48-3.

Refractometry has been used to detect boundaries in fractions during separations by electrophoresis (see Chapter 37).

The refractive index has been found to be a useful value in the analysis of a number of special materials. Methods included elsewhere in Standard Methods of Chemical Analysis are as follows:

1. Chapter 12, Volume III, Chemical Microscopy.
   a. Used for the identification of organic compounds by determining the refractive index of molten samples at a definite temperature
2. Chapter 37, Volume IIB, Paint, Varnish, and Lacquer.
   a. Identification of oils, page 1645.
3. Chapter 41, Volume IIB, Plastics.
   a. Refractive index for transparent plastics, pages 2052, 2053.
4. Chapter 48, Volume III, Natural Fats.
   a. Oil content of flaxseed

   Chapter 33, Volume IIB, Natural Fats.
   a. The refractive index is used as a *fat constant* as a measure of unsaturation, as a means of determining the fat content of some source materials, and as a control test for hydrogenation and other plant processes, page 1447 (also, Chapter 48, Volume III).
5. Chapter 50, Volume III, Foods.
   a. Determination of sucrose
   b. Determination of water

   Chapter 33, Volume IIB, Natural Fats.
   a. Fats, oils, waxes, page 1447.

RECENT DEVELOPMENTS IN REFRACTOMETRY

The current interest in instrumentation and in the application of refractometry to a wide variety of problems and materials may be demonstrated by citing some recent work. A group of representative references has been selected from the subject index for Volume 58 of Chemical Abstracts which covers papers and books abstracted between January and June, 1963.

Three books of refractometry were reviewed during this same period. One pertained to studies of flames and aerodynamics,[14] one to biological materials,[15] and one to ion-

[12] Shippy, B. A., and Barrows, G. H., J. Am. Chem. Soc., **40,** 185, 1918.
[13] Hirsch, Z. angew. Chem., **33,** I, 269, 1920.
[14] Chemical Abstracts, **58,** 8424h, 1963.
[15] Chemical Abstracts, **58,** 11786g, 1963.

ospheric layer models.[16] Designers of new and modified equipment were active, as there were five references to refractometers and eleven references to interferometers.

A wide variety of materials is being studied by refractometry. Typical of the eighteen references which appeared were those dealing with coal,[17] films on glass,[18] films on silicon,[19] alkali metal nitrates,[20] and paraffins and their halogenated derivatives.[21] Interferometry was cited in eleven references. These studies included the examination of germanium crystals,[22] research on the thermal diffusion of liquids,[23] and the investigation of sedimentation.[24]

[16] Chemical Abstracts, **58,** 9777d, 1963.
[17] Chemical Abstracts, **58,** 6617a, 1963.
[18] Chemical Abstracts, **58,** 6543h, 1963.
[19] Chemical Abstracts, **58,** 146f, 1963.
[20] Chemical Abstracts, **58,** 12058d, 1963.
[21] Chemical Abstracts, **58,** 149b, 1963.
[22] Chemical Abstracts, **58,** 2949f, 1963.
[23] Chemical Abstracts, **58,** 3917e, 1963.
[24] Chemical Abstracts, **58,** 13174h, 1963.

Chapter **15**

POLARIMETRY AND SPECTROPOLARIMETRY

By Gabor B. Levy
Photovolt Corporation
New York, New York

INTRODUCTION

Polarimetry is a classical method of quantitative analysis. It is an elegant, nondestructive technique. It consists of the simple measurement of the angle of rotation of linearly polarized light. This rotation is caused by the asymmetric chemical structure of the sample through which a beam of polarized light is passed, and the angle is a linear function of the concentration. The basic principles of polarimetry were established about 150 years ago, and the technique has served well in routine analytical work in several fields, notably in the quantitative analysis of sugars.

In fact, saccharimetry, as the polarimetric analysis of sugar is called, has become a specialized area with its own instrumentation and well established, standard procedures of international acceptance. Polarimetry in other fields is less standardized, but is widely used for the quantitation of several alkaloids, steroids, and other pharmaceutical and organic chemical products.

Recently, polarimetry underwent an explosive development with the availability of spectropolarimeters. The measurement of optical rotatory dispersion (ORD), *i.e.*, rotation dependent of wavelength, is an incisive tool of discovery and characterization of organic structure. Here polarimetry serves not so much for quantitative analysis but rather to solve complex qualitative problems involving asymmetric compounds.

The newest technique, which is operative with asymmetric molecules, is the direct measurement of circular dichroism (*i.e.*, the difference of absorption of the left and right circularly polarized light as it passes through the sample). This technique is analogous to absorptiometry (quantitative spectrophotometry), but it offers significant advantages over the latter in many situations.

GENERAL PRINCIPLES

Light is polarizable as are all electromagnetic waves. Considered as propagating by transverse vibration, an unpolarized beam simply means that the transverse vibrations are distributed over the plane perpendicular to the direction of travel. In a linearly polarized beam, the energy is sharply restricted in a definite direction on this plane. As the light beam passes through a medium, it can be conveniently considered to be split into two circular components which are coherent and have opposite sense of rotation.

As the light emerges from the medium, these two components, left- and right-handed, add up to yield the original plane polarized beam. If, however, the medium is *anisotropic*, the emergent beam is not identical with the original beam. In an anisotropic medium, the refractive index for the right- and left-hand polarized light is different, *i.e.*, the velocity of propagation differs. This causes a phase difference between the two component beams and the resultant beam is rotated in its plane of polarization as it emerges from the medium.

Molecules of inherent structural asymmetry are anisotropic; they are *optically active* and exhibit *optical rotation* in solution. The typical optically active center is a carbon atom with four different substituents. In addition, any structural dissymmetry which results in a spatial left- and right-handedness will cause optical activity. Compounds of these types come in a right-hand (D) and left-hand (L) form. When equal amounts of these two forms are mixed (racemic mixtures) there is no optical rotation because the activity of the two forms exactly cancel. Internal compensation of optically active centers in complex molecules is also found. Left- and right-handed optical isomers were first studied by Pasteur well over 100 years ago, and extensive surveys are found in most organic chemical texts.

Around the turn of the century, Cotton found that the refractive index changes rather abruptly near an absorption band which is associated with optical activity. In consequence, the Cotton effect gives rise to "anomalous" rotatory dispersion curves as contrasted with "plain" curves, which are found in the absence of absorption (Fig. 15–1).

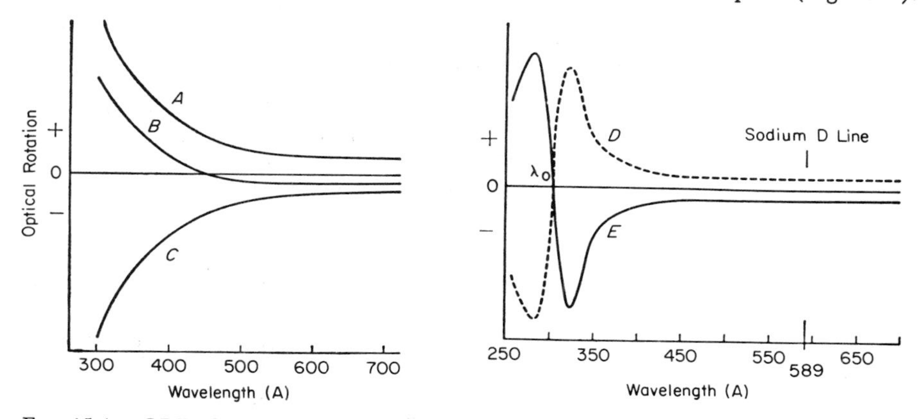

FIG. 15-1. ORD Curves: *a*, Typical Plain Curves; *b*, Typical Cotton Effect Due to an Absorption Band at λ_0. A curve is designated positive by starting at the long wavelength. Plain curves *A* and *B* are positive, and curve *D* shows a positive Cotton effect because the first extremum is in the positive direction. (Reprinted with permission from C. Djerassi, Science, **134**, 649, 1961.)

A good description of these conditions will be found in a review article by Djerassi.[1]

Near the "optically active" absorption bands, the light absorption for the left- and right-hand circularly polarized beams is also dissimilar. Thus, in addition to the extinction coefficient for unpolarized light (which is the basis of absorptiometry, *i.e.*, spectrophotometric analysis), there are two extinction coefficients, one for left- and one for right-hand circularly polarized light. The difference of these two, the dichroic absorption or extinction coefficient, is measurable and can be a valuable analytical

[1] Djerassi, C., Science, **134,** 649, 1961.

datum. The measurement of circular dichroism had been vigorously promoted by W. Kuhn, and recently by Velluz and Legrand.[2]

The detailed theory of optical activity is a fascinating study, but it goes far beyond the scope of the present review. A good summary including many references, will be found in a chapter by W. Heller.[3] Other excellent reviews are those of Moscowitz[4] and Mason.[5]

POLARIMETRY

As already mentioned, the concentration of an optically active compound can be determined by measuring the angle of rotation which the linearly polarized light beam undergoes during passage through the solution. The basic equation is:

$$[\alpha] = \frac{\alpha}{l \cdot c}$$

where: α = the angle measured;
l = light path in decimeters; and
c = concentration in g./100 ml.

$[\alpha]$ is the specific rotation, *viz.*, the rotation in degrees of a compound under *standard* conditions. Thus, $[\alpha]$ refers to a light path of unity (100 mm.), but the actual light path of the measurement is unimportant because the rotation increases precisely linearly with the light path, and the data are readily interconvertible. For instance, with low values of rotation, the use of a 200-mm. tube is usual, which will then exactly double the measured value. The concentration, however, may have a somewhat nonlinear effect. Therefore, the concentration range is usually indicated to which a given value of $[\alpha]$ refers. Similarly, the temperature has an unpredictable effect on rotation. Most data refer to room temperature (20°C.), but if the measurement is made at other temperatures, it is given with the corresponding value of rotation.

Most important is the wavelength, because of the slope of the ORD ($[\alpha]$ *vs.* λ), which may be quite steep. For this reason, monochromatic light must always be used. (The exception to this is saccharimetry, which will be described later.) Earlier measurements were taken at 589 mμ because sodium flames and arc lamps were the only convenient sources of monochromatic light (sodium *D* line). More recently, the mercury arc has been employed widely and the 546- and 436-mμ lines have been isolated by filters. These have the great advantage that the values of $[\alpha]$ are usually substantially greater at the shorter wavelengths. The notation is then, for instance, $[\alpha]_D^{20}$, *i.e.*, specific rotation at 20°C. and the sodium *D* line at 589 mμ. To this the concentration range may be added if it deviates from 1 g./100 ml. Additional data will refer to the solvent, pH, etc., which may have a substantial effect on the rotation if they affect the state of ionization or spatial conformation. In some compounds, notably sugars, mutarotation may be present. These compounds exist in two optically active forms at equilibrium. When the compound is dissolved, a considerable time may elapse before the equilibrium is reached. In these cases, the initial and final rotation will be listed.

In newer references, rotation may be expressed as molecular rotation $[\phi]$ rather than

[2] Kuhn, W., Am. Rev. Phys. Chem., **9**, 417, 1958; Velluz, L., Legrand, M., and Grossjean, M., La Mesure et l'Etude du Dichroisme Circulaire Optique, Centre de Recherches Reussel-UCLAF, Paris, 1963.

[3] Heller, W., "Polarimetry," in Physical Methods of Organic Chemistry Vol. 1, Part III, Interscience Publishers, New York, 1960.

[4] Djerassi, C., Optical Rotatory Dispersion, McGraw-Hill, New York, 1960, Chapter 12.

[5] Mason, S. F., Quart. Rev. Chem. Soc., **17**, 20, 1963.

specific rotation $[\alpha]$. These data are readily interconvertible by the value of molecular weight (M.W.). (Molecular rotation used to be symbolized by [M], and this will be found in older references instead of $[\phi]$.)

$$[\phi] = \frac{[\alpha]\cdot 100}{\text{M.W.}}$$

The basis of the analysis is then the known specific rotation of the compound. A rather complete list of all categories of organic compounds will be found in Section 6 of Handbook of Analytical Chemistry.[6]

INSTRUMENTATION

Visual Polarimeters.—A typical visual polarimeter is shown in Fig. 15-2. Light source may be a sodium or a mercury arc (less usual is the cadmium arc for the 509-mμ and

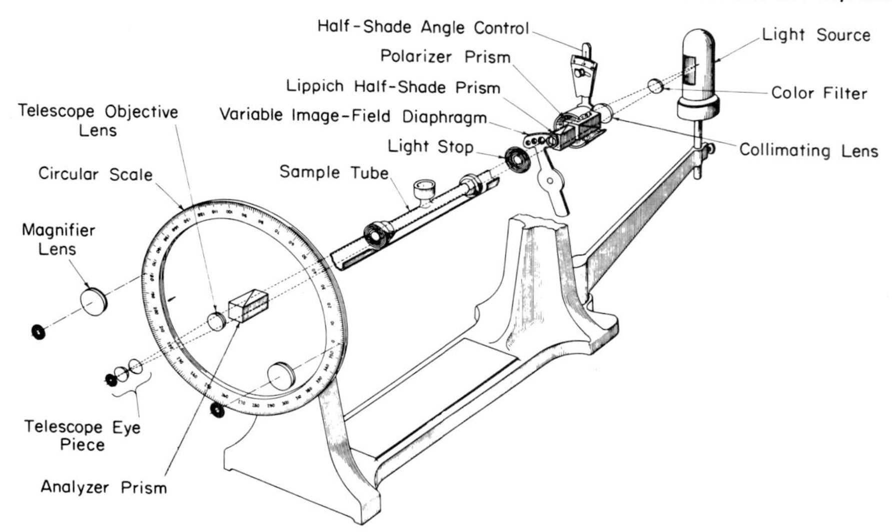

Fig. 15-2. Schematic of a Visual Polarimeter. (Courtesy O. C. Rudolph and Sons.)

644-mμ lines). A filter isolates the emission line for monochromatic illumination. The light then passes a polarizer prism system. This is usually a Nicol prism made of calcite which is cut and recemented in such way that the incident light is split into a linear polarized beam which is transmitted, while the second beam is reflected and absorbed. The polarized beam is then passed through the analyzer which is essentially identical with the polarizer. One of these two elements (usually the analyzer) can be rotated, and it is provided with a graduated circle for the precise read-out in angular degrees. By using a large circular scale and a vernier, a precision of 0.002° can be obtained in research-type polarimeters.

The principle of measurement is straightforward. If the two "Nicols" are oriented identically with respect to their optic axes, maximum light is passed. When they are crossed (90°), the intensity is at minimum (following a $\sin^2$ law). A refinement in all commercial visual polarimeters is that the observation of the crossed analyzer position

[6] Meites, L., Ed., Handbook of Analytical Chemistry, McGraw-Hill, New York, 1963.

is made easier by a half-shade field (Fig. 15-3). Because the human eye is a comparative, rather than absolute, light-measuring device, very much better precision can be obtained by comparing two adjacent fields, rather than attempting to evaluate the brightness of a single field. The half-shade fields are created by an auxiliary prism, and the details of the optical arrangement can be found in the literature.[3] Here we are only concerned with the operational features. The zero position of the instrument is that angle at which the two (or three) segments of the observed field are *equally* dim.

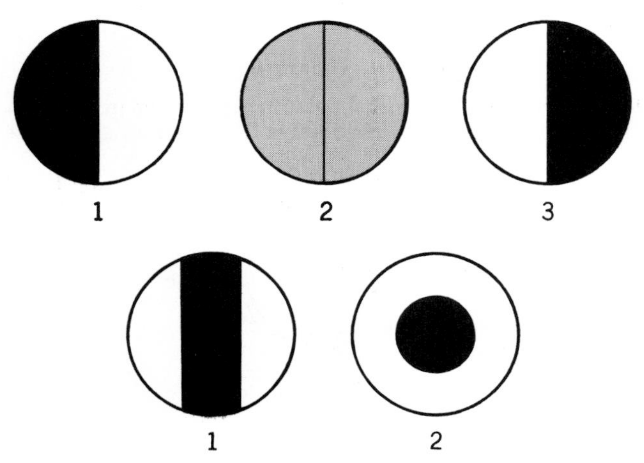

FIG. 15-3. Aspect of Half-Shade Fields. Above is conventional split field, 2 at balance, 1 and 3 off balance at minus and plus rotation. Below is special field configurations, off balance point. (Courtesy John Wiley and Sons.)

Between the polarizer and the analyzer, a space is provided to accept the sample. The sample is placed in a tube which has precisely ground ends corresponding to the light path. End windows are held to the tube by gasketed fittings.

Routine polarimetric determinations are simple enough. First the polarimeter is balanced to zero degrees with the solvent. Then the solution is placed into the instrument, the instrument is rebalanced, and the angle α read off the scale. Nevertheless, when many measurements are taken, this becomes somewhat tedious. For the assessment of the half-shade field, the operator's eyes must be dark-adapted. Extended work in a darkened room peering through the eyepiece at an almost black field is tiring. The precision of visual polarimetric measurements will tend to increase rapidly at first, as the observer's eyes become adapted, but then it will decrease gradually because of fatigue. These facts justified the introduction of photoelectric polarimeters whose popularity is growing steadily. Four models are briefly described below.

***Photoelectric Polarimeters.* O. C. Rudolph and Sons.**—This company, a pioneer in visual instruments, developed a line of photoelectric polarimeters which are particularly noteworthy because they paved the way for spectropolarimetry. Moreover, the Rudolph Photoelectric Polarimeters provide excellent precision at a reasonable cost. The design of these instruments is based on a research-type visual polarimeter with one important optical modification. There is no split half-shade field: instead, the analyzer is mechanically "flip-flopped" over an adjustable angle. At balance, and only at balance, the two extreme positions of the analyzer yield equal (low) intensity. A sensitive photomultiplier-photometer (Photovolt Model 520-M, modified) serves as a null indicator. The analyzer prism is manually rotated until a minimum deflection results on the large photometer-scale, and then the angle of rotation is read visually. In this sense, the instrument is not fully automated, but the critical half-shade observation is replaced by a convenient meter read-out.

Zeiss.—Besides their visual polarimeters, Zeiss introduced, some years ago, a fully automatic photoelectric polarimeter. It is furnished with a mercury arc (at 365, 405, 436, 546, and 578 mμ); an auxiliary sodium arc can also be used. The key element for automatic operation is a Faraday modulator.

Faraday cells are often used in photoelectric polarimeters, and their mode of operation merits a few words. Faraday found that a magnetic field can induce optical rotatory power in liquids and solids by its influence on the atomic electron configuration. By using an electromagnet surrounding a glass rod (in the Zeiss instrument) or a suitable crystal or solution, an alternating optical rotation can be introduced. This is exactly analogous to the mechanical flip-flop employed in the Rudolph instrument.

The Zeiss instrument uses a rotating polarizer, followed by the sample cell and the Faraday modulator. The emerging light passes through the analyzer and a photomultiplier pickup. The latter actuates a servosystem which drives the polarizer to balance. When the polarizer is exactly crossed with the analyzer, then, and only then, will the alternating polarization introduced by the Faraday modulator have equal magnitude. This is the null point for the servosystem which thus establishes the balance automatically. The operator places the sample into the instrument (after it has been set to zero with the solvent) and then reads off the value of rotation from a magnified scale which allows estimation to 0.0025°. This is a great convenience, but the price of the instrument is much greater than that of a visual instrument.

Perkin-Elmer Model 141.—This instrument is rather similar to the Zeiss machine in that it also uses a self-balancing servosystem, and the light source and filter arrangement are equivalent. It differs in that the modulation is introduced by a mechanically oscillated polarizer, and the analyzer is driven by the servosystem to balance. The read-out is obtained either on the integral digital counter in 0.001° or on an auxiliary recorder. The instrument reaches far into the ultraviolet, and is well engineered. A very interesting new light source for this instrument uses a narrow pencil of laser light. This light is sharply monochromatic, of course, but its merit lies in the fact that the minute beam dimension allows the measurement of microsamples. Less than 40 μl. with 100-mm. light path can be measured in this way. This is of great potential importance with scarce and valuable biological samples. Unfortunately, the single wavelength available at present with the laser source is at 632.8 mμ, and this seems rather limiting.

Bendix.—This instrument is somewhat different in concept as well as in features. It, too, incorporates a modulating Faraday cell, but in front of the analyzer there is a second, compensating Faraday cell. The automatic regulation of the current to this cell establishes balance. The optical rotation is thus reduced to an electrical current measurement that can be done with great ease and precision. The dynamic range of the instrument is small, 0.5° (*vs.* 360° with the Zeiss and Rudolph, and almost 90° with the Perkin-Elmer instrument). However, the sensitivity is incredibly high (of the order of 0.0001°) so that very short light paths are used, and small sample volumes are possible. A tungsten light is employed with interference filters, giving fairly monochromatic light selectable within the visible light range of 450–600 mμ.

QUANTITATIVE POLARIMETRY

The key limitation of quantitative analysis by polarimetry is the necessity of the precise knowledge of the qualitative composition of the sample. This is true, of course, of other methods of analysis to some extent, but here such knowledge is essential because optical rotation is an additive, cyclic, property. In a sense, this is an advantage, too, because added rotation does not decrease the precision of the measurement. For instance, it is possible to work with an optically active solvent, if its rotation is known, without impairing the accuracy of measurement. This is in contrast with spectrophotometry where high levels of absorbance are damaging. Moreover, the presence of optically inactive admixtures, even when they absorb appreciable light is of small moment in polarimetry.

Polarimetry is, therefore, well suited to detect small amounts of optically active impurities. More commonly, it is employed for the opposite purpose of determining the purity of optically active preparations, where the bulk of the sample is a well defined compound, and there is a fair knowledge of the nature of the potential contaminants. The polarimetric method is outstanding when optical activity and biological activity are corollary, and this is not unusual.

The Technique.—The unknown is dissolved in a suitable solvent at as high a concentration level as is practicable. Both solvent and concentration to be used will be found in a "standard" method or appended to the published value of specific rotation $[\alpha]$.[6] The polarimeter tube (sample holder) is then filled with solvent and, after a warm-up period, as prescribed by the manufacturer, the instrument is balanced to read zero. It is noted that the actual setting to exactly zero value is unnecessary. A blank value can be numerically subtracted equally well because of the additive nature of rotation. It is essential, of course, to subtract with the proper sign (for example, if the blank were to read $-0.10°$ and the sample $+1.10°$, the actual rotation is $+1.20°$).

Then the sample is placed in the tube and rotation, α, is read. The actual concentration is computed from the known value of specific rotation $[\alpha]$: $\frac{\alpha}{[\alpha]} = c$ (g./100 ml.). The purity expressed in percent equals $\frac{c \times 100}{\text{weighed in (g./100 ml.)}}$

There are a few general cautions. The polarimeter tubes can introduce spurious rotation if the end-windows are stressed by excessive tightening. This can be checked quite easily by blank readings with solvent. The light path can also be checked by using a standard optically active solution, but it will probably be found to be correct because of the precision-ground length of commerical tubes. Air bubbles in the tubes are extremely disturbing, and for this reason, tubes with enlarged ends or filler necks which trap the air, are very convenient. Jacketed tubes which can be thermostated are also recommended. Details on these and other experimental details will be found in NBS Circular C440.[7]

When using a visual polarimeter, the dark-adaptation of the eye is of decisive importance for the precision of measurement. It is best to work in a darkened room and not to attempt measurements before a few minutes' adaptation to darkness. The presetting of the half-shade angle before any measurement is also of importance. Small angles are preferable, but a compromise will have to be made corresponding to light transmission of the sample and the visual acuity of the operator. This angle must be set before starting and it must not be changed during a set of measurements.

The use of shorter wavelength is usually advantageous because most organic compounds show larger values of rotation toward the ultraviolet. In visual polarimetry, the use of the 546-mμ mercury line is particularly favorable because it is near to the maximum sensitivity of the eye. Unfortunately, most older published data are based on the sodium *D* line, and when the specific rotation is known only for that wavelength, work

[7] Polarimetry, Saccharimetry and The Sugars, Circular of the National Bureau of Standards, C440, Washington, D. C., 1942.

at 589 mμ will be necessary. This is much more tiring and yields lower absolute values of rotation.

The last caution is more theoretical than actual. Because of the cyclic nature of optical rotation, it is theoretically possible to exceed 180°, and then the rotation will appear as a reduced value with the opposite sign. Automatic polarimeters, too, will drive to the nearest balance point. This danger is not acute, because, in practical solutions which are dilute, the rotations will tend to be small. Doubt on this point can be resolved quite easily, too, by serial dilutions or correspondingly shorter sample tubes. When a set of such measurements yields a linear proportion, the original measured value is correct. Conversely, if the values "cycle," the true value can be computed. For example, if double-dilutions show values −90°, +135°, +67.5°, etc., then the original value should have been read as +270°.

Quantitative methods of analysis by polarimetry are widespread. Intraplant control methods based on polarimetry are quite common in the pharmaceutical industry, for instance. Many such methods also have official standing. Four assays are listed here as representative examples. The first is an AOAC method;[8] the other three are USP methods.[9]

Lemon and Orange Extracts.[8]—Determine rotation at 20° with any standard instrument, 50-mm. tube, and sodium light. State results in angular degrees on 100-mm. basis. If instruments having sugar scale are used, reading for orange oils is above range of scale, but readings may be obtained by use of standard levorotatory quartz plates, or by 25-mm. tube. True rotation cannot be obtained by diluting the oil with alcohol and correcting rotation in proportion to the dilution.

Estradiol Benzoate.[9]—The specific rotation of estradiol benzoate, determined in a solution in dioxane containing 250 mg. of estradiol benzoate in each 10 ml., is not less than +40° and not more than +47°.

Lactose.[9]—The specific rotation of lactose, calculated on the dried basis, determined in a solution containing 10 g. of lactose and 0.2 ml. of ammonia T.S. in each 100 ml., is not less than +54.8° and not more than +55.5°.

Calcium Pantothenate.[9]—The specific rotation of calcium pantothenate, calculated on the dried basis, determined in a solution containing 500 mg. of calcium pantothenate in each 10 ml., is not less than +25° and not more than +27.5°.

SACCHARIMETRY

The determination of sugar concentration offers an almost ideal field for polarimetry. The concentrations involved are high (or can be made high because of the great solubility of sugar in water). The impurities associated with the sugars show no excessive rotation, and the mixtures are not too complex by comparison. For these reasons, then, saccharimetry was one of the earliest practical applications of polarimetry, and it still represents the most important field of routine control work done by this technique.

It has been found that in the range of visible light, quartz has almost identical rotatory dispersion as sucrose. Consequently, saccharimeters have traditionally been built utilizing this effect. By positioning a quartz wedge in the light path of the polarimeter, a variable path through the quartz is obtained. The wedge is pushed in to a point where it exactly compensates the rotation of the sugar solution. In this system, both the analyzer and the polarizer are fixed in orientation, and the linear displacement of the wedge is the only variable. The small difference between the rotatory dispersion of quartz and

[8] Official Methods of Analysis of The Association of Official Agricultural Chemists, 8th Ed., 1955.

[9] Pharmacopoeia of the United States of America, 17th Revision, 1965.

of sucrose can be eliminated by spectral "trimming" with a potassium dichromate solution or an equivalent glass filter. The residual error is only about 0.12 sugar degrees at 100 degrees, and a solution of dichromate, whose concentration times the light path equals 9, compensates for this (*e.g.*, 3-cm. cell filled with a 3 percent solution).

A saccharimeter differs from a polarimeter quite radically. It uses white light, whereas, a polarimeter is operated with sharply monochromatic light. Consequently, a saccharimeter can only be used with sugar solutions (in which case the quartz compensates for the rotatory dispersion of sucrose). Conversely, a polarimeter is suitable for the measurement of optical rotation of any solution, including sugar. However, saccharimetric sugar determinations are the basis of internationally accepted *sugar degrees* (°S), and saccharimeters are appropriately calibrated. When a polarimeter is employed which utilizes monochromatic light rather than a quartz wedge, deviations from sugar degrees will be found in some solutions, and they may not be inconsequential. The International Sugar Scale assigns 100°S to a pure sucrose solution of normal weight (26 g. in 100 ml. of pure water) at 20°C., and a 200-mm. light path, measured in a saccharimeter with white light and a dichromate filter. Of course, an exact numerical conversion from sugar degrees to angular degrees is possible with pure sucrose (100°S corresponds to $\alpha = 34.6°$), but in practical, more or less impure solutions, the relationship is not exactly predictable, and the sugar scale is conventionally and legally binding.

It is not surprising, then, that virtually all sugar laboratories use visual saccharimeters (also called polariscopes). They differ in vintage, the half-shade presentation, and in construction features, but they all use the quartz-wedge compensating principle, and they read out in sugar degrees. A typical instrument will have a split half-shade field or a triple field for observation. The quartz wedge is equipped with a fine scale that is read off a second observation tube. It is graduated in °S (*e.g.*, −30 to +110°S) and comes with a vernier, readable to 1/10°S. Modern photoelectric and automatic polarimeters have found little favor in sugar laboratories because the potentially higher degree of precision is lost by the slight divergences between angular and sugar degrees. To get around this, Schmidt and Haensch in Germany and O. C. Rudolph and Sons in the United States have built photoelectric instruments which are true quartz-wedge saccharimeters. Both of these instruments utilize photoelectric servosystems so that the operator only places the sample into the instrument and reads off the results, and the instrument does the balancing. Extensive tests have shown that both of these instruments perform well (and actually also the automatic polarimeters using monochromatic light, such as the Zeiss and Bendix instruments). Nevertheless, at this writing, they have had negligible penetration into the sugar industry, and the classical saccharimeter (or polariscope) is the only instrument which needs to be considered.

It follows that the determination of sugar content of a solution can be determined conveniently and precisely with a saccharimeter. The instrument is first balanced with water to read zero °S and then the sample is placed into it. Rebalancing will yield a figure in °S which corresponds to 0.26 g./100 ml. of sucrose per degree. This is called the "direct method of polarization" or "simple polarization."

This approach is certainly valid for pure solutions of sucrose. However, actual cane sugar solutions are far from this ideal. First of all, they are more or less turbid. This difficulty is eliminated by adding a clarifying agent. Quite generally, lead subacetate is used for this purpose, and this is now part of the official sugar methods. (For the effect and "errors" inherent in the technique, see NBS C440.[7])

More importantly, cane sugar contains appreciable amounts of dextrose and fructose, besides the main constituent, sucrose. For this reason, its sucrose content is determined by the Clerget method of "double polarization." This involves the inversion (hydrolysis) of sucrose. First, the initial rotation is determined by simple polarimetry. Then the sucrose is inverted and a second reading is taken. Since neither dextrose nor fructose undergoes further changes, the total change of rotation can be attributed to sucrose, and a simple algebraic conversion of the difference in these two readings (Clerget constant) yields the sucrose concentration. The inversion can be catalyzed by acid or by the enzyme invertase. The latter is specific and tends to give more precise results. Inversion by hydrochloric acid is still practiced and it is acceptable, but the trend is towards invertase. Because this technique is rigidly standardized and widely used in the cane sugar and allied industries, it is reproduced below from the Cane Sugar Handbook.

STANDARD METHOD FOR SUCROSE WITH INVERTASE[10]

Direct Reading.—Dissolve the double normal weight (52 g.) of the substance in water in a 200-ml. flask. Add basic lead acetate solution carefully, avoiding any excess, then 1 to 2 ml. of alumina cream, and shake. Dilute to the mark with water, mix well, and filter, rejecting at least the first 25 ml. of the filtrate. Cover the funnel with a watch glass. When sufficient filtrate has collected, remove the lead from the solution by adding anhydrous sodium carbonate (ammonium dihydrogen phosphate is preferred; see note below), a little at a time, avoiding any excess. Mix well, and again filter, rejecting at least the first 25 ml. of the filtrate. (Instead of weighing 52 g. into a 200-ml. flask, two 26-g. portions may be diluted to 100 ml. each and treated exactly as described. Depending on the color of the product, multiples or fractions of the normal weight may be used, and the results reduced by calculation to the basis of 26 g. in 100 ml.) The amount of sample to be taken is given in the specific directions for analysis of various products in succeeding chapters.[10] Pipet one 50-ml. portion of the lead-free filtrate into a 100-ml. flask, dilute with water to the mark, mix well, and polarize in a 200-mm. tube. The result, multiplied by 2, is the direct reading (P of formula given below) or polarization before inversion. If a 400-mm. tube is used, the reading equals P.

Invert Reading.—First determine the quantity of acetic acid necessary to render 50 ml. of the lead-free filtrate distinctly acid to methyl red indicator; then, to another 50 ml. of the lead-free solution in a 100-ml. volumetric flask, add the requisite quantity of acid and 5 ml. of the invertase preparation. Fill the flask with water nearly to 100 ml., and let stand overnight (preferably at a temperature not less than 20°C.). Cool, and dilute to 100 ml. at 20°C. Mix well and polarize at 20°C. in a 200-mm. tube. If the analyst is in doubt as to the completion of the hydrolysis, allow a portion of the solution to remain for several hours and again polarize. If there is no change from the previous reading, the inversion is complete, and the reading and temperature of the solution should be carefully noted. If it is necessary to work at a temperature other than 20°C., which is permissible within narrow limits, the volumes must be completed and both direct and invert readings made at the same temperature. Correct the invert reading for the optical activity of the invertase solution and multiply by 2. Calculate the percentage of sucrose by the following formula:

$$S = \frac{100(P - I)}{132.1 + 0.0833(m - 13) - 0.53(T - 20)}$$

where: S = percentage of sucrose;
P = direct reading, normal solution;
I = invert reading, normal solution;
T = temperature at which readings are made; and
m = grams of total solids in 100 ml. of the invert solution in the polariscope (solids by refractometer multiplied by specific gravity of solution).

[10] Spencer-Meade, Cane Sugar Handbook, 9th Ed., John Wiley, New York, 1963. Reprinted with permission.

NOTE.—Sodium carbonate is specified for deleading by the AOAC, but others object to the reagent, as it tends to darken the solution, and may destroy levulose if added in excess, even a local excess, while neutralizing the solution. The ISSCT and ICUMSA specify deleading with anhydrous ammonium dihydrogen phosphate, and this practice is recommended here.

KINETIC POLARIMETRY

Polarimetry is particularly well suited for kinetic studies. The reason lies in the cyclic nature of the phenomenon which allows the measurement of small changes in the angle of rotation with equal precision in the presence and absence of large background values. Moreover, subtle changes in structure, which are common in enzyme reactions, are often strongly reflected in rotatory power.

The measurement of optical rotation *vs.* time is, consequently, a particularly attractive method for enzyme assay. The word "rotography" has been coined to describe the method.[11] However, neither the term nor the technique has found general acceptance. The reason, probably, is that recording polarimeters are not common in biochemical laboratories, and even when available, they are utilized for spectropolarimetry rather than routine assays.

Nevertheless, because of the good potential of such techniques in enzyme research and studies of stereospecific reactions, a brief discussion is included here. The procedure is quite analogous to the spectrophotometric determination of enzymes. In enzyme assays, an excess of substrate is employed and then the zero order rate constant reflects the enzyme concentration. In polarimetry, optically active substrates must be used, of course, but their concentration need not be known. The enzyme is then added and the change in rotation with time is recorded. The slope of the record (degrees per minute) is directly proportional to the enzyme concentration. This technique has been used to define the "unit" of penicillinase,[11] and it actually served in routine production control work in the manufacture of this enzyme.

The technique has also been used in enzyme research, and the specificity of mutarotase has been explored by "rotography."[12] An interesting analytical possibility is the simultaneous determination of the concentrations of both enzyme and substrate from the same record. The reaction rate (slope) is proportional to the enzyme concentration while the absolute change of rotation, from the addition of the enzyme to the break in the curve, is proportional to the substrate concentration. In this manner, the concentration of both penicillin and penicillinase has been determined simultaneously.[12]

It may be assumed that this technique will become more popular because the use of automatic polarimeters and automatic spectropolarimeters is increasing rapidly. There is absolutely no reason why the same instruments should not be used to plot $[\alpha]$ *vs.* time, as required here, and alternately $[\alpha]$ *vs.* $[\lambda]$ for spectropolarimetric work. The equipment is equally suited for both operations.

OPTICAL ROTATORY DISPERSION

The most exciting recent developments in polarimetry have been in spectropolarimetry. This field opened up with the availability of commercial spectropolarimeters. Early work of Werner Kuhn[13] gave an indication of the importance of determining optical rotatory dispersion (ORD), but the great push came through the work of Carl Djerassi and his students. ORD measurements had a tremendous impact on steroid research, and they are now being expanded into other fields of organic chemistry. A

[11] Levy, G. B., Anal. Chem., **23,** 1089, 1951.
[12] Levy, G. B., and Cook, E. S., Biochem. J., **57,** 50, 1954.
[13] Kuhn, W., Trans. Faraday Soc., **26,** 293, 1930.

good summary of what had been accomplished by 1959 will be found in Djerassi's book Optical Rotatory Dispersion.[14]

The instrument used in most of this work was the Rudolph Spectropolarimeter, introduced in 1955. The ORD accessory for Perkin-Elmer spectrophotometers also found use, as did, more recently, the fully automatic recording spectropolarimetery of the Rudolph Instrument Engineering Co. A number of new recording instruments have been announced during the past few years. It now seems that, perhaps, three of these will be commercially successful. They are briefly described below, together with a short report of the older, established instruments.

MANUAL AND SEMIAUTOMATIC SPECTROPOLARIMETERS

The visual research model was the starting point for the Rudolph spectropolarimeter line. The instrument was expanded to a photoelectric polarimeter, as already described. As the interest in ORD measurements increased, promoted among others by the late E. Brand of Columbia University, a relatively simple spectropolarimeter was developed. The photoelectric instrument already allowed the determination of several points of the ORD curves, *viz.*, at the 365, 405, 536, 546, and 578 mμ mercury lines, together with the traditional sodium D line at 589 mμ. The ORD curves obtained by this equipment are quite sketchy, of course. They can be of use only if plain curves are involved. The equipment was further expanded for this reason by Rudolph to include a light source emitting a continuum and a monochromator. A zirconium arc was used for the range 310–750 mμ, but a xenon arc is generally preferred because of its higher intensity and wider range into the shorter wavelength region. Because the penetration into the ultraviolet is of prime importance, quartz optics and xenon arcs have become standard equipment in spectropolarimetry. The monochromator originally used in the Rudolph instrument was that of the Beckman DU Spectrophotometer. This was then replaced by fast single and double monochromators of their own design, both with an effective aperture of F 1:6.

This equipment is a classic model in this new field. It is a manual instrument; the wavelength is selected manually, the analyzer is rotated by hand, based on the indication of the photometer, and finally, the angle is read on the polarimeter scale. Nevertheless, it is possible to plot a complete ORD curve in about an hour with little eyestrain and good precision. This instrument has a well deserved place in spectropolarimetry.

The Perkin-Elmer ORD Accessory (Model 262-0447 and -0448) extends the use of Perkin-Elmer and Cary ultraviolet spectrophotometers to rotatory dispersion measurements. While the basic double-beam instruments are fully automatic, the ORD operation itself is not because it requires point-by-point computation or graphical conversion. The principle of this accessory is similar to that of the Keston attachment for the Beckman single-beam DU Spectrophotometer. When a polarizer is placed in the light path of a spectrophotometer ahead of the sample, and an analyzer between the sample and the photometer, the instrument is converted to a spectropolarimeter. Keston utilized the well-known principle of symmetrical angles by providing the analyzer with two fixed positions of + and − rotation. The equipment is adjusted so that these two positions are symmetrical around the minimum intensity point (crossed polarizer and analyzer) with an optically inactive sample or the solvent. With optically active samples, the spectrophotometer is balanced at the one position of the analyzer, and the light attenuation is measured at the other. The corresponding angle of rotation is then read off the calibration curve. The drawback of this arrangement is not so much the manipulative effort, which is appreciable, but rather, the fact that the Polaroid elements used

[14] Djerassi, C., Optical Rotatory Dispersion, McGraw-Hill, New York, 1960.

by Keston limit the range to the visible spectral region. Both of these defects are eliminated by the Perkin-Elmer accessory. Here polarizing prisms are used so that the instrument can be used down to 240 mμ. Furthermore, two symmetrical analyzer-polarizer sets are placed in each sample and reference beams. Consequently, the balancing and reading is entirely automatic, and automatic wavelength scanning is possible. However, the resultant graph represents intensities which are related to, but are not identical with, optical rotation. The curves have the same general appearance, of course, with the extrema at the proven wavelengths. However, to obtain the exact ORD curve, it is necessary to make a graphical conversion point by point.

AUTOMATIC RECORDING SPECTROPOLARIMETERS

The first fully automatic recording spectropolarimeter was offered by the Rudolph Instruments Engineering Co., which deserves credit for this pioneering effort. The first commercial instrument goes back to May 1956, but full scale production dates to 1959–1960. The light source is a stabilized xenon arc. For best performance, a double-monochromator is used with quartz prisms. The analyzer is oscillated at 20 cycles per second in this system, and the 20-cycle signal of the photomultiplier pickup actuates a servosystem which drives the polarizer to the proper angle to compensate for the rotation of the sample.

This servosystem is mechanically linked to a pen mechanism, and so is the wavelength drive of the monochromator, resulting in an X-Y recorder which is unusually large, 20 in. × 40 in. The dynamic range in angular degrees is exceptionally large (2°, 20°, and 200°). The spectral range can be pushed down to 190 mμ. The basic sensitivity is 0.002°, but the actual sensitivity depends on the light transmission characteristics of the sample at a given wavelength. The response of a 20-cycle system is relatively slow, and a number of scanning speeds are provided ranging from 5 to 2500 minutes. Much useful information has been obtained by the approximately 30 laboratories using these instruments.

Of the more recent automatic recording spectropolarimeters, three are mentioned here because they show promise of a permanent place in the field. All of these became commercially available in 1964, and the experience with them is limited.

Durrum-Jasco ORD-5.—This instrument is actually a dual-purpose machine which can be used as a double-beam spectrophotometer and as a recording spectropolarimeter. It uses a quartz prism double-monochromator for both functions. The principle of operation is rather similar to that of the Rudolph, using an oscillating polarizer mechanically driven at 12 cycles per second. The photomultiplier pickup actuates a servosystem to drive the analyzer to balance until the angle of oscillation is symmetrical. The wavelength scan is fully automatic, and it is adjustable from 5 to 125 minutes for the full range from 700 mμ down to 185 mμ. The reproducibility is of the order of 0.001°, but the RMS noise in the ultraviolet rises to the equivalent of about 0.005°. The dynamic range of the instrument is 4°. Djerassi's group has reported work done with prototype models, and many recent papers of Japanese laboratories are based on work with this instrument.

Cary Model 60.—This instrument is the result of many years of careful development work. It, too, is a null-balance servoinstrument employing the principle of symmetrical angles. However, the oscillation of the rotation is introduced by a Faraday cell driven at 60 cps. The optical array consists of a 500-watt xenon arc, a double-prism monochromator, the servodriven polarizer, followed by the sample space, the Faraday cell, analyzer, and photomultiplier with associated circuitry. The spectral range of Model 60 extends down to 1875 A, where the RMS noise is equivalent to 0.0065° which drops to 0.0007° at 300 mμ. The light absorption tolerance is large (abs. 2 at 1875 A), and this is an important feature. The spectral resolution is high. The dynamic range of the instrument is ±2°, and an uncalibrated wide-range zero suppressor of ±10° is also available. The 10-inch chart will record 0.02° to 2.0° full scale in 7 steps. Pen speed can be set as fast as 1 second.

Bendix Model 460C.—This spectropolarimeter is a commercial version of the design developed at the British National Physical Laboratory, and then by Billingham and Stanley (London) and by Bendix-Ericsson (England). It incorporates interesting concepts and, similarly to the Bendix Photoelectric Polarimeter, it has essentially no moving parts. In this instrument, too, the optical balance is obtained by an auxiliary Faraday cell, and the current through its coil is the measure of optical rotation. The most novel feature of Model 460C is that the polarizing elements and the monochromator are physically the same prisms. This is done by cutting crystal quartz prisms with the optic axis perpendicular to the light path. In this way, polarized spectra are obtained, and the two prisms in the instrument are crossed with respect to polarization, and they also act as a double-monochromator. The optical path is very long (24 feet) for high resolution, and it is folded to obtain convenient overall dimensions. This design is inherently well suited to reach into the ultraviolet, and the instrument has a nominal range from 667 to 182 mμ. It has a dynamic range of ±1.4° in the ultraviolet, and a sensitivity of about 0.002°. Another interesting feature is that light transmission and optical rotation can be measured simultaneously and plotted on the same chart with a two-pen recorder.

SPECTROPOLARIMETRIC METHODS

The methods of spectropolarimetry vary a great deal. The manipulative steps in spectropolarimetry are essentially similar to those in polarimetry. They will differ slightly with the instrument used, but the result is always an ORD curve. The essential differences are due to the nature of the samples, the aim of the measurement, and the interpretation of the results. In this way, each set of data in spectropolarimetry is unique. Nevertheless, the techniques can be grouped in general types, as suggested by Professor W. Klyne.[15,16] The topics are organized in this manner in the following sections.

It may be added that spectropolarimetry represents a particularly difficult field for instrumentation. Of greatest interest are the spectral ranges in which the compounds exhibit a Cotton effect with characteristic sharp extrema. However, it is exactly at these points where the absorption bands of the compounds are located because the asymmetric centers exert an effect on the chromophone which causes the absorption bands. Consequently, at the very points of interest, the light signal is the weakest and the signal-to-noise ratio least favorable. It is not exceptional to find spurious peaks which are due to instrumental "noise" rather than to the rotation of the compound. It is often necessary to work with dilute solutions to get enough light signal through the system, and then the precision of the measurement suffers. This is counteracted to some extent by the extremely high values of specific rotation at the extrema. So, it is sometimes advisable to take measurements at higher concentrations off the peak values and at lower ones at the peaks. In any case, spectropolarimeters are extremely difficult to design and construct. The sensitivity has to be pushed to extreme limits where the signal is small and the noise most bothersome. The relatively high price of the commercial instruments is justified.

Recognition of Optical Activity.—It is impossible to use a fixed wavelength for the definitive determination of the existence of optical activity in a compound. Even compounds of appreciable rotatory power can show zero rotation if the wavelength chosen

[15] Klyne, W., private communication.

[16] Klyne, W., "Optical Rotatory Dispersion," in Advances in Organic Chemistry, Vol. I, Interscience Publishers, New York, 1960.

for measurement happens to coincide with a point of the rotatory dispersion curve where the sign of rotation changes (Fig. 15-1*a*, curve *B*). Admittedly, this would be an unusual coincidence, but the value of rotation, even though not exactly zero, may be so small that it escapes recognition. This is particularly true when the traditional sodium *D* line is used. There are numerous examples of this happening and the case of a derivative of Vitamin B_{12} is cited.[17] The degradation product of this vitamin shows a molecular rotation of only $+1°$ at the *D* line and $-165°$ at 365 mμ.

In view of these facts, it is mandatory to run an entire dispersion curve. Alternatively, determinations must be made at a few selected wavelengths (preferably in the ultraviolet) whenever it is to be established that a compound is optically active.

Quantitative Analyses.—The determination of a rotatory dispersion curve is a prerequisite to the establishment of a sensitive polarimetric technique. This is analogous to colorimetry, where a complete spectrophotometric curve is required to establish the absorption peak best suited for routine work at a fixed wavelength. Similarly, in polarimetry, the gain in sensitivity may be enormous when working at an extremum (peak or trough). Thus, spectropolarimetry plays a role even though the analytical technique is simply polarimetry at a fixed wavelength. Djerassi furnishes an excellent example of the judicious choice in wavelength in an industrial assay. This is the determination of cryptogenin as an impurity of diosgenin to which it is closely related chemically.[18] The difference in specific rotation of these two compounds is about $-2600°$ at 320 mμ, but only $-70°$ at the sodium *D* line. Even when working with dilute solutions, as is done in industrial practice, it is thus possible to determine as little as 0.1 percent of admixed cryptogenin at this properly chosen wavelength.

It is theoretically possible also to resolve a multicomponent mixture or to determine a specific compound in mixtures of optically active materials. If a dispersion curve is taken through an extremum which is characteristic of the compound, this will show up as a "modulation" superimposed on the resultant curve. The amplitude will be proportional to the concentration. This, too, is analogous to spectrophotometry. For instance, benzylpenicillin has been determined in penicillin preparations by an analogous spectrophotometric method.[19]

Despite this good potential, the bulk of spectropolarimetric work to date has not been directed to such analytical applications. Rather problems of functional groups, structure, and conformation have been the major directions, because in these spectropolarimetry is uniquely useful.

Recognition of Functional Groups.—Functional groups which absorb light in the visible and ultraviolet region can give rise to Cotton effect curves when attached to an asymmetric molecule, even though they are, themselves, symmetrical. Azide, xanthate, nitrate, dithiocarbamate, sulfoxides, conjugated double bonds, heterocyclic aromatic groups, give rise to this condition, and particularly the carbonyl group. In compounds in which the presence of carbonyl is difficult to establish by chemical means (*e.g.*, 11-oxosteroids), rotatory dispersion curves can serve. Similarly, acetoxyl and carbonyl groups are often indistinguishable by spectrophotometry, and ORD curves are used to advantage to recognize the carbonyl.[20]

Determination of Location of Functional Groups.—The change of location of a functional group, in an asymmetric compound, may have a dramatic effect on the ORD curve. This has been investigated in great detail with steroids by Djerassi and collabora-

[17] Clark, V. M., *et al.*, J. Chem. Soc., 2383, 1958.
[18] Djerassi, G., Bull. Soc. Chim. France, 741, 1957.
[19] Levy, G. B., *et al.*, Anal. Chem., **20,** 1159, 1948.
[20] Klyne, W., "Optical Rotatory Dispersion," in Advances in Organic Chemistry, Vol. 1, Interscience Publishers, New York, 1960, p. 302.

tors. For instance, cholestan-1-one and cholestan-2-one have radically different dispersion curves.[21] Conversely, androstan-17-ones all show essentially identical ORD even when the substituents at positions 3 and 5 (*i.e.*, far from the chromophore) are substantially different in kind and in orientation.

Admittedly, this approach is only possible if basic work on a group of compounds is already at hand. The best explored field is that of steroids,[22] where the results were of significant practical and theoretical importance. There are literally hundreds of ORD curves of steroid ketones on record, and also of many terpene ketones. Yet, a method of this kind is not "standard" in the sense that it is directly applicable to a new area. However, experience is accumulating and the reviews by Djerassi,[21] Klyne,[22] as well as by Lyle and Lyle,[23] will be helpful, as they give exhaustive references.

Conformational Analysis.—In the determination of conformation (*i.e.*, the spatial arrangement of a known organic structure or configuration), ORD curves proved to be a unique, practical tool. Problems of this type are the "chair" and "boat" conformation of cyclohexane or, more importantly, the two chair forms which are interconvertible in mobile cyclohexanes (Fig. 15-4), as well as the question of axial and equatorial con-

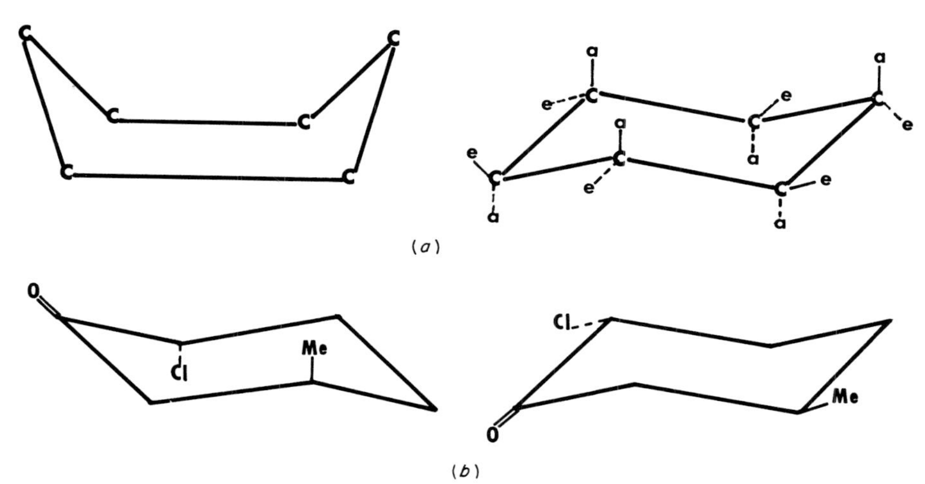

FIG. 15-4. *a*, Boat and Chair Conformations of Cyclohexane with Axial (*a*) and Equatorial (*e*) Substituents Marked. *b*, Two Chair Forms of *trans*-2-Chloromethylcyclohexanone: Diaxial form (left) favored in octane solution; diequatorial (right) in methanol.

formation of substituents, which is most pertinent in steroid chemistry. It was in the latter field that the octant rule[24] was developed. It was based on theoretical ideas of Moffitt, Moscowitz, and Woodward of Harvard, and extensive experimental proof was furnished by Djerassi. It provides the first really adequate link between theory and practice, and gives a solid basis for the interpretation of ORD curves in problems of this type. A sketchy description of the octant rule is given here.

[21] Djerassi, C., Optical Rotatory Dispersion, McGraw-Hill, New York, 1960, p. 47.
[22] A short exposition of this specialized field is Klyne, W., The Chemistry of Steroids, Methuen & Co., London, 1957.
[23] Lyle, G. C., and Lyle, R. E., in Determination of Organic Structures by Physical Methods, Vol. 2, Academic Press, New York, 1962.
[24] Moffitt, W., *et al.*, J. Am. Chem. Soc., **83,** 4013, 1961.

When a carbonyl group in cyclohexane gives rise to ultraviolet absorption (in the range of 280–330 mμ), assymmetry in the molecule will cause a Cotton effect ORD curve. Qualitatively, and semiquantitatively, the contribution of the substituents to the rotatory dispersion can be interpreted, and their spatial arrangement can be assigned. For instance, in a normal "chair" steroid cyclohexane ring, four octants in space (beyond the C=O bond) generally fall away because no substituent will extend beyond. The other four define space as shown schematically in Fig. 15-5. The upper left quadrant and

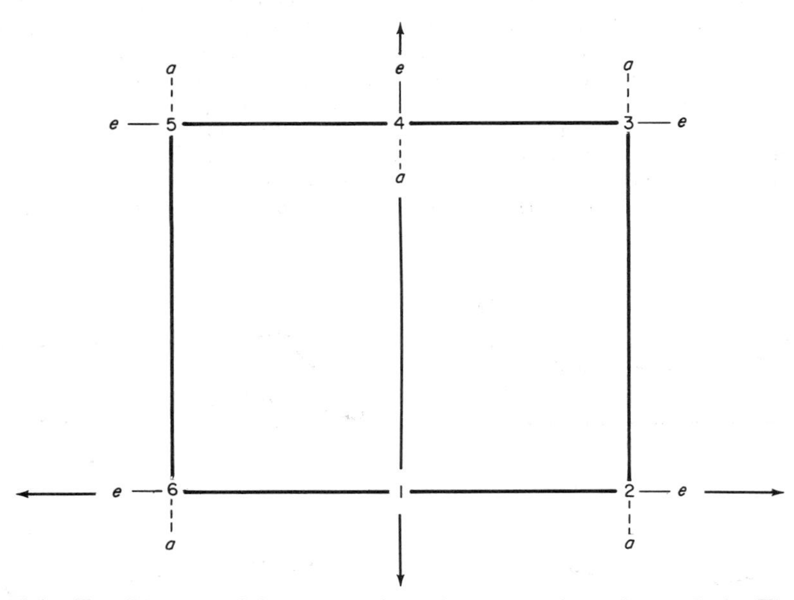

FIG. 15-5. Two-Dimensional Schematic of the Operation of the Octant Rule. The four octants are separated at the lines marked with arrows. The numbers refer to carbon atoms, and the axial and equatorial substituents are marked with *a* and *e*, respectively.

the lower right contribute to a positive Cotton effect at carbons 2 and 5, and equatorial substituents at carbon 5. The contributions in the other two quadrants have the opposite sign.

This technique has been refined and tested with a large number of ketones, mostly by Djerassi, Klyne, Ourisson, and their students,[25] with outstanding success. Because of the facility of interpretation and the favorable spectral conditions, it is actually of advantage to introduce chemically a carbonyl group when questions of configuration or conformation arise.

A very interesting example of the application of ORD curves in conformational analysis is in protein and polypeptide chemistry.[26] It was found that the α-helix and the percentage of α-helical conformation of the long chain molecule can be determined from the ORD curves. Earlier interpretation was based on plain curves in the near-ultraviolet, and more recently, on the Cotton effect region in the far-ultraviolet.[27] An interesting trick

[25] Djerassi, C., and Klyne, W., J. Chem. Soc., 4929, 1962; 2390, 1963.
[26] Blout, E. R., Chapter 17 in Djerassi, C., Optical Rotatory Dispersion, McGraw-Hill, New York, 1960.
[27] Simmons, N. S., and Blout, E. R., Biophys. J., **1**, 55, 1960.

used before the availability of spectropolarimeters reading down to 200 mμ, was the use of (optically inactive) acriflavine dye. When this dye is coupled to polypeptides, Cotton effect ORD curves result in the visible region, allowing conformational interpretation of the chain structure.[28]

Determination of Relative and Absolute Configuration.—It is evident from the foregoing that ORD curves can serve to determine the configuration, *i.e.*, the spatial relationship of substituents around an asymmetric carbon atom. A classical study in this area concerns natural L-α-amino acids. These are by no means all levorotatory at the sodium *D* line, which had been used. This necessitated the use of the unattractive symbolism L (+) and L (−). Pfeiffer and Christeleit utilized copper complexes[29] which have absorption in the visible region. The ORD curves of L (+) valine and L (−) phenylalanine were found essentially identical, despite the chance opposite rotation at 589 mμ of the parent compounds. This conclusively proved the identical configuration at the α-carbon atom. This approach is of historical interest only because the Cotton effects of the free amino acids around 225 mμ are now accessible with modern instrumentation.[30]

Much of the recent work is concerned with steroids which are of considerable pharmaceutical interest, and which represent particularly difficult stereochemical problems. An example is the beta configuration of the hydrogen at C-10 in 19-nor-Δ^4-3-oxosteroids. This configuration could be assigned by analogy of the ORD curves to the ordinary Δ^4-3-oxosteroids.

The question of *absolute* configuration (*i.e.*, actually which of two mirror-image representations fits a compound), is of substantial theoretical interest. The only direct method to obtain absolute configurations is x-ray analysis. However, once the absolute configuration of a typical compound is known, it can be used as reference. Employing ORD curves, which are tremendously sensitive to steric differences, the configurational features can be peeled off by working through analogies. A detailed discussion would exceed the scope of this review, but it should be stated that a substantial number of absolute configurations have been allotted by way of spectropolarimetry, particularly in the field of terpenes and steroids.[14,16]

CIRCULAR DICHROISM

The measurement of circular dichroism (CD) as dependent on wavelength (similarly to ORD) has long been advocated by Werner Kuhn.[31] This technique was recently vigorously pursued at the research laboratories of Roussel. The outcome was a commercial instrument, manufactured by Jouan in Paris, called the "Dichrograph."

The approach is similar to spectropolarimetry. A scanning monochromator is provided followed by a polarizing prism. In addition, there is a crystal of ammonium dihydrogen phosphate in the light path ahead of the sample. It is driven by an alternating voltage source to provide alternating circular polarization. The electronics associated with the photomultiplier sensor are so arranged that the dichroic absorption (*i.e.*, the difference in absorption coefficients between left and right polarized light) is recorded directly, as the wavelength is scanned right through the absorption bands. The problems in instrumentation are substantial because the total light absorption is two or more orders of magnitude greater than dichroic absorption, but this seems to have been solved.

[28] Blout, E. R., and Stryer, L. J., Am. Chem. Soc., **83,** 1411, 1961.
[29] Pfeiffer, P., and Christeleit, W., Z. physiol. Chem., **247,** 262, 1937.
[30] Dirkx, I. P., and Sixma, F. L. J., Rec. Trav. Chim., **83,** 522, 1964; Gaffield, W., Chem. & Ind., 1460, 1964; Craig, J. C., & Roy, S. K., Tetrahedron, **21,** 391, 1965; Jennings, J. P., Scopes, P. M., and Klyne, W., J. Chem. Soc., 264, 1965.
[31] Kuhn, W., and Biller, H., Z. phys. Chem., **B29,** 1, 1935.

To date, some 25 Dichrographs have been delivered, and results should be forthcoming in addition to the first reports from France,[32] by Snatzke (Bonn), and by Djerassi.

It is clear that the measurement of CD offers advantages in the analysis of optically active chemicals. In contrast to spectrophotometry, CD peaks are quite isolated, while spectral absorption peaks are often swamped by the strong absorbance of molecules not pertinent to the analytical problem. This is in contrast to ORD curves, too, because there is often a strong contribution from groups whose own extrema are spectrally far removed. CD curves originate at, or near, the zero line and then rise in a characteristic peak at defined wavelength ranges. Reversal in sign indicates reverse spatial arrangement, and, therefore, this technique may be used to assign absolute configurations. An advantage of the technique seems to be in the quantitative analysis of complex molecules (containing, for example, ketonic groups besides carbonyl) which may be difficult by other methods. Perhaps the greatest advantage of CD over ORD is the fact that CD measurements are now being made at very low temperatures, down to $-192°$ (largely due to the work of Djerassi and of Snatzke). These low temperature studies are already significant in dealing with problems of conformation and solvation—and this is undoubtedly a part of the field which will be developed greatly.[33]

APPLICATIONS IN THE ANALYSIS OF SPECIAL MATERIALS

A number of procedures have been discussed in Volume III in the chapters on the analysis of special materials. These are:

1. Chapter 50, Volume III, Foods.
   a. Determination of lactose in milk products
   b. Determination of starch in foods
   c. Determination of sugar in foods
2. Chapter 51, Volume III, Organic Functional Groups.
   a. The principal application is the determination of the concentration of a compound containing a functional group by relating its concentration to its optical rotation. For example, the determination of the relative amounts of hecogenin and tigogenin in a mixture is considered.

CONCLUDING REMARKS

The present review on methods of optical rotation is, admittedly, somewhat unbalanced. The main activity in this field is in spectropolarimetry. Literally, hundreds of research papers have appeared during the past few years dealing with spectropolarimetric applications. Of course, these are of far greater importance in organic and physical chemistry than in analytical chemistry. The character of this work, which is largely "nonstandard" precludes comprehensive treatment. However, the outline given here will indicate the direction and utility of spectropolarimetry. The short section on circular dichroism will serve to point up the potential of that new technique.

[32] Velluz, L., Legrand, M., and Grossjean, M., La Mesure et l'Etude du Dichroisme Circulaire Optique, Centre de Recherches Roussel-UCLAF, Paris, 1963.

[33] For details on CD see footnote 32 or, in English, a book by the same authors; Optical Circular Dichroism, Academic Press, New York, 1965. A review by Crabbe is in Tetrahedron, **20,** 1211, 1964, and a book by the same author is to be published by Holden-Day, San Francisco.

Chapter 16

TURBIDIMETRY AND NEPHELOMETRY

By Robert B. Fischer
California State College at Palos Verdes
Palos Verdes Peninsula, California

INTRODUCTION

Turbidimetric and nephelometric methods of analysis are based upon the phenomenon whereby light, passing through a medium with dispersed particles of a different refractive index than the medium, is attenuated in intensity by scattering. In turbidimetry, measurement is made of the intensity of light transmitted through the medium, that is, of unscattered light. In nephelometry, the intensity of the scattered light is measured, usually, but not necessarily, at right angles to the incident light beam.

Major attention in this chapter is directed to systems in which the incident light is in, or near to, the visible portion of the electromagnetic spectrum, and in which the medium and the dispersed particles are liquid and solid, respectively. When the light is of a considerably different wavelength, as x-radiation for example, the principles are closely related but the applications and instrumentation are very different. When the medium is a gas and the dispersed particles are either liquid or solid, the principles again are similar but the analytical applications are quite different.

Turbidimetric methods are similar to colorimetric in that both involve measurement of the intensity of light transmitted through a medium. They differ in that the light intensity is attenuated by scattering in turbidimetry and by absorption in colorimetry. Both may employ similar, or even identical, apparatus. Many practical analytical situations involve both scattering and absorption as, for example, when optical measurements are made on the colored "lakes" of aluminum.

Nephelometric methods are similar to fluorometric methods in that both involve measurement of scattered light. However, the scattering is inelastic in nephelometry and elastic in fluorometry. Thus, the scattered light which is measured in fluorometry is of a longer wavelength than the incident light, and both incident and scattered lights are of the same wavelength in a nephelometric determination.

Applications of nephelometry and turbidimetry in analysis are widely varied. Some determinations involve systems which are turbid prior to entering the analytical laboratory, such as in the determination of suspended material in river water. Other systems require that the turbidity be developed in the laboratory by addition of suitable chemical reagents and comparison to standard suspensions. Still other analytical applications involve titrations, with the turbidimetric or nephelometric measurements being used to construct titration curves for end-point detection. It is also possible, from certain measurements of scattered light intensity, to obtain information on size, shape, and uniformity of the scattering particles.

PRINCIPLES

Most analytical turbidimetric and nephelometric procedures are empirical. However, a brief consideration of the underlying principles should be informative in providing a proper basis for selection of the analytical method. Also, it is important to know why and under what conditions an analytical procedure is empirical and when it is not.

The intensity of light scattered at any particular angle is a function of the concentration of scattering particles, of their size, of their shape, of the wavelength of light and of the difference in refractive indexes of the particle and the medium. Consider first a particle which is small compared to the wavelength of the light. The scatter depends upon the area intercepting the beam, and so is proportional to the square of the effective radius of the particle. The total scatter from a number of particles, assuming no multiple scattering interactions, is simply the sum of the individual scatterings, and the optical density of the system is directly proportional to the concentration of particles. An equation similar to the Lambert-Beer equation in absorption colorimetry may be written to represent this scattering system:

$$\frac{I}{I_o} = e^{-\tau lc}$$

in which I and I_o are the intensities of transmitted and incident light, respectively, τ is a turbidimetric coefficient, and l and c are, respectively, the length of the scattering path and the concentration of scattering particles. The quantity $\log I_o/I$ is the "effective optical density."

The intensity of scatter is, as shown by Rayleigh, inversely proportional to the fourth power of the wavelength of the light. Thus, blue light is scattered to a greater extent than is red light.

Consider next a larger particle, with one or more dimensions not small compared to the wavelength of the light. Interference occurs among the portions of the scattered light beam, and the resulting angular dependence of the scattered light is indicative of the shape and size of the particle. The theoretical aspects of scattering by particles which are of a size comparable to the wavelength of the light have been developed by Mie and others; the calculations are very complex and have been limited generally to spherical particles. Suffice it to say that the relationships between effective optical density, or any other measurable indication of scattered light intensity, and concentration of particles are not simple. Furthermore, multiple scattering is encountered with more concentrated suspensions. Analytical determinations which necessarily involve this relationship must, therefore, be empirical. It is possible, however, to obtain information on the size and shape of small particles from measurements of the total scatter and its angular dependence, by methods which are experimentally and fundamentally sound. (See item 8 in Bibliography at end of chapter.)

There is, in addition to the optical consideration, another reason why most turbidimetric and nephelometric procedures are empirical. The phenomena of nucleation and crystal growth, of coagulation and dispersion are complex and quite irreproducible. Nucleation is generally a heterogeneous process and is influenced by trace impurities and other random conditions at the time of precipitation (Bibliography item 4). Only by rigid adherence to a fixed procedure is it possible even to approximate constancy of these precipitation factors in preparing a series of turbid standards and unknowns, and, thus, to obtain meaningful analytical results.

The irreproducibility of the physical form of a precipitate is less serious in a titration than when comparison must be made with standards (Bibliography item 5). The first increment of titrant forms a batch of particles, by nucleation and "initial growth," which largely determine the physical form of the precipitate present throughout the entire titration. It is conceivable that the next equal increment of mass of precipitate could form in one of four ways: (A) further nucleation and initial growth just as the first increment; (B) uniform growth on all crystal faces of the particles already present; (C) preferential growth on certain crystal face(s) of the precipitate already present; (D) combination of new nucleation and further growth on particles already present. Calculated curves of total surface area *vs.* mass of precipitate are shown in Fig. 16-1 for (A) and (B). The curve for (B) applies regardless of the particle shape (sphere, cube, etc.). Curves calculated for (C) lie intermediate between (A) and (B), and (D) is intermediate between (A) and either (B) or (C).

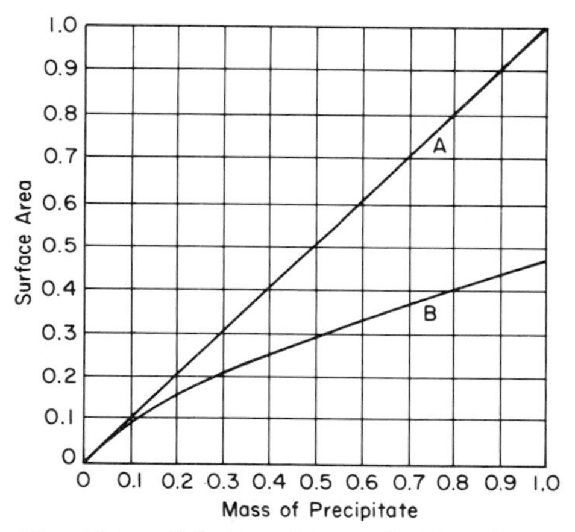

FIG. 16-1. Calculated Curves for Two Conditions of Nucleation and Crystal Growth (Both Axes in Arbitrary Units).

For a titration, the X-axis of Fig. 16-1 may be relabeled as volume of titrant up to the equivalence point. The relationship between surface area (on the y-axis) and effective optical density is not a simple one, particularly because the particles are not of constant size throughout the titration and because the sizes typically are of magnitude similar to the wavelength of the light. Nevertheless, a plot of effective optical density *vs.* volume of titrant is empirically analogous to Fig. 16-1 up to the equivalence point, and the plot should be horizontal beyond that point. Any settling of the precipitate would tend to decrease the optical density as measured through the liquid. It may be noted from Fig. 16-1 that a sharper end point "break" would be obtained with (A) than with (B), so it is desirable to enhance nucleation at the expense of crystal growth insofar as this is possible. A more precise treatment of these optical aspects of turbidimetric titrations has been presented by Meehan and coworkers (Bibliography items 7 and 8).

INSTRUMENTATION

Several instruments have been designed specifically for turbidimetry and nephelometry, and many colorimeters and spectrophotometers may also be used for this purpose.

The Parr turbidimeter is an extinction type instrument which consists of a cylinder to contain the turbid suspension, a lamp filament of fixed intensity at the base, and an adjustable plunger through which visual observation is made. Measurement is made of the depth of turbid medium necessary to extinguish the image of the lamp filament. Standard suspensions are used to prepare a calibration curve, which is a plot of depth *vs.* concentration.

The Hellige turbidimeter is also a variable depth type of instrument using visual detection. A combination of vertical and horizontal illumination of the sample and a split ocular permit the eye to function merely to compare the intensities of two images simultaneously appearing in the ocular. This is a special form of double-beam operation, and the intensity emitted by the light source need not be extremely constant from one sample to another. Adjustment is made of a slit in the path of the direct, or vertical, illumination of the sample, and the calibration curve consists of a plot of this slit opening *vs.* concentration.

The Brice-Phoenix light scattering photometer is a refined instrument for measuring total scatter and for measuring the angular dependence and disymmetry of the scattered light. The distinctive features of this instrument are not needed for the simpler turbidimetric and nephelometric analyses, but they do permit its use for additional applications, including particularly determinations of size and shape of macromolecules.

Virtually any colorimeter or spectrophotometer can be used for turbidimetry measurement, and, if provision is made for viewing at right angles, for nephelometry as well. The choice of wavelength is generally not critical and, in fact, an extremely narrow band of wavelengths is of no particular value. If the sample solution contains a colored solute in addition to the turbid component, a wavelength region of minimum absorption is preferable. If the scattering component itself absorbs characteristically, a wavelength region of maximum absorption should be used so as to utilize the combined absorption and scattering effects.

In an instrument designed strictly for absorption work, and used for turbidimetry, the light scattered from the sample may be rescattered from the walls and housing in such a way that some of it gets to the detector and interferes with the desired reading. A simple expedient is to use sample cells with black side walls to absorb the scattered light.

Several versatile instruments have been designed jointly for nephelometry, turbidimetry, and colorimetry. For example, the Coleman Nepho-Colorimeter uses a filter type monochromator and a photoelectric detector, and may be used for viewing either at right angles to or in direct line with the incident light.

Useful analytical results, particularly in titrations, can be obtained with a simple "home-made" apparatus consisting of a flashlight bulb and barrier-layer photocell, with the sample vessel in-between (Bibliography item 2). It is also possible to obtain useful results by the standard series comparison method with the turbid standards and the unknown in Nessler tubes, or even in test tubes, for visual observation.

Of particular significance is the choice of standards for all but the titration procedures. Rigid adherence to an empirical procedure of preparation is necessary when these turbid standards and unknowns are formed by precipitation reactions. It is not always necessary, however, to use working standards which are chemically the same as the unknowns. For example, suspensions of colloidal glass can be used as secondary standards, but these must be standardized empirically against known samples of the type to be analyzed. The Coleman Instrument Co. markets a series of standards in sealed containers which fit into the Nepho-Colorimeter and which cover the range from absolute clarity to a faintly perceptible haze in five steps assigned values from 0 to 100 "Coleman nephelos units." Use of these standards permits expression of results by one investigator or analyst in terms reproducible by others who use this same scale.

APPLICATIONS

Turbidimetry and nephelometry are applicable to the determination of suspended material in liquids encountered in nature and in manufacturing and processing streams. Numerous applications are found in water treatment plants, in sewage works, in power and steam generating plants, in the beverage bottling industry, in pulp and paper manufacturing, in the pharmaceutical industry, and in petroleum refineries. The turbidity may be due to a single chemical species, or it may be due to a combination of several components. For example, silica may be determined in the approximate concentration range of 0.1 to 150 p.p.m. SiO_2; composite turbidities are sometimes expressed as equivalent to silica. Higher concentrations may be determined by dilution.

Many applications are possible in which a turbidity is developed from the test sample under controlled conditions. Perhaps the most widely used single determination is that of sulfate after addition of barium chloride to form a suspension of barium sulfate. The procedure is particularly applicable within the concentration range of 0.2 to 100 p.p.m. sulfate. Routine procedures have been developed for the determination of sulfur in coal, oil, and other organic materials in which the sample is fused in a sodium peroxide bomb prior to precipitation of the sulfur as barium sulfate.

The accuracy may be limited by the optical device, but, more frequently, it is limited by the irreproducibility of the physical form of the precipitate or by the instability of the precipitate once it is formed. An accuracy of ± 5 percent of the quantity of the substance being determined is typical.

Many other typical determinations using these methods are applicable over a concentration range from 0.5 to 10 p.p.m. Nephelometric methods which permit measurement of scattered light against a dark background are often more sensitive than turbidimetric methods. As a general rule, nephelometric measurement should be made instead of turbidimetric measurement if the percent transmittance is greater than about 90.

The precipitation reaction used in this type of analysis should be one that takes place rapidly, and the precipitated particles should be low in solubility and small in particle size. Above all else, the physical form of the precipitate should be as reproducible as possible. Surfactants and other protective colloids are helpful, not only to make the process more reproducible but also to make the particles small by enhancing nucleation at the expense of crystal growth.

Turbidimetric titrations are of particular interest because no general types of chemical indicators have been developed for precipitation titrations as has been done for neutralization and oxidation-reduction titrations. Accuracies of the turbidimetric method are typically within a few percent. Among the numerous applications which have been developed are the titrations of sulfate as barium sulfate, of silver as a halide, of calcium as the oxalate, and of calcium or of fluoride as calcium fluoride.

Light scattering methods are applicable to continuous, "on-stream" analysis, including aerosol systems as well as solids suspended in liquids. The growth of test bacteria in a liquid nutrient can be measured turbidimetrically. The average molecular weight of a macromolecule and an estimate of its size may be determined from measurements of the angular dependence of light scatterings.

A number of turbidimetric and nephelometric methods have been described in other chapters of Standard Methods of Chemical Analysis. These are:

1. Chapter 22, Volume IIA, Commercial Acids and Bases.
   a. Determination of traces of zinc in sulfuric acid, page 550.
2. Chapter 41, Volume III, Air Pollutants.
   a. Determination of sulfate in air pollution studies
3. Chapter 54, Volume III, Paint, Varnish, and Lacquer.
   a. A method for the turbidimetric titration of polymers is described.
4. Chapter 59, Volume III, Rubber and Rubber Products.
   a. Nephelometric determination of inorganic fillers in rubber
5. Chapter 61, Soaps and Synthetic Detergents.
   a. Determination of cloud point of nonionic surfactants and liquid detergent compositions

6. Chapter 47, Volume IIB, Vitamins.
   a. Determination of biotin, page 2379.
7. Chapter 48, Volume IIB, Water Analysis.
   a. Determination of sulfate in water, page 2483.

SELECTED PROCEDURES

DETERMINATION OF SULFATE IN AQUEOUS SOLUTION

Procedure.—Prepare a standard sulfate solution by dissolving 0.443 g. of anhydrous sodium sulfate in water to 1 liter; (this solution, designated solution A, contains 100 p.p.m. S). Prepare another solution by dissolving 120 g. of Reagent grade sodium chloride in water, adding 10 ml. of concentrated hydrochloric acid, and diluting to 500 ml. (this solution, designated solution B, will be used to provide reasonably constant ionic strength in all test solutions and thus enhance reproducibility of the precipitation process). Prepare 250 ml. each of standard solutions containing 75, 50, and 25 p.p.m. S by using aliquots of solution A, adding 25 ml. of solution B to each before final dilution. Transfer each to a 500-ml. Erlenmeyer flask. Add 1 g. of 20-30 mesh barium chloride. Shake well. Pour the milky suspensions into the turbidimeter tubes (Parr or Hellige or other type). Measure the appropriate instrumental quantity. Plot a calibration curve, of instrument reading *vs.* concentration of standard. Treat the unknown in the same way and read its concentration from the calibration curve.

Other systems in which a turbidity is produced under controlled conditions can be handled similarly.

TURBIDIMETRIC TITRATION

No detailed procedure need be given here for a turbidimetric titration. Simply read the turbidity in any appropriate instrument quantity, such as optical density, after each increment of titrant, and plot the titration curve. The end point is determined from the titration curve. Equal increments of titrant should be used and a fixed procedure of adding titrant and shaking should be followed.

SELECTED BIBLIOGRAPHY

1. Bobtelsky, M., Heterometry, American Elsevier Publishing Co., New York, 1960. This book consists of information on principles and applications of titrations in which a precipitate is formed.
2. Brandt, W. W., and Duswalt, A. A., Anal. Chem., **30,** 1120, 1958.
3. Challis, H. J. G., in L. Meites, Ed., Handbook of Analytical Chemistry, pp. G-173–G-176. McGraw-Hill, New York, 1963. Includes a list of applications of turbidimetric and nephelometric methods for the determination of the elements.
4. Fischer, R. B., Anal. Chem. Acta, **22,** 501, 1960.
5. Fischer, R. B., Yates, M. L., and Batts, M. M., Anal. Chem. Acta, **20,** 501, 1959.
6. Hochgesang, F. P., in I. M. Kolthoff and P. J. Elving, Eds., Treatise on Analytical Chemistry, Vol. 5, Part I, pp. 3289–3328, Interscience Publishers, New York, 1964.
7. Meehan, E. J., and Beattie, W. H., J. Phys. Chem., **64,** 1006, 1960.
8. Meehan, E. J., and Chiu, G., Anal. Chem., **36,** 536, 1964.
9. Stacey, K. C., Light Scattering in Physical Chemistry, Academic Press, New York, 1956.
10. van den Hulst, H. C., Light Scattering by Small Particles, John Wiley and Sons, New York, 1957.
11. Selected Bibliography on Light Scattering, Phoenix Precision Instrument Co., Philadelphia, 1964.

Chapter 17

POTENTIOMETRIC TITRATIONS

By Donald G. Davis
Professor of Chemistry
Louisiana State University in New Orleans
New Orleans, Louisiana

PRINCIPLES

The measurement of the potential of an appropriate indicator electrode has been used for many years as a method of detecting the equivalence point of a variety of titrations. The method is based on the fact that the potential of a suitable indicator electrode, when measured in comparison with a reference electrode, is related to concentration changes in the solution being titrated. The potentiometric method is exceptionally versatile because indicator electrodes for almost every type of titration reaction have been developed. In addition to the establishment of equivalent points of reactions, further information about the sample and its reactions may be obtained by the complete recording of a potentiometric titration curve. Problems involved in the selection of an indicator are avoided, and multi-component or colored solutions can be more conveniently handled. The extensive use of potentiometric titrations is also due to the fact that the necessary apparatus is inexpensive and generally available.

The potential (e.m.f.) of a cell typically set up to accomplish potentiometric titrations is the sum of three potentials. These are the indicator electrode-solution potential; the reference electrode potential; and a liquid junction potential. If, for example, the following cell were set up to follow a titration of chloride by a standard solution of silver ion,

$$(-)\ \mathrm{Pt},\ \mathrm{H_2}(1\ \mathrm{atm.})|\mathrm{H^+}(a = 1)||\mathrm{Cl^-}(a = ?),\ \mathrm{AgCl}|\mathrm{Ag}\ (+)$$

the potential of the cell would be

$$E_{\mathrm{cell}} = E_{\mathrm{H_2|H^+}} + E_{\mathrm{j}} + E_{\mathrm{AgCl|Ag}} \tag{1}$$

In this case the hydrogen electrode, on the left hand side, serves as a reference electrode and by convention is said to have a potential of zero. Thus

$$E_{\mathrm{cell}} = E_{\mathrm{j}} + E_{\mathrm{AgCl|Ag}} \tag{2}$$

The liquid junction potential, E_{j}, arises across the liquid-liquid boundary, ||, or salt bridge due to unequal migration of ions. For the purposes of potentiometric titrations, experimental methods are used to keep E_{j} low and/or constant, or else this usually unknown quantity is ignored (provided only relative potentials are desired for equivalence point detection).

Thus the value of the cell potential is considered to be equal to the numerical value of the potential of the indicating electrode (here the silver-silver chloride electrode) if a standard hydrogen electrode is used as a reference. If another reference electrode is chosen, such as the commonly used saturated calomel electrode ($E_{cal.} = +0.242$ volts), its potential must be taken into account with the application of the proper sign conventions.[1]

The potentials of each electrode can be expressed by the well-known Nernst equation. In the case of the reference electrode the concentrations of the reacting species are set up so as to be essentially constant and the Nernst equation for this electrode need not be considered. For the indicator electrode, however, this relation is of primary importance. For a generalized reaction

$$\text{Ox} + ne^- = \text{Red} \tag{3}$$

the Nernst equation may be written

$$E = E^0 - \frac{RT}{nF} \ln \frac{[\text{Red}]}{[\text{Ox}]} \tag{4}$$

where E^0 is the standard potential of reaction (usually recorded on the scale in which the normal hydrogen electrode is zero), R is the molar gas constant, T the absolute temperature, n the number of electrons per molar unit of reaction, F the faraday (96,494 coulombs per equivalent) and [Ox] and [Red] the molar concentrations of the oxidized and reduced species, respectively. This equation clearly indicates the relation between the indicator electrode potential and the concentrations of the oxidized and reduced species. Actually, activities should be used rather than concentrations. However, for potentiometric titrations close to the equivalence point, activity changes are closely proportional to concentration changes and thus concentrations are used for simplicity.

The value of E^0 to be used in any particular case may be taken from a table of standard potentials such as that of Latimer[2] or Lingane.[3] In practical analytical applications, "formal" potentials are of more use than standard potentials because the former are measured under analytical conditions which often include relatively high concentrations of acids or other species in solution. This is done by simply preparing solutions of known concentrations, measuring the electrode potential, and applying Eq. 4. Activity coefficients are included in the E^0 term by this method. Lists of formal potentials are available.[3,4]

APPARATUS

ELECTRODE SYSTEMS

Electrode systems can be divided into several classes depending on the species that determines the electrode potential. The simplest case, first class electrodes, can be exemplified by a metal electrode in contact with a solution of a soluble salt of that metal. In the instance that a metallic electrode cannot be used, as in the case of nonmetals such as iodine or hydrogen, an "inert" electrode is used as the site of electron transfer. For example, Pt, $H_2|H^+$ represents the hydrogen electrode, with platinum acting as an inert electron collector or donor.

Second class electrodes are those which may be exemplified by:

$$\text{Ag}|\text{AgCl}, \text{Cl}^-$$

[1] Lingane, J. J., Electroanalytical Chemistry, 2nd Ed., Interscience Publishers, New York, 1958, Chap. 3.

[2] Latimer, W. M., Oxidation Potentials, 2nd Ed., Prentice-Hall, New York, 1952.

[3] Lingane, J. J., Electroanalytical Chemistry, 2nd Ed., Interscience Publishers, New York, 1958, pp. 639–51.

[4] Swift, E. H., A System of Chemical Analysis, W. H. Freeman and Co., San Francisco, 1939, pp. 540–3.

in which the metallic electrode in contact with a slightly soluble salt responds to changes in the anion concentration. The titration of anions can thus be followed. On the other hand if the anion concentration is held constant, electrodes of this class can be used as reference electrodes, *i.e.*, the much used saturated calomel reference electrode.

The third class electrode is an extension of the above principle in which the metallic electrode is in contact with one of its own slightly ionized salts or complexes and that of a second metal as well. The electrode then responds to changes in concentration of the second metal ion. Two examples are:

$$Ag|Ag_2C_2O_4,\ CaC_2O_4,\ Ca^{+2}$$

$$Hg|HgY^{-2},\ MY^{-2},\ M^{+2}$$

REDOX ELECTRODES

The special case of first class electrodes, the reactions between soluble oxidants and reductants, is of special interest in analytical chemistry. The "noble" metal electrodes, such as those of platinum or gold, which are ordinarily used in this case are subject to some limitations which must be recognized. At very reducing potentials, such as in an acidic chromous solution, platinum catalyzes the reduction of hydrogen[5] and does not indicate the true solution potential. Mercury electrodes, which have a much higher hydrogen overvoltage, should be substituted in this case. On the other hand, in solutions of strong oxidants, noble metals can become oxidized and covered with an oxide film which may adversely effect the attainment or rate of attainment of the solution potential.[6,7,8] Pretreatment of the electrode is helpful, as are long waiting periods for steady potentials near the end point. Potentiometry at constant current (p. 290) is also useful in some cases. In microanalysis this oxide film may cause significant errors by introducing oxidizing material into the solution.

MEMBRANE ELECTRODES

Electrodes of this type can be used as both reference and indicating electrodes. A refence half-cell is separated from the test solution by a suitable membrane. The membrane must be responsive to the activity of one species of ion. A typical example is the glass electrode so commonly used for pH measurements. A common cell of this type can be represented:

Ag|AgCl, HCl ⋮ Test solution|saturated calomel electrode

glass membrane

at 25°C. the potential of this cell obeys the equation

$$E = \mathcal{E} + 0.05916\ \text{pH}$$

over the pH range 2 to 11. The value of $\mathcal{E}$ depends on the reference electrode potential and the various junction potentials. The potential across the glass membrane is often very large and is termed the "asymmetry" potential. Because of this asymmetry potential, glass electrodes must be calibrated with a standard buffer before pH measurements can be accomplished. The high resistance of glass membranes (many megohms) makes

[5] Lingane, J. J., Anal. Chem., **20,** 797, 1948.
[6] Kolthoff, I. M., and Tanaka, N., Anal. Chem., **26,** 632, 1954.
[7] Ross, J. W., and Shain, I., Anal. Chem., **28,** 548, 1956.
[8] Davis, D. G., and Lingane, J. J., Anal. Chim. Acta, **18,** 245, 1958.

it essential that a sensitive vacuum-tube voltmeter be used for potential measurement.

Other membranes, such as fused silver halides, barium sulfate, and ion exchange membranes have found some use in titration indicator electrodes.

INSTRUMENTATION

The potential of a galvanic cell depends on the concentrations of chemical species involved in the electrode reaction as well as the nature of these species. When current of any magnitude is allowed to pass through the cell these concentrations will change due to electrode reactions. For this reason, a simple voltmeter is not useful for the exact measurement of potentials. Instruments which do not draw appreciable current from the cell must be used. The most commonly used are a potentiometer making use of a compensation arrangement and a vacuum tube voltmeter (pH meter).

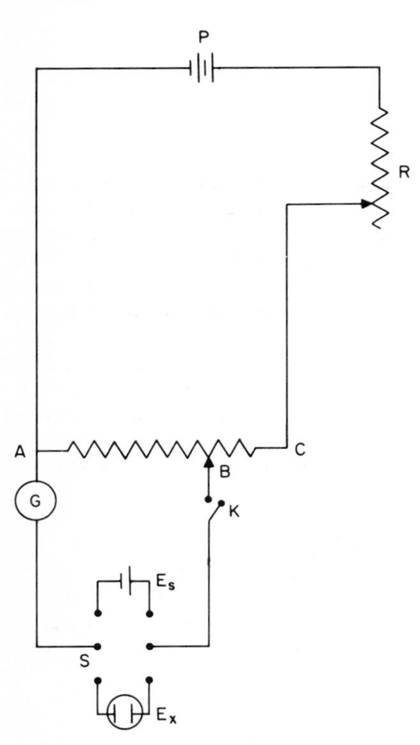

FIG. 17-1. Potentiometer

Apparatus for opposing the potential to be measured by an equal and opposite potential is shown in Fig. 17-1. A constant voltage from the battery P is impressed on the slide wire AC so that the voltage drop between A or C and any point B is proportional to the length AB or BC. The slide wire is provided with an accurate scale to measure the position of the sliding contact B. The potentiometer is calibrated by bringing the standard cell E_s into the circuit by means of the double pole-double throw switch, S. The slide wire is set at the scale value corresponding to the known voltage of the standard cell. The potentiometer is set by varying R and tapping the key until the sensitive galvanometer G shows no deflection. The key is used rather than a switch to avoid drawing more current than necessary through the cell. The titration cell E_x is then put into the circuit in place of the standard cell and its potential measured as a function of titrant volume.

The standard cell most normally used is the Weston cell:

$$(-)\ Cd(Hg)|3CdSO_4 \cdot 8H_2O\ (sat'd),\ Hg_2SO_4\ (solid)|Hg\ (+)$$

This cell is available from several manufacturers and is characterized by a low temperature effect on the voltage.

When the sensitivity of galvanometers is too low for the measuring electrode system, as when a glass electrode is used, a vacuum tube voltmeter becomes necessary. These electronic instruments, available from many manufacturers, draw very little current from the cell being measured. Because of their great convenience these voltmeters are now used very extensively. Some models can even be purchased at a lower price than a potentiometer and accessories.

The simplest modern potentiometric titration equipment consists of a line operated pH meter, a buret, and a magnetic stirrer. Since essentially any type of electrode system can be used with commercial pH meters this arrangement is also very versatile.

AUTOMATIC POTENTIOMETRIC TITRATIONS

When large numbers of similar titrations must be made, it is often profitable to purchase or construct apparatus to do potentiometric titrations in an automatic fashion. Automatic potentiometric titrators are usually constructed as continuous recording devices or as automatic "shut off" devices. In the former case, titrant is allowed to flow into the sample at a known rate and the potential of the indicator electrode or its derivative is recorded by an automatic plotting device. Titrant is usually dispensed by a motor-driven syringe buret. Care must be taken that the titrant is added at a relatively slow rate, especially near the end point, or errors will result. Difficulties due to oxide film formation may be troublesome in this method.[7]

Automatic titration to an end point is more analogous to the manual method. In this method titrant is allowed to flow into the solution being titrated until a pre-selected value of indicator electrode potential is reached. The signal from the indicator electrode is amplified and used to shut off a stopcock or a magnetic valve. In this case, also, the flow of titrant must be very slow, or, alternatively, an anticipation of the end point provided. This can be accomplished by locating the indicator electrode "down stream" from the buret tip, or sometimes by electronic means. The proper equivalence point potential must be known beforehand either by experiment or calculation.

APPLICATIONS

Potentiometric methods are generally considered to be among the most accurate available. Other than the ability of the experimenter to measure titrant volumes accurately, the limitation upon the accuracy of potentiometric titrations is generally only the equilibrium constant of the titration reaction. Naturally the reaction must go to analytical completion for accurate results to be obtained in a normal way. In certain cases, if the electrodes being used do not respond "reversibly" (according to the Nernst equation) to the species determining the potential, poor results are obtained even at high concentrations. Electrode "fouling" by impurities must be avoided as well.

Potentiometric titrations can be carried out on the microlevel if electrodes of the type necessary can be constructed in sufficiently small size, and dilute solutions (perhaps to 10^{-5} *M* in some cases) can be used successfully. Care must be taken to avoid drawing current from the cell in these cases (in extreme situations the vibrating reed electrometer can be used), and also to insure that the electrode systems are free of fouling, oxide formation and other interferences.

METHODS OF END POINT LOCATION

If the equilibrium constant of the titration reaction is large, the titrant concentrated, and the indicator electrode responsive, it is often possible to locate the end point by means of a drop by drop approach. The titration is then terminated at that drop which causes a large change in potential. Sufficient accuracy for the case at hand may sometimes be achieved very easily by this method. Frequently, however, one of the stated conditions cannot be attained. A more complex method is then necessary for accurate results, such as plotting the titration curve or its derivative, titration to the accurately known equivalence point potential, the Pinkhof-Treadwell method, or the use of other special apparatus.

GRAPHICAL DETERMINATION

The most obvious "exact" way of locating the equivalence point of a potentiometric titration is to plot the potential (or pH) as a function of titration volume, and to determine by inspection the volume corresponding to the point of maximum slope of the curve. When the titration curve is symmetrical, the maximum value of $\Delta E/\Delta V$ occurs exactly at the equivalence point. A symmetrical titration curve is obtained when the indicator electrode potential obeys the Nernst equation (Eq. 4) and the number of moles of titrant and reactant are equal in the balanced titration reaction (symmetrical reaction). If the reaction is not symmetrical, the point of maximum slope differs from the equivalence point. However, the error is usually very small if the potential change near the equivalence point is large.

The end point can be exactly located by a differentiation method rather than by plotting an actual graph. The data are obtained by adding small increments (say 0.10 ml.) of titrant near the end point and recording the potential. The maximum value of $\Delta E/\Delta V$ is then computed by taking it as the end point where $\Delta^2E/\Delta V^2$ becomes zero.[9] An illustration is given in Table 17-1.

TABLE 17-1. TITRATION DATA (NEAR THE END POINT) FOR A HYPOTHETICAL TITRATION

Vol. in ml.	E millivolts	$\Delta E/\Delta V$ mv./0.1 ml.	$\Delta^2E/\Delta V^2$
10.00	620		
		5	
10.10	625		+7
		12	
10.20	637		+20
		32	
10.30	669		+74
		106	
10.40	775		−36
		70	
10.50	845		−20
		50	
10.60	895		

$$V(\text{at } \Delta^2E/\Delta V^2 = 0) = 10.30 + 0.10\left(\frac{74}{74 + 36}\right)$$

Figure 17-2 illustrates the principle of this method. The best value of ΔV depends on the slope of the curve near the equivalence point. In general, the greater the value of the slope, the smaller the value of ΔV. Of course, practical considerations are important as well, in that the size of a drop is about 0.05 ml. and with ordinary apparatus an addition of smaller volumes would be troublesome.

TITRATION TO THE EQUIVALENCE POINT POTENTIAL

If the potential of the indicator electrode at the equivalence point is known or can be calculated, the titration can be carried out by adding titrant until this point is reached.[10]

[9] Hostetter, J. C., and Roberts, H. S., J. Am. Chem. Soc., **41,** 1337, 1919.
[10] Müller, E., Elektrometrische Massanalyse, 6 Auflage T. Steinkopf, Dresden, 1942.

This method is quite convenient since it is not necessary to record or plot data. If the equivalence point cannot be calculated, then often it may be measured experimentally. This method is especially useful for titrations involving small amounts of materials.[11]

PINKHOF-TREADWELL METHOD

The Pinkhof-Treadwell method of equivalence point detection[12] is actually a variation in the equivalence point potential method. The titration cell is made up of two electrodes which are often identical. One serves as the indicator electrode and is placed in the solution being titrated. The other serves as a reference electrode and is placed in a solution whose composition (or at least potential) is equal to the indicator electrode potential at the equivalence point. Contact between the solutions is accomplished with a salt bridge. As this electrode combination has a potential of zero at the equivalence point, very simple apparatus can be used. Only a galvanometer and tapping key are necessary—the end point being signified by no deflection of the galvanometer.

While this method is very rapid and the apparatus simple, care must be taken if there is the possibility that the indicator electrode potential might be established only slowly. This method is best used for the repetitive performance of well-studied titrations. Unfortunately it is not applicable in its simplest form to titrations with glass electrodes.

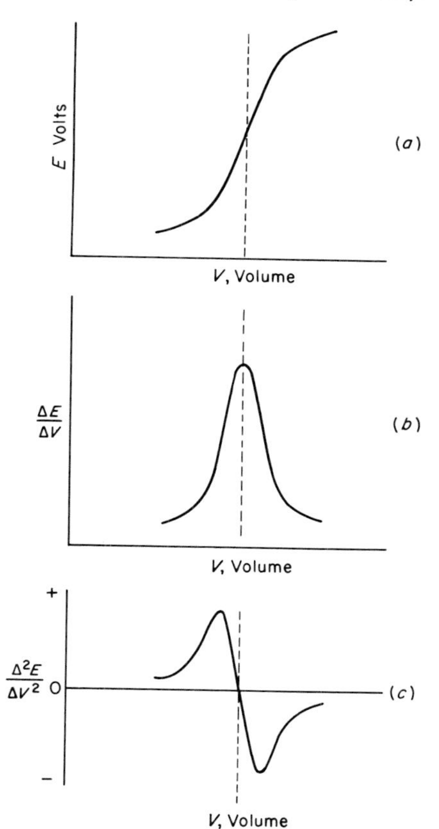

Fig. 17-2. Standard Titration Curve (*a*); First (*b*) and Second (*c*) Derivatives.

DIFFERENTIAL TITRATIONS

It is possible to set up cell arrangements which allow the direct measurement of $\Delta E/\Delta V$.[13] Two identical electrodes are used, one being isolated in a small portion of the solution being titrated. The isolation compartment can conveniently be a small medicine dropper dipping into the titrant solution and provided with a rubber bulb for flushing and refilling the compartment. The platinum or other metal electrode is sealed through the glass dropper, well above the tip so that it contacts only the solution inside the dropper. The titration is carried out by adding an increment of titrant and measuring the value of ΔE between the electrodes. The rubber bulb is then used to flush the isolated compartment and the next increment of titrant is added. Thus the solution in the compartment is a stage of the titration slightly behind the main body of solution. Before the equivalence point is

[11] Cooke, W. D., Reilley, C. N., and Furman, N. H., Anal. Chem., **23,** 1662, 1951.
[12] Treadwell, W. D., and Weiss, L., Helv. Chem. Acta, **2,** 680, 1919.
[13] MacInnes, D. A., and Cowperthwaite, I. A., J. Am. Chem. Soc., **53,** 555, 1931.

approached the value of ΔE is small but increases to a large maximal value at the equivalence point. A curve such as Fig. 17.2(b) is thus recorded.

The main advantage of this method is that no reference electrode is needed. The accuracy is as good, but no better than other methods of potentiometric titrations.

POTENTIOMETRY WITH POLARIZED INDICATOR ELECTRODES

A number of commonly used redox couples, such as thiosulfate-tetrathionate behave irreversibly at a platinum electrode and establish constant potentials only slowly when measurements are made by ordinary (zero current) potentiometry. Long waiting periods can be avoided and sometimes larger potential breaks measured, by forcing a slight amount of electrolysis to occur at the indicator electrode. Kolthoff[14] and also Lingane[15] have discussed the interpretation of potentiometric titrations with polarized electrodes. Either one or two indicator electrodes may be used. If the one indicator electrode method is selected, the cell is completed with a reference electrode (not of the asbestos fiber type) large enough to allow the polarizing current to pass. This single electrode may be polarized either cathodically or anodically, depending on the system under consideration. If two indicator electrodes, say two identical platinum wire electrodes, are used, one functions as an anode and the other as a cathode.

If both the titrant couple and the reactant couple are reversible, the use of one polarized indicator electrode will result in a curve similar to the ordinary (zero current) case; but two polarized indicator electrodes will yield a "peak" type curve. The main advantage in the use of polarized electrodes is in the case of irreversible reactions (often resulting in slowly attained or unsteady potentials). In such cases the resultant curve is usually characterized by a sharp increase (or decrease) in potential at or near the equivalence point—for either the one or two indicator electrode system. The literature should be consulted for some examples, instruments, and interpretations.[16,17,18] Of particular interest is the work of Bishop who developed these methods (designated as Differential Electrolytic Potentiometry) to a state of high accuracy[19] and sensitivity.[20]

Some caution must be exercised in the application of polarized electrodes because the current passed can cause reactant to be consumed (except in the two-electrode case applied to reversible systems). This can cause errors in the titration unless the polarizing current and the size of the electrodes are kept small. Currents of a few microamps are normal. In addition, the potential changes are sometimes not theoretically coincidental with the equivalence point. Again this error may be minimized by using small electrodes and current.

Several commercially available pH meters have sources of constant polarizing current built in which may be used to polarize the indicator electrode. These are used especially for "Karl Fischer" titrations.

ACID-BASE TITRATIONS

The practicality of any particular acid-base titration depends on the strength of the acid or base being titrated and its concentration. In general, the lower limit of the usefulness of a titration is reached when K_a approaches 10^{-8} at a concentration level of 0.1 *M*

[14] Kolthoff, I. M., Anal. Chem., **26,** 1689, 1954.

[15] Lingane, J. J., Electroanalytical Chemistry, 2nd Ed., Interscience Publishers, New York, 1958, pp. 153–157.

[16] Reilley, C. N., Cooke, W. D., and Furman, N. H., Anal. Chem., **23,** 1223, 1951.

[17] Bishop, E., Analyst, **83,** 212, 1958.

[18] Charlot, G., and Bezier, D., Methodes Electrochimiques D'Analyse, Masson et Cie, Paris, 1954.

[19] Bishop, E., and Dhaneshwar, R. G., Analyst, **87,** 207, 1962.

[20] Bishop, E., Mikrochim. Acta, **5–6,** 803, 1960.

in aqueous solutions. For each decrease in concentration by a power of 10 the K_a must be greater by at least a power of 10. The maximum value of $\frac{\Delta E}{\Delta V}$, that is to say $\left(\frac{\Delta pH}{\Delta V}\right)$, is ordinarily taken as the equivalence point, even though the titration curve of a weak acid with a strong base (or vice versa) is unsymmetrical. It has been calculated[21] that an error of 0.3% occurs between the maximum value of $\frac{\Delta E}{\Delta V}$ and the equivalence point if the product of K_a and concentration is 10^{-11}. This allows for no experimental error, however, which might be large at low concentrations.

If two weakly acidic or basic materials with pK's between 3 and 10 are titrated with a strong base or acid, two well defined potentiometric end points will be found provided the pK's of the two materials differ by 4 or 5. These figures assume roughly equal concentrations.

It has been reported that weak bases can be more effectively titrated in concentrated neutral salt solutions[22] such as 6 to 8 *M* sodium iodide or 6 *M* sodium chloride. Aniline gives a sharp end point in 7 *M* sodium iodide and, even more useful, some mixtures such as triethylamine and pyridine can be analyzed with higher accuracy than pyridine in water alone. A concentrated titrant (0.5 *M* HCl) is used so that the volume does not increase more than about 10 percent. This effect has been further studied by Rosenthal and Dwyer[23] and explained in terms of the variation of a composite activity term and its effect on the K_b.

Acid-base titrations can be carried out very conveniently in nonaqueous media. Almost any indicator electrode can be used for some nonaqueous solvents, but the glass electrode (with a suitable low resistance reference electrode—not an asbestos fiber type) is by far the most popular. Care must be taken with the glass electrode because water plays an important role in its pH response. Intermittent soaking of the glass tip in water allows successful application of the glass electrode to almost any solvent.

The theory[24] and procedures[25] for many nonaqueous titrations have been reviewed. One of the more useful procedures involving glacial acetic acid as a solvent is given below. Many amino acids (titrated as bases) and amines may be analyzed by this procedure.

TITRATION OF AMINO ACIDS[25]

Reagents. **0.1 *M* Perchloric Acid.**—Mix 8.5 ml. 72% perchloric acid with 200 to 300 ml. of glacial acetic acid and add 20 ml. of acetic anhydride. Dilute to 1 liter and allow to stand for several hours to permit complete reaction of acetic anhydride with the water present.

0.1 *M* Sodium Acetate.—Dissolve 8.2 g. of anhydrous sodium acetate in 1 liter of glacial acetic acid.

Potassium Acid Phthalate.—Primary standard.

Procedure.—Dissolve a sample containing 2 to 3 milliequivalents of amino acid in exactly 50 ml. of 0.1 *M* perchloric acid. Back titrate the excess acid with 0.1 *M* sodium acetate using a pH meter equipped with a water-soaked glass and sleeve type calomel electrode to identify the end point.

[21] Roller, P. S., J. Am. Chem. Soc., **50,** 1, 1928.
[22] Critchfield, F. E., and Johnson, J. B., Anal. Chem., **30,** 1247, 1958.
[23] Rosenthal, D., and Dwyer, J. S., Anal. Chem., **35,** 161, 1963; Can. J. Chem., **41,** 80, 1963; J. Phys. Chem., **66,** 2687, 1962.
[24] Kolthoff, I. M., and Elving, P. J., Treatise on Analytical Chemistry, Part I, Vol. I, John Wiley and Sons, New York, 1959, pp. 475–541.
[25] Fritz, J. S., Acid Base Titrations in Nonaqueous Solvents, G. F. Smith Chemical Co., Columbus, 1952.

The perchloric acid is standardized against potassium acid phthalate. About 0.5 g. of potassium acid phthalate is weighed out and dissolved in about 50 ml. of glacial acetic acid (with refluxing if necessary) and titrated, using the pH meter to identify the end point. The sodium acetate solution is then standardized against perchloric acid.

TITRATION OF AMINES

Reagents.—See preceding method.

Procedure.—Dissolve the sample containing two to four milliequivalents in about 50 ml. of chlorobenzene or glacial acetic acid and titrate with 0.1 *M* perchloric acid using the pH meter to locate the end point.

PRECIPITATION TITRATIONS

Much work has been done on the potentiometric end point detection of precipitation titrations due to the fact that the number of indicators available is not great and cannot usually be applied to mixtures. Most applications make use of a silver electrode (for titrations of halides, sulfide, cyanide, and tetraphenylborate) or a small mercury pool electrode for similar titrations. The platinum electrode is also often used, being particularly applicable to ferrocyanide and chromate titrations.

Care must be used in selecting a reference electrode, since precipitating titrants sometimes react with ions from the reference electrode, causing precipitation at the reference electrode solution junction, and thus erratic behavior. For instance, a saturated calomel electrode should not be allowed to contact directly a silver ion solution, because silver chloride precipitates. In such cases the use of salt bridges is recommended.

Many examples of useful precipitation titrations can be found in the literature.[26] The potentiometric method is particularly applicable to mixtures of halides[27] but special procedures are needed to compensate for mixed halide precipitation.

A typical potentiometric precipitation titration is outlined as follows:

TITRATION OF ZINC[28,29]

Reagents. **Potassium Ferrocyanide Solution.**—Prepare a standard solution of potassium ferrocyanide, using reagent grade potassium ferrocyanide and distilled water Standardize against a known zinc solution by the procedure descricbed below. Store in a dark bottle.

Potassium Ferricyanide Solution.—Prepare a 1 percent (by weight) solution of potassium ferricyanide, and store in a dark bottle. This solution should be freshly prepared each day.

Procedure.—A sample solution containing about 150 mg. of zinc is placed in a beaker and the pH adjusted between 1 and 3 with dilute hydrochloric acid or sodium hydroxide. About 10 drops of the 1 percent potassium ferricyanide is added The sample solution is then titrated with standard ferrocyanide, using a platinum and calomel electrode connected to a pH meter (millivolt scale) to establish the endpoint. The precipitate formed is $K_2Zn_3[Fe(CN)_6]_2$. The end point potential is approximately +0.6 volt *vs.* the calomel electrode.

If other metal ions such as iron(III), nickel(II), or lead(II) which precipitate with ferrocyanide are present, their interference may be eliminated by adding an approxi-

[26] Kolthoff, I. M., and Furman, N. H., Potentiometric Titrations, 2nd Ed., John Wiley and Sons, New York, 1931.

[27] Martin, A. J., Anal. Chem., **30,** 233, 1958.

[28] Lingane, J. J., and Hartley, A. M., Anal. Chim. Acta, **11,** 475, 1954.

[29] Davis, D. G., and McLendon, H. T., Talanta, **2,** 124, 1959.

mately equal amount of EDTA solution and controlling the pH more exactly to 2.10 ± 0.05.

COMPLEXOMETRIC TITRATIONS

Complexometric titrations can often be followed potentiometrically. For instance, cyanide ion may be titrated with silver to yield $[Ag(CN)_2]^-$ even in the presence of halides, using a silver metal indicating electrode. Of greater current interest is the use of chelating agents, such as EDTA, as complexometric titrants. Metal ions which establish reversible potentials at a platinum electrode, such as iron(III) ion, can be titrated with EDTA using that indicating electrode.

Since most metal ions do not fall into this category, a special type of third class electrode was developed by Reilley and his co-workers[30,31,32] which may be represented as

$$Hg|HgY^{-2}, MY^{-2}, M^{+2}$$

where Y^{-4} stands for the EDTA anion and M^{+2} the metal being titrated. This electrode, when attached with a reference electrode to a pH meter, functions as a pM electrode and may be used to titrate a large variety of metal ions.

POTENTIOMETRIC TITRATION OF METAL IONS WITH EDTA

Apparatus.—Amalgamate a clean gold wire by dipping it in pure mercury and connect it to a pH meter (millivolt scale). Connect also a saturated calomel electrode to be brought into contact with the solution to be titrated with an ammonium nitrate salt bridge.

***Reagents.* Ammonium Hydroxide–Ammonium Nitrate Buffer.**—For Mg, Ca, Ba (remove O_2), Zn, Co, Ni, Cu, Cd, Pb (add tartrate). Add ammonium hydroxide to a 0.5 *M* solution of ammonium nitrate until the pH is 10.

Acetate Buffer.—For Sc, Y, La, Rare earths(III), vanadium(IV), manganese(II), Cu, Zn, Cd, Hg, Bi. Add acetic acid to sodium acetate until the pH is about 4.6.

Mercury(II)–EDTA Complex.—Mix *equivalent* amounts of mercuric nitrate and EDTA solutions and dilute the resulting solution until the final concentration is 10^{-2} to 10^{-3} *M*.

Standard EDTA Solution.—Weigh out the appropriate amount of the pure disodium salt of EDTA and dissolve it in distilled and de-ionized water.

Procedure.—To a 25-ml. aliquot of the sample solution of the metal ion(s) to be titrated, add 25 ml. of the appropriate buffer (See NOTE below) and 1 drop of mercury-EDTA reagent. Titrate the solution with standard EDTA solution and take the end point as the point of maximum potential change.

The original papers of Reilley should be consulted for information on theory and on particular multicomponent mixtures.

NOTE.—The buffer is selected according to the metals to be titrated. In general, the buffer with the lowest pH for a particular metal ion should be selected. Metals listed for a low pH buffer generally interfere at higher pH's. Mixtures of metals to be titrated in the same buffer can sometimes but not always be differentiated. Mixtures of metal ions to be titrated in different buffers can be titrated to different end points. After the break for the first metal is found using the lower pH buffer, the more basic buffer is added and the second metal titrated.

[30] Reilley, C. N., and Schmid, R. W., Anal. Chem., **30,** 947, 1958.
[31] Reilley, C. N., Schmid, R. W., and Lamson, D. W., *ibid.*, 953.
[32] Reilley, C. N., and Vavoulis, V., Anal. Chem., **31,** 243, 1959.

OXIDATION-REDUCTION TITRATIONS

Perhaps the most frequently used potentiometric titrations involve the use of a strongly oxidizing or reducing titrant and a platinum indicator electrode. The basic requirement for a successful titration is that the E^0 for the titrant couple differ from the E^0 of sample couple by several tenths of a volt. Oxidants commonly used include potassium permanganate, potassium dichromate, ceric sulfate, and potassium iodate or bromate. Usually these titrations are carried out in acidic media. Often the sample must be reduced before titration and for this purpose a Jones Reductor containing amalgamated zinc metal is of use. Samples that can be conveniently titrated with the above oxidants include: nitrite (45°C.), oxalate (70°C.), iron, vanadium, tin, titanium, iodide, uranium, manganese, arsenic and many others. For more details, see the author's work.[33]

Reductants of great use include iron(II), arsenic(III), titanium(III), chromium(II), tin(II) and ascorbic acid. Frequently the sample must be preoxidized using persulfate and silver, argentic oxide, sodium perborate or sodium bismuthate. Samples analyzed frequently in this class include those containing chromium, manganese, gold, cobalt, nitrates, mercury, cerium, and the higher oxidation states of halogens.

Two procedures are given below which illustrate the use of oxidizing and reducing titrants as well as sample pre-treatment.

POTENTIOMETRIC TITRATION OF MANGANESE[34]

Apparatus.—A pH meter for the adjustment of pH (glass and calomel electrodes) and potentiometric titrations (platinum and calomel electrodes).

Reagents. **Potassium Permanganate Solution.**—Use a standardized 0.025 *M* solution.

Sodium Pyrophosphate Solution.—Use a freshly-prepared, saturated solution.

Procedure.—Take a sample containing about 140 mg. of manganese and dissolve in an appropriate acid or acids. Add an aliquot to about 250 ml. of saturated sodium pyrophosphate in a 600-ml. beaker and adjust the pH to between 5 and 7 with sulfuric acid or sodium hydroxide solution. Place the platinum and calomel electrodes in the solution and titrate with the standard potassium permanganate, recording the titration curve. The manganese(II) in the sample is oxidized to manganese(III) and the permanganate is reduced to manganese(III).

DETERMINATION OF CERIUM, MANGANESE, OR CHROMIUM[35]

Reagents. **Argentic Oxide, AgO.**—This compound is supplied by Merck and Co., Rahway, N. J.

Ferrous Ammonium Sulfate Solution, 0.1 *M*.—Dissolve the appropriate, accurately weighed amount of ferrous ammonium sulfate in 0.05 *M* sulfuric acid and standardize. This solution should be freshly-prepared every few days.

Procedure.—Add enough previously boiled nitric acid and water to the sample to result in a final volume of about 50 ml. and a nitric acid concentration of 3–5 *M*. Add small portions of solid argentic oxide until an excess is present as indicated by a dark brown or black color of the solution. Dilute the solution to about 150 ml. with 1 *M* sulfuric acid, warm to about 80°C., and allow the solution to stand until the argentic oxide has decomposed (about 15 minutes). Titrate the solution potentiometrically with the standard ferrous solution, using platinum and calomel electrodes. The end point is the point of maximum potential change.

[33] Davis, D. G., in Comprehensive Analytical Chemistry, Vol. 2, Part A, Wilson, C., and Wilson, D., Eds., Elsevier Publishing Co., Amsterdam, 1964.

[34] Lingane, J. J., and Karplus, R., Anal. Chem., **18,** 191, 1946.

[35] Lingane, J. J., and Davis, D. G., Anal. Chim. Acta, **15,** 201, 1956.

The titration may also be started without warming or waiting. In this case two potential breaks are found—the first for the reduction of excess silver(II), and the second for the permanganate, dichromate, or cerium(IV), or the sum of these ions if more than one is present.

APPLICATIONS IN THE ANALYSIS OF SPECIAL MATERIALS

Potentiometric methods have been used in the determination of various substances in the analysis of special materials. Those included in other chapters of Standard Methods of Chemical Analysis are:

1. Chapter 24, Volume IIA, Alloys: Iron and Steel.
   a. Manganese in iron, steel, and alloy steels, page 661.
2. Chapter 25, Volume IIA, Alloys: Ferro-alloys.
   a. Manganese in ferromanganese and silicomanganese, page 771.
3. Chapter 26, Volume IIA, Alloys: Nonferrous.
   a. Chromium in copper-base alloys, page 844.
   b. Manganese in nickel-copper alloys, page 888.
4. Chapter 46, Volume III, Portland Cement.
   a. Chloride
5. Chapter 50, Volume III, Foods.
   a. Sodium chloride in meat and meat products
6. Chapter 53, Volume III, Glass.
   a. Arsenic
   b. Iron
   Chapter 44, Volume IIB, Silicates: Glasses, Rocks, and Ferrous Slags.
   a. Boron in glass, page 2255.
   b. Chloride in glass, page 2255.
7. Chapter 59, Volume III, Rubber and Rubber Products.
   a. Determination of antioxidants in rubber
   b. Determination of isocyanate groups in bonding agents in rubber analysis
8. Chapter 61, Volume III, Soap and Synthetic Detergents.
   a. Determination of composition of "upper layer" obtained from sulfonation of alkylate
   b. Determination of soap in commercial products containing synthetic products
   c. Determination of water
   Chapter 45, Volume IIB, Soaps and Detergents.
   a. Borate in inorganic builders, page 2307.
   b. Chloride in inorganic builders, page 2303.
   c. Phosphate in inorganic builders, page 2304.
9. Chapter 63, Volume III, Water Analysis.
   a. Chloride
   Chapter 48, Volume IIB, Water Analysis.
   a. Acidity of water, page 2398.
   b. Alkalinity of water, page 2399.
   c. Boron, page 2405.

SELECTED BIBLIOGRAPHY

Kolthoff, I. M., and Furman, N. H., Potentiometric Titrations, 2nd Ed., John Wiley and Sons, New York, 1931.
Müller, E., Elektrometrische Massanalyses, 6 Auflage, Steinkopf, Dresden, 1942.

Lingane, J. J., Electroanalytical Chemistry, 2nd Ed., Interscience Publishers, New York, 1958, Chapters 3–8.
Davis, D. G., Comprehensive Analytical Chemistry, Volume II, Part A, editors C. Wilson and D. Wilson, Elsevier Publishing Co., Amsterdam, 1964.
Reviews by Furman, N. H.: J. Chem. Ed., **3,** 932, 1926; Ind. Eng. Chem., Anal. Ed., **2,** 213, 1930; **14,** 367, 1942; Anal. Chem., **22,** 33, 1950; **23,** 21, 1951; **26,** 84, 1954.
Reviews by Reilley, C. N.: Anal. Chem., **28,** 671, 1956; **30,** 765, 1958; **32,** 185R, 1960.
Review by Murry, R. W., and Reilley, C. N.: Anal. Chem., **34,** 313R, 1962; **36,** 370R, 1964.

Chapter 18

CONDUCTOMETRIC TITRATIONS

By J. W. Ross
Orion Research, Inc.
Cambridge, Massachusetts

INTRODUCTION

Measurements of electrolyte solution conductance can easily be made to a high degree of precision using relatively simple equipment. For this reason conductance measurements were among the first to be used by physical chemists for determining solubility products, dissociation constants, and other properties of electrolyte solutions. The possibility of using conductance to locate end points in titrations was also recognized early in the development of instrumental methods,[1] but in recent years the development of alternative methods of locating end points has displaced conductometric titrations to a large extent. Several analytically important applications remain, however, where conductance measurement makes possible titrations where other techniques fail. Additionally, conductometric titrations may frequently be used with a considerable saving in equipment complexity, even though other instrumental methods are available.

Conductance is an additive property of a solution depending on all the ions present. Solution conductance measurements, therefore, are nonspecific, and knowing the conductance of a given solution will tell little about its composition. If it is known in advance that only one ionized species is present, direct measurement of conductance can be of some analytical utility, for example, in standardizing reagent solutions, but the major application lies in the area of conductometric titration. When a solution is titrated with a reagent which reacts with a sought for constituent in such a way that the number or kind of ions present in the solution varies, then suitable graphical treatment of conductance data measured during the course of the titration will, in many cases, permit the location of the end point. In recent years a related technique, high-frequency conductometric titration, has been developed. This method, although similar in name, differs in a number of important respects and is the subject of a separate chapter.

DEFINITION OF CONDUCTANCE

Electrolyte solutions are ionic conductors and, except at very high electrical fields in excess of 1000 volts per centimeter, obey Ohm's law. The resistance of a solution expressed in ohms is defined as the ratio of an impressed potential difference in volts to the resulting current flow in amperes. Since a solution is a three dimensional conductor the exact resistance of any given solutions will depend on the geometry of the containing cell used in the measurement, and the spacing and area of the electrodes used to make contact with the solution. It is customary in conductance measurements to refer to a simple cell, consisting of a uniform column of solution of length, l, bounded by two plane

[1] Kuster, F. W., Gruters, M., and Giebel, W., Z. anorg. Chem., **42**, 225, 1904.

parallel electrodes of equal area, A. For this simple case the solution resistance, R, in ohms, is given by:

$$R = \rho \frac{l}{A} = \rho\theta \tag{1}$$

where: ρ is the specific resistance of the solution expressed in units of ohm cm.; and the ratio l/A is referred to as the cell constant, θ.

For chemical measurements it is more convenient to refer to the reciprocal of the solution resistance, called the conductance, expressed in reciprocal ohms or mhos. For the column of a solution in Eq. (1)

$$\frac{1}{R} = \frac{1}{\theta} k \tag{2}$$

where k is the specific conductance of the solution expressed in units of mho cm.$^{-1}$. Practical cells are never of such simple geometry as the one just described. In such cases l/A may be exceedingly difficult to calculate. However, it is possible to measure the absolute specific conductance of an unknown solution in any nonuniform cell if the cell constant is first calculated using a solution of known conductivity. Table 18-1 gives the

TABLE 18-1. SPECIFIC CONDUCTANCE OF STANDARD POTASSIUM CHLORIDE SOLUTIONS

Concentration Grams KCl/1000 g. Solution (in vacuo)	*Specific Conductance (mho cm.$^{-1}$) at*		
	0°C.	*18°C.*	*25°C.*
71.1352	0.06518	0.09784	0.11134
7.41913	0.007138	0.011167	0.012856
0.745263	0.0007736	0.0012205	0.0014088

specific conductance of standard KCl solutions at various temperatures as determined by Jones and Bradshaw.[2] In calibrating a cell it is advisable to choose the standard solution with the specific conductance which corresponds most closely to the sample solution being measured. Fortunately, in conductometric titrations it is only changes in conductivity, and not absolute values, which are significant. Therefore, it is rarely necessary to calibrate a cell precisely. It is desirable however, to have some idea of the cell constant to be used in order that measuring apparatus of an appropriate resistance range can be selected.

RELATIONSHIP OF CONDUCTANCE TO SOLUTION COMPOSITION

To a first approximation, each ion in solution acts as an independent current carrier; therefore, the conductance of a solution depends in a simple way on the solution composition as given by the following equation:

$$\frac{1}{R} = \frac{1}{\theta} \sum_i c_i z_i \lambda_i \tag{3}$$

The summation is made over all the ions in solution: c_i is the concentration of the ith ion in moles/cm.^{3}, z_i the absolute value of its charge, and λ_i its equivalent conductance expressed in mho-cm.^{2}/equivalent. Application of Eq. (3) is complicated to some extent by the fact that ionic equivalent conductances are dependent to some extent on the

[2] Jones, G., and Bradshaw, B. C., J. Am. Chem. Soc., **55**, 1780, 1933.

concentrations and nature of the other ions present, but in relatively dilute solutions the variation is not large and can be ignored for the purpose of interpreting titrations curves. The relative variation of λ_{Na^+} in several sodium salt solutions is shown in Fig. 18-1, and is typical of most ions. Table 18-2 gives a representative list of equivalent ionic

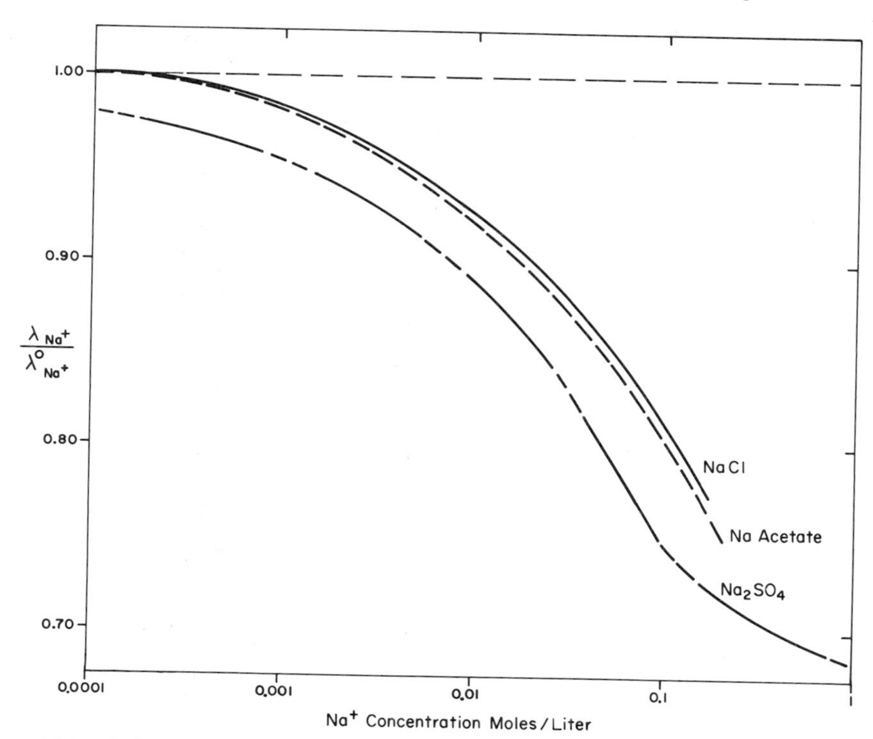

Fig. 18-1. Relative Change in Sodium Ion Equivalent Conductance in Sodium Salt Solutions.

conductivities at infinite dilution $\lambda°$. The magnitude depends principally on the hydrated ionic size, and can be estimated for ions not listed by taking the value of an ion of similar charge and radius.

The values of Table 18-2 refer to a temperature of 25°C. Ionic equivalent conductance is dependent on temperature and increases approximately 2 percent for each degree Centigrade rise in temperature. The values also refer to aqueous solutions. In other solvents the conductance values will be different, varying strongly with the viscosity of the solvent.

INSTRUMENTATION

All measurements of conductance and resistance require that some current pass through the solution. The most direct method of producing a current is to apply a potential between two inert metallic electrodes introduced directly into the solution under test. Under these conditions the solution will, in general, appear as a complex

TABLE 18-2. SPECIFIC IONIC CONDUCTANCES AT INFINITE DILUTION

Ion	$\lambda°$ *25°C., mho-cm.²/g. equiv.*	$\frac{1}{\lambda°}\frac{d\lambda°}{dT}$ *deg.⁻¹ at 25°C.*
Inorganic cations		
Ag^{+}	61.9	0.021
Ba^{++}	63.6	0.023
Ca^{++}	59.5	0.023
Co^{++}	53.0	0.02
$Co(NH_3)_6^{+++}$	102.3	—
Cs^{+}	77.0	0.18
Cu^{++}	54.0	0.02
H^{+}	349.8	—
K^{+}	73.5	0.019
Li^{+}	38.7	0.024
Mg^{++}	53.1	0.022
NH_4^{+}	73.4	0.019
Na^{+}	50.1	0.022
Pb^{++}	73.0	0.02
Rb^{+}	77.8	0.019
Sr^{++}	59.5	0.02
Tl^{+}	74.7	0.02
UO_2^{++}	51.0	—
Zn^{++}	52.8	0.02
Organic cations		
$(CH_3)_4N^{+}$	44.9	0.02
$(C_2H_5)_4N^{+}$	32.7	0.02
$(n\text{-}C_4H_9)_4N^{+}$	23.4	0.02
Inorganic anions		
$B(C_6H_5)_4^{-}$	18.0	—
Br^{-}	78.5	0.020
BrO_3^{-}	55.8	—
Cl^{-}	76.3	0.020
ClO_3^{-}	64.6	0.019
ClO_4^{-}	67.3	0.020
$CO_3^{=}$	69.3	0.020
$C_2O_4^{=}$	74.2	—
F^{-}	55.0	0.020
$Fe(CN)_6^{-4}$	110.5	0.020
$Fe(CN)_6^{-3}$	100.0	—
HCO_3^{-}	44.5	—
$HC_2O_4^{-}$	40.2	—
$H_2PO_4^{-}$	33.0	0.030
I^{-}	76.8	0.020
IO_3^{-}	40.8	0.020
IO_4^{-}	54.5	0.02
NO_3^{-}	71.4	0.02
OH^{-}	198.0	0.018
$SO_4^{=}$	80.0	0.022
Organic anions		
$HCOO^{-}$	54.6	
CH_3COO^{-}	40.9	
$C_6H_5COO^{-}$	32.3	

impedance to an external measuring system and not as an ohmic conductor. Polarization potentials appear at the electrode solution interface whose magnitudes depend on the electron transfer reaction of the electrolysis. At the interface large capacitances may be present due to the electrical double layers and the geometric capacity of the cell and the connecting leads. The presence of polarization potentials and capacity may combine to far overshadow the ohmic resistance in determining the cell current, making it impossible to measure solution resistance accurately. Furthermore, prolonged passage of current may affect the composition of the bulk of the solution, thereby changing the resistance. Many of the common techniques used in measuring the resistance of solid conductors must, as a consequence, be modified if they are to be applied to solution measurements. The most important schemes for overcoming polarization effects and measuring conductance are briefly discussed below.

ALTERNATING CURRENT METHODS

By using alternating applied voltages and platinum electrodes, polarization effects can be reduced to negligible values. If the applied voltage is sufficiently large, *i.e.*, 5–10 volts, the principal reaction occurring at the electrode surfaces is the oxidation and reduction of hydrogen produced from the decomposition of water. This reaction proceeds with a low polarization overvoltage at a platinum surface which can be decreased even more if the effective surface area is increased by coating the electrode with platinum black. Furthermore, since the current reverses with each half cycle, there can be no net change in solution composition as a result of electrolysis. The frequency used is not especially critical. At very low frequencies less than 20 c.p.s. some polarization difficulty may be experienced, probably due to loss of hydrogen and other electrolysis products from the electrode surface by diffusion, while at frequencies much above 10,000 c.p.s. the effect of cell capacity may become significant, particularly in high resistance solutions.

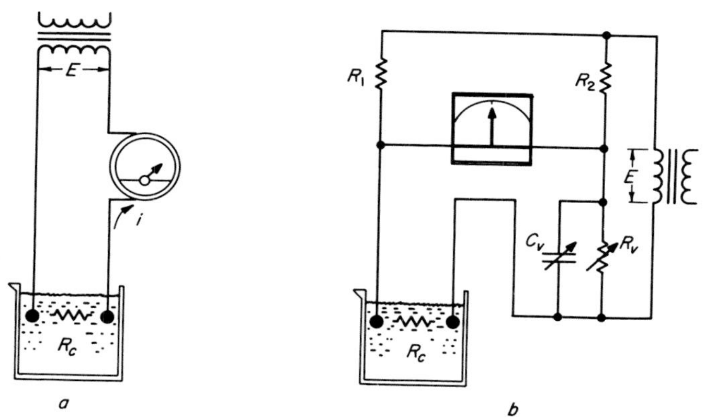

FIG. 18-2. Alternating Current Measuring Circuits. *a*, Direct reading instrument. *b*, Wheatstone bridge.

Direct-reading Instruments.—The simplest a.c. circuit for measuring conductance is shown in Fig. 18-2*a*. The applied voltage E is impressed across a series circuit containing the cell and an a.c. current meter or equivalent amplifier of negligible input resistance compared with the cell resistance R_c. The sources of the applied voltage might be a transformer winding at the output of an oscillator, or even a step down constant voltage transformer operating directly from the power line. Whatever method is used to generate the applied voltage, its output impedance should be low, so that the effective voltage applied across the cell and meter is effectively independent of changes in cell resistance. Under the above restrictions the current i flowing through the cell is limited entirely by the cell resistance and it follows from Ohm's law:

$$i = \left(\frac{1}{R_c}\right) E \qquad (4)$$

The meter reading is proportional to the current flowing in the cell and, therefore, to the conductance of the cell. Instruments of this type have the advantage of giving a continuous reading, and can be used to monitor changes in solution conductivity with time or serve as the nucleus of an automatic titrator. Disadvantages are that the accuracy of measurement depends on the linearity of the current measuring meter or amplifier and also the stability of E. With modern circuitry however, it is relatively simple to build direct-reading instruments accurate to 0.1 percent of the cell conductance. Circuit designs suitable for titration application have been described by several authors.[3]

Wheatstone Bridge.—The Wheatstone bridge is the classical circuit for determining solution conductance; a simple version is shown in Fig. 18-2*b*. The applied voltage is impressed across two resistance voltage dividers. One divider contains a precision resistance R_1, in series with the cell; the second divider contains a similar precision resistance R_2, in series with a variable resistance R_v. R_v is typically a precision decade resistance box and slide wire combination whose resistance value can be read directly. An a.c. null detector is connected between the midpoints of the two divider arms. The applied voltage will be distributed such that the voltage appearing at the midpoint of the divider arm containing R_c is $ER_c/(R_c + R_1)$, and the voltage at the similar point of the arm containing R_v is $ER_v/(R_v + R_2)$. If R_v is adjusted until no voltage appears across the midpoints as indicated by the null meter, then equating the two midpoint voltages gives the condition of balance

$$\frac{R_c}{R_c + R_1} = \frac{R_v}{R_v + R_2}$$

and

$$R_c = R_v \frac{R_1}{R_2} \qquad (5)$$

Knowing R_v, R_1, R_2, the value of R_c and, hence, the cell conductance may be obtained.

The bridge has the advantage that the accuracy of measurement is independent of E and the linearity of the null detector, and is dependent only on the accuracy of the precision resistors. This assumes of course that the point of balance can be accurately sensed by the null detector. A variety of sensitive null devices has been used; telephone receivers (for applied voltages in the audio frequency range), cathode ray oscilloscopes, a.c. galvanometers, and high gain a.c. amplifiers with meter or "magic eye" output have all been used successfully. A particularly sensitive and accurate bridge circuit is described by Jones and Josephs.[4] With their bridge, an accuracy of 0.001 percent in resistance measurements can be obtained.

With high resistance solutions, the capacity associated with the cell may prevent an accurate balance indication because of the phase shift introduced by a nonresistive component in the cell arm. Compensation and sensitive balance indication may largely be

[3] Calvin, D. W., and Propst, R. C., Anal. Chem., **32,** 1858, 1960; Reeben, V. A., Zh. Fiz. Khim., **35,** 934, 1961; Boardman, W., Chem. and Ind., 565, 1963; Goodwin, R. D., Anal. Chem., **25,** 263, 1953.

[4] Jones, G., and Josephs, R. C., J. Am. Chem. Soc., **42,** 1648, 1920.

restored by introducing a variable capacitor across R_v; R_v and C_v are then successively varied to achieve minimum signal at the null detector. When the detector reads zero, C_v will have introduced a phase shift in the reference bridge arm exactly equal to that caused by the cell capacity, and R_v will then be equal to the true cell resistance R_c. The principal disadvantage of bridge measurement is the necessity of manually rebalancing the bridge for each measurement. This can be time consuming in analytical work where many measurements must be made during the course of a single titration. Unfortunately, the more precise the bridge, the greater the complexity of the balancing operation.

DIRECT CURRENT METHODS

High Applied Voltage Measurements.—A direct measurement of solution conductance can be made using d.c., provided that the applied d.c. potential across the cell electrodes is very large compared with any polarization potential resulting from electrolysis. The circuit used is identical with the direct-reading a.c. circuit of Fig. 18-2*a* except for the substitution of a high voltage d.c. source and a d.c. current measuring device. If E_p is the net polarization potential in the cell, then:

$$i = \frac{E - E_p}{R_c} \tag{6}$$

E_p at platinum electrodes passing d.c. currents is variable depending on current density, stirring, and other parameters, but is typically of the order of 1–2 volts. E_p can be neglected for modest precision measurements, if E is greater than about 100 volts. The current through the cell, and, therefore, the meter reading, is proportional to the solution conductivity, as in the a.c. circuit. Unless the current is small and the duration of the measurement short, electrolysis may seriously change the composition of the solutions under test. The method is, therefore, practical only for measurements in very high resistance solutions where cell currents can be kept below the level of a few microamperes at the necessarily high supply voltage. The high voltage d.c. technique can be extremely useful for conductance measurements in nonaqueous solvents where cell capacity interferes with accurate measurements using a.c. instruments. Fuoss and Kraus[5] have applied the high voltage technique to measurements in low dielectric constant solvents such as dioxane and benzene.

Low voltage d.c. has been used for conductance measurements using electrochemically reversible electrodes instead of platinum.[6] In this case it is necessary that the ions to which the electrodes are reversible be present in the sample solution. This restriction, coupled with the fact that any complexing, oxidizing, or reducing agent which reacts with the components of the electrodes makes measurement impossible, seriously limits usefulness of the method.

Constant Current Measurements.—Many of the restrictions of other d.c. techniques have been overcome by Taylor and Furman.[7] The principal of their circuit is outlined in Fig. 18-3. A 500 d.c. voltage, E, is connected in series with a large resistor, R_1, a standard precision resistor, R_s, and the cell to which contact is made by two platinum electrodes. R_1 is chosen to be large compared with the total cell resistance R_t so that the cell current is independent of cell resistance and is equal to $E/(R_1 + R_s)$. Two rigidly mounted, identical, nonpolarizable electrodes are placed between the primary platinum electrodes and connected to a pH meter. The voltage indicated by the pH meter will be a constant fraction R_f/R_t of the total cell iR drop and, hence, proportional to the solu-

[5] Fuoss, R. M., and Kraus, C. A., J. Am. Chem. Soc., **55**, 21, 1933.
[6] Eastman, E. D., J. Am. Chem. Soc., **42**, 1648, 1920.
[7] Taylor, R. P., and Furman, N. H., Anal. Chem., **24**, 193, 1952.

tion resistance. Taylor and Furman used tungsten electrodes which are almost nonpolarizable in aqueous solution, but a number of other choices such as the common fiber junction calomel reference electrode could be used. Since no current is drawn by the pH meter, resistance in the liquid junction does not affect the pH meter reading or the measured cell resistance. In order to avoid changes in solution composition, a switch is provided which is closed only while making a measurement. Connecting the pH meter across the standard resistor permits calculating the cell current from the measured iR drop, should absolute resistance measurements be required. The method has as its chief advantage the fact that no specialized equipment is needed and relatively high conductance solutions may be handled (up to about 0.5 M sodium chloride). The accuracy of conductance measurement is equal to that of the direct-reading a.c. methods.

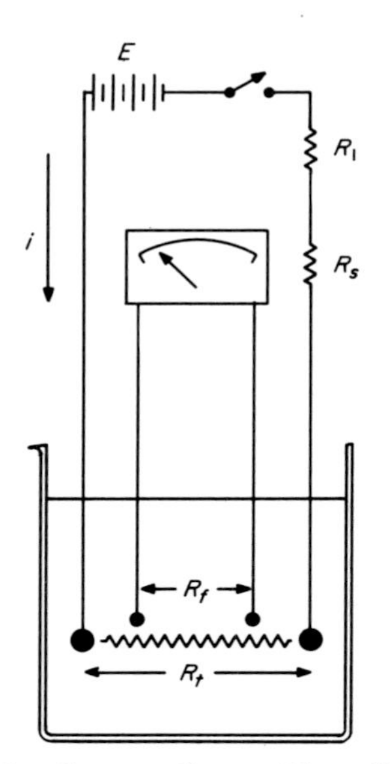

FIG. 18-3. Constant Current Direct Current Circuit.

MAGNETIC INDUCTION METHODS

It has already been pointed out that the chief difficulty in making conductance measurements is due to polarization at the electrode solution interface. Two methods are available which permit measurements without making direct contact with the solution; high frequency conductometry (discussed in a separate chapter) and

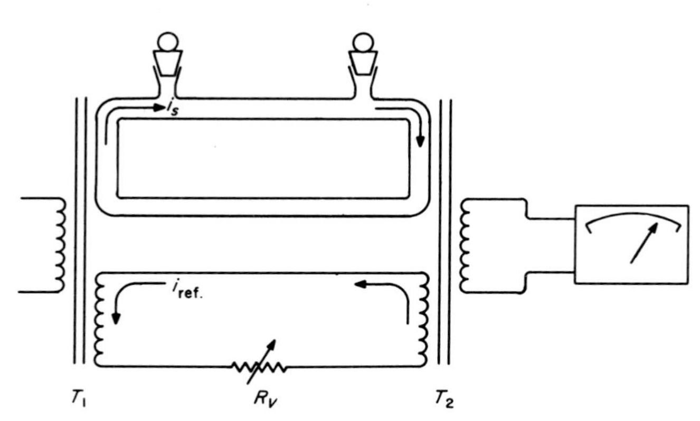

FIG. 18-4. Conductance Measurement by Magnetic Induction.

magnetic induction measurement. The principal of the magnetic induction method is illustrated in Fig. 18-4. A solution contained in an electrically-insulating glass or plastic tube connects the cores of two toroidal transformers T_1 and T_2, forming a single turn winding at each core. An a.c. audio frequency voltage is applied to the primary of transformer T_1 and the magnetic field produced in the core of T_1 in turn induces a current i_s in the solution winding. The magnitude of the current depends on the applied voltage, geometry, and on the conductance of the solution in the closed loop. The solution current in turn induces a magnetic field in T_2 which is detected as a signal across the terminals of the secondary winding of T_2. The detector meter reading is proportional to solution conductivity. The analogue of a Wheatstone bridge may be constructed by inducing a second electrical path containing resistor R_v connecting the two transformer cores. The magnetic field in T_2 produced by the current $i_{ref.}$ opposes that produced by the solution current, and a null indication at the detector may be obtained by adjusting R_v. At balance, R_v is then equal to the resistance of the solution path.

The theory of the magnetic induction method, together with cell designs, has been studied by Griffiths *et al.*[8] A suitable probe type electrode, which could be used for titrations, is shown in Fig. 18-5. The current induced by T_1 flows in the cylindrical hole through the probe and returns through a virtual short circuit provided by the external solution. The method is still quite new and very few applications to titrations have been attempted. Oliphant and Freund[9] have used a magnetic induction apparatus to titrate the alkalinity in sea water to 0.5 percent precision. Their work demonstrates that the technique is capable of high accuracy since this titration required measuring the small change in conductance produced by the neutralization of the small amount of bicarbonate in a high concentration of sodium chloride.

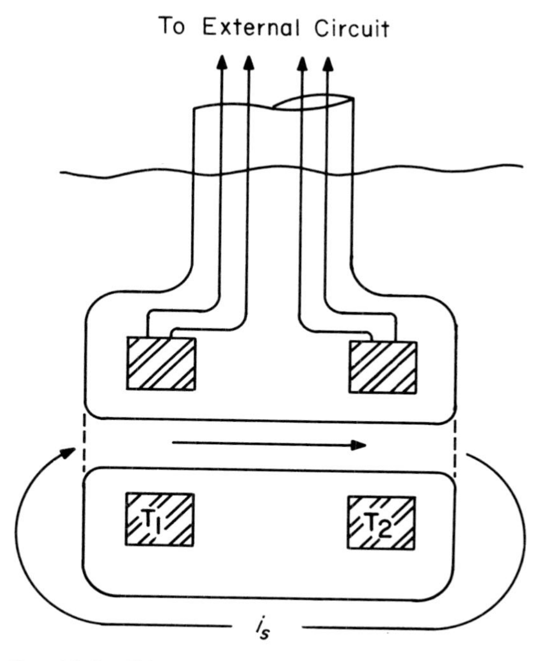

FIG. 18-5. Dipping Electrode Assembly for Magnetic Induction Conductance Measurement.

AUTOMATIC TITRATION

Any of the direct-reading d.c. or a.c. instruments can be combined with pen and ink recorders and motor driven syringe burets to function as automatic recording titrators. A considerable saving in titration time is possible since the end point can usually be read directly from the recorder chart, thereby eliminating the graphing of data points required by the manual instruments. Colvin and Propst[3] have described an automatic

[8] Griffiths, V. S., Talanta, **2,** 230, 1959; Anal. Chem. Acta, **18,** 174, 1958; Griffiths, V. S., and Stock, D. I., J. Phys. Chem., **62,** 47, 1958.

[9] Oliphant, M., and Freund, H., Anal. Chem., **35,** 1549, 1963.

recording titrator based on a direct-reading a.c. circuit with excellent linearity up to conductances of 10^5 mhos. Provision is made to expand any 50-mho range to occupy the full width of the recorder chart, permitting accurate titrations to be made where the change in conductance is small compared with the total conductance of the solution under test. Boardman[3] has designed a simple conductometric conversion unit consisting of an a.c. direct-reading circuit with a rectified output suitable for use with a pH meter feeding a commercial recording potentiometer.

COMMERCIAL INSTRUMENTS

A wide variety of measuring instruments is commercially available. The choice of a particular instrument obviously depends on the accuracy sought in a given titration. In this regard, sensitivity, *i.e.*, the ability to detect small changes in conductance, is more important than absolute accuracy. In most titrations, the ultimate precision is limited by the chemistry of the titration rather than by the instrument used. In favorable situations such as the strong acid–strong base titrations discussed in the next sections, a rough estimate of the required instrument sensitivity may be made. The instrument should be capable of discriminating at least that percent of the total conductance change in the titration as the percent accuracy sought in the end point determination. For example

TABLE 18-3. COMMERCIAL INSTRUMENTS

Model	*Frequency, c.p.s.*	*Total Range, µmhos*	*Sensitivity*	*Accuracy*	*Read Out*
Industrial Instruments, Inc. Cedar Grove, N. J.					
RC16B, Manual bridge	60, 1000	$0.4–5 \times 10^6$	0.3%	±1%	R, 1/R
RC18, Manual bridge	1000, 3000	$10–10^7$	0.01%	±0.1%	R
LKB Instruments, Inc. Washington, D. C.					
LKB3216, Manual bridge	1000, 2000	$10^3–10^6$	0.01%	±0.1%	R
LKB5300, Manual bridge with recorder output of cell resistance deviation from balance	2000	$10^2–10^7$ in three ranges	0.005%	±0.25%	R
Metrohm Ltd. (Brinkman Instruments, Inc.) *Great Neck, N. Y.*					
E365 Direct reading meter, recorder output	fixed	$0.1–3 \times 10^3$ in eight ranges	0.5% full scale	—	1/R
E382 Manual bridge	fixed	$1–10^5$	—	±1%	R
W. G. Pye and Co. Ltd. (The Ealing Corp., Cambridge, Mass.)					
11750 Direct reading meter, recorder output	fixed	0.1–100 one range	0.5% full scale	±3%	1/R
11700 Manual bridge	300, 5000	$0.1–10^4$	0.01%	±0.1%	1/R
Leeds and Northrup Co. Philadelphia, Pa.					
4866 Manual bridge	60	$0.1–1.2 \times 10^4$	0.5%	±1%	1/R, R
4666 Manual Jones bridge	50, 1000, 2000	$17–10^7$	0.001%	±0.01%	R
4958 Direct reading meter with recorder output	60	0–100 one range	0.5% full scale	±2%	1/R
Radiometer (The London Co., Westlake, Ohio)					
CDM2 Direct reading meter with recorder output	70, 3000	$0–5 \times 10^5$ in six ranges	0.5%	±0.5%	1/R
Arthur H. Thomas Co. Philadelphia, Pa.					
Serfass bridge, manual a.c. bridge	60, 1000	$1–10^6$	0.3%	±1%	R, 1/R
Wissenschaftlich-Technische-Werkstatten (Kahlsico Scientific Instruments Corp., San Diego, Calif.)					
WBR Manual bridge	1000	$1–5 \times 10^5$	0.001%	±0.02	R
LBR Manual bridge	60, 3000	$1–10^7$	0.3%		R, 1/R
LF3 Direct reading meter	60, 3000	$0.3–10^5$	0.05%	±1%	R, 1/R

if 1 percent precision is desired in a strong acid–strong base titration, where the total conductance change during the titration is 50 percent, then the instrument used should have a sensitivity of at least 0.5 percent.

The measurable conductance range of an instrument may be extended by at least a factor of 10 in either direction by choosing cells with cell constants of appropriate values. Most titrations in aqueous solutions are performed in the range of 10 to 10^5 mhos with cell constants of approximately 1.0.

Bridges with two voltage source frequencies are advantageous. Sensitivity of balance is improved in high conductance ranges if the higher frequency source is used, while measurement of low conductance solutions is facilitated with a lower frequency 50–60 c.p.s. source.

Table 18-3 gives a sampling of the conductance apparatus which is currently available in the U.S. Prices vary widely, from approximately $250 for the lower precision bridges and direct-reading instruments, to several thousand dollars for the more sophisticated bridges. Most of the manufacturers listed also supply cells, electrodes, and other associated equipment.

At the present time there does not appear to be a supplier of magnetic induction apparatus which can be conveniently used for titration. Industrial Instruments, Inc., however, does manufacture a power supply–detector unit which could be adapted to titration work by providing an appropriate probe electrode assembly.

TITRATION TECHNIQUE

Electrodes.—Probe electrode assemblies are most convenient for titrations. Figure 18-6 shows an arrangement consisting of two pieces of platinum foil sealed on opposite sides of a glass plate. Different cell constants are obtained by varying the area of the platinum foil to bring the cell resistance within the range of the measuring instrument. Many other configurations are possible. The only requirement is that the two platinum electrodes should be rigidly mounted so that their spacing does not change accidentally during the titration. Probe assemblies with protective glass shields surrounding the

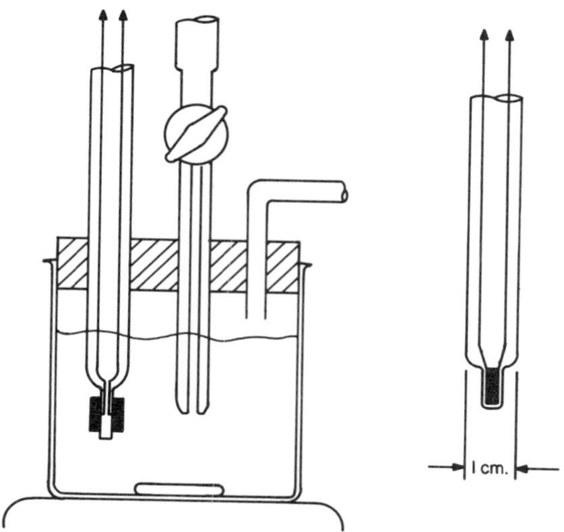

Fig. 18-6. Conductometric Titration Assembly.

electrodes are a nuisance in titrations because of the difficulty of obtaining rapid stirring inside the shield.

Most titrations can be performed with bright platinum electrodes. In systems where polarization is serious, some improvements in performance can be obtained by electroplating a platinum black coating on the electrode surfaces. This is simply done by immersing the electrode to be plated in a solution of potassium chloroplatinate, approximately 0.05 *M*, containing a trace of lead acetate together with a platinum foil anode. Connecting the electrodes to the terminals of a 1.5-volt dry cell for a few seconds results in the deposition of a grey coating of finely divided platinum on the cathode. The plating should not be continued past the point where the surface appears a dull grey to the eye, as too heavy a coating gives trouble from ion adsorption and adhesion of precipitates during titrations. When not in use, platinized electrodes should be stored in distilled water to prevent their drying out.

Cells.—Open beakers are most frequently used for titrations. Where oxygen, carbon dioxide, etc., must be excluded, it is an easy matter to provide a rubber stopper with holes to fit the buret tip, electrodes, and gas entry tubes as shown in Fig. 18-6.

Accurate measurement of absolute solution conductance cannot be made using dip type probe electrodes because the effective cell constant depends to some extent on the size of the solution container and the depth of immersion of the electrodes. Where absolute measurements are needed, a cell of the type shown in Fig. 18-7 should be used.

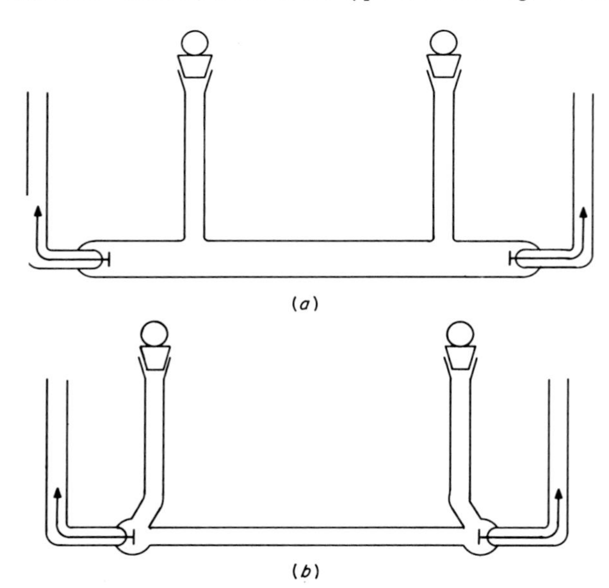

FIG. 18-7. Cells for Absolute Conductance Measurement. *a*, For medium conductance solutions. *b*, For high conductance solutions.

Other cell designs for accurate absolute work are discussed by Parker,[10] Jones and Bollinger,[11] and Shedlovsky.[12]

[10] Parker, H. C., J. Am. Chem. Soc., **45,** 1366, 2017, 1923.
[11] Jones, G., and Bollinger, J. Am. Chem. Soc., **53,** 411, 1931.
[12] Shedlovsky, T., J. Am. Chem. Soc., **52,** 1793, 1930.

Temperature Control.—For titration work all that is required is that the solution temperature remain constant to about 0.5°C. during the course of the titration. In most laboratories no precautions need be taken for elaborate thermostating. Where room temperature is subject to rapid fluctuation, or where there is a significant heat of reaction, as when concentrated acids are neutralized, it is usually sufficient to place the titration beaker in a large pan of water at ambient temperature.

If absolute conductance measurements are being made, either thermostating in an oil bath is necessary or some type of temperature compensation must be provided. Müller and Vogel[13] describe an apparatus for standardizing volumetric reagent solutions conductometrically; the apparatus includes a thermistor sensor and compensation circuit as an integral part of the bridge. Their apparatus permits standardization of reagents to an accuracy of 0.1 percent over a temperature range of 15°–35°C. without the need of thermostating the cell.

Burets.—Graphical determination of titration end points is considerably simplified if the assumption can be made that the solution volume does not change appreciably during the titration. For this reason it is desirable that the concentration of the titrant be at least ten times the concentration of the substance being determined and preferably much greater. Small volume burets capable of accurate reading are desirable. The many micrometer syringe burets available on the market are particularly suitable for conductometric work.

CONDUCTOMETRIC TITRATION CURVES

Strong Acid-Strong Base Titrations.—When a strong base is titrated with a more concentrated strong acid, the volume of the solution remains substantially constant, and the net effect of the neutralization reaction is simply to replace the OH^- ions originally present with an equivalent number of anions from the acid. The neutralization reaction goes essentially to completion so that during the course of the titration the OH^- concentration is decreasing in a linear manner with titrant volume, while the acid anion concentration is increasing linearly. The total ion concentration remains constant, but a change in solution conductance will be observed provided that the OH^- ion and the acid anion have different equivalent ion conductances. This will always be the case, since reference to Table 18-2 shows OH^- ion has an equivalent ion conductance greater than any other anion. Since the extent of anion replacement is proceeding in a linear fashion with titrant addition, it follows from Eq. (5) that the measured solutions conductance also varies linearly with acid additions. When the equivalence point is reached, the solution will have a conductance equal to that of the salt produced from the neutralization; further addition of the strong acid results in a linear increase in conductance due to the excess hydrogen ion and acid anion. The state of affairs during the titration is illustrated in Fig. 18-8 for the titration of 0.1 M sodium hydroxide with hydrochloric acid. The final titration curve of $1/R$ *vs.* the fraction titrated is obtained simply by summing the individual ion contributions to the conductance $z_i c_i \lambda_i$ at each point of the titration, and dividing the sum by the cell constant. The titration curve is seen to be composed of two straight line segments, which intersect at the titration equivalence point. In actual practice the equivalence point is determined by extrapolating the two straight lines defined by experimental conductance measurements in the regions before and after the end point. The titration of a strong acid with a strong base is the exact reverse of the example just discussed.

The precision of a strong acid–strong base titration depends on the acuteness of the

[13] Müller, R. H., and Vogel, A. M., Anal. Chem., **24,** 1590, 1952.

angle of intersection at the end point. This angle in turn depends to some extent on the nature of the acid anion, but as reference to Fig. 18-8 shows, the major change in conductance is due to changes in the concentrations of OH^- and H^+ and no great improvement in the angle of intersection will be expected if, for example, an acid with a lower

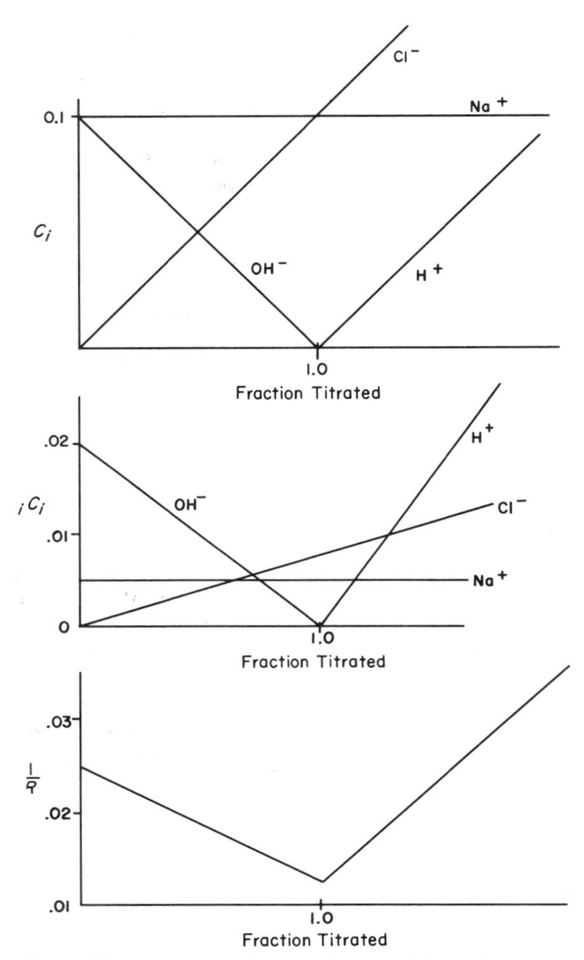

Fig. 18-8. Titration of 0.1 *M* NaOH with HCl. Cell constant 1.0.

mobility anion such as perchloric acid were used. The effects of varying the initial concentration of base and the amounts of foreign electrolytes are shown in Fig. 18-9, where the relative change in conductance rather than the absolute change in conductance is plotted *vs.* the fraction titrated. Clearly the addition of the foreign electrolyte, sodium chloride, acts adversely on the precision of end point determination. Interestingly, however, the dilution of the initial base has no effect on the shape of the relative change in conductance curve, making it possible to titrate dilute acids and bases with the same precision as more concentrated solutions. This is not true with potentiometric titration.

Kolthoff[14] and Dutoit[15,16] have shown that strong acids as dilute as 10^{-4} M may be titrated to a precision of 1 percent conductometrically, provided that carbon dioxide is excluded and carbonate free base is used. The ultimate limit is apparently set by the

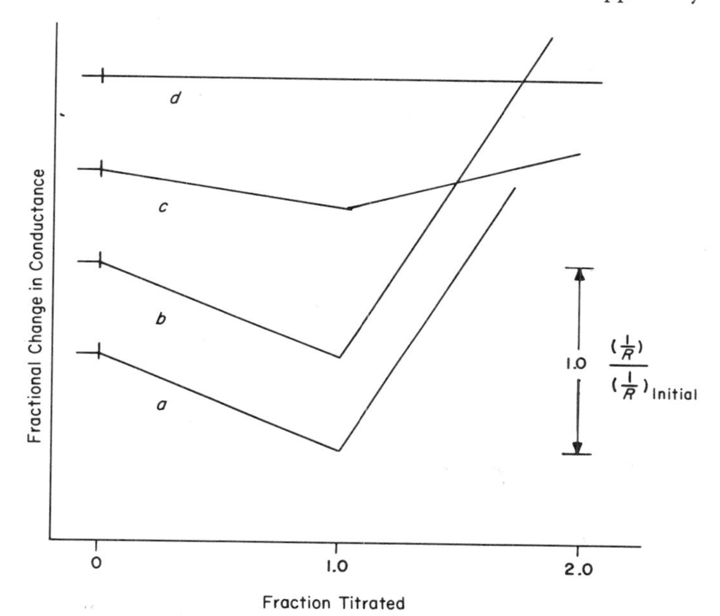

FIG. 18-9. Effect of Dilution and Foreign Electrolytes on the Titration of NaOH with HCl. *a*, 0.1 M NaOH. *b*, 0.01 M NaOH. *c*, 0.01 M NaOH + 0.1 M NaCl. *d*, 0.01 M NaOH + 1.0 M NaCl.

conductance of water itself whose specific conductance is about 0.06×10^{-6} mho cm.$^{-1}$ (2×10^{-6} mho cm.$^{-1}$ for equilibrium water). Correction for the contribution of the solvent conductance to acid-base titration curves is complicated due to the repression of the ionization of the solvent by the acids and bases present. Solvent corrections have been discussed by various authors,[17] but are usually not required for use in analytical work where the contribution of the solvent to the total conductance is negligible.

The effect of carbon dioxide on strong acid–strong base titrations was investigated by Poethke,[18] who found that, when using equilibrium water and a carbonate-free base, the presence of carbon dioxide did not affect the results when the acid was titrated with the base. The reverse titration was, however, subject to error.

Weak Acids and Bases.—Titration curves of weak acids with strong bases can be constructed by the same procedure as used in the preceding section, *i.e.*, by first determining the concentrations of all ions at each point in the titration and then summing the contribution of each ion to the total conductance. Figure 18-10 shows the result of this

[14] Kolthoff, I. M., Bull Soc. chim., France, **7**, 1, 1910.
[15] Dutoit, P., J. Chim. phys., **8**, 12, 1910.
[16] Dutoit, P., and Mojoiu, P. B., J. Chim. phys., **8**, 27, 1910.
[17] Kendall, A., J. Am. Chem. Soc., **38**, 1480, 2460, 1916; Washburn, B. W., J. Am. Chem. Soc., **40**, 110, 1918; Wynne-Jones, J. Phys. Chem., **31**, 1647, 1927.
[18] Poethke, W., Z. anal. Chem., **86**, 45, 1931.

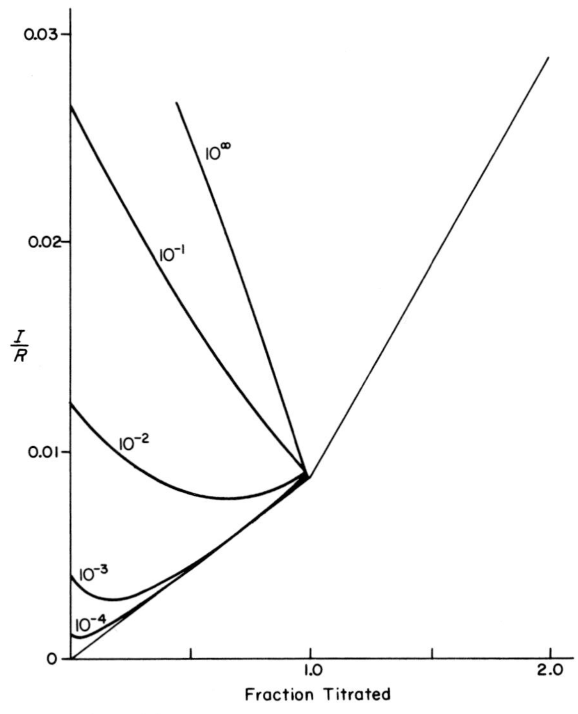

FIG. 18-10. Titration of 0.1 M Weak Acids with NaOH. Numbers on curves refer to values of the acid dissociation constant.

calculation made for a family of weak acids of variable dissociation constant, K, all at 0.1 M initial concentration, being titrated with a strong base. The conductance falls during the initial portion of the titration as H^+ is consumed, but then passes through a minimum and rises due to the repression of the dissociation,

$$HA \rightleftarrows H^+ + A^-$$

of the remaining acid by the acid anion A^-. Moderately strong acids with dissociation constants in the range of 10^{-2} to 10^{-3} are particularly difficult to titrate accurately with strong bases as their titration curves show pronounced curvature over the first half of the titration curve. With still weaker acids, K is in the range 10^{-5} to 10^{-10}, and the titration curves again approach straight lines as shown in Fig. 18-11. Further reduction in the acid dissociation constant, below approximately 10^{-10}, results in curvature near the equivalence point, due to the incompleteness of the neutralization reaction.

Acids in the moderately strong range of K equal to 10^{-1} to 10^{-4} can be handled successfully by a method discussed by Righellato and Davies.[19] Two aliquots of the sample are titrated separately, one with a strong base, the other with ammonia. In the ammonia titration the excess of undissociated reagent beyond the end point does not contribute to the solution conductance, and a horizontal titration curve results. When the two titration curves are superimposed, as shown in Fig. 18-12, it becomes possible to define

[19] Righellato, E. C., and Davies, C. W., Trans. Faraday Soc., **29**, 431, 1933.

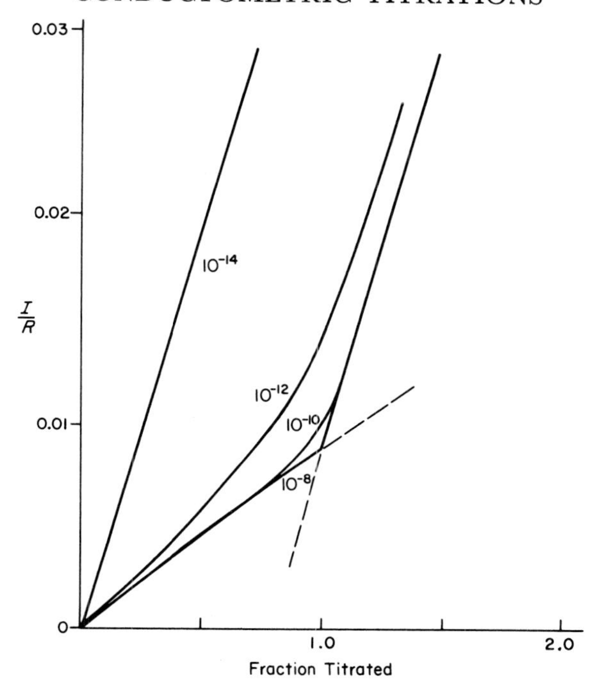

FIG. 18-11. Titration of 0.1 *M* Very Weak Acids with NaOH. Numbers on curves refer to values of the acid dissociation constant.

the end point as the intersection of the extrapolated straight line segments produced by the two excess bases. Since acids in this range of dissociation constant are easily titrated potentiometrically, the double titration technique is of value only for special situations; for example, where the presence of organic surface active material gives rise to sluggish response at the glass pH electrode.

Weak acids with dissociation constants in the range of 10^{-5} to 10^{-7} are usually titrated with ammonia in order to take advantage of the greater acuteness of the line intersections at the equivalence point. Dilute solutions of the weaker acids in this range may give trouble, due to curvature in the end point region and may require a strong base titrant. Kolthoff[20] has calculated that satisfactory titrations using ammonia are possible if the dissociation constant of the weak acid is greater than $6.7 \times 10^{-3}\ M$, where M is the initial molarity of the weak acid.

Titration of very weak acids with dissociation constants between 10^{-7} and 10^{-10} is possible if a strong base titrant is used. Kolthoff[20] for example was able to obtain good end points using sodium hydroxide to titrate phenols and boric acid with pKs on the order of 10. Such determinations of very weak acids are an example of an area where conductometric measurements offer a significant advantage over potentiometric end point determination. Since the conductometric end point is determined by extrapolation from measurements made at some distance from the equivalence point, considerable curvature of the titration curve can be tolerated. The requirements for completeness of the neutralization reaction are, therefore, much less stringent than for potentiometric

[20] Kolthoff, I. M., Z. anorg. Chem., **111**, 9, 28, 1920.

titrations, where acids with dissociation constants less than about 10^{-7} do not give discernible pH breaks at the equivalence point.

Gaslini and Nahum[21] have developed an indirect technique for titrating very weak acids and bases. In the case of a weak acid, excess ammonia is added to the sample, thereby converting the weak acid to its corresponding highly dissociated ammonium salt. The ammonium ion is then titrated with lithium hydroxide giving a much more distinct end point than would be obtained with a direct titration. A similar approach was used with weak bases. Adding excess acetic acid to a solution of a weak base followed by titration with trichloroacetic acid permits a determination of bases with dissociation constants as low as 10^{-12} with good precision.

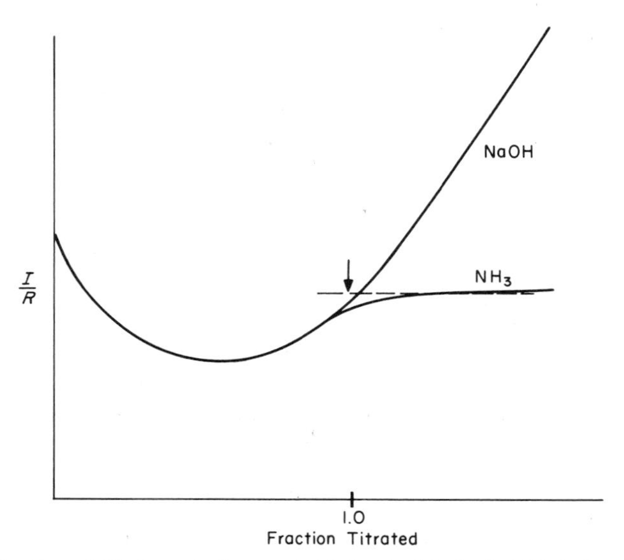

FIG. 18-12. Titration of Moderately Strong Acids by the Method of Righellato and Davies.

Grunwald[22] has treated mathematically the problem of locating end points from conductometric titrations curves where curvature in the equivalence point region due to incomplete reaction makes straight line extrapolation difficult. He suggests an alternative to the usual graphical extrapolation, as indicated in Fig. 18-13. The procedure consists in first determining a tentative end point by the usual extrapolation procedure. Three points, P_1, P_2, P_3, are then chosen such that two lie on the titration curve before the tentative end point and one lies beyond it. Fraction titrated values, f_1, f_2, f_3, are then computed for the three points and a fourth point P_4, is determined by calculating the value of f_4, from an equation which depends on the titration type. The formula for a strong acid–weak base or weak base–strong acid titration is

$$\frac{1 - f_2 f_1}{(1 - f_2)(1 - f_1)} = \frac{f_4 + f_3 - 2}{(f_3 - 1)(f_4 - 1)}$$

[21] Gaslini, F., and Nahum, L. Z., Anal. Chem., **31**, 989, 1959; **32**, 1027, 1960.
[22] Grunwald, E., Anal. Chem., **28**, 1112, 1956.

For weak acid–weak base titrations the appropriate equation is

$$\frac{f_2 + f_1 - 2f_1f_2}{(1 - f_2)(1 - f_1)} = \frac{f_4 + f_3 - 2}{(f_3 - 1)(f_4 - 1)}$$

Straight lines are then constructed by connecting P_2, P_1, and P_3, P_4, and the corrected end point is determined by the new intersection. Should even greater refinement be needed, the new equivalence point may be used to recalculate values of f_1, f_2, and f_3, and the process may be repeated in successive cycles. Convergence will be most rapid if the points are initially chosen to lie outside the range of greatest curvature.

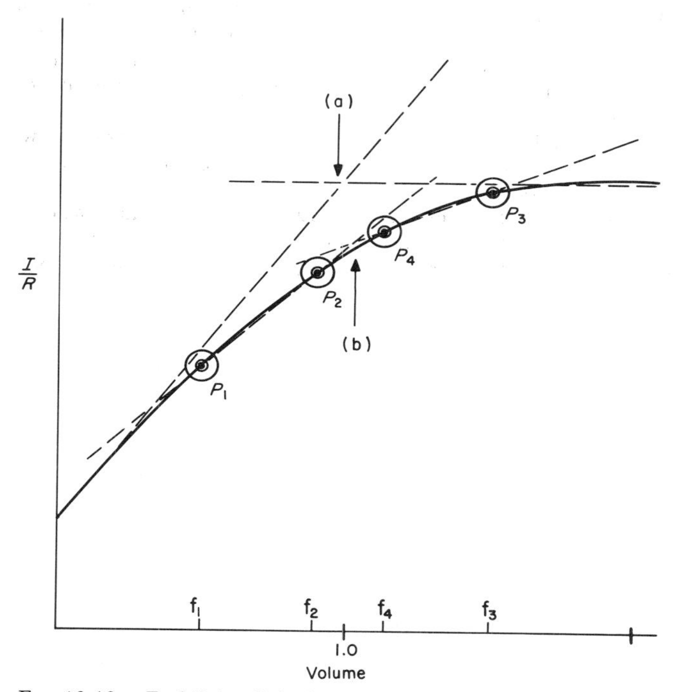

FIG. 18-13. End Point Calculation by the Method of Grunwald.

Polybasic Acids.—Separate end points from the stepwise neutralization of polybasic acids are rarely observed in conductometric titrations. The reason is that most anions have nearly the same equivalent ionic conductances, so that the various branches of the conductance titration curve have very nearly the same slope. Since most polybasic acids have stepwise dissociation constants sufficiently different in magnitude to provide measureable pH breaks at the various equivalence points, there would seem to be little value in using any method but potentiometric titration for these systems.

Mixtures of Acids.—Differentiating titrations of mixed acids suffer from the same problems outlined for the polybasic acid systems. Some special cases exist, however, where accurate titrations can be made.

Mixtures of strong acids with a weak acid, of a sufficiently low dissociation constant so that its titration curve would be substantially a straight line from the initial point if it were present alone, *i.e.*, a K of about 10^{-5} or less (see Fig. 18-10) show two sharp end points when titrated with either a strong base or a weak base.

Occasionally acid mixtures are encountered in which a weak base can be found which will neutralize the stronger acid, but is not sufficiently strong to neutralize the weaker acid appreciably. In this case the titration can be made to the first end point with the weak base and the remaining solution can be titrated with a strong base to an end point corresponding to neutralization of the weaker of the two acids. Righellato and Davies[19] used this technique to differentiate mandelic acid in the presence of the weaker acid, phenol, using pyridine as the weak base.

A mixture of a strong acid and a moderately strong acid with a dissociation constant in the range of 10^{-3} is difficult to perform potentiometrically. Righellato and Davies have shown how the titration may be made conductometrically. The total acidity is first determined as outlined previously under titrations of moderately weak acids. A second solution is prepared by adding sodium hydroxide in exactly equivalent amounts to the total acidity, as determined by the first titration. The solution which now contains the sodium salts of the two acids is back titrated with hydrochloric acid which reacts with the anion A^- of the moderately weak acid to form the undissociated acid. The end point for this reaction which gives the concentration of the weaker acid in the original mixture will be obscure due to curvature, but may be reconstructed by either the method of Grunwald described earlier, or by a graphical method due to the present authors. Figure 18-14 shows the titration curve for the back titration with hydrochloric acid. The

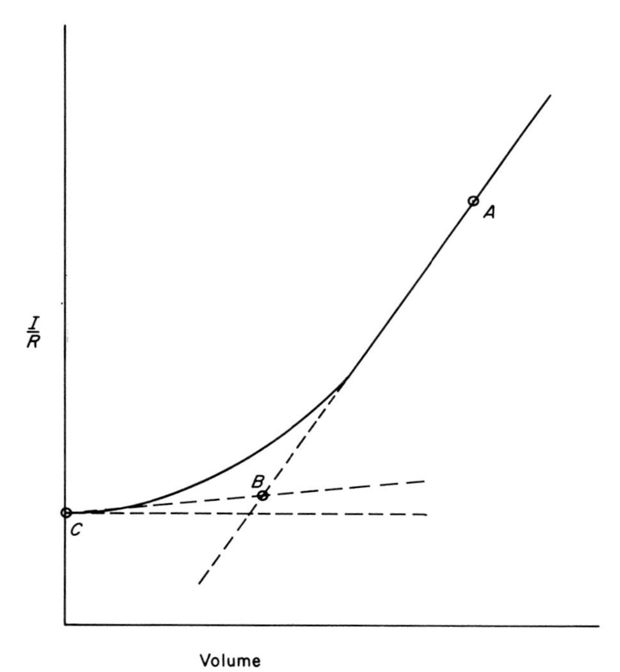

FIG. 18-14. Titration of a Weak Acid, Strong Acid Mixture by the Method of Righellato and Davies. The titration curve shown is the back titration with HCl.

slope of the final straight line portion AB of the titration curve is determined from the graph, and the slope of the constructed line BC is calculated from the relation,

$$\frac{\text{slope } AB}{\text{slope } BC} = \frac{\lambda H^+ + \lambda Cl^-}{\lambda Cl^- - \lambda A^-}$$

The intersection of the lines AB and BC defines the equivalence point for the weaker acid. The graphical method requires a fairly accurate estimation of λA^- but is somewhat simpler to perform than Grunwald's end point calculation.

Replacement Titrations.—Titration of salts of weak acids or bases may be performed with strong acids and bases respectively. The ion of the weak electrolyte is displaced from the corresponding salt by the strong acid (base). These so-called "replacement titrations" are in reality only titrations of weak acids and bases. The theory of the previous sections applies directly to these titrations as well; for example, the weak acid NH_4^+ ($K_A = 10^{-9}$) may be titrated in solutions of ammonium salts using strong bases.

Nonaqueous Acid-Base Titrations.—The usefulness of nonaqueous solvents in potentiometric titrations is well recognized, and makes possible titration of weaker acids and bases and differentiating titrations of mixtures which would be impossible in aqueous solution. In the case of conductometric titrations, however, the ability to work with extremely weak acids and bases in aqueous solution using the methods already outlined, coupled with the general conductometric problem of distinguishing successive neutralization end points for which nonaqueous media offer little advantage, somewhat restricts the practical use of nonaqueous media.

Should the sample already be in a nonaqueous solvent, conductometric titration is generally feasible using as titrant such reagents as alcoholic sodium hydroxide, perchloric acid, etc. In many cases conductometric measurement will give more rapid titrations than the glass electrode. Use of nonaqueous solvents is also dictated when the sought for constituent is water insoluble. Van Meurs and Dahmen[23] have titrated a large number of weak organic acids in methanol, dimethylformamide, and pyridine with good results using tetramethylammonium hydroxide and potassium methoxide in methanol-benzene and pyridine-benzene. In some cases differentiating titrations were possible. McCurdy and Galt[24] recommend a dioxane-formic acid solvent system for titration of mixtures of weak bases with perchloric acid. An interesting example of a titration requiring the use of a nonaqueous solvent is described by Higuchi and Rehm,[25] who successfully differentiated sulfuric and hydrochloric acids in anhydrous acetic acid, using lithium acetate in the same solvent as titrant.

Precipitation Titrations.—Generally, precipitation titrations are not as accurate as acid-base titrations when carried out conductometrically. The sharp end point characteristic of many acid-base titrations is due to the relatively high equivalent ionic conductances of H^+ and OH^-. The choice of a particular strong acid or base was usually immaterial in acid-base titrations, but in the case of precipitation titrations the nature of accompanying nonreacting ions in the titrating reagent may be critical. Additional considerations which limit precision are: the fact that many precipitation reactions are slow to reach equilibrium; coprecipitation may cause significant positive errors; and the precipitate may adhere to the electrode surfaces in amounts sufficient to change the effective cell constant. In spite of these difficulties it is still possible in most cases where stoichiometric precipitates are formed to choose conditions such that good end points may be obtained.

[23] van Meurs, N., and Dahmen, E. A. M. F., Anal. Chim. Acta., **19**, 64, 1958; **21**, 443, 1959.
[24] McCurdy, W. H., and Galt, J., Anal. Chem., **30**, 940, 1958.
[25] Higuchi, T., and Rehm, C. R., Anal. Chem., **27**, 408, 1955.

Precipitation titration curves are characterized by small initial slopes. While the precipitate is forming, the change in conductance is due to the relatively small differences in ionic conductances of the ions being replaced. After the end point the conductance will rise as excess electrolyte is added. The acuteness of the intersection at the end point will be increased if a titrant is selected whose cation has a low mobility where a cation is to be precipitated, or whose anion has a low mobility when an anion is to be precipitated. This choice will cause the conductance to decrease during the initial stages of the titration. The sharpness of the end point also depends on the slope of the conductance increase after the end point. Where several precipitating ions are available for a given determination, it is best to choose the ion with the greatest equivalent ionic conductance. Some rounding at the end point will be observed if the precipitate has a solubility sufficient to contribute measurably to the conductance. This curvature will be more pronounced at low concentration levels and may occasionally interfere with the end point extrapolation. Kolthoff[26] calculated that satisfactory titrations may be made where the solubility product of the precipitate is less than 5×10^{-5} at a sample concentration of 0.1 M, or 5×10^{-7} at a concentration of 0.01 M.

The technique of performing precipitation titrations differs in some respects from the procedure followed in acid-base titrations. Where sluggish equilibrium and excessive coprecipitation occurs, it is helpful to titrate at elevated temperatures, with the solution contained in a thermostated cell. Difficulties arising with moderately soluble precipitates are helped by addition of 10–30 percent alcohol or acetone to the titration solution. Occasionally supersaturated solutions are formed, as with barium sulfate. Equilibrium times in these systems can be improved if a suspension of the solid precipitate is added to the sample prior to the titration.

Complexometric Titrations.—Conductometric titrations based on complex formation reactions are similar to precipitation titrations in that the total conductance change is usually small. Complexation titrations are limited in scope because of the tendency of most metal ions to add ligands in a stepwise manner. Conductometric end point detection is restricted to the few cases where only one of the possible complex species is formed in the region before the equivalence point. Cyanide, for example, can be determined by titration with silver nitrate,[27] or mercuric perchlorate[28] with the formation of $[Ag(CN)_2]^-$ and $[Hg(CN)_4]^=$ respectively. Hall and coworkers[29] have studied EDTA titrations conductometrically and were able to determine accurately a large number of cations in dilute acetate buffer solutions which form stable EDTA complexes in the pH 5–6 range. Alkali earth ions could be determined with some sacrifice in precision by titrating in an excess of ammonia.

Oxidation-Reduction Titrations.—Although conductometric determination of end points in oxidation-reduction titrations is feasible, the technique offers no advantage over the potentiometric method using platinum indicator electrodes. Special attention must be given to solution acidity; too high a concentration obscures the conductance change unless a high precision bridge is used, while hydrolysis and precipitation of metal ions interfere at low acid concentrations. Simpson and Walter,[30] using an inexpensive a.c. bridge, showed that potassium dichromate could be used to titrate millimolar concentrations of ferrous and uranous ion to a precision of better than 1 percent. Ferrous ions and also iodide, bromide, and peroxide, could be titrated with potassium permanganate. The acid concentration in the solutions being titrated could range be-

[26] Kolthoff, I. M., Z. anal. Chem., **61,** 171, 1922.
[27] Kolthoff, I. M., Z. anal. Chem., **64,** 229, 1923.
[28] Kolthoff, I. M., Z. anal. Chem., **62,** 332, 1923.
[29] Hall, J. L., Gibson, J. A., Wilkinson, P. R., and Phillips, H. O., Anal. Chem., **26,** 1484, 1954.
[30] Walter, P. H. L., B.S. thesis, M.I.T., 1956.

tween 0.04 and 0.2 *M*. All the titration curves showed a pronounced linear decrease in conductance during the initial portion due to the replacement of H^+ in the solution via reactions such as:

$$14H^+ + 6Fe^{++} + Cr_2O_7^{=} \rightleftarrows 6Fe^{+++} + 2Cr^{+++} + 7H_2O$$

After the equivalence point the conductance increases slightly with addition of excess reagent.

APPLICATIONS OF CONDUCTOMETRIC TITRATIONS

Table 18-4 summarizes some of the more important conductometric titrations together with a brief indication of titration conditions where these might not be immediately obvious. Acid-base titrations have not been included since they were covered in some detail in the earlier sections. The type of titration is indicated by the symbol P for precipitation, C for complexometric, and OR for oxidation-reduction titrations. All the titrations may be performed to better than 1 percent precision using simple equipment under relatively ideal conditions. Where foreign electrolytes are present in high concentration in the sample, the expected precision will be lower, unless highly precise measuring equipment is available.

A number of conductometric methods have been included in other chapters of Standard Methods of Chemical Analysis. These are not titration procedures, but are based on conductance measurements. They are:

1. Chapter 42, Volume III, Air Pollutants.
   a. Determination of sulfur dioxide in air pollution studies
2. Chapter 48, Volume III, Natural Fats.
   a. Determination of soap in oil
3. Chapter 59, Volume III, Rubber and Rubber Products.
   a. Determination of accelerators in rubber
   b. Determination of total soap in latex
4. Chapter 48, Volume IIB, Water Analysis.
   a. Specific conductance of water, page 2425.
5. Chapter 64, Volume III, Determination of Water.
   a. In amines
   b. In grain
   c. In hydrogen fluoride
   d. In jute
   e. In paper
   f. In petroleum products
   g. In plastics
   h. In textiles

TABLE 18-4.

Substance Determined	*Reagent*	*Titration Type*	*Conditions*	*Reference*[a]
Inorganic				
Ag^+	NaCl, LiCl	P		(5)
	Na_2CrO_4	P		(6)
	$Li_2C_2O_4$	P		(6)
	H_2S (10^{-3} *M*)	P	Sample concentration 10^{-4} to 10^{-6} *M*. Precision 1–5%.	(11)
Al^{+++}	NaOH	P		(8)
Ba^{++}	Li_2SO_4	P		(5)
	Li_2CrO_4	P	30% ethanol.	(9)
Bi^{+++}	H_2S (10^{-3} *M*)	P	Sample concentration 10^{-4} to 10^{-6} *M*. Precision 1–5%.	(11)
Br^-	$AgNO_3$	P	Add ethanol for dilute samples.	(1)
Ca^{++}	Li_2SO_4	P	30% ethanol.	(5)
CN^-	$AgNO_3$	P		(1)
	$Hg(ClO_4)_2$	P		(2)
CNO^-	$AgNO_3$	P		(12), (13)
$CO_3^=$	$BaCl_2$	P		(14)
Cd^{++}	$Li_4Fe(CN)_6$	P		(7)
	EDTA	C	Dilute acetate buffer pH 5.	(3)
	H_2S (10^{-3} *M*)	P	Sample concentration 10^{-4} to 10^{-6} *M*. Precision 1–5%.	(11)
Cl^-	$AgNO_3$	P	Add ethanol for dilute samples.	(1)
	$Hg(ClO_4)_2$	P		(2)
Co^{++}	EDTA	C	Acetate buffer pH 5.	(3)
	$Li_3Fe(CN)_6$	P	Dilute acid solutions.	(7)
$CrO_4^=$	$BaCl_2$	P	Neutral solution.	(14)
$Cr_2O_7^=$	$Fe(NH_4)_2(SO_4)_2$	OR	0.05–0.2 *M*. H_2SO_4 solution.	(4)
Cu^{++}	$Ba(OH)_2$	P	Hot solution, excess $SO_4^=$ present.	(15)
F^-	$AlCl_3$	P	Dilute acetic acid.	(16)
	$La(CH_3COO)_3$	C	10% ethanol.	(17)
Fe^{++}	$K_2Cr_2O_7$	OR	0.05–0.1 *M* H_2SO_4.	(4)
	$KMnO_4$	OR	0.1 *M* H_2SO_4.	(4)
$Fe(CN)_6^{-3}$	$AgNO_3$	P		(1)
$Fe(CN)_6^{-4}$	$Pb(NO_3)_2$	P		(18)
	$ZnCl_2$	P	Neutral solution, 100°C.	(7)
Hg^{++}	H_2S (10^{-3} *M*)	P	Sample concentration 10^{-4} to 10^{-6} *M*.	(11)
I^-	$AgNO_3^-$	P		(1)
IO_3^-	HCl	OR	Neutral solution containing small excess of KI and $Na_2S_2O_3$.	
K^+	$NaB(C_6H_5)_4$	P		(19)
Mg^{++}	NaOH	P		(8)

TABLE 18-4 (cont.)

Substance Determined	*Reagent*	*Titration Type*	*Conditions*	*Reference*[a]
Inorganic (cont.)				
	EDTA	C	Dilute NH_3, buffer pH 10.	(3)
$MoO_4^{=}$	$Pb(NO_3)_2$	P	Neutral solution.	(20)
NO_3^-	Nitron in acetic acid.	P	Dilute acetic acid solution.	(22)
Ni^{++}	dimethylglyoxime in ethanol	P	Add excess DMG and back titrate. NH_3 buffer.	(29)
H_2O_2	$KMnO_4$	OR	0.05–0.1 M H_2SO_4.	(4)
PO_4^{-3}	$BiOClO_4$	P	0.3 M $HClO_4$ solution.	(21)
	$UO_2(CH_3COO)_2$	P	Dilute sodium acetate solution.	(32)
Pb^{++}	$Li_2C_2O_4$	P		(24)
	$K_4Fe(CN)_6$	P		(7)
	Na_2CrO_4	P		(6)
	H_2S (10^{-3} M)	P	10^{-4} to 10^{-6} M sample concentration. Precision 1–5%.	(11)
	EDTA	C	Dilute acetate buffer pH 5.	(3)
SCN^-	$AgNO_3$	P		(1)
	$Hg(ClO_4)_2$	P		(2)
$SO_4^{=}$	$Ba(CH_3COO)_2$ in 1% acetic acid	P	20% ethanol.	(24)
$S_2O_3^{=}$	$Pb(NO_3)_2$	P		(18)
$SeO_3^{=}$	$Pb(NO_3)_2$	P		(25)
	$AgNO_3$	P		(26)
$SeO_4^{=}$	$Pb(NO_3)_2$	P	5% ethanol.	(25)
	$AgNO_3$	P		(26)
Sr^{++}	EDTA	C	Dilute NH_3 buffer.	(3)
	$Li_2C_2O_4$	P		(23)
Tl^+	Na_2CrO_4	P		(6)
	$NaB(C_6H_5)_4$	P		(27)
	KSCN	P		(30)
UO^{++}	$KMnO_4$	OR	0.2–0.5 M H_2SO_4.	(4)
V^{+++}	$KMnO_4$	OR	Dilute H_2SO_4.	(4)
VO_3^-	$AgNO_3$	P		(31)
$WO_4^{=}$	$Pb(NO_3)_2$	P	Neutral solution.	(28)
Zn^{++}	NaOH	P	Dilute acid solution.	(8)
	EDTA	C	Dilute acetate buffer pH 5.	(3)
Organic Species				
benzoate	$Pb(NO_3)_2$	P		(18)
citrate	$Ba(CH_3COO)_2$	P	50% ethanol.	(14)
oxalate	$Pb(NO_3)_2$	P		(18)
	$Ba(CH_3COO)_2$	P	50% ethanol.	(14)
succinate	$Pb(NO_3)_2$	P		(18)
tartrate	$Pb(NO_3)_2$	P		(14)
	$Ba(CH_3COO)_2$	P	50% ethanol.	(18)

[a] Numbers refer to the following reference works:

(1) Kolthoff, I. M., Z. anal. Chem., **64,** 229, 1923.

TABLE 18-4 (cont.)

(2) Kolthoff, I. M., Z. anal. Chem., **62,** 332, 1923.
(3) Hall, J. L., Gibson, J. A., Wilkinson, P. R., and Phillips, H. O., Anal. Chem., **26,** 1484, 1954.
(4) Walter, P. H. L., B.S. thesis, M.I.T., 1956.
(5) Kolthoff, I. M., Z. anal. Chem., **62,** 1, 1923.
(6) Kolthoff, I. M., Z. anal. Chem., **62,** 97, 1923.
(7) Kolthoff, I. M., Z. anal. Chem., **62,** 209, 1923.
(8) Britton, H. T. S., Conductometric analysis, Chapman and Hall, Ltd., London, 1934.
(9) Kolthoff, I. M., Z. anal. Chem., **62,** 97, 1923.
(10) Gaslini, F., and Nahum, L. Z., anal. Chem., **31,** 989, 1959; **32,** 1027, 1960.
(11) Immig, H., and Jander, G., Z. Elektrochem., **43,** 207, 214, 1937.
(12) Pfundt, O., Z. angew. Chem., **46,** 218, 1933.
(13) Tilici, R. R., Z. anal. Chem., **99,** 415, 1934.
(14) Kolthoff, I. M., Z. anal. Chem., **64,** 433, 1923.
(15) Harned, H. S., J. Am. Chem. Soc., **39,** 256, 1917.
(16) Harms, J., and Jander, G., Z. Electrochem., **42,** 315, 1936.
(17) Kubota, H., and Surak, J., Anal. Chem., **31,** 283, 1959.
(18) Kolthoff, I. M., Z. anal. Chem. **61,** 399, 1922.
(19) Ruff, P., and Brotz, W., Z. anal. Chem., **133,** 241, 1951.
(20) Bye, J., Bull. soc. chim., France, **6,** 174, 1939.
(21) Harms, J., and Jander, G., Z. angew. Chem., **49,** 106, 1936.
(22) van Suchtelen, F. H. H., and Itano, A., J. Am. Chem. Soc., **36,** 1793, 1916.
(23) Kolthoff, I. M., Z. anal. Chem., **62,** 161, 1923.
(24) Kameda, T., and Kolthoff, I. M., Ind. Eng. Chem., Anal. Ed., **3,** 129, 1931.
(25) Tilici, R. R., Z. anal. Chem., **102,** 28, 1935.
(26) Ripan, R., and Tilici, R. R., Z. anal. Chem., **117,** 47, 1939.
(27) Wendlandt, W. W., Chemist-Analyst, **46,** 8, 1957.
(28) Rother, E., and Jander, G., Z. angew. Chem., **43,** 930, 1930.
(29) Boulad, J. H., J. Soc. Chem. Ind., **57,** 323, 1938.
(30) Rippan, R., and Popper, E., Gazz. chim. ital., **72,** 439, 1942.
(31) Britton, H. T. S., and Robinson, R. A., J. Chem. Soc., **135,** 2328, 1930.
(32) Chretien, A., and Kraft, J., Bull. soc. chim. France, **5,** 1399, 1938.

Chapter 19

POLAROGRAPHY

By Ward B. Schaap
Professor of Chemistry
Indiana University
Bloomington, Indiana

Polarography is that branch of voltammetry in which current-voltage relationships are obtained with an electrolysis cell in which one of the electrodes is a microelectrode, usually a dropping mercury electrode; the current-voltage relationships are then used to determine the identity or concentration of a species reacting at the microelectrode. The technique was first described by J. Heyrovsky in 1922.[1] Following the publication of its theoretical basis about 1935 to 1940,[2,3,4,5,6,7] interest in the method spread rapidly throughout the world.

Many excellent books, monographs, and review articles have been written concerning polarography. Notable among these are the two-volume reference work by I. M. Kolthoff and J. J. Lingane[8] and the volumes by G. W. C. Milner[9] and by J. Heyrovsky and J. Kuta.[10] Several books emphasizing more specialized or practical aspects of the subject have been written, including those by L. Meites,[11] M. von Stackelberg,[12] J. Heyrovsky,[13,14] P. Zuman,[15] and M. Březina and P. Zuman.[16] Comprehensive chapters on

[1] Heyrovsky, J., Chem. Listy, **16,** 256, 1922.
[2] Heyrovsky, J., "Polarographie," in Physik. Meth. der Anal. Chem., W. Böttger, Ed., Leipzig, 1936.
[3] Heyrovsky, J., and Ilkovic, D., Collection Czechoslov. Chem. Communs., **7,** 198, 1935.
[4] Ilkovic, D., Collection Czechoslov. Chem. Communs., **6,** 498, 1934.
[5] Ilkovic, D., Collection Czechoslov. Chem. Communs., **8,** 170, 1936.
[6] Kolthoff, I. M., and Lingane, J. J., Chem. Revs., **24,** 1, 1939.
[7] Lingane, J. J., J. Am. Chem. Soc., **61,** 2099, 1939.
[8] Kolthoff, I. M., and Lingane, J. J., Polarography, 2nd Ed., Interscience Publishers, New York, 1952.
[9] Milner, G. W. C., The Principles and Practice of Polarography and Other Voltammetric Processes, Longmans, Green, London, 1957.
[10] Heyrovsky, J., and Kuta, J., Základy Polarografie, Ceskoslovenski Akademie Ved, Prague, 1962.
[11] Meites, L., Polarographic Techniques, Interscience Publishers, New York, 1955.
[12] von Stackelberg, M., Polarographische Arbeitsmethoden, de Gruyter, Berlin, 1950.
[13] Heyrovsky, J., in Berl, W. G., Ed., Physical Methods in Chemical Analysis, Vol. II, Academic Press, New York, 1951.
[14] Heyrovsky, J., Polarographisches Praktikum, Springer-Verlag, Berlin, 1948.
[15] Zuman, P., Organic Polarographic Analysis, Pergamon-Macmillan, New York, 1964.
[16] Březina, M., and Zuman, P., Polarography in Medicine, Biochemistry and Pharmacy, Interscience Publishers, New York, 1958.

polarography include those by Lingane,[17] Delahay,[18] Meites,[19,20] Heyrovsky,[13] and Müller.[21] Reviews of current research are published biennially in Analytical Chemistry by D. Hume and by S. Wawzonek.

In this chapter those aspects of polarography that are important to its utilization as a quantitative method are emphasized. Sufficient theory is included to make the discussion understandable to the nonspecialist. Recent innovations in instrumentation and methodology are discussed. Further and more detailed information on most aspects of the subject may be obtained from the references cited.

CURRENT-VOLTAGE RELATIONSHIPS

The analytical applications of polarography arise through the use of a small-area microelectrode in an electrolysis cell. If one of the electrodes in the cell is a reversible electrode of relatively large area, not readily polarized, while the other is a polarizable microelectrode, then the potential of the microelectrode, *vs.* the larger electrode, will vary according to the external voltage applied to the cell, and the current flowing through the cell will be limited by whatever reactions occur at the microelectrode. The microelectrode may, therefore, be said to be acting as an "indicator" electrode.

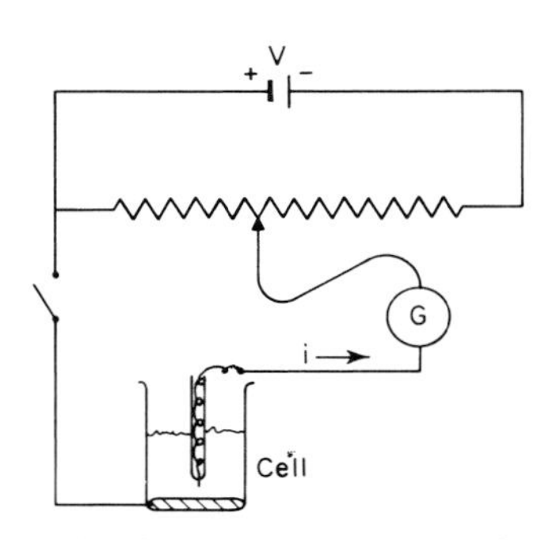

Fig. 19-1. Schematic Diagram of Apparatus Suitable for Obtaining Current-voltage Curves.

Consider, as an example, the electroreduction of a solution containing 1.0 *M* potassium chloride and 10^{-4} *M* thallium(I) chloride in a cell in which the anode is a mercury pool of large area in contact with the solution, and the cathode is a platinum wire not greater than several square millimeters in area. Suppose also that a variable voltage can be impressed across the cell from an external source, V, and that the current, i, flowing through the cell can be measured with a galvanometer, G. Such a set up is shown in Fig. 19-1.

Because there is no thallium metal present initially, there is no cell reaction that can occur spontaneously. However, an electrolysis reaction can be forced to proceed whenever the voltage applied to the cell exceeds the reversible potential (back e.m.f.) of a possible cell reaction.

Of the various reactions possible in the above cell, that with the smallest reversible potential, which will be the first to have its potential exceeded by the voltage applied to the cell, involves the electrodeposition of thallium and the oxidation of mercury:

[17] Lingane, J. J., Electroanalytical Chemistry, 2nd Ed., Interscience Publishers, New York, 1958.

[18] Delahay, P., New Instrumental Methods in Electrochemistry, Interscience Publishers, New York, 1954.

[19] Meites, L., Ed., Handbook of Analytical Chemistry, McGraw-Hill, New York, 1963, Sec. 5, pp. 5–38.

[20] Meites, L., "Voltammetry at the D.M.E. (Polarography)," in Kolthoff, I. M., and Elving, P. J., Eds., Treatise on Analytical Chemistry, Interscience Publishers, New York, 1963, Part I, Vol. 4, Chapter 46.

[21] Müller, O. H., "Polarography," in Weissberger, A., Ed., Physical Methods of Organic Chemistry, 3rd Ed., Part IV, Vol. I., Interscience Publishers, New York, 1960.

At cathode: $Tl^+ + e^- = Tl$ $\qquad E^0 = -0.336$ volts
At anode: $Hg + Cl^- = \frac{1}{2}Hg_2Cl_2 + e^-$ $\qquad E^0 = +0.268$ volts
Overall cell: $Tl^+ + Cl^- + Hg = Tl + \frac{1}{2}Hg_2Cl_2$ $\qquad E^0_{cell} = -0.604$ volts

If the actual concentrations are taken into account, the applied potential at which thallium will begin to be deposited can be calculated approximately (assuming activity coefficients are equal to one) by means of the Nernst equation written for the cell reaction, *i.e.*,

$$E_{cell} = -0.604 - 0.0591 \log \frac{1}{[Tl^+][Cl^-]} \quad (1)$$

$$E_{cell} = -0.604 - 0.0591 \log \frac{1}{10^{-4}} = -0.840 \text{ volts} \quad (2)$$

At this applied potential, a thin layer of thallium on the surface of the platinum electrode will be in equilibrium with thallium(I) ions at a concentration of 10^{-4} *M* at the surface of the electrode. If the applied voltage is now increased by 0.0591 volts, *i.e.*, the cathode (microelectrode) voltage is changed to −0.899 volts *vs.* the mercury pool anode, current will flow due to deposition of thallium on the electrode and the thallium(I) ion concentration at the electrode surface will decrease tenfold to 10^{-5} *M*. Similarly, if the applied potential is increased another 0.0591 volts (cathode potential = −0.958 volts), the equilibrium concentration of thallium(I) ion at the electrode surface will have decreased to 1 percent of its original value, and so on.

Consider now what would happen if an applied voltage of −0.958 volts were instantaneously applied to the cell (by closing the switch) and the solution were unstirred. A large resistance-limited current would flow at the instant electrical contact was made, but this would decrease rapidly as the thallium(I) ion concentration at the electrode surface decreased to its equilibrium value (at this potential) of 10^{-6} *M*. A more gradually decreasing cell current (no longer limited by resistance) would then be observed as thallium(I) ions from the bulk of the solution moved toward the electrode to relieve the concentration gradient caused by the deposition of thallium from the solution adjacent to the electrode surface. The current-time relationship of the cell current is shown in Fig. 19-2. Application of a still more negative potential after an appreciable time would change the current very little, since the concentration of unreduced thallium ions at the electrode surface is already only 1 percent of the original concentration. The current flowing is now limited by diffusion to the electrode surface.

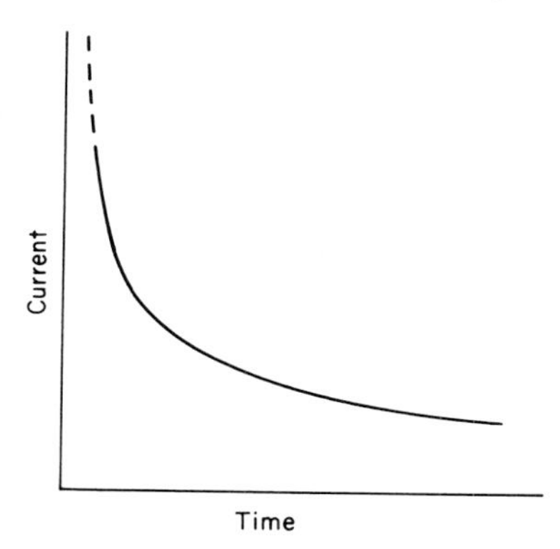

FIG. 19-2. Current-time Relationship Following Instantaneous Application of Electrolysis Voltage.

In general, there are three mass-transfer processes by which a reacting species may be brought to an electrode surface. These are: (1) *diffusion* under the influence of a concentration gradient; (2) *migration* of charged ions in an electrical field; and (3) *convection* due to motion (stirring) of the solution or the electrode. In polarography, the effect of migration is usually eliminated by adding a 50- or 100-fold excess of an inert "supporting electrolyte" salt, the ions of which migrate to relieve the electric fields, and convection may be minimized by using unstirred vibration-free solutions. Under such conditions, the limiting current is controlled solely by diffusion of the reacting species through the concentration gradient adjacent to the electrode.

According to Fick's law, the net rate of diffusion of a species to a unit area of electrode surface at any time is proportional to the magnitude of the concentration gradient, *i.e.*,

$$\text{flux} = -D\left(\frac{\partial C}{\partial x}\right)_{x=0} \tag{3}$$

where the flux is expressed as moles cm.$^{-2}$sec.$^{-1}$, and the proportionality constant, D (the diffusion coefficient), has units of cm.^{2}sec.$^{-1}$. Using the simplest model, as proposed by Nernst, which assumes a constant gradient of concentration, Fick's law becomes

$$\text{flux} = -D\frac{\Delta C}{\Delta x} = -D\frac{C_{\text{bulk}} - C_{x=0}}{\delta} \tag{4}$$

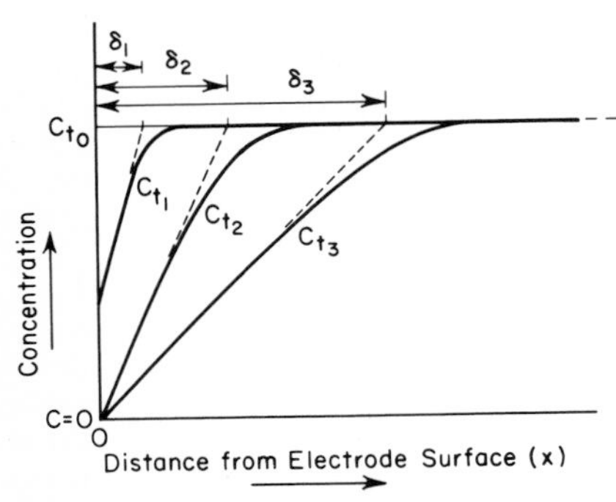

FIG. 19-3. Concentration Profiles for Reacting Species at Various Times after the Start of Electrolysis. ($C_{t_0} = C_{\text{bulk}}$; $t_3 > t_2 > t_1$; t_0 = before electrolysis; δ_i refers to thickness of the Nernst diffusion layer at time t_i.)

where δ is the thickness of the Nernst diffusion layer (see Fig. 19-3). When the potential of the electrode is set at such a value that the concentration of the reacting species at equilibrium at its surface is negligible in comparison to the concentration in the bulk of the solution, then $C_{x=0} \rightleftarrows 0$ and

$$\text{flux} = -DC_{\text{bulk}}/\delta \tag{5}$$

Expressing the flux in terms of electrical current density, i/A (amperes cm.$^{-2}$), the diffusion limited current is given by

$$i_{\text{lim}} = nFADC_{\text{bulk}}/\delta \tag{6}$$

showing that the limiting current is proportional to concentration and inversely proportional to δ, the thickness of the diffusion layer. Because δ increases with time, the limiting current to a stationary electrode decreases with increasing time, as illustrated in Fig. 19-2.

If the voltage applied to the above cell is not applied instantaneously, but is increased slowly and linearly through the region of discharge of thallium, the very large, resistance-limited current surge is avoided. In this case, the deposition begins gradually and a hump-shaped current-voltage curve is observed. The height of the hump (or peak) is proportional to the square root of the scanning rate and, in the limit of fast scanning rates, would approach the current observed when the circuit was closed instantaneously. Again, the diffusion-limited current decreases with time because of the build-up of the diffusion layer.

Current-voltage curves with several types of microelectrodes are shown in Fig. 19-4. All are typical of curves obtained with voltage scanning rates in the range 100–500 millivolts per minute. Curve A was obtained with a stationary gold wire microelectrode, and represents approximately the case described above.

Curve B in Fig. 19-4 was recorded using a rotating platinum microelectrode. In this case, the electrode is rotated rapidly through the solution so that the diffusion layer, δ, cannot increase in thickness, but remains constant and very thin. Under such conditions a larger constant limiting current is observed which depends upon both convection (rate of stirring) and diffusion, and which does *not* decrease with time.

Curve *C* was obtained with a dropping mercury microelectrode. This electrode consists of tiny mercury drops issuing out of a very small-bore capillary. The current oscilla-

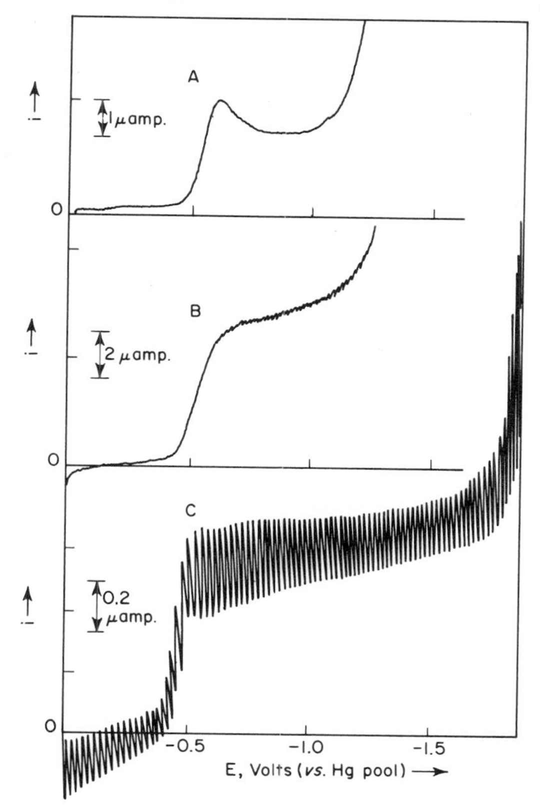

FIG. 19-4. Qualitative Comparison of Current-voltage Curves Recorded for 10^{-4} *M* Tl^+ in 1 *M* KCl with Various Types of Electrodes. Curve A, gold wire electrode (mercury coated; scanning rate = 500 mv. min.$^{-1}$); Curve B, rotating platinum wire electrode (600 r.p.m.); Curve C, dropping mercury electrode.

tions are due to the growth and fall of successive mercury drops. Note that a constant limiting current is attained, indicating that the growth of the drops offsets the effect of a widening diffusion layer. The dropping mercury electrode is the most important microelectrode for analytical purposes, and is discussed in detail below.

THE DROPPING MERCURY ELECTRODE

CHARACTERISTICS

The most commonly used type of microelectrode is the dropping mercury electrode (D.M.E.). This electrode consists of small mercury drops issuing from the orifice of a glass capillary and possesses several unique and useful advantages:

(1) During the growth of each drop, the increase in area of the drop and the outward movement of its surface more than compensate for the tendency, observed with the stationary electrode, to exhibit a decreasing current with time. At a constant applied potential, a steady average current, which is easily measured and is proportional to the concentration of the reacting species, may be observed for successive drops.
(2) Each successive mercury drop presents new surface at which the electrochemical reaction takes place. There is, therefore, no accumulation of products of the electrode reaction and, in the absence of vibration and stirring, each drop exhibits a remarkably reproducible current-time relationship at constant applied voltage. Because the reaction products and the diffusion layer are reproduced with each drop, a sudden change in applied potential is followed by a change in current to a new steady value with the succeeding drop.
(3) The high overvoltage for the discharge of hydrogen on a mercury surface allows the mercury electrode to be used at voltages considerably cathodic to the reversible potential of hydrogen discharge.

The characteristics of the growing mercury drop that can affect the magnitude of the current flowing are the rate at which its surface area increases and the maximum size it attains just before falling. These characteristics are expressed in terms of the rate of flow of mercury through the capillary, m (mg. sec.$^{-1}$), and the length of time the drop grows before falling, the "drop time," τ (sec.).

Curve *C* of Fig. 19-4 is a typical current-voltage curve recorded with a dropping mercury microelectrode. The reproducibility of the pen excursions is striking, and indicates the high degree of reproducibility in the growth and size of the drops. The current oscillates between a near-zero value, just after a drop falls, to a maximum value just before the next drop falls. Usually no attempt is made to follow or to record the entire current excursion, but rather a somewhat damped system is used to indicate the average current flowing during the life of the drop. The average current (averaged over the life of the drop) has been shown to be equal to $\frac{6}{7}$ of the maximum current flowing just before the drop falls.

The increase in current at the center of Curve *C* is the so-called "polarographic wave," and is typical of a cathodic wave arising from a reversibly reduced species. The most important characteristics of the wave are its height, *i.e.*, the magnitude of its diffusion-limited current, and its potential. The analytical applications of D.M.E. polarography are based on the measurement of these parameters, and are discussed in detail in later sections.

Voltage Range of the D.M.E.—The useful voltage range of the D.M.E. is limited in the cathodic direction by the discharge of hydrogen or of the cation of the supporting electrolyte present. In molar hydrochloric acid solution the limit is about -1.2 volts *vs.* the S.C.E., at which point hydrogen begins to be discharged. In neutral or alkaline solutions of alkali metal salts, the negative limit is changed to about -2.0 volts, the potential at which the alkali metal ions begin to be reduced to give amalgams. The most negative potentials are attainable in alkaline solutions in which quaternary ammonium salts or bases are used as supporting electrolytes. The limit in the presence of the tetramethylammonium cation is nearly -2.5 volts *vs.* the S.C.E., and with tetra-*n*-butylammonium hydroxide, the limit is about -2.7 volts.

The D.M.E. has a serious disadvantage in that mercury is relatively easily oxidized and is much more limited in its voltage range in the positive direction than are the more noble metals, such as platinum and gold. The potential at which the anodic dissolution of mercury begins depends upon the identity and concentration of other substances present in the solution. The most positive potentials, about $+0.3$ volts *vs.* the S.C.E., are attainable in the presence of noncomplexing anions that form soluble mercurous and mercuric salts, *e.g.*, nitrate or perchlorate ions. The anodic dissolution occurs more readily, *i.e.*, at less positive potentials, in the presence of anions that form insoluble mercury salts or stable complexes. The more insoluble the salt, or the more stable the complex, the less positive will be the potential at which the mercury of the D.M.E. is oxidized. The positive limit of the D.M.E. voltage range becomes progressively more negative as the supporting electrolyte anion is changed from chloride to bromide to iodide. In the presence of molar sodium cyanide, the oxidation of mercury proceeds at potentials more positive than -0.7 volt *vs.* the S.C.E. The standard electrode potential of the Hg/Hg_2X_2 couple can be used to estimate the approximate positive limit of potential for the D.M.E. in the presence of the anion, X^-.

The Charging Current.—Important features of the current-voltage curve obtained with a D.M.E. (Curve *C*, Fig. 19-4) that should be noted are the appreciable current that flows before the wave and the changing slope of the curve before and after the wave. Even when no reducible species is present in solution, an appreciable current flows because of the charging of the double layer at the surface of each growing mercury drop. This current has been called the "condenser" or "charging" current, and is the principal factor limiting the sensitivity of polarography and its accuracy at low concentrations.

The observed current flowing in a polarographic cell is the sum of the faradaic current, i_f, which arises from the oxidation or reduction reaction occurring at the D.M.E., and the charging current, i_c, *i.e.*, $i_{\text{total}} = i_f + i_c$. Because the analytical applications of polarography are usually related to the faradaic current alone, the separate estimation of each of these is an important problem. At concentrations of electroactive species of 10^{-3} *M* or greater, the charging current is negligible and may be ignored. At concentrations on the order of 10^{-4} *M*, the charging current is an appreciable fraction of the total current and a correction for it must be made. At concentrations around 10^{-5} *M*, the charging current is usually larger than the faradaic current and the precision of the polarographic determination depends principally on how precisely the contribution of the charging current can be estimated, compensated, or eliminated at the potential at which the diffusion current is measured. Because it is difficult to measure small faradaic currents precisely in the presence of larger charging currents, the useful range of conventional polarography is limited to concentrations of 10^{-5} *M* or greater. If special instrumental techniques are used to eliminate or compensate for residual current, as discussed below, the useful range of polarography can be extended to about 10^{-7} *M*.

The charging current may be understood in terms of the "electrocapillary curve" for mercury. If one measures the surface tension of mercury (or the drop times of a D.M.E.), as a function of applied voltage, and plots the data, the resulting curve has the shape of an inverted parabola, as seen in Fig. 19-5. In 0.1 *M* aqueous chloride, nitrate, or perchlorate solutions, and in the absence of oxygen and other reducible impurities, the maximum surface tension and maximum drop time occur at about -0.53 volts *vs.* the S.C.E. At this point the mercury surface is uncharged with respect to the solution, changing from positive to negative at this potential. When the mercury surface is charged, the repulsion between the charges decreases the surface energy and decreases the maximum size to which the drops grow before falling.

The charges at the mercury surface are induced by the ions or dipoles in the solution at the mercury-solution interface. For example, adsorption of negative ions or dipoles on the drop induces positive "image" charges at the inside surface of the drop by repelling electrons away from the drop and toward the mercury in the reservoir. This process is repeated as each drop grows and, if the potential of the D.M.E. is maintained constant, an anodic current will flow indefinitely. If the circuit is opened after the D.M.E. has been shorted to an S.C.E., the potential of the D.M.E. and reservoir will shift in the negative direction until the anion adsorption is just counteracted by the negative charge built up on the mercury. The potential at this point will correspond to the electrocapillary maximum (e.c.m.) for that solution (maximum drop time and surface tension), and the charging current will have decreased to zero.

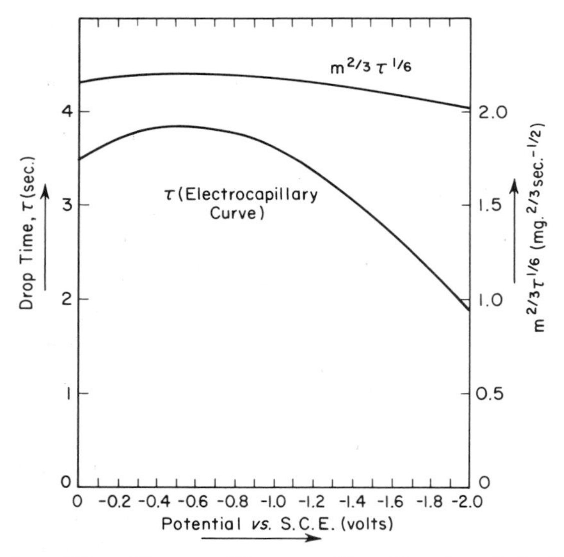

FIG. 19-5. Variation of Drop Time, τ, (Electrocapillary Curve) and of $m^{2/3}\tau^{1/6}$ as Functions of Potential for a Typical D.M.E. Capillary in a Solution Containing 0.1 *M* Potassium Nitrate.

The stronger the forces of attraction between the anion or dipole and mercury, the more negative will be the potential of the electrocapillary maximum. For example, the potentials of the e.c.m. in 1 *M* solution of chloride, bromide, iodide, and sulfide have been observed[8] to be -0.58, -0.67, -0.84, and -0.94 volts, *vs.* the S.C.E., respectively. Anions or molecules, inorganic or organic, which adsorb on mercury are said to be "capillary active." Such substances alter the potential of the e.c.m., and affect the amount of residual current flowing at potentials at which they are adsorbed. Adsorption or desorption of capillary active species is accompanied by a change in the charging current, and such processes may be detected by these means.[22]

The growing mercury drop with its adsorbed double layer acts as a capacitor which increases in area. At the potential of the electrocapillary maximum, $E_{\text{e.c.m.}}$, the surface is uncharged and the situation is analogous to an uncharged capacitor of capacity, c. The total charge, Q, on a mercury drop at any one instant is then seen to be

$$Q = cA(E_{\text{e.c.m.}} - E) \tag{7}$$

where: c is the capacity of the surface per unit area;
A is the area at any time, t; and
$E_{\text{e.c.m.}} - E$ is the difference between the applied potential and $E_{\text{e.c.m.}}$, the potential of zero charge.

[22] Breyer, B., and Bauer, H., Alternating Current Polarography and Tensammetry, Interscience Publishers, New York, 1963.

The capacity current, $(i_c)_t$, flowing at any instant to charge the mercury drop capacitor is equal to the derivative dQ/dt, *i.e.*,

$$(i_c)_t = \frac{dQ}{dt} = c(E_{\text{e.c.m.}} - E)\frac{dA}{dt} \tag{8}$$

in which it is assumed that the applied voltage does not change appreciably during the life of one drop. For a growing, spherical mercury drop issuing from a capillary it can be shown[8,18] that

$$\frac{dA}{dt} = 0.0057m^{2/3}t^{-1/3}\text{cm.}^2\text{sec.}^{-1} \tag{9}$$

and

$$(i_c)_t = 0.0057m^{2/3}t^{-1/3}c(E_{\text{e.c.m.}} - E) \tag{10}$$

in which $(i_c)_t$ is the current in microamperes, and c is the capacity expressed in microfarads per square centimeter. If the capacity current is averaged over the life of the drop (τ = drop time), the expression for the average capacity current in microamperes is

$$\bar{i}_c = 0.0085cm^{2/3}\tau^{-1/3}(E_{\text{e.c.m.}} - E) \tag{11}$$

It is important to note that the capacity current *decreases* with time, t, during the life of a single drop ($\propto t^{-1/3}$) and also decreases with increasing drop time, τ. This contrasts with the faradaic current, which *increases* with time ($\propto t^{1/6}$) during the life of a single drop, and also with drop time, τ. It has, therefore, been suggested that current measurements be made near the end of the drop time in order to minimize the effects of the charging current. This principle has been utilized in the Selector Tast-Polarograph produced by Atlas-Werke AG of Bremen, West Germany.

The capacity of a mercury surface in dilute aqueous chloride or nitrate solutions has been measured and found to be about 44 microfarads per square centimeter on the positive side of the electrocapillary maximum (e.c.m.) and about half that value, or 22 μf. cm.$^{-2}$, on the negative side. Consequently, the slope of the residual current curve after the e.c.m. is about half of what it is before the e.c.m. In the presence of a reducible ion, the slope of the current-voltage curve may become zero, or even negative, at potentials more negative than the wave. This is because the more rapid drop times at these potentials decrease the faradaic current significantly. Actually, the residual current should increase with decreasing drop time, but this may be overshadowed by the decrease in faradaic current if the faradaic current is larger than the charging current.

Because the slope of the charging current curve is not linear with changing voltage, and because a change in drop time affects the charging current and the faradaic current differently, estimation of residual currents by extrapolation techniques are inaccurate and questionable at low concentrations. Methods for correcting for residual currents are discussed below.

THEORY OF POLAROGRAPHIC WAVES

THE DIFFUSION CURRENT

The problem of calculating the polarographic diffusion current in terms of the characteristics of the diffusing species and those of the growing mercury drops will probably never be solved exactly, though increasingly accurate approximate solutions have been proposed.

The first solution to the problem was derived by Ilkovic[4,5,23] and later by MacGillavry

[23] Ilkovic, D., J. chim. phys., **35**, 129, 1938.

and Rideal,[24] using a more rigorous treatment. This solution, which has come to be known as the Ilkovic equation, is usually written in one of the following forms, the first of which is the expression for the instantaneous current (in microamperes) flowing at any time, t; the second is the expression for the average current flowing during the life of a drop of "drop time" equal to τ seconds, and the third is the expression for the maximum value of the current.

$$i_t = 709nCD^{1/2}m^{2/3}t^{1/6} \tag{12}$$

$$i_{\text{ave}} = 607nCD^{1/2}m^{2/3}\tau^{1/6} \tag{13}$$

$$i_{\text{max}} = 709nCD^{1/2}m^{2/3}\tau^{1/6} \tag{14}$$

In each equation n is the number of equivalents per mole of electrode reaction, C is the concentration of electroactive substance in millimoles per liter, D is its diffusion coefficient in cm.^{2} sec.$^{-1}$, m is the mass rate of flow of mercury through the capillary in mg. sec.$^{-1}$, and τ is the drop time in seconds.

Lingane[25] suggested rearranging Eq. (13) and defining a *diffusion current constant*, I, such that

$$I = i_d/Cm^{2/3}\tau^{1/6} = 607nD^{1/2} \tag{15}$$

For a given ion under fixed conditions of temperature and solution composition, I should be constant and should be independent of capillary characteristics. Values of I have been reported for many ions in various media.[11,19] For drop times between 2 and 8 seconds and with carefully reproduced conditions, such as supporting electrolyte concentration, maximum suppressor concentration, and the potential at which i_d is measured, published values of I may be used to evaluate C within ± 3 to 5 percent.[20] It is usually preferable, from the standpoint of precision, to evaluate I in one's own laboratory.

Although many experimental studies have shown I to be very nearly constant for drop times between 2 and 8 seconds, careful experimental studies by Meites[20,26] have shown that I increases markedly at drop times shorter than 2 seconds. The increase is attributed to stirring of the solution around the rapidly forming drops. With drops of normal size, drop times less than 2 seconds should not be used for analytical purposes. (There is evidence, however, that faster drop times can be used if the drop size is much smaller.[27])

The original Ilkovic equation is a very good, though approximate, solution to the problem of diffusion to an expanding spherical electrode. The equation is dimensionally equivalent to the case of diffusion to an expanding *p'anar* electrode, with an approximate constant factor added to account for curvature. Actually, the sphericity of the diffusion layer cannot be accounted for exactly with a constant, dimensionless factor, and thus the original Ilkovic equation does not express the exactly correct dependence of i_d upon electrode characteristics.

Lingane and Loveridge[28] and, independently, Strehlow and von Stackelberg[29] derived a more dimensionally correct modification of the diffusion equation, and since then even more rigorous derivations have been attempted.[30,31,32,33] The consensus of these derivations is that a more nearly correct equation is

[24] MacGillavry, D., and Rideal, E. K., Rec. trav. chim., **56,** 1013, 1937.
[25] Lingane, J. J., Ind. Eng. Chem., Anal. Ed., **15,** 583, 1943.
[26] Meites, L., J. Am. Chem. Soc., **73,** 1581, 3724, 1951.
[27] Smoler, I., J. Electroanal. Chem., **6,** 465, 1963.
[28] Lingane, J. J., and Loveridge, B. A., J. Am. Chem. Soc., **72,** 438, 1950.
[29] Strehlow, H., and von Stackelberg, M., Z. Elektrochem., **54,** 51, 1950.
[30] Koutecky, J., Ceskos, cas. fys., **2,** 117, 1952.
[31] Koutecky, J., and von Stackelberg, M., in Zuman, P., and Kolthoff, I. M., Eds., Progress in Polarography, Interscience Publishers, New York, 1962, Vol. I, p. 21.
[32] Markowitz, J., and Elving, P., J. Am. Chem. Soc., **81,** 3518, 1959.
[33] Matsuda, H., Bull. Chem. Soc. Japan, **26,** 342, 1953.

$$i_d = 607nD^{1/2}Cm^{2/3}\tau^{1/6}(1 + 34D^{1/2}\tau^{1/6}/m^{1/3}) \quad (16)$$

Careful experimental studies by Meites[26] have shown that this modified equation correctly expresses the dependence of i_d upon m and τ within experimental error. For typical values of D, m, and τ, the last term is on the order of 5 to 10 percent of the first term. Equation (16) should be used whenever maximum precision is desired for comparison of results using different capillaries and for calculation of the diffusion coefficient, D. In this case, the modified diffusion current constant is

$$I' = i_d/Cm^{2/3}\tau^{1/6}(1 + 34D^{1/2}\tau^{1/6}/m^{1/3}) = 607nD^{1/2} \quad (17)$$

For analytical applications of polarography, the original Ilkovic equation is still the most widely used. Its errors tend to cancel in practical applications and it is much more convenient. In this connection it is important to note that, regardless of which equation is used, (13) or (16), the diffusion current is directly proportional to concentration, other factors being constant.

FACTORS AFFECTING THE DIFFUSION CURRENT

The original and modified Ilkovic equations give the dependence of the diffusion current upon experimental parameters, which in turn depend upon the composition of the solution, temperature, potential of the electrode, etc. The diffusion coefficient, D, varies with the viscosity of the medium[34] and with the size and charge of the diffusing species. These properties, in turn, vary with the identity of the solvent, the composition of the solution, and with the temperature. With aqueous solutions, the viscosity of the solution may change appreciably when the concentration of dissolved solute exceeds 0.1 M.[35] In addition, the presence of molecules or anions which interact with the electroactive species, *e.g.*, via complex formation, may alter the composition and size of the diffusing species and change its diffusion coefficient. This effect is readily apparent in the case of metal ions in solutions containing large complex-forming anions, such as citrate, tartrate, malonate, etc. The relationship between i_d and C, or the value of I, should be considered constant only for a given composition of solution and should be redetermined, or at least verified, if the solution composition is changed appreciably.

Of the various factors in the Ilkovic equation, that which is most strongly temperature dependent is D, the diffusion coefficient, which has a temperature coefficient of about +2 percent deg.$^{-1}$ for most ions. The temperature dependencies of C, m and τ are much less and may be neglected in comparison. In order that the temperature factor may not cause an error of more than 1 percent, it is necessary to control the temperature to at least ±0.5 degree.[8] For currents controlled by kinetic or catalytic processes, rather than by diffusion, much higher temperature coefficients may be observed.

The Ilkovic and the modified Ilkovic equations predict the dependence of i_d upon m and τ. The mass of mercury flowing through the capillary per second, m, is directly proportional to h_{cor}, the corrected or effective height of the mercury level in the reservoir above the capillary tip, *i.e.*,

$$m = k'h_{cor} \quad (18)$$

where[20]

$$h_{cor} \cong h_{Hg} - 4.31\sigma(d/m\tau)^{1/3} \cong h_{Hg} - 3.1(m\tau)^{-1/3} \quad (19)$$

In Eq. (19), h_{Hg} is the measured height of the mercury level in the reservoir above the capillary tip in cm., d_{Hg} is the density of mercury and σ is its surface tension. Although σ is a function of potential, as discussed previously, it is usually sufficiently accurate to

[34] Lingane, J. J., Anal. Chem., **21**, 45, 1949.
[35] Schaap, W. B., Laitinen, H. A., and Bailar, J. C., J. Am. Chem. Soc., **76**, 5868, 1954.

use an average value for σ (400 dynes cm.$^{-1}$) in the calculation of h_{cor}. For typical values of h_{Hg}, m, and τ, the last term in the equation amounts to about a 5 to 10 percent correction, and is by no means negligible. This term, $3.1(m\tau)^{-1/3}$, expresses the correction for changing drop size with changing potential, assuming an average value of the surface tension. It is usually called "back pressure," and arises because the growth of the drop is resisted by the surface tension, the effect of which is greatest at small drop radii, for which the surface to volume ratio is greatest.

The drop time, τ, varies inversely with h_{cor}; thus, the net dependence of i_d upon the corrected height of the mercury column is

$$i_d = km^{2/3}\tau^{1/6} \cong k(k'h_{cor})^{2/3}(k''/h_{cor})^{1/6} \cong k'''h_{cor}^{1/2} \quad (20)$$

The square root dependence of i_d upon h_{cor} is valid only for diffusion controlled processes and constitutes a valuable test for distinguishing such processes from adsorption or kinetic-controlled processes.

The variation of drop time, τ, with applied potential in 0.1 *M* potassium chloride solution is shown in Fig. 19-5. The drop times change markedly with potential, decreasing by about a factor of 2 between the potential of the electrocapillary maximum and -2.0 volts. In contrast, the value of m is at a minimum at the e.c.m. and increases at both more positive and more negative potentials.[20] In this case, however, the proportionate change is small, amounting to less than 1 percent between 0.0 and -1.5 volts (*vs.* S.C.E.). For this reason, most workers measure m at only one potential and use this value, together with drop times measured at a series of potentials, to evaluate $m^{2/3}\tau^{1/6}$ for their capillaries. A plot of this quantity as function of potential is also shown in Fig. 19-5. In quantitative applications, the measurement of the diffusion current should always be made at the same potential in order to minimize the effect of the potential on m and τ. Also, values of m and τ should be measured at some specified potential and reported for each capillary used.

DEPARTURES FROM DIFFUSION-LIMITED CURRENTS

The discussion in the previous section, including the Ilkovic and modified Ilkovic equations, applies to polarographic currents that are limited by the diffusion of the electroactive species to the surface of the drop. A number of situations exist in which the cell current differs in magnitude or characteristics from a diffusion-limited current. It is important to recognize these, for the proportionality between diffusion current and concentration may not be realized in these situations.

Polarographic Maxima.[8]—Polarographic maxima are frequently observed when using a dropping mercury electrode, and are recognized by the appearance of a sharp peak or a rounded hump at the top of the polarographic wave. Usually the current will fall to the diffusion-limited value at potentials more negative than those encompassed by the maximum, but this may not be so if a second wave closely follows the wave exhibiting the maximum.[11] During the maximum, a surprising situation exists in which more ions or molecules are reacting at the electrode than can reach the electrode surface by diffusion through an unstirred solution. Direct, visual observation of the surface of the D.M.E. during a maximum has shown that there is "streaming" of the solution past the electrode.[8,36] Thus, the motion of the solution brings more electroactive species into contact with the electrode surface than would be the case if the solution were unstirred. The causes of the streaming and the reasons why it is observed only in the cases of certain species are not yet fully understood.[8]

A polarographic maximum can frequently be suppressed by adding to the solution a

[36] Antweiler, H. J., Z. Elektrochem., **43,** 596, 1937; **44,** 719, 831, 888, 1938.

capillary active substance which will adsorb on the mercury surface at the potential of the maximum. Recommended maximum suppressors and their maximum concentrations, as given by Meites,[11,20] are gelatin ($\leq 0.005\%$), Triton X-100 ($\leq 0.002\%$), methyl red ($\leq 0.0004\%$). The concentrations listed are usually ample to suppress maxima. Higher concentrations of suppressor may seriously affect i_d or the potential of the wave, and should not be used without careful testing.[37] Frequently, maxima that exist with species at concentrations $\geq 10^{-3}$ M will vanish at concentrations on the order of 10^{-4} M or lower.

Nonadditive and Mixed Currents.—When more than one electrode reaction occurs at the D.M.E., there is a possibility that the products of one of the reactions may interfere with the reacting species of the other. An example of such an interference is encountered if one attempts to obtain a polarogram using a neutral, unbuffered solution containing both cadmium and iodate ions.[8] If these ions are run separately, cadmium exhibits a reversible wave at -0.6 volts (*vs.* S.C.E.) and iodate gives a well-developed wave at about -1.2 volts. If these ions are run in the same solution, the cadmium wave is observed at -0.6 volts as before, but the second wave at -1.2 volts does not attain a total height equal to the sum of the waves run separately. (If thallium is substituted for cadmium, the total height of the second wave becomes equal to the sum of the separate individual waves.)

The nonadditivity of the waves in the mixed solution was studied in detail by Lingane and attributed to the precipitation of cadmium hydroxide in the vicinity of the drop due to reaction with the hydroxide ions liberated at the electrode surface as a result of the reduction of iodate in an unbuffered solution, *i.e.*,

$$IO_3^- + 3H_2O + 6e^- \rightleftarrows I^- + 6OH^-$$
$$3Cd^{++} + 6OH^- \rightleftarrows 3Cd(OH)_2 \downarrow$$

A study of this anomalous reaction by Schaap and Wildman,[38] using radioactive cadmium-115 tracer in order to separate the current due to the reduction of cadmium from that arising from iodate, showed that the activity in the amalgam (arising from reduction of radioactive cadmium-115 ions into the drop) increased at -0.6 volts in proportion to the polarographic current, but decreased to a small value at the potential of the iodate wave. The results show that the reduction current due to cadmium decreases during the iodate wave, and they suggest that Lingane's explanation is correct.

Lingane and coworkers have found other examples in which the production of OH^-, $S^=$, $Se^=$, and $Te^=$, as a result of an electrode reaction at the D.M.E., can interfere with the diffusion current for metal ions which form insoluble precipitates with these anions.[8]

Apparently anomalous currents can also be observed in situations where both anodic and cathodic reactions can occur at the same potential and tend to compensate each other.[8] Examples of these have been observed with sulfide ion and oxygen in basic solutions, with cyanide ion together with oxygen, and with tin(II) and copper(II) ions in tartrate medium. In each case the first-named species gives rise to an anodic current which tends to compensate the cathodic current arising from the reduction of the second species. Frequently, errors due to compensating currents can be avoided by proper choice of the potential at which i_d is measured.

Currents from Irreversible Waves: Kinetic and Catalytic Currents.—A wide variety of common ionic or molecular species do not reduce at the D.M.E. at their thermodynamic, reversible potentials, but exhibit overpotentials (or overvoltages) of varying magnitudes at a mercury surface. Examples of such species include most of the common

[37] Schmid, R. W., and Reilley, C. N., J. Am. Chem. Soc., **80,** 2087, 1958.

[38] Schaap, W. B., and Wildman, E., Proceedings, Sixth Conf. on Anal. Chem. in Nuclear Reactor Technology, U.S.A.E.C. Document TID-7655, 1963, p. 302.

inorganic oxy-anions, *e.g.*, nitrate, sulfate, perchlorate, peroxide, etc., molecules such as O_2, CO_2, and N_2, and most organic substances. In these cases the polarographic wave, if it is observed at all, is always irreversible. Nevertheless, in some cases the limiting current may still be diffusion controlled at potentials considerably beyond the half-wave potential if the reaction rate is not too slow. The theory of irreversible waves is discussed in the next section.

Kinetic Currents.—Some polarographic reactions have been observed in which the actual transfer of electrons at the electrode surface, *i.e.*, the charge transfer process, is preceded by a chemical reaction as well as by diffusion. If the transfer of electrons is sufficiently rapid, then the limiting current depends upon the rates of the other two processes and, if the chemical reaction is also rapid, the current may again be diffusion controlled, or nearly so. On the other hand, if the chemical reaction is slow, the current will be limited by the rate of this reaction and is called a *kinetic* current.

Examples of substances which produce kinetic currents are the undissociated forms of certain keto acids, such as pyruvic and phenylglyoxalic acid, and many of the reducing sugars, such as glucose, galactose, xylose, and dextrose. At intermediate pH values, solutions of the keto acids exhibit two waves, the first resulting from the reduction of the undissociated acid, and the second from reduction of the anion. The relative heights of the waves do not correspond to the relative concentrations of the undissociated acid and anion species in solution. The first wave is higher than expected because of the protonation of the anion in the immediate vicinity of the electrode to produce additional undissociated acid. The height of the first wave is, therefore, not diffusion limited, but is limited by the rate of the association reaction. In such cases the height of the first wave will be independent of the height of the mercury column, whereas the combined heights of the first and second waves will be proportional to the square root of the corrected column height.

In the case of the reducing sugars, a single wave is observed, the height of which is much less than would be predicted for a diffusion-controlled process. Actually, the current is controlled by the rate of the reaction by which the nonreducible form of the sugar is converted to the reducible form, which is then immediately reduced at the electrode, *i.e.*,

$$\underset{\text{(nonreducible)}}{\text{Sugar}} \underset{\text{(slow)}}{\xrightarrow{k}} \underset{\text{(reducible)}}{\text{Sugar}'} \underset{\text{(fast)}}{\longrightarrow} \text{Electrode Products}$$

Again, the height of the wave is independent of the height of the mercury column.

Temperature coefficients of kinetic currents are usually at least 5 to 10 times greater than the temperature coefficient of diffusion-limited currents. Kinetic currents are difficult to utilize for quantitative determinations and they do not have important applications in practical polarography. They are, however, useful in physical chemical studies of certain reactions, and the practical polarographer should be able to recognize and identify these situations whenever they are encountered.

Catalytic Currents.—In the case of *catalytic* currents, important practical applications do exist. In a catalytic electrode process, the species consumed in the primary electron transfer reaction at the electrode surface is regenerated by reacting chemically with a nonelectroactive substance in the solution immediately surrounding the electrode, and so is capable of reacting again and again at the electrode. The species involved in the primary electron transfer thus serves as a catalyst (C) to effect the reaction of the normally nonelectroactive substance (N). The reaction sequence may be written

$$C + e^- \rightarrow C_r$$
$$N + C_r \rightarrow N_r + C$$
$$C + e^- \rightarrow C_r, \text{ etc.}$$

If the reaction between N and the reduced form of the catalyst, C_r, is very rapid, then a small amount of catalyst will suffice to react with N as fast as the latter diffuses to the electrode. The overall reaction can then be limited by the diffusion of the normally non-electroactive substance, N, to the electrode, and will be suitable for the determination of N. An example of this application is the polarographic determination of nitrate ion in the presence of catalytic amounts of uranyl or molybdate ions.[39] In this type of application, the concentration of the catalyst and the rate of its reaction with N must be sufficient to effect complete reaction with N as fast as the latter diffuses to the electrode.

In the other type of application of catalytic waves, either the ratio of concentrations, C/N, is too low, or the rate of the reaction between N and C_r is too slow for all the N in the immediate vicinity of the electrode to react. The limiting current is then dependent on the concentration of the catalyst, C, but the magnitude of the current can be much larger than that expected from only the diffusion of the catalyst to the electrode. The method is useful for the determination of the catalytic species at extremely low concentrations. Examples include the detection and determination of micromolar concentrations of vanadate or molybdate in the presence of excess peroxide.[40] The reduction of tungstate and iron(III) ions also catalyzes the reduction of peroxide at potentials more positive than the normal peroxide wave, but with these ions the reaction rate is rather slow so that the increase in current and the sensitivity are not so great.[8,40]

Certain substances, such as platinum, rhenium, ruthenium, pyridine, quinoline-related alkaloids, strychnine, cysteine (in the presence of Co^{++}), and certain proteins are capable of decreasing the overvoltage for the discharge of hydrogen at the D.M.E. and producing catalytic hydrogen discharge waves.[8] These waves are not strictly proportional to concentration, and are very sensitive to traces of other substances in solution, to pH, and to temperature. The wave heights are expected to be independent of mercury column height for most of these. The original literature or reviews[8,18,41] should be consulted for more details on applications of catalytic currents.

EQUATIONS OF POLAROGRAPHIC WAVES

Reversible Waves.—A polarographic wave may be considered reversible if the concentrations (actually, activities) of the reactants and products *at the electrode-solution interface* are related to the potential of the electrode through the Nernst equation within experimental error, *i.e.*, for the reaction

$$\mathrm{Ox} + ne^- \leftrightarrows \mathrm{Red} \tag{21}$$

$$E = E^0 - \frac{RT}{nF} \ln \frac{C^0_{\mathrm{red}} f_{\mathrm{red}}}{C^0_{\mathrm{ox}} f_{\mathrm{ox}}} \tag{22}$$

where: E^0 is the standard potential of the electrode reaction;
C^0_{ox} and C^0_{red} are the concentrations of the oxidized and reduced species, respectively, at the electrode surface; and
f_{ox} and f_{red} are the corresponding activity coefficients.

Stated in another way, reversible behavior is observed when the rates of both the forward and reverse reactions are rapid enough so that equilibrium is maintained at the surface of the electrode in spite of changes in concentration produced by the flow of electrolysis current or by diffusion. Conversely, a reaction is irreversible when the concentrations of the oxidized and reduced species at the electrode surface are determined by the rate

[39] Johnson, M. G., and Robinson, R. J., Anal. Chem., **24**, 366, 1952.
[40] Kolthoff, I. M., and Parry, E. P., J. Am. Chem. Soc., **73**, 5315, 1951.
[41] Koutecky, J., Koryta, J., Electrochim. Acta, **3**, 318, 1961.

of some reaction rather than by electrolysis current and diffusion. A reaction is totally irreversible when the rate of the reverse reaction, Red $\rightarrow$ Ox + ne, is so slow that it may be neglected. The potential of the electrode is then not given by Eq. (22) and loses its thermodynamic significance.

Soluble Reactants and Products.—For a reversible reaction in which a soluble oxidized species is reduced to a lower oxidation state, also soluble in the solution, the flow of current establishes a concentration gradient between the surface of the electrode, where the reaction occurs, and points in the solution at some distance from the surface. The formation of the concentration gradient by the passage of current is opposed by the diffusion of the species from regions of higher to lower concentrations. Thus, for the oxidized and for the reduced species,

$$(C_{\text{ox}} - C^0_{\text{ox}}) = \frac{i}{k_{\text{ox}}} \quad \text{and} \quad (C^0_{\text{red}} - C_{\text{red}}) = \frac{i}{k_{\text{red}}} \tag{23}$$

where: $C - C^0$ (or $C^0 - C$) represents the concentration gradient;
i is the current; and
k_{ox} and k_{red} include the proportionality constants and the diffusion coefficients of the oxidized and reduced species, respectively.

For the dropping mercury electrode in a solution containing excess inert electrolyte, k may be evaluated from the Ilkovic equation at a potential at which all the species in contact with the electrode have reacted, *i.e.*, $C^0 = 0$; thus, *e.g.*,

$$k_{\text{ox}} = 607nD_{\text{ox}}^{1/2}m^{2/3}\tau^{1/6} \tag{24}$$

The limiting cathodic current ($C^0_{\text{ox}} = 0$) is given by the expression

$$(i_d)_c = k_{\text{ox}}C_{\text{ox}} \tag{25}$$

and the limiting anodic current ($C^0_{\text{red}} = 0$) becomes

$$-(i_d)_a = k_{\text{red}}C_{\text{red}} \tag{26}$$

Substituting Eqs. (25) and (26) into (23), one obtains

$$C^0_{\text{ox}} = \frac{(i_d)_c - i}{k_{\text{ox}}} \tag{27}$$

and

$$C^0_{\text{red}} = \frac{i - (i_d)_a}{k_{\text{red}}} \tag{28}$$

Inserting these expressions into the Nernst equation written for the D.M.E. yields for the case being considered, *i.e.*, a combined cathodic-anodic wave involving a change in oxidation state between two soluble species,

$$E_{\text{D.M.E.}} = E^0 - \frac{RT}{nF}\ln\frac{D_{\text{ox}}^{1/2}f_{\text{red}}}{D_{\text{red}}^{1/2}f_{\text{ox}}} - \frac{RT}{nF}\ln\frac{i - (i_d)_a}{(i_d)_c - i} \tag{29}$$

Usually, a cathodic or an anodic wave is studied separately. For a reversible, purely cathodic wave, $C_{\text{red}} = 0$, $(i_d)_a = 0$ and Eq. (29) simplifies to (at 25°C.)

$$E_{\text{D.M.E.}} = E^0 - \frac{0.0591}{n}\log\frac{D_{\text{ox}}^{1/2}f_{\text{red}}}{D_{\text{red}}^{1/2}f_{\text{ox}}} - \frac{0.0591}{n}\log\frac{i}{i_d - i} \tag{30}$$

Similarly, for a reversible, purely anodic wave at 25°C., $C_{ox} = 0$ and $(i_d)_c = 0$, so that

$$E_{D.M.E.} = E^0 - \frac{0.0591}{n} \log \frac{D_{ox}^{1/2} f_{red}}{D_{red}^{1/2} f_{ox}} - \frac{0.0591}{n} \log \frac{i - (i_d)_a}{-i} \quad (31)$$

Examining Eq. (30) further, at the point on the wave at which the current equals one-half the limiting diffusion current, *i.e.*, $i = i_d/2$, the last term in the equation equals zero. The potential of the D.M.E. at this point is a constant, independent of concentration, and is called the half-wave potential, $E_{1/2}$. The $E_{1/2}$ is numerically equal to the first two terms on the right hand sides of the above three equations, so that Eq. (30) for a cathodic wave is frequently written

$$E_{D.M.E.} = E_{1/2} - \frac{0.0591}{n} \log \frac{i}{i_d - i} \quad (32)$$

where

$$E_{1/2} = E^0 - \frac{0.0591}{n} \log \frac{D_{ox}^{1/2} f_{red}}{D_{red}^{1/2} f_{ox}} \quad (33)$$

The half-wave potential is important because it is a constant, independent of concentration, and is useful in identifying qualitatively the potential-determining reaction. For reversible reactions it is closely related to the standard electrode potential, as seen in Eq. (33). In fact, for the reduction of an ion to a lower oxidation state, soluble in the solution, the mercury of the D.M.E. acts as an inert metallic surface at which the electron transfer can occur, and does not enter into the chemistry of the redox reaction. In this case the $E_{1/2}$ is very nearly numerically equal to E^0 (*vs.* a common reference electrode), because the magnitude of the logarithmic term in Eq. (33) is small, usually not more than 10–20 millivolts at the most.

Soluble Amalgams.—When the reduction proceeds to an amalgam, a different reaction must be written which takes into account the participation of the mercury of the D.M.E., *i.e.*,

$$M^{+n} + x\,Hg + ne^- \rightarrow M(Hg)_x$$

The equations of the polarographic waves for this case turn out to be formally analogous to Eq. (29), (30), or (31), except that the E^0 term now refers to the standard potential of the amalgam electrode reaction, and D_{red} and f_{red} refer to the diffusion coefficient and the activity coefficient, respectively, in the amalgam phase. The standard potential of the amalgam formation reaction will be more positive than the ordinary standard potential of the metal, metal-ion electrode whenever the free energy of formation of amalgam is appreciable. Experimental results show that the energy of amalgamation is relatively small for the heavy metals close to mercury in the periodic table, *e.g.*, cadmium, lead, silver, thallium, and zinc, but that it is large for metallic elements far removed from mercury in the periodic table (long form), *e.g.*, the alkali and alkaline earth metals. Thus, the $E_{1/2}$ values obtained with the D.M.E. for Na^+ and K^+ are, respectively, 0.84 and 1.03 volts more positive than the standard E^0 values for these elements. Lingane[7,8] and von Stackelberg[42] have discussed the thermodynamic significance of the half-wave potentials of amalgam-forming reactions, and show that these can be calculated from the standard potentials of the metal, metal-ion electrodes, and data from saturated amalgam electrodes.

For a reversible cathodic wave a plot of $E_{D.M.E.}$ *vs.* $\log i/(i_d - i)$ should be a straight

[42] von Stackelberg, M., Z. Elecktrochem., **45**, 466, 1939.

line of slope $-0.0591/n$ volts at 25°C. The $E_{1/2}$ can be accurately evaluated from such a plot by locating the potential at which the logarithmic term equals zero. This can be done graphically or by a least-squares calculation. (Corrections for residual current and for resistance losses must be made.)

The agreement of the slope of the plot of $E_{D.M.E.}$ *vs.* $\log i/(i_d - i)$ with the theoretical value, $-0.0591/n$ volts, is a necessary (but not sufficient) condition for testing polarographic reversibility. More stringent criteria for reversibility are satisfied if there is agreement, within experimental error, between the $E_{1/2}$ values and slopes evaluated for both the cathodic and the anodic (or mixed cathodic-anodic) waves for the same couple. In applying these criteria, resistance losses should be corrected for, and the value of n should be known independently, *e.g.*, by coulometric determination.

An alternative property of a reversible polarographic wave that is easier to evaluate than the slope of the plot of $E_{D.M.E.}$ *vs.* $\log i/(i_d - i)$ is the difference in potential between points which are one-fourth and three-fourths the total wave height. This difference, $E_{1/4} - E_{3/4}$, should be $56.4/n$ millivolts at 25° for reversible waves. Irreversible waves are more drawn out and the difference in potential between $E_{1/4}$ and $E_{3/4}$ is greater.

Insoluble Products.—Equations of polarographic waves have also been derived for various other types of reversible reactions. For example, if the reduced form of the reaction $Ox + ne^- \rightarrow Red$ is insoluble at the D.M.E., then its activity is constant and independent of the current. The equation for a cathodic wave then becomes

$$E_{D.M.E.} = E^0 - \frac{0.0591}{n} \log \frac{D_{ox}^{1/2}}{f_{ox}} + \frac{0.0591}{n} \log (i_d - i) \tag{34}$$

and the half-wave potential is no longer independent of concentration.

$$E_{1/2} = E^0 - \frac{0.0591}{n} \log \frac{D_{ox}^{1/2}}{f_{ox}} + \frac{0.0591}{n} \log i_d/2 \tag{35}$$

This type of behavior is approached in the reduction of cations of metals which do not form soluble amalgams with mercury. In the case of anodic waves of halide anions which form insoluble mercury(I) salts at the electrode surface, the behavior and equations are very similar, except that in this case the activity of Ox (Hg_2X_2) is constant. The equation of the wave then becomes[8,43]

$$E_{D.M.E.} = E^0_{Hg_2X_2} - 0.0591 \log (f_{x^-}/D_{x^-}^{1/2}) - 0.0591 \log [i - (i_d)_a] \tag{36}$$

in which an anodic current is considered negative.

Complex Ions.—Polarography has been widely used in the study of coordination complexes, and is very convenient for such applications.[8,44,45] For the case in which a metal complex, MX_p (X is the complexing ligand), is reduced to a soluble amalgam, the complex-forming reaction, the electrode reaction, and the equation for the reversible cathodic wave are, respectively,

$$M^{+n} + pX \rightleftarrows MX_p$$

$$MX_p + ne^- \rightleftarrows M(Hg)_x + pX$$

$$E_{D.M.E.} = E_a{}^0 - \frac{0.0591}{n} \log \frac{D_{ox}^{1/2} f_{red}}{D_{red}^{1/2} f_{ox}} - \frac{0.0591}{n} \log K(C_x f_x)^p - \frac{0.0591}{n} \log \frac{i}{i_d - i} \tag{37}$$

[43] Kolthoff, I. M., and Miller, C. S., J. Am. Chem. Soc., **63,** 1405, 2732, 1941.

[44] DeFord, D. D., and Hume, D. N., J. Am. Chem. Soc., **73,** 5321, 1951.

[45] Vlcek, A. A., "Polarographic Behavior of Coordination Compounds," in Cotton, F. A., Ed., Progress in Inorg. Chem., Vol. 5, Interscience Publishers, New York, 1963, p. 211.

The half-wave potential is now given by

$$E_{1/2} = E_a{}^0 - \frac{0.0591}{n} \log \frac{D_{ox}^{1/2} f_{red}}{D_{red}^{1/2} f_{ox}} - \frac{0.0591}{n} \log K - p \frac{(0.0591)}{n} \log C_x f_x \tag{38}$$

and may be used to evaluate both p, the total number of ligand groups attached to the metal ion, and K, the overall formation constant of the complex. The values for p and K must be evaluated in the concentration range in which the plot of $E_{1/2}$ *vs.* log $C_x f_x$ is a straight line with a slope equal to $-p \frac{(0.0591)}{n}$.

The polarographic method may also be used in the determination of the formation constants of the successive complexes formed in a stepwise manner over a range of concentrations of the complexing ligand. The equations for this application were first derived by DeFord and Hume,[44] and make use of the graphical approach of Leden. The method has been extended by Schaap and McMasters[46] to an even more complicated situation, the determination of formation constants of mixed ligand complexes in solutions containing more than one type of ligand.

Nonaqueous Solvents.—In solvents of low dielectric constant, ion-pair formation becomes important and the half-wave potential of a metal ion, for example, will depend upon both the identity and concentration of the supporting electrolyte. Both the reducible metal ion and the supporting electrolyte will be involved in the ion pairing. Equations of polarographic waves which take ion-pair formation into account have been derived by Schaap.[47,48]

Irreversible Waves.[18, 20, 49]—Many polarographic waves do not satisfy the criteria for reversibility and must be considered irreversible. For such waves it is important to remember: (1) that the shape and potential of the waves are no longer governed solely by thermodynamic equilibrium conditions; and (2) that the limiting current may still be diffusion controlled and entirely suitable for quantitative determinations.

For irreversible waves, the current during the rising portion of the wave may be governed by the rate of the reaction, by diffusion, or both. If the reaction is totally irreversible, the rate constant for the forward reaction is much greater than the rate constant for the backward reaction, *i.e.*, $k_f \gg k_b$. The current flowing at any potential, E, for a cathodic reaction may then be written

$$i = n_a F A k_f C_{ox}^0 \tag{39}$$

where: n_a is the number of electrons transferred in the rate determining step;
A is the electrode area; and
C_{ox}^0 is the concentration of the reducible species at the electrode surface.

The rate constant for the forward reaction varies with the potential of the electrode, E, according to the equation

$$k_f = k_f' e^{-\alpha n_a F(E-E')/RT} \tag{40}$$

in which α is the transfer coefficient and may be regarded as that fraction of the change in the electrode potential in the cathodic direction which serves to increase the rate of

[46] Schaap, W. B., and McMasters, D. L., J. Am. Chem. Soc., **83,** 4699, 1961.
[47] Schaap, W. B., J. Am. Chem. Soc., **82,** 1837, 1960.
[48] Schaap, W. B., Bayer, R. E., Siefker, J. R., Kim. J. Y., Brewster, P. W., and Schmidt, F. C., Record of Chem. Progress, **22** (No. 4), 197, 1961.
[49] Reilley, C. N., "Fundamentals of Electrode Processes," in Kolthoff, I. M., and Elving, P. J., Eds., Treatise on Anal. Chem., Interscience Publishers, New York, 1963, Part I, Vol. 4, Chapter 42.

the cathodic reaction. If α is small, only a small fraction of the potential change is effective in increasing the value of k_f, so that the wave becomes severely distorted and drawn out.

The term k'_f is defined in Eq. (40) as the rate constant of the reaction when $E = E'$, the reference potential of the electrode couple. Two choices are common for the reference potential, E'. If the reversible, formal potential of the couple is known, it is convenient to define E' as this formal potential. Thus when $E = E' = E_{\text{formal}}$, the reactants and products of the reaction are present at equal concentrations and are at equilibrium, so that $i = 0$, $C^0_{\text{ox}} = C^0_{\text{red}}$ and $k_f = k_b = k'$. Alternatively, the reference potential may be taken to be the potential of the standard hydrogen electrode, *i.e.*, $E' = E^0 = 0$. In this case, k' becomes k^0, the rate constant of the electrode process at $E = 0$ *vs.* the hydrogen electrode. Regardless of the choice for E', it may be seen from Eq. (40) that, at sufficiently negative potentials, k_f will become large so that C^0_{ox} at the electrode surface will decrease to negligibly small values. At these potentials the current can be diffusion limited and vary in direct proportion to concentration.

The equation of an irreversible wave can also be written in terms of an observed half-wave potential and the limiting average diffusion current; but in this totally irreversible case the equation is[20, 50]

$$E \simeq E_{1/2} - \frac{0.0591}{\alpha n_a} \log i/(i_d - i) \tag{41}$$

where

$$E_{1/2} = \frac{0.0591}{\alpha n_a} \log [1.35 k_f{}^0 \tau^{1/2} / D^{1/2}_{\text{ox}}] \tag{42}$$

The half-wave potential becomes increasingly negative as the rate constant $k_f{}^0$ (or k_f) becomes smaller, *i.e.*, the overvoltage increases as the reaction rate decreases. A plot of $E_{\text{D.M.E.}}$ *vs.* $\log i/(i_d - i)$ for a totally irreversible reaction should be a straight line. Now, however, the slope is $0.0591/\alpha n_a$. At low values of α, the waves are drawn out and greatly distorted. This occurs because for $\alpha \ll 1$ only a small fraction of a given change in electrode potential serves to increase the rate of the cathodic reaction.

From the practical standpoint, quantitative applications are still possible for irreversible waves. It is only necessary to ascertain that the limiting currents are measured at potentials at which they are diffusion controlled. This can usually be determined by inspection of the wave or by measurement of the relation between i_d and the height of the mercury column or temperature.

INSTRUMENTATION

CONVENTIONAL POLAROGRAPHY

The essential functions of any polarographic instrument are to apply a known, variable potential across the cell and to measure the concomitant faradaic cell current. A simple, convenient circuit that performs these functions and would be suitable for a manually operated polarograph is given in Fig. 19-6.

In the schematic diagram, R_3 is a variable resistor (about 500 ohms) to drop the voltage of the 3 to 6 volt battery to some convenient, integral value desired for the overall voltage range to be applied to the cell by means of the slidewire AB. The voltage range selected is indicated by the voltmeter, V. The resistance of the slidewire should be low,

[50] Meites, L., and Israel, Y., J. Am. Chem. Soc., **83**, 4903, 1961.

preferably not more than 100 ohms, in order that the current flowing through the cell always remains a negligible fraction of the current flowing through the slidewire and does not affect the iR drop at any point along the slidewire. If the resistance of the slidewire is strictly linear, then the voltage applied to the cell can be determined from the position of the sliding contact and the overall voltage across the slidewire.

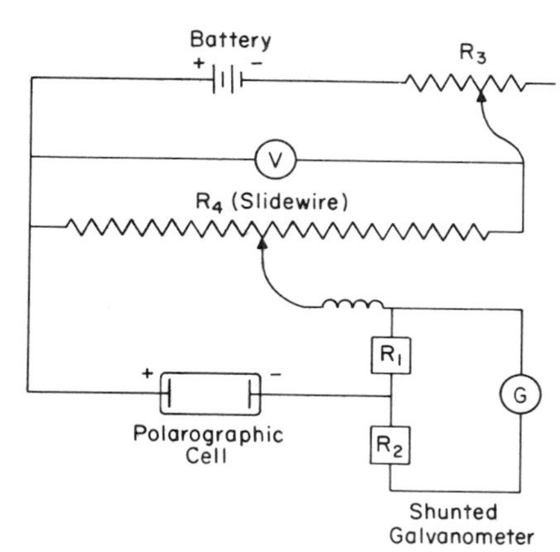

FIG. 19-6. Basic Circuit Suitable for a Manual Polarograph.

The current passing through the cell is measured with a galvanometer, G, provided with a shunt to increase its range. The shunt can consist of two variable resistance boxes in series, the total resistance of which is kept constant and serves as the damping resistance for the galvanometer. The sensitivity of the galvanometer varies as the ratio $R_1/(R_1 + R_2)$.

The circuit shown in Fig. 19-6 can be made the basis of a simple, workable, automatic recording polarograph if the slidewire is replaced by a linear 100-ohm, 10-turn potentiometer, driven at 1 r.p.m. with a synchronous motor, and if the galvanometer is removed and a recording millivolt potentiometer connected across R_1.

Manual polarographs, complete with built-in galvanometers, are available from several commercial sources at a cost of about $600 to $700, and are entirely adequate for quantitative determinations. In spite of their greater cost, recording instruments are preferred by most workers because a record is obtained and because the characteristics of the entire wave are readily observed. (An experienced observer can frequently detect abnormal solution, capillary, or circuit behavior from the appearance of the recorded polarogram.) More than a dozen different recording polarographs are available on U.S. and foreign markets. Prices start at about $1,400 and increase above that figure depending upon additional features and the quality of the recorder furnished. One of the more popular, low-cost American instruments is the E. H. Sargent & Co. Model XV Polarograph, for which are available as accessories a "micro-range extender" for low concentration use, and an "IR Compensator" for 3-electrode, controlled-potential operation. This instrument is shown in Fig. 19-7.

Significant advances in polarographic techniques and instrumentation have appeared in recent years. Those which are represented in commercially available instruments are discussed under the various headings below.

DERIVATIVE D.C. POLAROGRAPHY

The first derivative of a reversible cathodic polarographic wave can be shown[51] to attain its maximum value at the $E_{1/2}$, and to have a value at this point equal to

$$\left(\frac{di}{dt}\right)_{\max} = -\frac{2.303}{0.0591} \cdot \frac{ni_d}{4}\left(\frac{dE}{dt}\right) \tag{43}$$

where: di/dt is the derivative of the average current recorded with respect to time, dE/dt is the voltage scanning rate; and the other symbols have their usual significance.

[51] Kelley, M. T., and Fisher, D. J., Anal. Chem., **30**, 929, 1958.

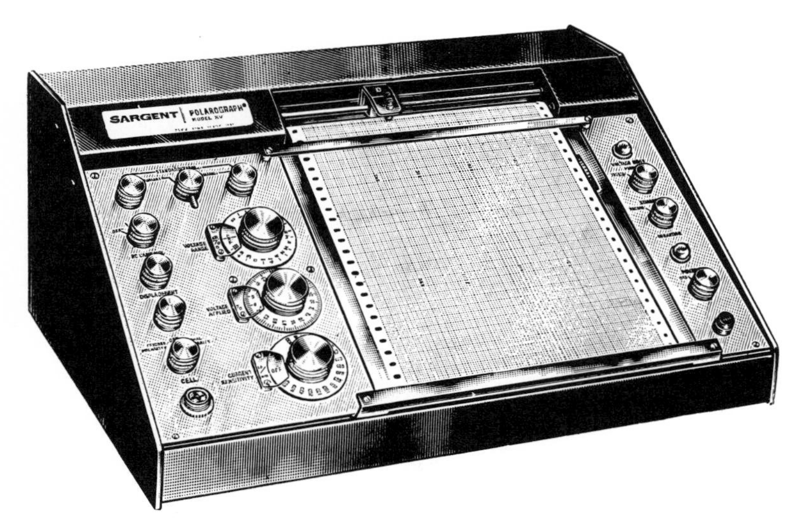

Fig. 19-7. Sargent Model XV, Pen Recording Polarograph. (Courtesy E. H. Sargent and Co.)

Because $i_d = knC$ (Ilkovic equation), the maximum (peak) height of the first derivative is proportional to concentration, to the square of the number of electrons involved, and to the scanning rate, *i.e.*,

$$\left(\frac{di}{dt}\right)_{\max} = -\frac{2.303}{0.0591} \cdot \frac{kn^2C}{4} \cdot \left(\frac{dE}{dt}\right) \tag{44}$$

where k is a proportionality constant which may be evaluated from the Ilkovic equation

Derivative d.c. polarography has several advantages over conventional d.c. polarography. First, because the derivative of a linearly increasing residual current is a constant, polarographic waves maintain their derivative shape at very low concentrations and are detectable even in the presence of large residual currents. Concentrations below 10^{-6} M are detectable.[52,53] Second, because the peak of the first derivative occurs at the $E_{1/2}$, and because the peak height-concentration relation obtains at this point, the derivative technique can yield quantitative data for species whose conventional waves overlap slightly and are incompletely resolved. Indeed, it can be shown that for less than 3 percent overlap (equal to experimental error), the separation in $E_{1/2}$ values of successive waves of equal height and identical n should be approximately $200/n$ millivolts for conventional S-shaped waves, but only $90/n$ millivolts if the first derivatives are recorded. Finally, the derivative signal returns to the base line following each wave, so that successive waves can be recorded at maximum sensitivity without requiring downscale compensation. The derivative of a small wave due to a minor constituent can often be recorded in the presence of a much larger concentration of a prior-reduced major constituent.

Various techniques for recording first derivatives of polarographic waves have been

[52] Cooke, W. D., Kelley, M. T., and Fisher, D. J., Anal. Chem., **33,** 1209, 1961.
[53] Kelley, M. T., Fisher, D. J., Cooke, W. D., and Jones, H. C., in Longmuir, I. S., Ed., Advances in Polarography, Vol. I, 158, Pergamon Press, 1960.

proposed, including classical resistor-capacitor differentiating networks,[54] electromechanical direct-current tachometers, a.c. signals superimposed on a d.c. scan, measurement of the difference in current between two dropping electrodes maintained at slightly different applied potentials throughout the scan (differential polarography), and derivative analog computer networks. These have been critically reviewed by

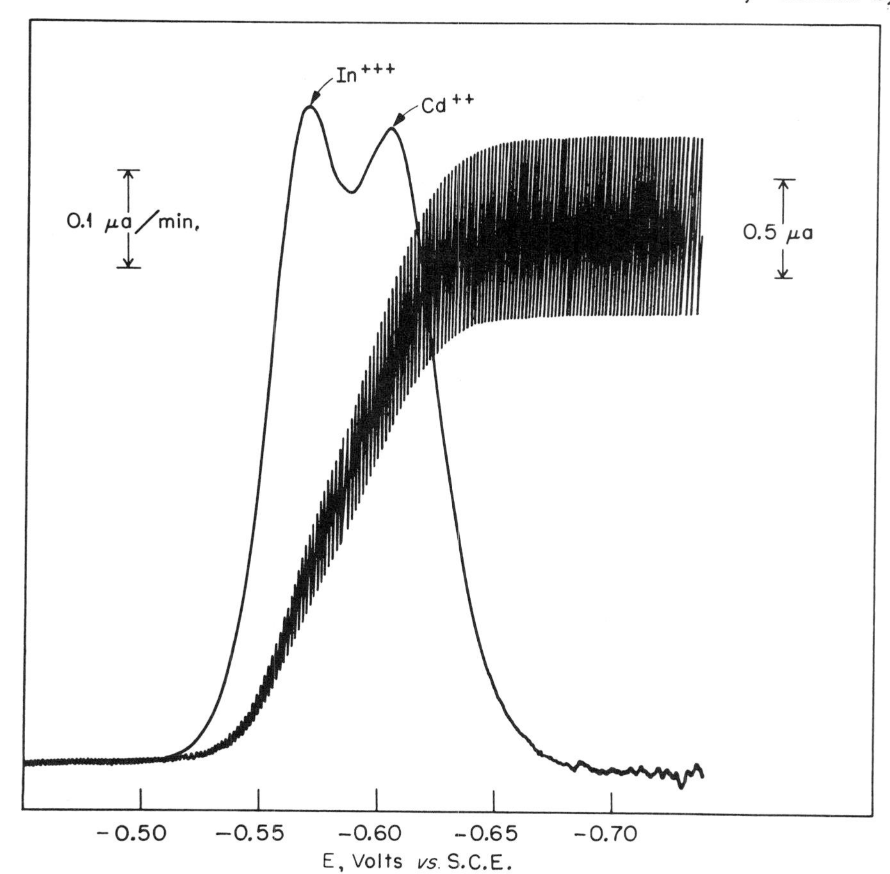

FIG. 19-8. Comparison of Resolution of a Regular and a Derivative Polarogram Recorded with a Solution Containing 1 × 10^{-4} *M* In^{+3} and 2 × 10^{-4} *M* Cd^{+2} in 0.1 *M* KCl. (Courtesy D. J. Fisher, W. L. Belew, and M. T. Kelley, Oak Ridge National Laboratory.)

Kelley and Fisher,[51] who recommend use of the derivative computer approach and present a design for a controlled potential and derivative-taking instrument capable of yielding first derivatives of theoretical shape.[55] An essential feature of this instrument is the complete filtering-out of the current oscillations due to the growth and fall of the mercury drops. A tuned, parallel-T RC filter network eliminates the current oscillations and allows a smooth curve to be recorded. The analog computer derivative-taking cir-

[54] Leveque, M. P., and Roth, F., J. chim. phys., **46,** 480, 1949.
[55] Kelley, M. T., Jones, H. C., and Fisher, D. J., Anal. Chem., **31,** 1475, 1959.

cuit then computes the first derivative of the smooth, S-shaped wave. Because the filter network has an appreciable time constant, the scanning rate applied by this instrument must be less than about $40/n$ millivolts per minute if derivatives of theoretical shape are to be recorded.[56] Thus, it is not possible to take full advantage of the fact that the peak height of the first derivative is proportional to the scanning rate, Eq. (44).

The Kelley-Fisher instrument design forms the basis of the polarographs commercially available from Numec Corp., Apollo, Pa., and from Indiana Instrument Corp., Bloomington, Ind. A regular and a derivative polarogram obtained with such an instrument and illustrating the increased resolving power of derivative waves is shown in Fig. 19-8. Duplicate derivative polarograms obtained for 2×10^{-6} M lead using the Kelley-Fisher instrument are shown in Fig. 19-9.

Several commercially available instruments provide derivative-taking circuitry based on classical resistor-capacitor differentiating networks such as suggested by Leveque and Roth.[54] Derivatives recorded with such instruments are not of theoretical shape and, depending upon the choice of R and C values, are either greatly overdamped and distorted, or lack sensitivity.

STATIONARY ELECTRODE (SLOW LINEAR SCAN) POLAROGRAPHY

With stationary electrodes of constant area in unstirred solutions, application of a linear voltage scan gives rise to peak-shaped polarograms, the peak height of which varies with the scanning rate and with the concentration of electroactive species. If the electrode is rotated, however, or if the solution is rapidly stirred or caused to flow over the electrode, then the current-voltage curve will generally be independent of the voltage scanning rate and a level limiting current will result.

The dependence of the magnitude of the peak current, i_{max}, on experimental conditions has been shown by Randles[57] and by Sevĉik[58] to be

$$i_{max} = 217An^{3/2}D^{1/2}CV^{1/2} \tag{45}$$

where: A is the area of the stationary electrode in cm.^{2};
C is concentration of electroactive species in moles liter^{-1};
D is the diffusion coefficient in cm.^{2}sec.$^{-1}$;
n is the number of electrons transferred at the electrode surface; and
V is the voltage scanning rate in volts sec.$^{-1}$.

This equation assumes semi-infinite linear diffusion, and applies most accurately to planar electrodes. The analogous equations describing the currents obtained during application of a linear voltage scan to a small, spherical, hanging mercury drop electrode have been described by Reinmuth[59,60] for the cases in which the diffusing species is either in the solution or within the mercury drop. Equations for other cases are summarized by Adams[61] as part of a complete review of the subject.

Streuli and Cooke[62] demonstrated that the variation of peak currents (i_{max}) with voltage scanning rate and with concentration agreed well with the predictions of the

[56] Schaap, W. B., and McKinney, P. S., Anal. Chem., **36,** 29, 1964.
[57] Randles, J. E. B., Trans. Faraday Soc., **44,** 334, 1948.
[58] Sevĉik, A., Collection Czechoslov. Chem. Communs., **13,** 349, 1948.
[59] Reinmuth, W., Anal. Chem., **33,** 185, 1961.
[60] Reinmuth, W., J. Am. Chem. Soc., **79,** 6358, 1958.
[61] Adams, R. N., "Voltammetry at Electrodes With Fixed Surfaces," in Kolthoff, I. M., and Elving, P. J., Eds., Treatise on Analytical Chemistry, Interscience Publishers, New York, Part I, Section D-2, Chapter 47, 1963.
[62] Streuli, C. A., and Cooke, W. D., Anal. Chem., **25,** 1691, 1953; **26,** 963, 970, 1954.

Randles-Sevĉik equation for the case of reactions at a quiet mercury pool in unstirred solutions. The ratio of peak current to background or residual current was observed to be about 10 times greater than for conventional polarography, thereby giving rise to a 10-fold increase in sensitivity. Useful analyses could be made in the concentration range 10^{-4} to 10^{-6} *M*. These workers also observed that the potential at half the maximum peak height was approximately equal to the conventional polarographic half-wave potential. Linear scan polarograms for 10^{-5} *M* lead are shown in Fig. 19-10.

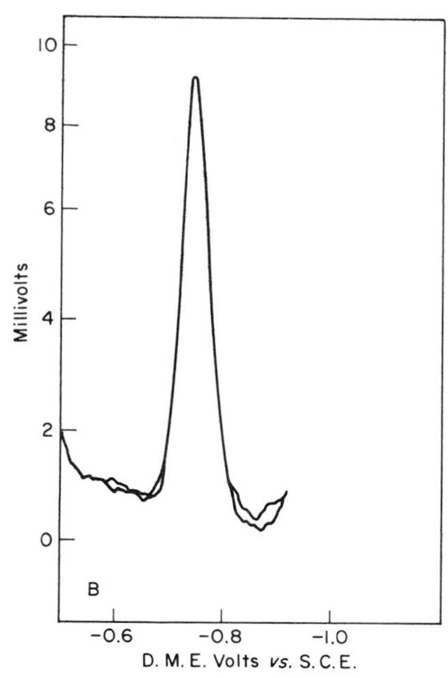

Fig. 19-9. First Derivative Polarograms (Two) of 2×10^{-6} *M* Lead in 0.1 *M* NaOH. (Recorded with the Kelley-Jones-Fisher Q-1988-ES Controlled Potential and Derivative Polarograph. Reproduced with permission from Analytical Chemistry.)

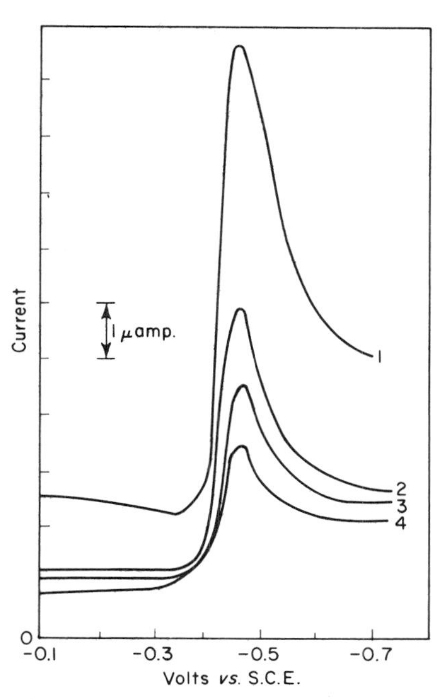

Fig. 19-10. Linear Scan Polarograms Obtained for 10^{-5} *M* Lead at a Quiet Mercury Pool Showing the Effect of Voltage Scanning Rate. Data: pool area = 2.86 cm.^{2}; curve 1 recorded at 1.2 volts/min., 2 at 0.4 volts/min., 3 at 0.2 volts/min., and 4 at 0.1 volts/min. (Reproduced with permission from Analytical Chemistry.)

Studies in the author's laboratory[63] have shown that linear scan–mercury pool polarography is convenient for amperometric titrations involving precipitation, complexation, or oxidation-reduction reactions. In such titrations only relative changes in the peak currents are needed; absolute calibrations are not needed. Titrations were performed with reactant concentrations approaching 10^{-6} *M*. The results appeared to be limited more by the incompleteness of the reactions, as determined by the magnitude of the equilibrium constants, than by the sensitivity of the method.

Solid electrodes composed of materials other than mercury retain the advantage of

[63] Samargachandra, A., "High Sensitivity Amperometric Titrations," M.S. thesis, Dept. of Chemistry, Indiana University, Bloomington, Indiana, June, 1956.

high sensitivity for linear scan voltammetry and, in addition, allow reactions to be studied at more positive potentials where mercury cannot be used. Other electrode materials studied include platinum, gold, graphite, wax-impregnated carbon rods, carbon paste, boron carbide, and pyrolytic graphite. The theory and practice of stationary-electrode polarography has been reviewed by Adams.[61]

Conventional polarographic equipment can be used to record current-voltage curves obtained with stationary electrodes, although provision should be made for faster voltage scanning rates. The instruments mentioned at the end of the following section are suitable for this application.

RAPID DROPPING MERCURY ELECTRODE POLAROGRAPHY

It has been demonstrated by Meites[26] and others that, with a vertical capillary of typical characteristics, a marked increase in value of the diffusion current constant, I ($= 607nD^{1/2}$), occurs at drop times shorter than 2 seconds. The increase is attributed to stirring of the solution caused by the rapidly forming drops of normal size. Smoler[27,64] found, on the other hand, that reproducible results could be obtained at drop times of about 0.5 second using capillaries bent at 90° so that the mercury issues from the orifice on a vertical face and the drops do not grow to normal size. Because the drops are much smaller with this arrangement, the stirring effect is minimized. Also, the use of mechanical devices to knock off small drops at times less than 1 second has been shown to yield reproducible currents.[65,66]

The use of small drops and short drop times does not result in any appreciable change in sensitivity, but is advantageous in that it allows faster scan rates to be used, thereby decreasing the amount of time required to run a polarogram. Using a scanning rate of 3 volts per minute, a range of 0.5 volt can be traversed in only 10 seconds. Moreover, the voltage change over the life of a single drop remains the same for a scanning rate of 0.3 volt per minute with a 5-second drop time and a rate of 3 volts per minute with a 0.5-second drop time. The recorded polarograms will look quite similar, except for a decrease in size of the pen excursions, if the rapid scan polarogram is recorded at a 10-fold increased recorder-chart speed.

Instruments suitable for rapid-scan, rapid dropping polarography are available from Metrohm Ltd., Herisau, Switzerland, and from E. H. Sargent & Co., Chicago, Ill. The electronic scan instrument available from the Indiana Instrument Corp., Bloomington, Ind., can be modified to allow scanning rates up to 5 volts per minute. A mechanical drop controller assembly is available as an accessory from Metrohm Ltd.

Another possible advantage resulting from the use of very short drop times (*ca.* 0.5 second) has been pointed out by Fisher, Belew, and Kelley,[67] but has not yet been utilized by any commercial instrument. This is that the much smaller current oscillations accompanying the use of the rapid dropping mercury electrode allow an *RC* averaging filter with a much shorter time constant to be used than can be used with conventional electrodes with 3- to 5-second drop times. Thus, derivatives may be recorded at much faster scan rates and the dependence of derivative peak height upon scan rate, Eq. (44), can be used to increase the sensitivity.

CATHODE RAY (RAPID LINEAR SCAN) POLAROGRAPHY

So-called cathode-ray polarography is in essence a very rapid scan form of linear scan (stationary electrode) polarography. It differs from the latter only in that the entire

[64] Smoler, I., Collection Czechoslov. Chem. Communs., **19,** 238, 1954.
[65] Airey, L., and Smales, A., Analyst, **75,** 287, 1950.
[66] Wolf, D., J. Electroanal. Chem., **5,** 186, 1963.
[67] Fisher, D. J., Belew, W. L., and Kelley, M. T., Anal. Chem., in press.

voltage sweep is made toward the end of the lifetime of a single drop, and in that the current-voltage curve is displayed on an oscilloscope or cathode-ray tube. The technique was originally suggested by Randles[57] and improved by Davis and Seaborn.[68] Commercial instruments are now available from Southern Analytical, Ltd., Camberley, England, and from Apparecchiature DiMisura Elettroniche (AMEL), Milan, Italy.

With the Southern A1660 instrument, a rapid scan covering 0.5 volt is applied during the last 2 seconds of the growth of a mercury drop. Because the drop area increases slowly toward the end of its life, the charging current is minimized. The rapid scan gives rise to a peaked polarogram, the peak height of which is directly proportional to concentration. At the scanning rate used, the sensitivity in terms of peak current per unit concentration is claimed to be about $4\sqrt{n}$ times greater than the usual diffusion current. The instrument can also be used with two synchronized dropping electrodes in two separate cells. If a blank solution containing only supporting electrolyte is placed in one cell and a test solution with the same concentration of supporting electrolyte in the other cell, then the difference in currents in the two cells can be displayed on the tube. In this way, the residual current and currents due to trace impurities are subtracted out, so that the gain of the difference signal can be increased and higher sensitivity can be attained. Curves obtained with 4×10^{-7} M tin (0.05 p.p.m.) are shown in Fig. 19-11. Curve A shows the oscilloscope trace obtained from a single cell; curve B shows the difference signal at maximum sensitivity after subtraction of residual current from the test solution current. The lower limit of concentration detectable appears to be about 10^{-7} M in favorable cases.

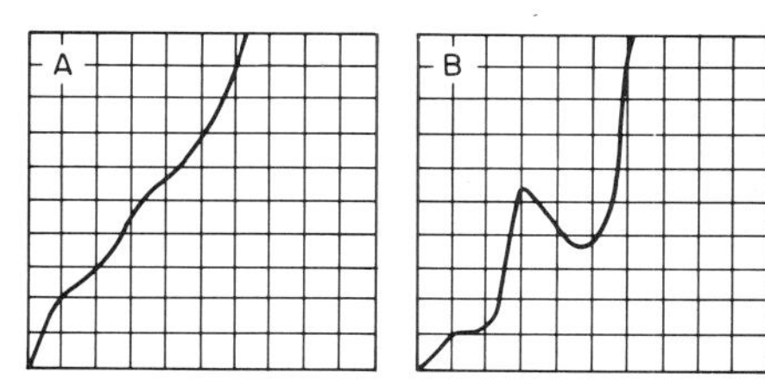

FIG. 19-11. Cathode-ray Polarograms (Oscilloscope Traces) Recorded with 0.05 microgram/ml. Tin (4×10^{-7} M) in 5 M Hydrochloric Acid. Curve A is uncompensated output of cell 1 at a sensitivity of 1/15. Curve B is the difference wave resulting from subtraction of current from blank (cell 2) from output of cell 1. Scanning rate = 0.25 volts per second. (Courtesy Southern Analytical Ltd. Camberley, England.)

ANODIC STRIPPING (INVERSE) POLAROGRAPHY[69]

Anodic stripping polarography is related to linear scan polarography discussed above in that the same scanning rates and instruments will suffice for both. In this technique a pre-electrolysis is used to concentrate the species to be determined on the electrode in the form of a solid deposit or an amalgam. After a sufficient concentration has been achieved, the current is reversed and the amount of deposited species is determined by some appropriate voltammetric technique. Frequently, the concentration step is effected by electrolysis for a carefully measured length of time into a hanging mercury drop, and the determination is made by recording an anodic polarogram of the resulting amalgam using a rapid, linear scan. It is not necessary that the pre-electrolysis be exhaustive (stoichiometric). For stoichiometric pre-electrolysis, the use of small electrodes, which increases the sensitivity of stripping measurement, would necessitate inconveniently long pre-electrolysis times. It is necessary only that the electrolysis time, stirring rate,

[68] Davis, H. M., and Seaborn, J. E., in Longmuir, I. S., Ed., Advances in Polarography, Vol. I, p. 239, Pergamon Press, London, 1961.

[69] Shain, I., "Stripping Analysis," in Kolthoff, I. M., and Elving, P. J., Eds., Treatise on Analytical Chemistry, Interscience Publishers, New York, Part I, Section D-2, Chapter 50, 1963.

stirrer position, and volume of solution be kept constant. The method has been studied extensively by Shain and coworkers[70] and a comprehensive review has been written.[69]

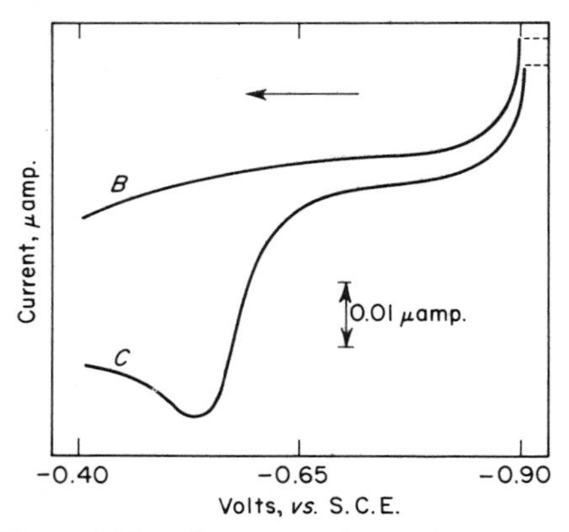

Fig. 19-12. Current Voltage Curves for Anodic Stripping Analysis. *B*, Anodic residual current curve; *C*, Anodic stripping wave for 10^{-8} *M* cadmium solution after a 15 min. pre-electrolysis. Voltage scanning rate = 21 mv. sec.$^{-1}$ (Reproduced with permission from Analytical Chemistry.)

A current-voltage curve for anodic stripping of a hanging mercury drop electrode after a 15-minute pre-electrolysis of a 10^{-8} *M* cadmium solution in 0.1 *M* potassium chloride is shown in Fig. 19-12. Also shown is the anodic residual current curve. Notice that the polarogram has a peak shape characteristic of a stationary electrode. Determination of trace concentrations of metal ions that form soluble amalgams is the most favorable application of stripping analysis, for in this case neither the pre-electrolysis nor the reverse oxidation need be exhaustive or stoichiometric. (If a solid electrode is used, or if a surface film is formed, then the stripping must be exhaustive and the amount of deposit must be determined by a coulometric measurement.) Longer pre-electrolysis times are necessary at lower concentrations. Whereas a 5-minute pre-electrolysis period is sufficient at 10^{-6} *M*, using a hanging drop electrode, a 60-minute electrolysis is needed for 10^{-9} *M* solutions.[69,70]

The principal advantages of the method are its great sensitivity (*ca.* 10^{-9} *M*) and its relatively good precision at very low concentrations (±4 percent at 10^{-9} *M*). Disadvantages of the method include the considerable care required to maintain reproducible conditions (stirring, etc.) within the cell, the length of time required to make a determination, and the inconvenience and tedium encountered in analyzing for more than one species in any solution.

ALTERNATING CURRENT, SQUARE WAVE, AND PULSE POLAROGRAPHY

If a small alternating voltage signal of relatively low frequency is superimposed on a slow, linear "d.c." potential scan, the alternating current signal that results will be enhanced in the region of a reversible polarographic wave, and will exhibit its maximum amplitude at the half-wave potential. This situation obtains because the reversible polarographic wave attains its maximum slope at the half-wave potential, so that a given alternating voltage signal causes the periodic changes in concentration (of the species participating in the electrode reaction) to be maximal at this potential. The periodic concentration changes occur through electron transfer at the electrode surface and, hence, are related to the faradaic alternating current. If this alternating faradaic current is rectified and damped, the resulting signal corresponds to the first derivative of the polarographic wave.

According to Breyer and Bauer,[22] who have reviewed the subject of a.c. polarography, the maximum height of the faradaic alternating current, Δi_{max}, for the case in which the applied alternating voltage signal is of low amplitude and low frequency, is given by the expression

[70] DeMars, R. D., and Shain, I., Anal. Chem., **29**, 1825, 1957.

$$\Delta i_{\max} = \frac{n^2F^2AVC\omega^{1/2}D_{ox}^{1/2}}{4RT} \tag{46}$$

where: n is the number of electrons transferred;
A is the electrode area;
V is the amplitude of the voltage signal;
C is concentration;
ω is the angular frequency; and
D_{ox} is the diffusion coefficient of the oxidized species.

It is interesting to note that the peak height in the a.c. case has the same dependence upon n, C, and D_0 as does the first derivative of a d.c. polarogram.

Although Eq. (46) predicts that $\Delta i_{\max}$ should increase with the square root of frequency, low frequencies are actually preferable because the capacitative component of the current increases as the first power of the frequency and because slower, irreversible reactions give greatly diminished response at higher frequencies. The optimum frequency of the alternating potential appears to lie in the range 10 to 60 c.p.s. and the optimum amplitude between 1 and 35 millivolts. Highly irreversible reactions, such as the reduction of oxygen, may not give a.c. polarographic waves, and slightly irreversible reactions may give distorted a.c. waves. The best range for analytical applications of a.c. polarography is 10^{-3} to 10^{-4} M and the detectability limit is 10^{-5} M.[71] Without further modifications, as described below, the method has little or no advantage over conventional d.c. polarography, except for kinetic studies of fast electrode reactions and for "tensammetric" studies of surface-adsorbed species.[22]

An a.c. modulator, suitable for simple a.c. polarography, is available at moderate cost from Metrohm Ltd. as supplementary equipment for the Polarecord Model E261R.

The more sensitive applications of a.c. techniques have all attempted in some way to separate the faradaic from the capacitative component of the overall alternating current passing through the cell. This separation was accomplished by Jessop[72] by means of a phase-sensitive detector capable of accepting the faradaic alternating current, which lags the applied alternating potential only slightly, while rejecting the capacitative alternating current, which is 90° out of phase with the applied voltage signal. Because even a moderate cell resistance serves to mix the phases, successful application of the phase discriminator requires very low cell resistances.

The Cambridge Instrument Co. supplies a "Univector Polarograph Unit" for converting a conventional d.c. polarograph into an a.c. instrument. Separation of the faradaic and capacitative components of the cell current is accomplished by means of a phase-sensitive detector. A 20-fold increase in sensitivity over d.c. polarographs is claimed for this instrument in the case of reversible reactions.[73] It is much less sensitive than d.c. polarographs for irreversible reactions. Instruments based on the same design are also manufactured by several Japanese firms.[22]

Another successful approach to the separation of faradaic and capacitative components of the cell current is through the measurement of second (or higher) harmonics of the alternating current. Second harmonics were first measured quantitatively by Bauer and Elving,[74] and have been studied extensively by Smith and Reinmuth.[75,76] The method is based on the fact that the capacitative current varies essentially linearly with

[71] Bauer, H., J. Electroanal. Chem., **1**, 256, 1960.
[72] Jessop, G., British Patent 640,768, 1950.
[73] Ferrett, D. J., Milner, G. W. C., Shalgosky, H. I., and Slee, L. J., Analyst, **81**, 506, 1956.
[74] Bauer, H., and Elving, P., Anal. Chem., **30**, 341, 1958.
[75] Smith, D. E., and Reinmuth, W., Anal. Chem., **33**, 482, 1961.
[76] Smith, D. E., Anal. Chem., **35**, 1811, 1963.

voltage, whereas the faradaic process varies nonlinearly. Thus, although the first derivative of the capacitative current may be appreciable, the second derivative will be near zero. Whereas the base-line current may be 75 percent of the peak current in the case of normal a.c. polarography, it is only about 5 percent or less when the second harmonics are recorded. The limit of detection with this approach is between 10^{-6} and 10^{-7} *M*.[75] The technique is insensitive to irreversible reactions, and demands very low cell resistances for successful application.

Another approach to the isolation of the faradaic component of the cell current was utilized by Barker in the development of both the "square wave" polarograph[77,78,79] and the "pulse" polarograph.[80,81] This approach takes advantage of the fact that, follow-

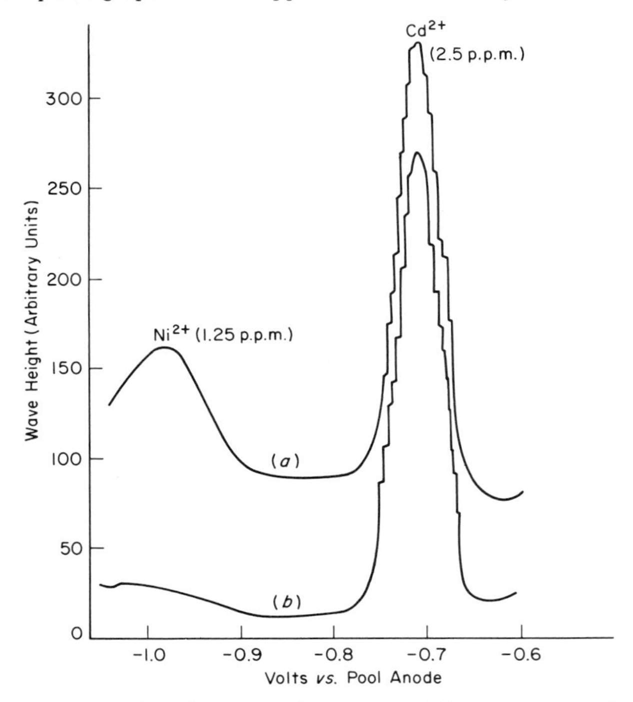

Fig. 19-13. Comparison of a Pulse and Square-wave Polarogram for Ni^{+2} (Irreversibly Reduced) and Cd^{+2} (Reversibly Reduced) in a Solution Containing 1 *M* NH_4OH and 1 *M* NH_4Cl. Curve *a*, pulse polarogram recorded at 1/64 maximum sensitivity; Curve *b*, square-wave polarogram recorded at 1/16 maximum sensitivity. (Courtesy, G. W. C. Milner.)

ing a sudden change in applied potential, the capacitative current surge decays much more rapidly than the faradaic current. Thus, if the a.c. voltage is applied in the form of a square wave and, if the amplitude, Δi, of the a.c. current is measured after a suitable time delay, essentially only faradaic current will be detected.

[77] Barker, G. C., and Faircloth, R. L., J. Polarog. Soc., **1,** 11, 1958.
[78] Barker, G. C., and Jenkins, I. L., Analyst, **77,** 685, 1952.
[79] Milner, G. W. C., Recent Developments in Polarography, Royal Institute of Chem., Lecture Series, 1961, No. 3.
[80] Barker, G. C., Anal. Chim. Acta, **18,** 118, 1958.
[81] Barker, G. C., and Gardner, A. W., Z. anal. Chem., **173,** 79, 1960.

The Mervyn Instruments Ltd. Modular Square-Wave Polarograph, in one of its modes of operation, superimposes a 225 c.p.s. square-wave voltage signal, 2 to 32 millivolts in height, onto a linearly increasing "d.c." voltage scan, and measures the current during the last 2.2 milliseconds of the square wave. In another mode of operation, a single square-wave pulse ("strobe") of longer duration is applied at a predetermined time in the life of a drop, and a single measurement of current is made after a predetermined delay following the application of the pulse. Both modes give rise to derivative-type polarograms. The latter mode, however, is more sensitive for irreversible reactions because of the effectively lower frequency. A comparison of a pulse and a square-wave polarogram recorded with a solution containing both nickel (irreversibly reduced) and cadmium (reversibly reduced) is made in Fig. 19-13.

The Southern-Harwell Mark II Pulse Polarograph, manufactured by Southern Ana-

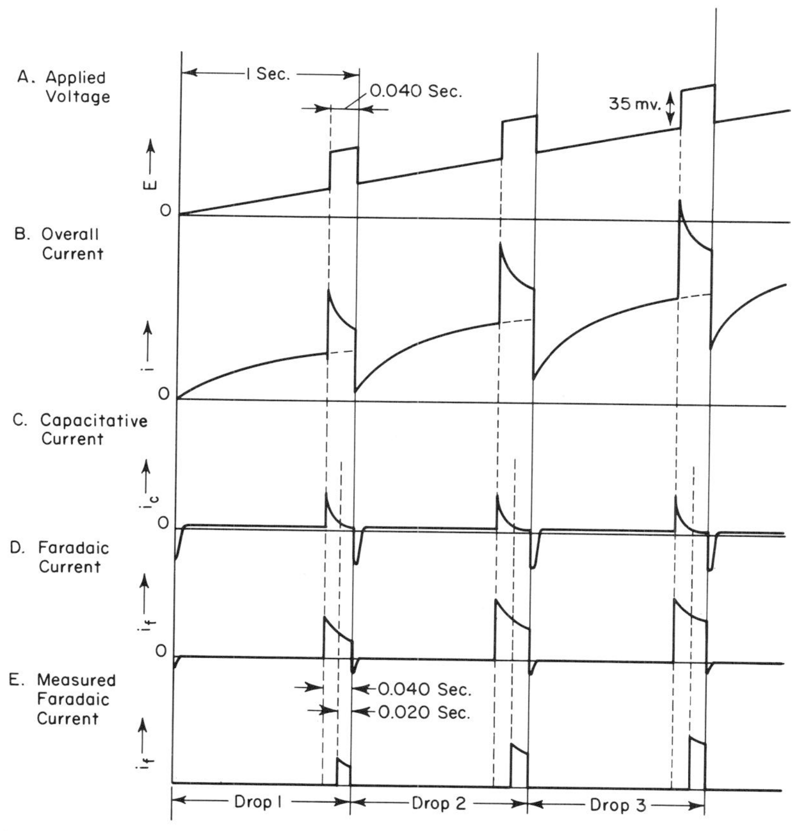

FIG. 19-14. Current and Voltage Diagrams Illustrating the Operation of a "Pulse Polarograph." Curve A, a linearly increasing scan voltage upon which a 35-millivolt pulse is superimposed during the last 40 milliseconds of the 1 second drip time; B, the overall current flowing through the cell as a result of the applied voltage; C, the capacitative component of cell current; D, the faradaic component of the cell current measured above the "d.c." background; E, the net current signal measured during the last 20 milliseconds of the life of the drop after the capacitative current has decayed to near zero.

lytical Ltd., is an elegant instrument derived from the work of Barker. In its present form the instrument utilizes a solenoid-energized hammer to control the drop time at 1.0 second and to synchronize the timing circuits. A 40-millisecond square-wave pulse is applied after a delay of 0.96 second from the start of growth of the drop and just before the next drop is detached. The cell current is then measured during the last half of the pulse, *i.e.*, during the last 20 milliseconds, at which time the capacitative component of the current has decayed to near zero, while the faradaic component is still appreciable. If an applied pulse of constant amplitude (7 or 35 millivolts) is superimposed on a linearly increasing "d.c." voltage scan, the measured current will correspond to the first derivative of each polarographic wave. If the "d.c." voltage is held constant, and the amplitude of the 40-millisecond pulse is increased in small increments from 0 to 1 volt, then the resulting current signal will correspond in shape to a conventional S-shaped wave. The voltage, current and time relationships for the derivative-taking mode of operation are shown in Fig. 19-14.

Both the Southern Analytical and the Mervyn instruments are said to possess: (1) a limit of detectability approaching 10^{-8} *M* in favorable cases; (2) increased resolution (*ca.* 50 millivolts) for closely spaced waves (in the derivative mode); and (3) indifference to the presence of large excesses (50,000 to 1) of prior-reduced substances. Both instruments possess the disadvantages that rather low cell resistances (<50 ohms) are required and that they are much more expensive than conventional d.c. recording polarographs.

AUXILIARY EQUIPMENT

THE CAPILLARY AND ITS CARE

Capillaries suitable for use as a D.M.E. must be of such length and internal diameter that drop times on the order of 2 to 6 seconds are obtained at mercury reservoir heights of 30 cm. or more. (The "height" of the mercury reservoir is the distance between the lower tip of the capillary and the top of the mercury meniscus in the reservoir.) At present, excellent capillaries are readily available from scientific supply houses, and so are seldom made by the experimenter. For example, E. H. Sargent & Co., Chicago, sells 21-cm. lengths of capillary tubing having drop times of either 2 to 5 or 6 to 12 seconds.[82] The latter can be divided to yield two shorter capillaries of suitable characteristics, but the long 2- to 5-second capillary has the advantage that, should it become "plugged" or erratic, a small section ($\frac{1}{2}$ to 1 cm.) can be cut off the end without making it inconveniently short or changing its characteristics greatly. On the other hand, the smaller bore of the 6- to 10-second capillary tends to reduce capillary noise.[67]

A Smoler-type capillary can be made by bending a Sargent 2- to 5-second D.M.E. capillary at right angles near its center and then breaking off the horizontal segment about one-half inch from the bend. Drop times on the order of 0.5 second are obtained with such capillaries at mercury reservoir heights of 60 to 120 centimeters.[67]

In order to obtain results with maximum reproducibility using a conventional D.M.E., care should be taken to insure that the capillary is mounted in a strictly vertical position (within 5°). Larger deviations from the vertical cause significant decreases in drop time. Furthermore, the D.M.E. is sensitive to low-frequency vibrations and should be used on a sturdy table standing on a firmly-supported floor.

With proper care and precaution a capillary can be maintained in good working condition for many months. The principal difficulty seems to arise from the precipitation of products of electrode reactions either on the flat end of the D.M.E., around the

[82] E. H. Sargent & Co., Chicago, Ill. Bulletin P-5, Sargent Polarographs and Accessories, 1965.

capillary orifice, or inside the orifice on the inner walls of the capillary. A capillary that has become dirty will usually exhibit a change in drop time from its original value and will give rise to erratic and irreproducible pen excursions during a recorded polarogram. Frequently, such a capillary can be restored to its original characteristics by immersing the tip (with mercury flowing) in warm 6 *M* nitric acid for several minutes followed by thorough washing with distilled water.

If the deposited solids are inside the capillary they are more difficult to remove, and the best procedure may be to cut off a $\frac{1}{2}$- to 1-cm. length from the end, or to replace the capillary with a new one. In either case, a recalibration is necessary.

Capillary difficulties can be minimized by: (1) thoroughly washing the capillary with distilled water immediately after each use, while the mercury is still flowing through the capillary; (2) avoiding positive potentials at which large anodic currents flow; and (3) making sure that the mercury head is never decreased to such an extent that solution can back up into the capillary. It is important to note at what reservoir height the mercury just ceases to flow through the capillary and then to maintain the reservoir several centimeters above this minimum height whenever the capillary is immersed in solution. After the capillary has been throughly washed with distilled water, it may be stored dry in the air or with its tip immersed in either a small amount of distilled water or a small amount of pure mercury.

Capillaries can be used in strongly basic solutions for long periods without adverse effect. Acidic fluoride solutions, however, ruin a capillary quickly. With such solutions the Teflon capillary of Raaen may be used.[83]

Mercury Reservoir Assembly.—A convenient dropping mercury electrode reservoir assembly is shown in Fig. 19-15. Many suitable designs for such assemblies have been proposed, ranging from the simplest possible setup in which the capillary and reservoir bulb are connected by a 2-foot length of plastic tubing to elaborate glass-metal commercial units which automatically maintain a constant head of mercury.[82] The important functions served by the D.M.E.-reservoir assembly are: (1) to provide a convenient means of initiating or ending the flow of mercury through the capillary; (2) to allow the column height to be set at some selected value in the range of about 30 to 60 cm. in order to produce an optimum drop time; and (3) to allow the height, *h*, of the mercury column to be measured accurately and to be reproduced easily. The greater the height the less precise need be the column adjustment for a given relative error in *h*.

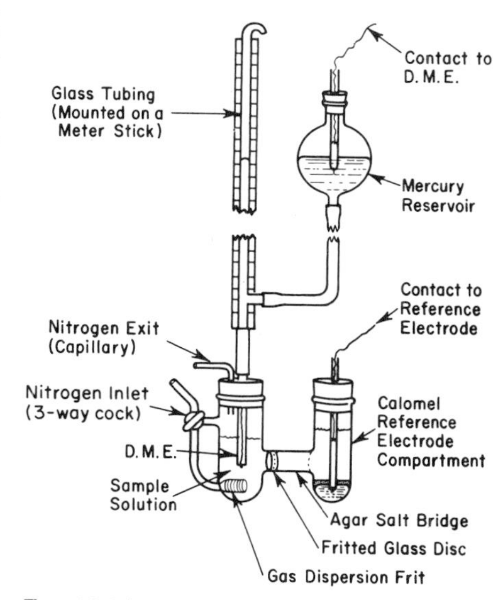

FIG. 19-15. Convenient H-cell and Reservoir Arrangement for Polarographic Studies.

Purification of Mercury.—Mercury used for the D.M.E. should be scrupulously free of solids, dirt, and dissolved metals. Triply-distilled, Instrument Grade mercury is commercially available and is usually satisfactory. (Occasionally, commercial C.P. mercury

[83] Raaen, H. P., Anal. Chem., **34,** 1714, 1962.

contains impurities at such levels of concentration that anomalous anodic waves are observed in residual current curves.) Used mercury can be exchanged for an equivalent amount of triply-distilled Instrument Grade mercury at the Bethlehem Apparatus Co., Hellertown, Pa., at a cost considerably below the price of new mercury.

Used mercury may be cleaned without distillation by placing it in a large suction flask, adding a volume of 1 M nitric acid several times that of the mercury, and then bubbling filtered air through the mercury and acid to effect oxidation of impurities and stirring. The nitric acid should be removed and replaced with fresh acid every 6–12 hours, and the process should be continued for several days. The mercury is then rinsed thoroughly with distilled water, blotted dry, warmed to 100°C. briefly in a *good hood,* cooled, and filtered through a filter paper containing several pinholes into a very clean, dry storage container.

Calibration of the Capillary.—Because diffusion currents obtained with different capillaries are proportional to the product $m^{2/3}\tau^{1/6}$, results with different capillaries can be compared if the values of m and τ are measured for each capillary at any one potential. The ratio $m_1{}^{2/3}\tau_1{}^{1/6}/m_2{}^{2/3}\tau_2{}^{1/6}$ for the two capillaries will be constant within experimental error at all other potentials.

The value of m, the mass of mercury flowing through the capillary (mg. sec.$^{-1}$), is quite insensitive to potential changes, and can be measured at any convenient potential, *e.g.*, with the D.M.E. shorted to the S.C.E. (zero applied potential); or with the D.M.E. at its open circuit potential (E_{ecm}). Sufficient accuracy is obtained if the mercury issuing from the capillary, inserted into an electrolyte solution, is collected for a sufficiently long time (10 to 30 minutes) and is then washed, dried, and weighed.

The drop time, τ (seconds per drop), is usually measured either at zero applied potential, at the potential of the electrocapillary maximum, or at the potential at which i_d is to be measured. The drop times can be measured satisfactorily with a stop watch (by measuring the total time for 10 or 20 drops to fall) or they can be computed at any potential by counting the number of oscillations (pips) per chart division on a recorded polarogram and knowing the chart speed of the recorder.

CELLS AND REFERENCE ELECTRODES

Initially, most polarographic work was carried out in simple, single-compartment cells, *e.g.*, Erlenmeyer flasks, using internal reference electrodes. At present, most polarographers prefer 2-compartment H-cells, such as shown in Fig. 19-15, which are commercially available in a variety of shapes and sizes, and which utilize external reference electrodes. The recent advent of controlled-potential polarographic instruments necessitates the use of 3 electrodes, which may be used with either 2-compartment or 3-compartment cells.

Single-compartment Cells.—Single-compartment cells have the advantages of economy and minimum chance of contamination from previous cell solutions. They are entirely adequate for most quantitative measurements, but possess the disadvantage that the potential of the internal reference electrode used in them depends upon the composition of the solution, so that potentials are not as easily reproduced as would be the case if external reference electrodes were used.

Criteria which should be satisfied by a half-cell if it is to be satisfactory for use as an internal reference electrode include the following: it should be reversible, stable, and reproducible in contact with the supporting electrolyte used in the cell; it should be able to supply currents of the magnitude of those flowing in a polarographic cell without becoming appreciably polarized itself; it should not react directly with the species being determined or studied (in the usual cathodic studies, this requirement will be satisfied if the potential of the reference electrode is more positive than the $E_{1/2}$ of the species being determined); and finally, the oxidized form of the half reaction occurring at the reference electrode should not give rise to a large residual current (satisfied if the oxidized form is insoluble). These criteria are met by a mercury pool several square centimeters in area or by a coil of silver wire (10–20 cm. in length) in contact with fixed concentrations of alkali metal halides, *e.g.*, 0.1 or 1 *M* KCl, and these are the internal electrodes most commonly used. These metals should not be used with supporting electrolyte salts having anions such as nitrate, perchlorate, or acetate, which form soluble mercurous and mercuric salts, if any significance is to be attached to the observed potentials. Similarly, the presence of complexing agents which dissolve mercurous halides will also alter the potential of the internal mercury electrodes, and may lead to high residual currents, especially in the presence of dissolved oxygen, which may then oxidize the mercury metal.

Removal of Oxygen.—Removal of dissolved oxygen from solutions in the D.M.E. compartment is almost always accomplished by bubbling nitrogen (or hydrogen) through the solution. The rate at which oxygen is removed depends on the total surface area of the nitrogen bubbles passing through the solution per unit time. If a sintered-glass gas dispersion frit is used, dissolved oxygen may be removed within 1 to 2 minutes, whereas if large bubbles of nitrogen pass through the solution, deaeration may require 20 to 30 minutes.[11]

It is convenient to have a 3-way stopcock on the nitrogen-inlet tube, so that the gas may be directed either through or over the surface of the solution (Fig. 19-15). To prevent re-entry of oxygen through the top of the cell, the stopper itself and all tubes passing through it should fit snugly, and the nitrogen exit tube should be of small bore and at least 2–3 inches in length. The purity of commercially available nitrogen gas is now such that no further purification is needed. Furthermore, "pre-purified" nitrogen, containing only 8 p.p.m. oxygen, is available from Matheson Co., at only a slight premium in cost.

Two-compartment Cells.—To avoid the possibility of a direct reaction between reference electrode components and species to be studied, and to permit a wider selection of anions in supporting electrolytes, most polarographic studies are carried out with 2-compartment cells in which the reference electrode is separated from the cell solution by means of a porous plug or a conducting bridge or diaphragm. If a sintered-glass disc is used to separate the compartments, as shown in Fig. 19-15, it should be placed as close to the D.M.E. compartment as possible in order to facilitate mixing of the solution and complete and rapid removal of oxygen. If mixing of solutions in the two compartments should be avoided, the plug should be backed with an agar salt bridge containing an electrolyte compatible with the solution in the D.M.E. compartment.

The principal disadvantage of the 2-compartment cell is the possibility of contamination of the sample solution with ions from previously used solutions which have migrated or diffused into the sintered-glass plug or the agar salt bridge or both. This is especially true in case a cell with an agar bridge is reused. Such cells should be thoroughly rinsed between runs or, preferably, allowed to stand for at least 10–15 minutes filled with a "blank" solution containing only supporting electrolyte. Cells containing a fine porosity glass frit and no agar bridge are easily cleaned by rinsing and then sucking wash solution through the frit.

Two of the best means of separating the sample compartment and the reference electrode are by means of a leached Vycor conducting glass bridge or a sheet of suitable ion-exchange resin. The former are available from Corning Glass Works, Corning, N.Y., in the form of tubes into which electrolyte and the salt bridge of a separate reference electrode can be inserted. Sheets of ion-exchange resin can be purchased from the British Drug Houses Ltd., B.D.H. Laboratory Chemicals Group, Poole, England, and a portion of this can be clamped tightly in place between two L-shaped tubes (smoothly ground edges) to give a demountable cell of a form approximating that shown in Fig. 19-15. Both the Vycor and the ion exchange bridges have fairly low resistances, less than several hundred ohms, and are not appreciably porous, so that cleaning is easy and chance of contamination is minimized.

Controlled Potential (Three-Electrode) Cells.—In any cell with only two electrodes, the reference electrode must also function as the electrolysis electrode counter to the D.M.E., and care should be taken to minimize the cell resistance and to prevent polarization of the combination reference and counter electrode by the cell current, if accurate measurements of half-wave potentials are desired. Both these possible sources of errors can be eliminated if three electrodes are used as in controlled potential polarography.[53,55,82,84,85,86] In such cells, the counter or auxiliary electrode to which the cell current flows does not serve as the reference electrode, and the reference electrode is placed on the side of the D.M.E. opposite the counter electrode so that it is out of the path of the cell current. The potential of the D.M.E. is then measured and controlled with respect to the reference electrode, and is not influenced by an iR drop across the salt bridge or diaphragm, or by possible polarization of the counter electrode.

The cell used for 3-electrode, controlled potential polarography can be in the form of an H-cell, as shown in Fig. 19-15, if the salt bridge connecting the reference electrode is inserted into the D.M.E. compartment and positioned so that its tip is at least 1 cm. above the end of the D.M.E. and out of the path of the cell current. Alternatively, a 3-compartment cell can be used, in which 2 compartments are attached to a central D.M.E. compartment, each separated by means of a sintered-glass disc.[84] In both these cells, high resistances due to electrode or cell design can be tolerated between the D.M.E. and either one or both of the electrodes. Commercial pH-type calomel electrodes can be used for reference and a piece of platinum wire suffices for the counter (auxiliary) electrode in controlled potential polarography.

It should be noted, however, as pointed out by Schaap and McKinney,[87] that if a nonaqueous solution of high specific resistance ($>10^3$ ohm cm.) is being studied, an appreciable iR drop can occur in the immediate vicinity of the D.M.E. (within 0.5 cm.), which is not compensated for in the usual 3-electrode cell.

PREPARATIONS

Agar Salt Bridge.—A satisfactory salt bridge can be made with a solution containing 3 to 4 percent agar by weight and 1 *M* inert electrolyte, *e.g.*, potassium chloride or sodium nitrate. The materials should be heated on a water or steam bath to liquefy them before use, pipetted into position, and then allowed to set until solidified. Excess agar should be refrigerated to prevent spoilage. A pure grade of agar is available from Difco Laboratories, Detroit, Mich.

Calomel Electrodes.—Many designs for calomel electrodes have been proposed. Three useful examples are shown in Fig. 19-16. The electrode at the left in Fig. 19-16 is useful for insertion directly into the D.M.E. compartment, but because of the length and narrowness of the salt bridge, it tends to have a higher resistance than the others. The center electrode has the advantages of very low current density, because of the large area of its mercury-solution interface, and very low resistance. It is inserted into one compartment of an H-cell and can be reused many times. The electrode at the right is made for use with demountable cells and is fitted with a standard tapered joint. The

[84] Arthur, P., Lewis, P. A., and Vanderkam, R. K., Anal. Chem., **33,** 488, 1961.
[85] Arthur, P., and Vanderkam, R. H., Anal. Chem., **33,** 765, 1961.
[86] Kelley, M. T., Fisher, D. J., and Jones, H. C., Anal. Chem., **32,** 1262, 1961.
[87] Schaap, W. B., and McKinney, P. S., Anal. Chem., **36,** 1251, 1964.

sintered-glass tip must be moistened and capped when the electrode is not being used.

The electrodes are prepared by first fixing in place the agar salt bridge, containing potassium chloride, adding pure mercury to a depth of about 1 cm., and then adding several grams of moist calomel paste, prepared by grinding together equal weights of mercurous chloride and potassium chloride to which was added 1 drop of mercury and enough saturated potassium chloride solution to moisten the mixture. The cell is filled to about three-fourths capacity with saturated potassium chloride solution, several addi-

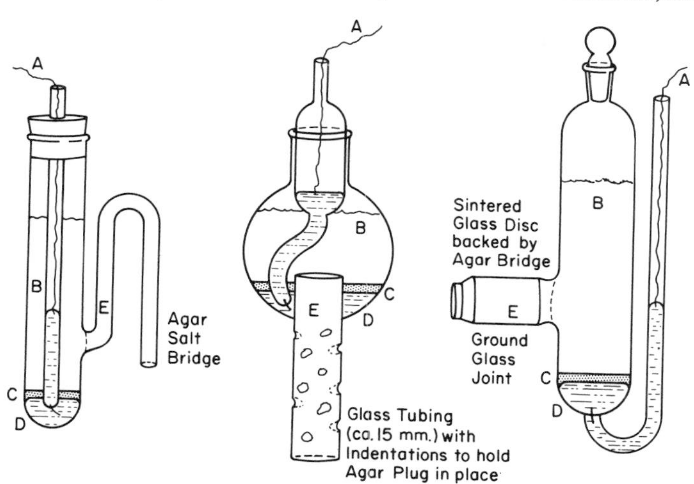

FIG. 19-16. Three Forms of Calomel Reference Electrodes. A, wire serving as electrical contact; B, saturated KCl solution; C, excess calomel paste and KCl crystals; D, mercury metal; E, agar salt (KCl) bridge.

tional grams of solid potassium chloride are added, and the compartment is sealed. After about a day, a constant, reproducible equilibrium potential is attained. (*Caution.* To prevent shrinkage, agar salt bridges must always be kept moist. They are best stored by dipping them into molar or saturated potassium chloride solution.)

It is very difficult to establish absolutely whether a single saturated calomel reference electrode is at its proper standard potential of +0.2464 volts. A practical way to check reference electrodes and to detect "bad" ones is to prepare several, at least three or four, at different times and to compare them against each other, always being careful to have one that is unused and relatively freshly prepared. Potentials of calomel electrodes should agree within ±0.5 millivolt. Electrodes showing larger deviations are suspect.

Solutions for Analysis or Standardization.—The procedure for preparing a sample for polarographic analysis depends on the nature and form of the original sample as well as on the composition desired for the final solution in which the polarogram is to be run. Although the procedure will generally be different for each sample, some general considerations regarding the preparation of solutions and the choice of reagents can be given.

(1) A convenient solvent and supporting electrolyte should be selected at the outset. Tables of half-wave potentials should be consulted for this selection.[11,19] The ideal supporting electrolyte should allow a well-developed wave to be recorded for the species being determined, free of interference from other constituents in the solution.

(2) All other reagents used in dissolving the sample, or in effecting necessary separa-

tions, must be compatible with the composition of the final solution, including the supporting electrolyte selected. If any reagents interfere they must be carefully removed.

(3) Supporting electrolytes and other reagents used in sample preparation should be of highest purity (Analytical Reagent Grade). For example, as little as 0.01 percent electroactive impurity in a reagent present at a concentration of 1.0 *M* could be a very serious interference. Water, or other solvents used, should be distilled.

(4) Large concentrations of electroactive species which react prior to or near the species being determined may have to be removed. Such separations may utilize, for example, precipitation, extraction, chromatographic, or controlled-potential electrolytic techniques.[8,11] They need not be complete unless the wave of the interference overlaps the wave of the constituent being determined. Moreover, a significant proportion of the species being determined must not be removed along with the interference.

(5) If sample size and solution volume can be varied, it is generally advisable to have a total of at least 0.1 *M* inert salt present as supporting electrolyte and to have the species being determined present at a concentration between 10^{-3} and 10^{-4} *M*.

(6) Because polarographic determinations are usually based on comparative rather than absolute measurements, the effects of traces of impurities in solvents and reagents tend to cancel out if the calibrating standard solutions are prepared and handled as much like the unknown sample as possible. For maximum precision, not only should concentrations be similar, but the solvent and reagents used should be from the same bottle or lot.

QUANTITATIVE APPLICATIONS

A brief resume of the general applicability and features of the quantitative applications of polarography is given here. For detailed information, the reader is advised to refer to the more comprehensive reviews of the subject[8,9,11,15,16,19] or to the original literature.

GENERAL FEATURES

Advantages.—The principal advantages of the polarographic method appear to be (1) its wide applicability (see below), (2) the possibility of determining several species (qualitatively and quantitatively) in the same solution and in the same experiment, (3) its relatively wide concentration range, (4) its sensitivity (down to part per million levels and below), and (5) its rapidity. In regard to the last point, although polarography is not to be regarded as a "rapid" method of analysis, in the hands of an experienced worker and with only the basic equipment available (no special standard or reagent solutions), rough quantitative data for a wide variety of substances can be obtained in from 10 to 30 minutes.

Applications.—Determinations can be performed of inorganic or organic species, molecular or ionic, which undergo oxidation or reduction at a mercury electrode in the region of potential bounded at the positive limit by the potential of oxidation of mercury in the medium employed, and at the negative limit by the potential at which the supporting electrolyte or the solvent is reduced. In aqueous solutions these limits are from about +0.3 volt to −2.7 volts *vs.* the S.C.E. If materials other than mercury are used for the microelectrode (*e.g.*, platinum, gold, graphite, or boron carbide) the positive limit can be extended considerably, and will be limited only by the oxidation of the solvent, the anion present, or the electrode material. Nonaqueous solvents can be used for organic substances which are insoluble in water, the only limitation being that, if the resistance of the medium is high, the polarographic wave may be severely distorted. In such cases a 3-electrode, controlled-potential polarograph may be used to advantage.[55,82,85,87] Substances which are not themselves electroactive, but which react quantitatively with another reagent which is electroactive, may be capable of being determined indirectly.[11]

Concentration Range.—The useful concentration range of polarography is generally regarded to be 10^{-2} to 10^{-5} *M*. Above 10^{-2} *M*, maxima are commonly encountered and the migration current may not be completely eliminated. Below 10^{-5} *M*, residual currents are much larger than faradaic currents, and they limit sensitivity and accuracy. Using special techniques and instrumentation to compensate for the residual current, the lower concentration range can be extended to about 10^{-7} *M* in favorable cases.

Precision.—A precision of ±3 to 5 percent is readily attainable at concentrations between 10^{-2} and 10^{-4} *M*. With additional effort and care to maintain the experimental conditions constant, *e.g.*, temperature, solution composition, capillary characteristics, and the potential at which the diffusion current is measured, a precision approaching ±1 percent can be obtained.

Interferences.—In cathodic polarography, substances which react at potentials more positive than that of the wave of the species being determined are troublesome, though they can be tolerated if present at not too high concentrations. Substances which give waves which overlap the wave being measured may prevent an accurate measurement of i_d. For reversible waves of equal height, it is easily shown that, for less than 2 percent overlap between adjacent conventional waves, the half-wave potentials should be separated by an amount not less than $(0.12/n_1 + 0.12/n_2)$ volt, where n_1 and n_2 are the numbers of electrons involved in the reactions. Thus, two 1-electron waves of equal height should be separated by 0.24 volt and two 2-electron waves should be separated by 0.12 volt for less than 2 percent overlap between the end of the first wave and the start of the second. As mentioned previously, smaller separations between waves can be tolerated in derivative polarography, as well as much larger concentrations of prior-reduced substances.

The separation between two interfering waves can sometimes be increased by a change in supporting electrolyte salt, or by complexation of one of the species. If such measures fail, a chemical separation may be necessary.[11] The chemical experience and judgment of the experimenter must be utilized in the solution of such problems.

MEASUREMENT OF DIFFUSION CURRENTS

Average and Maximum Currents.—In quantitative polarography either the *average* current flowing during the life of the drop or the *maximum* current flowing just before the drop falls should be measured. If the average current is to be measured, some degree of damping should be utilized to decrease the size of the oscillations of the galvanometer or the recorder pen so that the oscillations are not more than about 5 to 10 percent of full scale. Usually, the midpoint of these oscillations is assumed to be the average current, but this is true only if the damping is sufficient and the oscillations are small.

Measurement of maximum currents should not be attempted unless the pen speed of the recorder used is 2 to 4 seconds (full scale response) or faster. Experiments in the author's laboratory have shown that recorders with pen speeds on the order of 10 to 12 seconds are not quite fast enough to give true maximum currents and, if used without damping, are too fast to allow the midpoint of the oscillations to be used as a measure of the average current. Such recorders should be used only with appreciable damping in quantitative applications.

Measurement of Wave Heights and Correction for Residual Current.—At higher concentrations of the species being determined ($\geqslant 10^{-3}$ *M*), the residual current is negligible in comparison with the diffusion current and the measurement of the wave height presents no problems. Regardless of whether a manual or a recording polarograph is being used, the height of the wave may be determined simply from the difference in the average (or maximum) current measured at suitable potentials before the wave and after the wave, *i.e.*, $\bar{i}_d = (\bar{i}_2)_{E_2} - (\bar{i}_1)_{E_1}$. In order to select the potentials E_1 and E_2 which are suitable for the current measurements, it is always advisable to measure or record the current over a range of at least 0.1 to 0.2 volt before the wave begins and also for an equal range on the diffusion current plateau following the wave. The currents should be measured at points where the average-current polarograms have a constant slope and no curvature.

At concentrations on the order of 10^{-4} M the residual current is no longer negligible, and the measured difference in total current before and after the wave now includes a significant contribution from the residual current. The elimination of the residual current contribution from measurements of the diffusion current is indeed a vexing problem, and the suggested solutions for it using conventional instrumentation are empirical and only approximate. As mentioned previously, the slope of the residual current curve is not constant, but changes by a factor of 2 in the region of the electrocapillary maximum. Both the slope of the residual current curve and the potential of the electrocapillary maximum are dependent upon the composition of the solution.

Two general approaches which do not involve special instrumentation have been used to estimate and to correct for the residual current in conventional polarography. The first of these involves estimating the residual current at any selected potential by means of a linear extrapolation. If i_d is to be determined from measurements of the total current before and after the wave, the value of the residual current at E_2, the potential at which i_d is to be measured, is estimated by extrapolating the curve from E_1 to E_2 by means of a straight line drawn with its slope equal to the slope of the polarogram observed at E_1. The value of i_d is then given by

$$i_d = [(i)_{E_2} - (i_{\text{res}})_{E_2}] \tag{47}$$

The most common extrapolation technique involves extrapolation of both the prewave and postwave portions of the polarogram to the half-wave potential, and then measuring the diffusion current at this arbitrary but reproducible potential. This technique is illustrated in Fig. 19-17. The chief advantages of the method are that only one polarogram need be run and that the diffusion current measurements are made at a reproducible, definite potential.

The principal source of error in the extrapolation technique arises from the nonlinearity of the residual current curve, especially in the vicinity of the electrocapillary maximum. Only in limited ranges of potential, either before or after the electrocapillary maximum, is the slope of the residual current curve reasonably constant. If both segments of the curve, which are extrapolated to the half-wave potential, lie on the same side of the electrocapillary maximum, the technique attains its maximum accuracy.

An examination of residual current curves will show that extrapolated residual currents are always higher than the true residual current at potentials near the electrocapillary maximum. It is the opinion of the author that the best way to make extrapolations to the $E_{1/2}$ in the region of the electrocapillary maximum is to extrapolate both segments as curves, drawn parallel to an actual residual current curve recorded with a blank solution at the same sensitivity.

The second approach to separating the "true" diffusion current from the residual current involves an attempt to measure or record the residual current (at the potential at which i_d is to be measured) with a "blank" solution made up to simulate as nearly as possible the solution to be analyzed, except for the presence of the species to be determined. This compensation procedure is only approximate because the residual current arises both from reaction of traces of impurities in the solution and from the charging current. If the solution associated with the substance being determined (an aliquot of which must be added to the blank or compared with the blank) contains impurities different in identity or in concentration from those in the blank, the procedure becomes inaccurate. If the species being determined is itself capillary active, the approach will be seriously in error, because in this case the charging current will change and will not cancel out. Nevertheless, in most situations this type of approach appears to offer the best accuracy. It has the disadvantage of being rather time consuming because measurements must be made on two solutions, both of which must be deaerated.

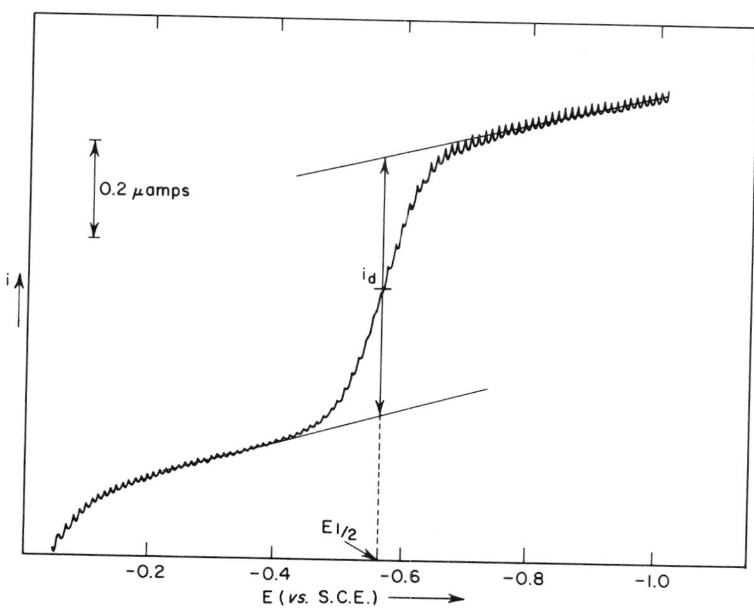

FIG. 19-17. Damped, Average-current Polarogram of 10^{-4} *M* Tl^+ in 1 *M* Potassium Chloride, Illustrating Measurement of the Diffusion Current by Extrapolation to the Half-wave Potential.

It should be remembered that elimination of residual current either by use of blank solutions or by extrapolation is essentially an empirical procedure, and that at low concentrations appreciable uncertainty is introduced.

Instrumental Methods for Automatic Compensation of Residual Current.—A variety of instrumental approaches have been suggested for automatic compensation for residual current. The oldest and most common of these is the linear compensation technique of Ilkovic and Semerano,[88] who subtracted from the total cell current a linearly increasing current which was adjusted to be approximately equal to the average residual current. This type of compensation is available on several commercial instruments.

Although the application of linear compensation greatly improves the appearance of polarographic waves of substances at low concentrations, the method is subject to precisely the same errors and uncertainties as the linear extrapolations discussed above. This type of compensation is most satisfactory in those regions of potential where the residual current maintains a reasonably constant slope, and is least satisfactory in the region of the electrocapillary maximum potential, where the residual current slope

[88] Ilkovic, D., and Semerano, G., Collection Czechoslov. Chem. Communs., **4**, 176, 1932.

changes by a factor of 2. The compensating current can be adjusted to compensate approximately for the residual current on one or the other side of the electrocapillary maximum, but not for both simultaneously.

The effects of large residual currents are apparently minimized in derivative polarography, as mentioned in a preceding section. But here again, the first derivative of a residual current polarogram is constant in only those regions of potential where the slope of the residual current curve is constant. In the region of the electrocapillary maximum, the baseline of a derivative polarogram changes and measurement of the derivative peak height becomes difficult because the position of the baseline must be arbitrarily interpolated. Use of a "blank" solution to establish the baseline in this region is a useful expedient, but is subject to the uncertainties mentioned above in regard to matching the solutions exactly.

Kanevskii[89] suggested the use of two dropping mercury electrodes, one dipping into a blank solution and the other into the test sample, and measuring the difference in their currents. At the same applied potential, the current flowing through the D.M.E. in the blank solution is caused to flow through the measuring galvanometer or resistor in a direction opposite to that of the current from the D.M.E. in the test sample. The residual current of the blank is then subtracted from the total cell current of the test sample. Compensation of this type will be effective only to the extent that both the capillaries and the solutions match. The Differential Cathode Ray Polarograph manufactured by Southern Analytical Ltd. has compensating circuitry of this general type.

Recent studies in this laboratory[90] have investigated the discharge of the capacitative current carried by mercury drops immediately after their detachment from the D.M.E. Integration of this discharge current and subtraction of it from the total cell current was effective in compensating for residual current in d.c. polarography.

In the area of alternating current polarography, several elegant approaches for residual current compensation have been suggested. In all of them the differences in the time responses of the signals arising from the faradaic and capacitative components are utilized to separate them. A phase-sensitive detector, first suggested by Jessop,[72] is incorporated in the Cambridge Instrument Co. Univector Polograph and in several instruments manufactured in Japan.[22] Although a number of very promising studies of second harmonic a.c. polarography have been made,[74,75,76] instruments with such capabilities are not at present available commercially. Square wave and pulse techniques effect compensation by measuring the faradaic component of the current after the capacitative component has decayed to a near zero value. Instruments incorporating such circuitry are commercially available,[22] and have been discussed in more detail in a previous section. The more effective methods of compensating for residual current using a.c. techniques, allow the useful range of quantitative polarography to be extended to about 10^{-7} *M* and the limit of detectability to lie below 10^{-8} *M*.

Calibration of Wave Heights.[8, 11]—Once the wave height is measured, it remains to relate the diffusion current to concentration. This may be done in a variety of ways.

Calculation from Diffusion Current Constant.—If an experimental value of the diffusion current constant, I $(= i_d/Cm^{2/3}\tau^{1/6})$, is available for the species being determined and for the same solution composition and temperature, then the concentration of the desired species can be calculated from the measured diffusion current and the capillary characteristics

$$C = i_d/Im^{2/3}\tau^{1/6} \tag{48}$$

Although published values of I are available,[8,11,19] and may be used for this purpose, it

[89] Kanevskii, E., J. Appl. Chem. (U.S.S.R), **17,** 514, 1944.
[90] DiSalvo, J., Ph.D. thesis, Dept. of Chemistry, Indiana University, 1965.

is always better to determine I in one's own laboratory with one's own equipment in order to minimize the effects of calibration errors in the instrument, etc. If this is done, then for drop times between 3 and 6 seconds, and for concentrations in the range 10^{-2} to 10^{-4} M, a precision of ± 3 percent may be expected for results calculated by this method.

It is also possible to calculate simply the ratio i_d/C, or its reciprocal, C/i_d, for a given species in a given solution using a particular capillary at a specified voltage (m and τ constant). Once the value of this ratio is evaluated for the capillary, it can be used for the calculation of C from diffusion current data. Obviously, it is better to evaluate I than to evaluate only i_d/C, for the latter value must be determined for each capillary used.

EXAMPLE.—Cadmium is to be determined in a dilute solution known to contain cadmium sulfate. A 5-ml. aliquot of the unknown solution is pipetted into a 50-ml. volumetric flask, sufficient solid potassium chloride is added to make the solution 0.1 M in potassium chloride, and the flask is filled to the mark with distilled water. A portion of this solution is placed in a polarographic cell, carefully deaerated and thermostatted at 25°C. A polarogram is recorded using a capillary having a drop time of 2.47 sec. at -0.60 volt (the $E_{1/2}$ of cadmium) and a value of $m = 3.299$ mg. sec.$^{-1}$ ($m^{2/3}\tau^{1/6} = 2.577$). The height of the wave as measured at the $E_{1/2}$ (see Fig. 19-17) with a ruler is 85.0 mm. If the sensitivity scale of the polarograph is set at 0.020 μamp. per mm., the measured wave height corresponds to a current, i_d, of 1.70 μamp.

Using the tabulated value[11] of 3.51 for the diffusion current constant, I, of cadmium ion in 0.1 M potassium chloride, the concentration of cadmium in the original solution can be calculated using Eq. (48). (The factor 10 arises because of the dilution.)

$$C_{\mathrm{Cd^{++}}} = \frac{10 \times 1.70}{3.51 \times 2.577} = 1.88 \text{ millimolar} = 1.88 \times 10^{-3}\ M$$

Use of Calibration Curves.—Calibration curves can be constructed corresponding to each of the two ratios mentioned in the preceding section. The first involves constructing a plot of $i_d/m^{2/3}\tau^{1/6}$ *vs.* C, and is preferable to the second, which consists merely in plotting i_d *vs.* C. In both cases, it is best to be as consistent as possible in reproducing the conditions under which both the calibration curve and the measurements are made. The plot of i_d *vs.* C is valid for only the particular capillary and potential used. At low concentrations, use of calibration curves tends to cancel the systematic errors involved in correcting for residual currents.

Use of Standard Solutions or Samples.—A *standard solution* is a synthetic solution made up to approximate the sample being analyzed in composition and in the concentration of the species being determined. If polarograms are run on both the standard and unknown solutions using the same capillary, then the concentration of the unknown, C_x, may be calculated from the known concentration of the standard, C_s, and the two measured diffusion currents, *i.e.*,

$$C_x = C_s(i_d)_x/(i_d)_s \tag{49}$$

This calculation assumes that m and τ are constant. Although m may be considered constant within experimental error, the value of τ is quite sensitive to the composition of the solutions and its constancy should be checked. Changes in τ may be taken into account by modifying Eq. (49) as follows:

$$C_x = C_s \frac{(i_d)_x}{(i_d)_s} \times \frac{\tau_s^{1/6}}{\tau_x^{1/6}} \tag{50}$$

A *standard sample* is a previously analyzed sample similar to that being analyzed. It is carried along and treated in a manner identical to that for the unknown sample. The concentration of the unknown is calculated by means of Eq. (49) or (50). If the two concentrations are roughly equal, most of the possible errors tend to cancel and maximum accuracy is attained, even at lower concentrations.

EXAMPLE.—The determination of cadmium in the previous example can be made more precisely by comparison with a standard solution prepared in a manner similar to that used for the unknown solution. A 5-ml. aliquot of a standard solution known to contain 2.40×10^{-3} M cadmium is diluted to 50 ml. and made 0.1 M in potassium chloride. The height of the polarogram, recorded with the deaerated solution at 25°C. using the same capillary, is measured to be 110 mm. at a polarograph sensitivity of 0.020 μamp. per mm., giving a diffusion current, i_d, of 2.20 μamp.

Assuming that the capillary characteristics are the same for the two polarograms, the concentration of cadmium in the unknown solution can be calculated using Eq. (49). (The dilution factors cancel out here because they are equal.)

$$C_x = (2.40 \times 10^{-3}) \frac{1.70}{2.20} = 1.85 \times 10^{-3} \ M$$

Standard Addition Methods.—The methods of standard addition possess the advantage that both the unknown polarogram and the calibrating polarogram are obtained with the same, or nearly the same, solution. In one type of standard addition method, after the polarogram of the unknown solution is recorded, an aliquot of standard solution of the species being determined is added to the unknown solution and a second polarogram is recorded. The increase in wave height produced by the addition of the standard aliquot enables the concentration of the unknown species to be calculated from the wave height of the original polarogram. It can be shown that, if C_u is the concentration of the species being determined in the original solution of volume V, and if v is the volume of the added aliquot of standard solution of concentration C_s, then

$$C_u = i_1 v C_s / [i_2(V + v) - i_1 V]. \tag{51}$$

where: i_1 is the measured wave height of the first wave; and
i_2 is the wave height after the addition of the standard solution.

In a modification of this type of standard addition method, two identical samples of the unknown are taken and an aliquot of standard solution is added to one. The calculation of the concentration of the unknown from the wave heights of the two polarograms is the same as above. These standard addition methods provide maximum accuracy if i_2 is at least twice i_1, if the volume, v, of the added aliquot is small compared to V, and if the standard solution is made up to contain supporting electrolyte and other inert salts at about the same concentration as the solution being analyzed. Under these conditions errors arising from differences in the composition of the solution and from changes in the characteristics of the capillary are minimized. Any error introduced by inaccurate correction for the residual current (likely at lower concentrations) will always be proportionately greater in the unknown (smaller) wave than in the second, larger wave and will not entirely cancel out. At higher concentrations the methods of standard addition are probably as accurate as any.

EXAMPLE.—The determination of cadmium in the unknown solution referred to in the previous examples is carried out by the method of standard addition. Exactly 25.0 ml. of the 50 ml. of 0.1 M potassium chloride solution containing the 5-ml. aliquot of the unknown solution is pipetted into the polarographic cell and the polarogram is run as before with the same results (wave height = 85.0 mm.; polarograph sensitivity = 0.020 μamp. mm.$^{-1}$, giving i_d = 1.70 μamp.). Then a 5-ml. aliquot of the standard cadmium solution (2.40×10^{-3} M) is added, the solution is deaerated, and another polarogram is recorded at 25°C. which gives a wave height of 127 mm. at a polarograph sensitivity of 0.04 μamp. mm.$^{-1}$ (i_d = 5.08 μamp.). For the calculation using Eq. (51), V = 0.025 liters, v = 0.005 liters, $V + v$ = 0.030 liters, $C_s = 2.40 \times 10^{-3}$ M, i_1 = 1.70 μamp. and i_2 = 5.08 μamp. (Again, the factor 10 must be introduced to take into account the 10-fold dilution of the original unknown sample.)

$$C_u = \frac{(10)(1.70)(0.005)(2.40 \times 10^{-3})}{(5.08)(0.030) - (1.70)(0.025)} = 1.86 \times 10^{-3}\ M$$

Pilot Ion Method.—The standard addition methods above have the disadvantage of requiring the recording of two polarograms. It is possible to carry out a determination by recording just one polarogram if the added aliquot introduces a standard solution of a second ion, different from the unknown, whose well-developed wave does not interfere with the wave of the substance being determined. If an empirical calibration is made of the ratio of wave heights at known concentrations of the two species, then the differences in m and τ (at the potentials at which the two different sets of diffusion currents are measured) are included in the calibration factor. Since both polarograms are recorded with the same solution at the same temperature and with the same capillary, changes in these factors affect the heights of the two waves similarly, and the effects of changes in these factors tend to cancel. Careful temperature control is not essential. The advantages of the use of pilot ions are the speed and the insensitivity to experimental variables.

ANALYTICAL PROCEDURES AND DATA

The literature pertaining to the applications of polarography in inorganic and organic analysis is enormous.[91] Many excellent and convenient compilations of polarographic data and procedures have been published, of which only brief summaries can be included in the tables at the end of this chapter.

In the case of inorganic analysis, extensive tables listing half-wave potentials and diffusion current constants in a variety of supporting electrolytes have been assembled by Meites.[11,19] Table 19-1 contains a summary of these in some of the more common supporting electrolytes. Procedures for the determination of many elements in various materials are given by Milner,[9] Kolthoff and Lingane,[8] Březina and Zuman,[16] von Stackelberg,[12] Heyrovsky,[13,14] and by Doležal and Zýka.[19] A summary of the applications of polarography in the determination of inorganic species in various materials is given in Table 19-2.

Applications of polarography in organic analysis have been summarized by Zuman,[15] Březina and Zuman,[16] Milner,[9] Kolthoff, Lingane, and Wawzonek,[8] von Stackelberg,[12] and Elving.[92] Schwabe[93] and Kabaskalian and McGlothen[19] have compiled extensive tables of data pertaining to the cathodic and anodic polarographic reactions of organic compounds. Biochemical, biological, and medicinal applications of polarography have been reviewed by Milner,[9] by Kolthoff and Lingane,[8] and, more extensively, by Březina and Zuman.[16] A listing of some of the principal polarographically active organic functional groups is given in Table 19-3, together with examples of specific organic compounds which exhibit polarographic waves.

Current research in polarography is reviewed biennially by Hume and Wawzonek in Analytical Chemistry. The published proceedings of the successive meetings of the International Congress of Polarography contain papers describing in detail recent advances in polarographic theory, instrumentation, and applications. A bibliography of polarographic literature, complete through 1955, has been published by E. H. Sargent & Co., Chicago, Illinois.[91]

The following section contains references to actual polarographic determinations used in the analysis of various materials which are described elsewhere in these volumes.

[91] E. H. Sargent & Co., Bibliography of Polarographic Literature, Chicago, Illinois, 1922–1955.

[92] Elving, P. S., "Application of Polarography to Organic Analysis," in Mitchell, J., Kolthoff, I. M., Proskauer, E., and Weissberger, A., Eds., Organic Analysis, Interscience, New York, 1954, Vol. II, p. 195.

[93] Schwabe, K., Polarographie und Chemische Konstitution Organischer Verbindungen, Akademie-Verlag, Berlin, 1957.

APPLICATIONS IN THE ANALYSIS OF SPECIAL MATERIALS

Procedures included in other chapters of Standard Methods of Chemical Analysis are:

1. Chapter 44, Volume III, Alloys: Nonferrous.
   a. Aluminum in bronze
   b. Antimony in lead
   c. Bismuth in aluminum-copper and zinc alloys
   d. Bismuth in cadmium
   e. Cadmium in aluminum
   f. Cadmium in zinc
   g. Copper in magnesium
   h. Copper in antimony alloys
   i. Copper in copper alloys
   j. Copper in lead alloys
   k. Copper in tin alloys
   l. Copper, lead, nickel, and zinc in aluminum alloys
   m. Copper, cobalt, chromium, and nickel in titanium alloys
   n. Indium in zinc
   o. Iron in nonferrous alloys
   p. Iron in nickel-molybdenum-iron alloys
   q. Lead in brass and bronze
   r. Lead in indium
   s. Lead in zinc
   t. Manganese in nickel and monel
   u. Nickel in cobalt
   v. Nickel and zinc in brass and bronze
   w. Tin in aluminum
   x. Titanium in aluminum
   y. Zinc in aluminum-copper alloys
   z. Zinc in brass

   Chapter 26, Volume IIA, Alloys: Nonferrous.
   a. Determination of zinc in antimony, lead, and tin, and their alloys, page 902.
2. Chapter 48, Volume III, Natural Fats.
   a. Tin in fats
3. Chapter 53, Volume III, Glass.
   a. Aluminum
   b. Antimony
   c. Barium
   d. Cadmium
   e. Lead
   f. Sodium + potassium
   g. Selenium
   h. Zinc
4. Chapter 51, Volume III, Organic Functional Groups.
   a. Anthraquinone in complex mixtures
   b. Maleic anhydride
5. Chapter 54, Volume III, Paint, Varnish, and Lacquer.
   a. Cobalt, lead, and titanium in paint pigments
   b. Trace elements in "pure" pigments and vehicles
   c. Cobalt, lead, and manganese in vehicles
   d. Copper and lead in zinc oxide
   e. Additives in rubber chemicals
   f. Antioxidants in hydrocarbon thinners
   g. Free acrylic or styrene monomers in polymers

   h. Maleic acid or anhydride in phthalic anhydride
   i. Peroxides in oils
6. Chapter 41, Volume IIB, Plastics.
   a. Determination of acrylic monomers in plastics, page 2089.
   b. Determination of acrylonitrile monomer in plastics, page 2064.
7. Chapter 59, Volume III, Rubber and Rubber Products.
   a. Accelerators in rubber analysis
   b. Antioxidants in rubber analysis
   c. Free sulfur in accelerators
   d. Zinc in rubber
8. Chapter 60, Volume III, Semiconductors.
   a. Bismuth
   b. Cadmium
   c. Copper
   d. Indium
   e. Lead
   f. Thallium
   g. Tin
   h. Zinc
9. Chapter 62, Volume III, Soil.
   a. Copper
   b. Manganese
   c. Nitrate
   d. Zinc
10. Chapter 47, Volume IIB, Vitamins.
   a. Determination of folic acid, page 2383.
   b. Determination of Vitamin K_3, page 2355.
11. Chapter 63, Volume III, Water Analysis.
   a. Cadmium
   b. Copper
   c. Lead
   d. Nickel
   e. Nitrate
   f. Dissolved oxygen
   g. Zinc

TABLE 19-1. POLAROGRAPHIC CHARACTERISTICS OF SELECTED INORGANIC SUBSTANCES[8,9,11,19,20]

Element	Reaction at D.M.E.	Supporting Electrolyte	$E_{1/2}$ (*vs.* S.C.E.)	*I*
Aluminum	$+3 \rightarrow 0$	0.025 *M* $BaCl_2$ or 0.1 *M* LiCl	−1.75	—
Antimony	$III \rightarrow 0$	1 *M* HCl, 0.01% gelatin	−0.15 (rev.)	5.54
		0.5 *M* H_2SO_4, 0.01% gelatin	−0.32	4.94
	$III \rightarrow V$	1 *M* KOH	−0.45	(max.)
	$\rightarrow 0$		−1.15	6.0
	$V \rightarrow III$	6 *M* HCl, 0.005% gelatin	(1) >0	3.00
	$\rightarrow 0$		(2) −0.26	7.50
Arsenic	$III \rightarrow 0$	1 *M* HCl, 0.0001% methylene blue	(1) −0.43	6.04
	$\rightarrow -III$		(2) −0.67	12.0
	$III \rightarrow 0$ (?)	0.5 *M* H_2SO_4, 0.01% gelatin	(1) −0.7	—
	$\rightarrow -III$ (?)		(2) −1.0	8.4
	$III \rightarrow V$	0.5 *M* KOH, 0.025% gelatin	−0.26	−3.82
	$V \rightarrow 0$	11.5 *M* HCl	(1) >0	—
	$\rightarrow III$		(2) −0.52	10.7
Barium	$+2 \rightarrow 0$	0.1 *M* LiCl or $(C_2H_5)_4NI$	−1.92	3.58
Bismuth	$+3 \rightarrow 0$	1 *M* HCl, 0.01% gelatin	−0.09 (rev.)	5.23
		0.5 *M* H_2SO_4	−0.04	4.31
		0.1 *M* EDTA, 2 *M* NaOAc	−0.70	—
Boron	$BH_4^- \rightarrow BO_2^-$	0.1 *M* NaOH	−0.064	−26
Bromine	$-1 \xrightarrow{Hg} Hg_2Br_2$	0.1 *M* KNO_3	+0.12 (10^{-3} *M*)	—
Cadmium	$+2 \rightarrow 0$	0.1 *M* KCl or 0.1 *M* HCl	−0.60 (rev.)	3.51
		0.1 *N* KNO_3	−0.58 (rev.)	3.53
		1 *M* NH_3, 1 *M* NH_4Cl	−0.81	3.68
		1 *M* ethylenediamine, 0.1 *M* KNO_3 0.01% gelatin	−0.93	3.13
Calcium	$+2 \rightarrow 0$	0.08 *M* $(C_2H_5)_4NI$ with Ba^{++} or La^{+3} as max. suppressor	−2.22	—
Cesium	$+1 \rightarrow 0$	0.1 *M* R_4NCl or R_4NOH	−2.09	—
Chlorine	$-1 \xrightarrow{Hg} Hg_2Cl_2$	0.1 *M* KNO_3	+0.25 (10^{-3} *M*)	—
Chromium	$+2 \rightarrow +3$	0.1 *M* NH_3, 5 *M* NH_4Cl, 0.005% gelatin	−0.85	−1.14
		1.0 *M* KCl, 0.005% gelatin	−0.40	−1.54
	$+3 \rightarrow +2$	1 *M* NH_3, 1 *M* NH_4Cl, 0.004% gelatin	−1.43	—
		1 *M* KCN	−1.38 (rev.)	1.55
		Sat'd. $CaCl_2$, 0.005% gelatin	−0.51 (rev.)	—
		0.1 *M* KCl, 0.01% gelatin (pH 4)	−0.9	—
	$VI \rightarrow +3$	1 *M* NaOH	−0.85	5.72
Cobalt	$+2 \rightarrow 0$	0.1 to 1 *M* KCl or 0.1 *M* KNO_3	−1.20	—
		1 *M* NH_3, 1 *M* NH_4Cl, 0.004% gelatin	−1.29	—
	$+2 \rightarrow +3$	0.1 *M* ethylenediamine, 0.1 *M* KNO_3	−0.46 (rev.)	—
	$Co(NH_3)_6^{+3} \rightarrow II$	1 *M* NH_3, 1 *M* NH_4Cl	(1) −0.5	—
			(2) −1.3	—
		0.1 *M* KNO_3	(1) −0.24	1.74
			(2) −1.21	5.36
Copper	$+1 \rightarrow 0$	1 *M* Cl^-	−0.18 (rev.)	2.34
		1 *M* NH_3, 1 *M* NH_4Cl	−0.50 (rev.)	—
	$+1 \rightarrow +2$	1 *M* NH_3, 1 *M* NH_4Cl	−0.22 (rev.)	—
	$+2 \rightarrow +1$	1 *M* Cl^-	(1) +0.04	—
	$\rightarrow 0$		(2) −0.18	3.44
	$+2 \rightarrow +1$	1 *M* NH_3, 1 *M* NH_4Cl 0.004% gelatin	(1) −0.22 (rev.)	—
	$\rightarrow 0$		(2) −0.50 (rev.)	3.75
	$+2 \rightarrow 0$	0.1 *M* ethylenediamine, 0.1 *M* KNO_3, 0.01% gelatin	−0.51 (rev.)	3.56
		0.1 *M* KNO_3	+0.02	3.41
		1 *M* KOH or NaOH	−0.41	2.91
		0.25 *M* EDTA (pH 7)	−0.41 (rev.)	2.83
Europium	$+3 \rightarrow +2$	0.1 *M* NH_4Cl	−0.67	1.47
		0.1 *M* EDTA (pH 6–8)	−1.17 (rev.)	1.3
Gallium	$+3 \rightarrow 0$	0.001 *M* KCl	−1.1	—
		1 *M* NH_3, 1 *M* NH_4Cl	−1.6	—
Germanium	$IV \rightarrow 0$ (?)	0.5 *M* NH_3, 1 *M* NH_4Cl	−1.45	—
		0.1 *M* EDTA (pH 6–8), 10^{-4} *M* fuchsin	−1.30	—
Gold	$+1 \rightarrow 0$	0.1 *M* KCN	−1.46	—
		0.1 *M* KOH	−1.16	—
	$III \rightarrow +1$	0.1 *M* KCN	>0	—
		2 *M* KOH	−0.2	—
Hydrogen	$+1 \rightarrow 0$	0.1–0.5 *M* KCl or LiCl	−1.58 (10^{-3} *M*)	5.60

TABLE 19-1 (cont.)

Element	Reaction at D.M.E.	Supporting Electrolyte	$E_{1/2}$ (*vs.* S.C.E.)	I
Indium	$+3 \rightarrow 0$	0.1 *M* KCl or HCl	−0.56	—
		1 *M* KCl	−0.60	—
		1 *M* KOH or NaOH	−1.09	—
Iodine	$-1 \xrightarrow{Hg} Hg_2I_2$	0.1 *M* KNO_3	−0.03 (10^{-3} *M*)	—
	$V \rightarrow -1$	1 *M* KCl, LiCl or NaCl	−1.16	—
		0.1 *M* OAc^-, 0.1 *M* KCl (pH 4.9)	−0.50	—
		0.1 *M* NaOH, 0.1 *M* KCl	−1.21	—
Iron	$+2 \rightarrow 0$	0.1 *M* KCl	−1.3	—
	$+3 \rightarrow +2$	0.15 *M* Na_3Cit (pH 6)	−0.18 (rev.)	—
		0.2 *M* $Na_2C_2O_4$ (pH 4)	−0.24 (rev.)	1.50
		0.5 *M* Na_2Tart (pH 6) 0.005% gelatin	−0.19	1.11
		0.1 *M* EDTA, 2 *M* NaOAc	−0.12	—
Lead	$+2 \rightarrow 0$	0.1 *M* KCl, 0.005% gelatin	−0.40	3.80
		0.1 *M* KNO_3 or $NaNO_3$	−0.39 (rev.)	—
		1 *M* NaOH, 0.005% gelatin	−0.76 (rev.)	3.40
Lithium	$+1 \rightarrow 0$	0.1 *M* $(C_4H_9)_4NOH$	−2.33	—
		0.1 *M* $(C_4H_9)_4NOH$ (50% ethanol)	−2.31	1.19
Magnesium	$+2 \rightarrow 0$	0.1 *M* R_4NCl	−2.3	—
Manganese	$+2 \rightarrow 0$	1 *M* NH_3, 1 *M* NH_4Cl, 0.004% gelatin	−1.66	—
		1 *M* KCl	−1.51	—
		1 *M* KOH or NaOH	−1.70	—
	$+2 \rightarrow +3$	1.5 *M* NaOH, 3% Mannitol	−0.64	—
		0.1 *M* KOH, 0.3 *M* Triethanolamine	−0.5 (rev.)	—
Mercury	$I \rightarrow 0$	0.1 *M* HNO_3	>0	3.68
	$+2 \rightarrow 0$	0.1 *M* HNO_3	>0	3.48
Molybdenum	$VI \rightarrow V, III$	0.3 *M* HCl	(1) −0.26	poor
	$\rightarrow III$		(2) −0.63	—
	$VI \rightarrow V$	0.1 *M* H_2Tart (pH 2)	(1) −0.22	—
	$\rightarrow III$		(2) −0.52	5.07
	$VI \rightarrow V$	12 *M* H_2SO_4	(1) 0	—
	$\rightarrow III$		(2) −0.13	1.24
	$VI \rightarrow ?$	0.1 *M* EDTA, 0.1 *M* HOAc, 0.1 *M* NH_4OAc	−0.63	—
Nickel	$+2 \rightarrow 0$	0.1 *M* KCl, 0.0003% methyl red	−1.1	3.38
		1 *M* NH_3, 1 *M* NH_4Cl	−1.10	3.56
		0.1 *M* KCN, 0.1 *M* KCl	−1.42	—
Niobium	$V \rightarrow IV$	0.1 *M* KCl (pH 2.6)	−1.28	—
		0.1 *M* KNO_3 (pH 2.6)	−1.03	—
		0.1 *M* EDTA (pH 3)	−0.61 (rev.)	—
Nitrogen	$N_2H_4 \rightarrow ?$	alkaline soln. (anodic wave)	—	—
	$NH_2OH \rightarrow ?$	1 *M* NaOH (anodic wave)	−0.4	—
	$NO \rightarrow ?$	Dil. HCl	−0.9	—
	$HNO_2 \rightarrow ?$	0.1 *M* KCl, 0.01 *M* HCl, 0.05 − 0.2 × 10^{-3} *M* $UO_2(OAc)_2$	−1.0	7.45
	$NO_3^- \rightarrow ?$	0.1 *M* KCl, 0.01 *M* HCl, 0.2 × 10^{-3} *M* $UO_2(OAc)_2$	−1.0	13.8 (catalytic)
	$NH_4^+ \rightarrow ?$	$(CH_3)NBr$	−2.21	—
Osmium	$VIII \rightarrow VI$	Sat. $Ca(OH)_2$	(1) >0	—
	$\rightarrow IV$	Sat. $Ca(OH)_2$	(2) −0.40	—
	$\rightarrow III$	Sat. $Ca(OH)_2$	(3) −1.16	—
Oxygen	$H_2O_2 \rightarrow H_2O$	0.1 *M* NaOH	−1.0	—
	$O_2 \rightarrow H_2O_2$	0.1 *M* NaOH	(1) −0.18 (rev.)	—
	$\rightarrow H_2O$		(2) −1.0	—
	$O_2 \rightarrow H_2O_2$	0.1 *M* KNO_3 or KCl	(1) −0.05	6.22
	$\rightarrow O_2$		(2) −0.9	12.3
Palladium	$+2 \rightarrow 0$	1 *M* NH_3, 1 *M* NH_4Cl	−0.75	—
		1 *M* pyridine, 1 *M* KCl	−0.34 (rev.)	—
Platinum	$+2 \rightarrow 0$	1 *M* KCl	(1) −0.1 (adsorp.)	4.06
	$\rightarrow 0$		(2) −1.35 (normal)	—
Potassium	$+1 \rightarrow 0$	0.1 *M* $(C_2H_5)_4NOH$	−2.14	—
		0.1 *M* $(C_2H_5)_4NOH$ (50% Ethanol)	−2.10	1.70
Rhenium	$-1 \rightarrow 0 + ?$	2.4 *M* HCl	(anodic waves at −0.47, −0.34, −0.17)	—
	$IV \rightarrow III$ (?)	2.4 *M* HCl (15°C.)	−0.53	—
	$VII \rightarrow ?$	2.4 *M* HCl (15°C.)	−0.40	—
Rhodium	$III \rightarrow I$ (?)	1 *M* KNO_3, 0.01% gelatin	−0.96	—
		1 *M* NH_3, 1 *M* NH_4Cl	−0.93	—

TABLE 19-1 (cont.)

Element	Reaction at D.M.E.	Supporting Electrolyte	$E_{1/2}$ (*vs.* S.C.E.)	I
Rubidium	$+1 \rightarrow 0$	0.1 *M* $(CH_3)_4NOH$	−2.03	—
Ruthenium	IV $\rightarrow$?	1 *M* $HClO_4$	(1) >0	0.91
	$\rightarrow$ III		(2) +0.20	1.53
	$\rightarrow$ II		(3) −0.34	2.89
Samarium	$+3 \rightarrow +2$	0.1 *M* $(CH_3)_4NI$, 0.0005 *M* H_2SO_4 0.01% gelatin	−1.80	3.85
Selenium	$-2 \xrightarrow{Hg} HgSe$	0.05 *M* NH_3, 1 *M* NH_4Cl	−0.84	−4.9
		1 *M* HCl	−0.49	−3.8
	$-2 \rightarrow Se_2^{--}$	1 *M* NaOH	(1) −1.02	−1.95
	$\rightarrow$ HgSe		(2) −0.94	−3.78
	IV $\rightarrow -2$	0.1 *M* NH_3, 0.1 *M* NH_4Cl	−1.64	11.0
		1 *M* KCl (pH 7.2) 0.01% gelatin	−1.8	—
	IV $\rightarrow$?	1 *M* HCl	(1) >0	—
			(2) −0.1	—
			(3) −0.4	—
			(4) −0.5	—
Silver	$+1 \rightarrow 0$	0.1 *M* KNO_3	>0	2.50
Sodium	$+1 \rightarrow 0$	0.1 *M* $(C_2H_5)_4NOH$	−2.12	—
		0.1 *M* $(C_2H_5)_4NOH$ (50% ethanol)	−2.07	1.40
Strontium	$+2 \rightarrow 0$	0.1 *M* $(C_2H_5)_4NI$	−2.11	3.46
Sulfur	$-2 \xrightarrow{Hg} HgS$	0.1 *M* NaOH or KOH	−0.76 (10^{-3} *M*)	—
	$S(O) \rightarrow H_2S$	1.1 *M* pyridine, 0.06 *M* py·HCl (in methanol)	−0.50	5.69
	$SO_2 \rightarrow H_2SO_2$	0.1 *M* HCl or HNO_3	−0.37	5.49
Tantalum	V $\rightarrow$ IV	0.9 *M* HCl	−1.16	—
		0.1 *M* K_2Tart (pH 3–5)	−1.57	—
Tellurium	$-2 \rightarrow 0$	0.1 *M* NH_3, 1 *M* NH_4Cl, 0.003% gelatin	−1.1	—
		1 *M* HCl, 0.003% gelatin	−0.73	—
		1 *M* NaOH	−1.2	−3.5
	IV $\rightarrow 0$	1 *M* NH_3, 1 *M* NH_4Cl	−0.67	—
		2 *M* NH_3, 1 *M* $(NH_4)_2$Tart	−0.70	6.4
		1 *M* NaOH, 0.003% gelatin	(1) −1.1 (small)	—
			(2) −1.19	9.75
	VI $\rightarrow$ −II	NH_3—NH_4Cl (pH 8) 0.0005% gelatin	−1.21	17.5
		Sat. $(NH_4)_2C_2O_4 + NH_3$ (pH 8)	−1.23	16.3
	VI $\rightarrow$?	0.1 *M* KCl or $NaClO_4$	(1) −1.1	—
			(2) −1.45	—
	VI $\rightarrow$?	1 *M* NaOH, 0.003% gelatin	−1.57	—
		12 *M* HCl	(1) >0	—
			(2) −0.43	—
			(3) −0.79	—
Thallium	$+1 \rightarrow 0$	0.1 *M* KCl, HCl, KNO_3, HNO_3 or NH_3	−0.46 (rev.)	2.70
		1 *M* KCl, HCl, KNO_3, HNO_3 or NH_3	−0.48 (rev.)	—
		0.01 *M* EDTA, 1 *M* HOAc, 1 *M* NaOAc	−0.46 (rev.)	—
	$+3 \rightarrow +1$	0.6 *M* HCl	(1) >0	3.83
	$\rightarrow 0$		(2) −0.45 (rev.)	5.72
Tin	$+2 \rightarrow +4$	1 *M* KCl, 0.01% gelatin	−0.1	—
	$\rightarrow 0$		−0.47	4.07
	II $\rightarrow$ IV	1 *M* NaOH, 0.01% gelatin	−0.73	−3.45
	$\rightarrow 0$		−1.22	3.45
	$+2 \rightarrow +4$	1 *M* $HClO_4$	+0.14	—
	$\rightarrow 0$		−0.43 (rev.)	
	$+4 \rightarrow +2$	1 *M* HCl, 4 *M* NH_4Cl, 0.005% gelatin	(1) −0.25	2.84
	$\rightarrow 0$		(2) −0.52	6.33
	$+4 \rightarrow +2$	12 *M* HCl, 0.002% Triton-X	(1) −0.50	—
	$\rightarrow 0$		(2) −0.83 (rev.)	—
Titanium	IV $\rightarrow +3$	Sat. $CaCl_2$	−0.12 (rev.)	—
		0.1 *M* HCl, 0.005% gelatin	−0.81	1.56
		0.1 *M* KSCN	−0.46 (rev.)	—
		0.2 *M* $H_2C_2O_4$ (pH 0.5)	−0.28 (rev.)	1.75
		EDTA (pH 1.0–2.5)	−0.22 (rev.)	—
Tungsten	V $\rightarrow$ III	12 *M* HCl	−0.56 (rev.)	2.53
	VI $\rightarrow$ V	12 *M* HCl	(1) >0	1.31
	$\rightarrow$ III		(2) −0.55	3.82
	VI $\rightarrow$ V	0.1 *M* H_2Tart, 5 *M* HCl	(1) −0.33	—
	$\rightarrow$ III (?)		(2) −0.68	4.40

TABLE 19-1 (cont.)

Element	Reaction at D.M.E.	Supporting Electrolyte	$E_{1/2}$ (*vs.* S.C.E.)	*I*
Uranium	III → IV	1 *M* HCl (0°C.)	−0.94 (rev.)	—
		0.5 *M* H_2SO_4 (0°C.)	−1.10 (rev.)	—
	IV → III	1 *M* HCl	−0.89	—
		0.1 *M* $HClO_4$	−0.86	1.57
	VI → V	2 *M* HOAc, 2 *M* NH_4OAc, 0.01% gelatin	−0.45 (rev.)	1.7
	VI → V	0.5 *M* $(NH_4)_2CO_3$	(1) −0.83	1.5
	→ IV		(2) −1.45	—
	VI → V	1 *M* NH_3, 1 *M* NH_4Cl	(1) −0.8	—
	→ III		(2) −1.4	—
	VI → V	0.1 *M* HCl	(1) −0.18	1.54
	→ III		(2) −0.94	—
	VI → V	0.5 *M* $NaClO_4$, 0.01 *M* $HClO_4$	−0.18 (rev.)	1.57
Vanadium	III → +2	1 *M* HCl, 1 *M* $HClO_4$ or 0.5 *M* H_2SO_4	−0.51 (rev.)	1.41
		0.1 *M* EDTA (pH 5–8.5)	−1.27 (rev.)	1.20
	IV → V	1 *M* NH_3, 1 *M* NH_4Cl, 0.08 *M* Na_2SO_3	−0.32	−0.94
	II		−1.28	1.92
	IV → III	12 *M* HCl, 0.002% Triton-X	(1) >0	—
	→ ?		(2) −0.62	—
	→ II		(3) −0.75	—
	IV → V	1 *M* NaOH or KOH, 0.08 *M* Na_2SO_3	−0.43	—
	IV → II	0.1 *M* EDTA (pH 9.5)	−1.25	2.20
	V → IV	1 *M* NH_3, 1 *M* NH_4Cl, 0.005% gelatin	(1) −0.96	1.6
	→ II		(2) −1.26	4.72
	V → IV	0.1 *M* HCl	(1) >0	—
	→ II		(2) −0.80	—
	V → ?	0.1 *M* NaOH or LiOH	−1.7	—
	V → II	0.1 *M* EDTA (pH 9.5)	−1.22	3.29
Ytterbium	+3 → +2	0.1 *M* NH_4Cl	−1.41	1.57
Zinc	+2 → 0	1 *M* KCl, 0.0003% methyl red	−1.00 (rev.)	3.42
		1 *M* $NaClO_4$	−1.00	—
		1 *M* NH_3, 1 *M* NH_4Cl, 0.005% gelatin	−1.35	3.82
		1 *M* NaOH, 0.01% gelatin	−1.53 (rev.)	3.14
Zirconium	IV → 0	0.1 *M* KCl (pH 3)	−1.65	—
	IV → ?	0.1 *M* LiCl (abs. methanol)	−1.4	—

TABLE 19-2. SELECTED APPLICATIONS OF POLAROGRAPHY IN INORGANIC ANALYSIS[91]

Element	*Materials Analyzed*
Aluminum	Clay, glass, light metals and alloys, sea water, steel, Sn–Pb alloys, titanium, water
Antimony	Alfalfa, Al alloys, babbit metal, glass, iron, steel, lead, Mg alloys, battery acid, white metals
Arsenic	Biological material, blood, urine, Pb metal and alloys, minerals, phosphoric acid, steel, iron, ores, sulfuric acid, water, zinc
Barium	Glasses, refractories
Bismuth	Alloys, babbit metal, biological media, Cd, Sn–Pb alloys and ores, zinc alloys, lead, water, zinc
Bromine (-ide)	Developers, oil-well water, pharmaceuticals, water
Cadmium	Air, alloys, aluminum, Al alloys, amalgams, babbit metal, bearing metals, biological materials, CdS–ZnS phosphors, Cu alloys, Pb metal and alloys, lithopone, nickel baths, pulp, rocks, Ag alloys, water, zinc, Zn alloys, Zn ores
Calcium	Biological materials, blood, epidermis, glass, refractories, lead, milk and serum, soils, water
Chlorine (-ide)	Beer, blood, blood serum, brines, pharmaceuticals, gas, insecticides, sewage, water
Chromium	Al alloys, calcium, plating baths, ash, dust, Fe alloys, steels, lubricating oils, soil, Ti alloys
Cobalt	Babbit metal, biological material, carbides, clay, iron, Fe alloys, marine animals, Ni ores, motor oil, rocks, soils, steel, Ti alloys, lacquers, water
Copper	Alfalfa, Al alloys, babbit metal, bearing metals, beverages, blood, brass, Cd, Sn–Pb alloys, calcium, ash, epidermis, milk fat, fertilizers, gelatins, glass, iron, Fe ores, lard, lead, liver, milk, oils, plant tissues, proteins, soil, Ag alloys, steel, Ti alloys, water, wine, zinc, metal, alloys, and ores
Europium	Rare earth mixtures
Gold	Blood, ruby glass, silver, urine
Indium	Be compounds, lead alloys, minerals, zinc metal and alloys
Iodine (-ide)	Pharmaceuticals, developers, NaCl, blood, organic compounds, urine, water
Iron	Al metal and alloys, babbit metal, biological fluids, brass, calcium, epidermis, clay, H_2O_2, iron ores, lead, Mg alloys, nickel, oils, phosphate coatings, soil, sulfuric acid, tin, titanium, wine, Zn metal and ores
Lead	Air, Al metal and alloys, babbit metal, beryllium, biological materials, blood, bone, brass, cadmium, Cd, Sn–Pb alloys, Cu metal and alloys, feces, foods, gasoline, glass, lead alloys, lead salts, Mg alloys, oils, organic materials, paint, plants, soil, steel, tin, urine, varnish, water, wine, Zn metal, alloys and ores
Lithium	Natural waters, silicates
Magnesium	Brine, sea water, ash, epidermis, light metals and alloys, serum, water
Manganese	Air, alfalfa, Al alloys, blood, Ca metal, clay, ferromanganese, iron ore, lead, Mg alloys, plants, pulp, steels, Ti alloys, varnish, wine, zinc
Mercury	Urine
Molybdenum	Ferromolybdenum, iron, steels, ores, plants, soil, Ti alloys

TABLE 19-2 (cont.)

Element	*Materials Analyzed*
Nickel	Al metal and alloys, babbit metal, bearing metal, clay, cobalt salts, Cu metal and alloys, iron metal and alloys, lead, Ni ores, organic materials, pulp, rocks, soil, steels, Ti alloys, water
Nitrate	Blood, brines, propellants, plants, water and wastes
Oxygen	Atmosphere, aqueous solutions, bacterial media, beer, blood, cells, foods, gases, sewage, soil, water, wastes, wine
Potassium	Biological liquors, blood, epidermis, glass, refractories, salts, soil, water, urine
Selenium	Pyrites, ores, water
Silver	Lubricating oils, photographic baths, plating baths, zinc
Sodium	Al metal and alloys, biological liquors, blood, epidermis, glass, salts, water, wine
Sulfur	Bacteria, nickel, oil, organic compounds, paper, pyrites
" (sulfate)	Aluminate liquors, Al salts, fluoride solutions, Ni plating baths, water
" (sulfide)	Bacterial cultures, developers, oil-well water
Thallium	Biological material, bone, Cd metal, In metal, urine, Zn metal and alloys
Tin	Al alloys, Cu metal and alloys, food, iron, lead metal and alloys, oils, ores, steel, tin-plated iron, plating solutions, Ti metal, water, white metals, Zn metal, alloys and ores
Titanium	Al alloys, clays, Fe alloys, ores, pigments, soap, steels, Ni alloys
Tungsten	Alloy steels, ores and rocks
Uranium	Blood, dust, minerals and ores, solutions
Vanadium	Crude oils, salt, steel, alloy steels, uranium
Zinc	Alcohols, alfalfa, Al metal and alloys, amalgams, atmosphere, babbit metal, bearing metals, biological materials, blood, brass, Cd metal, Cu metal and alloys, fertilizers, foods, galvanized iron plate, glasses, Fe minerals, Pb metal and alloys, Mg alloys, Ni plating baths, organic material, oil, paints, plants, pulp, Ag and Au alloys, soil, water, Zn alloys and ores

TABLE 19-3. POLAROGRAPHICALLY ACTIVE ORGANIC FUNCTIONAL GROUPINGS[8,9,15,19,92,93]

Type of Grouping	*Structure (Examples)*	*Examples of Specific Compounds*
Conjugated Carbon—Carbon Double Bonds	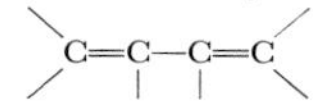 >C=C—C=C<	Butadiene, diacetylene, styrene, cyclo-octatetraene, naphthalene maleic acid, phthalic acid, acrylonitrile
Carbon–Halogen Bonds	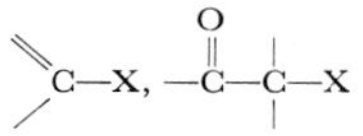 >C—X, —C(=O)—C—X	Chloroform, carbon tetrabromide, dibromoethylene, DDT, phenacyl fluoride, allylbromide, bromobenzene, benzyl iodide
Carbon–Oxygen Bonds	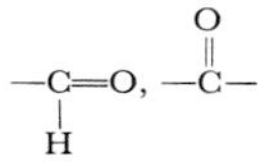 —C(H)=O, —C(=O)—	Formaldehyde, chloral, acrolein, benzaldehyde, acetone, acetophenone, mesityloxide, fural, glyoxal, *p*-benzoquinones, biacetyl, pyruvic acid, oxalic acid
Carbon–Nitrogen Bonds	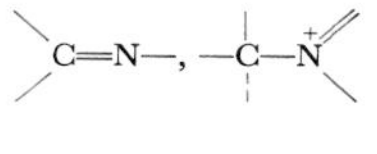 >C=N—, —C—N⁺<	Acetonimine, butyraldoxime, acetaldehyde, amidine, benzil monoxime, α-keto-acid oximes, benzalaniline, salicylaldoxime, diacetyldioxime, phenacylamine, aminoacetonitrile, pyridoxamine
Nitrogen–Nitrogen Bonds	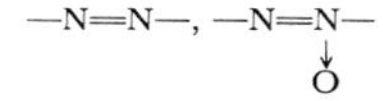 —N=N—, —N=N(→O)—	Azobenzene, formazane, azoxybenzene, benzenediazonium chloride
Nitrogen–Oxygen Bonds	$—NO_2$, —N=O, —NHOH	Nitromethane, nitrocyclohexane, nitrobenzenes, picric acid, nitrofurans, nitropyridines, *N*-nitrosodimethylamine, ethyl-nitrate, nitroglycerine, pyridine-*N*-oxide, nitrones, nitrosobenzene, phenylhydroxylamine
Carbon–Sulfur Bonds	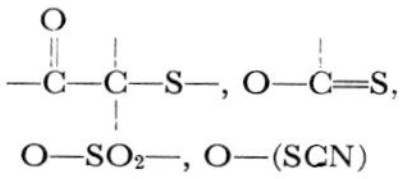 —C(=O)—C—S—, O—C=S, O—SO_2—, O—(SCN)	Phenyl phenacyl sulfide, thiobenzophenone, benzene sulfochloride, diphenylsulfone, rhodanbenzenes, phenylisothiocyanate
Oxygen–Oxygen Bonds	—O—OH, —O—O—	Ethylhydroperoxide, peracetic acid, dimethylperoxide, benzoylperoxide
Sulfur–Sulfur Bonds	—S—S—, —S—SO_2—	Diethyldisulfide, cystine, lipoic acid, thiothiosulfonates
5-Ring Heterocycles	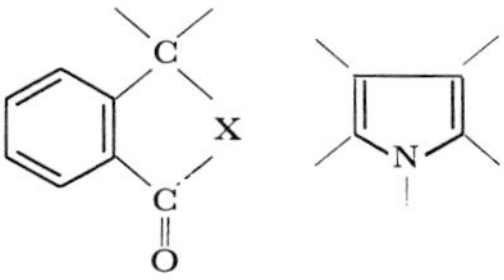 C, X, C, O; N	Phthalides, phthalimidine, indolenine, carbazolenine, pyrazolanthrone, maleic acid anhydride, ninhydrin, phthalimides isatine, saccharine, penicillic acid, digitoxine, tetrazolium salts
6-Ring Heterocycles	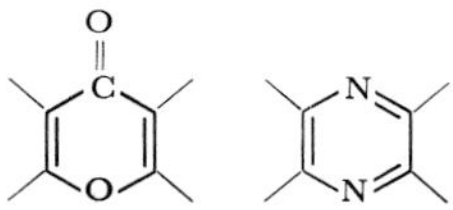 O, C, O; N, N	γ-pyrone, flavones, xanthone, flavanones, quinoxalines, phenazines, pyrimidines, adenine, nicotinamide, *N*-alkyl pyridinium ions, oxazines, coumarines, folic acid, riboflavin, 8-quinolinol, quinine, acridines
Organometallics	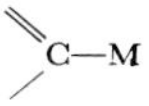 >C—M	Ethylmercurihalides, *p*-chloromercuribenzonic acid, tetraphenylphosphonium chloride, chlorotriethyl lead, triphenyl tin, tetraphenylarsonium chloride, tetraphenylstibonium chloride, diarylselenoxides, tetraphenylboride ion.

Chapter **20**

AMPEROMETRIC TITRATIONS

By Jan Doležal and Jaroslav Zýka

Department of Analytical Chemistry
Charles University
Prague, Czechoslovakia

INTRODUCTION

Electrometric methods based on measuring changes of potential, current intensity, or conductivity are widely used for determining the equivalence point in titrimetric determinations. In addition to the classical potentiometric and conductometric methods, others have been developed during the past few decades, which have followed the discovery of polarography. These are titrimetric determinations based on measuring the changes in the diffusion current (see Chapter 19) which flows between two electrodes at constant potential in a solution of the substance to be determined, and which is related to the amount of titrimetric reagent added. The use of polarographic diffusion currents for such titrations was first reported by Heyrovský and Berezicky (Ref. 1). These titrations were originally called *polarographic titrations*, but Majer (Ref. 2) later recommended the term *polarometric titrations*. The expression *titrations by means of limiting currents* has also been proposed. Kolthoff (Ref. 3) and his group, who have contributed largely to the general acceptance of this method, have recommended the use of *amperometric titrations*, and it is by this term that the method is now best known.

Polarometric or amperometric titrations have developed along with the development and application of polarography, or in the broader sense with the development of voltammetric methods.

Until recently the principle of amperometric titrations has been regarded as a part of the description of polarography, and has been considered as one of the "titration modifications" of polarography (Chapter 19). The very rapid development of electroanalytical determinations in recent years, however, has led to the necessity of a more precise classification, which is not related to the historical development or to the traditional manner of presentation, but rather to the character of the electrochemical processes which are the basis for the application of individual electroanalytical methods. Thus, amperometric titrations are those which are based on the use of polarized electrodes, and the measurement, at constant potential, of the changes in the current which flows between these electrodes upon the addition of the titrant.

The expression *classical amperometric titrations* is used for titrations at constant potential and in which one polarized indicator electrode is used. This may be a dropping mercury electrode, a rotating or vibrating platinum electrode, or one made of another suitable metal. Within this group, the expression *polarometric titrations* is limited to those cases in which the indicator electrode is a dropping mercury electrode. This agrees with the use of the term *polarography* for those voltammetric methods in which this special electrode is used. The reference electrode in such titrations is usually a saturated calomel electrode or a mercury pool.

In the present discussion only the *classical amperometric titrations* (and polarometric titrations) will be described. Thus, titrations in which two polarized electrodes are used will not be considered, although these methods (chiefly dead stop end point or biamperometric titrations) have been reported in analytical practice.

For more detailed information a number of monographs and comprehensive reviews are available which deal with general theory, classification, and mutual relationships of electrochemical methods (Ref. 4–18). The classification and nomenclature is summarized in a comprehensive review by Delahay, Charlot, and Laitinen (Ref. 19).

For methods other than those based on classical amperometry (or polarometry), or principally those titration methods in which two polarized electrodes are used, the reader is referred to the above-mentioned monographs and reviews, and in addition to publications devoted especially to such specific methods as dead-stop end point titrations (Ref. 20), polarization current titrations (Ref. 12), diamperometric end point titrations (Ref. 21), and biamperometric titrations (Ref. 22).

The fundamentals of amperometric titrations and examples of their applications are dealt with comprehensively in some of the above-mentioned monographs in the form of separate chapters (Ref. 3–8, 11). In book form, these topics have been treated only in three monographs (Ref. 23–24a), but numerous comprehensive reviews have been published, among these the regular reviews by Laitinen (Ref. 25) and Konopik (Ref. 26). Others which merit mention are those devoted particularly to the theoretical problems related to amperometric titrations (Ref. 27–30), and to the numerous reviews of the present state of this type of analysis (Ref. 31–52), or those which are concerned with the application of amperometric titrations, such as in pharmacy (Ref. 53–55), in the determination of organic compounds (Ref. 55a), alkaloids (Ref. 56), narcotics (Ref. 57), and others.

A review of the application of organic titrimetric reagents in amperometric titrations has also been published (Ref. 51), and the determination of organic compounds has been treated in a special monograph (Ref. 58–59). A number of the more recent monographs (Ref. 60–67) also report recommended amperometric titration methods, together with procedures.

Citations of the literature on amperometric titrations have been published and amplifications are published regularly as an appendix to the journal, *Collection of Czechoslovak Chemical Communications*. The literature is abstracted regularly in specialized journals, such as the *Journal of Electroanalytical Chemistry*, Abstract Section; *Leybold Polarographische Berichte;* and *Radiometer Polarographics* (now *Radiometer News*).

PRINCIPLES OF AMPEROMETRIC TITRATIONS

As shown in the chapter on polarography (Chapter 19) any substance capable of depolarizing a small indicator electrode will cause a definite limiting current to flow through the electrolytic solution. On a diffusion current plateau (Fig. 20-1) the limiting current is independent of the applied voltage on the microelectrode due to the extreme state of concentration polarization existing at the surface of the microelectrode. The only factor affecting the limiting current, if the migration current is almost eliminated by the addition of sufficient inert electrolyte, is the rate of diffusion of electroactive substance from the body of the solution to the electrode surface. Hence, the diffusion current is proportional to the concentration of the electroactive material in the solution.

If a portion of the electroactive material is removed from the solution by interaction with another reagent, the diffusion current will decrease. This is the fundamental principle of amperometric titrations. The observed diffusion current at a suitable applied voltage is measured as a function of the volume of the titrating solution. The end point is determined by the point of intersection of two straight lines representing the change of current before and after the equivalence point. In amperometric titrations, points on the curve near the end point are neglected.

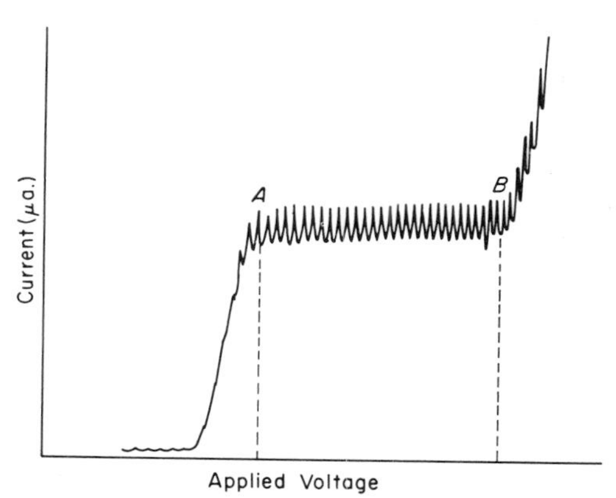

FIG. 20-1. Polarographic Wave of Lead(II) Ion.

If the current-voltage characteristics of the substance to be titrated and the reagent are unknown, it is necessary first to determine the polarographic curves for both under the same conditions as those under which the titration is to be carried out. The applied voltage is then adjusted at the beginning of the titration to a value such that the limiting diffusion current of the substance to be titrated, or of the reagent, or of both, is obtained. Depending on the nature of the substance to be determined and the nature of the titrant several types of titration curves are obtained.

Types of Titration Curves.—In Fig. 20-2 are shown the more common types of titration curves, together with the corresponding hypothetical polarographic curves of each individual substance: in these figures R represents the polarographic curve of the substance used as the titrant and X represents the curve of the substance to be titrated. For each amperometric titration the applied voltage is adjusted to a value corresponding to a point between A and B shown in the figures.

In order for amperometric methods to be applicable, it is necessary that at least one of the reacting substances, *i.e.*, the substance to be titrated, the titrant, or the reaction product, act as a depolarizer and give a diffusion current.

Amperometric titrations which have been most frequently studied are those based on the formation of precipitates of low solubility or of slightly ionized complexes. Titrations based on oxidation-reduction and neutralization reactions have received less attention.

The principle of amperometric titrations may be illustrated by considering the titration of the lead(II) ion. The polarographic wave of the lead(II) ion is shown in Fig. 20-1. This curve is obtained by using an electrode system consisting of the dropping mercury indicator electrode and a saturated calomel reference electrode. Another suitable polarization curve, such as the voltammetric curve which expresses the dependence of current intensity on potential, using other electrodes, could be used. The polarographic wave considered is due to the reduction of lead(II) ions (Pb^{++}) acting as a depolarizer on the indicator electrode in a suitable supporting electrolyte. If the external electromotive force is greater than that represented by point *A*, the current will remain constant (in polarography this is referred to as the *limiting current*) as long as the electromotive force does not exceed that value at which further depolarization of the electrode occurs due to the presence of another substance in the solution. This will take place at a voltage corresponding to point *B*.

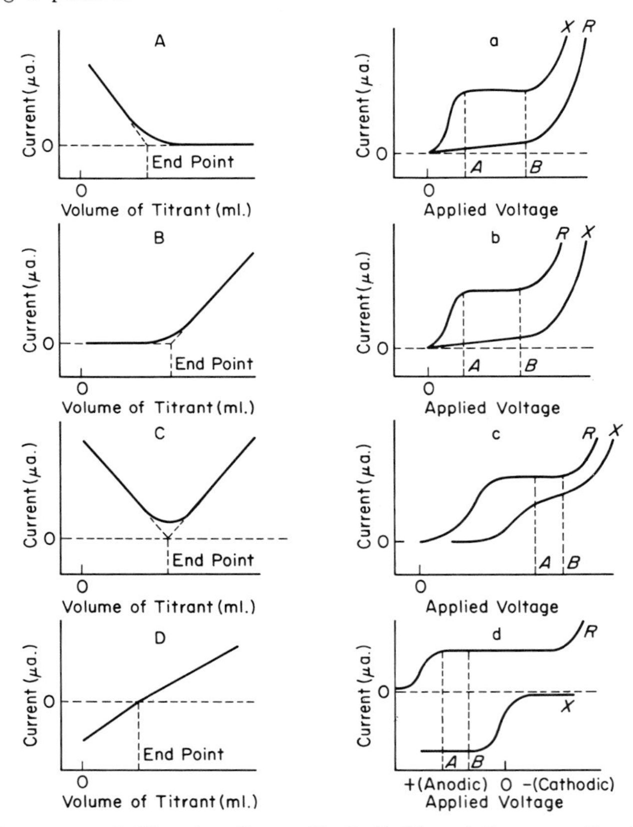

FIG. 20-2. Amperometric Titration Curves (A, B, C, D) and Corresponding Polarographic Curves (a, b, c, d) of Substance to be Titrated (*X*) and Titrating Reagent (*R*).

The current is directly proportional to the concentration of the active substance over the potential range between points *A* and *B*. Now, consider the titration of the polarographed solution of the lead salt by adding a reagent such as sulfate or oxalate which forms with the lead ions a precipitate of low solubility, and which is not reduced on the dropping mercury electrode at a potential within the range represented between points *A* and *B*. At the same time a constant potential having a value within this range is applied to the dropping mercury electrode. On adding the sulfate or oxalate solution, lead ions precipitate from the solution, and the limiting current due to the lead ions decreases linearly with the decrease in the concentration of the lead ion in the solution, *i.e.*, with the amount of reagent added. This decrease occurs after each addition of the sulfate or oxalate solution until all lead ions are precipitated as lead sulfate or lead oxalate. At the equivalence point the current decreases practically to zero, and it does not change on the addition of further portions of the titrant, since the latter is not reduced on the dropping mercury electrode in the applied potential range.

The course of such a titration is shown in Fig. 20-3, which was carried out in such a manner that after each addition of the titrant the decrease in the polarographic wave

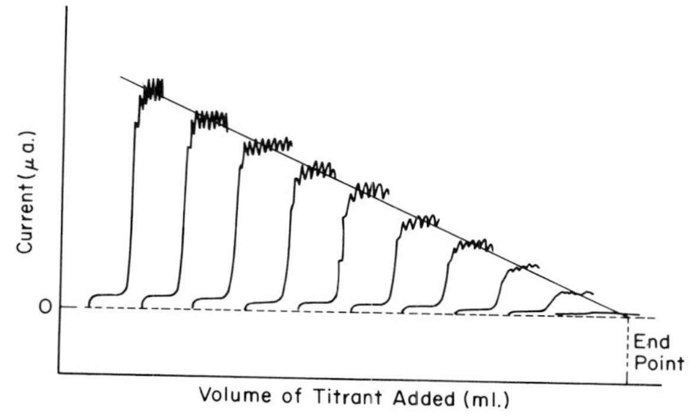

Fig. 20-3. Polarographic Titration of Lead(II) Ion by Sulfate Solution.

was registered. This is in fact a *polarographic* titration. In amperometric titrations this lengthy procedure is not used, but instead there is applied on the electrode a potential having a magnitude corresponding to the range of the limiting current and the decrease of this current as the titrant is added is measured by means of a microammeter.

The course of the titration may be demonstrated graphically by plotting on the ordinate axis values of current intensity in microamperes (the magnitude of the limiting current) and on the abscissa the volume of titrant added. Thus, two straight lines intersecting at the equivalence point are obtained (Fig. 20-4). For comparison, note Fig. 20-3.

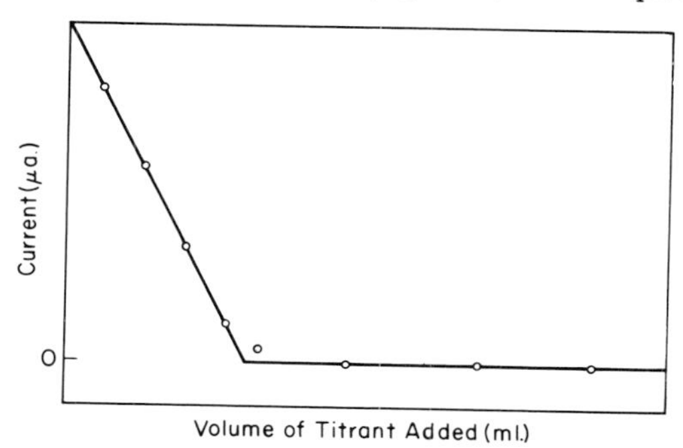

Fig. 20-4. Amperometric Titration of Lead(II) Ion by Sulfate Solution.

In the titration just described, a polarographically reducible substance is titrated by a substance which is polarographically inactive under the conditions employed, *i.e.*, composition of solution, potential, pH, etc. The titration curve obtained in such cases resembles somewhat the letter L (Fig. 20-2, A). As will be explained later, the titrant should always have a concentration greater than that of the solution to be titrated.

If the titration described above is reversed, *i.e.*, if a substance polarographically irreducible or inactive is titrated by a substance that is polarographically reducible or active, or, in general by a depolarizer, the plot of quantity of titrant *vs.* current consists of two intersecting straight lines in the form resembling somewhat a reversed letter L (Fig. 20-2, B). This is due to the fact that before the equivalence point the limiting current remains practically at zero, but after the equivalence point it increases linearly with the quantity of titrant added. An example of such methods is the titration of the sulfate ion with a solution of a lead(II) salt. The current intensity does not drop completely to zero in these titrations, and this is due to incomplete precipitation of the reaction product, and also to the presence of oxygen which has not been completely removed from the solution to be titrated.

If the substance to be determined and the titrant are both depolarizers, the titration curve consists of two intersecting straight lines, and resembles the letter V (Fig. 20-2, C). The limiting current due to the substance being determined decreases with the addition of the reagent to the equivalence point, after which the limiting current due to the added titrant increases linearly. An example of such titration is the determination of a nickel salt solution by means of dimethylglyoxime.

A number of substances give anodic limiting currents, which may also be utilized in amperometric titrations. When, for example, the substance titrated gives an anodic limiting current and the titrant a cathodic limiting current, the resulting titration curve is a straight line. Because the diffusion coefficient of the reagent is usually slightly different from that of the substance being titrated, the slope of the line before the end point differs slightly from that after the end point. The equivalence point corresponds to the point of intersection of the curve representing current intensity values before and after the equivalence point with the zero line of the measuring instrument (Fig. 20-2, D). This type of titration is exemplified by the determination of iodide by means of a solution of mercury(II) nitrate. Titrations of this type are frequently used in amperometric oxidation-reduction determinations.

It is possible in some instances to use an amperometric method to determine two substances by a single titration. This is illustrated by the curve in Fig. 20-5, A, which is the plot obtained from the titration of a mixture of lead and barium ions by means of a chromate solution at an applied potential of -1.0 volt. At this potential lead as well as chromate ions give a cathodic diffusion current. This method is based on the difference in solubility of lead chromate and barium chromate. Upon the addition of chromate to a solution containing lead and barium ions the diffusion current due to lead ions decreases practically to zero. Only after the end point of the titration of lead does the added chromate precipitate barium ions. Since the solubility product constant for barium chromate is small, the concentration of barium and chromate ions in the solution remains low, and the diffusion current remains practically zero until all barium ions are precipitated. Only then does the diffusion current due to chromate ions increase linearly.

Another case of an amperometric titration is represented by Fig. 20-5, B. An example of this type of determination is afforded by the titration of arsenate by iodide ions. An equivalent amount of iodine is liberated on the addition of the iodide due to its oxidation by the arsenate. Thus, iodine is formed until the equivalence point is reached. When following the course of this reaction amperometrically only the iodine formed gives a limiting current, and a gradual increase in current intensity values is at first observed. After the end point has been reached, however, the current remains constant.

Substances of the type of ethylenediaminetetraacetic acid (EDTA) behave polarographically as depolarizers, yielding a well-developed anodic wave. Some stable EDTA complexes with metals are not active in the same way in the accessible potential range. When titrating with EDTA a solution of the cation of some metal which is not a depolarizer a curve is obtained having the shape shown in Fig. 20-5, C. The current intensity decreases only when the equivalence point has been reached, and the decrease is caused by the formation of an anodic EDTA wave. The course of the reverse titration is shown in Fig. 20-5, D.

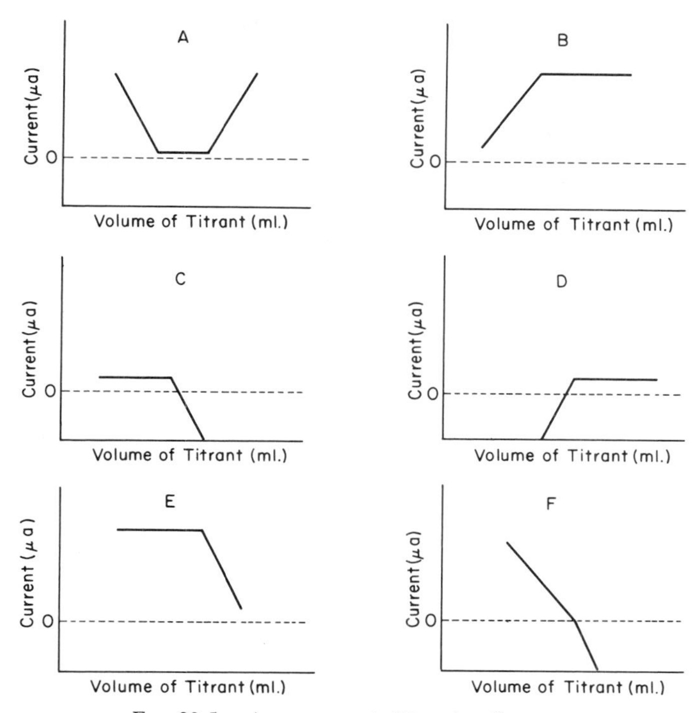

FIG. 20-5. Amperometric Titration Curves.

In some cases, in which neither the substance to be determined nor the titrant is a depolarizer, it is still possible under certain conditions to carry out an amperometric titration, using so-called polarographic or amperometric (polarometric) indicators. This is illustrated by the titration of calcium ions with an oxalate solution, using a soluble cadmium salt as indicator. After the calcium has been precipitated as calcium oxalate, the limiting current of the cadmium ions decreases due to the formation of cadmium oxalate. This change indicates the end point of the titration.

Another example of the above type of titration is the titration of calcium or aluminum ions by a soluble fluoride, using iron(III) ions as an amperometric indicator (Fig. 20-5, E). In this method of end point determination it is necessary that the indicator react with the titrant practically immediately after the end of the reaction with the substance determined in the same way as with visual indicators in precipitations. It should be emphasized that the above methods, while theoretically interesting, are not particularly useful, and in practical analysis they require relatively large corrections.

Still another example of an amperometric titration is that in which no chemical reaction takes place between the substance to be titrated and the titrant, but in which the cathodic or anodic current of the substance to be determined is "compensated" in the course of the titration by the anodic or cathodic current of the titrant. An example of this type is the "titration" of a tin(II) salt by a copper(II) salt. Tin(II) ions give, in a tartaric acid solution, an anodic polarographic wave with a half-wave potential of −0.1 volt. At room temperature there is no oxidation-reduction reaction between tin(II) and copper(II) ions, but it is possible to carry out an amperometric titration, since the added copper(II) ions compensate the anodic diffusion current of the tin(II) ions. (Ref. 68–69.)

INSTRUMENTATION

The equipment required for amperometric titrations is relatively simple. It consists of the following: (a) an e.m.f. source, such as a battery, dry cells, or a power supply; (b) a potential-regulating device, such as a calibrated slide-wire; (c) a current-sensing device, such as a microammeter or galvanometer; (d) an electrolysis and titration cell; (e) an indicator electrode; (f) a reference electrode or reference electrode plus a salt bridge; (g) a titrant delivery device, such as a buret or microburet; and (h) a stirrer.

Electrical Circuit.—Any available manually operated instrument for determining current-potential curves can be used for amperometric titrations. Since the applied potential need not be exactly adjusted in most cases, a battery or some type of potential divider arrangement, usually a voltmeter, is adequate to provide a satisfactory voltage. The remainder of the circuit consists of a device for measuring the current, either a microammeter or galvanometer and shunt, and the electrolytic cell.

Amperometric titrations may be carried out with advantage by means of a polarograph. The indicator and reference electrodes are simply connected to the terminals of the instrument, and the required potential is applied by means of the potentiometric wire of the polarograph. The current values are read on the galvanometer. Conditions for registering current intensity values may be adjusted on the polarograph by means of the sensitivity reductor as required. This may be done in the assembled amperometric apparatus by means of a shunt.

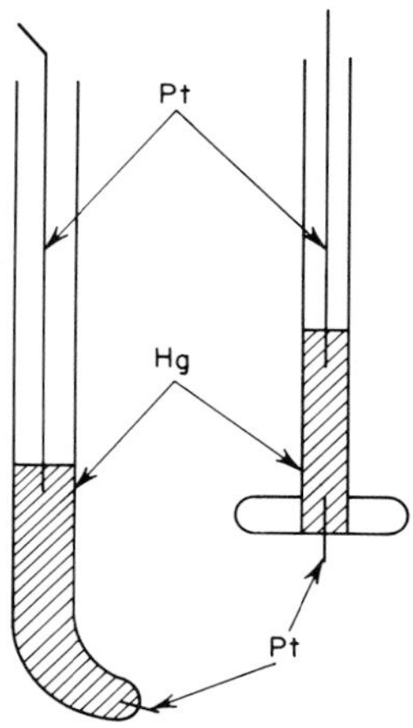

Indicator Electrodes.—The dropping mercury electrode and the rotating platinum electrode are used most frequently as indicator electrodes in amperometric titrations. The broad possibilities of application of the dropping mercury electrode are well known from polarography: with the use of this electrode reduction processes may be followed through negative potential values down to −2.7 volts. The scope of its application for studying anodic oxidations is, however, limited by the fact that mercury itself begins to be oxidized at about 0.4 volt.

Fig. 20-6. Types of Rotating Platinum Electrodes.

The rotating platinum electrode is also very suitable for amperometric titrations, especially for oxidation-reduction determinations. Electrodes of this type are not manufactured commercially, but the following has practically become standardized in laboratory design: a platinum wire 6 to 8 mm. in length and about 0.5 mm. in diameter is sealed into a glass tube in such manner as to make contact with mercury which fills the tube (Fig. 20-6). A wire is inserted into the mercury in the tube to connect the electrode with the measuring device (microammeter or galvanometer). The electrode is driven by a synchronous motor. It is advantageous to arrange the equipment for rotating the electrode so that a hole is bored through the motor axis, and the wire which is in contact with the mercury in the tube is passed through this hole. The glass tube is fixed to, or driven by, the motor, which should so far as possible have a regular and controllable speed.

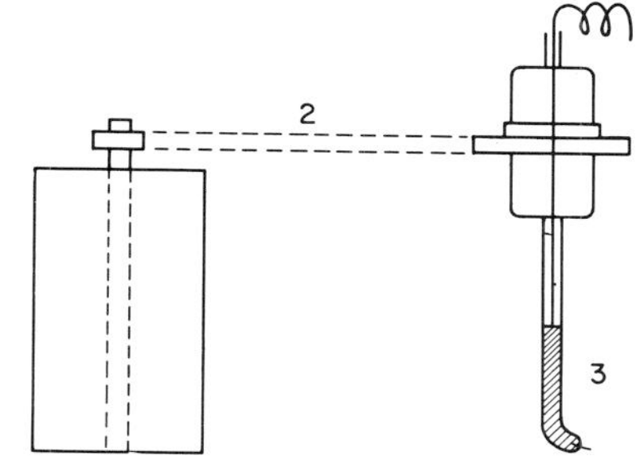

Fig. 20-7. Rotating Platinum Electrode: 1, Motor; 2, Driving Belt; 3, Electrode.

The rotating platinum electrode allows higher limiting currents to be attained than with the use of the dropping mercury electrode. This is especially advantageous in microanalysis. The most frequently used form of this electrode was first described by Kolthoff and Laitinen (Ref. 70). Some designs are shown in Figs. 20-6 and 20-7.

Vibrating platinum electrodes are now being used to some extent in polarography, as well as in amperometric titrations (Ref. 71–74) (Fig. 20-8).

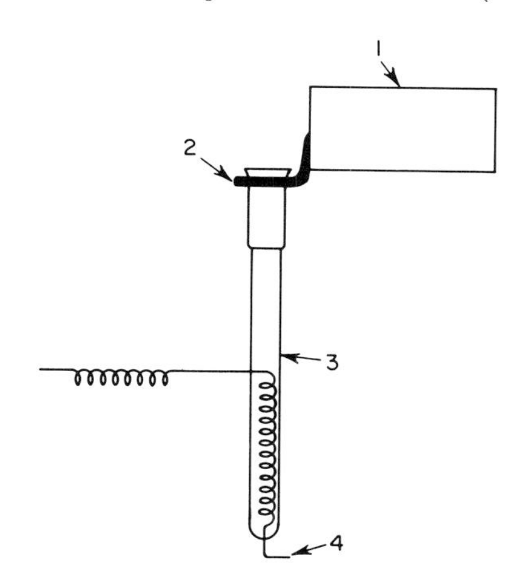

Fig. 20-8. Vibrating Platinum Electrode: 1, Electric Bell; 2, Hammer; 3, Glass Tube; 4, Platinum Wire.

The use of the dropping mercury electrode or of the rotating or vibrating platinum electrode as an indicator electrode is sufficient for all conventional types of amperometric titrations or determinations. In most cases the selection of one of these types is not a major problem. Many other possibilities, however, of applying other types of indicator electrodes have been described in the literature, either with respect to design or to the material of which the electrode is composed. These have usually been developed in the study of some special problem, and it is unlikely that they will find broader use. Such electrodes include the rotating gold, palladium, aluminum, silver, tantalum, or tungsten electrodes. Various new types of platinum electrodes, such as the submersible electrode for measurements in molten salts, the platinum amalgam electrode, and others have been described. Vibrating or rotating dropping mercury electrodes, mercury jet electrodes, and electrodes with a layer of mercury have also been tested experimentally as indicator electrodes. The possibility of titrating with two lead electrodes, and even with copper, zinc, or graphite electrodes has been studied. In most cases these electrodes were used in an attempt to increase the sensitivity of polarographic as well as of amperometric determinations.

Reference Electrodes.—Reference electrodes used most frequently in polarography are a mercury pool or a saturated calomel electrode. Attempts to introduce other reference electrodes have largely been motivated by an effort to find a system with a potential difference suitable to eliminate the need for branching off the voltage required for the amperometric titration itself, and to achieve the corresponding potential difference by connecting the indicator electrode with a suitable reference electrode into a "short-circuited" system. This would result in a simplification of the equipment required. This ideal, *i.e.*, a series of reference electrodes of different potentials, is, however, limited by the fact that various metals which could be considered for such an application may react with the titrating medium, or have similar drawbacks. Nevertheless, various publications have appeared in the literature dealing with this problem. In addition to the mercury–mercuric iodide and the silver–silver chloride electrodes, which are well known, electrodes composed of zinc amalgam, metallic hydroxides, mercuric bromate, cadmium sulfate, cadmium amalgam, bismuth, and platinum with a large surface area have been described. The aim in each case has been to obtain a system with the highest possible negative potential. The reader is referred to the various chemical abstracts and original journals for more detailed information regarding these more specialized problems.

TITRATION PROCEDURE

As described above the equipment required for an amperometric titration is very simple. A scheme for such apparatus is shown in Fig. 20-9. Very many modifications of the apparatus and equipment for amperometric titrations have been described. None of them, however, are universally applicable. The apparatus as described above is, however, satisfactory for conventional types of titrations. For routine work the simple equipment shown in Fig. 20-10 is very satisfactory. The titration vessel is fitted with a plastic cap, which is removed by simply turning in its thread. The cap contains the necessary openings for the electrodes, for the introduction of the inert gas, and for the buret.

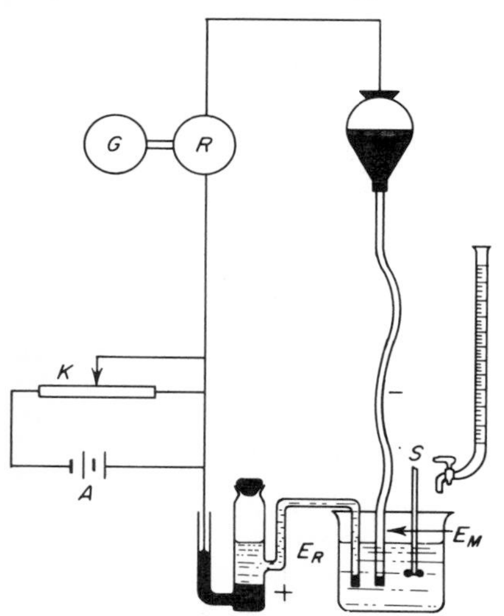

FIG. 20-9. Scheme of Amperometric Apparatus: *A*, Battery; *G*, Galvanometer (Microammeter); *K*, Potential Regulating Device; *R*, Sensitivity Reductor; *S*, Stirrer; E_M, Dropping Mercury Electrode; E_R, Reference Electrode.

The solution to be titrated is placed in the beaker or polarographic vessel. The capillary of the dropping mercury electrode (or a platinum or other type of electrode) is then immersed in the solution. The connection to the reference electrode, usually a salt bridge filled with a potassium nitrate solution, is also immersed in the solution. Both the indicating electrode and the reference electrode are connected by a sensitive dial-type (needletype) or mirror-type galvanometer, or by a microammeter (sensitivity about 10^{-7} amperes) for reading current intensity values. The sensitivity is controlled by a sensitivity reductor.

The buret containing the titrating reagent solution is also introduced into the titration vessel. Since during the course of the titration the solution must be stirred well after each addition of the titrant, the propeller of an electric stirrer is also immersed in the solution to be titrated. This step may be omitted when using a rotating platinum electrode, since the electrode itself acts as the stirrer. Stirring may also be accomplished by means of a magnetic stirrer, or by passing a stream of nitrogen or other inert gas through

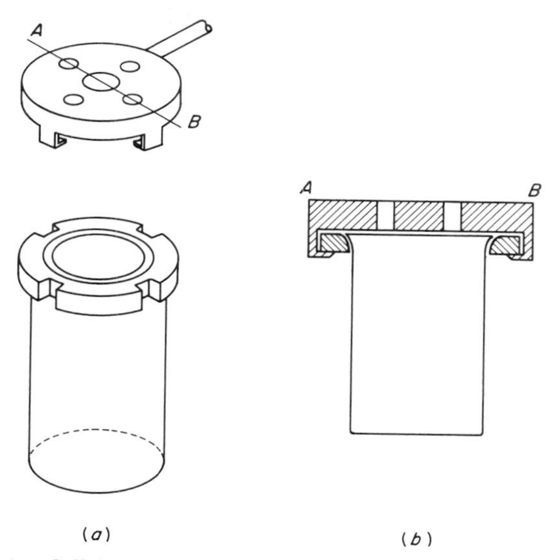

FIG. 20-10. Titration Cell for Amperometric Titrations: a, Overall View; b, Cross-section.

the solution. This is particularly desirable if it is necessary to remove oxygen from it.

Oxygen need not be removed from the solution as completely in amperometric titrations as it must be in polarography. For the purpose of determining the end point of the titration from the titration curve, it is unimportant whether the current value is stabilized at zero, or at a point above the zero point of the measuring equipment, *i.e.*, at the current value of oxygen, since the end point is determined as the point of intersection of two straight lines.

As in polarography, it is often necessary to add some surface-active substance, such as gelatin or fuchsin, to the solution to depress possible maxima.

By the use of a battery and some type of potential divider, a suitable potential is applied to the electrode. The potential must be selected as that value, determined from the appropriate polarization curves (usually from polarographic behavior), at which a limiting current (usually a diffusion current) will be attained, the measurement of this current is the basis of the determination. In order to determine the necessary potential, it is advantageous to record a polarographic wave of a solution of the substance whose diffusion current is to be measured, or whose polarization curve is required. This must be done under the same conditions, *i.e.*, the same supporting electrolyte, surfactants, pH, etc., as those under which the titration itself is to be performed.

The procedure for an amperometric titration is practically the same as that for a potentiometric titration. After each addition of the titrant, and after stirring, the current is allowed to become stabilized, and is then measured, as by noting the galvanometer deviation. The current intensity is then plotted against the volume of titrant added, and the end point determined from the intersection of the two straight lines of the graph. In potentiometric titrations it is necessary to record a sudden potential change that occurs very near the end point, and consequently the titrant must be added slowly and in small portions. In amperometric titrations, on the other hand, it is necessary only to record a few points before and after the equivalence point, and then to determine the end point from the graph. Values close to the end point may be neglected. This fact is of advantage, for example, in precipitation titrations which are used for reactions in which the product is somewhat soluble, so that the end point cannot be determined potentiometrically or visually.

In some cases, due to the polarographic behavior either of the substance to be determined or of the titrating reagent, or by the selection of a suitable reference electrode, it is unnecessary to apply an external voltage to the indicator electrode. In such instances the so-called "short-circuited" system is used, *i.e.*, the titration is carried out at the potential difference given by the indicator and reference electrodes. The apparatus required is then quite simple: the indicator electrode is connected to the reference electrode through a galvanometer (Fig. 20-11).

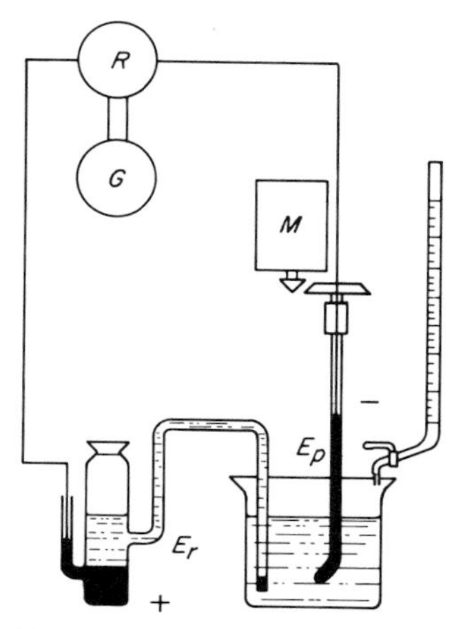

FIG. 20-11. Scheme of "Short-Circuited" System for Amperometric Titration (With Rotating Platinum Electrode): *G*, Galvanometer (Microammeter); *R*, Sensitivity Reductor; E_P, Rotating Platinum Electrode; E_R, Reference Electrode; *M*, Motor.

In order to avoid large changes in the volume of the solution during the course of the titration, the concentration of the titrant is usually greater than that of the solution to be titrated. Better results are also obtained by correcting current intensity values for volume changes due to added titrant before constructing the graph. This is done according to the formula

$$i_{\text{corr.}} = i \times \frac{V + v}{V}$$

where i is the measured current intensity value, V, the volume of the solution before titration, and v, the volume of titrant added. If the titrating solution is considerably more concentrated than the solution to be titrated (by a factor of 50 to 100 or more), the theoretically necessary correction may be ignored. If the titrant is more dilute, however, and especially if there is so much curvature near the end point that extrapolation necessary for end-point location is relatively great, the observed values of the current should be corrected by multiplying them by the $(V + v)/V$ factor.

The graphical determination of the end point is adequate for all analytical applications of amperometric titrations, but a number of publications have appeared in which other methods are discussed. These references consider the possibility of calculating the results, and give a mathematical derivation of the end point of the titration (Ref. 3, 23).

Generally, solutions titrated are of the order of 10^{-3} *M*. However, one of the advantages of amperometric titration, as compared to other methods, is the possibility of titrating very dilute solutions, due to the great precision of the method. For example, a 10^{-5} *M* solution of an arsenite may be titrated with a potassium bromate solution with a precision of better than ± 1 percent, using a rotating platinum electrode. In some cases the precision is even greater than in polarographic analysis.

Many foreign salts may be present without interference, and in fact are usually added as the supporting electrolyte to eliminate the migration current.

The temperature need not be known, provided it is kept constant during the titration.

APPLICATIONS (REF. 71–76)

Various amperometric titrations are summarized in Tables 20-1 and 20-2. The examples included have been selected from more than 1200 publications on amperometric titrations which have been published up to the present time. The selections have been based on the importance of the amperometric titration, and the fact that often the amperometric method is more advantageous to use than other methods of end point detection. Wherever possible the applications are accompanied by detailed procedures, or at least by the data necessary for testing the method. Most of these determinations have been tested or verified by the authors. They have not included methods for investigating chemical reactions or the composition of precipitates, but have restricted the tables to determinations which are suitable for practical analytical application.

For more detailed data concerning the methods included in the table, as well as for other amperometric determinations, the reader is referred to the monographs and comprehensive reviews cited in the references to this chapter.

The following abbreviations have been used in the tables to denote the electrodes:

Hg, dropping mercury indicator electrode
rot. Pt, rotating platinum indicator electrode
vibr. Pt, vibrating platinum indicator electrode
S.C.E., saturated calomel electrode
Hg pool, mercury layer used as reference electrode

The types of curves obtained in the titrations described in Tables 20-1 and 20-2 are designated by letters according to the notation shown in Fig. 20-12.

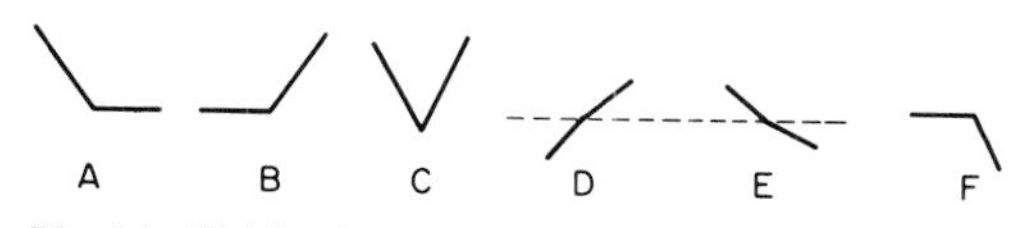

FIG. 20-12. Letters Used in Tables 20-1 and 20-2 to Designate Types of Curves Obtained in Titrations.

APPLICATIONS IN THE ANALYSIS OF SPECIAL MATERIALS

Amperometric titration methods reported in other chapters of Standard Methods of Chemical Analysis are:

1. Chapter 53, Volume III, Glass.
   a. Potassium
2. Chapter 41, Volume IIB, Plastics.
   a. Inorganic Chloride in plastics, page 2070.
   b. Lauryl mercaptan in plastics, page 2089.
3. Chapter 59, Volume III, Rubber and Rubber Products.
   a. Mercaptobenzothiazole accelerator in rubber analysis
4. Chapter 48, Volume IIB, Water Analysis.
   a. Residual chlorine in water

TABLE 20-1. AMPEROMETRIC TITRATES OF INORGANIC SUBSTANCES

Element	Titrimetric Reagent	Medium	Electrodes	Applied Potential	Procedure	Notes	Type of Curve	Literature
Ag^+	KI	neutral	Pt-S.C.E.	0 v.	To a solution of the sample (containing at least 1 mg. Ag) add EDTA, 5 drops of bromothymol blue and neutralise dropwise with 0.2 *M*-NaOH (blue-green colour). Dilute to 50–100 ml. and add 5 drops of 0.5% gelatin solution.	Pb, Bi, Cu, Fe, Zn, Cd, Tl, As, Sb do not interfere. Hg^{2+}, Ca, Sr, Ba interfere. Application: determination of Ag in Pb concentrates, in black copper and iron raw materials.	A	77*, 78, 79
Al^{3+}	NaF	ethanol + NaCl pH 2.5–3.5	Hg-S.C.E. (Pt-S.C.E.)	0 v.	Determination in refractory mineral materials: to 0.1 g. of the sample add 0.4 g. of Na_2CO_3; heat in a platinum crucible for 2 minutes to 1000°C; digest with water and ethanol; heat with dilute HCl for 1 to 2 minutes; transfer to a 100-ml. volumetric flask; heat till dissolved. Then add 5 g. NH_4Cl, the same volume of ethanol and 2 drops of methyl orange. Neutralise with NH_3 to a pink colour and add one drop of ascorbic acid. Oxidise the excess with 0.1 *M*-$FeNH_4(SO_4)_2$. Add ammonia to precipitation, add 1 drop of HCl, 0.1 ml. 0.1 *M* $FeNH_4(SO_4)_2$ and titrate.	The determination takes 30 minutes. Ca, Mg, Ti, Fe, and Cr do not interfere. Further application: Al in high-alloyed steel, Al in bronze	F	80, 81, 82, 82a
As^{3+}	$KBrO_3$	HCl + KBr	Pt-S.C.E.	0 v.	Use a medium of 1 *M* HCl with 0.05 *M* KBr; other conditions are the same as in potentiometric titration.	Concentrations down to 10^{-6} *M* As(III) may be determined. Applications: mineral waters, glass, pharmaceuticals.	B	83, 8, 85, 86, 87, 88, 89
Au^{3+}	hydroquinone	H_2SO_4	Pt-S.C.E.	1.0 v.	Down to 0.2 mg. Au in 1 liter may be determined in a medium of 2 *N* H_2SO_4 at about 60°C.	Se, Te, Pd do not interfere. Error: ±1 to 10%. Application: determination of Au in ores and electroplating baths.	B	90
B	fructose	LiCl + LiOH	Hg-AgCl	−2.05 v.	0.05 to 2 mg. B may be determined in a volume of 25 ml. at pH 12, in a medium of 0.1 *M* LiCl and 0.1 *M* LiOH.	The decrease of the fructose wave is measured. Mg, Ca, Cu, Zn do not interfere.		91
Ba^{2+}	K_2CrO_4	NH_4OAc (possibly with 25% acetone)	Hg-S.C.E.	−1.0 v.	To determine Ba in ores, heat 0.5 to 1 g. of the sample for 15 minutes with 10 to 15 ml. 38% HCl and 5 ml. HNO_3. Add more HNO_3 and evaporate till dry; add 8 drops of H_2SO_4 (1 + 1) and 10 ml. 38% HCl and evaporate. Then add 5 to 10 g. NH_4Cl	The titration has also been used for indirect determinations of SO_4^{2-}	B	92, 93, 94, 95

	Li_2SO_4	$N(C_2H_5)_4Br$ with ethanol (pH over 4)	Hg-S.C.E.	−2.0 v.	and 25 ml. HCl (1 + 3) and boil for 3 to 5 minutes; dilute with hot H_2O to 100 ml., boil and filter. Wash the $BaSO_4$ 5 to 6 times with 1 to 2% HCl and hot water. Dry, add 6 g. Na_2CO_3, oxalic acid and KNO_3 mixture (10 + 4 + 0.75) and heat in a porcelain crucible for 1 to 2 hours at 600 to 700°C. Add 1 g. Na_2CO_3 to the melt and boil with H_2O in a volume of 100 ml. Filter, wash with 1 to 2% Na_2CO_3 solution; dissolve in 10 ml. of hot HOAc and filter; wash with water. Neutralise the filtrate with NH_3 to phenolphthalein, add 2 to 3 drops of 10% HOAc and make up to volume. Take an aliquot and titrate.	Solutions containing down to 5×10^{-5} *M* Ba^{2+} may be titrated in the presence of NaF, KCl, NaCl, $AlCl_3$ and Be^{2+}.	A	96
Be^{2+}	NaF (KF)	HCl + $CoCl_2$ + $FeCl_3$ + ethanol (pH 2.1–2.3)	Hg-S.C.E. Pt-S.C.E.	0 v.	Electrolyte composition: 35 ml. 1% HCl, 3.2 ml. 0.5 *M* $CoCl_2$ in 1% HCl and 9.3 ml. 0.5 *N* $FeCl_3$ in 1% HCl (pH 2.1 to 2.3).	Fe^{3+} ions act as amperometric indicator.	F	97
Bi^{3+}	EDTA	HNO_3, pH 1 to 2 (citrate or tartrate may be used)	Hg-S.C.E.	−0.16 to −0.20 v.	To determine Bi in lead, dissolve up to 50 g. of the sample in concentrated HNO_3 and add citrate or tartrate so that the resulting concentration is 0.3 to 0.5 *M*. Adjust pH to 2 and make up to 100 ml. Titrate an aliquot with 0.02 *M* EDTA. 0.004 % Bi may be determined.	Zn, Cd, Co, Al, As, Cr, Mn do not interfere. Using a rot. Pt electrode (0.9 v.) down to 10^{-5} *M* Bi^{3+} may be determined.	A	98 99
Br^-	$AgNO_3$	HNO_3	Pt-S.C.E.	0 v.	Down to 10^{-4} *M* Br^- may be determined by titrating with 10^{-3} to 5.10^{-2} *M* $AgNO_3$ in a medium of 0.8 *N* HNO_3.	An indirect determination of Ag in copper alloys. Application to pharmaceuticals.	B	100 101 102
Ca^{2+}	EDTA	NH_4OH	Hg-S.C.E.	−1.5 v.	To a solution of the sample add enough NH_3 to bring the final concentration to 4–5 *M*; add enough $Zn(NO_3)_2$ to make the solution 10^{-3} *M*, and several drops of 0.5% gelatin solution. Titrate with 0.01–0.02 *M* EDTA solution.	Zn ions act as amperometric indicator. Use is made of the different stability of Ca and Zn complexes.	F	103
Cd^{2+}	EDTA	neutral or alkaline	Hg-S.C.E.	−0.7 to −0.92 v.	The titration takes place in a weakly acid (HOAc and NaOAc), neutral (0.01 to 0.1 *M* KNO_3), or weakly ammoniacal medium.	When a large-surface mercury electrode is used as indicator electrode, 10^{-7} *M* Cd^{2+} may be determined.	A	98
	sodium diethyldithiocarbamate	KNO_3 KCl	Hg-S.C.E. Pt-S.C.E.	−1.1 v. 0.8 v.	A medium of 0.1 *M* KNO_3 is used. A medium of 0.1 *M* KCl is used. Indirectly:	see NH_4^+, Reference (141)	C B	105 106 107

* Literature references follow tables.

TABLE 20-1 (cont.)

Element	Titrimetric Reagent	Medium	Electrodes	Applied Potential	Procedure	Notes	Type of Curve	Literature
Ce^{4+}	ascorbic acid	H_2SO_4	Pt-S.C.E.	0.3–0.5 v.	Down to 0.35 mg. Ce may be determined in 10 ml. of 5 N H_2SO_4 at 20°C. Fe(III) ions do not interfere. After diluting with water to 0.1 N H_2SO_4 determine Fe(III) at 40 to 60°C. and 0 v.	The rise of the limiting current of ascorbic acid is registered.	B	108
	hydroquinone	H_2SO_4	Pt-S.C.E.	0.8 v.	Down to 10^{-5} N Ce(IV) may be determined in a medium of H_2SO_4.	The rise of the anodic hydroquinone current is registered. VO_3^-, $Cr_2O_7^{2-}$ interfere.	F	
Cl^-	$AgNO_3$	HNO_3	Hg-S.C.E. Pt-S.C.E.	0 v. 0 v.	5.10^{-5} M Cl^- may be determined in solutions of 0.8 M HNO_3.		B	109, 110 111, 112 113
Cl_2 (active)	AsO_3^{3-}		Pt-Ag/AgCl	0 v.	The sample, which may be a mixture of Cl_2, ClO^-, ClO_2^- and chloramine, is hydrolysed for 5 minutes at pH 11. (A) in one portion, Cl_2 and ClO^- are titrated in phosphate buffer with AsO_3^{3-}. (B) a second portion is treated as above, 2 g. KI are added and Cl_2 and chloramine are determined.* (C) a third portion is adjusted to pH 7, KI is added and Cl_2, ClO_2^- and chloramine are determined. (D) H_2SO_4 is added to the fourth portion to pH 2, KI is added and after 5 minutes pH is adjusted to 7 and Cl_2, ClO^-, ClO_2^- and chloramine are determined.	Application: determination of Cl_2 in water.	A	114, 115
Co^{2+}	$K_3Fe(CN)_6$	NH_3 + tartrate	Pt-S.C.E.	−0.2 v.	To determine Co in alloys, heat 0.1 to 0.2 g. of the sample with HNO_3 (1 + 1) and 3 to 5 ml. H_2SO_4 (1 + 1); neutralise with NH_3, add 1 to 2 g. sodium tartrate, 10 to 15 ml. 25% NH_3 and 10 to 15 ml. 0.1 M $K_3Fe(CN)_6$ solution; titrate with 0.1 M Co(II) solution. Cu(II) ions must be removed electrolytically.	Down to 0.3 mg. Co may be determined with an error of ±0.5%.	A	116 117
$Cr_2O_7^{2-}$	Fe^{2+}	acid	Pt-S.C.E.	1.0 v.	The same conditions apply as in other titrimetric methods.	VO_3^- and MnO_4^- interfere.	B	118
Cu^{2+}	α-benzoinoxime	NH_3 + $(NH_4)_2SO_4$	Hg-HgI$_2$	0 v.	To determine Cu in ores, digest 1 to 2 g. of the sample with 20–25 ml. aqua regia add 10 ml. H_2SO_4 (1 + 1) and evaporate. Then add 50 ml. water and boil; after cooling, transfer to a 100-ml. volumetric flask, make up to volume with NH_3 (1 + 1). Add to an aliquot (20 to 25 ml.) 0.1–0.2 g. Na_2SO_3 and let stand for 2–5 minutes. Titrate with an ethanol solution of the		A	

F^-	Fe^{3+}	ethanol + NaCl	Hg-S.C.E.	0 v.	Approximately 25 mg. F^- may be determined in a volume of 50 ml., containing 50% ethanol and 8 g. NaCl (pH 5 to 7). The error is not greater than ±0.5%.		B	119
F^-	Al^{3+}	HOAc + NaOAc	Al-S.C.E.	−0.75 v.	3.10⁻⁴ *M* to 10⁻⁵ *M* fluoride may be determined in an acetate buffer solution of pH 3, titrating with $Al(NO_3)_3$ solution.	Application: water analysis.	B	120
Fe^{2+}	$Cr_2O_7^{2-}$	acid	Pt-HgI_2	1.0 v.	To determine Fe in chromite minerals, melt the sample with Na_2O_2 and carbonate. Separate $Fe(OH)_3$ by filtering, dissolve in 2 *N* H_2SO_4 reduce with Bi and titrate.		A	
Fe^{3+}	EDTA	HOAc + NaOAc	Hg-S.C.E.	0.02–0.1 v.	Determination of Fe in ores: pH 3 to 4.5	MoO_4^{2-}, WO_4^{2-} and a number of bivalent cations do not interfere.	see: E	121 122
Hg^{2+}	EDTA	HOAc + NaOAc	Hg-S.C.E.	0.2 v.	The titration proceeds best in HOAc-NaOAc buffer solution of pH = 6.4. The method may be applied to micro-determination of Hg in organic compounds after combustion according to Schöniger in a stream of oxygen.		E	123 124 125
In^{3+}	EDTA	weakly acid	Hg-S.C.E.	−0.7 to −1.1 v.	Determination of In in sphalerite: to 2 g. of the sample add 15–20 ml. HBr (h = 1.4), evaporate on a water bath to a volume of 2–3 ml., add 1 ml. HNO_3 and evaporate till dry. Add 5 ml. HBr and 1 ml. HNO_3 and evaporate; add 10–15 ml. 5 *N* HBr. Then add 0.1 g. KI and $Na_2S_2O_3$ till the solution is colorless and add a few more crystals of $Na_2S_2O_3$. Filter through a dry filter paper and wash with 5 *N* HBr 2–3 times; shake with an equal volume of butyl acetate for 1 minute. Discard the lower layer. Add to the extract 5 ml. 5 *N* HBr and some $Na_2S_2O_3$; shake, discard lower layer, wash the extract with 5 *N* HBr. In is then obtained from the organic phase by shaking with water. Repeat the extraction process. Evaporate the aqueous In solution to 5 ml., add 1 ml. 4 % ascorbic acid solution and 0.1–0.2 ml. 5% urea solution; neutralise with NH_3 (tropaeolin indicator), add 15 ml. buffer solution (5 ml. 0.2 *M* $KClO_4$ and 97 ml. 2 *N* HCl in 200 ml. Titrate with 0.005 *M* EDTA solution.	Indium may be determined in the presence of large amounts of cadmium by titrating with EDTA in a medium of 0.5 to 5 *M* potassium iodide.	A	126 127 128

* By titrating the liberated iodine.

TABLE 20-1 (cont.)

Element	Titrimetric Reagent	Medium	Electrodes	Applied Potential	Procedure	Notes	Type of Curve	Literature
Ir^{4+}	hydroquinone or ascorbic acid	HCl + NaCl	Pt-S.C.E.	0.4 to 0.5 v.	Down to 10^{-5} *M* Ir(IV) may be determined in a weakly acid solution of HCl and NaCl at pH 1.	Rh, Pd, Pb, Cu, Ni, Fe, Se, Te do not interfere, Au, Os interfere.	A	129
I^-	$AgNO_3$	50% acetone	Pt-S.C.E.	0 v.	When determining very small amounts of I^- (1.5 μg. I^- in 5–10 ml.) titrate with 5×10^{-5} *M* $AgNO_3$ solution.	In a medium of 0.8 *N* HNO_3 it is possible to titrate 0.01 *M* Br^- in the presence of 0.1 *M* Cl^-; in 0.1 *M* NH_3 medium, 0.01 *M* I^- may be titrated in the presence of 0.1 *M* Br^- and 0.1 *M* Cl^- (Pt-HgI_2). After acidifying to 0.8 *N* HNO_3, Br^- is determined at 0.0 v. (S.C.E.); after adding gelatin, Cl^- is determined at 0.0 v. (S.C.E.).	B	130 131 130 131
I_2	$S_2O_3^{2-}$	NaCl, or dilute HCl + NaCl	Pt-S.C.E.	0 v. 0.1–0.2 v.	Down to 1 μg. I_2 may be determined in a volume of 40 ml.	This method may be applied to the indirect determination of sulphides (as CdS).	A	132
K^+	dipicrylamine	phosphate buffer	Hg-S.C.E.	+1.3 to −1.4 v.	Not more than 0.15 *M* KCl may be determined in phosphate buffer medium at pH 12, at 0°C. A 0.7 *M* solution of the reagent is used. Interference by NH_4^+ is eliminated by evaporating. Mg^{2+}, Zn^{2+}, Mn^{2+}, Fe^{3+}, Al^{3+} are separated by precipitating with 8-hydroxyquinoline.	For contents of 4 to 120 mg. K the error is ±4%. Large concentrations of Li^+, Na^+, Ca^{2+}, NO_3^-, SO_4^{2-}, Cl^-, SiO_3^{2-} and $H_2BO_3^-$ do not interfere. Application: silicate analysis.	B	133 134 135
K^+ $B(C_6H_5)_4^-$	$AgNO_3$	acetate buffer	Hg-S.C.E.	0 v.	To a solution of K salts in acetate buffer solution at pH 5–6, in a volume of 20 to 100 ml. add Na or Li tetraphenylboron in excess. After precipitating, titrate the excess with 0.005 to 0.1 *M* $AgNO_3$.	Error: ±1 to 2%.	B	136
Mg^{2+}	8-hydroxyquinoline	$NH_3 + NH_4Cl$	Hg-S.C.E.	−1.5 to −1.9 v.	10^{-3} *M* solutions of Mg^{2+} are titrated with a titrimetric solution of 8-hydroxyquinoline in ethanol, in a medium of 0.5 *M* $NH_3 + NH_4Cl$. Indirect determination: see under NH_4^+.	The limiting current of the reagent reduction is measured. According to Ref. 137, better results are obtained by dissolving a Mg oxinate precipitate in mineral acid and titrating in a medium of HOAc and NaOAc by $CuSO_4$ solution (0.0 v.; Hg-HgI_2).	B	137
Mn^{2+}	MnO_4^-	pyrophosphate, pH 4.5–8	Pt-S.C.E.	0.0 v.	Modification of the method according to Lingane-Karplus.		B	138
MnO_4^-	Fe^{2+}	acid	Pt-S.C.E.	1.0 v.	The same conditions apply as in the potentiometric determination. Error: ±0.002%	Ag, Cu, Zn, Ni, Co, Ti, Fe, Al, Mo do not interfere.	A	138a

[illegible]	$Pb(NO_3)_2$	NaOAc + KCl	Hg-S.C.E.	−0.8 v.	To determine Mo in alloys, add to 0.3 g. of the sample HCl (1 + 1) and dropwise HNO_3. Boil off the nitrogen oxides, neutralise with 10% NaOH until $Fe(OH)_3$ precipitates. To an aliquot add HNO_3 (1 + 2), neutralise to methyl orange, add 10 ml. 0.5% NaOAc and 10 ml. ethanol and titrate.		C	139
Mo^{III}	Fe^{3+}	NaCl + HCl	Hg-S.C.E.	−0.25 v.	MoO_4^{2-} is reduced by an amalgam to the red-brown Mo(III) chlorocomplex (in a medium of 20% HCl). The titration is carried out in a medium of 0.5–1 *N* NaCl and 4 to 7% HCl.	This method allows an indirect determination of phosphorus in steels.	B	140
NH_4^+	$Ca(ClO)_2$ (Chloramine T)	$KHCO_3$ KBr	Pt-S.C.E.	0 v.	Precipitate Mg^{2+} as $MgNH_4PO_4$ xH_2O, wash with dilute and then absolute ethanol and dissolve in the least possible amount of EDTA. Add enough $NaHCO_3$ to make a 5% solution; add 0.5 g. KBr and titrate with 0.1 *N* $Ca(ClO)_2$ in a volume of about 50 ml.	The method is suitable for an indirect determination of phosphates, of 5 to 100 mg. Zn, 1–50 mg. Mg, 5–100 mg. Mn or 10–200 mg. Cd. The error is ±0.5%. Application: analysis of phosphatisation concentrates and of brass-plating salts.	B	141
Ni^{2+}	dimethylglyoxime	$NH_4OH + NH_4Cl$	Hg-S.C.E.	−1.85 v.	30 to 60 µg. Ni may be titrated by a solution of the reagent in 98% ethanol in a medium of NH_3 and NH_4Cl. F^- must be masked by Fe(III) ions.	Al, Cu, Cr interfere.	C	142
PO_4^{3-}	uranyl acetate	HOAc + NaOAc	Hg-S.C.E.	−0.7 to −0.8 v.	10^{-2} to 3×10^{-4} *M* phosphate may be determined in a medium of HOAc, neutralised to bromocresol green, 0.1 *M* KCl and 20% ethanol, with an error of ±1%. Larger amounts of Fe(III) ions must be separated by extracting with cupferron in ether medium. Before titrating, phosphates may be separated by means of ion-exchange. For an indirect determination, see under NH_4^+.	UO_2KPO_4 is formed. Mg, Ba, Fe, Pb, Al, Cr, VO_3^- and AsO_4^{3-} do not interfere. Phosphorus may thus be determined in organic substances after melting with Na_2CO_3.	B	143 144
Pb^{2+}	$Cr_2O_7^{2-}$	HOAc + NaOAc	Pt-S.C.E.	0.8 to 1 v.	Determination of Pb in bronze: after decomposing the sample in acids add acetate buffer and 10 to 15% ethanol. 0.2 mg. Pb may be determined in 1 ml.	The applied voltage depends on pH: 5.5–0.8 v. 4.5–1.0 v. 4.1–>1.0 v.	A	145
Pd^{2+}	dimethylglyoxime salicylaldoxime 8-hydroxyquinoline	acetic acid + sodium acetate HCl + HNO_3 HCl + HNO_3	Hg-S.C.E. Hg-S.C.E. Hg-S.C.E.	0 v. 0 v. 0 v.	(A) To determine 0.5–10 mg. Pd, use 25 ml. acetate buffer (pH 4.8 to 5) containing 0.1 *M* KNO_3. (B) Use 25 ml. of a medium, containing 0.1 *M* HCl, 0.05 *M* HNO_3 in 0.1 *M* KNO_3. (C) Use 25 ml. of a medium, containing 0.5 *M* HCl and 0.05 *M* HNO_3 in 0.1 *M* KNO_3.	Best results are obtained with methods B and C. Ag, Au, Cd, Pb, Bi, Co, Ni, Zn, Mn, Al do not interfere.	A	146

TABLE 20-1 (cont.)

Element	Titrimetric Reagent	Medium	Electrodes	Applied Potential	Procedure	Notes	Type of Curve	Literature
SO_4^{2-}	$Pb(NO_3)_2$	KNO_3 + ethanol	Hg-S.C.E.	−0.7 v.	Down to 10^{-3} *M* sulphate may be determined in a medium of 0.01–0.05 *M* KNO_3 and 20 to 30% ethanol.	The error of the determination is ±3%. Application: determination of sulfur in organic substances.	B	147 148 149
Sb^{3+}	$KBrO_3$	HCl KBr	Pt-S.C.E.	0.2 to 0.4 v.	5 to 800 μg Sb may be determined in a medium of 1 to 2 *N* HCl and 0.05 *M* KBr by titrating with 0.002 *M* $KBrO_3$ solution.		B	150 151
Sb^{3+}	I_2	$NaHCO_3$	Pt-S.C.E.	0.2 v.	The same conditions apply as in the potentiometric determination.	If As is present, both elements will be determined together. A possibility of determining As in the presence of Sb is mentioned; Fe, Cr, Zn, Cd, Al, Pb, Ni do not interfere.	B	152
SeO_3^{2-} SeO_4^{2-}	ascorbic acid	HCl or H_2SO_4	Hg-S.C.E.	−0.05 v.	3 to 34 mg. Se may be determined at 60°C. in a medium of 20–100 ml. HCl or H_2SO_4, pH 1 to 2. Fe(III) are masked by F^-, Cu(II) ions are precipitated as ferrocyanide. When analysing mineral raw materials, melt the sample with Na_2CO_3 and KNO_3 (Se → SeO_4^{2-}) or decompose the sample with aqua regia (Se → SeO_3^{2-}).	Large concentrations of Te, As, Sb, Pb, Cd, Bi, Al, Cr, Co, Ni, Zn, Mg, U, Mo, Ca do not interfere.	E	153
Sn^{2+}	$KBrO_3$	HCl	Hg-S.C.E.	−0.2 v.	0.12 to 54 mg. Sn may be determined in about 30 ml. of 3.5 to 4% HCl.	When using a HgI_2 electrode, the titration may be carried out at 0 v.	D	154
Te ($Cr_2O_7^{2-}$)	Fe^{2+}	H_2SO_4	Pt-S.C.E.	1.15 v.	Determination of Te in anodic sludge and fly-dust; melt 2–5 g. of the sample with Na_2O_2 in a nickel crucible. Dissolve in dilute HCl, boil and reduce Te(VI) with NaH_2PO_2 to metallic Te (thus precipitating also Au, Sb, Se, Sn). Filter, wash with dilute HCl, boil with HNO_3 and evaporate with 18 *M* H_2SO_4. Add water and 5 to 10 ml. $K_2Cr_2O_7$ solution (1 mg. Cr in 1 ml.) and titrate after 30 minutes.	5 mg. tellurium may be determined in 100 ml with an error of ±0.5%.	B	155 156
Th^{4+}	MoO_4^{2-}	NaCl + HOAc	Hg-S.C.E.	−0.95 v.	To determine Th in monazite melt with KHF_2, dissolve the melt in $AlCl_3$ and Br_2 water, heat, add acetate buffer. The chloride concentration should be about 2.5 *M*, the final pH value should be 1.9.	Error: ±2%. The determination takes three hours.	B	157

Ti^{4+}	Cupferron	HCl	Pt-S.C.E.	0.8 v.	To determine Ti in steel, dissolve 0.2 g. of the sample in 20 ml. of a mixture containing 600 ml. H_2SO_4 (1 + 1), 150 ml. concentrated HNO_3 and 300 ml. concentrated HCl. Evaporate, add 50 ml. HCl (1 + 5), filter into a 250-ml. volumetric flask and make up to volume with water. Neutralise an aliquot with NH_3 to methyl violet, add 5 ml. 1% EDTA solution and titrate.	Al, Mg, SiO_2 do not interfere.	B	158
Tl^+	I^-	HOAc + NaOAc	Hg-S.C.E.	−0.7 v.	To a solution, in which the Tl concentration is at least 10^{-3} *M*, add EDTA and acetate buffer pH 4, some drops of 0.5% gelatin solution and titrate with 0.1–0.5 *M* KI.	Bi, Cu, Fe, Pb do not interfere.	A	159
Tl^{3+}	EDTA	acid, pH = 2	Pt-S.C.E.	0 v.	To determine Tl in cadmium, dissolve 1–1.5 g. of the sample in 10 ml. 2 *M* H_2SO_4 and 1 to 2 ml. concentrated HNO_3. Boil off nitrogen oxides, add 0.1 g. $(NH_4)_2S_2O_8$, boil, neutralise with 2 *N* NH_3 and adjust pH to 2.	Cd, Pb, Zn do not interfere. Bi^{3+}, Cu^{2+}, Fe^{3+}, $Cr_2O_7^{2-}$ and MnO_4^+ interfere.	A	160
U (NH_4^+)	Calcium hypochlorite; (Chloramine T)	$NaHCO_3$	Pt-S.C.E.	0 v.	Precipitate U with NH_3 in the presence of EDTA. Filter the ammonium diuranate precipitate ($U{:}NH_4 = 2{:}1$), wash with ethanol, dissolve in saturated $NaHCO_3$ solution and titrate with ClO^- in the presence of KBr. Sn and Sb must be separated before the determination.	This is an indirect determination. Be and Ti do not interfere.	B	161
VO_3^-	Fe^{2+}	acid	Pt-S.C.E.	1.0 v.	Determination of V in steel: dissolve 0.5 g. of the sample in 20 ml. H_2SO_4 (1 + 3) and 10 ml. HNO_3 (1 + 3), and evaporate to remove the HNO_3. Dilute to 80 ml., add 5 ml. 5% $AgNO_3$ solution and 20 ml. 10% $(NH_4)_2S_2O_8$, boil, dilute to 100 ml. and titrate.	$Cr_2O_7^{2-}$ and MnO_4^- interfere; these must be removed in the conventional way.	F	162 163
WO_4^{2-}	8-hydroxyquinoline	HOAc + NaOAc	Hg-S.C.E.	−1.4 v.	To determine W in ferrotungsten, dissolve 2.5 g. of the sample in 10 ml. HF, and add HNO_3 dropwise till the sample dissolves. Evaporate with 25–30 ml. H_2SO_4 (1 + 1), cool, transfer to beaker together with the tungstic acid precipitated, neutralise with 30% NaOH adding an excess until tungstic acid dissolves. Transfer to 500-ml. volumetric flask, filter to remove $Fe(OH)_3$, neutralise an aliquot with HOAc (1 + 3) to litmus paper. Dilute with water to 100 ml., add 3 g. NaOAc and titrate with a 2% solution of the reagent in HOAc.		B	164

TABLE 20-1 (cont.)

Element	Titrimetric Reagent	Medium	Electrodes	Applied Potential	Procedure	Notes	Type of Curve	Literature
Zn^{2+}	$K_4Fe(CN)_6$	$NaCl + H_2SO_4$	Pt-S.C.E.	0.7 v.	Determination of Zn in nickel-plating baths: Evaporate the sample and melt with NaOH. Digest with water, filter, neutralise with HCl (resulting concentration 0.5 *N* NaCl). Add enough H_2SO_4 to make the final concentration 0.4 *N*.	The analysis takes 10 minutes.	F	165
Zn^{2+}	$K_4Fe(CN)_6$	$NH_4Cl + HCl$	Pt-S.C.E.	1.0 v.	To determine Zn in ores and fly-dust, take 0.5–2 g. of sample, add 0.1 g. $Fe_2(SO_4)_3$ to remove As, Sb, Se, Te, add 10 ml. concentrated HCl, 15 to 25 ml. 18 *N* H_2SO_4 and 10 ml. concentrated HNO_3. Heat until SO_2 is liberated. Add 40 ml. water and at 80°C. add 5 g. NH_4Cl, 0.25 g. $(NH_4)_2S_2O_8$ and 25 ml. concentrated NH_3, boil for 5 minutes. Remove the precipitate, wash with NH_3 and NH_4Cl. Acidify the filtrate to methyl orange. Add 3 ml. HCl, dilute to 250 ml. and titrate. The compound formed is $K_2Zn_3[Fe(CN)_6]_2$. For indirect methods, see under NH_4^+.		G	166
Zr^{IV}	Cupferron	H_2SO_4 ($HClO_4$)	Hg-S.C.E.	−0.8 to −0.9 v.	Determination of Zr in ores containing U and Nb: after decomposition add 10 ml. concentrated H_2SO_4. If oxalic acid is present, add 20 ml. concentrated HNO_3 and evaporate till white vapors are liberated. Transfer to 100-ml. volumetric flask and make up with water. Centrifuge an aliquot containing 10 mg. Zr with 50 ml. 10% H_2SO_4, 3 ml. 30% H_2O_2 and 25 ml. 10% $(NH_4)_2SO_4$ saturated with $NH_4H_2PO_4$; wash with a solution containing phosphate and H_2SO_4 then with a mixture of 50 ml. 10% H_2SO_4 with 3 ml. 30% H_2O_2. Dissolve the residue in 50 ml. 10% H_2SO_4 and titrate.		B	167

TABLE 20-2. AMPEROMETRIC TITRATIONS OF ORGANIC SUBSTANCES

Organic compounds

(Only those types have been selected, for which amperometric titration is more advantageous than other commonly used analytical methods: for a review of the amperometric titration of organic compounds, see for example J. Březina and P. Zuman, "Polarography in Medicine, Biochemistry and Pharmacy," Interscience Publishers, New York, 1958.)

Aldehydes and ketones (carbonyl group)	2,4-dinitrophenylhydrazine	acid medium	Hg-S.C.E.	−0.4 to −0.8 v.	Dissolve the sample in H_2O on ethanol, respectively, add 2.5 ml. conc. HCl 16 to 17 ml. of a 0.05% aq. thymol solution, titrate with 0.01 *N* 2,4-dinitrophenylhydrazine solution (in 2 *N* HCl).		B	168
Alkaloids and other organic bases	Silicotungstic acid	slightly acid medium (0.1–2 *N* HCl)	Hg-S.C.E.	−0.4 to −0.8 v.		Suitable for all bases forming addition precipitates with organic reagents (1 mole of the reagent with 2 or 4 moles of the base). The method can be used for a rapid testing of tablets and other pharmaceuticals.	B	169 See literature quotations in Březina-Zuman
Unsaturated bonds, styrene	$KBrO_3$ + KBr	methanol + HCl	rot. Pt-S.C.E.	0 v.	Cool 75 ml. methanol, and 5 ml. concentrated HCl to 5–10°C., add the sample solution (>10 mg. styrene), add 1 g. KBr, cool for another 5 minutes and titrate with 0.002 *N* $KBrO_3$ solution containing 0.1 *N* KBr.	The method is also suitable for the determination of xylenols, cresols, etc.	B	171, 170
Iodine number	Br_2 in glacial acetic acid	glacial acetic acid + 0.5 *M* Na acetate + 0.1 *M* NH_4 acetate	rot. Pt-S.C.E. or chloranil electrode	0 v.		Suitable for fats and volatile oils, resins, etc. For microanalytical purposes the titration in methanol medium is recommended.	B	172 173
-SH groups	$AgNO_3$, Hg(II) salts, Cu(II) salts, $K_3Fe(CN)_6$ etc.		rot. Pt-S.C.E. (or HgI_2)			For all possibilities of the determination of SH-groups in all materials, chiefly with regard to the biological problems, see for instance the monograph by Březina and Zuman: "Polarography in Medicine Biochemistry and Pharmacy," Interscience Publishers, New York, 1958.	B	59
α-Tocopherol	$AuCl_3$	benzoate buffer solution	Hg-S.C.E.	−0.075 v.		Suitable for microamounts.	B	175 174
Barbituric acid derivatives	Hg(I) and Hg(II) salts	slightly acid or neutral medium	Hg-S.C.E.	0 v.	Dissolve 0.05–0.2 g. of the sample in ethanol or acetone and titrate, in 0.5 *N* KOH medium (adding, if necessary, 10% sodium acetate to give a final concentration of 0.2 *M*) with 0.05 *N* $Hg(ClO_4)_2$ or nitrate.	The method is suitable for the testing of pharmaceuticals.	B	176 177

SELECTED BIBLIOGRAPHY

1. Heyrovský, J. and Berezicky, A., Collection Czechoslov. Chem. Commun. **1,** 19, 1929.
2. Majer, V., Z. Elektrochem. **42,** 120, 122, 1936.
3. Kolthoff, I. M., and Lingane, J. J., Polarography, 2nd Ed., Interscience Publishers, New York, 1952.
4. Berl, W. G., ed., Physical Methods in Chemical Analysis, Vols. 2 and 3, Academic Press, New York, 1951, 1956.
5. Lingane, J. J., Electroanalytical Chemistry, Interscience Publishers, New York, 1953, 2nd Ed., 1958.
6. Delahay, P., New Instrumental Methods in Electrochemistry, Interscience Publishers, New York, 1954.
7. Meites, L., Thomas, H. E., and Bauman, R. P., Advanced Analytical Chemistry, McGraw-Hill Book Co., New York, 1958.
8. Charlot, G., Badoz-Lambling, J., and Trémillon, B., Les Réactions Électrochimiques: Les Réactions Electrochimiques d'Analyse, Masson et Cie., Paris, 1959.
9. Bertin, C., Anal. Chim. Acta, **5,** 1, 1951.
10. Duyckaerts, G., *ibid.*, **5,** 233, 1951; **8,** 57, 1953.
11. Charlot, G., and Bézier, D., Méthodes Électrochimiques d'Analyse, Masson et Cie., Paris, 1954.
12. Cruse, K., Angew. Chemie, **65,** 232, 1953.
13. Kolthoff, I. M., Anal. Chem., **26,** 1685, 1954.
14. Stock, J. T., Chem. Age, London, **71,** 575, 719, 1954.
15. Dubois, J. E., and Walisch, W., Comptes Rendus, **242,** 1161, 1956.
16. Kozlovskii, M. T., Zhur. Anal. Khim., **12,** 623, 1957.
17. Stock, J. T., Microchem. J., **3,** 543, 1959.
18. Ashworth, M. R. F., Titrimetric Organic Analysis, Part I, Direct Methods, Interscience Publishers, New York, 1964.
19. Delahay, P., Charlot, G., and Laitinen, H. A., Anal. Chem., **32,** 103A, 1960.
20. Foulk, C. W., and Bawden, A. T., J. Am. Chem. Soc., **48,** 2045, 1926.
21. Jännti, O., Suomen Kemistilehti, **280,** 65, 1955.
22. Delahay, P., Charlot, G., and Laitinen, H. A., J. Electroanal. Chem., **1,** 425, 1960.
23. Songina, O. A., Amperometrichesko'e polarometrichesko'e titrovani'e v analize mineralnovo syrá, (Amperometric and Polarometric Titrations in the Analysis of Mineral Ores), Gosgeolizdat, Moscow, 1957.
24. Doležal J. and Zýka, J., Polarometrické titrace, (in Czech), (Polarometric Titrations), Státní Nakladatelstvi Technické Literatury, (State Publishing House of Technical Literature), Prague, 1961.

24a. Stock, J. T., Amperometric Titrations, John Wiley, New York, 1965.

25. Laitinen, H. A., Anal. Chem., **21,** 66, 1949; **24,** 46, 1952; **26,** 666, 1956; **30,** 657, 1958; **32,** 180R, 1960; **34,** 307R, 1962.
26. Konopik, N., Österr. Chemiker-Ztg., **54,** 289, 325, 1953; **55,** 117, 1954; **57,** 181, 1956.
27. Delahay, P., Anal. Chim. Acta, **4,** 635, 1950.
28. Kao, S-S., Hsu, K-H., and Tien, T-Ch., Acta Chim. Sinica, Hua Hsüch Pao, **24,** 12, 1958; **24,** 1, 1958.
29. Khadeev, V., Uzbek. Khim. Zhur. **27,** 1959.
30. Bradbury, J. H., Trans. Faraday Soc., **49,** 304, 1953.
31. Stock, J. T., Metallurgia, **46,** 209, 1952; **55,** 48, 1957.
32. Nikolić, K., Archiv. farm., **5,** 217, 1955.
33. Kitagawa, T., Japan Analyst, **6,** 877, 1957.
34. Kies, H. L., Anal. Chim. Acta, **18,** 14, 1953.
35. Songina, O. A., Zavodskaya Lab., **24,** 160, 1958.
36. Songina, O. A., Collection Czechoslov. Chem. Commun., **25,** 3179, 1960.
38. Svatiskaya, I. S., and Songina, O. A., Zavodskaya Lab., **26,** 282, 1960.
39. Stock, J. T., Microchem. J., **2,** 229, 1958; **3,** 543, 1959.
40. Smit, W. M., Chem. Weekblad, **56,** 25, 1960.
41. Fujinaga, J., Rev. Modern Polarography, No. 11, 23, 1950.
42. Furman, N. H., Anal. Chem., **23,** 21, 1951.
43. Kolthoff, I. M., Anal. Chim. Acta, **2,** 606, 1948.
44. Kolthoff, I. M., Frontiers in Chemistry, **7,** 1, 1949.
45. Kolthoff, I. M., J. Ass. Off. Agric. Chem., **39,** 47, 1956.
46. Kolthoff, I. M., Österr, Chemiker-Ztg., **44,** 179, 1941.
47. Kolthoff, I. M., Trans. Electrochem. Soc., **78,** 191, 1940.

48. Kolthoff, I. M., Burk, R. E., and Grummitt, O., Recent Advances in Analytical Chemistry, Vol. VII., Interscience Publishers, New York, 1949.
49. Majer, V., Proceedings 1st Intern. Polarogr. Congress, Vol. III, Přírodovědecké Vydavatelství, Prague, 1952.
50. Parks, T. D., Anal. Chim. Acta, **6,** 553, 1952.
51. Pyatnitskii, I. V., Zavodskaya Lab., **21,** 798, 1955.
52. Souchay, M. P., Chim. anal., **41,** 471, 1959.
53. Anastasi, A., Gallo, N., Mecarelli, E., and Novaćić, L., J. Pharm. Pharmacol., **8,** 241, 1956.
54. Kalvoda, R., and Zýka, J., Českoslov. farm. **1,** 98, 1952.
55. Kalvoda, R., and Zýka, J., Pharmazie, **7,** 535, 1952; Acta Pharm. Intern., **2,** 365, 1953.
55a. Berka, A., Doležal, J., and Zýka, J., Chemist-Analyst, **53,** 122, 1964; **54,** 24, 1965.
56. Zýka, J., Pharmazie, **10,** 170, 1955.
57. Zýka, J., J. Bull. Narcotics, **10,** 35, 1958.
58. Zýka, J., in P. Zuman and I. M. Kolthoff, Progress in Polarography Vol. 2, 649, Interscience Publishers, New York, 1962.
59. Březina, M., and Zuman, P., Polarography in Medicine, Biochemistry and Pharmacy, Interscience Publishers, New York, 1958.
60. Kryukova, I. A., Sni'akova, S. J., and Aref'eva, T. V., Polarograficheskii analiz (in Russian), (Polarographic Analysis), Gos. Nauch. Tekhn. Izdat. Khim. Lit., Moscow, 1959.
61. Meites, L., Polarographic Techniques, Interscience Publishers, New York, 1958.
62. Mika, J., Die Methoden der Mikromassanalyse, 2nd Ed., J. Enke Verlag, Stuttgart, 1958.
63. Milner, G. W. C., The Principles and Applications of Polarography and other Electroanalytical Processes, Longmans, London, 1957.
64. Stackelberg, von M., Polarographische Arbeitsmethoden, W. de Gruyter, Berlin, 1950.
65. Heyrovský, J., and Zuman, P., Einführung in die praktische Polarographie, Verlag Technik, Berlin, 1959.
66. Vinogradova, E. I., Gallai, Z. A., and Finogenova, Z. M., Metody polarograficheskovo i amperometricheskovo analiza (in Russian), (Methods of polarographic and amperometric analysis), Izd. Mosk. Univ., Moscow, 1963.
67. Jordan, J., and Clausen, J. H., in Meites, L., Handbook of Analytical Chemistry, McGraw-Hill, New York, 1963.
68. Proceedings 1st Intern. Polarographic Congress, Přírodověd. Vydavatelství, Prague, 1951.
69. Lingane, J. J., J. Am. Chem. Soc., **65,** 866, 1943.
70. Laitinen, H. A., and Kolthoff, I. M., J. Phys. Chem., **45,** 1079, 1941.
71. Rosenberg, S., Oerrone, J. C., and Kirk, P. L., Anal. Chem., **22,** 1187, 1955.
72. Robert, E. B., and Meek, J. S., Analyst **77,** 43, 1952.
73. Alimarin, I. P., and Gallai, Z. A., Zavodskaya Lab., **21,** 244, 1955.
74. Petrikova, M. N., and Alimarin, I. P., Zhur. Anal. Khim., **12,** 462, 1957.
75. Kolthoff, I. M., and Sambucetti, C. J., Anal. Chim. Acta, **21,** 17 (1959).
76. Lyalikov, Yu. S., Zhur. Anal. Khim., **8,** 38, 1953.
77. Doležal, J., Henzl, V., Simon, V., Chem. Listy, **46,** 272, 1952.
78. Erdey, L., and Karsay, A., Acta Chim. Hung., **9,** 43, 1956.
79. Songina, O. A., Zavodskaya Lab., **19,** 887, 1953.
80. Usatenko, J. J., and Bekleshova, G. E., Zavodskaya Lab., **19,** 147, 1953.
81. Shemyakin, F. M., and Belyakov, N. Y., Zavodskaya Lab., **20,** 552, 1954.
82. Usatenko, J. J., and Bekleshova, G. E., Zavodskaya Lab., **20,** 266, 1954.
82a. Usatenko, J. J., Bekleshova, G. E., Grenberg, J. E., Genis, M. J., and Karpusha, E. E., Zavodskaya Lab., **21,** 26, 1955.
83. Harris, E. D., and Lindsay, A. J., Analyst, **76,** 650, 1951.
84. Ishibashi, M., Fujinaga, T., and Saitô, Ch., J. Chem. Soc. Japan, Pure Chem. Sect., **79,** 12, 1958.
85. Ishibashi, M., and Fujinaga, T., J. Chem. Soc. Japan, Pure Chem. Sect., **79,** 14, 1958.
86. Kobrová, M., Chem. Listy, **49,** 1039, 1954.
87. Konopik, N., Österr. Chem. Ztg., **55,** 46, 1954.
88. Konopik, N., Slaczka, K., Österr. Chem. Ztg., **52,** 205, 1951.
89. Shaw, R., Riedel, B. E., and Harris, W. E., Can. Pharm. J., **90,** 303, 1957.
90. Reishakhrit, L. S., and Sukhobokova, N. S., Zhur. anal. khim., **12,** 146, 1957.
91. Swan, N. B., McNabb, D., and Hazel, J. F., Anal. Chim. Acta, **22,** 76, 1960.
92. Kalmykova, E. N., Zavodskaya Lab., **20,** 397, 1954.
93. Rulfs, Ch. L., Mackela, A. A., Chemist Analyst, **25,** 660, 1953.
94. Tenkovtsev, N. V., Zhur. anal. khim., **12,** 504, 1957.

95. Warshovsky, B., Shook, T. E., and Schantze, J., Anal. Chem., **26**, 1051, 1954.
96. Zittel, H. E., Miller, F. J., and Thomason, P. F., Anal. Chem., **31**, 1351, 1959.
97. Usatenko, J. J., and Bekleshova, G. A., Zavodskaya Lab., **19**, 892, 1953.
98. Přibil, R., Matyska, B., Chem. Listy, **44**, 305, 1950.
99. Usatenko, J. J., and Vitkina, M. A., Nauch. dokl. vys. shkol. khim. i khim. tekhnol., 502, 1958; Chem. Abstr., **53**, 964, 1959.
100. Laitinen, H. A., Jennings, W. P., and Parks, T. D., Ind. Eng. Chem., Anal. Ed., **18**, 358, 1946.
101. Bozsai, J., Magyar Kém. Foly., **62**, 386, 1956.
102. Parks, T. D., and Lykken, L., Anal. Chem., **22**, 1503, 1950.
103. Přibil, R., and Vicenová, E., Chem. Listy, **46**, 535, 1952.
104. Přibil, R., and Matyska, B., Chem. Listy, **44**, 305, 1950.
105. Tanaka, N., Oiwa, J. T., and Kodama, M., Anal. Chem. **28**, 1555, 1956.
106. Calzolari, C., Ref. Leybold Ber., **1**, Nr. 257, 1953.
107. Usatenko, J. J., and Tulyupa, F. M., Zavodskaya Lab. **26**, 783, 1960.
108. Gallay, Z. A., Tiptsova, V. G., Peshkova, V. M., Zhur. anal. khim., **12**, 469, 1957.
109. Kolthoff, I. M., and Lingane, J. J., Chem. Rev., **24**, 1, 1939.
110. Müller, O. H., J. Chem. Educ. **18**, 320, 1941.
111. Laitinen, H. A., Jennings, W. P., and Parks, T. D., Ind. Eng. Chem., Anal. Ed., **18**, 355, 1946.
112. Laitinen, H. A., Kolthoff, I. M., J. Phys. Chem., **45**, 1079, 1941.
113. Seagers, W. J., and Frediani, H. A., Anal. Chem., **26**, 1098, 1954.
114. Haller, J. F., and Listek, S. S., Anal. Chem., **20**, 637, 1948.
115. Shegol, S. S., Zavodskaya Lab., **22**, 1043, 1958.
116. Zhdanov, A. K., Khadeev, V. A., and Moiseeva, G. T., Zavodskaya Lab., **24**, 137, 1958.
117. Bozsai, J. Magyar Kém. Foly., **65**, 207, 1959.
118. Grenberg, E. J., and Genns, M. J., Zavodskaya Lab., **19**, 174, 1954.
119. Kadič, K., and Řezáč, Z., Chem. Listy, **49**, 570, 1955.
120. Kolthoff, I. M., and Sambucetti, C., J. Am. Chem. Soc., **81**, 1516, 1959.
121. Alimarin, I. P., and Frid, B. J., Zavodskaya Lab., **18**, 1300, 1952.
122. Usatenko, J. J., and Vitkina, M. A., Zavodskaya Lab., **23**, 1058, 1957.
123. Matyska, B., Doležal, J., and Roubalová, D., Chem. Listy, **49**, 1012, 1955.
124. Michel, G., Anal. Chim. Acta, **10**, 87, 1954.
125. Southwarth, B. C., Hodecker, J. H., and Fleischer, K. D., Anal. Chem., **30**, 1152, 1958.
126. Tsyvina, B. S., Vladimirova, V. N., Zavodskaya Lab., **24**, 278, 1958.
127. Doležal, J., and Zýka, J., Collection Czechoslov. Chem. Commun., **26**, 1964, 1961.
128. Treindl, L., Chem. listy, **50**, 534, 1956.
129. Pshenitsyn, N. K., and Ezerskaya, N. A., Zhur. Anal. Khim., **14**, 81, 1959.
130. Laitinen, H. A., Jennings, W. P., and Parks, T. D., Ind. Eng. Chem., Anal. Ed., **18**, 355, 1946.
131. Laitinen, H. A., Jennings, W. P., and Parks, T. D., Ind. Eng. Chem., Anal. Ed., **18**, 358, 1946.
132. Knowles, G., and Lowden, G. F., Analyst, **78**, 159, 1953.
133. Sandberg, B., Proceedings 1st Intern. Polarographic Congress, Vol. I, 227, Prague, 1951.
134. Sandberg, B., Svensk Kem. Tid., **58**, 197, 1946.
135. Yasumori, Y., Bull. Soc. Japan, **24**, 107, 1951.
136. Heyrovský, A., Chem. listy, **52**, 40, 1958.
137. Ishibashi, M., and Fujinaga, T., Proceedings 1st Intern. Polarographic Congress, Vol. 1, 115, Prague, 1951.
138. Duyckaerts, G., Anal. Chim. Acta, **5**, 233, 1951.
138a. Bozsai, J., and Hegedüs, Z., Magyar. Kém. Foly., **58**, 339, 1952.
139. Mukhina, Z. S., Zavodskaya Lab., **14**, 1194, 1948.
140. Chlebovský, T., Hutnické listy, **13**, 252, 1958.
141. Simon, V., Sekerka, J., and Doležal, J., Chem. Listy, **46**, 617, 1952.
142. Kolthoff, I. M., Langer, A., J. Am. Chem. Soc., **62**, 211, 1940.
143. Kolthoff, I. M., and Cohn, G., Ind. Eng. Chem., Anal. Ed., **14**, 412, 1942.
144. Boss, R. N., and Conn, J. B., Anal. Chem., **23**, 674, 1951.
145. Khadeev, V. A., and Nikurashina, A. G., Zavodskaya Lab., **24**, 283, 1959.
146. Tomíček, O., Čihalík, J., Doležal, J., Simon, V., and Zýka, J., Chem. Listy, **46**, 710, 1952.
147. Kolthoff, I. M., and Pan, J. D., J. Am. Chem. Soc., **62**, 3332, 1940.
148. Kolthoff, I. M., and Pan, J. D., J. Am. Chem. Soc. **61**, 3402, 1939.
149. Gildenberg, L., Microchem. J., **3**, 167, 1959.
150. Harris, E. D., and Lindsay, A. J., Analyst, **76**, 650, 1951.

151. Konopik, N., and Slaczka, K., Österr. Chem. Ztg., **52**, 205, 1951.
152. Abramov, M. K., and Teodorovich, J. L., Zhur. anal. khim., **12**, 566, 1957.
153. Simon, V., and Grim. V., Chem. Listy, **48**, 1774, 1954.
154. Subrumanian, N., J. Sci. Ind. Res., 16B, 516, 1957; Chem. Abstr., **52**, 7926, 1958.
155. Bozsai, J., Acta Chim. Hung., **9**, 195, 1956.
156. Bozsai, J., and Hegedüs, Z., Magyar. Kém. Foly., **58**, 335, 1952.
157. Tung, S. C., and Wang, E. K., Acta Chim. Sinica, **25**, 37, 1959.
158. Usatenko, J. J., Bekleshova, G. E., Grenberg, J. E., Genis, M. J., and Karpusha, E., Zavodskaya Lab., **22**, 528, 1956.
159. Přibil, R., and Zábranský, Z., Chem. Listy, **46**, 16, 1952.
160. Busev, A. J., and Tiptsova, V. G., Zhur. Anal. Khim., **13**, 180, 1958.
161. Sekerka, J., and Vorlíček, J., Chem. Listy, **47**, 512, 1953.
162. Bozsai, J., Kohaszali Lapok, **9**, 271, 1954; Leybold Ber., **3**, Nr. 123, 1955.
163. Butenko, G. A., Bekleshova, G. E., and Sorochonskii, E. A., Zhur. Anal. Khim., **6**, 105, 1951.
164. Degterev, N. M., Zavodskaya Lab., **22**, 167, 1956.
165. Kao, S. S., Yun, W., Acta Chim. Sinica, **21**, 253, 1955.
166. Parks, T. D., Smith, O. D., and Radding, S. B., Anal. Chim. Acta, **10**, 485, 1954.
167. Elving, P. J., and Olson, E. C., Anal. Chem., **28**, 338, 1958.
168. Berka, A., Doležal, J., Janata, J., and Zýka, J., Anal. Chim. Acta, **25**, 379, 1961.
169. Zýka, J., Bull. Narcotics, **10**, 35, 1958.
170. Kolthoff, I. M., and Bowey, F. A., Anal. Chem., **19**, 498, 1947.
171. Haslam, J., Whatten, S. M. A., and Newlands, G., Analyst, **78**, 340, 1953.
172. Tomíček, O., Blažek, A., and Roubal, Z., Chem. zvesti, **4**, 479, 1950.
173. Baltes, J., and Hiller, A., Fette u. Seifen, **56**, 371, 1954.
174. Beaver, I. I., and Kunitz, H., J. Biol. Chem., **152**, 363, 1944.
175. Smith, L. I., Kolthoff, I. M., and Spillane, L. G., J. Am. Chem. Soc., **64**, 646, 1942.
176. Kalvoda, R., and Zýka, J., Čas. Čes. Lékárn. Věd. Příl., **62**, 134, 1949.
177. Cohen, E. M., and Lordi, N. G., J. Pharm. Science, **50**, 661, 1961.

Chapter 21

CHRONOPOTENTIOMETRY

By Dennis G. Peters
Department of Chemistry
Indiana University
Bloomington, Indiana

Chronopotentiometry is the name given by Delahay and Mamantov[1] to the electroanalytical technique in which the potential-time behavior of a working electrode in an unstirred solution during a constant-current electrolysis is indicative of the nature and the quantity of the electrode reaction which is occurring.

Consider, as a typical chronopotentiometric experiment, the electro-reduction of iron(III) in dilute hydrochloric acid medium at a platinum electrode. Suppose that this electrolysis is performed with a constant current and under conditions where the sole means of mass transfer of iron(III) to the electrode surface is diffusion.

At a platinum cathode, iron(III) is reduced to iron(II) in hydrochloric acid according to the reaction

$$Fe^{+++} + e^{-} = Fe^{++}$$

Since the iron(III)-iron(II) couple is more or less reversible in hydrochloric acid medium, the potential E of the platinum electrode at 25°C. is given reasonably closely by the Nernst equation

$$E = E^{0\prime} - 0.059 \log \frac{[Fe^{++}]}{[Fe^{+++}]} \qquad (1)$$

where $E^{0\prime}$, the formal potential for the iron(III)-iron(II) couple in 1 F hydrochloric acid, is +0.46 v. *vs.* S.C.E. (saturated calomel electrode) and $[Fe^{+++}]$ and $[Fe^{++}]$ are the concentrations of iron(III) and iron(II), respectively, at the electrode surface.

NOTE.—The relationship between the formal potential $E^{0\prime}$ and the standard potential E^0 is

$$E^{0\prime} = E^0 - \frac{0.059}{n} \log \frac{f_R}{f_O}$$

where f_R and f_O are the activity coefficients, respectively, for the reduced and oxidized species.

A representative potential-time curve, called a *chronopotentiogram*, for the reduction of iron(III) in dilute hydrochloric acid at a platinum cathode is shown in Fig. 21-1.

Because the solution initially contains virtually no iron(II), the potential of the platinum electrode prior to the commencement of the electrolysis will be more oxidizing or more positive than the formal potential of the iron(III)-iron(II) couple. At the instant the electro-reduction begins, the iron(II) formed at the electrode surface causes the potential to shift rapidly to a more reducing value (segment AB of Fig. 21-1). As the electrolysis continues, the potential of the working cathode changes more slowly (seg-

[1] Delahay, P., and Mamantov, G., Anal. Chem., **27**, 478, 1955.

ment BC) because the ratio of the concentrations (activities) of iron(III) and iron(II) which determines the potential is in the neighborhood of unity at the electrode surface. Finally, however, all the iron(III) which is initially present at and which diffuses toward the electrode surface is reduced to iron(II), and the potential undergoes a very abrupt change to a much more reducing value (segment CD). If the concentration of iron(III) at the electrode surface reached zero precisely, the potential should become infinitely reducing; but the potential changes only enough to permit the occurrence of some other

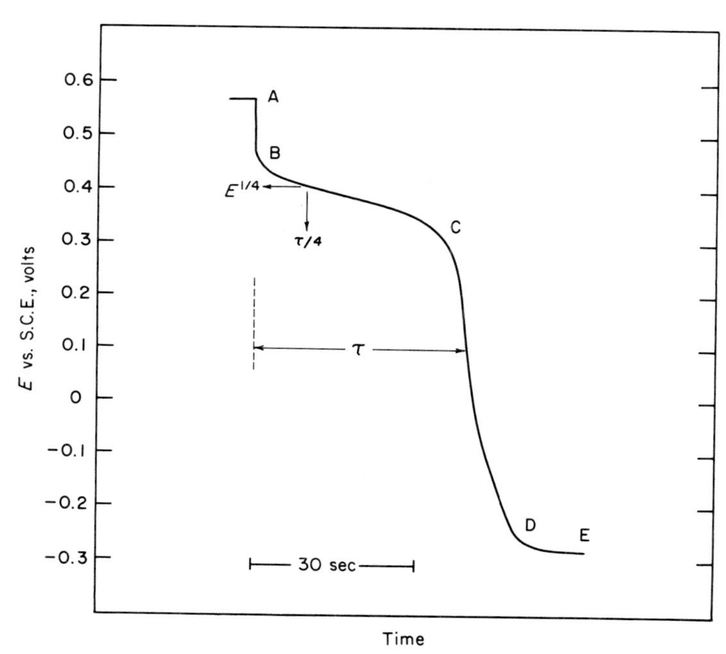

Fig. 21-1. Chronopotentiogram for the Reduction of Iron(III) at a Platinum Cathode. The concentration of iron(III) was 0.0250 *M*, the supporting electrolyte solution was 1 *F* hydrochloric acid, and the temperature was 25°C. A cylindrical (wire) electrode of area 0.281 cm.^{2} and radius 0.0255 cm. was used and the constant current was 2.79×10^{-4} ampere.

electrode reaction. Therefore, the iron(III) concentration at the electrode surface does become infinitesimally small, but never zero. In order that the requirement of constant current be fulfilled after the potential transition, a second electrode reaction must occur. For the case of iron(III) in hydrochloric acid, this second reaction is the reduction of hydrogen ion, and the potential of the platinum electrode is stabilized by the steady evolution of hydrogen (segment DE).

These are the essential features of chronopotentiometry. The theory and practice of chronopotentiometry have been excellently reviewed by numerous authors. Several of the most useful discussions are to be found in monographs by Delahay[2] and by Lingane,[3]

[2] Delahay, P., New Instrumental Methods in Electrochemistry, Interscience Publishers, New York, 1954, pp. 179–216.

[3] Lingane, J. J., Electroanalytical Chemistry, 2nd Ed., Interscience Publishers, New York, 1958, pp. 617–638.

in a summary by Delahay,[4] and in the pioneering studies by Delahay and Mamantov,[1] by Reilley, Everett, and Johns,[5] and by Gierst and his co-workers.[6,7]

THEORY

Discussion of the theory of chronopotentiometry in a chapter primarily intended to describe practical aspects of the method must of necessity be brief. Therefore, the majority of emphasis will be placed on the theory which pertains to a single electrochemical process, such as the reduction of iron(III) to iron(II). Very important, however, is the fact that this theory is also applicable to the first reaction which occurs in the electrolysis of a multicomponent system. To conclude this discussion, the theory relating to successive reactions in multicomponent systems, stepwise reaction of a single substance, and current-reversal chronopotentiometry will be mentioned.

The Transition Time and the Sand Equation.—In the application of chronopotentiometry to chemical analysis, the time required for the abrupt change in potential to occur is of special interest and importance, because it is related to the concentration of the electroactive substance. This so-called *transition time* is defined theoretically as the time, measured from the start of the electrolysis, that is required for the concentration of the electroactive species to reach zero at the electrode surface. The term *transition time* was suggested by Butler and Armstrong,[8,9] and in chronopotentiometry it is denoted by the Greek letter τ (Fig. 21-1). However, since the concentration of the electroactive species never quite reaches zero at the electrode surface, a more practical and precise definition of τ is to state that it is the electrolysis time required to establish a diffusion layer such that the concentration of the electroactive substance at the electrode surface becomes negligibly small in comparison to the bulk concentration.

The fundamental relation which endows chronopotentiometry with analytical usefulness is the Sand equation,[10]

$$\tau^{1/2} = \frac{\pi^{1/2} nFAD^{1/2}C}{2i} \tag{2}$$

where τ is the transition time (seconds), π is 3.1416, n is the number of electrons per molar unit of the electrode reaction, F is the Faraday constant (96,487 coulombs/equivalent), A is the electrode area (cm.^{2}), D is the diffusion coefficient (cm.^{2}/sec.) of the electroactive species, C is the bulk concentration (moles/cm.^{3}) of the substance, and i is the constant electrolysis current (amperes).

The Sand equation applies equally well to reversible and irreversible electrode reactions, but it pertains strictly only to diffusion-controlled processes occurring with 100 percent current efficiency at a plane electrode. This latter requirement limits the applicability of the Sand equation to single electrochemical processes or to the first reaction which takes place during the electrolysis of a multicomponent system. Conversely, the obeyance of the Sand equation over a range of transition times is a good criterion for a linear diffusion process.

Two other modes by which the electroactive substance may reach the electrode sur-

[4] Delahay, P., "Chronoamperometry and Chronopotentiometry," in Kolthoff, I. M., and Elving, P. J., Ed., Treatise on Analytical Chemistry, Part I, Volume 4, Interscience Publishers, New York, 1959, pp. 2233–2267.
[5] Reilley, C. N., Everett, G. W., and Johns, R. H., Anal. Chem., **27,** 483, 1955.
[6] Gierst, L. E., and Juliard, A. L., J. Phys. Chem., **57,** 701, 1953.
[7] Gierst, L. E., and Mechelynck, P., Anal. Chim. Acta, **12,** 79, 1955.
[8] Butler, J. A. V., and Armstrong, G., Proc. Royal Soc. (London), **A139,** 406, 1933.
[9] Armstrong, G., and Butler, J. A. V., Trans. Faraday Soc., **30,** 1173, 1934.
[10] Sand, H. J. S., Phil. Mag., **1,** 45, 1901.

face, namely electrical migration and convection, must be prevented. Electrical migration is virtually eliminated, as in polarography, by the presence in the test solution of a 50-fold to 100-fold excess of an innocuous supporting electrolyte. A study of electrical migration in chronopotentiometry has been reported by Morris and Lingane.[11] Although chronopotentiometric analysis is performed in unstirred solutions, convection can become a serious problem if solution density gradients arise at the electrode surface during electrolysis. Some electrodes and techniques designed to minimize or eliminate such effects will be described below.

In addition to planar electrodes, cylindrical (wire) electrodes and spherical electrodes are frequently employed in chronopotentiometry. Theoretical transition-time relations which are analogous to the Sand equation have been derived and tested for cylindrical[12,13,13a] and spherical[14,15] electrodes.

Equation of the Chronopotentiometric Wave.—Provided an electrode reaction proceeds more or less reversibly, the potential at which a chronopotentiometric wave appears can serve as a qualitative indication of the reaction responsible for the particular wave, in much the same way as the more familiar half-wave potential in polarography.

At 25°C. the relation between potential and time, or the equation of the chronopotentiometric wave, for a single electrochemical process or the first reaction in a multicomponent system is

$$E = E_{1/4} - \frac{0.059}{n} \log \frac{t^{1/2}}{\tau^{1/2} - t^{1/2}} \tag{3}$$

where E is the potential of the working electrode, t is the electrolysis time, τ is the transition time, and $E_{1/4}$, the chronopotentiometric *quarter-wave potential*, is defined by the expression

$$E_{1/4} = E^{0\prime} - \frac{0.059}{n} \log \frac{D_O^{1/2}}{D_R^{1/2}} \tag{4}$$

in which $E^{0\prime}$ is the formal potential for the electrode reaction and D_O and D_R are the diffusion coefficients of the oxidized and reduced species, respectively. It should be emphasized that the chronopotentiometric $E_{1/4}$ and the polarographic $E_{1/2}$ are synonymous, if there are no kinetic complications. The equation of the chronopotentiometric wave was originally derived by Karaoglanoff,[16] and is truly applicable only to perfectly reversible processes occurring at a plane electrode. A further restriction is that Eq. (3) pertains specifically to reactions for which (1) both the reactant and product are soluble in the supporting electrolyte solution, *e.g.*, iron(III) and iron(II), or (2) either the reactant or product species is soluble in the solution phase while the other species is soluble in the electrode phase (as is the case for mercury, mercury amalgam, or other liquid metal electrodes). In other words, for Eq. (3) to be valid, the laws of diffusion must govern the movement of the reactant and product, respectively, to and from the electrode surface. Relations for the chronopotentiometric waves obtained in the anodic oxidation of a metal with formation of a soluble complex and with formation of an insoluble film have been derived and verified by Delahay, Mattax, and Berzins.[17]

[11] Morris, M. D., and Lingane, J. J., J. Electroanal. Chem., **6,** 300, 1963.
[12] Peters, D. G., and Lingane, J. J., J. Electroanal. Chem., **2,** 1, 1961.
[13] Lingane, J. J., J. Electroanal. Chem., **2,** 46, 1961.
[13a] Evans, D. H., and Price, J. E., J. Electroanal. Chem., **5,** 77, 1963.
[14] Mamantov, G., and Delahay, P., J. Am. Chem. Soc., **76,** 5323, 1954.
[15] McKeon, M. G., J. Electroanal. Chem., **4,** 93, 1962.
[16] Karaoglanoff, Z., Z. Elektrochem., **12,** 5, 1906.
[17] Delahay, P., Mattax, C. C., and Berzins, T., J. Am. Chem. Soc., **76,** 5319, 1954.

For a system which obeys Eq. (3), the important conclusion is that the potential E of the working electrode is exactly equal to $E_{1/4}$ when the electrolysis time t is $\tau/4$, and, since D_O and D_R are usually similar in magnitude, E at $t = \tau/4$ is nearly the same as $E^{0'}$. Expressions for cylindrical and spherical diffusion processes, which are analogous to Eq. (3), predict a small but, for practical purposes, negligible difference between E at $t = \tau/4$ and $E_{1/4}$. Note that $E_{1/4}$ in Fig. 21-1 is +0.40 v. *vs.* S.C.E., a value which is close to the formal potential $E^{0'}$ for the iron(III)-iron(II) couple in 1 F hydrochloric acid (+0.46 v. *vs.* S.C.E.). The experience of the writer has shown that in chronopotentiometry many reactions proceed with some overpotential which usually increases as the current density increases or as the transition time decreases. Therefore, for reduction reactions $E_{1/4}$ may be somewhat more cathodic than $E^{0'}$, whereas $E_{1/4}$ will be slightly more anodic than $E^{0'}$ for oxidation processes.

Irreversible Chronopotentiometric Waves and Kinetics.—A discussion of the theory for irreversible chronopotentiometric waves and of electrode processes complicated by kinetics surpasses the purpose and intent of the present chapter. However, information about these subjects can be gleaned from the monograph by Delahay[2] and from papers by Reinmuth[18,19] and by Delahay and collaborators.[17,20–22]

Multicomponent Systems.—One of the undeveloped applications of chronopotentiometry is the analysis of mixtures of electroactive substances. If a solution contains two electroactive species and if the potentials at which these species undergo reduction or oxidation differ by at least 100 millivolts, the resulting chronopotentiogram will exhibit two successive waves, one corresponding to each species. Because the first substance is reduced or oxidized with 100 percent current efficiency, the transition time (τ_1) for the first wave is given by the Sand equation, the subscript 1 being appended to τ, n, D, and C in Eq. (2) to designate the first substance. While the second species is reacting, however, the first substance still continues to diffuse toward and to react immediately at the surface of the electrode. Consequently, the current efficiency for the reduction or oxidation of the second substance is substantially less than 100 percent, and the transition time (τ_2) for the second wave is longer than it would be if only the second substance alone is present. Berzins and Delahay[23] have shown that the theoretical equation which describes this situation is

$$(\tau_1 + \tau_2)^{1/2} - \tau_1^{1/2} = \frac{\pi^{1/2} n_2 F A D_2^{1/2} C_2}{2i} \tag{5}$$

where each symbol has the same significance as in the Sand equation and the subscripts 1 and 2 refer, respectively, to the first and second substances. The non-additivity of transition times is an important characteristic for successive reactions and for stepwise processes in chronopotentiometry, and serves to distinguish chronopotentiometry from polarography. Equation (5) has been corroborated by Kambara and Tachi.[24] Reilley, Everett, and Johns[5] deduced a general relation for any number of electroactive substances. Analogous equations for chronopotentiometry with cylindrical[25,26] and spherical[26] electrodes are available.

Stepwise Reaction of a Single Substance.—Attention has also been directed to the

[18] Reinmuth, W. H., Anal. Chem., **32,** 1514, 1960.
[19] Reinmuth, W. H., Anal. Chem., **33,** 322, 1961.
[20] Delahay, P., and Berzins, T., J. Am. Chem. Soc., **75,** 2486, 1953.
[21] Delahay, P., and Mattax, C. C., J. Am. Chem. Soc., **76,** 874, 1954.
[22] Delahay, P., Disc. Faraday Soc., **17,** 205, 1954.
[23] Berzins, T., and Delahay, P., J. Am. Chem. Soc., **75,** 4205, 1953.
[24] Kambara, T., and Tachi, I., J. Phys. Chem., **61,** 1405, 1957.
[25] Peters, D. G., and Lingane, J. J., J. Electroanal. Chem., **2,** 249, 1961.
[26] Murray, R. W., and Reilley, C. N., J. Electroanal. Chem., **3,** 182, 1962.

theory of the diffusion-controlled stepwise reduction or oxidation of a single electroactive species. If a substance undergoes a two-step reduction or oxidation ($A \xrightarrow{n_1e^-} B \xrightarrow{n_2e^-} C$), and if the difference in the potentials for the half-reactions corresponding to each step is 100 millivolts or more, a chronopotentiogram showing two waves will be obtained. Again, the Sand equation, with τ and n set equal to τ_1 and n_1, respectively, is valid for the interpretation of the first step of the reaction. During the second step, however, both the parent electroactive substance, A, and the intermediate oxidation state, B, are reduced or oxidized to form the final product, C. The theoretical relation which pertains to the transition time for the second step (τ_2) was also derived by Berzins and Delahay,[23] and is identical to Eq. (5), except that D_2 and C_2 are replaced, respectively, by D and C which represent the diffusion coefficient and the concentration of the parent substance. It is interesting that the second transition time (τ_2) is dependent on D and C for the parent substance and not for the intermediate oxidation state, B, in spite of the fact that the latter species is reduced or oxidized during the second step. A further significant point, shown by Evans,[26a] is that, during the second step of the reaction (which corresponds formally to the reduction or oxidation of the intermediate oxidation state B to the final product C), the reduction or oxidation of the parent substance A to form B also occurs.

By algebraically combining the theoretical relations for τ_1 and τ_2 for a two-step process, one can obtain the following equation.[23]

$$\frac{\tau_2}{\tau_1} = \left[\frac{n_2}{n_1}\right]^2 + 2\left[\frac{n_2}{n_1}\right] \qquad (6)$$

Frequently, the identity of stepwise electrode reactions can be established with the aid of this relation. Berzins and Delahay[23] showed that for the two-step reduction of oxygen to hydrogen peroxide to water at a mercury pool cathode the transition time for the second step is three times that for the first step. The reduction of uranium(VI) occurs in two steps at a mercury electrode in a potassium chloride–hydrochloric acid solution. In the latter case $\tau_2 = 8\tau_1$ which indicates that uranium(VI) is reduced first to uranium(V) and then to uranium(III). For the stepwise chronopotentiometric oxidation of iodide at a platinum or gold electrode in dilute acid medium, Anson and Lingane[27] correlated the two waves with the one-electron oxidation to iodine and the five-electron oxidation to iodate.

An equation for the stepwise reaction of a single substance at a cylindrical (wire) electrode has been tested with data obtained for the stepwise reduction of copper(II) in chloride media.[27a]

Current-Reversal Chronopotentiometry.—Another useful electroanalytical technique is current-reversal chronopotentiometry. The theory for this method was developed by Berzins and Delahay.[23] The technique consists essentially of reversing the direction of current flow at some preselected point on the chronopotentiometric wave. Usually, current reversal is performed at the moment the transition time is reached. The most straightforward result and interpretation are achieved when (1) both the reactant and product species are soluble (either in the solution phase or in the electrode phase), (2) the reactions occurring before and after current reversal are simply the reverse of each other, and (3) the current is the same throughout the experiment. For these conditions Berzins and Delahay[23] proved that the transition time (τ_r) for the current-reversal wave is exactly one-third of the transition time (τ) for the forward reaction at a plane electrode. For some systems the equality of τ_r and τ indicates that the product of the forward

[26a] Evans, D. H., J. Electroanal. Chem., **9**, 267, 1965.
[27] Anson, F. C., and Lingane, J. J., J. Am. Chem. Soc., **79**, 1015, 1957.
[27a] Peters, D. G., and Cruser, S. A., J. Electroanal. Chem., **9**, 27, 1965.

reaction is insoluble and is precipitated on the electrode surface. Murray and Reilley[26] have derived the theoretical expressions for current-reversal chronopotentiometry with cylindrical and spherical electrodes. Chief interest in the method of current-reversal chronopotentiometry stems from its application to kinetics studies.[28-31]

INSTRUMENTATION AND METHODOLOGY

The basic instrumentation required for chronopotentiometric measurements, as shown in Fig. 21-2, consists essentially of a three-electrode cell and two electrical circuits—an

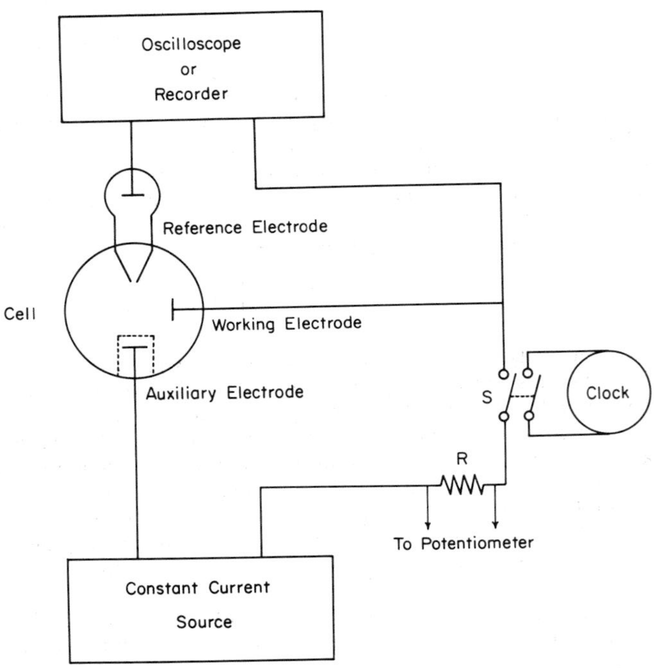

Fig. 21-2. Schematic Diagram of Essential Instrumentation for Chronopotentiometry.

electrolysis circuit and a recording circuit. Each of these experimental aspects of chronopotentiometry will be discussed below.

Electrodes. **Working Electrodes.**—The *working electrode* is defined herein as that electrode at which the reaction of interest occurs. The selection of a working electrode is governed to a large extent by the electrochemical system under study. In turn, the particular working electrode has an influence on the design of the chronopotentiometric cell.

The use of mercury working electrodes in chronopotentiometry is limited, by and large, to cathodic processes. Mercury exhibits a large hydrogen overpotential which

[28] Testa, A. C., and Reinmuth, W. H., Anal. Chem., **32,** 1512, 1960; *ibid.*, **32,** 1518, 1960.
[29] Furlani, C., and Morpurgo, G., J. Electroanal. Chem., **1,** 351, 1960.
[30] King, R. M., and Reilley, C. N., J. Electroanal. Chem., **1,** 434, 1960.
[31] Christie, J. H., and Lauer, G., Anal. Chem., **36,** 2037, 1964.

renders mercury pool, dropping mercury, and hanging mercury drop electrodes useful for the reductimetric determination of both inorganic and organic substances. Probably most, if not all, of the information which has been accumulated from polarographic studies with the dropping mercury electrode can be extrapolated for the purposes of chronopotentiometric analysis.

Of the three kinds of mercury electrodes mentioned, by far the most extensive use has been made of mercury pool electrodes. Descriptions of chronopotentiometric cells which incorporate mercury pool electrodes are contained in papers by Delahay and Mattax,[21] Nicholson and Karchmer,[32] Reilley, Everett, and Johns,[5] and Bruckenstein and Rouse.[33] Some words of qualification concerning the use of mercury pool electrodes seem warranted. A mercury pool is more sensitive than many other electrodes to vibrations which perturb the diffusion layer at the electrode surface and which produce positive errors in the observed transition time. Also, depending upon the specific electrode and cell design and the procedure employed for introduction of the mercury and solution, a thin film of the test solution can become entrapped between the mercury and container; the result can be spurious chronopotentiometric waves, irreproducible electrode areas, or erroneous transition-time measurements. This difficulty can be circumvented by coating the glass surface of the cell which contacts the mercury with a non-wetting silicone oil. A better alternative, however, is the use of a *Teflon*® or *Lucite*® cup for the mercury pool. With electrodes of a small diameter (up to perhaps five millimeters), the variation with potential of the interfacial tension between the mercury pool and the solution causes changes in the surface area of the electrode. In addition, the meniscus of small mercury pool electrodes introduces the complicating factor of nonlinear diffusion and gives rise to significant differences between the apparent (projected) and real electrode area.

The dropping mercury electrode (D.M.E.) was employed in some of the early research in chronopotentiometry. The chief problems associated with the use of this electrode are (1) performing chronopotentiometric experiments of a duration very short compared to the lifetime of the drop in order that the electrode area remain virtually constant, and (2) beginning the electrolysis always at the same stage in the growth of the drop so that the electrode area will be reproducible from one trial to the next. A conventional dropping mercury electrode may be employed for which the drop time ranges from two to ten seconds and the chronopotentiometric electrolysis lasts on the order of tenths of a second. By forming a constriction in a polarographic capillary, one can obtain drop times as long as several hundred seconds, and transition times of a few seconds can be reproducibly measured. Since the mercury thread momentarily retracts up into the capillary at the instant of drop detachment, clogging of the capillary may ensue, particularly if a metal ion reduction is being studied. Some details about the dropping mercury electrode and the required supplementary instrumentation for chronopotentiometric studies can be found in papers by Gierst and Juliard[6] and by Delahay, Mattax, and Berzins.[17]

The hanging mercury drop electrode (H.M.D.E.) offers the advantage of being a stationary mercury microelectrode of exceptionally reproducible area. In addition, the instrumentation problems which attend the use of the dropping mercury electrode are not encountered. The design and construction of a hanging mercury drop electrode have been described by Ross, DeMars, and Shain.[34]

Finally, two other mercury-type electrodes deserve mention. The first of these, the mercury-film electrode, recently described by Moros,[35] has not been used for chrono-

[32] Nicholson, M. M., and Karchmer, J. H., Anal. Chem., **27**, 1095, 1955.
[33] Bruckenstein, S., and Rouse, T. O. Anal. Chem., **36**, 2039, 1964.
[34] Ross, J. W., DeMars, R. D., and Shain, I., Anal. Chem., **28**, 1768, 1956.
[35] Moros, S. A., Anal. Chem., **34**, 1584, 1962.

potentiometry. It possesses the characteristic of being a very close approximation to a planar mercury electrode. Kuwana and Adams[36,37] added the mercury chloride film anode to the roster of electrodes for chronopotentiometry. These authors found that a mercury pool electrode could be anodized in chloride medium to a potential well above +1.0 v. *vs.* S.C.E. because of the formation of a passivating film of mercurous chloride on the surface of the pool.

For the study of anodic reactions, a long list of solid electrodes has been employed, including platinum, gold, graphite, carbon paste, boron carbide, and pyrolytic carbon.

Platinum electrodes have been used for a wide variety of chronopotentiometric studies. For exploratory work, platinum foil electrodes are perfectly satisfactory. However, for careful work, including analysis, ordinary foil electrodes may be inadequate in several respects. With small, unshielded, planar electrodes, the electrolysis occurring at the edges of the platinum foil may produce experimental results which deviate significantly from linear diffusion theory. The use of platinum foil electrodes of a large area may minimize these "edge-effects," but the constant-current source must deliver higher currents and the nonuniform current flow around any large electrode may cause the effective area to be different from the apparent, geometric area. In addition, with unshielded planar electrodes (and, for that matter, any other unshielded electrode), the precise measurement of transition times above, say, 25 to 30 seconds is a very uncertain proposition because the diffusion layer becomes so thick that any difference in the densities of the bulk solution and the diffusion layer causes stirring of the solution (natural convection). Therefore, shielded platinum foil electrodes which have a well-defined area and which can be oriented for either upward or downward diffusion are recommended. If the density of the diffusion layer is less than that of the bulk solution, the shielded electrode should be positioned for upward diffusion; and, if the densities of the diffusion layer and bulk solution are reversed, downward diffusion is preferred. The correct orientation must usually be determined empirically. Bard[38] has reported on a chronopotentiometric study in which platinum foil electrodes in glass sleeves were employed. Shielded platinum electrodes recessed into *Teflon,*® *Nylon,*® or *Lucite*® have been described by Bruckenstein and Rouse[33] and by Morris and Lingane,[11] and a shielded planar electrode of almost any metal could be similarly fabricated.

Wire electrodes of platinum, gold, silver, palladium, and other metals are especially convenient to use from an experimental and manipulative standpoint, although the theory of chronopotentiometry for cylindrical diffusion[12,13,25,26] is more complicated than that for linear diffusion. Platinum wire sealed into a soft-glass tube provides a suitable electrode. Electrical contact is best obtained by extending the wire through the entire length of the glass tube. The all-too-common practice of filling the glass tube and obtaining electrical contact with mercury seems ill-advised. The "end-effect" (diffusion of the electroactive species to the end of the wire) may be eliminated if the end of the wire is sealed into a small glass bead or otherwise covered. The "end-effect" is negligible to within one percent if the length of exposed wire is at least 25 times greater than the diameter of the wire. With thick wire, a satisfactory platinum-glass seal is difficult, if not impossible, to achieve. Furthermore, many metals, such as gold, palladium, and silver, cannot be sealed into glass because they melt at a relatively low temperature. The writer has used Tygon paint (commercially available from the U. S. Stoneware Co., Akron, Ohio) to coat platinum, gold, and silver wires and to leave exposed perfectly cylindrical surfaces of known area. The wire should be dipped into the Tygon paint so that a one-to-two-cm. length of wire remains exposed at one end; then, to eliminate the

[36] Kuwana, T., and Adams, R. N., J. Am. Chem. Soc., **79,** 3609, 1957.
[37] Kuwana, T., and Adams, R. N., Anal. Chim. Acta, **20,** 51, 1959.
[38] Bard, A. J., Anal. Chem., **33,** 11, 1961.

"end-effect," the tip of the exposed wire can be coated. Electrical contact to the electrode can be made by scraping the paint from the upper end of the wire. Such a coating adheres well in aqueous acid or base and does not suffer from chemical reactions or from loss of electrical insulating properties. The coating is soluble in many organic solvents, *e.g.*, acetone, so that the wire may be reclaimed or recoated.

The surface oxidation and reduction of platinum is now well known. In fact, chronopotentiometry is particularly suited for studies of this surface oxidation and reduction and of the profound effects on other electrode reactions which this ignobility causes. Gold electrodes behave similarly. However, gold undergoes surface oxidation at a potential approximately 200 to 300 millivolts more oxidizing (positive) than does platinum. Therefore, many chronopotentiometric oxidations occur prior to the formation of a gold oxide film, but simultaneously with the production of the platinum oxide film. This important difference in the two classical electrode materials, platinum and gold, has yet to be fully exploited. It is worthy of serious consideration in any contemplated analytical procedure. The reduction of hydrogen ions or water at a gold cathode generally occurs at a potential 100 to 200 millivolts more reducing (negative) than at platinum, which provides the former electrode with a slightly greater cathodic working range in chronopotentiometry.

Studies of the other four electrode materials cited—graphite, carbon paste, boron carbide, and pyrolytic carbon—have been carried out, at least in part, in an effort to circumvent the obvious problems associated with the surface oxidation and reduction of platinum and gold.

The use of the graphite electrode in chronopotentiometric studies was introduced by Elving and his students.[39,40] These workers employed wax-impregnated graphite electrodes in order to overcome the irreproducible surface area which stems from the high porosity of ordinary graphite. Adams and his co-workers[41–43] developed a carbon paste electrode, and designed and tested a boron carbide electrode. One of the apparent disadvantages of some samples of commercially-obtained boron carbide rods is that the binding agent which cements the boron carbide granules together is destroyed by the anodic cleaning procedure recommended by the authors. Recent use of the pyrolytic carbon electrode has been reported by Beilby, Brooks, and Lawrence,[44] who compared the chronopotentiometric behavior of ferrocyanide and ferricyanide at pyrolytic carbon and wax-impregnated graphite electrodes.

Auxiliary and Reference Electrodes.—In the present discussion, the *auxiliary electrode* is that electrode which, in conjunction with the working electrode, completes the electrolysis circuit. The *reference electrode* is the electrode against which the potential of the working electrode is compared as a function of time during the electrolysis. Generally speaking, the selection of auxiliary and reference electrodes for chronopotentiometry is the same as for other electrometric methods of analysis.

It is customary to separate the auxiliary and reference electrodes from direct contact with the test solution by placing them in compartments which are physically isolated from but in electrolytic contact with the test solution. For the auxiliary electrode compartment, a glass tube closed at the bottom with a sintered-glass disc is commonly used. To decrease solution flow through the sintered-glass disc, an agar plug may be placed behind the disc. Alternatively, a cracked-glass bridge tube, patented by and com-

[39] Elving, P. J., and Krivis, A. F., Anal. Chem., **30,** 1648, 1958.
[40] Elving, P. J., and Smith, D. L., Anal. Chem., **32,** 1849, 1960.
[41] Adams, R. N., Anal. Chem., **30,** 1576, 1958.
[42] Mueller, T. R., Olson, C. L., and Adams, R. N., Proc. 2nd Intern. Polarog. Congr., Cambridge, 1959, p. 198.
[43] Mueller, T. R., and Adams, R. N., Anal. Chim. Acta, **23,** 467, 1960; *ibid.*, **25,** 482, 1961.
[44] Beilby, A. L., Brooks, W., Jr., and Lawrence, G. L., Anal. Chem., **36,** 22, 1964.

mercially available from the Leeds and Northrup Company and described by Lingane,[45] or a Vycor conducting-glass tube (Corning Glass Works, Corning, New York) serve equally well as auxiliary electrode compartments. Vycor tubes cannot be used in strongly alkaline media. Any of the above-mentioned devices may function as a reference electrode compartment. When special significance is to be attached to the potential measurements, however, the familiar Luggin capillary should be employed as a reference electrode compartment.

The auxiliary electrode is usually nothing more than a bare platinum or gold wire placed in the auxiliary electrode compartment. The auxiliary electrode compartment is filled with a portion of pure supporting electrolyte solution or of the test solution itself, due attention being paid, however, to the ever-present possibility that the products of electrolysis at the auxiliary electrode may eventually contaminate the test solution.

By and large, the saturated calomel electrode (S.C.E.) is the most universal reference electrode for studies in aqueous and nonaqueous solutions at room temperature. The silver chloride reference electrode is another possibility. If the exclusion of chloride ion from a system is mandatory, a mercury-mercury(I) sulfate electrode may be suitable. For chronopotentiometric studies in molten salts, Laitinen and his students[46,47] have employed a platinum-platinum(II) chloride reference electrode, while Liu[48] utilized a silver-silver chloride electrode. The most comprehensive treatment of reference electrode systems is the book edited by Ives and Janz.[49]

Chronopotentiometric Cells.—The design and construction of chronopotentiometric cells is limited only by the imagination and ingenuity of the investigator. Almost any cell employed for polarography or coulometric methods of analysis can be used in chronopotentiometry with little or no modification. Typical cells may be found in papers by Delahay and Mattax,[21] Nicholson and Karchmer,[32] Reilley, Everett, and Johns,[5] and Lingane.[45] An arrangement for chronopotentiometric analysis of a single drop of solution was devised by Iwamoto, Adams, and Lott.[50]

The chronopotentiometric cell shown in Fig. 21-3 is of a conventional design. Any of the working electrodes previously described, except the mercury pool, could be readily incorporated into such a cell. Chronopotentiometric cells must ordinarily be three-electrode cells, as opposed to the familiar two-electrode polarographic cells in which the functions of the auxiliary and reference electrodes are performed by the same electrode. This is because the magnitudes of constant currents employed are relatively large and may cause polarization of the reference electrode and necessitate corrections for iR effects. Utilization of the dropping mercury or hanging mercury drop electrodes for chronopotentiometry might render feasible a two-electrode cell because of the small electrode areas and constant currents involved. However, a three-electrode cell is recommended for all measurements.

Naturally, since the Sand equation includes as a parameter the diffusion coefficient of the electroactive species, accurate chronopotentiometric analyses demand precise control of the solution temperature. As diffusion coefficients for most substances increase about two percent per degree, the temperature of the test solution should be kept constant to within approximately one-tenth degree. For this purpose the writer prefers a water-jacketed cell as pictured in Fig. 21-3.

Good chronopotentiometric practice requires that between each trial the solution be

[45] Lingane, J. J., J. Electroanal. Chem., **1,** 379, 1960.
[46] Laitinen, H. A., and Ferguson, W. S., Anal. Chem., **29,** 4, 1957.
[47] Laitinen, H. A., and Gaur, H. C., Anal. Chim. Acta, **18,** 1, 1958.
[48] Liu, C. H., Anal. Chem., **33,** 1477, 1961.
[49] Ives, D. J. G., and Janz, G. J., Reference Electrodes, Academic Press, New York, 1961.
[50] Iwamoto, R. T., Adams, R. N., and Lott, H., Anal. Chim. Acta, **20,** 84, 1959.

stirred to restore the original bulk concentration of the electroactive species at the electrode surface. This is accomplished by the use of a magnetic stirrer or by bubbling an inert gas (employed to remove oxygen) through the solution. After the period of stirring, about one or two minutes must be allowed for the solution to become quiescent before the subsequent trial. Obviously, the chronopotentiometric cell must be mounted so that it is unaffected by vibrations.

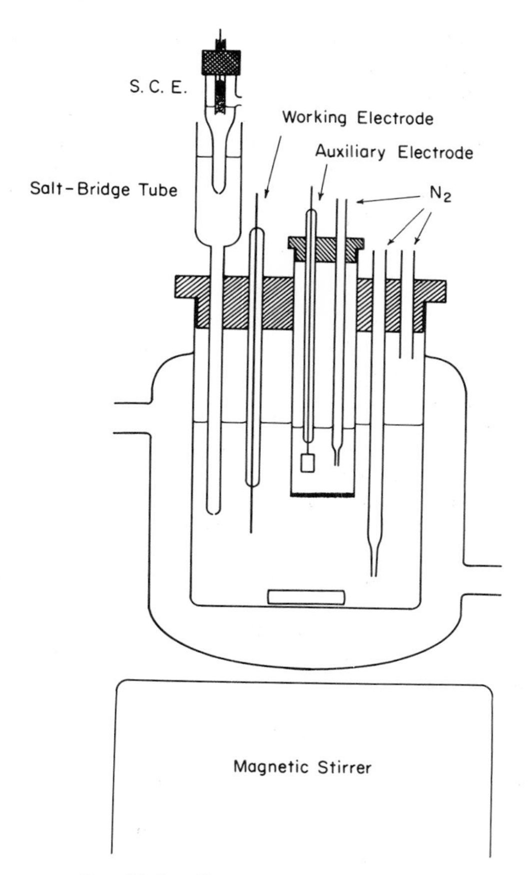

FIG. 21-3. Chronopotentiometric Cell.

The exclusion of dissolved air from test solutions is almost mandatory because oxygen is electroactive. In addition, in the chronopotentiometric study of species such as uranium(IV), iodide, plutonium(III), or copper(I), oxygen must be absent because it reacts with these substances. Oxygen may be conveniently removed from test solutions, as is done in polarography and coulometry, with pure nitrogen, carbon dioxide (in acid media), helium, and other inert gases. Ordinary high purity, commerically-available, tank gases are very satisfactory for most work. However, in very unusual situations, the residual traces of oxygen present in commercial gases can be removed by one of several accepted procedures.[51,52] It is advisable to presaturate tank gases with water vapor or other appropriate solvent to prevent the evaporation of solvent from the test solution itself. The gas may be employed to stir the solution between chronopotentiometric trials. During a trial a stream of gas should flow over the surface of the quiescent solution to prevent reabsorption of oxygen. With some cells, the removal of oxygen from the auxiliary and reference electrode compartments is also necessary to prevent its diffusion into the test solution.

A factor relating to the electrode area and the volume of test solution contained in the cell should be mentioned. Each chronopotentiometric trial results in a certain, usually very small, depletion of the electroactive substance. For a prescribed set of experimental conditions, the larger the electrode area, the larger will be the amount of this substance electrolyzed in a single trial. If the total quantity of electroactive species is small (because the volume of solution in the cell happens to be not very large), the concentration of the electroactive substance may decrease significantly with each successive trial. In order that the depletion of the electroactive substance be negligible, the ideal situation is that of a small electrode (*e.g.*, 0.25 to 0.50 cm.^{2} in area) and a relatively large solution volume of 50 to 100 ml. The brief quantitative discussion of this problem by Lingane[3] should be consulted.

Constant-Current Sources; Current Measurement; Programmed Current.—A wide variety of constant-current sources has been proposed for chronopotentiometry. Most of these originate from the practice of coulometric analysis. Any constant-current source used for coulometric titrations can serve well for chronopotentiometry. It is preferable, therefore, that the interested reader consult the literature of coulometric analysis for comprehensive information. A useful starting reference is the monograph by Lingane.[53]

Probably the simplest, and certainly very widely used, constant-current source consists of a bank of heavy-duty radio B-batteries placed in series with a large, current-limiting resistance. The writer has employed three or four 45-volt batteries in series to provide an e.m.f. of 135 or 180 volts, and it is not uncommon for six to eight batteries to be utilized in this manner. The current-limiting resistance need be nothing more than a one-watt or two-watt carbon radio resistor.

The foregoing constitutes the most straightforward example of a constant-voltage current source. For such devices it must be recognized that the factor which governs the constancy of the current is the magnitude of the e.m.f. developed across the cell during the electrolysis relative to that of the batteries. For example, if the cell e.m.f. is approximately one volt (as it frequently will be), a bank of three B-batteries, totalling 135 volts, can guarantee at best a current constant to within one percent. A further consideration is that battery constant-current sources should be used only in conjunction with microelectrodes, *e.g.*, 0.25 to 0.50 cm.^{2} in area. Because of the limited strength of batteries, it is impractical to draw constant currents much larger than a few milliamperes from them. When large currents are drawn from batteries, a current surge followed by a current decay normally occurs during the first few seconds of the electrolysis. To alleviate this undesirable feature of battery constant-current sources, it is helpful to "pre-polarize" the batteries. This operation can be accomplished most simply with the aid of a two-position switch or relay; the first position connects the batteries across a resistor of the same size as the cell resistance for 15 to 20 seconds prior to the actual experiment,

[51] Kolthoff, I. M., and Lingane, J. J., Polarography, 2nd Ed., Interscience Publishers, New York, 1952, pp. 395–396.

[52] Meites, L., Polarographic Techniques, Interscience Publishers, New York, 1955, pp. 32–34.

[53] Lingane, J. J., Electroanalytical Chemistry, 2nd Ed., Interscience Publishers, New York, 1958, pp. 499–511.

then, immediately, the relay or switch is thrown to the second position to initiate the electrolysis.

The other type of constant-current source is one which employs electronic or servo-mechanical regulation of the current. In contrast to constant-voltage current sources, a regulated constant-current source produces currents of the much greater constancy (± 0.1 percent or better) required for coulometric titrations and for precise chronopotentiometric work.

For all chronopotentiometric experiments, the accepted procedure for determination of the constant current is to measure the iR-drop across a calibrated resistor with a precision potentiometer, as indicated in Fig. 21-2.

According to the Sand equation, a linear relationship exists between the square-root of the transition time ($\tau^{1/2}$) and the concentration of the electroactive substance. Senda[54] has pointed out that, if the electrolysis current increases as the square-root of time, the transition time (τ) will be directly proportional to concentration. Hurwitz and Gierst[55,56] have derived theoretical expressions appropriate to this modification of chronopotentiometry, and have discussed various experimental methods for achieving the desired dependence of current on the square-root of time. More recently, Murray[57] has described the utilization of operational amplifiers to obtain a variety of time-dependent electrolysis currents. Using this technique, one could obtain chronopotentiograms for mixtures of two or more electroactive substances in which the successive transition times are additive. The advantage of this technique for chemical analysis is obvious, but little work has been done to exploit the analytical potentialities of the method.

Observation and Recording of Chronopotentiograms; Measurement of Transition Times.—In the graphical presentation of chronopotentiograms, the writer recommends recording or plotting the potential of the working electrode (Y-axis) as a function of time (X-axis) because the former quantity is the dependent variable. Figure 21-1 exemplifies this preference.

For the purpose of observing and recording chronopotentiograms, the most popular instruments are oscilloscopes (with auxiliary equipment for photographing potential-time curves) and fast-response, pen-and-ink X–Y or strip-chart recorders. The fast-response characteristic is more important in chronopotentiometry than in conventional polarography because the duration of the majority of routine chronopotentiometric experiments is in the neighborhood of 5 to 25 seconds. As indicated below, this feature is of special significance when transition times are very short.

Another important requirement of the recording instrument is that it possess a high input impedance in order to minimize polarization of the working electrode prior to the actual chronopotentiometric trial. Typically, most commercially-available recorders and oscilloscopes have input impedances of two or three megohms. Suppose, for example, that the open-circuit potential of the working electrode versus the reference electrode is $+0.5$ v. and that the input impedance of the recorder is two megohms. If, prior to the actual electrolysis, the working and reference electrodes are connected through the recorder, a current of 0.25 μa. will flow and the working electrode will undergo cathodic polarization. Such an event can be especially deleterious in two different experimental situations. First, in solutions which contain very small concentrations of electroactive substances, *i.e.*, 10^{-4} M or less, the potential of the working electrode is not well poised, and the electrode is particularly prone to such polarization. Second, for microelectrodes, such as the dropping mercury or the hanging mercury drop electrode, the current which

[54] Senda, M., Rev. Polarography (Japan), **4,** 89, 1956.
[55] Hurwitz, H., and Gierst, L., J. Electroanal. Chem., **2,** 128, 1961.
[56] Hurwitz, H., J. Electroanal. Chem., **2,** 142, 1961; *ibid.*, **2,** 328, 1961.
[57] Murray, R. W., Anal. Chem., **35,** 1784, 1963.

flows through the recording circuit can be an appreciable fraction of the electrolysis current and can cause inconstancy of the electrolysis current as well as pre-polarization of the working electrode. Transition times measured under such circumstances can be very erroneous. Experiments involving an electrode of area at least 0.25 $cm.^2$, a concentration of the electroactive substance greater than 0.01 *M*, and a recorder with an input impedance of one megohm or more are not usually affected by the small current which flows through the recording circuit. However, such a conclusion should always be confirmed by preliminary calculations and verified by experiment.

To further eliminate pre-polarization of the working electrode, it is always preferable that the recording circuit remain open during the one or two minutes just before the electrolysis that the test solution is allowed to reach quiescence. The recording circuit should be closed only slightly in advance of the electrolysis circuit. Another solution to this problem is the incorporation into the recording circuit of a voltage follower[58] with an input impedance of 100 megohms.

Numerous methods for the measurement of transition times have been proposed. Regardless of the technique used, however, an important fact to be remembered is that an experimentally-measured transition time is almost never precisely the same as the transition time defined theoretically by the Sand equation, because the concentration of electroactive substance at the electrode surface never reaches zero in an actual trial. Any method for the experimental evaluation of transition times is at best an approximation, albeit possible in many situations to approach the true value.

Direct measurement of the transition time from a complete recorded chronopotentiogram requires that the time scale of the recording instrument be perfectly linear. Otherwise a precisely-known timing signal must be superimposed upon the time-base function of the recorder. In addition, the response of the recorder must be sufficiently rapid to prevent the introduction of a significant positive error to the measurement. Provided the recorded chronopotentiogram is well defined, the transition time may be taken from the commencement of the electrolysis to some suitable point, usually the point of inflection, on the potential-time curve. In suitable cases, this method is undoubtedly preferable because it permits easy measurement of the transition time as well as observation of the complete chronopotentiogram. For the well-defined chronopotentiogram shown in Fig. 21-1, this technique would be very successful, and it would be reasonable to measure the transition time from the start of the electrolysis to a potential of +0.1 v. *vs.* S.C.E.

When the concentration of the electroactive species is much below 10^{-3} *M*, charging of the electrical double layer at the electrode surface distorts the chronopotentiogram by decreasing the slope or sharpness of the curve before and after the wave. Thus, measurement of the transition time by the method outlined in the preceding paragraph introduces a positive error. In this eventuality, several graphical techniques have been suggested which parallel the practice employed in polarography to correct for residual current. Different graphical methods for the measurement of transition times as well as a comparison of the several techniques are described by Delahay and Berzins,[20] by Reinmuth,[59] and by Russell and Peterson.[60]

In recapitulation, the measurement of transition times from complete recorded curves by either the direct or the graphical methods just surveyed can succeed only if the recording instrument is capable of rapid response to changes in the electrode potential and possesses an accurate and precise time-base. Chronopotentiograms with transition

[58] Malmstadt, H. V., Enke, C. G., and Toren, E. C., Jr., Electronics for Scientists, W. A. Benjamin, New York, 1962, p. 355.
[59] Reinmuth, W. H., Anal. Chem., **33**, 485, 1961.
[60] Russell, C. D., and Peterson, J. M., J. Electroanal. Chem., **5**, 467, 1963.

times greater than two to three seconds can be reliably obtained with high quality X-Y or strip-chart recorders. Recording of chronopotentiograms with transition times shorter than one to two seconds should always be accomplished with the aid of an oscilloscope and photographic equipment. Many workers have measured transition times in the millisecond range by means of oscilloscopic and electronic recording techniques; however, such very short transition times are of interest only in kinetics studies.

Frequently, it is more convenient to measure the transition time at a pre-selected potential. The procedure requires two preliminary steps. First, a complete chronopotentiogram must be recorded and, second, a suitable potential at which the transition time is to be measured is chosen by inspection of the potential-time curve. This latter potential is frequently termed the *transition potential*. Transition-time measurements then proceed as follows: (1) the electrolysis is begun and is continued until the pre-selected transition potential is just reached, at which time the electrolysis is interrupted, and (2) a suitable timing device, actuated by the closing and opening of the electrolysis circuit, is read to obtain the transition time directly without recourse to graphical measurement.

For the application of this technique, the potential of the working electrode as a function of time may be monitored in a variety of ways. Obviously, the potential may be observed in a conventional manner with a pen-and-ink recorder. Unlike the measurement techniques described earlier, the accuracy of the time scale of the recorder is unimportant. In order to obtain accurate measurements of short transition times, however, the recorder pen response must be rapid enough to follow and indicate the potential correctly. To a lesser extent, such instruments as pH meters and potentiometers have been similarly used. The importance of the rapid response characteristic gives preference to the use of a cathode ray oscilloscope with a long-persistence phosphor. By means of the procedure described, transition times as short as 0.5 second are easily measurable with an oscilloscope, but with other instruments it is unrealistic to attempt to measure transition times less than approximately two to three seconds. An additional advantage in the use of an oscilloscope or a recorder is that the potential at which the electrolysis is actually interrupted can be observed in relation to the pre-selected transition potential, and, if the two potentials differ markedly, the transition-time measurement can be immediately rejected. As suitable timing devices, precision electric stopclocks and electronic pulse counters have been employed. Gierst and his collaborators[7,61] have described automatic instruments for the determination of transition times.

The measurement of the transition time at a pre-selected potential, either by manual or automatic means, has two disadvantages. First, because the complete chronopotentiogram is usually not recorded, any changes in the wave character are undetected. Second, many, if not all, electrode processes exhibit increased overpotential with increasing current density; that is to say, the chronopotentiometric wave shifts with increasing current density toward more cathodic potentials for reduction reactions and toward more anodic potentials for oxidation reactions. Therefore, the transition potential may actually change with current density, and anomalous results may be encountered if this effect is not taken into consideration.

If the first derivative with respect to time of the chronopotentiogram is monitored, a maximum value of this first derivative occurs at the point which corresponds to the very rapid change in potential following the wave. This maximum may be utilized for the measurement of transition times. Two methods by which this procedure can be made applicable for transition-time measurements involve the automatic differentiation of potential-time curves as suggested by Iwamoto[62] and alternating-current chronopotenti-

[61] Gierst, L., Anal. Chim. Acta, **15,** 262, 1956.
[62] Iwamoto, R. T., Anal. Chem., **31,** 1062, 1959.

ometry as reported by Takemori and co-workers.[63] The original papers should be consulted for complete details.

The fundamental problem which derives from this discussion is the selection of the correct method for the measurement of transition times. None of the various techniques has been subjected to an absolute or critical test. For well-defined chronopotentiograms, it is safe to conclude that all of the methods agree to within perhaps two to three percent. For poorly defined waves, however, each method invariably gives a different result. Since the Sand equation stipulates that, for linear diffusion processes, the quantity $i\tau^{1/2}/AC$ is a constant, preference for a particular method of measurement of transition times for analytical purposes can be based on the demonstration that $i\tau^{1/2}/AC$ remains constant over a wide range of concentrations and transition times.

Transition-Time Limits.—The purpose of the following section is to point out the upper and lower transition-time limits for most practical chronopotentiometric work and to discuss briefly the various factors which govern these limits.

The onset of natural convection is the factor which sets the upper limit for transition-time measurements. During an electrolysis, depletion of the electroactive substance and generation of the product species cause the density of the diffusion layer to become different from that of the bulk solution. This difference in density, together with the increasing thickness of the diffusion layer at longer electrolysis times, eventually initiates natural stirring or convection. With unshielded electrodes, these effects limit the duration of transition times to the range of about 25 to 50 seconds, depending on the nature of the reaction. For a substance with a large diffusion coefficient, the thickness of the diffusion layer becomes appreciable even after electrolysis times of only 10 to 15 seconds, and the upper limit for transition times may be in this latter range. Bard[38] has shown that, with shielded electrodes suitably oriented for either upward or downward diffusion, transition times as long as 300 seconds may be reproducibly measured.

Several factors influence the lower limit for practical transition-time measurements—charging or discharging of the electrical double layer, adsorption phenomena, and surface oxidation and reduction of the working electrode. Each of these factors can cause problems at long transition times, but it is for short transition times that serious difficulty may be encountered. The nature of the chronopotentiometric diffusion process is such that the amount of electroactive substance that is electrolyzed decreases as the square-root of the transition time decreases. However, the quantities of electricity due to charging or discharging of the double layer, adsorption phenomena, and surface oxidation or reduction of the electrode are largely independent of the transition time. Therefore, at short transition times the quantity of electricity associated with these extraneous processes becomes larger and larger relative to the amount of electroactive substance which reacts. Each of these factors, by decreasing the average current efficiency for the diffusion-controlled electrode reaction below the requisite 100 percent, causes positive deviations from the Sand equation or other appropriate relation. Valuable discussions of empirical methods for correcting transition-time data for the effects of extraneous processes, such as those mentioned above, may be found in papers by Lingane,[45] Reinmuth,[59] and Bard.[64]

It is not a simple matter to assign a definite value as the lower limit for transition-time measurements. The importance of the double layer and the adsorption effects and the surface oxidation or reduction of the working electrode varies with the nature of the electroactive species, the supporting electrolyte, the electrode material, and the range of working potentials during the electrolysis. For routine analytical work, there appears to be little advantage in attempting to measure transition times less than a few seconds.

[63] Takemori, Y., Kambara, T., Senda, M., and Tachi, I., J. Phys. Chem., **61,** 968, 1957.
[64] Bard, A. J., Anal. Chem., **35,** 340, 1963.

Routinely, the precision of transition-time measurements is or should be on the order of one percent. Excluding from the present discussion any electrode reaction which involves kinetic processes, irreproducible results are more likely to be obtained in the measurement of relatively long transition times, *e.g.*, 25 to 50 seconds, when such factors as natural convection or unavoidable external laboratory vibrations act to disturb the diffusion layer. In such cases, special electrode and cell designs may be employed, but, in reality, for analytical applications there is little necessity for long transition-time measurements. As a final generalization, a suitable range of transition times for chronopotentiometric analysis might be from about 5 to 25 seconds.

Concentration Limits.—Any statement that chronopotentiometry is superior to polarography with respect to accuracy and sensitivity in analysis seems unfounded. Although certain kinds of analyses, such as those involving electrochemistry in molten salts or anodic processes, may be preferably accomplished by means of chronopotentiometry, still not enough genuine analytical applications or critical performance tests of chronopotentiometry have been made to enable its ultimate, overall analytical usefulness to be assessed.

In chronopotentiometric studies reported to date, the highest concentration to be employed has been in the neighborhood of 0.05 M. Undoubtedly, higher concentrations may be determined, provided a large excess of supporting electrolyte is maintained and a suitable constant-current source is available. On the other hand, the lowest concentration amenable to chronopotentiometric analysis is governed fundamentally by the quantity of electricity produced by the electrode reaction of interest in relation to the quantities of electricity associated with extraneous processes, including charging or discharging of the double layer, reaction of adsorbed species or impurities in solution, and surface oxidation or reduction of the working electrode. In other words, the minimum concentration in chronopotentiometric analysis is limited by the occurrence of certain "background" phenomena, just as the residual current sets the lower concentration limit in conventional polarography. Depending upon circumstances discussed below, this lower concentration limit may range from 10^{-3} to 10^{-4} M, and perhaps slightly smaller.

Any factor which increases the quantity of the electroactive species electrolyzed in a single trial will lower the minimum concentration limit for practical analysis. A low concentration limit is favored for electrode reactions which have large n-values and for substances with large diffusion coefficients. As an example, for borohydride ion with an n-value of eight and a diffusion coefficient of 2.1×10^{-5} cm.^{2}/sec., chronopotentiometric analysis with a gold anode in sodium hydroxide medium is accurate for solutions as dilute as 2×10^{-4} M to within five percent.[65] Surface oxidation of the gold electrode causes large positive errors in the analysis of more dilute borohydride solutions. For some electrochemical systems for which n is only one or two and D is less than 1×10^{-5} cm.^{2}/sec., it is very disappointing to attempt chronopotentiometric analysis of solutions at or below a concentration level of 10^{-3} M, particularly when the electrode, being of platinum or gold, is subject to surface oxidation and reduction.

A conclusion derived from a survey of numerous papers is that, at low concentrations, chronopotentiometry is more successful with mercury than with platinum or gold electrodes, for with mercury there is less problem with surface oxidation or reduction of the electrode, and the double-layer capacitance of mercury is only one-fourth or one-fifth as great as that of platinum and gold. Therefore, for a given determination, when the range of working potentials permits a choice of electrodes, a mercury electrode should be selected, especially for low concentrations.

In summation, for solid electrodes such as platinum or gold, available information

[65] Cutchens, C. E., M.S. Thesis, Indiana University, 1964.

indicates that the optimum concentration range is from 0.001 to 0.05 *M*, while for mercury electrodes a reasonable concentration range is from 0.0001 to 0.05 *M*. However, any such statement is intended only as a guide; each proposed application of chronopotentiometry must be evaluated on its own merits.

ANALYTICAL APPLICATIONS

The aim of this section is to describe some research in the area of chronopotentiometry which seems pertinent to the solution of analytical problems. As implied previously in this chapter, much work remains to be performed, not only to extend the number of analytical applications but to stimulate further interest in the analytical potentialities of chronopotentiometry.

Some Specific Analytical Applications.—Up to the present time, there have been relatively few authentic analytical applications of chronopotentiometry, although a large number of substances has been investigated. Parenthetically, it should be pointed out that chronopotentiometry, aside from its analytical interest, is an exceedingly valuable tool for gathering information about the electrochemistry of many substances, especially those which react at potentials outside the range accessible to polarography with the dropping mercury electrode. Some representative, analytically-oriented studies will now be cited; but, this list should not be construed as a complete compilation of all substances which have been investigated chronopotentiometrically. Somewhat arbitrarily, the following list includes studies for which a range of concentrations of the substance of interest has been used and for which, in most instances, the Sand equation appears to be reasonably well obeyed. The writer suggests that, even for a majority of these procedures, more extensive work is required to establish them as routine and useful applications.

Among the inorganic species which have been determined are cadmium,[5] cerium(IV),[66,67] chromium(VI),[67] ferricyanide,[40] ferrocyanide,[5,40,43] gallium(III),[68] iodide,[69] iron(III),[67] lead,[5,32] permanganate,[67] thallium(I),[15] and zinc.[5] In addition, some indirect methods have been described for arsenic(III)[66] and for uranium(VI).[70] The determination of organic substances by means of anodic chronopotentiometry appears to be a field worthy of further exploitation. Such compounds as 5-amino-2-naphthalenesulfonic acid,[69] aniline,[37,69] anthracene,[71] ascorbic acid,[40] catechol,[39] hydroquinone[12,39] and resorcinol,[39] 2-mercaptobenzothiazole,[72] oxalic acid,[45] the isomeric phenylenediamines,[39] sulfanilimide and other sulfa drugs,[71,73] and *p*-toluidine[69] have been studied. For purposes of brevity, other applications discussed specifically at a later point in this section are not included in the above list.

Determination of Metal Cations in Molten Salts.—For the analysis of molten salt solutions, chronopotentiometry has definite advantages over voltammetry (polarography) or potentiometry because, as pointed out by Laitinen and Ferguson,[46] experimental conditions can be established which correspond closely to the theoretical requirements of chronopotentiometry. An up-to-date review of chronopotentiometry in molten salts has been written by Laitinen and Osteryoung.[74]

[66] Davis, D. G., Anal. Chem., **33,** 1839, 1961.
[67] Davis, D. G., and Ganchoff, J., J. Electroanal. Chem., **1,** 248, 1960.
[68] Moorhead, E. D., and Furman, N. H., Anal. Chem., **32,** 1507, 1960.
[69] Adams, R. N., McClure, J. H., and Morris, J. B., Anal. Chem., **30,** 471, 1958.
[70] Davis, D. G., Anal. Chim. Acta, **27,** 26, 1962.
[71] Voorhies, J. D., and Furman, N. H., Anal. Chem., **31,** 381, 1959.
[72] Voorhies, J. D., and Parsons, J. S., Anal. Chem., **31,** 516, 1959.
[73] Voorhies, J. D., and Furman, N. H., Anal. Chem., **30,** 1656, 1958.
[74] Laitinen, H. A., and Osteryoung, R. A., "Electrochemistry in Molten Salts," in Sundheim, B. R., Ed., Fused Salts, McGraw-Hill Book Company, New York, 1964, pp. 255–300.

Laitinen and his co-workers[46,47] have demonstrated the usefulness of cathodic chronopotentiometry with a platinum microelectrode for the determination of bismuth(III), cadmium(II), silver(I), copper(I), thallium(I), lead(II), and cobalt(II) in fused lithium chloride-potassium chloride eutectic mixtures at 450°C. For the conditions employed by these workers, the accuracy of the chronopotentiometric method, as evidenced by obeyance of the Sand equation, is between two and four percent over the following concentration ranges: bismuth (5 to 60 millimolar); cadmium (2 to 80 millimolar); silver (2 to 50 millimolar); copper (2 to 35 millimolar); thallium (14 to 80 millimolar); lead (20 to 50 millimolar); and cobalt (10 to 60 millimolar). Mixtures of bismuth and silver and of bismuth and copper were successfully analyzed. Liu[48] reported that copper(I) in a lithium sulfate–potassium sulfate melt at 625°C. and over a concentration range from two to eight millimolar can be determined with an accuracy of approximately ±4 percent.

For analytical purposes, it seems equally feasible either (1) to calculate the concentration of the electroactive substance using a single transition-time measurement in conjunction with the Sand equation or (2) to construct a calibration curve for a suitable working range of concentrations under the desired experimental conditions.

Two problems arise for chronopotentiometry in molten salts. Because the molten salt is at the same time both the solvent and the supporting electrolyte, care must be taken by purification of the molten-salt system to minimize the presence of impurities. In addition, the use of molten salts at elevated temperatures precludes the complete absence of natural convection, so to ensure that diffusion is, or almost is, the sole means of mass transfer the transition times must be restricted to no more than a few seconds.

Analysis of Liquid Alloys and Amalgams.—Another application of chronopotentiometry lies in the determination of minute quantities of metals in liquid alloys or in amalgams.

Using anodic chronopotentiometry, Van Norman[75] designed a procedure for the determination of traces of lithium and zinc in liquid bismuth and verified the obeyance of the Sand equation for 0.003 to 0.009 *M* zinc (20 to 60 parts per million) and for 0.005 to 0.03 *M* lithium (3.5 to 21 parts per million) to within ±4 percent. The liquid bismuth electrode was contained in a borosilicate glass cup and was maintained at 450°C. in contact with a fused lithium chloride–potassium chloride electrolyte. The success of the method depends upon the facts that bismuth has a low melting point (271°C.), but a high boiling point (1560°C.), and that it is a relatively noble metal under the extant conditions, *i.e.*, bismuth is much more difficultly oxidized than either lithium or zinc.

A technique, related to the above experiments and reported by Mamantov, Papoff, and Delahay,[76] essentially involves the anodic chronopotentiometric analysis of metals dissolved in mercury. The procedure described is one of a family of so-called stripping analysis methods[77] in which, first, a metal ion in solution is reduced and deposited into a mercury pool or a hanging mercury drop electrode usually by means of controlled-potential (potentiostatic) coulometry and, second, the resulting amalgam is subjected to anodic polarization to re-oxidize the dissolved metal with any of several possible electroanalytical techniques, *e.g.*, chronopotentiometry, being used to determine the particular metal. Such a stripping analysis technique is capable of much higher sensitivity than conventional chronopotentiometry because the deposition of a metal into mercury serves to increase the effective concentration of the electroactive substance by as much as a factor of 500 or 1000. Thus, in a typical experiment, an aqueous solution containing 10^{-5} *M* reducible metal ion might, by the approach outlined, yield a concen-

[75] Van Norman, J. D., Anal. Chem., **33**, 946, 1961.
[76] Mamantov, G., Papoff, P., and Delahay, P., J. Am. Chem. Soc., ***79***, 4034, 1957.
[77] Shain, I., "Stripping Analysis," in Kolthoff, I. M., and Elving, P. J., Eds., Treatise on Analytical Chemistry, Part I, Vol. 4, Interscience Publishers, New York, 1959, pp. 2533–2568.

tration of metal in the mercury of 5×10^{-3} M. The latter concentration is definitely amenable to determination by means of anodic chronopotentiometry. Solutions as dilute as 10^{-8} M could presumably be analyzed according to this method. Except for the paper of Mamantov, Papoff, and Delahay, the chronopotentiometric determination of metals dissolved in mercury has received little attention.

To simplify both the theory of the method and the interpretation of experimental data, conditions should be arranged so that a uniform concentration of the dissolved metal exists throughout the mercury prior to anodization. Moreover, the anodic transition time should be short in order that the diffusion layer thickness be much smaller than the dimensions of the mercury drop or pool. If these provisions are correctly met, the conditions of semi-infinite linear or spherical diffusion will obtain, and the Sand equation or its spherical-diffusion counterpart (suitably modified to account for the diffusion process occurring within a mercury drop) will be applicable.

Measurement of Thickness of Metal Plating and Oxide and Tarnish Films on Metals.—The chronopotentiometric technique is well-suited to the determination of the thickness of plating and oxide or tarnish films on metals.

Consider how the thickness of a copper(I) oxide (Cu_2O) film on copper metal may be determined. Suppose that a sample of the metal of known area A (cm.^{2}) is made to serve as the cathode in a chronopotentiometric cell, that this electrode is polarized with a constant current i (amperes), and that the potential of the cathode is observed versus a reference electrode as a function of time. This potential will remain almost constant as long as any oxide film is still present, but will shift abruptly to a much more reducing value at the instant the Cu_2O film is completely reduced. By measuring the time t (seconds) required to reduce the film, one can calculate its thickness T (cm.) from the relation

$$T = \frac{itM}{nFA\rho}$$

where M is the gram-formula-weight of the film material, *e.g.*, Cu_2O, n is the number of electrons required to reduce or oxidize one gram-formula-weight of the film material, F is the Faraday constant, and ρ is the density (g./cm.^{3}) of the film material.

Since the experiment described above constitutes a quantitative reduction of the Cu_2O film, the procedure is essentially a coulometric one. At the same time, however, the observations which characterize the technique, namely, the potential-time behavior of an electrode during a constant-current electrolysis, are closely related to chronopotentiometry. The method also may be considered an example of stripping analysis.[77]

Grower,[78] who determined the thickness of tin coatings on copper wires, appears to have been the first worker to employ this technique. Campbell and Thomas[79] measured the thicknesses of Cu_2O, Cu_2S, Ag_2O, and Ag_2S films and analyzed mixed films of Cu_2O Cu_2S and of Ag_2O and Ag_2S. Allen[80] has employed the same technique for copper(I) oxide films. Oxide film thicknesses on tin plate have been determined by Frankenthal, Butler, and Davis,[81] and by Willey and Kelsey.[82] Francis[83] has reported the results of an extensive study in which anodic chronopotentiometry was used to determine films of cadmium, chromium, copper, gold, lead, silver, tin, and zinc on steel as well as chromium, lead, tin, and zinc plating on pure copper and on brass. Kunze and Willey[84] found

[78] Grower, G. G., Proc. Am. Soc. Testing Materials, **17,** II, 129, 1917.
[79] Campbell, W. E., and Thomas, U. B., Trans. Electrochem. Soc., **76,** 303, 1939.
[80] Allen, J. A., Trans. Faraday Soc., **48,** 273, 1952.
[81] Frankenthal, R. P., Butler, T. J., and Davis, R. T., Jr., Anal. Chem., **30,** 441, 1958.
[82] Willey, A. R., and Kelsey, D. F., Anal. Chem., **30,** 1804, 1958.
[83] Francis, H. T., J. Electrochem. Soc., **93,** 79, 1948.
[84] Kunze, C. T., and Willey, A. R., J. Electrochem. Soc., **99,** 354, 1952.

that the technique could be used to identify and measure the films of tin and tin-iron alloy on tin-plated steel. The discussions by Lingane[3] and by Shain,[77] and the bibliographies contained in the papers cited, list additional references to other work.

An obvious extension of this technique involves the use of anodic chronopotentiometry to determine a metal which has been previously plated onto a platinum or gold electrode from a very dilute solution in order to increase the effective concentration of this metal. The method is similar to the stripping analysis procedure described briefly in the preceding section for the determination of metals dissolved in mercury, and would ordinarily be employed when the metal to be determined is more noble than mercury. As another example, the technique would also be useful for the analysis of dilute halide solutions. A silver electrode could be anodized to form an adherent silver halide coating, and then subsequently cathodized to determine the quantity of the silver halide and, hence, the concentration of the unknown halide solution. Again, the chapter by Shain[77] contains a useful and recent survey of such applications.

When one is interested, as most workers have been, in the application of the above technique to the determination of the thickness of plating or oxide films on real metal samples, several factors should be considered. First, in calculating the thickness of a film from the above relation, it is assumed that the film material uniformly covers the metal surface and that the apparent area of the metal sample is equal to the microscopic area. Second, it must be assumed that the density of the material composing the thin film is the same as that for the film material in bulk. The reliability of either of these assumptions is always subject to question.

Analysis of Mixtures.—As implied earlier, the use of chronopotentiometry for the analysis of mixtures of electroactive substances remains an almost unexplored field. Aside from the study by Reilley, Everett, and Johns[5] on the consecutive reductions of lead, cadmium, and zinc at a mercury pool electrode, little work has been reported. The nonadditivity of transition times in conventional chronopotentiometry detracts somewhat from the appeal of the technique for analytical purposes, especially if the particular application of interest can be performed polarographically.

More recently, Morris and Lingane[85] have performed anodic chronopotentiometric analysis of mixtures of hydrazine and hydroxylamine in dilute sulfuric acid with a platinum electrode. In spite of the minor disadvantage of the nonadditivity of transition times in the analysis of mixtures, chronopotentiometry is, fundamentally, an exceedingly valuable technique for anodic determinations because it is one of the simplest electroanalytical methods for use in conjunction with solid electrodes. The method proposed by Morris and Lingane overcomes several difficulties of classical titrimetric procedures. In particular, it allows the determination of as little as two percent hydrazine in the presence of 98 percent hydroxylamine or two percent hydroxylamine in the presence of 98 percent hydrazine. The study encompassed a range of hydrazine concentrations from 5×10^{-4} to 0.01 M, while the concentration of hydroxylamine ranged from 2×10^{-4} to 0.05 M. The method is accurate to within ± 5 percent. When the hydrazine concentration exceeds 5×10^{-3} M, however, low results are obtained for hydroxylamine because the formation of nitrogen bubbles on the electrode surface from oxidation of hydrazine decreases the effective area of the platinum anode. Chloride ion at a concentration of 2×10^{-3} M or higher causes negative errors and, for 0.2 M hydrochloric acid, no hydroxylamine wave is observed.

The study of Morris and Lingane is of further general interest because the problem of surface oxidation of platinum was encountered. In anodic chronopotentiometry with platinum electrodes, the factor which limits the lower concentration capable of accurate determination and which may profoundly affect the reproducibility of transition-time

[85] Morris, M. D., and Lingane, J. J., J. Electroanal. Chem., **8**, 85, 1964.

measurements is oxidation of the working electrode. In chronopotentiometric experiments, surface oxidation of platinum to PtO and PtO_2 commences at about +0.7 to +0.8 v. *vs.* S.C.E. in 1 *F* sulfuric acid or perchloric acid solutions. The formation of an oxide film decreases the current efficiency for any reaction which occurs at or above these potentials and causes positive errors in any analytical procedure. For the chronopotentiometric determination of small concentrations of substances, these positive errors may amount to several hundred percent.

There is no theoretically justifiable way to correct chronopotentiometric data for the effect described. This is so because the current efficiency for oxide film formation and, hence, for the reaction of analytical interest depends in an unknown and probably complex manner upon such variables as the actual current in an experiment, the concentration of the electroactive species, and the range of working potentials. Despite these fundamental uncertainties, Lingane[45] and Bard[38,64] have proposed and tested different empirical methods to correct for the effect of electrode oxidation. Testimony to the usefulness of these correction procedures is provided by the results of Morris and Lingane.

Determination of End Points in Titrations.—The use of chronopotentiometry to determine end points has been evaluated by Reilley and Scribner[86] for the titrations of arsenic(III) with iodine, of copper(II) with ethylenediaminetetraacetic acid (EDTA), of iron(II) with cerium(IV), and of a mixture of tin(II) and iron(II) with cerium(IV). The results agreed very well (one or two parts per thousand) with those obtained in potentiometric and conductometric titrations. The chronopotentiometric technique does not appear to possess any advantages over the more well-known potentiometric and amperometric end-point detection methods.

Other Applications and Innovations.—Chronopotentiometry is an extremely valuable technique for obtaining information about the electrochemistry of various elements or compounds. The identification of electrode reactions, *i.e.*, the evaluation of *n*-values, the determination of diffusion coefficients, information concerning the degree of reversibility of an electrode reaction, and the influence of electrode phenomena on the electrode reaction of interest are important aspects of the electrochemistry of any substance which can be ascertained through the application of chronopotentiometry. A report[87] of the results of studies of plutonium(III), plutonium(IV), and plutonium(VI) serves to demonstrate these capabilities of chronopotentiometry.

Anson and his co-workers[88,89] have introduced the method of chronopotentiometry in thin layers of solution. Basically, this technique involves chronopotentiometric experiments performed under special conditions in which (1) a very small volume of test solution is confined in a thin layer next to the working electrode and (2) the thickness of this layer of solution is smaller than that of an ordinary diffusion layer in chronopotentiometry. As a result, all of the electroactive substance in the thin layer of solution undergoes reaction in a single chronopotentiometric trial. If the product of the first electrode reaction is itself electroactive, a current-reversal wave can be recorded which (unlike the usual situation in current-reversal chronopotentiometry) has a transition time equal to that for the first wave. This is because the product of the first reaction remains confined in the thin layer of solution. The technique of thin-layer chronopotentiometry, which is essentially constant-current coulometric analysis on a microscopic scale, appears to be particularly applicable in the study of reaction kinetics and in the evaluation of rate constants. For kinetics studies the method has important advantages over conventional current-reversal chronopotentiometry. The original papers should be consulted for details.

[86] Reilley, C. N., and Scribner, W. G., Anal. Chem., **27,** 1210, 1955.
[87] Peters, D. G., and Shults, W. D., J. Electroanal. Chem., **8,** 200 ,1964.
[88] Christensen, C. R., and Anson, F. C., Anal. Chem., **35,** 205, 1963; *ibid.*, **36,** 495, 1964.
[89] Hubbard, A. T., and Anson, F. C., Anal. Chem., **36,** 723, 1964.

Herman and Bard[90] have proposed and tested another technique, cyclic chronopotentiometry, for the elucidation and study of electrode reaction mechanisms. The method consists essentially of a succession of 10 to 20 current reversals at the potentials which correspond to the transition times of the various waves. The oxidation of *p*-aminophenol and the reduction of titanium(IV) in the presence of hydroxylamine were employed in the experimental evaluation of this technique. According to the authors, cyclic chronopotentiometry enables kinetic, catalytic, and adsorption processes to be easily recognized and distinguished.

A significant advance toward promoting the use and further development of chronopotentiometry as an analytical method has been suggested by Shults, Haga, Mueller, and Jones[91] at the Oak Ridge National Laboratory. These workers have designed and constructed an all-electronic chronopotentiometer which compensates for charging of the electrical double layer, thereby giving chronopotentiograms with sharply defined and easily measured transition times. Two chronopotentiometric cells are utilized in this technique, one of which contains the electroactive species of interest plus the supporting electrolyte solution (cell I), and the second of which contains only the supporting electrolyte solution (cell II). The instrument forces the potential of the working electrode in cell II to equal the potential of the working electrode in cell I at all times, *i.e.*, the potential-time behavior is identical in the two cells. The current which flows through cell II is the current required for charging the double-layer (and perhaps other extraneous processes) because cell II contains only the supporting electrolyte solution. The cell II current is scaled (to allow for physical differences in the two working electrodes) and added to the preselected constant current for cell I to achieve compensation. Chronopotentiograms obtained with this instrument and technique at and below the 10^{-4} *M* concentration level are as well defined as those at the 0.05 *M* level, and the observed values of $i\tau^{1/2}/AC$ are virtually constant over this concentration range. This method of compensation for an extraneous process, such as charging of the double layer, may also be applicable to chronopotentiometric analysis in situations were the working electrode undergoes surface oxidation and reduction.

[90] Herman, H. B., and Bard, A. J., Anal. Chem., **35**, 1121, 1963; *ibid.*, **36**, 510, 1964.
[91] Shults, W. D., Haga, F. E., Mueller, T. R., and Jones, H. C., Anal. Chem., in press.

Chapter 22

ELECTROGRAVIMETRIC ANALYSIS

THEORY

ELECTRODE POTENTIALS

The principles of electrogravimetric analysis are reviewed briefly in this section. For a more detailed treatment, reference should be made to Volume II, Part A of this work, page 166.

The fundamental quantity in electrolysis is the potential of electrodes, that is, the potential difference established between an element (or other substance) and a solution containing its ions. The magnitude and sign of this potential depend upon the activity of the element itself, the activity (and hence the concentration) of its ions, the solvent, and the temperature. Since it is impossible to measure the potential of a single electrode in contact with a solution, because the necessary other contact between the solution and the exterior circuit is itself an electrode-solution interface, it is necessary to measure the potential relative to another electrode. Therefore, a table of standard electrode potentials has been established by the International Union of Pure and Applied Chemistry[1] by determining experimentally the values of the potentials of the elements against a hydrogen electrode at arbitrarily chosen values of the variables. These values are (1) the stable form of the element, at unit activity, free from mechanical strain or other anomaly, (2) unit activity (approximately 1 *M* concentration) of the ions with the concentration-potential function extrapolated to infinite dilution, at which the activity is equivalent to the concentration, (3) water as the solvent, (4) a temperature of 25°C., (5) a given direction for the electrode reaction (*i.e.*, a reduction) in relation to its sign, as shown in Table 22-1. The hydrogen electrode is the standard, as is seen from the zero value of the standard potential of hydrogen in the table.

In addition to elements in equilibrium with their ions, the table also gives the standard potentials of a number of compounds in equilibrium with their ions, or with ions and other compounds. There are also standard potentials of ions for reactions whereby other ions are formed. As shown by the reactions in the table, the values given are reduction potentials in the direction written, *i.e.*, from left to right. If the direction of the reactions is from right to left, the signs of all the potentials must be changed, and they are then oxidation potentials.

EFFECT OF CONCENTRATION ON ELECTRODE POTENTIALS

Computations of the potentials under other conditions than the standard ones are made by forms of the Nernst equation such as the following,

$$E = E^0 + \frac{RT}{nF} \ln \frac{a_{\text{ox}}}{a_{\text{red}}} \tag{1}$$

[1] Licht, T. S., and de Bethune, A. J., J. Chem. Educ., **34,** 433, 1957.

TABLE 22-1. STANDARD ELECTRODE POTENTIALS AT 25°C.

Electrode Reaction	E^0, *volts*
$Li^+ + e^- \rightleftharpoons Li$	−3.045
$K^+ + e^- \rightleftharpoons K$	−2.925
$Ba^{+2} + 2e^- \rightleftharpoons Ba$	−2.90
$Sr^{+2} + 2e^- \rightleftharpoons Sr$	−2.89
$Ca^{+2} + 2e^- \rightleftharpoons Ca$	−2.87
$Na^+ + e^- \rightleftharpoons Na$	−2.714
$La^{+3} + 3e^- \rightleftharpoons La$	−2.52
$Ce^{+3} + 3e^- \rightleftharpoons Ce$	−2.48
$Mg^{+2} + 2e^- \rightleftharpoons Mg$	−2.37
$Th^{+4} + 4e^- \rightleftharpoons Th$	−1.90
$Al^{+3} + 3e^- \rightleftharpoons Al$	−1.66
$Ti^{+3} + 3e^- \rightleftharpoons Ti$	−1.63
$Zr^{+4} + 4e^- \rightleftharpoons Zr$	−1.53
$Mn^{+2} + 2e^- \rightleftharpoons Mn$	−1.18
$Zn^{+2} + 2e^- \rightleftharpoons Zn$	−0.763
$Cr^{+3} + 3e^- \rightleftharpoons Cr$	−0.74
$U^{+4} + e^- \rightleftharpoons U^{+3}$	−0.61
$H_3PO_3 + 2H^+ + 2e^- \rightleftharpoons H_3PO_2 + H_2O$	−0.50
$2CO_2 + 2H^+ + 2e^- \rightleftharpoons H_2C_2O_4$	−0.49
$Fe^{+2} + 2e^- \rightleftharpoons Fe$	−0.440
$Cr^{+3} + e^- \rightleftharpoons Cr^{+2}$	−0.41
$Cd^{+2} + 2e^- \rightleftharpoons Cd$	−0.403
$Ag(CN)_2^- + e^- \rightleftharpoons Ag + 2CN^-$	−0.31
$Co^{+2} + 2e^- \rightleftharpoons Co$	−0.277
$V^{+3} + e^- \rightleftharpoons V^{+2}$	−0.255
$Ni^{+2} + 2e^- \rightleftharpoons Ni$	−0.25
$N_2 + 5H^+ + 4e^- \rightleftharpoons N_2H_5^+$	−0.23
$Mo^{+3} + 3e^- \rightleftharpoons Mo$	−0.2 (approx.)
$AgI(s) + e^- \rightleftharpoons Ag + I^-$	−0.151
$Sn^{+2} + 2e^- \rightleftharpoons Sn$	−0.136
$Pb^{+2} + 2e^- \rightleftharpoons Pb$	−0.126
$2H^+ + 2e^- \rightleftharpoons H_2(g)$	0.00
$AgBr(s) + e^- \rightleftharpoons Ag + Br^-$	0.095
$TiO^{+2} + 2H^+ + e^- \rightleftharpoons Ti^{+3} + H_2O$	0.10
$CuCl + e^- \rightleftharpoons Cu + Cl^-$	0.137
$S(s) + 2H^+ + 2e^- \rightleftharpoons H_2S$	0.14
$Sn^{+4} + 2e^- \rightleftharpoons Sn^{+2}$	0.15
$S_4O_6^{-2} + 2e^- \rightleftharpoons 2S_2O_3^{-2}$	0.17
$SO_4^{-2} + 4H^+ + 2e^- \rightleftharpoons H_2SO_3 + H_2O$	0.17
$SbO^+ + 2H^+ + 3e^- \rightleftharpoons Sb + H_2O$	0.212
$AgCl(s) + e^- \rightleftharpoons Ag + Cl^-$	0.2222
$BiO^+ + 2H^+ + 3e^- \rightleftharpoons Bi + H_2O$	0.23
$Hg_2Cl_2(s) + 2e^- \rightleftharpoons 2Hg + 2Cl^-$	0.2676
$UO_2^{+2} + 4H^+ + 2e^- \rightleftharpoons U^{+4} + 2H_2O$	0.334
$Cu^{+2} + 2e^- \rightleftharpoons Cu$	0.337
$Fe(CN)_6^{-3} + e^- \rightleftharpoons Fe(CN)_6^{-4}$	0.36
$VO^{+2} + 2H^+ + e^- \rightleftharpoons V^{+3} + H_2O$	0.361

TABLE 22-1 (cont.)

Electrode Reaction	E^0, *volts*
$Cu^+ + e^- \rightleftharpoons Cu$	0.52
$I_3^- + 2e^- \rightleftharpoons 3I^-$	0.536
$H_3AsO_4 + 2H^+ + 2e^- \rightleftharpoons H_3AsO_3 + H_2O$	0.559
$Hg_2SO_4(s) + 2e^- \rightleftharpoons 2Hg + SO_4^{-2}$	0.615
$2HgCl_2 + 2e^- \rightleftharpoons Hg_2Cl_2(s) + 2Cl^-$	0.63
$O_2(g) + 2H^+ + 2e^- \rightleftharpoons H_2O_2$	0.682
$Fe^{+3} + e^- \rightleftharpoons Fe^{+2}$	0.771
$Hg_2^{+2} + 2e^- \rightleftharpoons 2Hg(l)$	0.789
$Ag^+ + e^- \rightleftharpoons Ag$	0.7991
$2Hg^{+2} + 2e^- \rightleftharpoons Hg_2^{+2}$	0.92
$NO_3^- + 3H^+ + 2e^- \rightleftharpoons HNO_2 + H_2O$	0.94
$HNO_2 + H^+ + e^- \rightleftharpoons NO(g) + H_2O$	1.00
$VO_2^+ + 2H^+ + e^- \rightleftharpoons VO^{+2} + H_2O$	1.00
$Br_2 + 2e^- \rightleftharpoons 2Br^-$	1.065
$IO_3^- + 6H^+ + 5e^- \rightleftharpoons \frac{1}{2}I_2 + 3H_2O$	1.09
$O_2(g) + 4H^+ + 4e^- \rightleftharpoons 2H_2O$	1.229
$MnO_2(s) + 4H^+ + 2e^- \rightleftharpoons Mn^{+2} + 2H_2O$	1.23
$Cr_2O_7^{-2} + 14H^+ + 6e^- \rightleftharpoons 2Cr^{+3} + 7H_2O$	1.33
$Cl_2 + 2e^- \rightleftharpoons 2Cl^-$	1.36
$PbO_2 + 4H^+ + 2e^- \rightleftharpoons Pb^{+2} + 2H_2O$	1.455
$MnO_4^- + 8H^+ + 5e^- \rightleftharpoons Mn^{+2} + 4H_2O$	1.51
$BrO_3^- + 6H^+ + 5e^- \rightleftharpoons \frac{1}{2}Br_2 + 3H_2O$	1.52
$H_5IO_6 + H^+ + 2e^- \rightleftharpoons IO_3^- + 3H_2O$	1.6
$Ce^{+4} + e^- \rightleftharpoons Ce^{+3}$	1.61
$MnO_4^- + 4H^+ + 3e^- \rightleftharpoons MnO_2(s) + 2H_2O$	1.70
$H_2O_2 + 2H^+ + 2e^- \rightleftharpoons 2H_2O$	1.77
$S_2O_8^{-2} + 2e^- \rightleftharpoons 2SO_4^{-2}$	2.01
$F_2(g) + 2H^+ + 2e^- \rightleftharpoons 2HF$	3.06

where: E^0 is the standard electrode potential given in Table 22-1;
E is the potential under the existing conditions;
R is the molar gas constant (8.316 volt-coulombs per degree);
T is the absolute temperature (°K.);
n is the number of electrons transferred in the electrode reaction;
F is the faraday (96,493 coulombs);
ln is the natural logarithm; and
the a-terms are the activities of the oxidized and reduced forms of the substances entering into the reaction.

For many calculations the Nernst equation is used more conveniently in the form

$$E = E^0 + \frac{0.0591}{n} \log \frac{[\text{ox}]}{[\text{red}]} \tag{2}$$

where E, E^0, and n have the same values as in Eq. (1), the values of the constants have been substituted (the temperature being taken as 25°C.), the logarithm is to base 10, and the oxidized and reduced forms are expressed in concentrations rather than activities. A change of one unit in the logarithmic term moves the value of E by $59.15/n$ mV. For many analytical purposes, a system is considered quantitatively converted when 0.1

percent or less of the original electroactive species remains. For a metallic ion-metal system, such as the Ag^+/Ag^0 system,

$$E = E^0 + 0.0591 \log [Ag^+] \tag{3}$$

the value of the potential need shift by only $3 \times 0.0591 = 0.177$ v., or for metallic ion-metal systems in general, by $3 \times 0.0591/n$ volt for a quantitative conversion. On the other hand, for an ion-ion system (with an electrode of platinum or other inert conductor), such as Fe^{+3}/Fe^{+2}

$$E = E^0 + 0.0591 \log \frac{[Fe^{+3}]}{[Fe^{++}]} \tag{4}$$

the shifts would need to be $6 \times 0.0591/n = 0.354/n$ volt.

ELECTROLYTIC CELLS

The fundamental structural parts of an electrical cell are a vessel containing an electrolyte and two electrodes which are connected to an external circuit. When such a cell is used for electrolysis, as is the case in analytical separations or depositions, the external circuit must provide a potential difference across the electrodes sufficient to cause current to flow through the electrolyte and produce electrolytic reactions at the electrodes. The magnitude of this potential difference can be treated by consideration of a simple example.

Consider a solution of copper(II) sulfate which is 1 *N* in sulfuric acid from which it is desired to deposit the copper on a cathode for gravimetric determination. Since copper(II) ions are discharged at the cathode, using electrons from the external circuit, a reaction must occur at the anode which yields electrons. Under the conditions described, this reaction is the electrolysis of water to form protons and molecular oxygen, which yields electrons:

$$2H_2O \rightarrow O_2 + 4H^+ + 4e^- \tag{5}$$

The potential equation for this system may then be written

$$E_{\text{applied}} = (E_1 + \omega_1) - (E_2 + \omega_2) + IR \tag{6}$$

where the *E*-terms on the right-hand side of the equation are the electrode potentials of the two reactions, the ω-terms are the overvoltages at the electrodes, and the IR term is the voltage drop across the cell, excluding the overvoltages.

Taking the value of $+0.337$ volts from Table 22-1 for the reduction potential of copper(II) ions to copper, the value of that electrode potential becomes, by Eq. (2)

$$E_1 = 0.337 + \frac{0.0591}{2} \log \frac{[Cu^{++}]}{[Cu^0]} \tag{7}$$

Since the metallic copper is at unit activity (and hence unit concentration), Eq. (7) becomes

$$E_1 = 0.337 + 0.0295 \log [Cu^{++}] \tag{8}$$

Since from Table 22-1, the standard electrode potential for the electrolysis of water to oxygen and protons is 1.229 v., that electrode potential becomes

$$E_2 = 1.229 + \frac{0.0591}{4} \log \frac{[O_2][H^+]^4}{[H_2O]^2} \tag{9}$$

Since the oxygen is evolved at one atmosphere pressure, O_2 can be taken as unity, as can H_2O. Since the solution was 1 M in sulfuric acid, H^+ is also unity, giving unity for the logarithmic expression, so that the value of the logarithm is zero. Thus

$$E_2 = 1.229 \tag{10}$$

Overvoltage.—Overvoltage is the excess of voltage—over the value calculated by the Nernst equation from standard electrode potentials—needed to maintain a certain rate of deposition on an electrode. There are several types of overvoltage, occurring both at cathodes and anodes. One type is due to the formation close to an electrode of a layer that is either less concentrated in an ion or other substance that in reacting at the electrode, or more concentrated in one that is being formed there. This type is commonly called concentration overpotential, and is reduced by the use of electrodes of large area, and by limiting the current. Stirring the solution or raising its temperature also reduces this type of overvoltage.

Another type of overvoltage is gas overvoltage, which occurs when a gas is formed at an electrode. This type of overvoltage may reach fairly high values, especially for hydrogen and oxygen. It is also reduced by decreasing the current density and raising the temperature. It varies markedly with the metal of the electrode, its surface condition (being lower for rough surfaces) and somewhat with the pH.

IR Drop.—The IR drop is merely the product of the current passing through the cell and the resistance of the cell. Obviously, the IR drop will be very small when small currents are flowing, but becomes significant for large resistances. In most electrolytic separations from aqueous solution, the resistance of the cell is small (less than 5 ohms) and the IR drop is usually considered to be small. However, if only 0.2 ampere is flowing, the IR drop is 1 volt with a 5 ohm resistance, and the applied voltage may have exceeded the potential of another reaction that could occur in the same solution. This effect often leads to very poor current efficiencies and to contaminated deposits.

PHYSICAL CHARACTERISTICS OF DEPOSITS

Obviously a substance separated by electrolysis from a solution must remain separated, whether the purpose of the separation is to determine it gravimetrically or merely to remove it from the solution. Thus adherence to the electrode is a most important property of a deposit. Generally the smoother the deposit, the more adherent it is. For this reason, hydrogen evolution at a cathode along with metal deposition is objectionable, since it produces spongy deposits. Moreover, the discharge of hydrogen tends to leave an alkaline film close to the cathode, forming oxides or basic salts. This codeposition of hydrogen can be prevented by controlling the cathode potential, or using nitrate or some other potential buffer.

Other factors whose influence serves to produce smooth deposits are (1) stirring of the solution and (2) the proper selection of anions. Stirring tends to reduce the type of overvoltage known as concentration overpotential, and permits a higher current density to be used without the danger of a second ion discharging at the electrode and lowering the current efficiency. As stirring will allow this use of higher current density without the risk of adverse effects, the electrolysis can proceed more rapidly. The proper selection of anions is a particularly salient factor. Smooth deposits are generally produced from solutions of complex ions (other than aquo-ions). For example, a coarse, treelike deposit of silver is obtained from nitrate solutions, while cyanide solutions, in which the silver is present as the complex ion $Ag(CN)_2^-$, give a smooth deposit. Halide ions facilitate the deposition of many metals, probably because the overpotential is lower for ions of the type MCl_x^{m-x} than for the corresponding aquo complex. Complex ions also exhibit what is known as throwing power to a greater extent—that is, the property of a solution by virtue of which a relatively uniform deposit of metal may be obtained on irregular surfaces.

METHODS OF ELECTROGRAVIMETRIC ANALYSIS

CONSTANT CURRENT ELECTROLYSIS

Principle.—Probably the oldest method of electrodeposition is that in which the current is held constant by periodic or continuous adjustment of the voltage applied to the cell. Under this system the reaction with the most positive reduction potential occurs first at the cathode. As the concentration of cation or other reactant in that process falls, its reduction potential also decreases, and the rate at which it can be brought to the cathode surface also falls. If the applied voltage is then increased to maintain the current, it may reach a point at which another cathode reaction occurs. However, if the cation being deposited has a positive reduction potential (as does Cu^{++}) and any other metallic ions in the solution have negative reduction potentials, codeposition of them will not occur, since the reduction potential of H^+ will be reached and will prevent further increase in cathode potential, although it may cause poor deposits of the copper. The more complete statement is that for this separation to be successful, the hydrogen overpotential on the cathode plus the reversible reduction potential of the hydrogen ions must be less than the negative reduction potential of any of the metallic ions that are to remain in solution. For example, cupric ions in a solution containing 1 M hydrogen ions may be separated from all metallic ions whose reduction potentials are more negative than about -0.4 v.—the hydrogen overpotential on a copper electrode for relatively large current densities. Additional selectivity can be achieved through use of masking agents or potential buffers, or control of pH.

Apparatus.—A diagram of a manual apparatus for electrodeposition is shown in Fig. 22-1. It is operated by a battery and manually adjusted resistance, or else its power

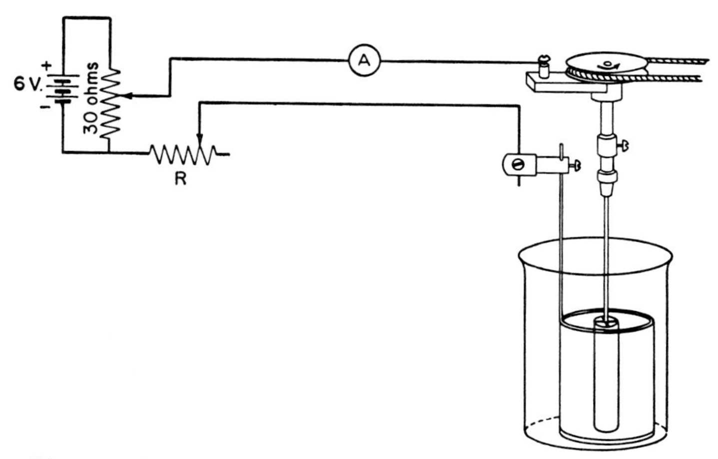

Fig. 22-1. Diagram of Minimum Equipment for Continuous-current Electrodeposition, Battery-powered. (Reprinted from Willard, Merritt, and Dean, Instrumental Methods of Analysis, 4th Ed., 1965, D. Van Nostrand Co., Inc.)

supply may be a transformer-rectifier combination drawing power directly from the 110 v. a.c. line, as shown in Fig. 22-2. The cathode is usually a gauze or perforated cylinder of platinum, although other metals, such as silver or tantalum, have been used

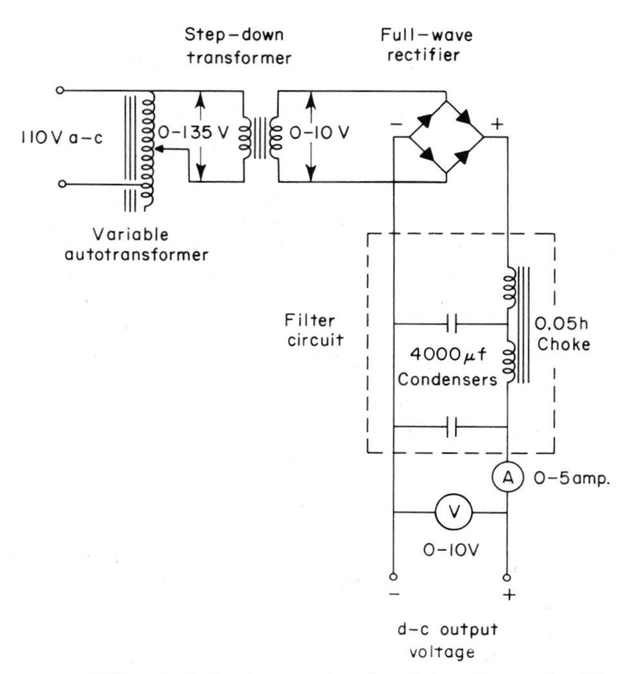

Fig. 22-2. Diagram of Electrical Equipment for Supplying Power for Electrodeposition from 110 v. a.c. Circuit. Dashed lines enclose fitter sufficient to reduce ripple below 1 percent. (Reprinted from Willard, Merritt, and Dean, Instrumental Methods of Analysis, 4th Ed., 1965, D. Van Nostrand Co., Inc.)

in some determinations. The anode is a smaller cylinder than the cathode, usually platinum also. To avoid the use of a stirrer, the anode is often used for that purpose, especially in Controlled Potential Electrolysis, described in that section.

DETERMINATIONS BY CONSTANT CURRENT ELECTROLYSIS

COPPER

General Directions.—Deposition may be carried out at a low current density (about 0.4 amps. per sq. dm. for the deposition of 1 g. of copper) over a period of about 15 hours or at high current density (over 2 amperes per sq. dm. for the deposition of 1 g. of copper) over a period of about 1 hour. The more rapid deposition requires efficient circulation of the electrolyte by a mechanical stirrer, a solenoid, or agitation with compressed air. It is advantageous to add 5 ml. of 5 percent sulfamic acid about 15 minutes before the termination of electrolysis to assist in plating out the last traces of copper. Two methods are used to remove the cathode containing the copper from the electrolyte without loss of copper. The electrolyte may be slowly siphoned off from the bottom of the electrolysis beaker (without breaking the circuit) while adding water to the top to maintain the solution level above the copper plate until the current falls to zero, or the electrolysis beaker (previously mounted on a block) may be slowly lowered (without breaking the circuit) while directing a gentle, continuous stream of water from a wash bottle over the exposed copper plate. The cathode may be dipped in 2 or 3 successive baths of acetone and dried in a current of warm air (hair dryer) or for a few minutes in an oven at 100°C.

With Nitric Acid-Sulfuric Acid Electrolyte.—When the sample is free from silver, mercury and bismuth, and contains less than 0.5 mg. of arsenic, antimony, selenium, and tellurium combined, less than 10 mg. of tin, less than 50 mg. of iron, and less than 1 mg. of lead, this is the preferred method. The electrolyte solution should be free of chlorides and should contain about 3.5 ml. of sulfuric acid and 2 ml. of nitric acid per 100 ml. of solution. Simple brasses (tin up to 1%) nickel silvers, and similar alloys are readily analyzed by this method.

With Nitric Acid Electrolyte.—When the sample is free of tin (and appreciable amounts of other interfering elements listed above), electrolysis in a nitric acid solution containing a trace of chloride offers a convenient method for the simultaneous determination of copper and lead (lead is deposited on the anode as the dioxide)[2] and for preventing the interference of small amounts of molybdenum. The electrolyte solution should contain about 3% nitric acid and 1–2 drops of 0.1 N hydrochloric acid. A mesh anode somewhat larger than ordinary must be used if much lead is to be deposited. This is an excellent method for the analysis of leaded brasses. If tin is present it may be precipitated as metastannic acid and filtered off before electrolysis.

With Electrolytes Containing Special Oxidants.—The interference of moderate amounts of arsenic, antimony, selenium, and tellurium may be prevented by keeping these metals in their highest state of oxidation.[3] Ammonium nitrate (5 g. per sample) is often used to prevent deposition of arsenic and antimony, but manganese nitrate (2 ml. of a solution containing 1 g. manganese per 100 ml.) is more effective and also prevents deposition of tellurium, but is not effective for selenium. To oxidize selenium the solution must be made ammoniacal and boiled with 1 g. of ammonium peroxydisulfate. The solution is then acidified and electrolyzed as usual. For samples containing large amounts of iron the amount of nitric acid present should be limited to 1 ml.

Hydrazine Buffering.—In a number of methods for the electrodeposition of copper from its solution as complex ions, hydrazine has been used successfully as a buffer to prevent competing oxidation of the complex ions to copper(II) ions at the anode, the hydrazine being preferentially oxidized there.[4] In this way, copper can be deposited quantitatively from chloride solutions in which it is present as $[CuCl_3]^=$ ions.

COBALT

General Directions.—Cobalt is electrolyzed in a strongly ammoniacal solution in the presence of ammonium sulfate. Copper and other Group 2 metals are removed with hydrogen sulfide, and iron removed with zinc oxide or ether and cobalt precipitated by α-nitroso-β-naphthol, or iron is eliminated by means of phosphate. Where only small quantities of iron are present, several precipitations with ammonium hydroxide will liberate virtually all the cobalt. Where cobalt has not been isolated by means of α-nitroso-β-naphthol prior to electrolysis, any nickel, of course, will be deposited with cobalt and must be determined by dimethylglyoxime on the dissolved plating.

If cobalt is precipitated with α-nitroso-β-naphthol and ignited to oxide, transfer to a beaker, add a little hydrochloric acid, nitric acid, and 5 ml. 1 : 1 sulfuric acid. Evaporate to fumes of the latter, cool, neutralize with ammonia and add 40 ml. excess. If the sample has been fumed to dryness, add more 1 : 1 sulfuric acid or ammonium sulfate to ensure the presence of the latter after making ammoniacal. Electrolyze overnight on a stationary cabinet at 0.5 amp., or on a rotating electrolytic apparatus at 2 amp. for 1 hour. Test the

[2] Scherrer, J. A., *et al.*, J. Research, NBS, **22,** 697, 1939, R. P. 1213.
[3] Skowronski, S., A.S.T.M. Bull., #174, 60, 1951.
[4] Lingane, J. J., and Jones, S., Anal. Chem., **23,** 1804, 1951.

solution for complete deposition by withdrawing a few drops with a pipet onto a spot plate and testing with potassium thiocarbonate, phenylthiohydantoic acid, nitroso-R-salt, or ammonium sulfide, by the usual spot tests for these reagents.

Wash the cathode, rinse in alcohol, dry on a hot plate or in a blast of warm air from a hair dryer, and weigh the previously tared cathode.

CONTROLLED POTENTIAL ELECTROLYSIS

Principle.—As has been shown earlier in this chapter, the potential at which an ion deposits from solution is a function, not only of its standard electrode potential at an electrode of the corresponding metal, but also of a number of other factors, including its concentration. When that concentration decreases, as it must if the deposition is to be quantitative, the voltage applied to the cell is necessarily increased to continue the deposition. This increase may be great enough to bring about the codeposition of other ions present in the solution, thus introducing errors into the analytical results. In general, the closer the standard electrode potential of the other ion to that of the one under analysis, the greater the likelihood of this kind of error, particularly if both electrode potentials are positive or negative (in the case of cathodic deposition) so that the discharge of protons as hydrogen does not intervene. To extend the range of use of electrogravimetric methods to solutions containing such ions, close control of potential is necessary, and various methods, manual and automatic, have been developed to effect it.

Manual Apparatus.—Figure 22-3 shows a simple manually-operated circuit for measuring the cathode potential by means of a reference electrode (shown diagramatically as a

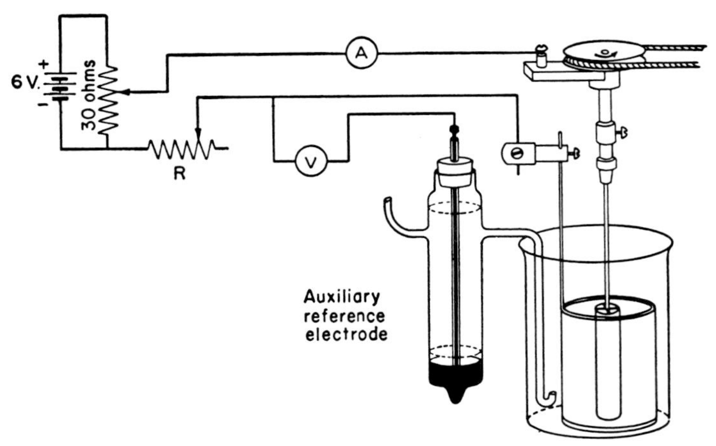

Fig. 22-3. Diagram of Fig. 22-1 Showing Reference Electrode and Circuit for Measuring Cathode Potential. (Reprinted from Willard, Merritt, and Dean, Instrumental Methods of Analysis, 4th Ed., 1965, D. Van Nostrand Co., Inc.)

standard calomel electrode) placed close to the cathode of the cell. This arrangement, which is a modified version of Fig. 22-2, also has means for manual adjustment of the voltage applied to the cell.

Automatic Control Circuit.—Figure 22-4 shows[5] an apparatus for automatic control of the potential of the working electrode, which operates from the 110 a.c. line. It

[5] Caldwell, C. W., Parker, Robert C., and Diehl, Harvey, Ind. Eng. Chem., Anal. Ed., **16,** 533,1944.

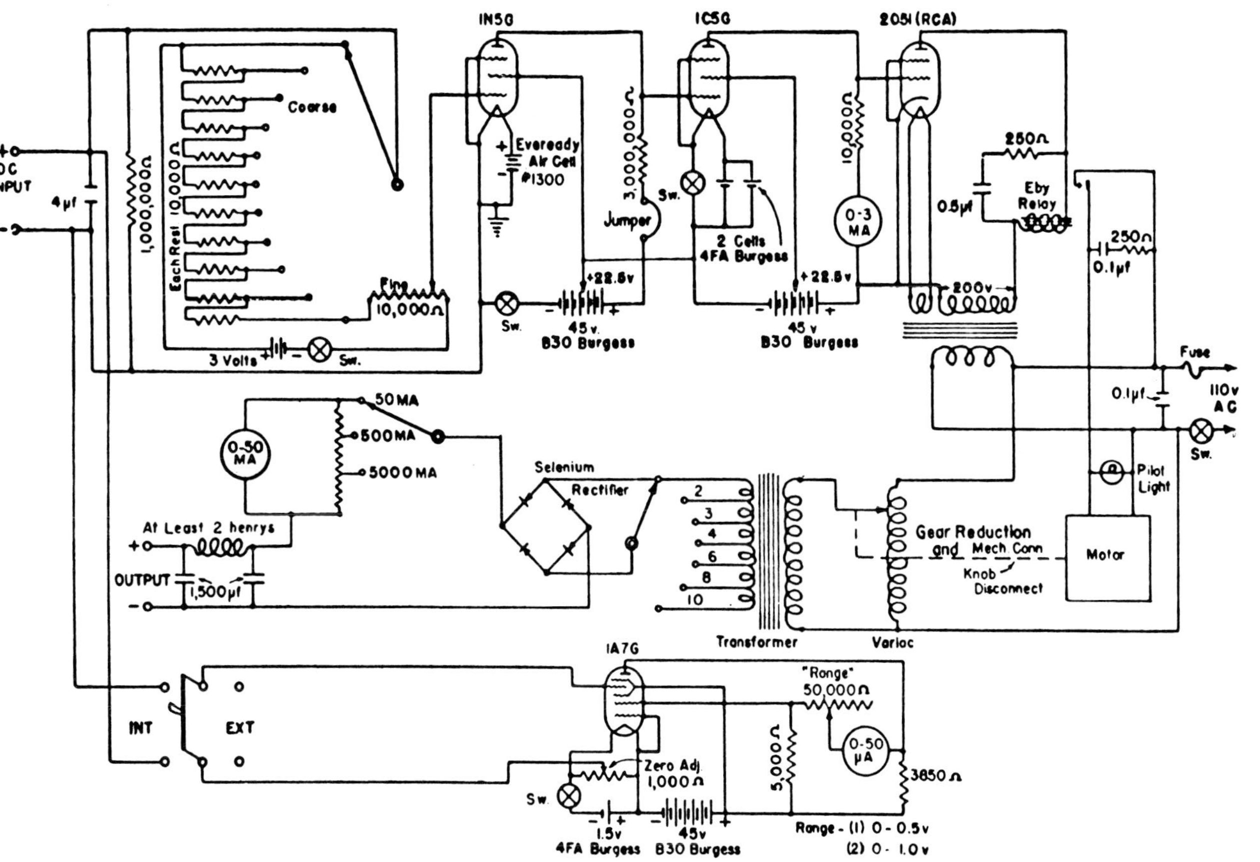

FIG. 22-4. Diagram of Caldwell-Parker-Diehl Circuit for Automatically Controlled Electrodeposition at Constant Cathode Potential. (Courtesy Industrial and Engineering Chemistry.)

consists of a vacuum tube amplifier which multiplies the potential difference between the cathode in the cell and that of the standard calomel electrode sufficiently to actuate a relay and motor which drives a Variac; the Variac controls the magnitude of the a.c. which when rectified is used as to effect the deposition in the cell.

Operation of Automatic Control Circuit.—The filament voltage, bias voltage, and vacuum tube voltmeter filament are turned on, and the apparatus is given a 20-minute warming up period before starting the electrodeposition. Connections from the d.c. output are made to the cathode and anode and from the d.c. input to the cathode and calomel cell. In the case of copper and metals higher than copper in the electromotive series, the calomel cell is connected to the positive terminal. The bias controls are set for the limited potential wanted. The stirring motor is started and the electrolysis is begun by turning the alternating current switch on, setting the Variac to full value, and turning the voltage regulator to give a suitable current.

It is best then to test the d.c. input circuit by breaking contact at the calomel cell junction. The reading of the vacuum tube voltmeter should change on breaking the contact or upon altering the size of the electrolyzing current. If a variation is not observed, the other contacts should be examined and the calomel cell inspected for air bubbles. If the circuit is closed, the electrolysis can proceed without further attention from the operator.

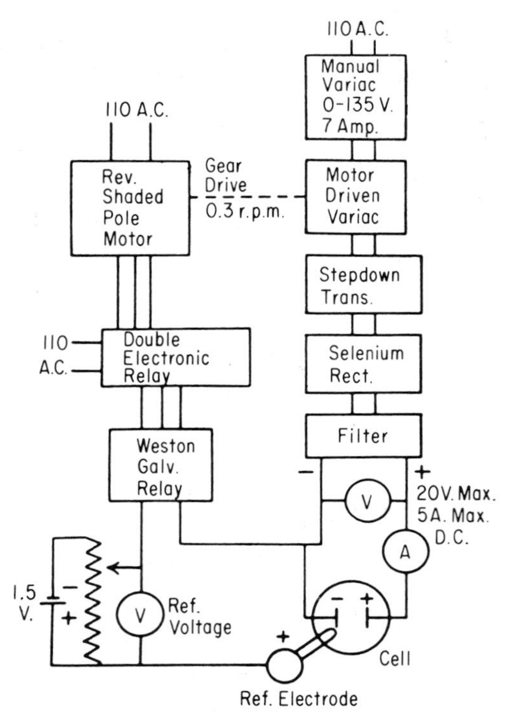

Fig. 22-5*a*. Lingane-Jones Potentiostat for Automatically-controlled Electrodeposition at Constant Cathode Potential. Schematic circuit. (Reprinted from Analytical Chemistry, **22,** 1169, 1950. Copyright 1950 by the American Chemical Society and reprinted by permission of the copyright owner.)

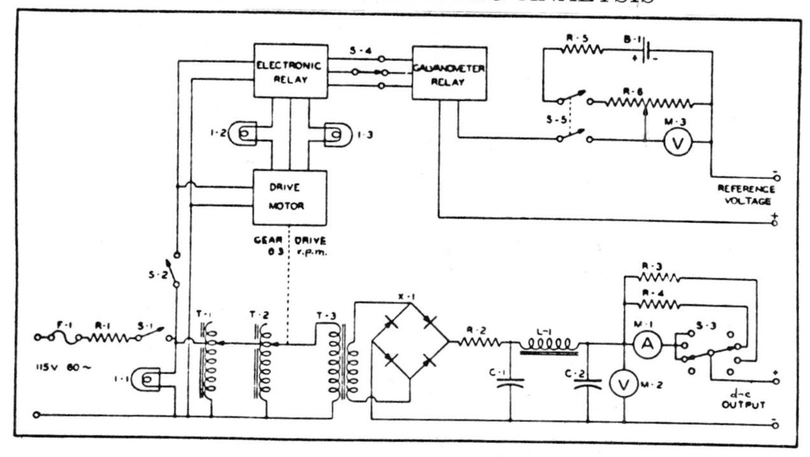

B-1. 1.5-volt dry battery
C-1, *C*-2. 6000-μfd. electrolytic capacitors (50 volts)
F-1. 3-ampere fuse (250 volts)
L-1. Choke (0.015 henry, 5 amperes)
M-1. Milliammeter (0–100 ma. d.c.)
M-2. Voltmeter (0–30 volts d.c.)
M-3. Voltmeter (0–1 volt, ±1% or better; Weston Model 741)
I-1. Pilot lamp (115 volt a.c.)
I-2, *I*-3. Pilot lamps (G.E. No. 47, 6.3 volt, 0.15 ampere)
R-1. 5 ohms, 50 watts, wire wound (±5%)
R-2. 1 ohm, 100 watts, wire wound (±5%)
R-3, *R*-4. Empirically adjusted shunts
R-5. 40 ohms, 5 watts, wire wound (±5%)
R-6. 100-ohm potentiometer (General Radio No. 214)
S-1, *S*-2. S.p.s.t. toggle switches
S-3. 4-position rotary switch (low resistance contacts)
S-4. 3-position single pole switch
S-5. D.p.s.t. toggle switch
T-1, *T*-2. General Radio Co. Type V-5 Variac autotransformers (0–135 volts, 7.5 amperes)
T-3. Power transformer (U.T.C. Special Series Type S-63, stepdown ratio 5 to 1, 10 amperes)
X-1. Selenium rectifier (48 volts, 5 amperes)

Drive motor. Barber-Coleman Model No. gYAz 804 (110-volt a.c., shaded pole, reversible)
Galvanometer relay. Weston Model 30 (±15 microamp. per mm., 1100 ohms internal resistance)

FIG. 22-5*b*. Lingane-Jones Potentiostat for Automatically-controlled Electrodeposition at Constant Cathode Potential. Complete circuit. (Reprinted from Analytical Chemistry, **22**, 1169, 1950. Copyright 1950 by the American Chemical Society and reprinted by permission of the copyright owner.)

In the use of this apparatus, or any other method of automatic potential control, the current must not be allowed to fall below a certain limiting value, below which the deposit redissolves more rapidly than it is being formed. All methods of determining substances under controlled potential must give consideration to this limiting current.

A later development in a circuit for automatic control of electrode potential is that of Lingane and Jones (see Fig. 22-5).[6]

Automatic Analyzer.—There are automatic analyzers embodying control circuits for electrogravimetric determinations (or separations) at controlled potential applied to the cell. The Sargent Electrolytic Analyzer is shown in Fig. 22-6 and its circuit diagram is shown in Fig. 22-7. As is shown there, this instrument has self-contained rectifying and filter circuits which provide a d.c. output with negligable a.c. ripple. The deposition potential between electrodes is adjusted to the preset value by means of an autotransformer. There is also a self-contained magnetic stirrer that functions as long as current is passing through the cell. This instrument is also available in two-position models,

[6] Lingane, J. J., and Jones, S., Anal. Chem. **22**, 1169, 1950.

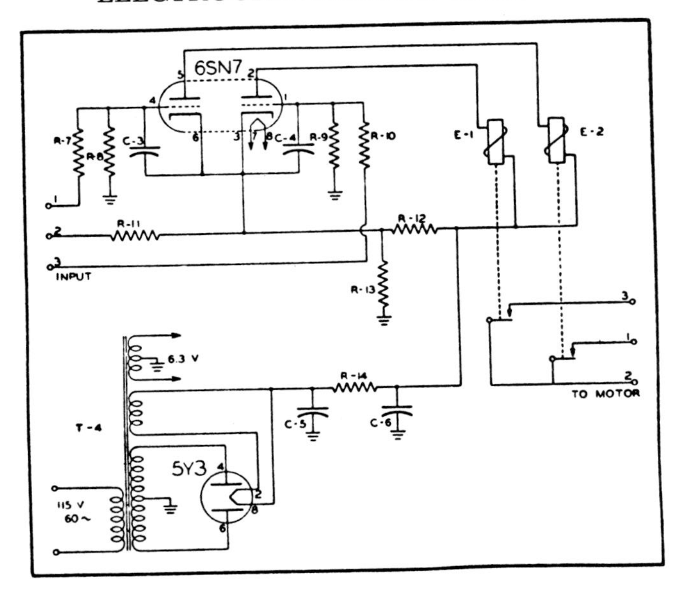

C-3, *C*-4. 0.003 μfd. mica capacitors (200 volts)
C-5, *C*-6. 8 μfd. electrolytic capacitors (450 volts)
E-1, *E*-2. S.p.s.t. relays (10,000 ohms, 30 volts d.c.)
R-7, *R*-10. 4 megohms, 1 watt, carbon (±10%)
R-8, *R*-9. 10 megohms, 1 watt, carbon (±10%)
R-11. 100,000 ohms, 1 watt, carbon (±10%)
R-12. 34000 ohms, 10 watts, wire wound (±5%)
R-13. 2000 ohms, 5 watts, wire wound (±5%)
R-14. 4000 ohms, 10 watts, wire wound (±5%)
T-4. Thordarson T-22R00 transformer or equivalent (primary 115 volts, secondary 250-0-250 volts at 40 ma., 5 volts at 2 amperes, 6.3 volts at 2 amperes)
5Y3. Rectifier tube (glass envelope)
6SN7. Twin triode (glass envelope)

FIG. 22-5*c*. Lingane-Jones Potentiostat for Automatically-controlled Electrodeposition at Constant Cathode Potential. Electronic relay circuit. (Reprinted from Analytical Chemistry, **22**, 1169, 1950. Copyright 1950 by the American Chemical Society and reprinted by permission of the copyright owner.)

each of which may take currents up to 15 amperes, and which are suitable for use when a number of determinations are to be made daily.

DETERMINATIONS BY CONTROLLED POTENTIAL ELECTROLYSIS

DETERMINATION OF COPPER, LEAD, AND TIN IN BRASSES AND BRONZES[7]

Transfer 1.0 g. of sample to a covered 250-ml. conical beaker and add 7.5 ml. of hydrochloric acid, sp. gr. 1.16, and 5 ml. of water. Warm gently on a hot plate, adding the minimum amount of nitric acid, sp. gr. 1.42, dropwise to dissolve the sample. Then add 2 g. of ammonium chloride and approximately 25 ml. of water and boil for 5

[7] Milner, G. W. C., and Whittem, R. N., Analyst, **52**, 11, 1952.

minutes. Cool, transfer to a 400-ml. squat beaker, add 2 g. of hydrazine hydrochloride and about 25 ml. of water containing 10 mg. of gelatin and dilute to about 200 ml. with water. Immerse the platinum-gauze electrodes (cathode 6 cm. high, 6 cm. in diameter; anode 3.5 cm. high, 3.5 cm. in diameter) in the solution, adjust an electrically-driven, paddle-shaped stirrer to pass centrally through the electrodes, and position a saturated calomel electrode so that the connection bridge touches the outside surface of the cathode. Adjust the speed of the stirrer to give efficient stirring of the solution. Begin the electrolysis by controlling the cathode at −0.36 volt with respect to the saturated calomel electrode using unidirectional control and also limiting the current in the first stages to

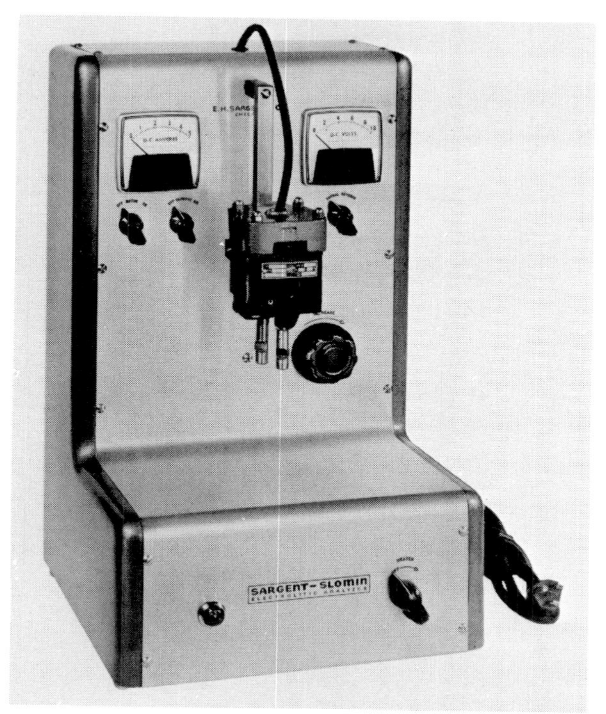

FIG. 22-6. S-29460 Sargent-Slomin Electrolytic Analyzer. (Courtesy E. H. Sargent and Co.)

a maximum of 4 amp. After the current has become constant (usually at about 20 mamp., after electrolyzing for 30 to 45 minutes) switch off the controller motor, remove the saturated calomel electrode and then lower the beaker, at the same time washing the cathode with a stream of water from a wash bottle. Switch off the stirrer, shut off the current, and remove the cathode. Rinse the cathode in ethyl alcohol, dry at not more than 105°C. for 5 minutes and measure its increase in weight. If the alloy contains more than trace amounts of antimony, correct this weight for the codeposited antimony and the final weight then corresponds to the copper content of the sample.

Add 10 ml. of hydrochloric acid, sp. gr. 1.16, to the electrolyte remaining after the copper determination and immerse the electrodes as before, but this time use a copper-plated cathode. Prepare this electrode by plating about 50 mg. of copper from a conventional sulfuric–nitric acid solution, washing with water and with alcohol, drying at not more than 105°C. and weighing. Add water to the solution until the cathode gauze is completely immersed in the solution and then electrolyze with the cathode maintained at −0.70 volt with respect to the saturated calomel electrode. Continue the electrolysis for 45 minutes, as this time has been found to be sufficient for the deposition of the lead and tin in most types of copper-base alloys with the above electrodes, whereas the final value of the current has proved an unreliable indication of the completion of the electrolytic process. Switch off the controller and neutralize the electrolyte by adding 30 ml.

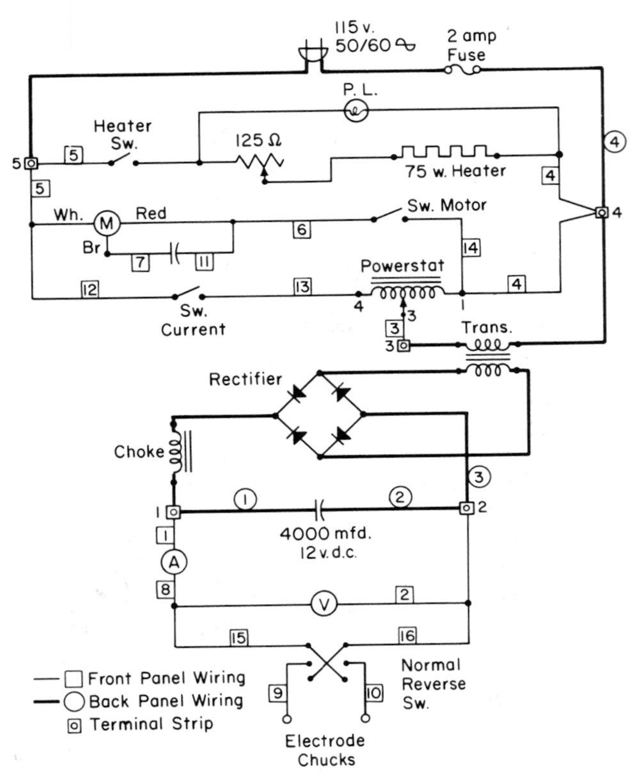

FIG. 22-7. Circuit of S-29460 Sargent-Slomin Electrolytic Analyzer. (Courtesy E. H. Sargent and Co.)

of dilute (1 + 1) ammonia solution, and immediately lower the beaker while washing the electrodes with water. Rinse the cathode in alcohol, dry it, and determine the increase in weight to give the combined percentage of lead and tin in the sample. Make the remaining electrolyte acid by adding hydrochloric acid, sp. gr. 1.16, transfer to a 1-liter conical beaker, and boil down to a volume of less than 200 ml. Cool, accurately dilute to 200 ml. in a volumetric flask, and reserve for the determination of the remaining alloying elements.

Strip the deposit from the cathode with 25 ml. of nitric acid, sp. gr. 1.20, in a 400-ml. squat beaker, and finally wash the cathode with water. Evaporate the resulting solution almost to dryness, then cool and add a further 25 ml. of nitric acid, sp. gr. 1.20. Digest hot for a time and then filter the metastannic acid on paper-pulp pad, and wash it about four times with hot water. Collect the filtrate and washings in a 400-ml. squat beaker and dilute the resulting solution to about 100 ml. with water. Heat the solution to boiling and electrolyze while it is as hot as possible with a small platinum-gauze anode and a current of 4 to 5 amp. Electrolyze until the deposition of the lead is complete, which generally takes about 5 minutes. Remove the anode, wash it with water and then dry and weigh as before. Calculate the percentage of lead from the weight of lead dioxide by using the empirical factor of 0.863 and determine the tin content by subtraction from the combined tin and lead percentage.

ANALYSIS OF NICKEL BRONZES[8]

(Alloys of copper, tin, lead, zinc, and nickel, together with small amounts of iron, aluminum, and manganese)

From 0.5 to 1.0 g. of the alloy, in the form of fine sawings or drillings, are heated with 10 ml. of hydrochloric acid (sp. gr. 1.16) and 1 g. of ammonium chloride, the latter being added to minimize loss of tin as the volatile tin(IV) chloride. Complete solution is effected by the addition, drop by drop, of a saturated solution of potassium chlorate, with boiling after each addition. The solution is then evaporated in order to decompose excess of chlorate, and diluted to 100 ml., and 5 ml. of hydrochloric acid and 1 g. of hydrazine hydrochloride are added. Copper is deposited by electrolyzing the solution at 50°C. with an auxiliary potential of 0.4 volt. The current falls rapidly almost to zero, and reaches a minimum after about 10 minutes. After a further 5 minutes, the liquid in the tip of the auxiliary electrode is flushed out into the electrolysis vessel, and the electrolysis is continued for a further 5 minutes. The solution is cooled to room temperature, and electrolyzed similarly, for 20 minutes, at 20°C., with an auxiliary potential of 0.7 volt. The tin and lead are deposited together and are separated.[9] The residual solution is evaporated with 5 ml. of sulfuric acid (sp. gr. 1.82) until fumes appear, and then taken up in 50 ml. of water, and ammonia is added until the liquid is just alkaline to phenolphthalein. The mixture is boiled, and the hydroxides of iron and aluminum are filtered off and thoroughly washed with hot water. The iron is separated from the aluminium by boiling the precipitate with a little sodium peroxide and water, and refiltering the undissolved iron, which is determined gravimetrically, volumetrically, or, if present only in traces, colorimetrically.[10] The aluminium is determined colorimetrically by the use of aluminon.[11]

Twenty ml. of ammonia solution (sp. gr. 0.880) in excess and 2 g. of sodium sulfite are added to the filtrate, and nickel is deposited by electrolyzing for 20 minutes, at 70°C., with an auxiliary potential of 1.0 to 1.1 volts. The solution is cooled to room temperature, 5 ml. of ammonia solution are added, and the zinc is deposited by electrolyzing the solution for 30 minutes at 20°C. with a current of 3 amp. The residual solution is heated to boiling, and any manganese present is precipitated as the sulfide by passing hydrogen sulfide gas for 5 to 10 minutes. The precipitate is filtered off, washed with water saturated with hydrogen sulfide, dissolved in a little nitric acid and oxidized to permanganate with some sodium bismuthate. This permanganate is determined colorimetrically, or, if the amount of manganese present warrants, volumetrically.[12]

[8] Torrance, S., Analyst, **63,** 488, 1936.
[9] Torrance S., Analyst, **62,** 719, 1937.
[10] Sutton, F., Volumetric Analysis, Longmans Green, Ltd., London.
[11] Hopkins, R. A., and Williams, L. N., Organic Reagents for Metals, Chapman & Hall, Ltd., London,
[12] Sutton, *op. cit.*

MERCURY CATHODE ELECTROLYSIS

Principle.—The mercury cathode is not widely used for determination of deposited metals chiefly because of difficulties in drying and weighing the mercury before and after the determination. However, it is most useful for the removal of certain base metals that interfere in the determination of metals high in the electromotive series; and it is also useful in the separation of noble metals from other metals. It should be added that a large number of metals have been determined quantitatively by mercury cathode separation even though the method is not practical for general use for this purpose. Two factors set mercury apart from other electrode materials. Many of the metals depositing on mercury can form an alloy (amalgam) with the mercury. Owing to the alloy formation, the deposition potentials of these metals on mercury are displaced from their normal value in the positive direction with respect to reduction potentials. Their deposition is also aided by the fact that the hydrogen overpotential on mercury is particularly large. As a result the deposition from a fairly acid solution is possible for such metals as chromium, iron, nickel, zinc, and even manganese under certain conditions.

Apparatus.—While mercury cathodes may be constructed by amalgamating a brass or platinum gauze electrode, the simplest type consists of a pool of mercury in the bottom of a beaker, to which a platinum wire is conducted by sealing it inside a glass tube that passes through the beaker, or inside the base of the vessel itself. A cell of this type as designed by Melaven[13] is shown in Fig. 22-8. The cathode consists of 35 to 50 ml. of pure mercury in a modified separatory funnel. The apparatus has a conical base fitted with a three-way stopcock. One arm of the stopcock is connected to a leveling bulb that controls the level of the mercury in the cell; the other permits removal of the electrolyte. With a beaker, this removal is accomplished by siphoning. The anode is a platinum wire in the form of a spiral. Agitation is accomplished by a mechanical stirrer or a stream of air.

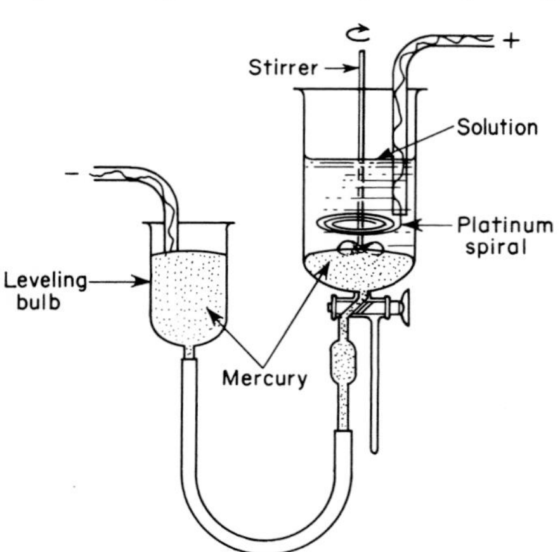

Fig. 22-8. Mercury Cathode Cell. (Reprinted from Willard, Merritt, and Dean, Instrumental Methods of Analysis, 4th Ed., 1965, D. Van Nostrand Co., Inc.)

As in the case of other electrodeposition processes already discussed, control of the potential of the mercury cathode extends considerably the usefulness of this method. By using it prior to other electrometric methods, such as polarography, the operation of removing certain metals from a solution can be performed as a step preliminary to other determinations in the same apparatus.

A more compact and easily handled mercury cathode has been devised,[14] the unitized cell, as shown in Fig. 22-9. The cell is a glass disc about 30 mm. in diameter by 15 mm. high, from the side of which extends a glass tube carrying the wire for electrical contact. A flat, spiral anode completes the cell. The unitized electrode is easily removed from the

[13] Melaven, A. D., Ind. Eng. Chem., Anal. Ed., **2,** 180, 1930.
[14] Johnson, H. O., Weaver, J. R., and Lykken L., Anal. Chem., **19,** 481, 1947.

electrolyte and washed with a stream of wash solution quickly enough to prevent appreciable re-solution of the deposited metals. The consumption of mercury is a minimum, usually 5 ml. per electrolysis, and the simplicity with which duplicate assemblies are interchanged encourages frequent substitution of fresh mercury. This increases the

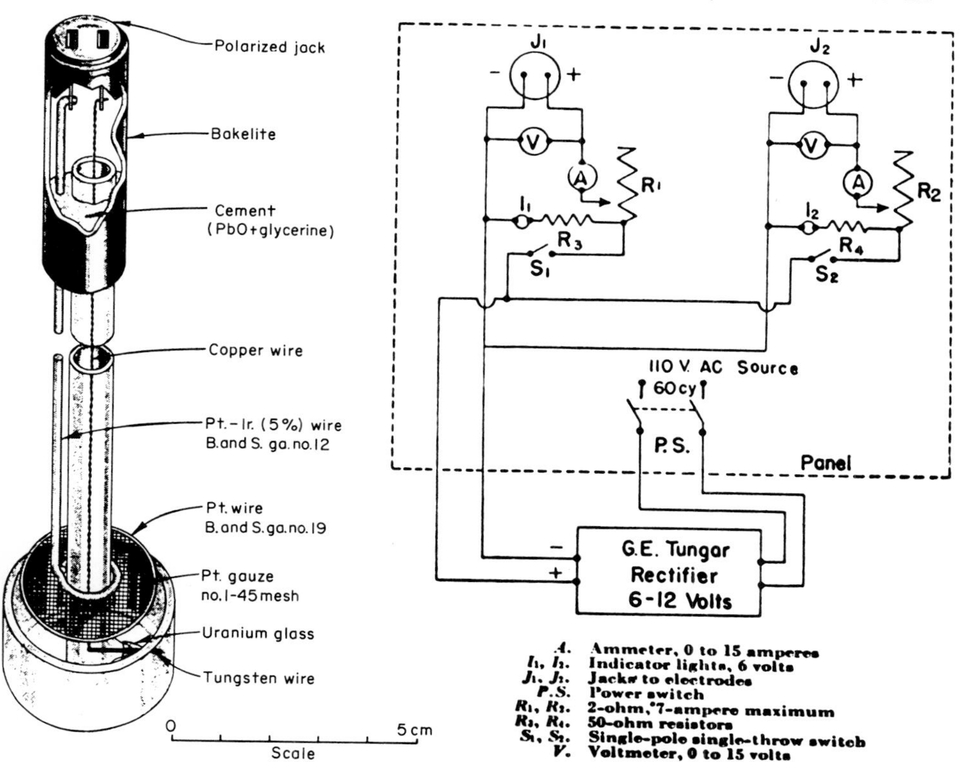

FIG. 22-9. Unitized Mercury Cathode. Sketch of electrode at left, wiring diagram at right. (Reprinted from Analytical Chemistry, **19**, 481, 1947. Copyright 1947 by the American Chemical Society and reprinted by permission of the copyright owner.)

efficiency of a separation and decreases the time for electrolysis. Finally, the difficulty from loss of mercury in handling and from dispersion during electrolysis is minimized. Automatic mercury-cathode electrolysis equipment is also available, such as the DYNA-CATH shown in Fig. 22-10. The instrument is 16 inches wide, 14 inches deep, and 22½ inches in overall height. The probe assemblies can be raised a maximum of 5½ inches. The sloping instrument panel carries: (1) a cell selector switch for operation of right or left cell only, or both cells simultaneously; (2) an ammeter reading 0 to 25 amp. showing d.c. input to cell or cells; (3) a 4-amp. fuse held in a panel receptacle which is mounted in the a.c. circuit and protects the electrical components; (4) a pilot light indicating power to unit (on or off); (5) a variable autotransformer knob controlling d.c. input to cell or cells; (6) a needle valve controlling the volume of water flowing through the heat exchangers in the cells; and (7) an off-on toggle switch controlling a.c. power into unit from line source.

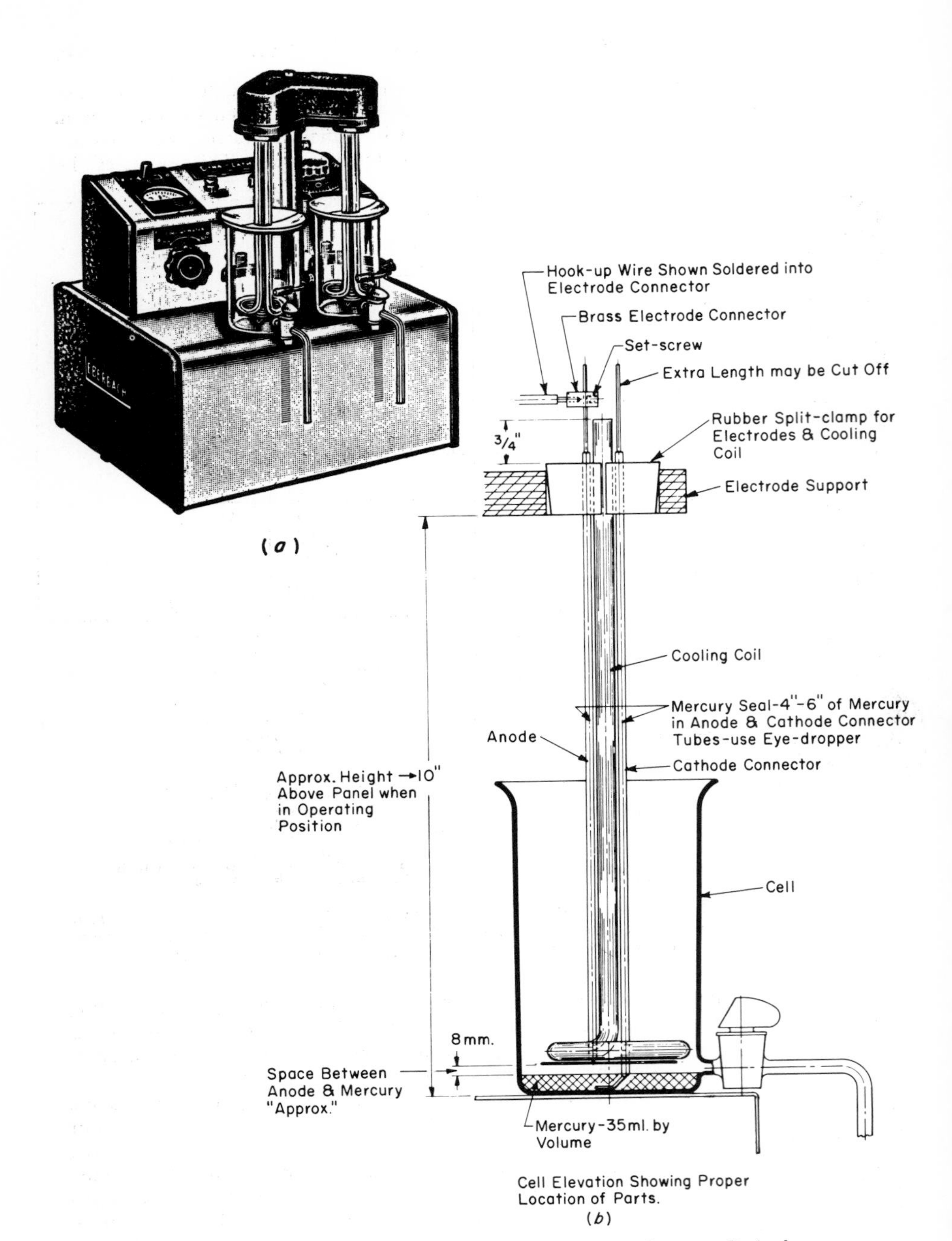

FIG. 22-10. The DYNA-CATH, a High-speed Mercury Cathode Instrument. (*a*) View of equipment. (*b*) Cell elevation showing proper location of parts. (Courtesy Eberbach Corp., Ann Arbor, Mich.)

The pillar in the center of the DYNA-CATH carries the probe support which can be raised $5\frac{1}{2}$ inches when the operator desires to remove the cells for cleaning. Electrical and heat-exchanger leads pass through the pillar and probe support to each of the probe assemblies. The probe support is made of stainless steel and bakelite with a hammertone gray finished aluminum cap covering the connections in the head of the probe support.

The two cathode cells are held in place with a stainless steel and bakelite clamp which provides positive centering of the probe unit with the cell. There is complete visibility of the electrolyte, mercury, and control panel in all operations.

The cathode cells are constructed of heavy borosilicate glass with a special fast-drain stopcock outlet above the mercury level. Spray losses are completely avoided by the cooling unit and plastic cell covers. The cells are designed to hold 25 to 45 ml. of mercury and 50 to 400 ml. of electrolyte. Special cells to hold approximately 70 ml. of mercury are available as accessories.

The anode is fabricated from heavy sandblasted platinum wire. Platinum is also used as a cathode contact to the mercury.

As shown, the instrument has two cells which can be operated over a current range of 0–20 amp.

Operation.—The steps in the operation of the assembled DYNA-CATH are as follows:

1. Raise probe units and place a cathode cell in each position.
2. Lower probes carefully to see that the cathode lead just clears the bottom of the cell (adjustment is made by removing the housing over the probe units and loosening the probe holder).
3. Pour mercury into the cells until the level is just flush with the lower edge of the cell drain and then add the electrolyte.
4. Place the split plastic cover glasses over the cells.
5. Connect power cord to 115-v., 50/60-cycle a.c. outlet and high-pressure hose to water supply.
6. With power control at the low end of its scale, and the cell selector switch in the desired position, turn on the main switch.
7. Adjust power setting to the required amperage (since the resistance of the cell decreases as the electrolysis proceeds, the initial setting should be low enough or a re-adjustment made later to prevent exceeding 20 amp.).*
8. Turn on and adjust cooling water, if necessary, by means of the needle valve on the sloping instrument panel.
9. At the completion of electrolysis, drain electrolyte from cell and wash as required. In cases requiring a minimum of cathode-group metals remaining in the electrolyte (*i.e.*, less than 50 μg. per 100 ml.) the washing should be done with the current on. This is easily accomplished by draining the electrolyte to a level just above the anode, adding a small amount of water (or 0.1 *N* acid) and again draining to the

* Occasionally during the electrolysis of concentrated iron solutions in excess of 5 g. and at very high current densities, trees may form on the surface of the mercury. They increase the effective area of the cathode and thus aid in deposition to some extent. Since the trees disappear at the completion of electrolysis, they are of no importance unless they grow sufficiently to short circuit the cell. Should this condition occur, it can be remedied by increasing the electrode spacing by raising the probe unit slightly, or avoided entirely by using a larger cell. The presence of trees should not be confused with the formation of ammonium amalgam. The latter occurs in the presence of ammonium salts at a pH of approximately 2.0 or greater and is characterized by a puffy, gassy condition in the mercury. The action of the cell can be restored to normal by the addition of a few drops of sulfuric acid; when sufficient acid has been added, ammonia is released from the cathode and the mercury assumes its normal appearance.

same level. This technique is particularly important with metals which are not ferromagnetic.*

SEPARATIONS AND DETERMINATIONS WITH THE *DYNA-CATH*

In addition to certain elements (arsenic, selenium and tellurium) which are quantitatively separated from the solution but not quantitatively deposited in the mercury, the following elements are quantitatively deposited in the mercury: bismuth, cadmium, cerium, chromium, copper, gallium, gold, indium, iridium, iron, mercury, molybdenum, nickel, palladium, platinum, polonium, rhenium, rhodium, silver, thallium, tin, and zinc. For the separations, there are a considerable number of electrogravimetric determinations for analyses of commercial products in which they are widely used to separate interferences prior to determinations by other methods of the elements sought. Representative procedures of this kind are given below:

DETERMINATIONS OF ALUMINUM IN STEEL

***Insoluble Aluminum* (Al_2O_3).**—Dissolve 20 g.** of drillings in 210 ml. of 1:9 sulfuric acid. Digest on the hot plate at a temperature below boiling until action ceases. Filter through a Whatman No. 40 with pulp and wash well with hot water. Reserve the filtrate for the determination of soluble aluminum.

Ignite the residue in a platinum crucible. Cool, add 6 to 8 drops of 1:1 sulfuric acid and 10 to 15 ml. of hydrofluoric acid. Evaporate to fumes and continue fuming until all of the sulfuric acid is gone. Fuse this residue in potassium bisulfate, leach in water, and add enough sulfuric acid to make the solution approximately 0.2 *N*.

Transfer the solution to a DYNA-CATH cell and electrolyze until a test shows no iron present.† Transfer the solution to a 400-ml. beaker, heat nearly to boiling, and add ammonia from a buret to a methyl red end point and 2 or 3 drops in excess. Digest for half an hour (keeping solution ammoniacal) and filter on a Whatman No. 41 with pulp. Wash well with a 2 percent solution of ammonium nitrate. Ignite in a tared platinum crucible, treat with hydrofluoric acid in the usual manner to eliminate any silica, re-ignite, and weigh as Al_2O_3 at 1100°C.

Soluble Aluminum.—Adjust the filtrate to approximately 200 ml. and heat to boiling.‡ While stirring briskly, add a sodium bicarbonate solution (80 g. per liter) from a buret until a permanent precipitate is formed (about 36 ml.), then add 4 to 6 ml. in excess.

Cover the beaker and boil for 1 minute. Let the precipitate settle and filter rapidly through an open-texture paper containing a little paper pulp. The filtrate will become cloudy owing to oxidation and hydrolysis of the iron, but this is of no consequence. Transfer the paper to the original beaker, add 20 ml. of nitric acid, and rotate to dis-

* This test is conveniently made on a spot plate using a mixed indicator consisting of 4 g. each of potassium ferrocyanide and potassium ferricyanide dissolved in 100 ml. of water. For maximum sensitivity, this solution should be discarded and renewed after 2 or 3 days.

** The sample weight, of course, is adjusted to the expected range of aluminum in the steel. 10 to 20 g. are normally used for plain-carbon steels of the S.A.E. 1020 type. Al-killed steels require a much smaller sample and correspondingly less sulfuric acid.

† The procedure given above is intended for use with plain-carbon and low-alloy iron and steel. Obviously, separations and/or corrections must be made if appreciable zirconium, titanium, etc., are present; also in work of the highest accuracy and in high-phosphorus iron, the aluminum trioxide obtained in the soluble aluminum procedure should be examined and corrected for phosphorus pentoxide.

With some alloys it is more convenient to complete the analysis by a colorimetric method.

‡With smaller sample weights (*i.e.*, 1 to 10 g.), the bicarbonate separation may be omitted, if desired, and the filtrate placed directly in the DYNA-CATH.

integrate the paper. Add 5 ml. sulfuric acid and heat to sulfur trioxide fumes. If solution blackens, add 5 ml. nitric acid and heat again to fumes.

After cooling, dilute to about 75 ml., and nearly neutralize with ammonia. The final solution in about 100-ml. volume should contain not more than 0.2 ml. of free sulfuric acid.

Place solution in a DYNA-CATH cell and electrolyze to the absence of iron. Complete the determination as outlined for insoluble aluminum.

DETERMINATION OF Al_2O_3 IN IRON ORE

Weigh a 1.0-g sample into a 250-ml. beaker. Add approximately 25 ml. of concentrated hydrochloric acid and digest on hot plate (adding more acid if necessary) until no further action is noted. Add a few drops of concentrated nitric acid and evaporate to a syrup. Cool, add 10 ml. of concentrated hydrochloric acid, digest, and transfer to a platinum dish. Add 5 ml. of 1:1 sulfuric acid and 5 to 10 ml. of hydrofluoric acid. Evaporate to heavy fumes.

Cool, leach, and digest with hot water. (Any insoluble residue is filtered, ignited (platinum crucible), fused with a small amount of sodium carbonate and added to the filtrate.)

Add ammonia (buret) until a precipitate just forms and then clear the solution by adding 1:1 sulfuric acid dropwise with vigorous stirring.*

Place in a DYNA-CATH cell and electrolyze to the absence of iron.

Complete as in the "Determination of Aluminum in Steel."**

DETERMINATION OF ALUMINUM AND MAGNESIUM IN ZINC-BASE ALLOYS (4–6% Al, 0.3–3% Cu, 0.04% Mg, BALANCE Zn)

Dissolve a 2-g. sample in 20 ml. of 1:3 sulfuric acid; when solution is complete, remove from the hot plate and reduce the acidity of the sample by adding ammonia until the solution is slightly turbid. Clear the solution with a few drops of 1:1 sulfuric acid, adding 3 to 4 drops in excess. Transfer to a DYNA-CATH cell and electrolyze until no test for zinc† is obtained. Any undissolved copper will alloy with the mercury.

Drain the clear solution into a 400-ml. beaker. Add about 5 g. of ammonium chloride, heat almost to boiling, and add ammonia until it is just alkaline to methyl red, then 2 to 3 drops in excess. Digest for half an hour and filter on a Whatman No. 41 paper (or equivalent) with a small amount of paper pulp in the apex of the funnel. Wash well with a hot 2 percent solution of ammonium nitrate.

Transfer to a weighed platinum crucible, dry thoroughly, and ignite. Cool, add a few drops of 1:1 sulfuric acid and about 10 ml. of hydrofluoric acid. Evaporate to dryness and ignite at 900° to 1000°C. Cool and weigh as Al_2O_3.

Place the filtrate in an ice bath and add 20 ml. of a 25 percent solution of diammonium phosphate. Add 15 ml. of concentrated ammonia and stir vigorously. Allow the solution to stand for 3 to 4 hours, then filter on a tight paper, washing well with 2 percent ammonium nitrate. Transfer the precipitate and paper to a weighed porcelain crucible, char well under the hot plate, and ignite at 900° to 1000°C. Cool and weigh as $Mg_2P_2O_7$.‡

* Make sure that the solution is sufficiently acid to prevent the formation of ammonium amalgam.

** Calcium and magnesium can be conveniently determined in the filtrate from the aluminum hydroxide if desired. However, with high-grade iron ores, a larger initial sample weight is used.

† A drop of 4 percent ferrocyanide solution on a black spot plate is used to test the solution.

‡ Magnesium may also be determined by precipitation with 8-hydroxyquinoline after the aluminum is removed.

DETERMINATION OF VANADIUM IN STEEL

Dissolve a sample containing 2 to 25 mg. of vanadium in a 1:9 sulfuric acid solution containing 1 ml. concentrated sulfuric acid for each gram of sample plus an excess of about 5 ml.* If hydrochloric or nitric acids, or a combination of both, is necessary to dissolve the sample, the solution must be evaporated to fumes of sulfuric acid before proceeding.

When solution is complete, cool and add ammonia until the solution becomes slightly turbid. Clear by adding 1:1 sulfuric acid dropwise, with stirring, and add 3 to 4 drops in excess.

Transfer to a DYNA-CATH cell and electrolyze until the iron has been removed. Drain the solution into a 400-ml. beaker, washing out the cell with water. Place on the hot plate and heat to boiling for 5 minutes.

Remove from the hot plate, cool in a water bath, and add 5 ml. of approximately 0.1 *N* iron(II) sulfate. Now add 5 percent potassium permanganate solution dropwise until the pink color persists and allow the solution to stand at room temperature for 10 min., adding more permanganate if the pink color disappears. Add 5 percent sodium nitrate freshly prepared solution dropwise until the permanganate color is gone, then add 2 to 3 g. of urea. Allow to stand for 2 to 3 minutes, then add about 10 drops of 0.001 *M* sodium diphenylbenzidine sulfonate indicator.**

After allowing the indicator color to develop fully (2 to 3 minutes), titrate with 0.02 *N* ferrous ammonium sulfate† to an apple-green end point.

DETERMINATION OF ZIRCONIUM IN STEEL

Weigh a 5-g. sample into a 600-ml. beaker and dissolve with 50 ml. 1:3 sulfuric acid. Evaporate to fumes of sulfuric acid. Cool; add 100 ml. of water, and boil (with stirring) until salts have dissolved. Add a little paper pulp and filter through 11-cm. Whatman No. 40 paper. Wash with hot water and reserve filtrate.

Ignite the residue in porcelain at a low temperature (500° to 600°C.) to prevent fusion with the glaze. Transfer the residue to a platinum crucible. Add a few drops of 1:1 sulfuric acid (enough to moisten the residue) and a few milliliters of hydrofluoric acid. Evaporate carefully to fumes of sulfur trioxide. Add a small amount of potassium pyrosulfate and fuse over a burner. Remove fused button by gently heating with a little water and add to the main filtrate.

Place in the DYNA-CATH cell and electrolyze until spot plate tests indicate absence of iron.‡ Remove from cathode, washing the mercury 3 times. Filter through a Whatman No. 2 (or equivalent) paper and wash 3 times with hot water.

Adjust volume to 300 ml. Add 20 ml. concentrated sulfuric acid and 1 ml. of 30 percent hydrogen peroxide. Warm to about 60°C. and add 25 ml. of a 20 percent solution of $(NH_4)_2HPO_4$. Stir vigorously for 5 minutes and allow to digest at about 60°C. for 2 to 4 hours. Stir in a little pulp, allow to settle, and filter on 11-cm. No. 44 Whatman paper. Wash thoroughly with 5 percent ammonium nitrate. Transfer to clean weighed platinum crucible. Burn paper off at low temperature and finally ignite at 1000°C. Cool and weigh as ZrP_2O_7.

* If a large sample (10 to 20 g.) of a steel soluble in dilute sulfuric acid is needed, a bicarbonate separation may be made at this point. This operation is described in detail under "Soluble Aluminum," above.

** Manufactured by The G. Frederick Smith Chemical Co., Columbus, Ohio.

† 1 ml. of 0.02 *N* ferrous ammonium sulfate is equivalent to 0.00102 g. of vanadium.

‡ Use a mixed indicator solution of ferricyanide and ferrocyanide.

SPECTROGRAPHIC DETERMINATION OF CERIUM AND LANTHANUM IN STAINLESS STEELS

Sample Preparation.—Dissolve 1.25 g. of drillings in an acid mixture (10 ml. conc. sulfuric acid, 10 ml. conc. nitric acid, 20 ml. 70 percent perchloric acid, all diluted to 100 ml. with water) with low heat. Fume down to oxidize the chromium, dehydrate the silica, and remove the carbon and nitric acid, then add conc. hydrochloric acid dropwise to remove the bulk of the oxidized chromium. Evaporate sample to low volume, add 2.5 ml. conc. sulfuric acid, and fume to remove most of the perchloric acid. Dilute to 50 ml. with water, filter off the remaining silica and wash the filter paper several times with hot water. Adjust volume to 100 ml., transfer to a DYNA-CATH cell and electrolyze to absence of iron. Drain the solution into a beaker, washing the cell out with water. Place on hot plate and evaporate to a volume of 25 ml. Add 1 ml. of cobalt solution (0.001 g. per ml.) as an internal standard.

Spectrographic Procedure.—The sample is excited by a low-voltage spark discharge as follows:

Prepare a Lucite-cup assembly* and place it in the lower holder of a Petrey-type spark stand. Transfer a portion of the sample to the Lucite cup, filling it completely (about 0.5 ml.). Use a pointed $\frac{1}{4}$-inch pure graphite rod as the upper electrode. After spark excitation, refill the Lucite cup with sample, change the upper electrode and spark again for duplicate check.

INTERNAL ELECTROLYSIS

Principles and Apparatus.—In an internal electrolysis, the current is obtained, not from an external source, but by the conversion of the chemical energy of another reaction within the cell itself, *i.e.*, by the use in the cell of an anode which reacts with the electrolyte of the cell. It is connected to the cathode, so that the system becomes, in effect, a short-circuited battery (or galvanic cell). In many cases the material of the consumable anode can be chosen so that it does not affect the potential of the electrolysis system.

A typical application is the removal of small amounts of copper and bismuth from pig lead. Since the reduction potential of lead is sufficiently far apart from the reduction potentials of the copper and bismuth systems, the anodes can be constructed from helices of pure lead wire. The arrangement of equipment is shown in Fig. 22-11. Dual anodes are often used to provide a larger electrode area. These are inserted within a porous membrane (Alundum shell) in order to isolate them from the sample and forestall any direct plating on the lead itself. A platinum gauze electrode is placed between the anode compartments. The electrolysis is begun by short-circuiting the cathode to the anode.

However, the driving force—that is, the difference between the potential of the system plating at the cathode and the dissolution of the anode—is small, and in consequence, the cell resistance is a critical factor in determining the rate of metal deposition.

* The Lucite-cup assembly is prepared as follows: Cut a $\frac{1}{2}$-inch-diameter Lucite rod into $\frac{5}{8}$-inch lengths. Hollow out the center of this Lucite cylinder using a $\frac{3}{8}$-inch center mill containing a $\frac{3}{16}$-inch pilot drill. The cylinder is cut to within $\frac{1}{16}$-inch of the bottom with the end mill and a $\frac{3}{16}$-inch hole is drilled through the bottom. Insert a $\frac{3}{16}$-inch-diameter pure graphite rod, 1-$\frac{1}{4}$ inches long into the prepared Lucite cylinder, extending the rod $\frac{1}{16}$ inch above the open end of the cylinder. Seal the graphite rod to the Lucite cup with an organic sealer. These Lucite cups may be reused by pressing out the graphite rod, cleaning the Lucite with acid, and putting in a new graphite rod. When the solution sample is placed in the cup assembly, capillary action carries it to the top of the rod for excitation.

The application of the method is restricted to small amounts of material if the time of electrolysis is not to be excessively long.

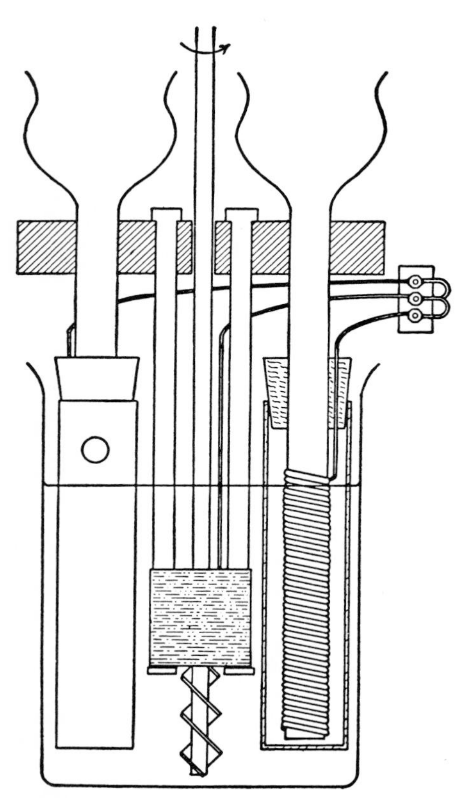

Fig. 22-11. Apparatus for Internal Electrolysis. (Reprinted from Willard, Merritt, and Dean, Instrumental Methods of Analysis, 4th Ed., 1965, D. Van Nostrand Co., Inc.)

Calculations by the Nernst equation show that the potential in a cell in which a lead anode is dissolving (to form Pb^{++}) and Cu^{++} being reduced to metallic copper, cannot have an electrode potential of the cathode exceeding -0.12 v.

Only those metal ions will deposit whose electrode potentials are more positive than this value. In the sample taken, as the electrolysis progresses, the concentration of copper(II) ions diminishes and the electrode potential of the cathode becomes more negative until it becomes equal to the anode potential (or the decomposition potential of another substance is exceeded). At no time will the decomposition potential of lead at the cathode be exceeded. There is no danger of lead contamination due to concentration-overpotential factor because the rate of cathodic deposition is controlled by the rate of anodic dissolution.

The anode need not always be constructed of the material that constitutes the matrix of the sample. For selective reduction of several trace constituents in zinc, for example, four separate samples would be dissolved for the separation of traces of cadmium, copper, lead, and silver. In the first, an attackable anode of copper would permit the complete removal of silver but control the cathode potential below the deposition potentials of the others. Similarly, a lead anode would make it possible to remove silver plus copper; a cadmium anode would remove silver, copper, and lead; and with a zinc anode, all four elements would be removed.

The amount of deposit is generally limited to quantities not exceeding 25 mg. Although larger quantities have been handled, the deposit is apt to be spongy and some of the metal ions may diffuse to the anode during the longer time required for complete electrolysis. Little attention is required during an analysis except to flush the anolyte compartments once or twice. Halide solutions may be employed without removing the halide ion and without adding an anodic depolarizer. Average running time is 30 minutes per sample.

As commonly used, the principal application of internal electrolysis is the plating out of small quantities of noble metals in a solution of a more active metal. Its suitability is readily apparent in those solutions where conventional electroanalytical procedures would permit large chloride ion concentrations to attack the platinum anode. Nor is the process restricted to cathodic depositions; the use of strong oxidizing agents as a catholyte has led to anodic depositions as well.

DETERMINATIONS BY INTERNAL ELECTROLYSIS

METHOD FOR THE DETERMINATION OF BISMUTH AND COPPER IN LEAD BULLION[15]

Five g. of the sample are dissolved in 50 ml. of 20 percent nitric acid, with the addition of 1 g. of tartaric acid. (If the bismuth content is known to be low, 10 g. of the sample are taken and the amount of nitric acid is increased proportionately.) Two ml. of 2 percent hydrochloric acid are added, and the precipitate of silver chloride is allowed to coagulate at a gentle heat, and then filtered off, together with any insoluble residue from the lead. The precipitate is washed well with hot water, and the filtrate is diluted to about 100 ml. and cooled; then a 2 percent solution of potassium permanganate is added as long as it is decolorized, to convert any trivalent antimony present into the pentavalent condition. Five ml. of a 5 percent solution of hydroxylamine hydrochloride are added, and the solution, after dilution to about 200 ml. in volume, is electrolyzed in the internal electrolysis apparatus at a temperature of 85–90°C. for 15 minutes. The cathode is then washed, dried, and weighed to determine the total copper and bismuth.

The combined deposit of copper and bismuth is dissolved in 20 percent nitric acid, heated gently, and the excess of acid neutralized with ammonia. Then 1 ml. of concentrated nitric acid is added for each 3 g. of deposit, and 3 drops of a 50 percent solution of hydrazine hydrate added to decompose any oxides of nitrogen present. The solution was heated to 85–90°C., and placed in the apparatus, after a 5 percent solution of lead nitrate, acidified with nitric acid, had been placed in the anode compartment. Deposition of bismuth is complete within 15 minutes, after which the cathode is washed with water, dipped in ethanol and then in ether, dried in a current of warm air, and weighed for its bismuth deposit.

DETERMINATION OF COPPER IN CARBON STEELS

(Copper present to extent of 0.2-0.5 percent)

Apparatus.—The anode can be made from a thistle funnel, the stem of which is wound for a length of approximately 8 cm. with 1-mm. diameter iron wire. The anode is placed in a Whatman 16-mm. by 100-mm. diffusion cell, the top of which is bound tightly to the glass stem of the funnel. One end of the anode wire projects through the neck of the diffusion cell and is connected to the stationary cylindrical cathode of platinum gauze. The catholyte, contained in a 600-ml. beaker, is stirred by a worm-ended glass rod driven by an electric motor, the glass rod passing axially through the cathode. The beaker is heated by a Bunsen burner and the temperature of the liquid may be measured by a mercury thermometer.

Procedure.—Dissolve 5 g. of steel millings in 100 ml. of dilute (1:10) sulfuric acid to which 10 ml. concentrated hydrochloric acid is added. Filter, neutralize with ammonia, and add 3 ml. concentrated sulfuric acid. Add an excess of hydrazine sulfate, and dilute to 300 ml. Reserve this solution for electrolysis, but first prepare for use as anolyte a solution of 5 g. iron(II) sulfate, 3 ml. concentrated sulfuric acid, and 0.2 g. hydrazine sulfate in 100 ml. of water. Pour the anolyte through the thistle funnel into the diffusion cell, add the reserved solution to the cell proper, and connect the anode assembly and fix the platinum cathode in place in the catholyte. Start the stirrer, and heat the solution to 75°C. After 30 minutes lower the beaker slowly while washing the cathode, wash it with isopropanol, and dry it in air at 105°C. Weigh the cathode for the copper deposited.

[15] Collin, E. M., Analyst, **55**, 312, 1930.

ANODIC DEPOSITION

A number of electrogravimetric procedures have been developed for the determination of metals by depositing their oxides upon the anode of an electrolytic cell. For this purpose cells are used with cylindical platinum gauze electrodes, but the electrical connections are reversed so that the larger electrode becomes the anode, and the smaller, inner one, often operated as a rotating stirring device, the cathode. Lead(IV) dioxide is quite commonly deposited in this form in determinations of lead; it is usually electrolyzed as the nitrate, with added nitric acid. Temperatures close to boiling are necessary because of the tendency of the deposited oxide to form hydrates, and even then a correction must be made by determining the extent of the hydration by trial runs. Thallium and plutonium have also been determined as their oxygen compounds, the latter being determinable in quantities down to the order of a microgram by the use of special electrolytic cells.

The determination of cobalt in the presence of nickel is a noteworthy use of this method. The cobalt is deposited on the anode as cobalt(III) oxide (Co_2O_3). To reach practical speeds of deposition, however, it is necessary to use Sand's revolving-diaphragm electrode[16,17] to separate the cathode from the cobalt solution, in order to inhibit the deposition of metallic cobalt.

Cobaltic oxide is not deposited from a solution with acidity much stronger than pH 3.5, and as by screening the cathode the anolytic solution becomes more strongly acid with the progress of the electrolysis, it was found necessary to buffer the anolyte with sodium acetate.

DEPOSITION OF COBALT AS COBALTIC OXIDE[18]

If the solution is acidic, neutralize it with sodium hydroxide solution, and adjust the pH to 5 with acetic acid and sodium acetate, using 10 g. of the latter to act as a buffer. Dilute to 100 ml. and electrolyze, using the Sand revolving-diaphrogm electrode as cathode and a platinum gauze electrode as anode; the cobalt solution is the anolyte, and a 2 *N* nitric acid solution the catholyte. The electrolysis is carried out at a temperature of 90°–95°C., beginning with a current of 0.5 amp. This is raised, after 10 minutes, to 1.0 amp., and the catholyte is flushed into the anolyte by the addition, to the catholyte, of about 5 ml. of 2 *N* nitric acid. The deposition is continued for a further 20 minutes, the catholyte being once more flushed out after 10 minutes. Under these conditions a firm adherent deposit of cobaltic oxide is obtained. The deposit is weighed and dissolved by warming the electrode with 20 ml. of 20 percent sulfuric acid, 2 drops of sulfurous acid solution being added to facilitate solution, and excess of sulfur dioxide boiled off. The solution is neutralized with ammonia, and 20 ml. of ammonia (sp. gr. 0.880) added in excess. The mixture is diluted to about 150 ml. and cobalt is deposited as metal by conventional electrolytic methods. This second electrolysis is necessary only when the amount of nickel in the original sample is greater than ten times the cobalt, otherwise the cobalt content can be computed directly from the weight of cobaltic oxide deposited.

SUMMARY OF METHODS FOR THE ELEMENTS

(Platinum electrodes to be used unless otherwise specified)

Manganese.[19]—(1). Dissolve 0.05–0.1 g. as sulfate, dilute to 125 ml., add 5 ml. formic acid and 1 g. sodium formate. Electrolyze in platinum dish anode at 1 amp. per

[16] Sand, H. J. S., Analyst, **54,** 279, 1929.
[17] Torrance, S., Analyst, **62,** 29, 1937.
[18] Torrance, S., Analyst, **64,** 109, 1939.
[19] Smith, Electroanalysis, Blakiston, 1907.

square decimeter for 5 hours. Weigh as hydrated manganese dioxide. (2). For quantities of manganese somewhat greater, omit sodium formate from above procedure.

Iron.[20]—(1). For solutions containing 1 to 10 mg. of iron, add to heated solution 0.5 ml. concentrated nitric acid and 2 g. tartaric acid and, after cooling, 10 g. sodium hydroxide, then make up to 200 ml. with water. Electrolyze by internal electrolysis at 50°C., using platinum cathode and zinc anode, with an anolyte solution consisting of equal parts *N* solutions of sodium chloride and sodium hydroxide. (2).[21] For smaller quantities iron (0.02–0.08) g., form the ferrous ammonium sulfate, dilute to 100 ml., add 1 ml. concentrated hydrochloric acid and 5 g. ammonium oxalate. Electrolyze at 6 amp. for 30 minutes.

Cobalt.[22]—(1). In acid solution as sulfate, add excess ammonia and ammonium sulfate. Electrolyze overnight at 0.5 amp., or for 1 hour at 2.0 amp. and 70°C. Copper, nickel and zinc codeposit if present. (2). Neutralize with ammonia, add 15 g. ammonium oxalate, electrolyze for 20 min. at 5.0 amp. and 95°C. A number of metals codeposit. See also detailed directions in this chapter.

Nickel.—(1).[23] Dissolve quantities of 0.05–0.2 g. in sulfuric acid, dilute to 100 ml., neutralize with ammonia and add 30 ml. excess. Add 0.5 g. hydrazine hydrochloride and 1 g. hydrazine in aqueous solution. Electrolyze at 0.5 amp. for 3 hours, using copper-plated platinum cathode. (2).[24] For somewhat greater quantities of nickel sulfate, dilute solution to 100 ml., add 30 ml. ammonia, 5 g. sodium sulfate and 3 g. sodium sulfite. Then dilute to 300 ml. Electrolyze at 90°C. using copper-plated platinum cathode at potential of −0.95 v.

Nickel in Presence of Zinc.[25]—Dissolve in hydrochloric acid, and add 30 g. ammonium chloride and 2 g. sodium sulfate. Dilute to 250 ml., and electrolyze at 65°C. for 45 min. with an anolyte prepared by dissolving 10 g. ammonium chloride, 10 g. zinc chloride and 20 ml. ammonia in 100 ml. water, using a zinc anode. Weigh anode for nickel.

Copper.—See detailed directions in this chapter.

Copper, Nickel and Zinc.[26]—Dissolve 1 g. in mixture of 5 ml. concentrated nitric acid and 10 ml. water. Evaporate to expel nitric acid, dilute to 100 ml., add 5 ml. concentrated hydrochloric acid and 1 g. hydrazine hydrochloride, and electrolyze at −0.4 v. for 30 min. Weigh cathode for copper. Neutralize with ammonia, adding 20 ml. excess, and 2 g. sodium sulfate. Electrolyze at −0.25 v. and 75°C. Weigh the cathode for nickel, and resume electrolysis at room temperature and 2 amp. for 30 min. to deposit zinc.

Silver in Presence of Lead and Bismuth.[27]—Dissolve in conc. nitric acid, add 5 ml. excess and 0.1 ml. hydrazine hydrochloride in solution. Dilute to 300 ml. and electrolyze at 65°C. by internal electrolysis, using an anolyte consisting of 2 g. bismuth nitrate and 3 ml. conc. nitric acid in 100 ml. of water, with a cast bismuth anode. After 20–25 min., weigh anode for silver.

Copper, Lead, Tin and Zinc.[28]—Dissolve 0.4 g. of alloy in 20 ml. 8 *N* hydrochloric acid to which 1 g. ammonium chloride and 2 ml. concentrated nitric acid have been added. Dilute to 150 ml., and add 1 g. hydrazine hydrochloride and 5 ml. conc. hydrochloric acid. Electrolyze at cathode potential of −0.4 v. and 50°C. Weigh the cathode

[20] Searano, J., and Ippoliti, D., Ann. Chim., Rome, **45,** 502, 1955.
[21] Bay, J., Metallurgia, **48,** 313, 1953.
[22] Torrance, S., Analyst, **64,** 109, 1939.
[23] Llacer, Anales farm. y biochim. Buenos Aires, **19,** 48, 1948.
[24] Ishibashi *et al.*, Japan Analyst, **4,** 365, 1956.
[25] Fife, J. G., Analyst, **61,** 681, 1936.
[26] Lassieur, A., Electroanalyse Rapide, Les Presses Universitaires de France, 1927.
[27] Fife, J. G., Thesis, Univ. of London, 1941.
[28] Torrance, S., Analyst, **64,** 109, 1939.

for copper. Add to remaining solution 1 g. hydrazine hydrochloride and electrolyze at −0.7 v. and 25°C. for 20 minutes. Weigh the cathode for lead and tin. Add bromine water in excess and boil until its color disappears. Adjust pH to 9.5 with ammonia, add 10 ml. excess, and electrolyze at 3 amp. and 25°C. for 20 min. Weigh cathode for zinc. The lead and tin may be separated by dissolving the deposit in 30 ml. 8 *N* nitric acid to which 5 ml. hydrochloric acid has been added, boiling to expel red fumes, adding 10 ml. concentrated nitric acid, electrolyzing at 5 amp. and 95°C. for 10 minutes. The anode is then weighed as lead(IV) dioxide, PbO_2.

Silver.—(1).[29] Dissolve about 0.5 g. in 200 ml. water, add 1 *N* potassium hydroxide solution, enough to precipitate silver, and add 10% potassium cyanide to redissolve the oxide precipitate. Electrolyze at 2 amp. for 20 min. (2).[30] In alloys samples containing 0.05–0.5 g. silver, dissolve in 6 ml. 8 *N* nitric acid, boil to expel nitrogen oxides, dilute with water to 150 ml., add 9–10 ml. ammonia. Electrolyze at −0.24 v. for 25 min. with oxygen bubbling through solution.

Gold.[31]—(1). Dissolve in aqua regia, add 5 ml. hydrochloric acid, and 1 g. hydroxylamine hydrochloride per 100 ml. solution. Electrolyze at 3 amp., +0.23 v. and room temperature for 20 min. (2). In solution as chloride, neutralize with 3 *N* sodium hydroxide, add 1.5 g. sodium hydroxide. Electrolyze at 3 amp. and room temperature for 20 min.

Zinc.[32]—(1). For 0.05–0.025 as the sulfate, dissolve in 50–75 ml. water, add 1–1.5 g. Rochelle salt and just enough 4 *N* potassium hydroxide solution to redissolve the precipitate. Electrolyze with copper-plated platinum cathode at −1.4 v. until current falls to 0.08 amp., then change to potential to −1.5 v. for 20 min. (2). For 0.4–0.5 g. zinc as the sulfate, dissolve in 50–75 ml. water, add 2 *N* sodium hydroxide solution until precipitate just redissolves, then add 1 g. potassium cyanide dissolved in 10 ml. ammonia. Dilute to 125–150 ml. Electrolyze with copper-plated platinum electrode for 30 min. at 3 amp.

Cadmium.—(1).[33] Dissolve 0.05–0.15 cadmium sulfate in 150 ml. 0.2 *N* sulfuric acid, add 20 ml. 6 *N* sodium hydroxide solution, and acetic acid until precipitate redissolves. Electrolyze with copper-plated platinum cathode at −1.00 v. and 65°C. (2).[34] Dissolve 0.25 g. cadmium as chloride or sulfate in 10 ml. 5*N* sulfuric acid, dilute to 200 ml. and add 5 ml. 0.2 percent gelatin solution. Electrolyze with copper-platinum cathode at 3 amp. for 45 min.

Cadmium and Zinc.[35]—Dissolve in concentrated hydrochloric acid, add 1 g. hydroxylamine hydrochloride, and then add 4 *N* sodium hydroxide solution to pH 1.5. Electrolyze at −0.8 v. and about 1 amp., at room temperature. Weigh cathode for cadmium deposit. To remaining solution, add 4 *N* sodium hydroxide to pH 6.0, then add 1 g. potassium cyanide and 10 ml. ammonia. Electrolyze at constant current of 3 amp. for 30–40 min. Weigh cathode for zinc.

Mercury.—(1).[36] Dissolve 0.1–0.5 g. in 15 ml. concentrated sulfuric acid. Dilute to 100 ml. Electrolyze with gold cathode and platinum anode at 1 amp. for 35–45 min. (2).[37] Dissolve 0.3–1.0 g. in 15 ml. concentrated nitric acid. Dilute to 75 ml. and add 30 ml. ammonia, using platinum cathode and gold-plated platinum anode. Electrolyze at anode potential of 0 v. at 90°C. for 6 minutes.

[29] Norwitz, G., Z. anal. Chem., **131,** 410, 1950.
[30] Diehl, Harvey, and Butler, J., Analyst, **77,** 268, 1952.
[31] Sand, H. J. S., Electrochemistry and Electrochemical Analysis, Blackie, 1939.
[32] Sand, H. J. S., Electrochemistry and Electrochemical Analysis, Blackie, 1939.
[33] Penther, C. G., and Pompeo, S. K., Anal. Chem., **21,** 178, 1949.
[34] Osborn, R., Metallurgia, **40,** 111, 1949.
[35] Sand, H. J. S., Electrochemistry and Electrochemical Analysis, Blackie, 1939.
[36] De Meeus, R. Bull. soc. chim. Belg., **31,** 202, 1922.
[37] Sand, H. J. S., Electrochemistry and Electrochemical Analysis, Blackie, 1939.

Thallium.—(1).[38] For 0.01 to 0.2 g. as thallium(I) sulfate, dissolve in 5 ml. concentrated nitric acid, dilute to 200 ml., add 1 g. benzoic acid. Electrolyze with amalgamated platinum electrode at 5 amp., and 45°C. for 15 minutes. (2).[39] For traces up to 0.2 g. present as thallium(I) or thallium(III), dissolve in 20 ml. concentrated nitric acid, add 0.2 g. copper(II) nitrate and dilute to 100 ml. Neutralize with ammonia and add excess to alkalinize (up to 3 ml. for 0.2 g. thallium or up to 10 ml. for greater amounts). Electrolyze for 1 hour at 2 amp. Weigh deposit on anode as trioxide (Tl_2O_3).

Lead.—(1).[40] For 5–50 mg. lead as lead nitrate, dissolve in 100 ml. *N* nitric acid containing 0.08 g. copper as copper sulfate. Electrolyze at 2 amp. per square decimeter for 1 hour at room temperature. Weigh as lead(IV) dioxide on anode. (2).[41] For alloys with antimony, dissolve in 30 ml. concentrated nitric acid and 5 ml. hydrofluoric acid, dilute to 150 ml., and add potassium dichromate solution to permanent yellow color. Electrolyze at 2 amp. for 20 min. Weigh as Pb(IV) dioxide on anode.

Tin.—(1).[42] Dissolve 0.1 to 0.3 g. tin salt in 15 ml. concentrated hydrochloric acid, dilute to 200 ml., add 2 g. hydroxylamine hydrochloride. Electrolyze at cathode potential of −0.75 v. (2).[43] Dissolve alloy sample containing 0.1 to 0.3 g. tin in acid mixture consisting of 10 ml. concentrated sulfuric acid, 15 ml. concentrated nitric acid, and 5 ml. perchloric acid. Evaporate and heat gently until fumes cease. Dissolve in water, make up to 200 ml., add 5 ml. conc. hydrochloric acid and 5 g. hydroxylamine hydrochloride. Electrolyze at 2 amp. per square decimeter for 2 hours with copper-plated platinum cathode.

Bismuth.—(1).[44] Dissolve up to 0.25 g. in 5 ml. concentrated hydrochloric acid, dilute to 100 ml., add 15 ml. 5 *N* sodium hydroxide solution, 2 g. Rochelle salt, and 1 g. hydroxylamine hydrochloride (also 3 g. sodium cyanide if copper is present). Electrolyze at 80°C. and −0.90 v. for 20 min. (2).[45] For smaller amounts of bismuth (0.01–0.1 g.) dissolve in 5 ml. concentrated nitric acid, fume with 10 ml. perchloric acid, add water to 200 ml. and then 5 ml. saturated solution of hydrazine sulfate. Electrolyze for 1 hour at 1 amp. See also detailed directions in this chapter.

Bismuth, Lead and Tin.[46]—Dissolve 1 g. alloy in 2 ml. concentrated nitric acid, add 10 ml. concentrated hydrochloric acid and boil. Add 10 ml. more hydrochloric acid, dilute to 100 ml., and then add 0.5 g. hydrazine hydrochloride and 5.0 g. oxalic acid. Electrolyze for 20 min. at cathode potential of 0.15 v., increasing to 0.3 v. at 80°C. Weigh cathode for bismuth. The lead and tin may then be deposited at the same temperature at a current of 2 amp. for 25 min. The deposit is weighed for the two metals, and then dissolved in 8 *N* nitric acid to which $\frac{1}{3}$ its volume of hydrofluoric acid is added, and the lead anodically deposited as directed under Lead.

Arsenic (present as As_2O_3).—(1).[47] Dissolve estimated 40–60 mg. in concentrated hydrochloric acid (15 ml.), dilute with water to 150 ml., add 1 g. hydroxylamine hydrochloride and 4 ml. 1 *M* copper(II) sulfate solution. Electrolyze at −0.40 v. for 20 min. Deposit is Cu_3As_2. (2).[48] Dissolve estimated 20–30 mg. in 10 ml. 1 *N* sodium hydroxide solution, dilute with water to 200 ml., add 1 g. hydrazine hydrochloride and 8 ml. 1 *M* copper sulfate solution. Electrolyze at 1 amp. for 90 min. Deposit is Cu_3As_2.

[38] Crétien, L., and Longi, G. Bull. soc. chim. France, **11**, 245, 1944.
[39] Ippoliti, P., and Burrati, A., Alluminio, **45**, 452, 1955.
[40] Tucker, N., Analyst, **71**, 319, 1946.
[41] Sand, H. J. S., Electrochemistry and Electrochemical Analysis, Blackie, 1939.
[42] Lindsay, A. J., Analyst, **75**, 104, 1950.
[43] Norwitz, G., Z. anal. Chem., **131**, 266, 1950.
[44] Kny-Jones, F. G., Analyst, **64**, 172, 1939.
[45] Norwitz, G., Analyst, **75**, 473, 1950.
[46] Collin, E. M., Analyst, **54**, 654, 1929.
[47] Torrance, S., Analyst, **63**, 104, 1938.
[48] Norwitz, G., Z. anal. Chem., **131**, 410, 1950.

Antimony.—(1).[49] Dissolve up to 0.5 g. in 15 ml. concentrated sulfuric acid, dilute to 150 ml., add 10 ml. concentrated hydrochloric acid and 10 ml. 3 percent hydrogen peroxide, boil for 10 min., dilute to 200 ml., and add 5 g. hydroxylamine hydrochloride. Electrolyze at 2 amp. per square decimeter for 15 min., then reduce current to 1 amp. for 45 min. more. (2).[50] Antimony(III) trioxide up to 0.5 g. Dissolve in 25 ml. concentrated hydrochloric acid, dilute to 200 ml., add 2 g. hydroxylamine hydrochloride. Electrolyze at 50°C. with copper-plated platinum cathode at potential of −0.40 v.

Chloride or Bromide.[51]—To the solution of 30–300 mg. sodium chloride, add 2.5 g. sodium acetate and acetic acid to make pH 4.7. Electrolyze at 50°C. for 30 min., using platinum cathode and silver anode, holding anode potential at +0.25 v. Silver chloride is deposited on anode.

APPLICATIONS IN THE ANALYSIS OF SPECIAL MATERIALS

Methods based on electrodeposition which have been reported in other chapters of Standard Methods of Chemical Analysis are:

1. Chapter 25, Volume IIA, Alloys: Iron and Steel.
   a. Copper in iron, steel, and alloy steels, pages 685, 686.
2. Chapter 26, Volume IIA, Alloys: Nonferrous.
   a. Copper in antimony, lead, and tin and their alloys, page 902.
   b. Copper in copper-base alloys, pages 814, 865.
   c. Copper in copper-beryllium alloys, page 848.
   d. Copper in nickel-copper alloys, pages 880, 881.
   e. Copper in copper-tellurium alloys, page 846.
   f. Copper in zinc-base diecasting alloys, page 918.
   g. Lead in copper-base alloys, pages 817, 865.
   h. Nickel in nickel-copper alloys, page 882.
3. Chapter 32, Volume IIB, Explosives and Propellants.
   a. Copper in aluminum, page 1309.
   b. Lead in aluminum, page 1309.

[49] Norwitz, G., Anal. Chem., **23,** 168, 1951.
[50] Schock, V. and Brown, C. D., JACS, **38,** 1660, 1916.
[51] MacNevin, R. C., *et al.*, Anal. Chem., **25,** 274, 1953.

Chapter 23

COULOMETRIC METHODS

By W. D. Shults
Analytical Chemistry Division
Oak Ridge National Laboratory*
Oak Ridge, Tennessee

INTRODUCTION

DEFINITION AND BASIS OF COULOMETRIC METHODS

Coulometric methods of analysis are those methods in which the quantity of electricity corresponding to a chemical change is utilized as the measure of that change. Such methods are founded upon Faraday's First Law, which states that the quantity of chemical change that occurs as a result of electrolysis is directly proportional to the quantity of electricity that passes. The proportionality constant is the faraday (F) which has the value 96,487 ± 1.6 coulombs per equivalent, based upon the carbon-12 atomic weight scale.[1] Utilizing this constant and recalling that the quantity of electricity (Q coulombs) is given by the integral of current (i amperes) over the time interval (t seconds), Faraday's Law may be stated

$$\int_0^t i\,dt = Q = \frac{nwF}{M} \tag{1}$$

where w is the weight in grams of the species that is consumed or produced during electrolysis, M is its gram-molecular weight, and n is the number of faradays (equivalents) of electricity required per gram mole, *i.e.*, the number of electrons appearing in the equation for the net reaction of interest. Equation (1) is the basic equation of coulometry. It indicates that w can be determined directly if two requirements are met: (a) Q must be accurately evaluated, and (b) experimental conditions must be arranged such that a single reaction of known stoichiometry occurs as a result of electrolysis. To the extent that these two requirements are met, coulometric methods are both accurate and precise.

TECHNIQUES OF COULOMETRIC ANALYSIS

Several techniques comprise coulometric methods, two of which are employed far more than the others. The simpler one, in principle at least, is *coulometry at controlled electrode potential*. Here, the substance being determined reacts directly at an electrode whose potential is maintained at such a value that other unwanted electrode reactions are precluded under the prevailing experimental conditions. The current decreases exponentially as the electrolysis proceeds, ultimately attaining so small a value that the reaction is virtually complete. The electrolysis is then terminated, Q is evaluated, and

* Operated for the United States Atomic Energy Commission by the Union Carbide Corporation.

[1] J. Chem. Ed., **40**, 642, 1963; Natl. Bur. Std. (U. S.), Tech. News Bull., **47**, 175, 1963.

the weight of the substance is calculated by means of Eq. (1). For some time, the development of this technique as a common analytical tool was impeded because completely satisfactory equipment was not available: the technique requires both an accurate coulometer (a device for measuring Q) and a precise potentiostat (a device for maintaining the electrode potential at a constant value). In recent years, however, advances in analytical instrumentation have made potentiostatic coulometry a simple and rapid technique, suitable for routine use. It is treated in the section on Coulometry at Controlled Potential (page 461).

The second widely used coulometric technique is *coulometry at controlled current*. Here, the electrolysis is performed with a current that is maintained at a constant value so that the evaluation of $Q \left[= \int_0^t i\,dt = i \int_0^t dt = it \right]$ involves simply the measurement of the current and the time during which electrolysis occurs. Indeed, this simplicity in the evaluation of Q is the reason for historical precedence of the controlled-current coulometric technique. However, with this technique it is more difficult to establish experimental conditions such that effectively a single reaction occurs as a result of electrolysis. This is because the concentration of the substance being determined decreases during electrolysis and ultimately falls to so low a value that that species cannot itself support all of the current. Some other electrolytic reaction must then occur, since the current is held at a constant level. Under suitable experimental conditions, however, the product of this second electrolytic reaction reacts rapidly with the substance being determined, resulting in the same net chemical change that occurs when the latter substance reacts directly at the electrode. The effective reaction is then a single one of known stoichiometry, but it is accomplished through a *secondary* process during some portion of the electrolysis. Because the overall result is the same as if a titrant were generated electrolytically and then caused to react with the substance being determined, this technique is frequently referred to as a *coulometric titration*. The progress of the electrolysis (*i.e.*, titration) is monitored with an appropriate end-point detection technique and the titration is terminated when the end point is signaled. The weight of the substance being determined can then be calculated by means of Eq. (1) after evaluating Q, the current-time product. Coulometry at controlled current is treated in a later section (page 474).

Several other techniques that are rightfully classified as coulometric methods are treated very briefly in the section on Other Coulometric Methods (page 489).

GENERAL CHARACTERISTICS OF COULOMETRIC METHODS

Both of the coulometric techniques mentioned above give results that are as accurate and precise as those obtained by classical methods at usual concentration levels. Coulometric methods become more accurate and precise than classical methods as the concentration level is decreased, primarily because electric currents can be controlled and measured with greater precision than can volumes of standard solutions. For the same reason—and also because the preparation, storage, and handling of standard titrant solutions are obviated when the determination is made electrolytically—coulometric methods are ideally suited for both routine and remote analysis. Accordingly, they have been applied widely to both usual and unusual analytical problems. It is not only possible to perform coulometrically many of the neutralization, redox, precipitation, and complexation titrations that are commonly known, but it is also possible to perform many titrations coulometrically which cannot be done by classical techniques. Examples are titrations in molten salt media, remote titrations of highly hazardous materials, and titrations which utilize unstable or difficultly prepared titrants such as bromine, chlorine, silver(II), uranium(IV) or (V), copper(I), tin(II), titanium(III), and chromium(II). Of the two techniques mentioned above, the controlled-current technique is more widely used. It is faster, requires simpler instrumentation and is therefore less expensive, and can be applied to many reactions with excellent accuracy and precision. It is also the more sensitive technique. On the other hand, potentiostatic coulometry is also a very accurate and precise method, is also quite sensitive, and has the important attribute of selectivity. The references cited in the sections that follow will illustrate the nature and utility of these techniques.

COULOMETRY AT CONTROLLED POTENTIAL (POTENTIOSTATIC COULOMETRY)

PRINCIPLES OF POTENTIOSTATIC COULOMETRY

The Nernst equation relates the equilibrium potential of a redox couple with the activities of the participating members of that couple. For the general reaction

$$\mathrm{Ox} + ne^- \rightleftharpoons \mathrm{Red}$$

the equation states

$$E = E^0 - \frac{RT}{nF} \ln \frac{a_{\mathrm{Red}}}{a_{\mathrm{Ox}}} = E^0 - \frac{RT}{nF} \ln \frac{\gamma_{\mathrm{Red}}[\mathrm{Red}]}{\gamma_{\mathrm{Ox}}[\mathrm{Ox}]}$$

where E is the equilibrium potential in volts, E^0 is the standard reduction potential in volts, a_{Red} and a_{Ox} are the activities of Red and Ox, respectively, R is the gas constant = 8.3143 joules (deg. K)$^{-1}$ mole^{-1}, T is the absolute temperature, F is the faraday, the brackets indicate molar concentrations, and γ_{Red} and γ_{Ox} are the activity coefficients of Red and Ox, respectively. For practical purposes, it is convenient to combine E^0 with the γ-term (which is virtually constant under the experimental conditions usually employed in coulometry) into a *formal* reduction potential, $E^{0\prime}$. The equation then becomes, at 25°C. and after converting to common logarithms,

$$E = E^{0\prime} - \frac{0.05914}{n} \log \frac{[\mathrm{Red}]}{[\mathrm{Ox}]} \tag{2}$$

It is important to realize that formal reduction potentials vary with chemical environment, whereas standard reduction potentials do not.

Figure 23-1 presents graphically the potential-composition behavior that is demanded by Eq. (2). The two sigmoid curves refer to two hypothetical reversible one-electron redox couples; the $E^{0\prime}_{(1)}$ of the first is arbitrarily set equal to zero potential and that of the second is $E^{0\prime}_{(2)} = -0.356$ volt. Note that for each couple the equilibrium potential equals the formal potential when $\mathrm{Ox}_{(i)}$ and $\mathrm{Red}_{(i)}$ are present in a 50:50 ratio. At potentials more negative than $E^{0\prime}$, the [Red] to [Ox] ratio must assume a larger value at equilibrium. Similarly, at potentials more positive than $E^{0\prime}$ the [Red] to [Ox] ratio must shift to a smaller value at equilibrium. For example, the potential of a mixture of 99 percent $\mathrm{Red}_{(1)}$ and 1 percent $\mathrm{Ox}_{(1)}$ is seen to be -0.119 volt, whereas a 1 percent $\mathrm{Red}_{(1)}$ and 99 percent $\mathrm{Ox}_{(1)}$ mixture is at equilibrium when the potential is $+0.119$ volt. If the latter solution (99 percent $\mathrm{Ox}_{(1)}$, $E = +0.119$ volt) is placed in contact with an electrode whose potential is controlled at -0.119 volt, electrolysis will occur until equilibrium is attained at this new potential, that is, until the amount of $\mathrm{Ox}_{(1)}$ decreases from 99 to 1 percent. The quantity of electricity required to accomplish this reduction is related by Eq. (1) to the quantity of $\mathrm{Ox}_{(1)}$ that is reduced. Now it has already been stated that a potentiostatic coulometric electrolysis takes place at an electrode whose potential is held at such a value that the desired reaction occurs while undesirable reactions do not occur.

For the determination of $Ox_{(1)}$ in the presence of $Ox_{(2)}$, -0.177 volt is such a potential, for at that potential 99.9 percent of $Ox_{(1)}$ is reduced while only 0.1 percent of $Ox_{(2)}$ is reduced. Assuming that only a moderate amount of $Ox_{(2)}$ is present (so that the reduction of 0.1 percent of it requires an insignificant amount of electricity), it is possible to deter-

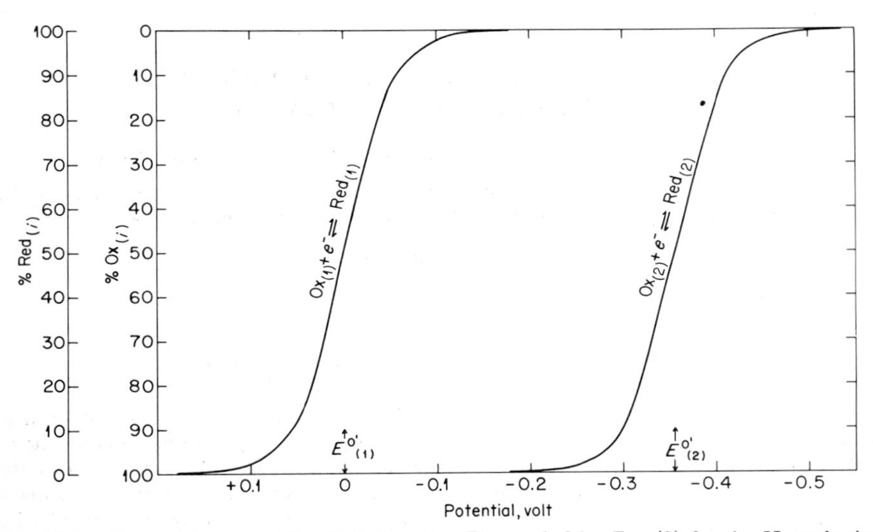

FIG. 23-1. Potential-composition Relationships Demanded by Eq. (2) for the Hypothetical Species 1 and 2.

mine $Ox_{(1)}$ by electrolytic reduction at -0.177 volt, measuring Q for the entire electrolysis, and computing the value of w in Eq. (1). Under these ideal conditions, the error in the analysis should be near 0.1 percent. A more detailed discussion of the factors that are involved in the choice of electrode potential and of the assumptions that are made in this type of calculation is reserved for the section on Applied Potentiostatic Coulometry (page 467). The above example only illustrates the basis for the accuracy and selectivity of potentiostatic coulometry.

Figure 23-1 also illustrates other possibilities that are inherent in this type of technique. Upon completion of the reduction of $Ox_{(1)}$, a second electrolysis at -0.532 volt would accomplish reduction of 99.9 percent of $Ox_{(2)}$. Thus, successive determinations are possible. Electrolytic oxidations are also feasible, of course. In practice, therefore, potentiostatic procedures of various types are utilized—reductions, oxidations, reduction-oxidation cycles—in order to obtain the desired analytical result with utmost selectivity and accuracy.

One question remains unanswered in the hypothetical determination of $Ox_{(1)}$, namely, when should the electrolysis be terminated? The most frequently used method for "end-point detection" in this type of electrolysis is based upon the variation of the current itself. For a diffusion-controlled, kinetically unhindered potentiostatic electrolysis, the current obeys the exponential rate law[2]

$$i = i_0 e^{-kt} \tag{3}$$

[2] Lingane, J. J., J. Am. Chem. Soc., **67**, 1916, 1945; Anal. Chim. Acta, **2**, 591, 1948.

where i is the current at time t, i_0 is the initial current at $t = 0$, and k is a constant that is characteristic of the experimental conditions. According to Eq. (3), the electrolysis is never really complete because $i = 0$ only when $t = \infty$. However, when Eq. (3) is obeyed, as indicated by a linear relationship between log i and t, then the magnitude of the current can be used to indicate when the electrolysis is *sufficiently* complete. This is true because Eq. (3) applies to electrolyses whose rates are controlled by the mass transfer process(es), by the rate at which the electroactive species is brought to the electrode surface. Consequently, the observed current is really a *limiting* current and is proportional to the concentration of the electroactive species in the bulk of the solution. This means that the electrolysis is *sufficiently* complete when the current decreases to $i = i_0 (1 - f)$, where f is the desired fraction titrated, because at that time the concentration has decreased by an amount corresponding to f. Returning to the determination of $Ox_{(1)}$ as an example, $f_{(1)} = 0.999$ since $Ox_{(1)}$ was to be reduced to 99.9 percent completion, so the electrolysis would be terminated when the current decreased to one one-thousandth of its initial value. Other "end-point detection" techniques are treated in later paragraphs, as are the implications of Eq. (3) upon cell design.

APPARATUS FOR POTENTIOSTATIC COULOMETRY

Cells and Cell Design.—Three electrodes are necessary for electrolysis at controlled electrode potential: (a) a controlled electrode (C) at which the desired electrode reaction occurs, (b) an auxiliary electrode (A) to complete the electrolysis circuit, and (c) a reference electrode (R). [This terminology is not standardized. The controlled electrode is sometimes called the working or analytical electrode and the auxiliary electrode is often termed the counter or separated electrode.] These electrodes have been incorporated into various electrolysis cells in a host of ways. Drawings of two typical cells are shown in Fig. 23-2 and many others may be found within the general references cited in the bibliography at the end of the chapter. Both cells depicted in Fig. 23-2 are of the double-diaphragm design, *i.e.*, the auxiliary and reference electrodes are separated physically but not electrically from the controlled electrode and sample solution. Cell I is convenient for nonroutine work because it will accept either a mercury pool or platinum gauze working electrode and because chemical pretreatments can be done in the cell itself. Cell II is a double-diaphragm version of the Lingane cell[2] and is useful for routine analyses that utilize the mercury pool.

A cell of good design provides for transfer of the electroactive material to the controlled electrode at a maximum rate so that the analysis requires a minimum of time and also incurs a minimum of error from time-dependent interferences. The parameters that are important in good cell design are implied in Eq. (3). Lingane[3] has shown that the constant k in that equation is equal to $DA/V\delta$ where D is the diffusion coefficient of the electroactive species in cm.^{2}/sec., A is the electrode area in cm.^{2}, V is the solution volume in cm.^{3}, and δ is the diffusion layer thickness in centimeters. [The diffusion layer is pictured as a thin layer of solution that remains stationary about the electrode surface even though the bulk of the solution is in motion; diffusion into and out of this layer occurs during electrolysis.] Optimum cell design implies a maximum value of k, hence a large electrode area, small solution volume, and a high rate of stirring (to minimize δ). Operation at elevated temperature may also decrease the electrolysis time because diffusion coefficients generally increase by approximately 2 percent per degree. These factors determine the speed of a controlled-potential electrolysis by their influence upon the rate of mass transfer to the electrode surface. In most cases, this is the rate-controlling factor and electrolysis times range from 5 to 45 minutes with an average of about 20

[3] Bibliography item 1, pp. 225–228. The Selected Bibliography appears at the end of the chapter, on page 492.

minutes. In some instances, however, the kinetics of the reaction itself is rate-controlling, cell design being of less importance. The electrolysis time may then be considerably longer, even if the cell is well-designed, unless experimental conditions can be selected which enhance the reaction rate.

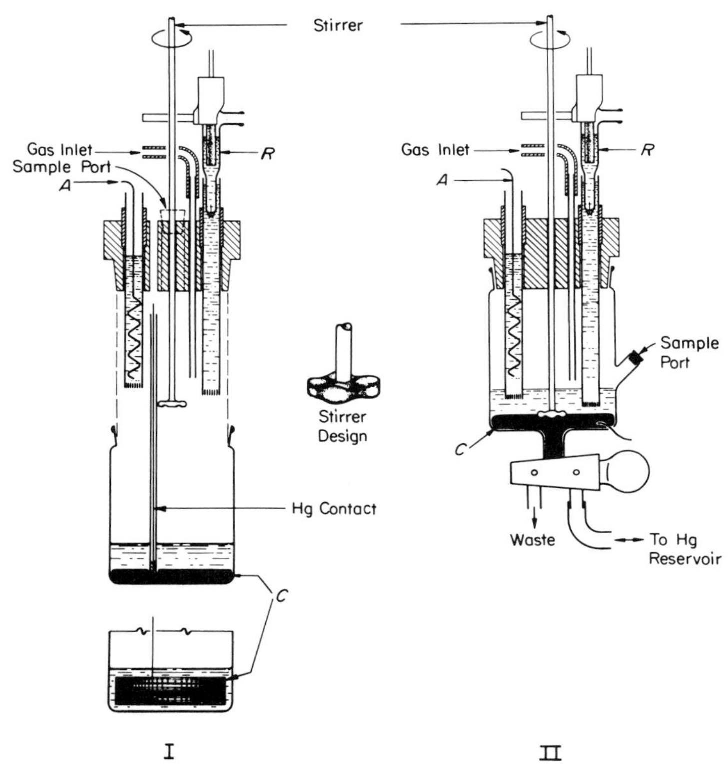

Fig. 23-2. Typical Cells for Potentiostatic Coulometry. Electrodes: A = Auxiliary; C = Controlled; R = Reference.

Instrumentation for Potentiostatic Coulometry.—The essential components of an instrument for performing controlled-potential coulometric analyses are shown in Fig. 23-3. The power supply, monitor, control potential selector, and control units comprise the potentiostat. Its function is to maintain the potential of the controlled electrode (C) with respect to the reference electrode (R) at the value specified by the control potential selector unit. It does this by applying between the auxiliary electrode (A) and the controlled electrode whatever potential is necessary to make the C *vs.* R potential equal to the specified control potential. Hence, the monitor observes the actual C *vs.* R potential and presents it to the control unit. The control unit compares this observed potential with the selected control potential, and minimizes any difference between them by suitable adjustment of the A *vs.* C potential. The analyst himself may perform the functions of the monitor and control units, of course, but manual control is tedious, time-consuming, and inaccurate; it is not a practical mode of operation. Accordingly, many designs for automatic potentiostats have appeared in the literature since about 1940, several of which are described in Chapter XIII of Bibliography item 1. These differ primarily in the manner in which the difference signal is minimized—electrically, mechanically, or electromechanically—and have generally had a good degree of success. In recent years, the trend has been toward all-electronic instruments[4–10] that are completely automatic and provide very precise potential control.

A second and important component of the instrument depicted in Fig. 23-3 is the

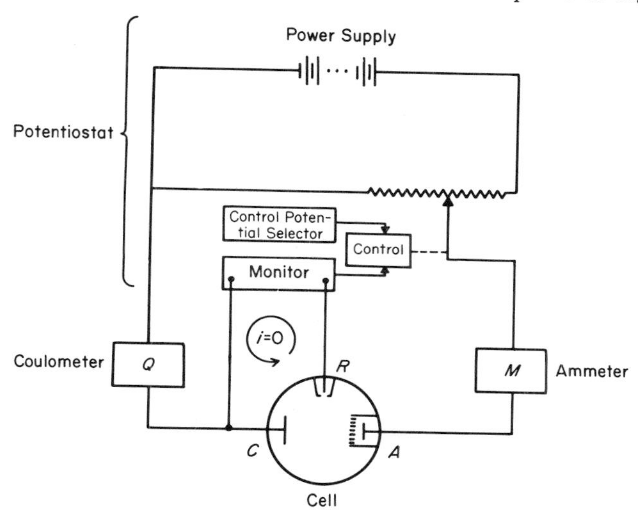

FIG. 23-3. Essential Components of a Potentiostatic Coulometric Titrator.

coulometer, labeled Q. Its function is to measure the quantity of charge that flows during the course of the electrolysis. Not only must the coulometer be extremely accurate, but it should maintain its accuracy over a wide range of current levels and regardless of whether a large or small amount of electrolysis transpires. It should also be convenient to use. Chemical coulometers of the weight, gas, titration, and colorimetric types have been used, but these are inconvenient and often are inaccurate unless a relatively large quantity of electrolysis occurs. Several devices for electromechanical integration of the current-time function have also been employed, but they vary considerably in accuracy and range of applicability. Schoedler[11] has reviewed the requirements and principal types of integrators that are employed in coulometric analysis. The work of Sawyer and Barr[12] is also pertinent. Currently, two types of integrators exist which appear to be almost ideally suited for use in coulometric analysis: those based upon operational amplifier circuitry[5,7,13] and those based upon voltage-to-frequency conversion, plus fre-

[4] Kaufman, F., Ossofsky, E., and Cook, H. J., Anal. Chem., **26**, 516, 1954.
[5] Booman, G. L., Anal. Chem., **29**, 213, 1957.
[6] Merritt Jr., L. L., Martin Jr., E. L., and Bedi, R. D., Anal. Chem., **30**, 487, 1958.
[7] Kelley, M. T., Jones, H. C., and Fisher, D. J., Anal. Chem., **31**, 488, 956, 1959.
[8] Wadsworth, N. J., Analyst, **85**, 673, 1960.
[9] Harrar, J. E., Stephens, F. B., and Pechacek, R. E., Anal. Chem., **34**, 1036, 1962.
[10] Lindstrom, F., and Davis, J. B., Anal. Chem., **36**, 11, 1964.
[11] Schoedler, C., J. Electroanal. Chem., **3**, 390, 1962.
[12] Sawyer, D. T., and Barr, J. K., Anal. Chem., **34**, 1213, 1962.
[13] Stephens, F. B., and Harrar, J. E., U. S. Atomic Energy Commission Report UCRL-7165, Jan. 21, 1963.

quency counting.[14–16] Both types are accurate to ± 0.05 percent or so over a range of current levels from zero up to at least several amperes, and both are very convenient to use.

It should be mentioned that satisfactory accuracy can sometimes be obtained without carrying the titration to completion. One way of doing this is to determine, for a particular analysis and set of operating conditions, the value of the constant k in Eq. (3) from the slope $[= -k/2.303]$ of a plot of log i *vs.* time and then to use that value of k to calculate Q in subsequent titrations via the relationship $Q = i_0/k$. The result is accurate to about ± 2 percent.[17] Another approach is to measure the values Q_1, Q_2, and Q_3 at two equally spaced times $[(t_2 - t_1) = (t_3 - t_2)]$ after the electrolysis is about half complete, then to calculate Q for the complete electrolysis by means of the equation

$$Q = \frac{Q_2^2 - Q_1 Q_3}{2Q_2 - (Q_1 + Q_3)}.$$

An accuracy of ± 0.2 to ± 0.5 percent is claimed for this technique.[18] Another "quick" method for obtaining Q is to plot i *vs.* Q: the curve is virtually a straight line (after the initial rise occurs) and can be extrapolated to $i = 0$ to get an estimate of Q early in the titration.[19, 19a] Results accurate to ± 1 percent have been reported[20] with milligram and submilligram quantities of material (Q less than one coulomb). It should be noted that these techniques effect a savings in total titration time at the expense of operator time and therefore may not afford a greater number of analyses in a given amount of time. Utilization of these "quick" techniques incurs some sacrifice in accuracy, particularly when graphical readout—with or without extrapolation—is involved. Their real advantage lies in the fact that Q can be estimated in cases where an accurate measure of Q cannot be obtained by continued electrolysis. Electrolyses in which a satisfactorily low background current cannot be obtained are in this category.

This discussion of the instrumental requirements of controlled-potential coulometric analysis has necessarily been cursory. For detailed information, one may consult the Selected Bibliography at the end of the chapter, the original papers that have been cited, or the literature that is available from the manufacturers of commercial instruments.

Commercially Available Instrumentation.—Each issue of the *Buyer's Guide* of *Analytical Chemistry* lists a number of companies that market instruments or instrumental components that are suitable for potentiostatic coulometry. There are others. Analytical Instruments, Inc. (Walcott 16, Conn.) has for several years produced electro-mechanical potentiostats and companion integrators that have proven quite popular. Electronic potentiostats of more recent vintage are marketed in this country by Duffers Associates, Inc. (Box 296, Troy, N. Y.), Magna Corp. (Santa Fe Springs, Calif.), Standard Scientific Supply Corp. (808 Broadway, New York, N. Y.) and Brinkman Instruments, Inc. (Great Neck, N. Y.). The potentiostats offered by the latter two companies are of foreign design. Several foreign companies also market potentiostats: Apparecchiature Di Misura Ellettroniche and Societa Italiana Di Tecnologia in Milan, Italy, Strohlein and Co. in Dusseldorf, Germany and Tacussel Electronique in Lyon, France. In general, these companies offer an integrator unit that can be used as a companion to their potentiostat when coulometric analyses are to be performed. An integrator unit, utilizing opera-

[14] Ammann, R., and Desbarres, J., J. Electroanal. Chem., **4,** 121, 1962.
[15] Bard, A. J., and Solon, E., Anal. Chem., **34,** 1181, 1962.
[16] Wise, E. N., Anal. Chem., **34,** 1181, 1962.
[17] MacNevin, W. M., and Baker, B. B., Anal. Chem., **24,** 986, 1952.
[18] Meites, L., Anal. Chem., **31,** 1285, 1959.
[19] Hanamura, S., Talanta, **2,** 278, 1959.
[19a] Hanamura, S., Talanta, **3,** 14, 1959.
[20] Hanamura, S., Talanta, **9,** 901, 1962.

tional amplifier circuitry, is also marketed by W. G. Pye and Co., Ltd. in Cambridge, England. Finally, it should be mentioned that controlled-potential coulometric titrators (potentiostat plus integrator in a single unit) are produced in the U. S. by Numec Instruments and Controls Corp. (Apollo, Pa.) and by Indiana Instrument and Chemical Corp. (Box 37, Bloomington, Ind.). These instruments are completely electronic, being constructed according to the circuit of Kelley, Jones, and Fisher.[7] The characteristics of these—and other—instruments for coulometry are given in two pertinent review articles by Lott.[20a]

APPLIED POTENTIOSTATIC COULOMETRY

Selection of Experimental Conditions.—The experimental conditions for any potentiostatic coulometric analysis are selected so as to give the best compromise between the desired accuracy, selectivity, and speed of analysis. The experimental variables of importance in the compromise, in addition to cell geometry and stirring efficiency, are the electrode potential; the electrode material; the solvent; the nature and concentration of the supporting electrolyte, complexing agent, or surface active agent; and the temperature. Selectivity depends primarily upon the difference between the formal reduction potential of the species being determined and that of the nearest interfering neighbor. Accordingly, solution conditions, which determine $E^{0'}$ values, are of paramount importance in designing selectivity into a procedure; conditions are selected to give the greatest difference between the formal reduction potentials of the competing reactions. In seeking the optimum conditions, one may make use of tabulated formal potentials[21,22] and of a wealth of voltammetric and polarographic information that is available (for references, consult the chapter in this volume that deals with Polarography). Often, a promising medium can be selected from that literature, but further polarographic work is frequently necessary to optimize the solution conditions to the particular problem at hand. Final optimization is best accomplished by consideration of *coulograms*, *i.e.*, curves relating Q *vs.* control potential, because they depict the progress of the electrolysis under the actual experimental conditions. [Data for the construction of coulograms are obtained simply by electrolyzing a known amount of electroactive species under representative conditions, periodically adjusting the control potential to such a value that the current equals 0, and noting at each point the values of Q and the corresponding control potential.]

Having chosen a suitable medium, one must next select the optimum control potential. This again involves compromise. For reversible reactions the Nernst equation is obeyed and there are several important parameters to be considered: (a) the analytical accuracy that is desired, *i.e.*, the fraction, $f_{(1)}$ of the substance to be determined that must be electrolyzed; (b) the fraction, $f_{(2)}$, of any neighboring reaction that may occur without causing the accuracy limits of the analysis to be exceeded; (c) the difference between the formal reduction potentials of the desired and possible interfering couples; (d) the number of electrons, n_1 and n_2 involved in the competing reactions; and (e) the nature of the reactions themselves. The interdependence of these factors is best illustrated by example. Consider again the two general reactions

$$\mathrm{Ox}_{(1)} + n_1\mathrm{e}^- \rightleftharpoons \mathrm{Red}_{(1)}$$

$$\mathrm{Ox}_{(2)} + n_2\mathrm{e}^- \rightleftharpoons \mathrm{Red}_{(2)}$$

[20a] Lott, P. F., J. Chem. Ed., **42,** A261, A361, 1965.

[21] Meites, L., Ed., Handbook of Analytical Chemistry, McGraw-Hill Book Co., New York, 1963.

[22] Charlot, G., Tables de Constantes et Donnees Numeriques, IUPAC, Vol. 8, Pergamon Press, New York, 1958.

where $Ox_{(1)}$ represents the substance being determined, $Ox_{(2)}$ is a neighboring and possibly interfering species, and all species are soluble (NOTE). Then Eq. (2) may be written

$$E = E^{0'}_{(1)} - \frac{0.05914}{n_1} \log \frac{f_{(1)}}{1 - f_{(1)}} \tag{4}$$

for Species 1 and an analogous equation can be written for Species 2.

NOTE.—For illustrative purposes, we shall consider only the situation in which all species are soluble. However, the nature of the reaction(s) should be considered because the Nernst equation assumes slightly different forms when a solid or amalgam phase is involved. Other forms of the equation are given in Bibliography item 4 and are tabulated in Appendix 1 of Bibliography item 2.

Moreover, both couples must attain the same potential at equilibrium, so the difference in formal reduction potentials is given by

$$E^{0'}_{(1)} - E^{0'}_{(2)} = \frac{0.05914}{n_1} \log \frac{f_{(1)}}{1 - f_{(1)}} - \frac{0.05914}{n_2} \log \frac{f_{(2)}}{1 - f_{(2)}}. \tag{5}$$

For the determination of $Ox_{(1)}$ in the absence of $Ox_{(2)}$, one would select an electrode potential that corresponds to virtually complete reduction of $Ox_{(1)}$, *e.g.*, 99.99 percent or $f_{(1)} = 0.9999$. By Eq. (4), the potential should be $E = E^{0'}_{(1)} - 0.2366/n_1$ volt. If, however, the same number of equivalents of $Ox_{(1)}$ and $Ox_{(2)}$ are present in the test portion, then the electrolysis of either contributes equally to the Q of the electrolysis. To determine $Ox_{(1)}$ with an accuracy of 99.9 percent, no more than 0.1 percent of $Ox_{(2)}$ should be electrolyzed at the selected control potential: $f_{(1)} = 0.999$ and $f_{(2)} = 0.001$. Equation (5) states that, under these conditions, the minimum difference in formal potentials must be

$$E^{0'}_{(1)} - E^{0'}_{(2)} = \frac{0.1774}{n_1} + \frac{0.1774}{n_2}.$$

If the difference in formal potentials is this much or greater, a satisfactory control potential is calculated by Eq. (4) with $f_{(1)} = 0.999$: $E = E^{0'}_{(1)} - 0.1774/n_1$. If the difference is less than the above amount, there are two alternatives: a smaller fraction of $Ox_{(1)}$ can be reduced at an appropriate control potential and the analytical result corrected for the portion that remains unreacted or a preliminary separation can be made to improve the $Ox_{(1)}$:$Ox_{(2)}$ ratio. Suppose the test portion contains $Ox_{(1)}$ and $Ox_{(2)}$ in an equivalents ratio of 10:1. The fraction of $Ox_{(2)}$ electrolyzed may now increase by a factor of ten over what it was in the equal-equivalents example (for the same analytical accuracy): as much as 1 percent of $Ox_{(2)}$ can be electrolyzed without causing an error of greater than 0.1 percent in Q. By Eq. (5), with $f_{(1)} = 0.999$ and $f_{(2)} = 0.010$, therefore,

$$E^{0'}_{(1)} - E^{0'}_{(2)} = \frac{0.1774}{n_1} + \frac{0.1183}{n_2}$$

which shows that the required separation in formal reduction potentials becomes smaller when the relative concentration of the neighboring interfering species becomes smaller. For this reason, it is sometimes desirable to carry out even a rough separation prior to electrolysis and then to take advantage of the inherent selectivity of the potentiostatic technique. The importance of the number of electrons involved in the possible electrode reactions is evident upon inspection of the above equations.

The discussion thus far has assumed reversible behavior. What has been stated is applicable to many real situations. There are also many irreversible reactions that are amenable to potentiostatic coulometric analysis, but for these, the correct control potential cannot be calculated; it must be chosen empirically. The utilization of voltammetric or polarographic data (gathered with an electrode of the same material to be used for the potentiostatic electrolysis) and the analysis of standard solutions are mandatory for selection of a suitable control potential. It is often stated that any potential is a suitable choice so long as it corresponds to the voltammetric diffusion current region. However, the rate of an irreversible reaction can often be increased markedly by operating (potentiostatically) at a potential in excess of that necessary to attain a voltammetric diffusion current. Consequently, although the control potential for an irreversible reaction must be established empirically, it too can be optimized to give the best compromise between the desired accuracy, selectivity, and speed of the analysis. A discussion of the effects of controlled electrode potential on the rates and extents of controlled-potential electrolyses for both reversible and irreversible reactions has been presented by Meites.[23]

Current Efficiency and Procedural Design.—The current efficiency for a given reaction is the percentage of the total current that acts to accomplish that reaction. In designing coulometric procedures, one attempts to attain as closely as possible a net current efficiency of 100 percent, then ignores or corrects for the difference between the actual current efficiency and the ideal 100 percent. The so-called "background current" prevents attainment of current efficiencies of exactly 100 percent, even when the electrolyzed solution is free of interfering reactants. The "background current" is a collective term that refers to any current that flows but does not accomplish the desired reaction when a pure solution is electrolyzed; it is itself a type of interference. The simplest way to minimize background current errors in practical analysis is to utilize a relatively large quantity of the electroactive species, thereby making insignificant the contribution of the background current to the total Q. This is common practice when the sample permits it, but when a large quantity of the substance cannot be utilized or when the background current is large and its contribution cannot be made insignificant, then the error introduced by the background current must be evaluated and corrected for. Such corrections become increasingly important with decreasing amount of the substance being determined. In fact, it is the accuracy of these corrections that determines the ultimate sensitivity of the potentiostatic coulometric method.[24]

Meites and Moros[25] divided "the background current" into five component currents as follows.

Charging Current.—The charging current is the current required to charge the electrical double layer that exists at the solution-electrode interface. The magnitude of this current depends upon the experimental conditions, cell design, medium, electrode material, and electrode potential. Errors caused by the charging current can sometimes be minimized by adding the test portion to a pre-electrolyzed supporting electrolyte solution while the controlled electrode is held at the control potential. A suitable correction can often be made by subtracting the result of a blank electrolysis from the result of a sample electrolysis.

Impurity Faradaic Current.—The impurity faradaic current arises from the electrolysis of impurities that are present in the medium and in or on the electrode, but not in the sample test portion. This current can be minimized by purification or pretitration of the medium; it also contributes to the result of a blank electrolysis.

Continuous Faradaic Current.—The continuous faradaic current is due to the electrolysis of some component of the medium itself, excluding the electroactive species and

[23] Meites, L., J. Electroanal. Chem., **7,** 337, 1964.
[24] Meites, L., Anal. Chim. Acta, **20,** 456, 1959.
[25] Meites, L. and Moros, S. A., Anal. Chem., **31,** 23, 1959.

impurities. This is a function of the extant chemical conditions and of the controlled electrode potential. The contribution of this current to the total Q for the electrolysis can be evaluated by performing a blank electrolysis of the same duration as the sample electrolysis or it can be estimated by the product: length of electrolysis by minimum attainable current value. These evaluation techniques are valid when kinetic and/or induced processes are inoperative. Alternatively, graphical correction for the effect of the continuous faradaic current can be accomplished by linear extrapolation of the plateau of a plot of Q *vs.* time back to $t = 0$.

Kinetic Background Current.—The kinetic background current arises when a product of the electrolysis is slowly converted to some other form (*e.g.*, back to the starting material) which is itself electroactive under the existing conditions.

Induced Background Current.—The induced background current results when the electrode reaction induces another reaction to occur, one which would not normally occur under the existing conditions. Kinetic and induced background currents are functions of the electrode reaction and chemical environment. Since they arise only when the major electrode reaction occurs, evaluation of and correction for them is difficult and sometimes impossible. A detailed discussion of the problems involved is given in the original paper.[25]

With real samples, a satisfactory operating technique is to pre-electrolyze the sample at a potential near (but not at) which the electrode reaction of interest occurs, to zero the integrator, and then to adjust the control potential to its final value *without turning the potentiostat off*. This technique, plus correction for the result of a blank electrolysis, is entirely adequate for all but the most exacting analyses. Such analyses, as for example the determination of minute amounts of materials,[24] may require exact evaluation and correction for the contribution from each type of background current. These and other practical aspects of procedural design *vs.* background current corrections have been discussed.[25a]

By proper design of a procedure, it is often possible to circumvent difficulties deriving from unduly large background currents or side reactions. One technique that has been used is the "cycle" procedure in which the first or pre-electrolysis may not proceed with 100 percent current efficiency because of a high background current, yet is satisfactory for quantitative preparation of a given oxidation state of the substance being determined. The second electrolysis in the "cycle" is the conversion of that oxidation state back to the original one, also electrolytically, but this time with essentially 100 percent current efficiency. This technique makes possible the determination of chromium[26] and europium:[27] the respective divalent ions can be prepared quantitatively by electrolytic reduction, then determined by potentiostatic coulometric oxidation back to the trivalent oxidation state. The "cycle" technique can be used to advantage in other ways. Copper(II) and uranium(VI) have closely lying formal reduction potentials in sulfuric acid medium, but their reactions differ markedly in reversibility. Accordingly, these species can be determined in the presence of each other with excellent precision and accuracy by a "cycle" procedure:[28] coulometric reduction of both copper(II) and uranium(VI), followed by coulometric reoxidation of only the copper amalgam back to copper(II). Copper is determined from the Q of the reoxidation electrolysis, while uranium is determined by difference. A final example of the utility of the "cycle" technique is the determination of the oxidation-state distribution of a species. This entails performing a sequence of reduction and oxidation electrolyses so as to determine the

[25a] Jones, H. C., Shults, W. D., and Dale, J. M., Anal. Chem., **37,** 680, 1965.
[26] Meites, L., Anal. Chim. Acta, **18,** 364, 1958.
[27] Shults, W. D., Anal. Chem., **31,** 1095, 1959.
[28] Shults, W. D., and Thomason, P. F., Anal. Chem., **31,** 492, 1959.

total quantity of the species as well as how that quantity is distributed among the various possible oxidation states. This technique has been applied to neptunium,[29] plutonium,[30] and antimony.[31]

One further illustration of the importance of procedural design is warranted. Hydrogen peroxide can be determined by coulometric oxidation at controlled-potential[32] in spite of the fact that the controlled electrode (platinum) catalyzes the spontaneous decomposition of hydrogen peroxide. This is possible because the design of the procedure insures that the current is controlled by mass transfer at all times—there is no opportunity for catalytic decomposition to occur. This procedure emphasizes the importance of strict adherence to procedural detail.

Sensitivity, Accuracy, and Precision.—Meites[24] has studied the potentiostatic oxidation of zinc amalgam in an attempt to extend the controlled-potential coulometric method to its ultimate sensitivity. As little as 0.07 μg. (*ca.* 0.002 μeq.) of zinc could be determined to about ±10 percent by this carefully designed procedure, provided accurate corrections for background currents were made. The "accuracy and precision" were ±1 percent at the 1 μg. level and ±0.1 percent at the 10 μg. or greater level. This was admittedly an ideal situation. The determination of uranium(VI)[33] gives results that are more typical of the performance that can be obtained with present instrumentation and by conscientious procedural design; the relative standard deviation for the determination of uranium(VI) is 2.2 percent at the 7.5 μg. level, 0.4 percent at the 75 μg. level, and 0.03 percent in the 7.5 to 75 mg. range. Under normal laboratory conditions the precision is less, but it is easily possible to operate this procedure routinely within 95 percent confidence limits of ±0.2 percent (7.5 mg. quantities of uranium(VI)). The upper concentration limit of controlled-potential coulometry is determined only by the range and stability of the coulometer and by the patience of the operator.

EXEMPLARY PROCEDURE: THE DETERMINATION OF URANIUM(VI)[33–37]

The determination of uranium(VI) by controlled-potential coulometric reduction is an accurate, precise, convenient, selective, and fairly rapid method. Because the method performs well with milligram quantities, is amenable to remote operation, and is not affected adversely by extremely high radiation fields, it has received a great deal of study within the atomic energy field. It illustrates many of the points that have been made in the preceding paragraphs of this chapter.

Apparatus.—In the procedure that follows, it is assumed that the coulometer (*i.e.*, integrator) functions accurately and precisely at Q values of about 40 μeq.; otherwise the sample size should be altered appropriately. Either of the cells diagrammed in Fig. 23-2 is suitable; it should be of such size that the volumes of mercury and of solution are each approximately 10 ml. A satisfactory stirring motor is the 1800-r.p.m. syn-

[29] Stromatt, R. W., Anal. Chem., **32,** 134, 1960.
[30] Shults, W. D., Talanta, **10,** 833, 1963.
[31] Dunlap, L. B., and Shults, W. D., Anal. Chem., **34,** 499, 1962.
[32] Harrar, J. E., Anal. Chem., **35,** 893, 1963.
[33] Booman, G. L., Holbrook, W. B., and Rein, J. E., Anal. Chem., **29,** 219, 1957.
[34] Shults, W. D., Uranium, Automatic Controlled-Potential Coulometric Titration Method, Method Nos. 1 219225 and 9 00719225 (R. 12-20-60), ORNL Master Analytical Manual, TID-7015, suppl. 4 (June, 1962).
[35] Thomason, P. F., and Booman, G. L., Controlled-Potential Coulometric Determination of Uranium in Irradiated-Fuel Dissolver Solutions, Method 1.302 in R. Jones, Ed., Selected Measurement Methods for Plutonium and Uranium in the Nuclear Fuel Cycle, USAEC Office of Technical Information, 1963.
[36] Booman, G. L., and Holbrook, W. B., Anal. Chem., **31,** 10, 1959.
[37] Shults, W. D., and Dunlap, L. B., Anal. Chim. Acta, **29,** 254, 1963.

chronous motor manufactured by Bodine Electric Co., Chicago, Ill.; it drives a corrugated, disc-shaped glass stirrer positioned at the mercury-solution interface so as to provide maximum stirring of both the solution and the mercury surface, without splashing. Either Vycor glass tubes with unfired bottoms (Type 7930 glass, Corning Glass Works, Corning, N. Y.) or coarse-porosity fritted-glass filter tubes (with 5 percent K_2SO_4–3 percent agar gel in the frits) can be used to isolate the electrode compartments. Each tube contains 0.5 *M* sulfuric acid. The reference electrode is a small, commercially available saturated calomel electrode (fiber type, Beckman type 39270, Beckman Instruments, Inc., Fullerton, Calif.); the auxiliary electrode is a short length of platinum wire. The cell cap must fit snugly to prevent air leaks. A stream of pure helium or nitrogen gas is used to sparge the solution and protect it from oxygen. When the stirring rate is adjusted properly and the solution is completely protected from oxygen, the electrolysis requires approximately 15 minutes.

Procedure.—Place 10 ml. of pure mercury and 10 ml. of 0.5 *M* sulfuric acid containing 5 to 10 mg. of uranium(VI) in the titration cell. Deaerate 10 minutes with pure nitrogen or helium gas, then continue with the gas passing over the solution. Pre-reduce with the mercury electrode controlled at +0.075 volt *vs.* S.C.E. until the current decreases to 50 μa. Zero the integrator. Readjust the control potential to −0.325 volt *vs.* S.C.E. and allow the electrolysis to continue until the current again decreases to 50 μa. Record the coulometer readout, Q. Flush the cell with distilled water and prepare for the next titration. The weight of uranium(VI) in the test portion is given by

$$w = \frac{QM}{nF} = \frac{Q \times 238}{2 \times 96{,}487},$$

that is,

$$\text{uranium(VI), mg.} = 1.233 \times 10^{-3} \times Q, \text{ mcoul.}$$

Relative error: ±0.1 percent; relative standard deviation, s = 0.1 percent.

The electrode reaction here is the reversible one-electron reduction of uranium(VI) to uranium(V), but uranium(V) is unstable in this medium and rapidly disproportionates to uranium(VI) and (IV). Hence, the overall reaction is the irreversible two-electron reduction of uranium(VI) to (IV). Uranium(VI) does not react with the electrode material (mercury) under these conditions, yet most other species that have formal reduction potentials even slightly more positive than uranium do oxidize mercury spontaneously. Pre-reduction at +0.075 volt *vs.* S.C.E., where mercury ions are reduced back to mercury metal, therefore accomplishes the reduction of oxidants stronger than uranium(VI) and effectively narrows the potential span within which an interference may react to 400 mvolts. The method is therefore inherently selective. A number of separation schemes have been developed to further improve the selectivity of the method.[35–37] Since uranium(IV) is a moderately strong reductant and reacts with oxygen at a significant rate, the procedure requires exclusion of oxygen from the solution during electrolysis. If oxygen leaks into the system, the current does not decrease to 50 μa. or less, but stops at some larger value that depends upon the oxygen leakage rate; a positive error is incurred. The use of 50 μa. as the cut-off current is consistent with the initial current values of 50 to 150 ma. that are obtained when this reduction is carried out in an efficiently designed and operated cell and at the specified concentration level. If other operating conditions are used, or if smaller quantities of uranium are taken, the above *modus operandi* may not be satisfactory. It may then be necessary to continue the electrolysis until a true, continuous faradaic background current is attained, and to apply appropriate corrections.[25a] Finally, it should be mentioned that the control potential of −0.325 volt *vs.* S.C.E. is specified in order to shorten the titration time; the reduction may be performed quantitatively at control potentials more negative than approximately -0.200 volt *vs.* S.C.E.

SCOPE OF POTENTIOSTATIC COULOMETRY

ANALYTICAL APPLICATIONS

Reference is given here to several of the recent and more complete tabulations of published analytical applications of controlled-potential coulometry.

(a). Meites, L., Ed., Handbook of Analytical Chemistry, McGraw-Hill Book Company, Inc., New York, 1963. Israel and Meites present, in Tables 5-56 and 5-57, summaries of the conditions that have been used and the results that have been obtained in determining various substances by controlled-potential coulometry. Only analytical determinations are listed, but both inorganic and organic materials are included and the tabulation is complete through 1962.

(b). Page, J. A., Maxwell, J. A., and Graham, R. P., Analyst, **87**, 245, 1962. This article is a review of the analytical applications of the mercury electrode; it contains a section that deals with controlled-potential coulometry at such an electrode. Applications other than analytical, such as separations or purification electrolyses, are included in this tabulation and are so marked.

(c). Rechnitz, G. A., Controlled-Potential Analysis, Pergamon Press, MacMillan, New York, 1963. Chapter IV deals with the analytical application of potentiostatic coulometry to inorganic substances. The determination of each element is discussed briefly with pertinent references. The tabulation is fairly complete through 1962.

(d). The Annual Reviews (Fundamental Part) published by Analytical Chemistry contain review articles on Electroanalysis and Coulometric Analysis biennially (even-numbered years). These articles should be consulted for information about developments in coulometry subsequent to those reported in the above references.

OTHER APPLICATIONS OF POTENTIOSTATIC COULOMETRY

The non-analytical utility of controlled-potential coulometry warrants some, though necessarily brief, mention.

Determination of Formal Potentials.—A plot of extent of reaction, as measured by Q, as a function of zero-current electrode potential (*i.e.*, a coulogram) was recognized early as a means for estimating formal redox potentials.[38,39] This technique is feasible because the curve assumes the form predicted by the Nernst equation when the electrode process is a reversible couple. Moreover, when the electrode process is not reversible, coulograms for the forward and reverse processes together provide estimates not only of the formal redox potential, but also of the departure of the process from reversibility. An instrument for automatically recording such curves has been described.[40]

Determination of n-Values.—Potentiostatic coulometry is frequently used for the direct measurement, via Eq. (1), of n-values. It is a particularly effective method when n does not assume an integral value or when the value is greater than one or two. In this capacity, potentiostatic coulometry is often employed as an auxiliary technique in investigations of the voltammetric or chronopotentiometric behavior of inorganic or organic compounds.

Kinetic and Mechanism Studies.—Because n-values can be determined simply and accurately by potentiostatic coulometry, the technique has been used with increasing frequency for kinetic and mechanistic studies in recent years. The approach is to determine the apparent value of n as a function of experimental conditions, then to use that

[38] Wehner, P., and Hindman, J. C., J. Am. Chem. Soc., **72**, 3911, 1950.
[39] Stromatt, R. W., Peekema, R. M., and Scott, F. A., HW-58212, Nov. 12, 1958.
[40] Propst, R. C., Anal. Chem., **35**, 958, 1963.

knowledge (along with the current-time relationship and perhaps the results of analysis of the solution) to deduce the kinetics and mechanism of the overall reaction.[41–45]

Preparations and Purifications.—Another way in which potentiostatic coulometry is used to augment voltammetric, chronopotentiometric, or other techniques is in the preparation of standard solutions that contain an electroactive species in a known oxidation state or as a mixture of known oxidation states. The advantages of this scheme are that no impurities are introduced into the solution during adjustment of the oxidation state and that species which are prepared only with difficulty by chemical means often are easily prepared by electrolysis. Electrolysis at controlled electrode potential is also well known as a purification technique and for the preparation of compounds, intermediates, metals, or amalgams in known quantities.

COULOMETRY AT CONTROLLED CURRENT (COULOMETRIC TITRATION; AMPEROSTATIC COULOMETRY)

PRINCIPLES OF COULOMETRY AT CONTROLLED CURRENT

The preceding section of this chapter dealt with coulometry when there is external control of the potential of the controlled electrode. In this section we shall consider coulometry when there is external control of the cell current. The electrode potential varies widely and abruptly during this type of electrolysis, yet is subjected to a degree of internal potential control through the action of a "depolarizing intermediate" species. Such a species supports the current when the substance being determined does not do so, thereby limiting the electrode potential to a value dependent upon the species itself and the prevailing experimental conditions. This means that undesirable reactions, which might cause a loss of current efficiency, are precluded. It also means that if there is rapid quantitative reaction between the substance being determined and the product(s) of electrolysis of the depolarizing intermediate, then the net reaction is identical to the reaction that would occur if the substance being determined reacted directly with an electrolytically generated titrant. This net reaction is accomplished at a constant rate determined by the magnitude of the cell current. Hence, this technique has been likened to a volumetric titration performed with a constant-rate buret. Indeed, this type of analysis is frequently called a "coulometric titration."

A better understanding of the factors involved in this type of coulometric analysis can be gained by consideration of the curves in Fig. 23-4. These are idealized current-potential curves (in arbitrary units) for the two general reactions that were considered in the previous section,

$$\mathrm{Ox}_{(1)} + n_1\mathrm{e}^- \rightleftharpoons \mathrm{Red}_{(1)}$$

and

$$\mathrm{Ox}_{(2)} + n_2\mathrm{e}^- \rightleftharpoons \mathrm{Red}_{(2)}$$

which have the formal reduction potentials $E^{0'}_{(1)}$ and $E^{0'}_{(2)}$, respectively. $\mathrm{Ox}_{(1)}$ corresponds to the substance being determined, $\mathrm{Ox}_{(2)}$ to the depolarizing intermediate, and $\mathrm{Red}_{(2)}$ to the electrolytically generated titrant. The net reaction is therefore analogous to the reaction

$$\mathrm{Ox}_{(1)} + \mathrm{Red}_{(2)} \rightarrow \mathrm{Ox}_{(2)} + \mathrm{Red}_{(1)}$$

[41] Geske, D. H., and Bard, A. J., J. Phys. Chem., **63**, 1057, 1959.
[42] Rechnitz, G. A., and Laitinen, H. A., Anal. Chem., **33**, 1473, 1961.
[43] Spritzer, M., and Meites, L., Anal. Chim. Acta, **26**, 58, 1962.
[44] Bard, A. J., and Mayell, J. S., J. Phys. Chem., **66**, 2173, 1962.
[45] Bard, A. J., and Solon, E., J. Phys. Chem., **67**, 2326, 1963.

The curves in Fig. 23-4 assume that both reactions behave reversibly, that $n_1 = n_2 = 1$, that the diffusion coefficients of the oxidized and reduced forms of each species are equal, and that initially only the two oxidized forms are present with the concentration of $Ox_{(2)}$ twice that of $Ox_{(1)}$. Curves A, B, C, and D indicate the relationship between cell current

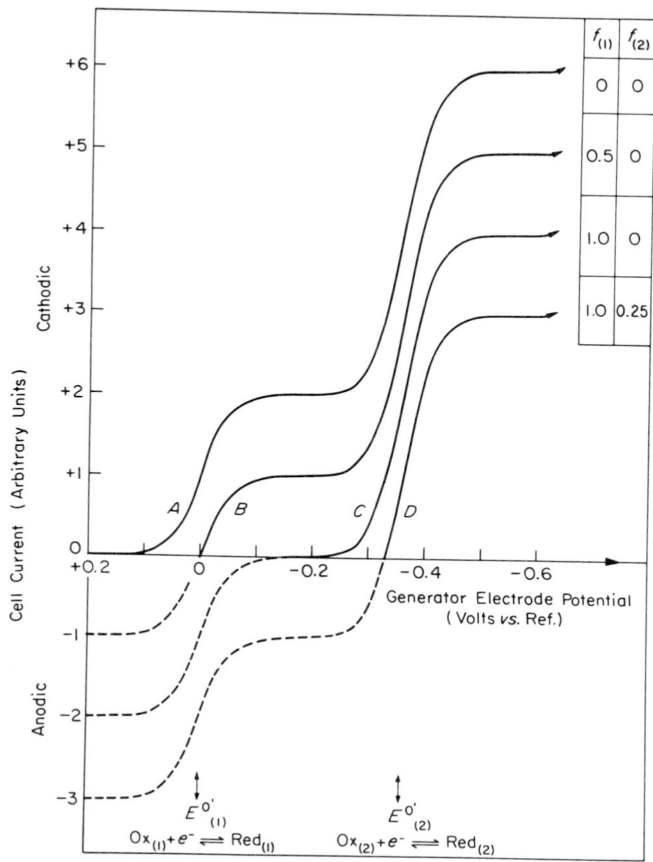

FIG. 23-4. Relationship between Cell Current and Generator Electrode Potential at Different Stages in a Hypothetical Coulometric Titration of Ox_1 with Red_2. $[Ox_1] = 0.5\,[Ox_2]$. $n_1 = n_2 = 1$.

and electrode potential at four different times during the titration: A = initial condition, B = midway through the titration, C = equivalence point, and D = beyond the equivalence point. The fractions of each species that have been titrated, $f_{(1)}$ and $f_{(2)}$, are indicated beside each curve. It should be noted that real curves of this type would depend markedly upon such experimental conditions as electrode area, stirring rate, and temperature. For consideration of a reduction reaction, which is the present case, only the cathodic portions of the curves are of interest; the anodic (dashed) portions are shown for completeness only. Finally, note that the electrode at which the reactions of interest occur is termed the *generator electrode* when the coulometric analysis is performed at controlled current.

Suppose the cell current is maintained at +1.5 (cathodic) units. In that case, the generator electrode will assume initially a potential given by curve A at a current level of +1.5 units, *i.e.*, about −0.03 volt *vs.* REF (hypothetical reference). At this potential, the species that supports the current is $Ox_{(1)}$, the substance being determined. As the electrolysis proceeds, $Ox_{(1)}$ is reduced to $Red_{(1)}$ at a constant rate corresponding to $i = 1.5$ units. Accordingly, curve A moves downward steadily towards curve B. A current-potential curve taken when half of $Ox_{(1)}$ has been reduced ($f_{(1)} = 0.5$) would appear as curve B. At that point in the titration, the generator electrode has assumed a potential corresponding to $i = 1.5$ units on curve B, *i.e.*, about −0.31 volt *vs.* REF. It is apparent that an abrupt shift in generator electrode potential must have occurred when the cell current became equal to the limiting current of $Ox_{(1)}$. At that time, the concentration of $Ox_{(1)}$ had decreased to so low a value that $Ox_{(1)}$ could no longer support +1.5 units of current so the next most reactive species (here $Ox_{(2)}$) was forced to carry the remainder of the 1.5 units of current. $Ox_{(2)}$, the depolarizing intermediate, assumes a larger fraction of the current as the titration proceeds because the concentration of $Ox_{(1)}$ decreases steadily. Note, however, that there is no accumulation of $Red_{(2)}$, the electrolytically generated titrant, in the solution because it reacts spontaneously with $Ox_{(1)}$ according to the equation stated above. Hence, at the midpoint in the titration $f_{(1)} = 0.5$ and $f_{(2)} = 0$, even though $Ox_{(2)}$ is supporting one-third of the cell current.

Curve C corresponds to the equivalence point in the titration: $f_{(1)} = 1$ and $f_{(2)} = 0$. The generator electrode potential is about −0.35 volt *vs.* REF at this point and is not changing significantly. Beyond the equivalence point, when the supply of $Ox_{(1)}$ is exhausted, $Ox_{(2)}$ would support all of the current and $Red_{(2)}$ would accumulate in the solution. In fact, however, the titration is not allowed to continue past the equivalence point except as necessary to signal an end-point. Several properties of any system signal an equivalence point, of course, all of which may in principle be employed for end-point detection. Various techniques are utilized in practice; these are discussed in the section on End-Point Detection Techniques (page 480).

It is convenient at this juncture to mention other implications of the curves in Fig. 23-4. The magnitude of the cell current is not critical. Suppose, for example, that a current of +3 units were selected. Initially the generator electrode potential would be (curve A) approximately −0.33 volt *vs.* REF with both $Ox_{(1)}$ and $Ox_{(2)}$ reacting at the electrode. However, the net chemical change in the solution is the same as when a current of +1.5 units is used. Indeed, the net reaction remains the same even if $Ox_{(1)}$ does not react directly at the electrode provided chemical reaction between $Ox_{(1)}$ and $Red_{(2)}$ is rapid and quantitative. The maximum current that can be used depends upon the experimental conditions: the cell current must not exceed the limiting current of the depolarizing intermediate at any time during the titration. If a current level of +5 units were used in the present example, the limiting current of $Ox_{(2)}$ would be exceeded before the equivalence point of the titration were attained. The generator electrode potential would then shift to a more negative value at which some other species, perhaps the solvent, is reduced. Such a reaction is undesirable because it may not proceed with 100 percent current efficiency or its product(s) may not react rapidly and quantitatively with the substance being determined: there would be a decrease in current efficiency *for the titration* with a concomitant error (positive) in the analytical result. To prevent such an undesirable reaction is the function of the depolarizing intermediate, and to minimize such errors is the object of procedural design (page 484).

It is quite simple to calculate the analytical result of a titration such as has been described if the cell current is constant throughout. First, the number of coulombs of electricity can be determined simply by timing the electrolysis, measuring the current level, and using the expression

$$Q = \int_0^t i\, dt = it$$

Second, since all of the charge that flows prior to the equivalence point is effectively used to accomplish the reduction of $Ox_{(1)}$, one may use Eq. (1) to calculate the weight of $Ox_{(1)}$ titrated. The assumptions are that (a) the current remains constant throughout the electrolysis, (b) the current level and time are measured accurately, (c) the overall titration current efficiency for the reduction of $Ox_{(1)}$ is 100 percent. To the extent that these assumptions are valid—and it is possible to design procedures so that they are quite closely approached—amperostatic coulometry is an accurate and precise method of analysis. The above discussion has been restricted to the reduction of an oxidant but the amperostatic coulometric technique can be applied equally well to oxidation, precipitation, complexometric, and neutralization reactions provided the titrant can be generated by a satisfactory electrolytic process. The same principles apply. Finally, while the titrant in the above example is generated electrolytically within the reaction medium, it should be mentioned that it is sometimes desirable to generate the titrant externally and flow it into the reaction medium (Mode of Generation, page 484).

APPARATUS FOR COULOMETRY AT CONTROLLED CURRENT

CELLS

Cell design is of less importance in amperostatic than in potentiostatic coulometry. The only demands upon the cell are that (a) a cell current of reasonable magnitude (for the application at hand) can be used without exceeding the limiting current of the depolarizing intermediate, (b) the contents of the cell are mixed rapidly and thoroughly, (c) the indicator system responds quickly, and (d) oxygen can be excluded when necessary. The literature is affluent with cell designs that meet these demands. Two designs of wide applicability are diagrammed in Fig. 23-5. The double-diaphragm cell, I, is convenient for applications that involve internal generation of the titrant because the generator electrode can be either a mercury pool or a solid electrode (platinum, silver, gold). Cell II in Fig. 23-5 is useful for titrations that require external generation of the titrant: the titrant is generated within a tubular platinum electrode and flows through the capillary tube into the solution being titrated. Potentiometric redox or pH-indicator electrode systems such as those depicted in cells I and II, respectively, are frequently employed in coulometric titrimetry for end-point detection. Other systems are also employed (*cf*: section on End-Point Detection Techniques (page 480)). The indicator electrode is positioned close to and "downstream" from the point of formation (or entry) of the titrant so that the indicator system senses an advanced stage of the titration at all times; this is a practical way to obtain a degree of "anticipation" in the end-point detection system. Other coulometric cells of specific and of general utility are described in Bibliography items 1 through 4; several are also marketed by the larger chemical supply houses.

INSTRUMENTATION FOR COULOMETRY AT CONTROLLED CURRENT

The essential components of any constant current coulometric titrator are diagrammed in Fig. 23-6: an amperostat, an end-point control unit, and a coulometer. The function of the amperostat is to impose a constant current, usually 1 to 25 ma., on the generator circuit, *i.e.*, the generator-auxiliary electrode system. In its simplest form the amperostat may consist of one or more 45-volt dry cells in series with a large variable

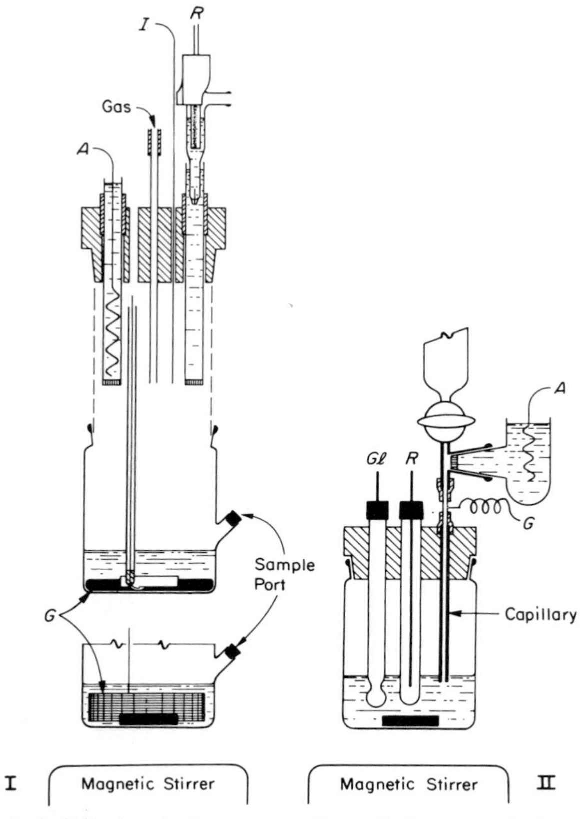

FIG. 23-5. Typical Cells for Coulometry at Controlled-current. I, Internal Generation, Potentiometric Redox End-point Detection. II, External Generation, Potentiometric pH End-point Detection. Electrodes: A = Auxiliary; G = Generator; Gl = Glass; I = Indicator; R = Reference.

load resistor and a smaller standard (precision) resistor (for current measurement). This arrangement is satisfactory when current levels of no more than 1 to 2 ma. are required and when results accurate to 0.5 percent are adequate. If larger currents or greater accuracy is desired, one must utilize a servo-controlled or preferably an electronically-regulated current source. Many have been described in the literature (see also Bibliography items 1 and 3) and several are available commercially.

The end-point control section consists of at least three components: a detector or indicator system which detects and signals the progress of the titration, an end-point criterion system which states what detector signal corresponds to the end point, and a control unit that terminates the electrolysis when the indicator and end-point criterion signals agree that the end point has been reached. In its simplest form, the end-point control section may consist of a colored indicator in the solution being titrated plus the analyst himself. He observes the solution color during the titration and terminates the electrolysis when the appropriate color change occurs. In this capacity, he may also function as a device that is not included in Fig. 23-6 but which may be part of the control unit: an "anticipation" device. This means that the analyst may sense when an equivalence point is near and stop the electrolysis beforehand to allow the system to come to equilibrium. He may do this several times in order to insure that when the titration is finally terminated, the chemical system is truly at the equivalence point.

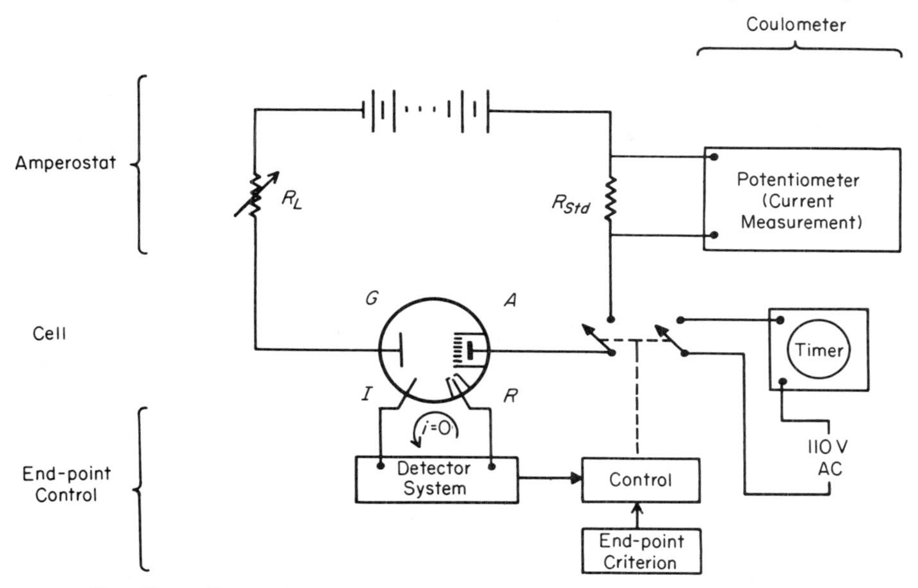

FIG. 23-6. Essential Components of an Amperostatic Coulometric Titrator.

Contrast this with the result obtained without "anticipation." The analyst terminates the electrolysis only once, when he receives the first indication that an end point has been reached. Because a finite amount of time is required for the solution to become homogeneous, for the reaction to occur, and for the indicator to respond, the true state of the solution may at that time be before or after the correct equivalence point and the resulting titration error may be either negative or positive (it is usually negative). A common technique for avoiding this error is to first titrate a small amount of the sample to the end point, then add the sample test portion and titrate it back to the same end point, holding all experimental conditions constant. The assumption is made that end-point errors are identical and cancel in the two electrolyses. Many of the instruments that are available commercially incorporate end-point control circuitry without anticipation, so that the above technique is frequently specified in a given procedure. It should be noted that the disadvantage to that procedure is that it precludes the successive titration of more than one species.

Whether anticipation circuitry is provided or not, the more advanced instruments are so designed that they will function with one or more of the end-point detection techniques mentioned in the section on End-Point Detection Techniques (page 480). Some include time differentiation of the indicator signal in order to provide a very abrupt change in signal to the control unit at the end point. An example is the Sargent-Malmstadt Model SE Automatic Titrator (E. H. Sargent and Co., Chicago, Ill.) which can be used in conjunction with the Sargent Coulometric Power Supply as a unit that provides optical or electrometric end-point detection. Moreover, this unit provides for automatic control of the end point based upon the detector signal itself or its second or third time derivative. Such instruments as this, and others available commercially, find wide application in analytical control laboratories. Finally, it should be mentioned that the control unit of instruments for automatic volumetric titrimetry can be adapted, often quite easily, to coulometric titrimetry. An example is the Beckman Model K Automatic Titrator.[46]

The "coulometer" component of the titrator diagrammed in Fig. 23-6 consists of a standard resistor in series with the cell, a potentiometer for measuring $iR_{Std.}$, and a timer. Since the current is held constant in this type of electrolysis, the number of coulombs of current can be evaluated simply by the product of current and time as mentioned earlier. Because of its simplicity and its accuracy over a wide range of Q values, this is by far the most frequently used method for evaluating Q during coulometric titration. However, as was demonstrated by Meites,[47] it is possible to use an integrator in conjunction with an unregulated current source to perform coulometric titrations. This technique has not been widely adopted, but the development of integrators based upon operational amplifier circuitry or voltage-to-frequency conversion (see section on Commercially Available Instrumentation, page 466) should give it impetus.[48] Another proposal has been "pulse coulometry" in which the current is imposed upon the generator circuit in pulses of controlled magnitude and duration; integration then is accomplished by counting the number of pulses.[49,50] For most analytical applications, however, the combination of an electronically-regulated current source with an accurate timer leaves little to be desired. This integration system is used exclusively by the several chemical supply houses and analytical instrument manufacturers that market instruments for performing coulometric titrations. See the annual Buyer's Guide of Analytical Chemistry or Lott's two review articles[20a] on instrumentation for electrodeposition and coulometry for a listing of these companies. A good discussion of coulometric titrators, including the commercially-available instruments, is given in Chapters VI and VIII of Phillips' monograph.[51]

END-POINT DETECTION TECHNIQUES

In principle any end-point detection technique that can be used in volumetric titrimetry can also be used in coulometric titrimetry. Most of the techniques are well known. Accordingly, the following discussion is concerned only with the general features and utility of the various techniques as employed in coulometric titrimetry. The references given are to procedures that illustrate a particular end-point technique. Discussions of these techniques are given in the appropriate chapters of the present volume. Detailed treatments of these techniques are given in Chapter 10 of Bibliography item 2 and in the papers of Kolthoff[52] and Gauguin.[53]

End-point detection techniques may be divided broadly into two classes: those based upon optical properties and those based upon electrical properties.

Optical Methods.—These methods include visual, photometric, and spectrophotometric end-point techniques, with or without the aid of a colored indicator. (If an indicator is added, it must not react electrolytically, of course.) Generally, visual end points

[46] Lingane, J. J., Anal. Chem., **26**, 622, 1954.
[47] Meites, L., Anal. Chem., **24**, 1057, 1952.
[48] Scott, P. G. W., and Strivens, T. A., Analyst, **87**, 356, 1962.
[49] Devanathan, M. A. V., and Fernando, Q., Trans. Faraday Soc., **52**, 1332, 1956.
[50] Fernando, Q., Devanathan, M. A. V., Rasiah, J. C., Calpin, J. A., and Nakulesparan, K., J. Electroanal. Chem., **3**, 46, 1962.
[51] Phillips, J. P., Automatic Titrators, Academic Press, New York, 1959.
[52] Kolthoff, I. M., Anal. Chem., **26**, 1685, 1954.
[53] Gauguin, R., Chim. anal., **36**, 92, 1954.

give quite precise (*ca.* 0.1 percent) results when macro (greater than 1 meq.) quantities are titrated, the photometric method is applicable to somewhat smaller amounts with equal accuracy, and the spectrophotometric method can be extended into the micro range with good accuracy (*e.g.*, 1 μg. or more can be determined to ± 2 percent or less). Typical uses of the visual technique are in neutralization reactions[54] or in the oxidimetric determination of arsenic(III) with electrolytically generated iodine.[54,55] These same titrations also illustrate photometric end-point detection.[56] The determination of arsenic(III) with electrolytically generated cerium(IV) exemplifies spectrophotometric end-point detection.[57] In most titrations that utilize spectrophotometric end-point detection, as in the latter example, the absorbance of the solution is monitored at a wavelength at which one or more of the reacting species absorbs strongly so that a plot of absorbance, A, *vs.* time (in the case of a coulometric titration) can be constructed. The end point is located by extrapolating the linear "before" and "after" portions of the curve to their intersection. Procedures that employ this type of detection can be automated simply by recording the A *vs.* t curve with a recording spectrophotometer[58] or by utilizing the time derivative(s) of the absorbance to terminate the cell current at the end point.[59]

Electrometric Techniques.—These techniques for end-point detection comprise three subclasses: potentiometry, amperometry, and conductometry.

Potentiometry includes those techniques in which a potential difference signals the progress of the titration. In this class falls "classical" potentiometry with zero faradaic current, in which the potential difference between a polarizable indicator electrode and a non-polarizable reference electrode indicates the conditions prevailing in the solution being titrated. This technique is frequently used in coulometric titration procedures not only because it is a familiar and well understood technique but also because a given potential value is characteristic of the composition of the solution, not of such experimental variables as electrode area, temperature, and stirring rate. Hence, titrations which utilize this end-point technique are easily automated either by titration to the true equivalence point potential or to the abrupt change that occurs in the time derivative of the indicator signal near the equivalence point. There is a possibility of error when this latter method is used, however, because the true equivalence point may not coincide with the point of maximum slope of the indicator potential *vs.* time curve. That is, the familiar potentiometric sigmoid curve may be distorted somewhat when a large excess of depolarizing intermediate is present in the solution. Errors deriving from this distortion are usually insignificant at the macro level so that classical potentiometry can be conjoined with coulometric titrations to obtain results accurate and/or precise to better than 0.1 percent. This is not true at the micro level where the "asymmetry" error may become significant (while the precision remains relatively good). Even at that level, such errors can be avoided or at least minimized by first titrating the medium to an end-point potential, then adding the sample and titrating it back to the same potential. A more serious disadvantage of "classical" potentiometry in the micromolar concentration range is that the response of the electrode system becomes sluggish. This fact has prompted a great deal of developmental work on other end-point detection methods for use in the micromolar concentration range. Among these are potentiometric methods in which a finite current is imposed upon the indicator circuit.

Potentiometric techniques with finite current may utilize one polarizable indicator

[54] DeFord, D. D., Pitts, J. N., and Johns, C. J., Anal. Chem., **23,** 938, 1951.
[55] Reilley, C. N., J. Chem. Ed., **31,** 543, 1954.
[56] Wise, E. N., Giles, P. W., and Reynolds Jr., C. A., Anal. Chem., **25,** 1344, 1953.
[57] Furman, N. H. and Fenton Jr., A. J., Anal. Chem., **28,** 515, 1956.
[58] Malmstadt, H. V., and Roberts, C. B., Anal. Chem., **27,** 741, 1955.
[59] Malmstadt, H. V., and Roberts, C. B., Anal. Chem., **28,** 1412, 1956.

electrode plus a non-polarizable reference electrode, or may utilize two polarizable indicator electrodes. Two single-indicator-electrode methods exist. One involves connecting a battery and large resistor in series with the indicator circuit so that a constant current of a few microamperes is maintained in the circuit.[60] The potential that develops between the indicator and reference electrode varies during titration in much the same fashion as when "classical" zero-current potentiometry is used, depending somewhat upon the reversibility of the electrode reaction and upon whether a cathodic or an anodic reaction occurs at the indicator electrode. The advantage here is that the small constant current improves the response of the indicator system. This technique is suitable for automatic end-point detection. The other finite-current single-indicator-electrode technique involves placing a bucking potentiometer and sensitive galvanometer in series with the indicator circuit. If the bucking potentiometer is adjusted beforehand to (or near to) the equivalence point potential, then a current is established in the indicator circuit so long as the solution potential differs from the preset equivalence point potential. This current decreases during the titration, falling to zero at the end point. It is clear that this is a potentiometric-type procedure that utilizes current as an indication of the solution potential. The indicator system reaches equilibrium within one minute in the vicinity of the end-point even when extremely dilute solutions are titrated.[61] For example, this technique was used for the titration of 1 μg. of manganese(VII) with electrolytically generated iron(II) in a total volume of 10 ml.; the average error was only ± 1.5 percent.[62] This technique is used primarily for the determination of minute quantities of a species as in this example; it is not readily automated.

Potentiometry with two polarizable electrodes[63] involves establishing a small constant current of 0.1 to 5 μa.—from a battery and large series resistor—in an indicator circuit which in this case contains two identical microelectrodes. The potential difference between these two electrodes varies markedly during a titration because one electrode functions anodically, the other functions cathodically, and each assumes a potential governed by the electrode reaction occurring at it at any given stage in the titration. As the titration progresses through an equivalence point, these governing reactions change and an abrupt change in the potential across the two microelectrodes occurs. The variation in potential at an equivalence point may comprise a peak if the couples of both the substance being determined and the titrant are reversible. Alternatively, the potential difference decreases very sharply at the end-point if the titrant couple is reversible and the other couple is irreversible, or a sharp increase in potential difference between the two indicator electrodes occurs when an irreversibly reacting titrant is used to titrate a substance whose couple behaves reversibly. The advantages of this technique are that steady potential differences are attained within 5 to 30 seconds, even when an irreversible couple is involved, and that no reference electrode is needed. Successive end points can be detected. This is a suitable technique for automatic end-point detection.

Amperometry.—The second subclass of electrometric end-point detection techniques is amperometry, which relates the magnitude of indicator current to the progress of the titration. There are two amperometric techniques, one of which might properly be called "classical" amperometry. A polarizable microelectrode plus a non-polarizable reference electrode comprise the indicator circuit in this technique. A voltage that corresponds to the limiting current of the substance being determined, or of the titrant, or perhaps of a product of the reaction, is impressed across the electrodes. Since the limiting current is proportional to the concentration of that particular species, a plot of indicator (*i.e.*,

[60] Lee, J. K., and Adams, R. N., Anal. Chem., **30**, 240, 1958.
[61] Cooke, W. D., Reilley, C. N., and Furman, N. H., Anal. Chem., **24**, 205, 1952.
[62] Cooke, W. D., Reilley, C. N., and Furman, N. H., Anal. Chem., **23**, 1662, 1951.
[63] Reilley, C. N., Cooke, W. D., and Furman, N. H., Anal. Chem., **23**, 1223, 1951.

limiting) current *vs.* time exhibits linear portions with different slopes before and after the equivalence point. These linear portions are extrapolated to their intersection point to locate the end point. An example of the application of this end-point detection technique is the titration of chromium(II) and vanadium(II) with iron(III) in molten LiCl-KCl eutectic.[64]

Amperometry with two polarizable electrodes is used more frequently than the above technique in coulometric titrimetry. A constant voltage of 50 to 300 mv. is impressed across two polarizable electrodes and the current that results is monitored. This indicator current is virtually zero at the end point, but is much greater than zero after or before or both before and after the end point (depending respectively upon whether the titrant couple, or the couple of the substance being determined, or both couples react reversibly). When macro quantities are titrated, quite accurate and precise results (*ca.* 0.1 percent) can be obtained simply by titrating until the indicator current decreases to zero. This is the so-called "dead-stop" end-point technique. With micro quantities, better results are obtained by plotting indicator current *vs.* time through the equivalence point, then extrapolating back to the end point or to an arbitrary current level that serves as the end point. An example of the use of this technique is the determination of aniline by bromine substitution: an excess of bromine is generated first and allowed to react, then the excess is back-titrated with electrolytically generated copper(I) employing amperometric end-point detection.[65] This end-point detection technique owes its popularity to the fact that it is simple, sensitive, and relatively free from sluggish response in the vicinity of an end point. It is not very adaptable to automation for several reasons, the principal one being that magnitude of indicator response is affected by experimental conditions which may vary from one run to another, *e.g.*, pretreatment of electrodes, rate of stirring, temperature, position and size of electrodes, and even magnitude of the generation current.

Conductometry.—The final subclass of electrometric end-point detection methods is *conductometry*. This approach is seldom used in coulometric titrations because solutions which conduct well enough to be useful for electrolytic generation of a titrant are rarely satisfactory for precise measurement of small changes in conductance. A clever application of this technique is the determination of water in liquid ammonia by reduction with electrolytically generated potassium, as described by Klingelhoeffer.[66] The end point is signalled by the sharp increase in the conductance of liquid ammonia when potassium is generated in excess.

There has been some disagreement as to which is more sensitive, potentiometry or amperometry. Some have pointed to the superior sensitivity of amperometry, stating that amperometric methods are, in fact, best for determining traces with high precision. Concentrations from 0.1 to 0.0001 *M*, and even, in favorable cases, to 0.000001 *M* can be measured with ease and accuracy. At least one investigation has been addressed to that question.[67] These investigators agreed upon the conclusion, identical with the general feeling prevalent today, that amperometry may be slightly more sensitive than potentiometry but that a significant advantage cannot be awarded to either technique. Published procedures always specify an indicator system that is known to work satisfactorily. Often, however, alternative techniques have not been investigated. The nature of the reaction, the concentration range of interest, the instrumentation that is used, whether or not the analysis is to be automated—all these are prominent factors in selection of the optimum end-point detection technique for any specific application.

[64] Laitinen, H. A., and Bhatia, B. B., Anal. Chem., **30,** 1995, 1958.
[65] Buck, R. P., and Swift, E. H., Anal. Chem., **24,** 499, 1952.
[66] Klingelhoeffer, W. C., Anal. Chem., **34,** 1751, 1962.
[67] Purdy, W. C., Burns, E. A., and Rogers, L. B., Anal. Chem., **27,** 1988, 1955.

APPLIED AMPEROSTATIC COULOMETRY

PROCEDURAL DESIGN

Mode of Generation.—In a previous paragraph it was mentioned that the titrant in a coulometric titration may be generated internally or externally. Internal generation—which involves titrant generation and chemical reaction within the same cell—gives slightly more accurate and precise results and is also more convenient than external generation. Accordingly, it is by far the more frequently used mode of operation. However, the external generation technique—which involves titrant generation in one compartment and chemical reaction in a second compartment—can sometimes be used to advantage. Thus, a titrant can be prepared externally and then used to titrate a sample that contains electroactive materials which would interfere if the titrant were generated internally. The usual example is a neutralization reaction involving hydrogen or hydroxyl ions generated by the electrolysis of water. In that situation, generation is best done externally because if the internal technique were used, any material that is more electroactive than water would also react electrolytically, causing a loss of current efficiency for the titration. Any titrant that can be generated internally can also be generated externally, but note that the external generation technique requires that *the titrant be generated* with virtually 100 percent current efficiency. This is not the same as a *net* current efficiency *for the titration* (see next section). Of course, it is easier to generate titrants efficiently when the external technique is employed because optimum electrolytic conditions can be utilized. The subsequent reaction can then be carried out under different, but chemically optimum, conditions if desirable. It is apparent, therefore, that some procedures require internal generation of titrant, others require external generation, and many can be performed by either mode of generation. Both modes of operation should be considered when a procedure is to be designed for a specific application.

Choice of Experimental Conditions.—If a reaction is to be suitable for volumetric titrimetry, it should be quantitative, stoichiometric, and reasonably rapid or amenable to back-titration. Some means is also needed to detect the equivalence point. If the same titration is to be done coulometrically, two additional requirements should be considered. First, the depolarizing intermediate should react at the electrode at a potential that precludes interfering *electrode* reactions, *i.e.*, the titrant must be generated at high, but not necessarily 100 percent current efficiency. Second, the titrant and chemical conditions should be chosen such that the titrant is no more reactive than is necessary for quantitative reaction with the substance being determined. This minimizes interfering *chemical* reactions and is the only way that some degree of selectivity can be incorporated into a coulometric titration procedure. These requirements are rather easily satisfied in practice, as evidenced by the wide variety of titrants that can be generated and the large number of determinations that can be made by this technique.

It was mentioned in the section on Principles of Coulometry at Controlled Current (page 474) that the cell current must not exceed the limiting current of the depolarizing intermediate at any time during the titration. The magnitude of this limiting current is determined largely by electrode area, stirring rate, and concentration of the intermediate species. These facts are important in procedural design because they dictate the maximum magnitude of generation current on the one hand and the concentration of depolarizing intermediate and electrode area on the other hand. Lingane (p. 490, Bibliography item 1) has suggested a value of 0.5 ma. cm.$^{-2}$ millinormal^{-1} as an average value for the limiting current density of most substances. Accepting that value, the choice of procedural details becomes rather straightforward. This is best illustrated by example. Suppose the procedure is to accommodate samples that contain about 5 mg. of unknown of equivalent weight 50, *i.e.*, about 0.1 meq. The problem is to select suitable values of electrolysis time, generation current, electrode area, and concentration of depolarizing intermediate. Let us choose 250 seconds as a reasonable titration time; it is a conveniently short duration, yet can be measured quite precisely with a timer accurate to ± 0.02 second per start-stop cycle. The generation current can be calculated by means of Eq. (1),

$$Q = it = \frac{nwF}{M} = \frac{wF}{(M/n)}, \text{ as follows}$$

$$i, (\text{in ma.}) \times 250 \text{ sec.} = \frac{5 \text{ mg.} \times 96{,}487 \text{ mcoul. meq.}^{-1}}{50 \text{ mg. meq.}^{-1}}$$

$$i \cong 38.6 \text{ ma.}$$

Therefore, a current of 40 ma. is selected. By means of this value and the average value of the limiting current density, 0.5 ma. cm.$^{-2}$ mN^{-1}, one calculates the concentration of the depolarizing intermediate to be

$$\frac{40 \text{ ma.}}{0.5 \text{ ma. cm.}^{-2} \text{ m}N^{-1}} = 80 \text{ m}N\text{-cm.}^2 = 0.08\ N\text{-cm.}^2$$

i.e., 0.08 N if the electrode area is 1 cm.^{2}, 0.04 N if the electrode area is 2 cm.^{2}, etc. Because the above limiting current value is an average one, it is wise to increase the calculated concentration of depolarizing intermediate by a factor of at least two in practice.

Recalling again the discussion in the section on the Principles of Coulometry at Controlled-Current, it has been mentioned that when the substance being determined is electroactive it will support the entire cell current so long as its limiting current exceeds the cell current. When the substance being determined is not electroactive under the existing conditions or when its limiting current is exceeded by the cell current, then the depolarizing intermediate must be electrolyzed so as to maintain the cell current at a constant value. It is obvious, therefore, that titrant may not be generated at all until the latter stages of the titration if the substance being determined is itself electroactive. This means that by judicious procedural design it is sometimes possible to employ titrants which are generated with considerably less than 100 percent current efficiency. That is to say, it is the *net titration current efficiency* that determines the accuracy of the titration, not the *current-efficiency for titrant generation.* If 75 percent of the substance being determined undergoes direct electrode reaction and the remaining 25 percent undergoes chemical reaction with a titrant that is generated at 95 percent current efficiency, the net current efficiency for the titration is $75 + (25)(0.95) = 98.75$ percent and the titration error is only $+1.25$ percent. Greatest accuracy is obtained in this type of procedure when most of the substance being determined reacts directly at the electrode, *i.e.*, when its limiting current is large relative to the cell current. This implies the use of a small cell current. However, the current efficiency for titrant generation may depend upon current density—especially when the titrant is a strong oxidant or reductant—so these two competing factors will have to be considered in a carefully designed procedure. For this reason, it is wise to adhere closely to specified experimental details.

The different types of background currents mentioned in the section on Current Efficiency and Procedural Design (page 469) pertain to amperostatic as well as potentiostatic coulometry, but to different extents. The charging current is inherently larger in amperostatic coulometry than in potentiostatic coulometry because of the relatively large variations in generator electrode potential during an amperostatic electrolysis. Errors due to charging current are magnified when incremental (i.e., anticipatory) generation of titrant occurs near the end point. On the other hand, the continuous faradaic current, and the kinetic and induced background currents if they are operative, make a smaller contribution when the electrolysis is done at constant current; they are time dependent quantities and the total electrolysis time is generally smaller in an amperostatic than in a potentiostatic electrolysis. The faradaic impurity current is likely to be of the same magnitude in both techniques but again it can be minimized by electrolysis of the medium and reagents to the equivalence point before adding the sample test portion. In general then, amperostatic coulometry is subject to less error from background current contributions than is potentiostatic coulometry, and this means that amperostatic coulometry can be employed for the determination of smaller quantities with more convenience and greater accuracy than can potentiostatic coulometry.

SENSITIVITY, ACCURACY, AND PRECISION

It is axiomatic that the control of minute currents and the measurement of time are more convenient and accurate than the control and measurement of tiny volumes of standard solutions. Accordingly, coulometric generation is the best method for precise addition of minute amounts of titrant during a determination. An example of the extreme sensitivity of this technique is the titration of solutions containing 0.001 to 0.0005 μg. of manganese(VII) per ml. (total volume, 5 ml.) with electrolytically generated iron(II); the average error was only ± 5 percent.[62] A current of about 5 μa. was used, giving titration times of five seconds or so. One microgram of manganese(VII) could be determined with an average error of only ± 1.5 percent by the same procedure. Amperostatic coulometry is suitable not only for the determination of microgram amounts of materials, but also for the titration of microliter volumes of samples. This has been demonstrated[68] by the titration of microgram quantities of hydrogen, hydroxyl, and arsenic(III) ions in a total solution volume of 30–40 μl. (test portions were 10 μl.) with accuracy comparable to that obtained with larger quantities and volumes. Such results are striking examples of the capability of coulometric titrimetry as a microanalytical technique, but such extremely small quantities and volumes are rarely encountered in practice. Generally, one may expect to determine microgram quantities with an accuracy and precision of 1 to 2 percent, quantities of about 100 μg. with an accuracy and precision of about 0.5 to 1 percent, and milligram quantities to about 0.1 to 0.5 percent.

Recently, investigations have been directed towards establishing the ultimate precision and accuracy that can be obtained by coulometric titrimetry. A relative standard deviation of $s = 0.003$ percent was obtained when test portions containing 500 mg. of chromium(VI) were titrated with electrolytically generated iron(II).[69] Equivalent quantities of halides were also determined with a relative standard deviation of 0.005 percent by titration with electrolytically generated silver(I).[70] This order of precision requires extreme care in procedural design and operation. Under normal laboratory conditions, however, it is easily possible to operate within 95 percent confidence limits of 0.2 percent with macro quantities, assuming *a priori* that the procedure and instrument are designed properly.

[68] Schreiber, R., and Cooke, W. D., Anal. Chem., **27**, 1475, 1955.
[69] Marinenko, G., and Taylor, J. K., J. Res. Natl. Bur. Std., **67A**, 31, 1963.
[70] Marinenko, G., and Taylor, J. K., J. Res. Natl. Bur. Std., **67A**, 453, 1963.

EXEMPLARY PROCEDURE: THE DETERMINATION OF CHLORIDE[46,70]

The coulometric titration of chloride with electrolytically generated silver(I) is an accurate and precise method, of great practical importance. It illustrates many of the points that have been mentioned in earlier paragraphs. The method was developed originally by Lingane[46] and it is essentially his method that is given here.

Apparatus.—Cell I of Fig. 23-5 is suitable. It should be constructed of dark glass, accommodate 25 to 50 ml. of solution, and be fitted with a pure silver wire, gauze, or foil of large (10–20 $cm.^2$) surface area to act as generator anode. A platinum wire helix may be used as the generator cathode; it is placed in a separate compartment that contains only the supporting electrolyte solution. A saturated calomel reference electrode of the commercially available type is placed in a second compartment that contains 0.1 *M* sodium nitrate. These compartments or salt bridge tubes are connected electrically with the solution being titrated by means of coarse-porosity sintered glass discs which are plugged with a gel of 5 percent agar and 10 percent sodium nitrate. The indicator electrode is a silver wire. The procedure assumes an instrument that is capable of stopping the titration within 2 mvolts of a preset end-point potential.

Procedure.—Place 25 to 30 ml. of supporting electrolyte solution—0.4 *M* sodium nitrate + 0.05 *M* perchloric acid in 80 vol. percent ethanol-water—in the titration cell. Add 2 drops of 0.2 *M* hydrochloric acid and position the cell for electrolysis. Adjust the current level (cell switched OUT) to about 20 ma. and set the end-point potential to +0.230 volt *vs.* S.C.E. Switch the cell IN and allow this preliminary titration to proceed until an end point is reached. Switch cell OUT, zero the timer, but do not change the current level. Pipet into the pretitrated solution a test portion that contains 2 to 5 mg. of chloride. Switch the cell IN and allow the titration to proceed until an end point is again reached. Record the electrolysis time and current level. The titration of several successive test portions in the same solution is possible. Flush the cell with distilled water. The silver anode may be used until it has passed about 5 coulombs of electricity per square centimeter of surface area, then the accumulated deposit should be removed with a cyanide or ammonia bath. The weight of chloride titrated is calculated as follows:

$$\text{w (in g.)} = \frac{MQ}{nF} = \frac{35.453 \text{ g.mole}^{-1} \times i \text{ (in amp.)} \times t \text{ (in sec.)}}{1 \text{ eq. mole}^{-1} \times 96{,}487 \text{ coulombs eq.}^{-1}}$$

$$\text{Cl (in mg.)} = 3.674 \times 10^{-4} \times i \text{ (in mamp.)} \times t \text{ (in sec.)}$$

Relative error: ±0.2%; standard deviation, s = 0.005 mg. = 0.1%.

The primary reaction, $Ag + Cl^- \rightarrow AgCl(solid) + e^-$, supports the cell current during the early stages of this titration, *i.e.*, when the limiting current for chloride is greater than the cell current. During the latter stages of the titration, a *secondary* process occurs, namely an electrode reaction

$$Ag \rightarrow Ag^+ + e^-$$

followed by a chemical reaction

$$Ag^+ + Cl^- \rightarrow AgCl \downarrow$$

These facts are observable during the first titration of a series because the solution remains clear during the early stages, becoming turbid only during the latter portion of the electrolysis. Because of the reversible nature of the silver-silver(I) couple, potentiometric end-point detection is quite satisfactory. The end-point "breaks" are improved by the use of the alcoholic medium because of the decreased solubility of silver chloride. The equivalence point potential in this alcoholic medium is theoretically equal to +0.255 volt *vs.* S.C.E., but the recommended value of +0.230 volt *vs.* S.C.E. was found to give more accurate results. No asymmetry about the equivalence point is observed in the potentiometric titration curve because the titrant is generated from a solid depolarizing intermediate, rather than a solution containing a large excess of depolarizing intermediate. The method can be used for determining other species that can be titrated with silver(I). The original paper should be consulted for a thorough discussion of those (as well as the present procedures).[46]

SCOPE OF COULOMETRY AT CONTROLLED CURRENT

In a previous paragraph it was mentioned that all common types of titration reactions can be performed coulometrically, including neutralization, redox, precipitation, and complexometric titrations. It is not surprising, therefore, that a very large number of titrations that can be performed volumetrically can also be carried out coulometrically. In addition to these, there is a large number of reactions that either must be done or are best done by the coulometric technique. Titrants such as bromine or chlorine, uranium(IV) or (V), copper(I), tin(II), titanium(III), and chromium(II) are difficult or impossible to use in the form of standard solutions, but they can be generated electrolytically with ease. Likewise, titrations in such media as molten alkali halide eutectic mixtures are impossible by conventional techniques, but have been done coulometrically. It is quite clear that the generation of titrant *in situ* obviates the preparation, standardization, and handling of standard solutions. This alone is an important advantage of coulometric titrimetry, but it is of particular importance where the analyst has only limited or perhaps no access to the sample itself. Remote analysis of highly hazardous samples is greatly simplified when the analysis requires the manipulation of an electric current rather than a standard solution. Similarly, amperostatic generation of titrant is advantageous in kinetic studies where precise control of the rate of addition of a reactant is desirable. Finally, amperostatic coulometric electrolysis is a convenient method for preparing standard solutions of numerous reagents, solutions that are free of contamination and whose titer does not depend upon chemical standards or other analytical procedures.

The references that have been cited throughout the section Coulometry at Controlled Current illustrate the versatility of this technique as an analytical tool. Reference is given here to several of the recent and more complete tabulations of the analytical applications of coulometric titrimetry.

1. Meites, L., Ed., Handbook of Analytical Chemistry, McGraw-Hill Book Company, Inc., New York, 1963. P. S. Farrington summarizes the applications of controlled-current coulometry in two tables, each containing many references. Table 5-54 is organized according to the titrant that is generated, presenting optimum solution composition and conditions for each. Table 5-55 is organized according to the substance determined and is divided into two major portions, one dealing with inorganic and the other dealing with organic substances. A total of 150 of the more common procedures are included in this table. For each procedure, there is brief mention of the recommended titrant, solution conditions, and end-point detecting technique, plus pertinent references.

2. Lingane, J. J., Electroanalytical Chemistry, 2nd Ed., Interscience Publishers, New York, 1958. Chapter XXI deals exclusively with specific applications of the coulometric method of titration. It is arranged according to titrant. A discussion is given of all the applications of each titrant with pertinent references through 1957.

3. K. Abresch and I. Claasen, Die coulometrische Analyse, Verlag Chemie, GMBH, Weinheim/Bergstr., 1961. In German. Table 2 is divided into two major portions, one dealing with neutralization titrations and the second dealing with redox, precipitation,

and complexometric titrations. Each section is arranged according to substance determined whether inorganic or organic. Information on solution conditions, electrodes, end-point detection technique, concentration range, and accuracy is included, plus references. An English translation is available.

4. The Annual Reviews (Fundamental Part) published by Analytical Chemistry contain biennially in even-numbered years a review article on Electroanalysis and Coulometric Analysis. These articles should be consulted for information about developments in coulometry subsequent to those reported in the above references.

OTHER COULOMETRIC METHODS

The emphasis in this chapter has necessarily been placed upon the two techniques that find widest analytical application. There are, however, other methods that are rightfully called *coulometric;* they are treated very briefly in this section.

THE DETERMINATION OF FILMS AND COATINGS

Grower's[71] method for determining the quantity of tin and tin-copper alloy on tinned copper wire was probably the first truly "coulometric" method. He anodically oxidized the sample specimen until its potential showed an abrupt change which indicated complete dissolution of the coating. The quantity of coating was calculated from the quantity of electricity passed, measured by a gas coulometer. The method was improved by Miley[72] who conducted the electrolysis at constant current so that Q could be evaluated simply as the current-time product. This technique is now used widely for the determination of the quantity and/or thickness of metal coatings[73,74] and various types of tarnish or corrosion films.[75–77] The method is basically chronopotentiometry with coulometric measurement. Further details are given in the chapter of this volume that deals with chronopotentiometry (Chapter 21).

STRIPPING COULOMETRY

Stripping coulometry also involves the electrolytic removal of a film or deposit from an electrode, but is distinguished by the fact that the film is first prepared by electrodeposition. Thus, *anodic stripping coulometry* involves electrolytic deposition of a metal onto an electrode under carefully controlled conditions, then measuring the quantity of electricity required to remove the deposit. Some non-metals can be determined by *cathodic stripping coulometry* which is analogous except that the film is formed by oxidation and stripped by reduction.[78,79] In principle, stripping methods are both sensitive and selective.[80] Selectivity is possible through proper choice of electrode potential for the electrodeposition, while sensitivity is gained by continuing the electrodeposition electrolysis until a relatively large amount of deposit is accumulated. In practice, however, the method proves to be rather empirical because the electrodeposition is not usually carried to completion; the quantity of deposit depends upon such experimental variables as condition and type of electrode, its area, the temperature, the stirring rate if the solution is

[71] Grower, G. G., Proc. Am. Soc. Testing Materials, **17**, Part II, 129, 1917.
[72] Miley, H. A., Iron and Steel Inst. London, Carnegie Schol. Mem., **25**, 197, 1936.
[73] Francis, H. T., J. Electrochem. Soc., **93**, 79, 1948.
[74] Kunze, C. T., and Willey, A. R., J. Electrochem. Soc., **99**, 354, 1952.
[75] Campbell, W. E., and Thomas, U. B., Trans. Electrochem. Soc., **76**, 303, 1939.
[76] Allen, J. A., Trans. Faraday Soc., **48**, 273, 1952.
[77] Willey, A. R., and Kelsey, D. F., Anal. Chem., **30**, 1804, 1958.
[78] Maddox, W. L., Kelley, M. T., and Dean, J. A., J. Electroanal. Chem. **4**, 96, 1962.
[79] Laitinen, H. A., and Lin, Z., Anal. Chem., **35**, 1405, 1963.
[80] Mamantov, G., Popoff, P., and Delahay, P., J. Am. Chem. Soc., **79**, 4034, 1957.

stirred, and even the quantity of deposit that forms. After electrodeposition, the quantity of deposit may be determined in one of several ways: by potentiostatic coulometry[78] or more often by amperostatic coulometry[79] or from the current-potential curve (potential scanned at constant rate) obtained during the electrolytic dissolution of the film.[81,82] In any event, the analysis of very dilute solutions can be made by rigid control of experimental conditions and use of calibration curves. Solutions containing as little as 10^{-10} g. of silver(I) in volumes of 20 μl. to 25 ml. have been analyzed by anodic stripping coulometry under near ideal conditions.[81] More common concentrations fall in the range 10^{-4} to 10^{-9} M, in which range analyses may be run with a precision of about 5 percent. For a detailed discussion of stripping analysis, see Chapter 50 of Bibliography item 4.

VOLTAGE-SCANNING COULOMETRY

Voltage-scanning coulometry involves quantitative electrolysis at a working electrode whose potential is scanned through the potential region of interest in such a way that electrolytic equilibrium is maintained at all times. Two methods have been used to achieve this equilibrium. In the first, the voltage is scanned at a constant rate that is slow enough to allow equilibrium to be maintained at all times simply by vigorous mixing of the solution.[83] A plot of either instantaneous current (i) or total electricity (Q) *vs.* electrode potential (E) is recorded during the scan and an analogous plot is recorded for a reagent blank. When Q *vs.* E is plotted, the resulting curve (a coulogram) provides a measure of Q and hence a measure of the weight of the electrolyzed species. A plot of i *vs.* E is, of course, the time derivative of the coulogram if the voltage is scanned at a constant rate. From the value of i at the derivative maximum it is possible to calculate directly the weight of electrolyzed species; no integrator is necessary. Alternatively, the electrode potential can be scanned at a rate that is inversely proportional to the current, the proportionality constant insuring that equilibrium is maintained throughout the scan, and a plot of Q *vs.* E recorded. This is accomplished electronically.[40] Both of these methods attempt to increase the sample-signal-to-blank-signal ratio, thereby increasing the sensitivity of an analysis which might otherwise be done potentiostatically. Traces of iron (10^{-7} M) have been analyzed by the first technique mentioned: the detection limit was 0.025 μg. of iron in a total volume of 5 ml. and the standard deviation was $s = 0.02$ μg. based upon i_{MAX} or 0.04 μg. based upon Q.[83] Plutonium has been determined by the second method: 2 to 5 μg. in a 10 ml. volume were determined with a relative standard deviation of $s = 1$ percent.[40]

COULOMETRIC INTERNAL ELECTROLYSIS

Internal electrolyses are carried out without an external power supply simply by designing the cell so that the desired reaction occurs galvanically rather than electrolytically. This type of electrolysis can be used for coulometric analysis, of course, provided Q can be evaluated. Thus, manganese(VII), chromium(VI), vanadium(V), and acids have been titrated[84] by short-circuiting a platinum cathode in the sample compartment with a zinc anode in a second compartment (separated from the first by a salt bridge). By regulating the depth of submersion of the zinc rod, the current was maintained at a fairly constant value so that Q could be evaluated as the current-time product. The end point was determined potentiometrically. More sophisticated applications of the internal electrolysis technique exist as exemplified by the determination of small

[81] Lord Jr., S. S., O'Neill, R. C., and Rogers, L. B., Anal. Chem., **24**, 209, 1952.
[82] Nikelly, J. G., and Cooke, W. D., Anal. Chem., **29**, 933, 1957.
[83] Scott, F. A., Peekema, R. M., and Connally, R. E., Anal. Chem., **33**, 1024, 1961.
[84] Oelsen, W., Haase, H., and Graue, G., Angew. Chemie, **64**, 76, 1952.

quantities of oxygen in gas samples.[85] Oxygen in the gas sample is reacted with copper(I) to form copper(II), then the copper(II) formed is reduced back to copper(I) by internal electrolysis employing a copper anode and platinum cathode. The current-time curve, recorded after sample injection, provides a measure of Q (the area under the curve). It is obvious that such procedures are quite analogous to potentiostatic coulometric analyses with external potential control.

COULOMETRY IN CONJUNCTION WITH OTHER MEASUREMENTS

Controlled-potential coulometry has been used in conjunction with other analytical techniques to effect the simultaneous determination of two substances which for some reason cannot be determined independently in the presence of each other. The general procedure involves three steps: (a) a controlled-potential coulometric determination of the quantity of electricity consumed by electrolytic reaction of both substances, (b) the evaluation of some other concentration-dependent quantity for both substances, and (c) setting up and solving the appropriate simultaneous equations to obtain the respective weights of the two substances. Several such procedures have been used.

Coulometry Plus Gravimetry.[86, 87]—The controlled-potential coulometric determination of chloride and of bromide successively in mixtures of the two is not accurate because of coprecipitation of chloride on silver bromide. However, a simultaneous indirect determination is possible if both silver chloride and silver bromide are coulometrically deposited on a tared electrode, for then it is possible to weigh the electrode and obtain the total weight of the halide deposit. Two equations in two unknowns can be set up—one in terms of weight and one in terms of coulombs—and solved simultaneously for the individual weights of chloride and bromide. MacNevin and McIver[86] determined chloride and bromide in various ratios by this procedure with excellent accuracy: the relative errors were -0.1 and -0.3 percent for chloride and bromide, respectively, in a 1:1 mixture of the two. Here, as in all indirect procedures, the experimental error for the determination of one species is magnified when that species is present in much smaller quantity than the other. Zinc and cadmium have also been determined simultaneously by this *coulogravimetric* technique, utilizing a mercury electrode.[87]

Coulometry Plus Polarography.[88]—Coulometry has been used in conjunction with polarography to effect the simultaneous indirect determination of thallium and lead. In this case the polarographic diffusion current for the total reduction of the two ions was evaluated in addition to the number of coulombs required to reduce both species in a potentiostatic electrolysis. Employing these two experimental measures, two equations in two unknowns were solved simultaneously for the individual weights of thallium(I) and lead(II). This procedure is applicable even when both species have identical polarographic half-wave potentials; it is most accurate when the two species have quite different diffusion coefficients. For a 1.6:1 mixture of thallium(I) and lead(II), the relative errors were $+2.7$ and -2.1 percent respectively. Again, the error is larger for the determination of one species if it is present in relatively small amounts.

Coulometry Plus Volumetry.[89]—Mixtures of picric acid and dinitrophenol have been analyzed by utilizing a controlled-potential coulometric reduction along with a conventional volumetric titration. Coulometric reduction gave a measure of the coulombs of

[85] Knapp, W. G., Anal. Chem., **31,** 1463, 1959.
[86] MacNevin, W. M., and McIver, R. D., Anal. Chem., **25,** 274, 1953.
[87] MacNevin, W. M., and McIver, R. D., Anal. Chem., **27,** 1994, 1955.
[88] Meites, L., Anal. Chem., **27,** 1114, 1955.
[89] Meites, L., and Meites, T., Anal. Chem., **28,** 103, 1956.

electricity required to reduce all of the nitro groups present in the sample, while the titration gave a measure of the total milliequivalents of replaceable hydrogen present in the sample. With these data, two equations were set up and solved simultaneously for the weights of the two species present. The feasibility of this procedure derives from the fact that the two species have widely different n-values: $n = 18$ for picric acid, $n = 12$ for dinitrophenol.

APPLICATIONS IN THE ANALYSIS OF SPECIAL MATERIALS

Coulometric methods which are included in other chapters of Standard Methods of Chemical Analysis are:

1. Chapter 42, Volume III, Air Pollutants.
   a. Determination of ozone in air
2. Chapter 47, Volume III, Instrumental Methods in Clinical Medicine.
   a. Chloride
3. Chapter 64, Volume III, Water Determination.
   a. Water in liquid ammonia

SELECTED BIBLIOGRAPHY

The goal of this chapter has been to present the different types of coulometric methods, the basic principles of each, something of the experimental techniques that are commonly employed, and the practical utility of these methods in the analysis of real samples. Frequent reference has been made to other sources where a particular point or technique is treated in more detail than is possible here. Below are listed several works that are suitable for general reference.

1. Lingane, J. J., Electroanalytical Chemistry, 2nd Ed., Interscience Publishers, New York, 1958. Theory, technique, specific application.

2. Delahay, P., New Instrumental Methods in Electrochemistry, Interscience Publishers, New York, 1954. Mostly theory, some general technique.

3. Abresch, K., and Claasen, I., Die coulometrishe Analyse, Verlag Chemie, GMBH, Weinheim/Bergstr., 1961. In German. A survey of coulometric analysis with many references. An English translation is available.

4. Kolthoff, I. M., and Elving, P. J., Ed., Treatise on Analytical Chemistry, Part I, Vol. 4, Interscience Publishers, New York, 1963. Chapter 49, contributed by D. D. DeFord and J. W. Miller, is a general survey of coulometric analysis.

5. Rechnitz, G. A., Controlled-Potential Analysis, Pergamon Press, Macmillan, New York, 1963. A recent concise treatment of potentiostatic coulometry.

6. Weissberger, A., Ed., Technique of Organic Chemistry, 3rd Ed., Vol. I, Part IV, Interscience Publishers, New York, 1960. Chapter XLIX, contributed by L. Meites, is an informative treatment of potentiostatic electrolysis (including coulometry) with emphasis upon the practical application of the technique, particularly to organic compounds.

ACKNOWLEDGMENT

The author wishes to express his sincere appreciation to T. R. Mueller, D. G. Peters, R. W. Stelzner, W. E. Thomas, Jr., and P. F. Thomason for reading and commenting critically upon the content of this chapter.

Chapter 24

HIGH FREQUENCY METHODS

By Robert B. Fischer
School of Natural Sciences and Mathematics
California State College at Palos Verdes
Palos Verdes Peninsula, California

INTRODUCTION

Analytical methods in which a radiofrequency electrical field is applied to the substance undergoing analysis, and in which the electrical conductance and/or the dielectric constant of that substance govern the response of the measuring instrument are described in this chapter. The frequencies involved fall within the approximate range of one to 100 megacycles. Excluded are (a) methods employing higher frequency fields as, for example, microwave absorption, (b) methods employing lower frequency fields as, for example, alternating current polarography, and (c) methods based upon the imposition of strong magnetic fields upon radiofrequency fields, as in nuclear magnetic resonance spectrometry.

High frequency methods have been developed primarily for measurement upon liquid specimens. In a typical application, two electrodes are applied to the specimen, either by direct immersion or with the electrodes external to the vessel containing the liquid, and a radiofrequency potential is applied to, or developed across, this system. In addition to liquid-phase analyses, a few applications have been developed of high frequency methods for the analysis of gases and of solids, and it is probable that further such applications will be forthcoming in the future.

The electrical conductivity and the dielectric constant of a liquid sample may both be influenced by any or all components of that sample. Therefore, high frequency methods are generally not specifically selective for any one component. Useful applications generally involve samples of which one component is dominant in determining the overall conductivity or dielectric constant, or of which only one such component varies from one sample to another. Of particular practical utility are two types of measurement: dielectric constant measurement with immersed electrodes of nonionic liquids; conductance and/or dielectric constant measurement in a system in which it is not feasible to immerse any electrodes. The possibility of measurement without immersing any electrodes in the analytical sample is very appealing, not only for simplicity and convenience, but also because the test liquid and the electrodes are not contaminated by each other and because polarization effects are nonexistent.

PRINCIPLES

High frequency methods of analysis are frequently empirical. It is important to note, however, what properties of the test sample are of significance in determining instrument response. It is also important to note why, and under what circumstances, the methods are empirical rather than fundamental.

With Immersed Electrodes.—Two nonreactive electrodes, of any area and shape, immersed in a liquid medium, are electrically equivalent to a parallel resistance and capacitance, Fig. 24-1. The magnitudes of both R and C are influenced by the physical factors of electrode area and spacing. In addition, the magnitude of R is governed by the electrical conductivity of the liquid, and the magnitude of C is governed by its dielectric constant. Thus, measurement of R and of C leads to the determination of these characteristics of the sample.

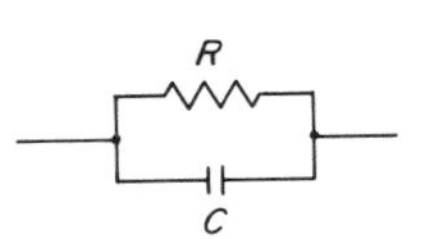

FIG. 24-1. Equivalent Circuit With Immersed Electrodes.

The measurement of R or of C must involve application of a potential between the electrodes; this must be an alternating potential—assumed in the following discussion to be sinusoidal—in order to eliminate polarization effects. The current which flows through R is in phase with the applied potential, and the current through C is 90° ahead of the potential. The total current flow is the vectorial sum of the two. The opposition which C offers to the flow of current, X_C, is designated capacitive reactance, and is dependent upon the frequency, f, as well as the capacitance, C:

$$X_C = \frac{1}{2\pi f C}$$

If either R or X_C is made considerably larger than the other, essentially all of the current goes through the path of lower opposition, and the branch of higher opposition is of no consequence in determining the electrical behavior of the system. Thus, for the measurement of dielectric constant, a high frequency should be selected to render X_C sufficiently small relative to R. Similarly, a low frequency should be chosen for the measurement of electrical conductivity, to make X_C sufficiently large relative to R.

It is also possible to measure R and C, when both R and X_C are of comparable magnitude. This can be done by means of an a.c. bridge, in which separate adjustments are provided for R and for C in the comparison arm. A single adjustment cannot suffice because of the phase difference in the current flow through each component.

With Nonimmersed Electrodes.—The situation is more complex when the electrodes are placed outside the vessel containing the sample. The vessel must be nonconducting as, for example, glass or plastic. The liquid itself is still a parallel R-C combination as in Fig. 24-1. In addition each electrode is capacitively coupled to the liquid as shown in Fig. 24-2, in which R and C are the same as in Fig. 24-1, and in which C_C is the series sum of the capacitance between each electrode, through the wall of the container, to the liquid. Inasmuch as C_C is characteristic of the physical apparatus only and not of the liquid undergoing analysis, this system is of no particular interest in analysis unless X_{C_C} defined as

$$X_{C_C} = \frac{1}{2\pi f C_C}$$

is sufficiently low that it does not dominate the combined opposition of R and C to the flow of electrical current. Thus, this system is useful only when used in high frequency circuits, a requirement fully acceptable if the dielectric constant is to be measured, and then particularly so if R is not overly low compared to X_C. Therefore, measurements with nonimmersed electrodes are of analytical interest only with high frequencies, and then primarily, but not solely, for measurements based upon the dielectric constant of a medium with little or no ionic conductivity.

Experimental measurement upon the system represented by Fig. 24-2 is generally accomplished by inserting the system either into a high frequency bridge circuit or into the tank circuit of a radiofrequency oscillator. Both methods generally, but not necessarily, treat the system as if it were either a parallel or series combination of a resistance and a capacitance, Figs. 24-3 and 24-4, rather than as the three-component system of Fig. 24-2. The circuits of Figs. 24-2, 24-3, and 24-4 are equivalent in the sense that all three exhibit the same opposition, both in magnitude and in phase relationships, to the flow of electrical current when proper values are selected for all components.

FIG. 24-2. Equivalent Circuit With Nonimmersed Electrodes.

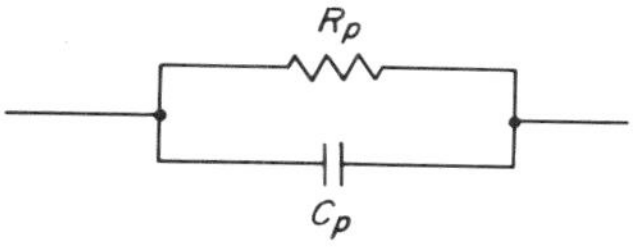

FIG. 24-3. Parallel R-C Equivalent of Fig. 24-2.

Equations for the values of C_p and R_p, and of C_s and R_s, in terms of the R, C, and C_C values of Fig. 24-2 may be calculated by conventional methods of circuit analysis. One of several forms in which these relationships may be derived is as follows:[1]

$$R_p = \frac{R^2\omega^2(C + C_C)^2 + 1}{R\omega^2 C_C^2}$$

$$C_p = \frac{C_C[R^2\omega^2 C(C + C_C) + 1]}{R^2\omega^2(C + C_C)^2 + 1}$$

$$R_s = \frac{R^2}{R^2\omega^2 C^2 + 1}$$

$$C_s = \frac{(R^2\omega^2 C^2 + 1)C_C}{(R^2\omega^2 C^2 + R^2\omega^2 C C_C + 1)}$$

in which ω is the frequency in radian units (*i.e.*, $\omega = 2\pi f$), and all other symbols are as already used in this chapter. Of utmost importance is the fact that each component of Figs. 24-3 and 24-4 is influenced by both the conductivity and the dielectric constant of the test liquid. Even if a direct experimental measurement is made of either the resistive or the capacitive component of Figs. 24-3 or 24-4, as with a radiofrequency bridge, both the R and the C of the test liquid contribute to the measured quantity. Thus, high frequency methods of analysis with nonimmersed electrodes involve a combination of the conductance and dielectric constant of the sample, rather than either one singly, although one or the other may be the dominant factor in a particular series of analyses. Furthermore, because of the complexity of the relationships between the parameters of the sample and the quantities which are experimentally measurable, it is necessary to treat most analyses by high frequency methods with nonimmersed electrodes on an empirical basis.

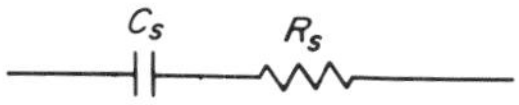

FIG. 24-4. Series R-C Equivalent of Fig. 24-2.

[1] Blaedel, W. J., and Petitjean, D. L., in Physical Methods of Chemical Analysis, W. G. Berl, Ed., Vol. III, Academic Press, New York, pp. 107–134.

The test system represented by Figs. 24-3 or 24-4 may be inserted as part or all of the capacitance in a radiofrequency oscillator tank circuit, Fig. 24-5. For oscillations to develop, this circuit must be in a resonant condition, in which the capacitive and inductive reactances are equal:

$$X_L = X_{C_r}$$

$$2\pi fL = \frac{1}{2\pi fC_r}$$

or

$$f = \frac{1}{2\pi\sqrt{LC_r}}$$

The effects of C_s or of C_r with nonimmersed electrodes, or of C with immersed electrodes, may be determined by a direct measurement of the resonant frequency or by a null adjustment method for the establishment of the same resonant frequency both with and without the test system in the circuit. The effects of the resistive component of Figs. 24-1, 24-3, or 24-4 upon the resonant frequency are not necessarily negligible, but they may be disregarded in this discussion. The resistive component does, however, influence the electrical characteristics of the oscillator in other measurable ways as, for example, in the amount of high frequency power consumed in this resonant circuit. The results of these measurements must be considered as highly empirical, but as based upon a combination of the electrical conductivity and the dielectric constant of the sample.

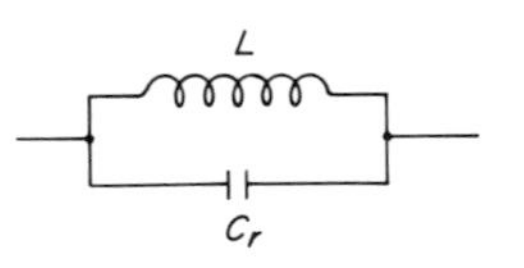

Fig. 24-5. Radiofrequency Oscillator Tank Circuit.

It is also of interest to note that inductance values, L, in the tank circuit may be measured similarly to capacitance values. The magnitude of any inductance is governed both by physical factors, such as the number, spacing, and diameter of the turns of wire, and by the magnetic permeability of the medium surrounding the wire. This permeability is somewhat characteristic of the chemical composition of that medium. Relatively little use has been made as yet of this relationship in chemical analysis.

INSTRUMENTATION

The principles of low frequency bridge circuits may be extended to the higher frequencies with appropriate choice of voltage source and detector and with proper design of bridge components to include appropriate ranges of resistance, capacitance, and, if needed, inductance values. The resistive and the reactive components must be balanced separately because of the phase difference in their current flows. Special attention must be paid to eliminating, or correcting for, stray capacitances between various portions of the apparatus, as these effects may be particularly significant at higher frequencies.

Many applications of high frequency methods of analysis involve inserting the test system as part of a radiofrequency oscillator tank circuit, but there is wide variety in what circuit parameter is measured. The measurement may involve a readjustment of some other component of the tank circuit to establish the same resonant frequency, both with and without the test liquid present, or it may be a direct reading of the resonant frequency or shift thereof upon insertion of the test liquid. Alternatively an anode, grid, or cathode current or voltage in the oscillator may be read, related in any event to the state of the resonant circuit.

Relatively few commercial instruments are being marketed which are directly designed for use in high frequency methods of analysis. Probably the most widely used of these is the Sargent Oscillometer (Fig. 24-6), which is primarily a capacitance measuring

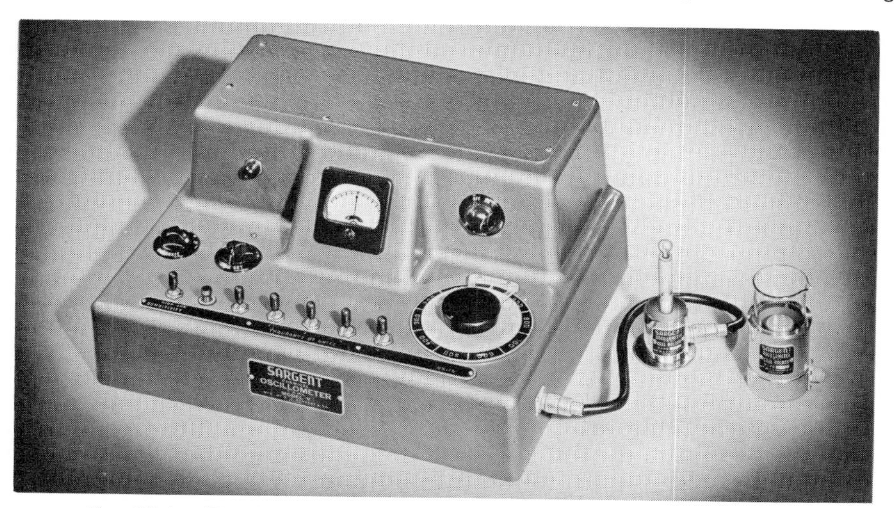

Fig. 24-6. The Sargent Oscillometer. (Courtesy E. H. Sargent and Co.)

device. It must be noted again, however, that a capacitance value as obtained with nonimmersed electrodes is a combined function of the conductivity and the dielectric constant of the sample, not just of the dielectric constant. The General Radio Company markets high frequency bridges (Fig. 24-7), and several manufacturers produce radio-frequency oscillators and other devices upon which the required instrumentation may be based. Many "home-made" instruments have been reported in the literature. All must be considered as devices for the measurement of some empirical combination of conductivity and dielectric constant when used with nonimmersed electrodes. Straightforward dielectric constant measurements are possible, however, with immersed electrodes.

APPLICATIONS

The high frequency method of analysis is of possible applicability whenever dielectric constant or electrical conductivity can be taken as indicative of the identity or the composition of the sample. The most common method of measuring the dielectric constant of a liquid is the high frequency method with immersed electrodes. The dielectric constant of a pure liquid is of interest in establishing its identity and is also of importance relative to its structure. Binary mixtures of nonionic liquids can be analyzed with calibration data obtained with known mixtures; the accuracy and precision are directly related to the difference in dielectric constant between the two components. Mixtures of more than two components cannot be analyzed readily by this method. If, however, all but one component of a multicomponent mixture are of similar dielectric constant, the system may be treated as a binary mixture.

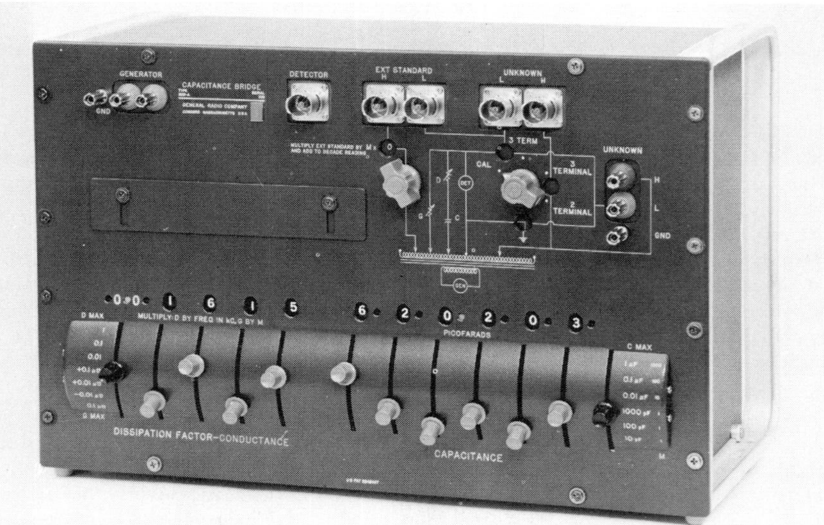

Fig. 24-7. Two of General Radio's High-frequency Bridges. (Courtesy General Radio Co.)

It is also possible to determine the dielectric constant of a nonionic liquid with nonimmersed electrodes, but the empirical nature of this type of measurement must be noted. Whenever an empirical calibration is acceptable and the use of immersed electrodes is undesirable for any reason, the method with nonimmersed electrodes is preferable to the more fundamental method with immersed electrodes.

Ionic species can also be measured and titrated by the high frequency method with nonimmersed electrodes. Again, the method is highly empirical. It is also generally limited to solutions which are dilute in all ionic components, although some apparatus does permit meaningful measurement in solutions with ionic strengths as high as about one molar. Therefore, conventional, lower frequency conductivity methods with immersed electrodes are preferable to the high frequency method for the titration of ionic solutions except when it is not feasible for any reason to immerse electrodes into the test solution or when the empirical combination of the R and C factors yields better end points than does any more fundamental type of measurement. A number of useful procedures have been developed involving precipitation and complex formation reactions. Titrations both in aqueous and in nonaqueous media are feasible by the high frequency method.

The apparatus for high frequency methods can readily be designed so as to provide a direct reading output, as contrasted to a null adjustment type of reading. Accordingly, a significant and distinctive area of practical application of the method with nonimmersed electrodes is in continuous analysis. Three types of such application are: (a) reaction rate studies, for example in the hydrolysis of esters and in polymerizations; (b) in monitoring the effluent of a chromatographic column; (c) in process control as, for example, in monitoring process streams in a petroleum refinery.

The high-frequency method of analysis is also applicable to process control systems. The output of the measuring instrument can readily be adapted to "on-off" or other desired types of control function. A further variation of the apparatus permits combining the high frequency electric field with a mercury column, as in a barometer or thermometer, to provide for an "on-off" type of operation.

Electrical conductivity and dielectric constant of liquid-phase substances are both temperature-sensitive properties. Thus, in any series of analyses by the high frequency methods, either the temperature must be maintained constant, or correction must be made for any variations in temperature.

Another area of application which merits mention is the measurement of actual dielectric constants of highly conducting media. Lengthy calibration and calculation are required to achieve data that are fundamental rather than empirical, but this can be accomplished.[2]

[2] Fischer, R. B., and Fisher, D. J., Trans. Indiana Acad. Sci., **62,** 160, 1953.

SELECTED BIBLIOGRAPHY

1. Blaedel, W. J., in Handbook of Analytical Chemistry, L. Meites, Ed., pp. 5-204 to 5-208, McGraw-Hill Book Co., New York, 1963. (This includes lists of applications of titrations in aqueous and nonaqueous media and of measurements of composition or properties dependent on composition.)
2. Daniels, F., Williams, J. W., Bender, P., Alberty, R. A., and Cornwall, C. D., Experimental Physical Chemistry, 6th Ed., pp. 212–231, McGraw-Hill Book Co., New York, 1962. (This includes discussion of principles and procedures for high frequency measurement of dielectric constant with immersed electrodes.)
3. Delahay, P., Instrumental Analysis, pp. 151–158, The Macmillan Co., New York, 1957.
4. Loveland, J. W., in Treatise on Analytical Chemistry, I. M. Kolthoff and P. J. Elving, Eds., Vol. 4, Part I, pp. 2569–2629, Interscience Publishers, New York, 1963.
5. Sherrick, P. H., Dawe, G. A., Karr, R., and Ewen, E. F., Manual of Chemical Oscillometry, E. H. Sargent and Co., Chicago, 1954.

Chapter 25

ELECTROGRAPHY AND ELECTROSPOT TESTING

By Harold W. Hermance and Harold V. Wadlow[1]
Bell Telephone Laboratories, Inc.
Holmdel, New Jersey

INTRODUCTION

Over the years, workers in many analytical fields have contributed to a growing collection of ingenious techniques to which the descriptive term *chemical contact printing* has been applied. The common objective in these methods is to obtain identification of surface components of a specimen by chemically transferring small amounts of that surface to a suitable receiving medium, usually paper. There, appropriate color reactions effect the identification, while the distributive pattern of the transferred products reflects any compositional differences on the original surface. It is this localized identification that justifies the term *printing.*

In chemical printing, the transfer is usually accomplished by moistening paper with a suitable dissolving agent, and then bringing it into intimate contact with the specimen surface. The resulting transferred material may have inherently characteristic color, but more often specific color producing agents are added before the transfer or are applied subsequently to "develop" the print.

In 1929, Glazunov[2] proposed electrolytic solution as a means of obtaining controlled transfer from metal surfaces. To his modification of chemical printing, he applied the term *electrography*. Electrolytic dissolution greatly enhanced the usefulness of printing methods. It eliminated the use of drastic transfer agents such as acids, which often interfered with specific color development. Furthermore, it reduced the transfer time to seconds and provided a close control of the amount of surface transferred.

As used by Glazunov, the term *electrography* was applied to the mapping of surface compositional patterns. Used loosely, it has often been extended to methods where electrolytic dissolution into paper is simply a very convenient means of obtaining a spot for purposes of identification. The abbreviated term *electrotransfer* used in this chapter applies to both uses, but since the equipment and techniques often differ considerably, the term *electrospot testing* will be used where identification is the primary objective, while *electrography* will apply to the printing of compositional patterns.

The basic electrotransfer assembly is shown in Fig. 25-1. It consists of two metal surfaces between which is sandwiched the printing pad of paper or other absorbent material containing an appropriate electrolyte and, in some cases, the identifying reagent. One of the metal surfaces will be that of the test specimen, the other, an inert

[1] The authors wish to acknowledge the experimental work done by Miss Nancy McKinney in preparation for this chapter.

[2] Glazunov, A., Chemie et Industrie, Special No., page 425, 1929.

or noninterfering metal. Together, these three members comprise the electrotransfer cell. Pressure is applied to the sandwich in some convenient manner to insure intimate contact. An external source of voltage is connected to the metal elements of the cell, the polarity of which will depend on whether cations or anions are to be driven from the specimen surface. Most often, it is metal ions, in which case the specimen is made the anode. Occasionally, however, anions such as chloride or sulphide may be under study in tarnish films. Then the specimen is made cathodic.

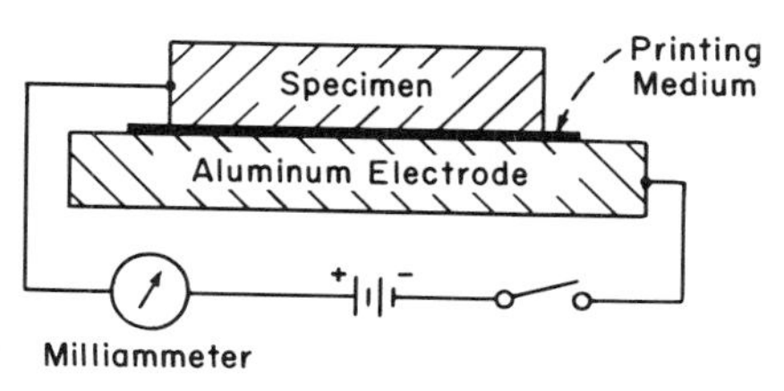

FIG. 25-1. Basic Electrotransfer Assembly.

With the two metal surfaces parallel and in good contact with the paper, a uniform electrical field drives ions released from the surface in a straight line toward the cathode. Reaction of these ions in the paper to form insoluble colored compounds preserves their spatial distribution, and reproduces patterns present on the specimen surface. In this manner, pinholes or scratches in a surface coating, contaminants or segregations on a surface may be printed in identifying colors.

APPARATUS

The electrotransfer equipment will, of course, depend on the specific objective. For electrospot testing, the essential equipment often may be contained in a portable unit. It might include an aluminum base platen with wire lead for electrical connection, a current supply from flashlight cells, and a probe for making electrical connection to the specimen together with the necessary papers, solutions, and trays for applying the electrolyte and developing the print.

Press for Electrotransfer.—For electrography and for those uses which require a more controlled technique, a press is a necessity. Besides applying a constant, measurable force to the printing sandwich, it allows the operator freedom to attend to the electrical adjustments and the timing. One form of press is shown in Fig. 25-2. An overhead screw compresses the electrotransfer sandwich against a spring-loaded table made of non-conducting material, such as bakelite or hard rubber. The compressing force is measured by the depression of the table, shown on a suitable vertical scale. The table is mounted on a plunger which slides in a cup containing one of several interchangeable calibrated springs. An axial aligning rod through the bottom of the cup keeps the spring centered. Further details of the press are purposely omitted here since other designs will undoubtedly occur to the reader. The size, too, will depend on the specific use.

The electrode surface opposed to the specimen in the sandwich must not contribute ions which might interfere with the test. Surfacing with an inert metal such as gold will avoid this. Aluminum can be used for most work, however, since it produces few interferences with identification reactions. It does have a tendency to become passive, and it should, therefore, be cleaned frequently with a fine abrasive.

Current Supply.—For a portable kit used for occasional electrospot testing of small areas, the current drain may be light enough to permit the use of flashlight cells. Four

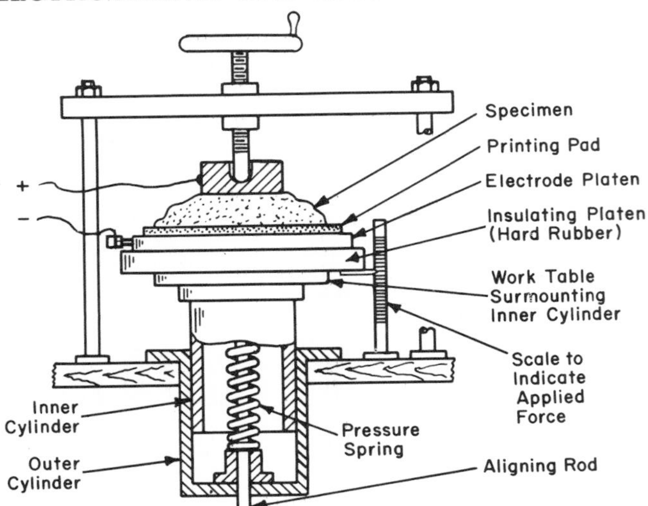

FIG. 25-2. Press for Use in Electrography.

of these, with a selector switch to add them in one at a time, will provide an adequate voltage range for most simple testing needs. An inexpensive milliammeter, range 5 to 500, to indicate the progress of the printing and a push button switch may be added for convenience.

For the more exacting uses of electrography, control of current and time become important. This is especially so when rough quantitative estimations are made by comparing the prints of known and unknown specimens. Successful electrographic printing, as in "pin hole" testing, often depends on reproducing experimentally determined conditions. Also, in some instances, selectivity may be improved by careful regulation of voltage.

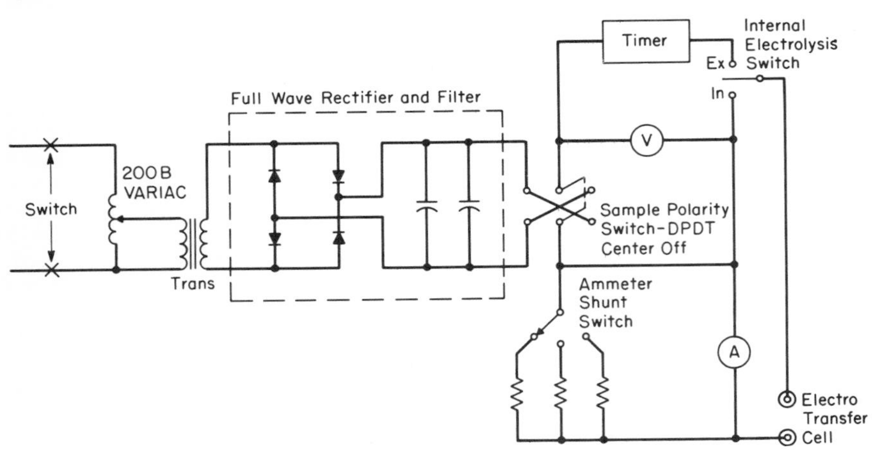

FIG. 25-3. Laboratory Circuit for Electrography.

A suitable laboratory circuit is shown in Fig. 25-3. A variable transformer feeds the primary of a second, fixed transformer, the output of which is converted to direct durrent by a full-wave rectifier with suitable filter. This arrangement permits close regulation of the output voltage by adjustment of the variable transformer. A polarity switch eliminates the need for changing connections at the press. Provision should be made for inserting a timing switch in the d.c. circuit. Timers used for switching photographic enlargers have a range suitable for electrography. The circuit has a center zero milliammeter with several scale ranges. A center zero voltmeter with a 0–10 range is placed across the electrotransfer cell. Another feature that is sometimes useful is a switch which cuts out the external current supply and short circuits the electrographic cell through the milliammeter. This permits the printing to proceed by "internal electrolysis," a technique occasionally used to print only the more electropositive metal in a heterogeneous structure.

THE TRANSFER MEDIUM

The obvious functions of the transfer medium are to contain the electrolyte and to receive the ions from the surface under test. If original distributive patterns are to be reproduced, however, that medium must be uniformly permeable, with a structure that does not impose any gross density variations on the print. So far as possible, it should restrict lateral diffusion of the transferred ions or their reaction products. Thus, filter paper with long-fibered open structure permits diffusion, while close textured paper tends to preserve transfer detail. Another important quality that the medium should have is high wet strength. In many procedures, the final identifying spot is obtained only after a series of treatments to remove interfering elements. Throughout these multiple immersions and washings, the paper must resist disintegration and must hold the transferred material with a minimum of loss or diffusion. Hardened, tight filter papers, such as Whatman No. 50 or Schleicher and Schull No. 576, have these qualities and give reasonably faithful prints. It is generally advisable to employ a thick, soft paper beneath the printing sheet. This provides greater capacity for electrolyte, preventing drying out, and the resulting cushioning improves contact with the specimen. This lower paper also protects against possible interferences from the opposite electrode. Photographic blotting paper is a good material for this purpose.

Where fine detail is required, the closest filter paper may be too coarse. A medium then is needed with a texture finer than the structure to be recorded. A number of materials have been employed to meet this objective. Of these, the most generally useful is a gelatin coated paper used in photography for dye transfer processes.[3] It is similar to photographic printing paper, except that the silver salts are absent. Since the gelatin coating is practically structureless, it places no limit, *per se*, on the detail attainable. Furthermore, lateral diffusion is retarded by the gelatin coating. Another material is unplasticized cellophane sheet, which adds the advantage of a transparent print, although its capacity for holding electrolyte and transferred products is somewhat limited. It is best used where sensitive reactions require only a small amount of ion transfer. Use has also been made by the writers of the porous membrane media such as "Millipore." [4] Since the extremely fine pores of this material do not communicate laterally, diffusion is negligible and very sharp prints can be obtained. These prints can also be made transparent by mounting in a fluid of suitable refractive index. The chief drawbacks are the high cost and the fragile nature of this material. Yagoda[5] has

[3] Marketed by Eastman Kodak Co. as Dye Transfer Paper-F.
[4] MF-Type HA-White −0.45 microns. Millipore Filter Corp., Bedford, Massachusetts.
[5] Yagoda, H., Ind. and Eng. Chem., Anal. Ed., **12,** 698, 1940.

made excellent prints on thin plaster of Paris wafers. He used this same material to make casts of irregular specimens, after which the casts were impregnated with appropriate electrolytes and prints were made on their surfaces.

Unlike paper, both gelatin and cellophane take up impregnating solutions slowly. They must, therefore, be soaked in the electrolyte for 10 minutes or more before use. This fact must also be remembered in applying developing solutions to prints on these materials.

TECHNIQUE

Preparation of the Specimen.—For electrospot testing and for differentiation of gross structures, a surface freshly renewed with fine abrasive and washed free of abrasion products and oily films is generally satisfactory. For electrographic reproduction of thin surface features, such as applied coatings, frictional transfers, tarnish, and other contaminants, any treatment beyond removal of dusts and oily films is precluded by the nature of the test.

The electrographic mapping of inclusions, segregations, or deep structural features requires more involved preparation of the specimen. A suitable section is ground and polished as for metallurgical examinations. A light etching, to remove the disordered polishing layers, usually enhances the printing of more delicate structures. Irregularly shaped metal specimens may be oriented and mounted in plastic before sectioning and polishing. Electrical contact to the back of such mounted specimens may be made by drilling a hole in the plastic and filling with solder or Wood's metal. When printing a mineralogical specimen which is not uniformly conducting, it is necessary to provide electrical continuity over the back surface of the specimen, which may be irregular in shape. A convenient means of doing this is afforded by silver-conducting paints, which are commercially available.

Making the Transfer.—After soaking in the electrolyte, the pad (composed of printing and backing sheets) is drained, but not blotted, and is then placed on the lower electrode platen, printing face up. The prepared specimen surface is placed on the pad and pressure is applied. The excess electrolyte which squeezes out is taken up in blotting paper, applied around the specimen edges. This sequence of operations reduces the likelihood of trapping air in the sandwich, particularly if the specimen surface is slightly rough. Pressures of 25 to 50 pounds per square inch are satisfactory for most work. However, where tiny voids, such as pin holes, in a surface coating are to be reached for printing, it may be necessary to increase the pressure to several hundred pounds per square inch. With the proper polarity of the sandwich first assured and the voltage adjusted, the current is then applied. If the surface of the test specimen contains minor irregularities, that are, however, too great to be compensated for by the cushioning of the printing pad, the lower electrode may be a sheet of thin tin or aluminum foil resting on a compressible material such as rubber.

Current, Time, and Voltage.—The current and time required will be determined by the quantity of ion transfer needed. This will vary, depending on the sensitivity of the color reactions employed. For present purposes, this specific sensitivity may be defined as the number of micrograms per square centimeter of the ion under test required to produce a satisfactory color density. If we assign to the sensitivity, the symbol k, from Faraday's second law,

$$i_d t = \frac{96.5k}{Q}$$

where: i_d is the current density in ma./cm.^{2};
t is the time in seconds;
k is the specific sensitivity value (as defined above); and
Q is the equivalent weight of the element under test.

Obviously, the value of k is only approximate and will vary with the transfer medium and the purposes of the test. In the case of pin holes or inclusions where the element under test occupies very small areas, a greater color density is usually required. For general guidance, a value of 30 for k provides a good starting point. From k, the trial current and time may be calculated.

For example: a good depth of color is obtained for nickel with dimethylglyoxime when the density is 20 μg./cm.^{2} Under test conditions, a current density of 15 ma./cm.^{2} is obtained. The required time is obtained from the equation:

$$15t = \frac{96.5 \times 20}{29.3} = 4.4 \text{ sec.}$$

The voltage measured across the electrotransfer cell is the algebraic sum of the IR drop through the pad and the EMF generated internally by the cell. This internal EMF is the potential difference between the specimen and its opposing electrode in the electrolyte used. It may aid the applied EMF or it may oppose it. Thus, if a copper specimen were being printed, using an aluminum cathode plate, the EMF of the sandwich would oppose the applied potential and no printing would occur until this back EMF is exceeded. A zinc specimen, on the other hand, being printed against a copper cathode plate, theoretically would require no applied potential. If the wires from the two sandwich members were joined, current would flow, the zinc would dissolve, and printing would take place by "internal electrolysis," although the process might be slow for practical use.

In general, the voltage applied to a specimen should not greatly exceed the solution potential of the metal to be detected. In this way, all of the electrical energy is used to dissolve the metal and Faraday's law may be applied to the transfer. This will not be the case when high current densities are used which raise the voltage above the decomposition potential of the electrolyte, for then part of the energy is used to release oxygen and hydrogen. This gassing also tends to break the contact between the specimen surface and the printing pad and drives the electrolyte out of the pad, producing poor prints.

The surface of a nonhomogeneous specimen in contact with an electrolyte will not be at uniform potential, but will have local anodic and cathodic areas set up between the different metal species appearing there. To obtain an electrotransfer of the whole surface, the applied potential must, therefore, exceed any local potential differences so as to render the whole surface anodic. Thus, to print a copper inclusion in a zinc specimen, the Zn-Cu couple potential must be exceeded. A detailed discussion of the conditions on such surfaces has been given by Hunter, Churchill, and Mears.[6]

As the electrotransfer progresses, the resistance of the cell tends to increase due to depletion of electrolyte, precipitation of reaction products, and polarization effects. For more quantitative work where the current is to be held as constant as possible, it is, therefore, important to minimize these effects. Sensitive reactions should be chosen which require a minimum of transferred material and electrolytes selected to reduce polarization and precipitation at the specimen surface.

[6] Hunter, M., Churchill, J., and Mears, R., Metal Progress, **42,** 1070, 1942.

Known Specimens.—A collection of known metals and alloys should be acquired. In devising a test for a particular alloy component, for example, it is essential to know how each of the other components will respond to a proposed sequence of printing and processing. A useful arrangement for testing combinations of known metals and alloys is shown in Fig. 25-4. A block of insulating material, such as Teflon, is drilled with a

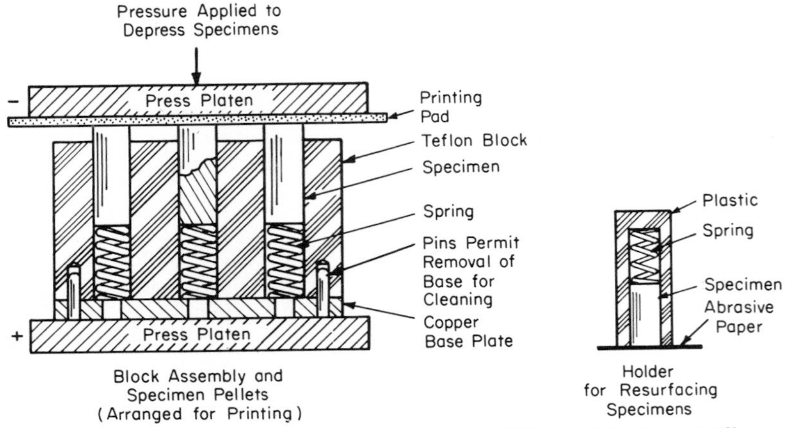

FIG. 25-4. Test Arrangement for Combinations of Known Metals and Alloys.

series of holes of uniform diameter. Known metals are machined into cylindrical pellets of uniform length which slide freely in the holes in the block. Coiled phosphorbronze springs placed in the holes support the pellets and provide electrical contact to a base plate. The lengths of the pellets and the springs are so adjusted that the pellets project part way out of the block, but when depressed to a flush position, each will exert an adequate force against the printing pad. The block is placed in the press with the specimens made positive; the printing pad, surmounted by the negative platen, is pressed into contact with the block face, and the transfer is obtained in the usual manner. Thus, any desired combination of metals may be electrospotted simultaneously and under identical conditions of timing, applied voltage, and paper impregnation. The resulting spots may then be given various treatments to the end that only the spot of the metal sought will remain after the processing.

THE ELECTROLYTE

In the electrotransfer, solution depends primarily on oxidation (or reduction in the case of anions) brought about by the potential difference at the specimen-electrolyte interface. The composition of the electrolyte, however, may have important secondary effects. It may determine whether the products of electrolysis build up on the surface of the specimen to form a partial or complete barrier to further passage of ions (polarization and passivation) or whether the ions will move unobstructed into the printing medium. Thus, copper, silver, and lead dissolve well with a nitrate electrolyte, but poorly with chloride, which coats their surfaces with insoluble products. Conversely, iron, aluminum, nickel, and gold tend to become passive in nitrate, but dissolve well in chloride electrolytes. Lead gives excellent prints with acetate. There are circumstances, however, in which passivation may be employed to advantage, particularly in porosity tests. These will be discussed later.

While it is essential to maintain smooth, continuous solution *at the specimen surface*, control of lateral diffusion of the transferred ions is also important if detailed patterns are to be obtained. In gelatin and similar media, diffusion is slow enough that sufficient detail may be preserved in a direct print. In open structures such as paper, however, it is desirable to control diffusion by regulated conversion of the transferred ions into insoluble products. In this way, patterns are better preserved, and an adequate concentration of the transferred material is obtained in the paper. When such prints are required to undergo further development treatments, this interim fixation becomes a necessity.

By buffering the electrolyte with sodium carbonate, practically all metals can be precipitated in the print as carbonates or basic carbonates. Carbonate fixation has several advantages: since precipitation of metal carbonates is readily controllable by pH adjustment, it is easily reversed to recover the metal ions for subsequent identification reactions and no anions are introduced which might later interfere with such reactions.

If the ratio of sodium carbonate in the electrolyte is properly adjusted, precipitation at the anodic metal specimen surface is prevented by the acidity developed there; hence, no barrier films are formed. However, a sharp increase in pH occurs away from the specimen surface due to the buffering action of the sodium carbonate. Precipitation then takes place in the deeper layers of the paper with no interference with anodic solution. The prints in Fig. 25-5 show the control of diffusion of copper obtained by the addition of sodium carbonate to a nitrate electrolyte, using C.S. & S. No. 576 paper.

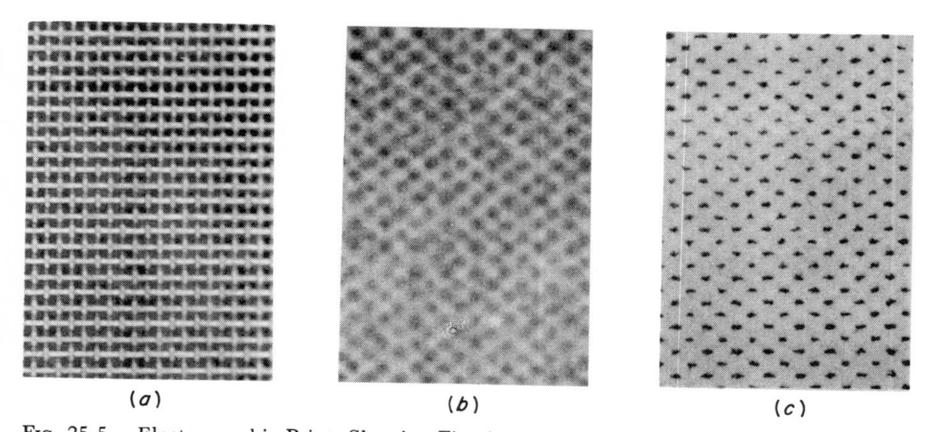

FIG. 25-5. Electrographic Prints Showing Fixation by Use of Buffered Electrolyte. *a*, Specimen copper screen (5×). *b*, Print made with 0.5 *M* $NaNO_3$ electrolyte only. Note diffusion (5×). *c*, Print made with 0.5 *M* $NaNO_3$ but with 0.5 *M* Na_2CO_3 added. Note improved definition (5×).

Generally, satisfactory transfers are obtained with electrolytes having a salt concentration of 0.1 to 0.5 *M*. By using equivalent concentrations of the several electrolytes commonly used, they may be interchanged or mixed without large changes in the cell resistance, thus facilitating comparison of experimental prints.

RECOGNITION OF THE ELECTROTRANSFER

Recognition of a transferred material involves its ultimate conversion to a characteristically colored product. Whether this is accomplished immediately in the transfer process, or only after a sequence of treatments, will depend on the nature of the identifying reaction and on the need to remove interfering materials also transferred.

Thus, iron inclusions in an aluminum surface may be electrographed directly with a 0.1 *M* potassium ferrocyanide solution, the iron areas showing as the deep blue ferric ferrocyanide. The only processing of the print would be to wash out the residual electrolyte. This exemplifies the simplest procedure, in which detection and differentiation are favored by the particular combination of metals and the availability of a color producing electrolyte.

On the other hand, let us suppose lead is to be detected in a brass. Direct detection is not feasible because of interferences by the large amounts of copper and zinc. A heavy electrospot is made on paper using a nitrate-carbonate electrolyte. It is then washed with ammonia–ammonium chloride solution which removes the copper and zinc. Lead remains as colorless basic carbonate. The washed spot is then transferred to a sodium chromate solution acidified with acetic acid. The lead carbonate thus is converted to the yellow chromate. Washing out the excess sodium chromate completes this procedure. This is an example of the indirect method in which a "latent" print contains all of the transferred metals in a temporarily fixed condition. Specific identification is obtained after removal of the interfering metals by one or more treatments, followed by an appropriate color-producing reaction.

Electrospot Testing.—Let us first consider those applications of the electrotransfer which emphasize identification of transferred materials, without particular regard for the printing of distributive patterns.

As pointed out earlier, electrospot testing can be regarded simply as a very convenient variation of the paper spot technique so ingeniously advanced by Feigl and others. As such, the reader will be aided in the specific identification methods by consulting Feigl's book.[7] It is beyond the capacity of this chapter to do more than suggest some general procedures when the test spot is obtained by electrotransfer.

Electrospots of uniform size and contour provide certain operational advantages, particularly when capillary separations or comparison of color densities are to be made. This can be accomplished by a mask of thin polyethylene having the desired opening, placed over the transfer pad, thus limiting the area of the specimen to be electrolyzed. An alternative is the "spotting electrode" of desired dimensions in which the area electrolyzed is defined by placement of this electrode on the backing sheet. This method is especially useful for unwieldy specimens. Slight diffusion may occur around the edges of the spot, but for usual purposes, this is not objectionable.

Single Metal Surfaces and Identifying Reactions.—Clearly, the simplest identifications involve single metal surfaces. A practical example would be electrodeposited coatings. In such cases, prior knowledge will often limit the number of possibilities so that one need only insure that the applied tests are specific within those limits. Then, it is often feasible to choose the pad impregnation so that the transfer and identification are effected in one operation. Thus, a ferrocyanide electrolyte would give distinctive colors directly for iron, copper, nickel, and molybdenum.

Many useful color-producing reagents cannot be added to the electrolyte because of their limited solubility. The difficulty may be circumvented by using papers in which

[7] Feigl, Fritz., Spot Tests in Inorganic Analysis, Elsevier Publishing Co., New York, 1958.

the reagents have been incorporated beforehand from a suitable solvent. Most papers, so prepared, will keep for several weeks if stored away from light and humidity. Another form of reagent paper employs moderately insoluble salts of certain anions precipitated in its fibers.[8] These papers offer several advantages over the soluble salts. For field work, they are convenient, reducing the number of solutions to be carried. They usually afford better control of "bleeding" and diffusion. Thus, copper prints made with cadmium diethyldithiocarbamate paper (impregnated from a 1 percent acetone solution of the salt) have better detail than when made with paper soaked in a water solution of the sodium salt. "Fixed" reagent papers may provide desirable control of the reactive anion. Thus, zinc, cadmium, and antimony sulfide papers provide a decreasing order of sulfide ion concentration. Lead will print on zinc sulfide paper, but not on antimony sulfide. Copper and silver print on all three. Table 25-1 lists a number of reagent papers useful for electrotransfer work.

When it is not possible to obtain a suitable electrospot test directly, identifying reagents are applied to the undeveloped spot as a separate step. This is also necessary when reagents are unstable under conditions of electrolysis. The spot may also require intermediate treatments before the final color is developed. A manganese spot, for example, may first require oxidation to managnese dioxide with hydrogen peroxide, after which application of benzidine acetate develops the confirming blue color. Zinc gives no suitable direct color reactions. However, it can be converted to white zinc sulfide in the spot with sodium sulfide. After washing out the excess sodium sulfide with dilute acetic acid, immersion in lead acetate will turn the white spot dark as the zinc sulfide is converted to lead sulfide. This sequence confirms the presence of zinc.

Alloys, Separations, and Elimination of Interferences.—When the specimen is an alloy, identification of its components may become more involved. Few color reactions are specific enough, *per se*, to identify directly one metal in the presence of other alloy elements. The most practical plan is to prepare a series of spots, using a general purpose electrolyte such as sodium nitrate or chloride with sodium carbonate buffer. Each spot may then be used for a specific identification, and given such treatment as may be necessary to eliminate interference by other metals. Useful preliminary information may be derived from the color of the untreated spots and from the application of a few simple treatments such as those listed in Table 25-2.

Interferences may be eliminated in several ways. One is to mask the interfering metals with an agent that reduces their ion concentration below the interference threshold.[9] Zinc in a copper-nickel alloy may be confirmed by the sulfide sequence mentioned earlier if cyanide is added to tie up the copper and nickel as complex ions.

Another method of removing interfering metals, which follows classical analytical procedure, is to apply treatments which render the unwanted metals soluble, while those under test remain fixed as insoluble products in the spot. This procedure is particularly useful when the test is for minor constituents which need to be freed from the bulk metals. Small amounts of iron, aluminum, lead, or beryllium in copper may be isolated in this manner by washing the spot with warm ammonia–ammonium chloride solution until the blue color of the copper has completely disappeared. Nickel in iron can be revealed by electrospotting on dimethylglyoxime paper with sodium acetate electrolyte, then washing out the iron with dilute acetic acid.

When spots are to be washed as in the above procedures, the washing fluid should be drawn through the spot. A Büchner funnel with a circular pad of blotting paper to

[8] Clarke, B. L., & Hermance, H. W., Ind. Eng. Chem., Anal. Ed., **9**, 272, 1937.

[9] An excellent treatment of masking agents is contained in Fritz Feigl's Chemistry of Specific, Selective and Sensitive Reactions, Academic Press, New York, 1949.

TABLE 25-1. FIXED REAGENT PAPERS[a]

Reagent	Preparation	Paper Color	Color of Reaction Products[b] Cu	Ag	Pb	Bi	Cd	Zn	Ni	Co	Fe	Mo	Al	Sn	Cl	S	Remarks
Zinc sulfide	1. Zn acetate 0.25 *M* 2. Na sulfide	White	Bk	Bk	Bn	Bn	Yl					[c]					Na_2CO_3-$NaNO_3$ electrolyte
Cadmium sulfide	1. Cd acetate 0.25 *M* 2. Na sulfide	Yellow	Bk	Bk	Bn	Bn						[c]					Same
Antimony sulfide	1. Na sulfantimoniate, 2–5% 2. HCl, dilute	Orange	Bk	Bk	Bn	Bn						[c]					Same
Zinc ferrocyanide	1. Zn acetate 0.25 *M* 2. K ferrocyanide	White	Brick Rd						Lt Gn		Bl	Bn					Same
Lead carbonate	1. Pb acetate 0.1 *M* 2. Na carbonate	White														Bk	Cathodic redn., for sulfide
Silver chromate	1. Ag nitrate 0.1 *M* 2. Na chromate	Red													Wh		Cathodic redn., for chloride
Cadmium diethyldithio-carbamate	1% soln., in acetone or chloroform	White	Lt Bn	[c]								[c]					Am. citrate electrolyte[d]
Dimethyl-glyoxime	1% alcoholic soln.	White		[c]					Rd			[c]					Am. citrate electrolyte Wash-NH_4OH-Am. citrate[d]
α-Benzoinoxime	1% alcoholic soln.	White	Gn	[c]								[c]					Na_2CO_3-$NaNO_3$ electrolyte wash dil. acetic acid[d]
Cinchonine	1% alcoholic soln.	White	Bn	Yl	Yl	Or			Or	Or		[c]					KI electrolyte, bleach-H_2SO_3
Morin	0.5% alcoholic soln.	Pale Yellow	Lt Yl	[c]	Wk Fl	Wk Fl	Wk Fl	Br Fl		Bn	Bn	[c]	Br Fl	Wk Fl			Fluorescent reagent, examine-UV
Salicylic acid	2% alcoholic soln.	White	Gr Yl					Fl		Gn	Vi		Fl				Na_2CO_3-NaCl electrolyte
Barium rhodizonate	1. 0.5% Na rhodizonate 2. 0.25 *M* Ba acetate	Orange														(SO_4) Wh	Cathodic redn., for sulfate

[a] Reproduced with permission from W. Berl, "Physical Methods in Chemical Analysis," Vol. II, Table III, p. 188, Academic Press, New York, 1951.
[b] Yl, Yellow; Rd, Red; Bl, Blue; Or, Orange; Gn, Green; Vi, Violet; Wh, White; Gy, Gray; Bn, Brown; Bk, Black; Fl, Fluorescence; Wk, Weak; Br, Bright; Lt, Light.
[c] Reduction (or Ag or Mo).
[d] Suggested electrolyte and/or treatment to obtain color reactions indicated.

TABLE 25-2. PRELIMINARY EXAMINATION OF ELECTROSPOTS

Test	Ag	Au	Bi	Cd	Co	Cr	Cu	Fe	Mn	Mo	Ni	Pb	Pd
Original Spot $NaCl + Na_2CO_3$	Wh.	Yel.	Wh.	Wh.	Pink	Yel.	Blue-Green	Gr.-Or.	Wh.	Indigo	Gr.	Wh.	(5V) Yel.-Or.
Fumed over NH_4OH		Yel.			Brown	Yel.	Blue	Or.-Br.	Br.	Br.	Violet	—	—
Fumed over HCl	Wh.	Yel.		—	Blue	Yel.	Yel.	Yel.	—	Br.	Yel.-Gr.	Wh.	Wh.
Treated with 10% HI	Yel.	—	Yel.	—	—	—	[a]	[a]	—	—	—	Yel.	—
Treated with 1% Na_2S	Blk.	Br.	Blk.	Yel.	Blk.	—	Blk.	Gr.-Blk.	Br.	Yel.-Br.	Blk.	Blk.	Br.
Treated with hypophosphorous acid as reducing agent	Br.-Blk.	Violet	—	—	—	—	—	—	—	Gray	—	—	Br.

[a] Iodine released.

distribute the suction evenly accomplishes this. The transfer, print side up, is placed on the moistened pad, suction is applied, and the wash fluid is delivered in a gentle stream over the spot area.

Separations are also possible by using the controlled flow of fluids in the capillary structure of the paper. To illustrate, one may wish to confirm chromium in an alloy steel. A circular spot is made, using a nitrate-carbonate electrolyte. The chromium transfers as soluble chromate, while the iron and other components will form insoluble basic compounds. The spot is allowed to become nearly dry, then water is introduced at its center from a capillary pipet. As the water spreads radially, it carries the soluble chromate with it, ultimately forming a yellow ring outside the transfer spot. Chromate may be confirmed by spotting the ring with silver nitrate in dilute acetic acid.

The radial spreading technique has been refined by Weisz[10] and applied to systematic spot separations. Weisz makes use of a ring-shaped heater block (Ring Oven, Vol. II, Part A, P. 84) to effect continuous evaporation of the wash fluid in a sharply defined ring zone. This permits the use of more wash fluid to effect more complete separations. He has indicated its applicability to electrospot testing, following an original suggestion by Stephen.[11]

ELECTROGRAPHY

As defined earlier, electrography is concerned primarily with the making of prints which localize compositional patterns found on a nonhomogeneous specimen surface. The circumstances are usually such that there is some prior knowledge of the nature of the patterns. Their printing may involve areas of different ionic species, or it may depend on variations in the transfer of a single species as a result of crystal orientation and stresses. The problem is to select printing conditions and reactions that will produce contrasting colors or contrasting print intensities with the pattern elements. Thus, specificity of the color reaction is not a controlling requirement, so long as recognizable contrast is obtained. Sometimes this contrast can be gained by careful regulation of the potential at the specimen surface so that there is a selective solution of the more positive areas. Sometimes it is possible to heighten contrast by repressing the solution of one component through formation of passive or barrier films.

The detail obtainable in an electrograph will depend on the control exercised over lateral diffusion. The part played in this control by the transfer medium has been discussed, as well as the advantages of immediate fixation of the transferred material. Another factor in reducing diffusion might be emphasized here. It is the use of color reactions of high sensitivity, which, therefore, require a minimum of transferred material. Where there is a choice, direct printing usually gives sharper detail than when development is done as a separate step. When the latter is necessary, diffusion can be minimized through the use of gelatin-coated papers.

A brief discussion of some of the practical uses of electrography follows. For more detailed information the reader is referred to the bibliography at the end of this chapter.

Pores and Discontinuities in Protective Coatings.—This is probably the most common application of electrographic printing. Its superiority over chemical contact printing derives from its rapidity, its more precise control of the solution, its sharper prints, and, also, its applicability to coatings which are electropositive to the base.

In making such prints, in which the basis metal may be exposed through pinholes and fine scratches, it is especially important to assure intimate contact with the printing

[10] Weisz, Herbert, Micro-analysis by the Ring Oven Technique, Pergamon Press, 1961.
[11] Stephen, William, "The Use of the Weisz Ring Oven in Electrographic Analysis," Mikrochim. Acta, **10,** 1531, 1956.

medium. The specimen surface should be clean and wettable by the electrolyte and a pressure of about 500 p.s.i. applied to force the pad and electrolyte into the discontinuities. For detailed reproduction, gelatin paper or Millipore material is best, but where the size and shape of the pores is of secondary importance to the number and distribution, CS&S No. 576 paper is less expensive and permits faster operation.

In porosity printing, it is obviously desirable to avoid the creation of false pores through undue solution of the coating. With organic or noble metal coatings and the right choice of electrolyte, this is rarely a problem. Gold, platinum, palladium, and similar metals will remain practically unattacked at 2 volts if an electrolyte such as sodium acetate is used. Basis metals, such as iron, nickel, or copper, then can be made visible with their usual color reagents without background color.

When the protective coating is a soluble metal, however, and particularly when it is electropositive to the basis metal, porosity printing may require a more critical selection of conditions. Since in most cases there will be some loss of coating metal, it is again important to employ sensitive color reactions so that the total transfer needed will be minimized. The ferrocyanide blue color for iron is amply visible in pin-point areas at a density of 0.3 mg. per square inch (.003 mils). Removal of this much coating metal where the commercial thickness ranges from 10 to 200 mg. per square inch probably would not be serious if only one printing is made. The diethyldithiocarbamate reaction for copper is even more sensitive. It should be remembered that the applied voltage, if the basis metal is negative to the coating, must be sufficient to cancel the opposing EMF and bring the basis metal into solution.

As mentioned above, it is sometimes possible to retard the solution of the coating by an electrolyte which passivates it or produces a barrier layer without interfering with the solution of the basis metal. Two examples which illustrate this approach are afforded by chromium and lead coatings. At an applied voltage below 3, lead goes into solution as the divalent ion. If a sodium sulphate electrolyte is used, a protective layer of lead sulphate forms and further solution of the coating is greatly retarded, while a copper or iron basis metal dissolves unhampered through any existing pores. At higher voltages, however, lead is oxidized to the tetravalent state with formation of a spongy non-protective peroxide. Chromium coatings illustrate the use of voltage control and passivation to limit solution of the coating. Above 2 volts chromium dissolves readily as the chromate ion. Below 1.5 volts, however, in ammonium acetate electrolyte it is oxidized only to the trivalent state with the formation of a thin passivating film which retards further solution. Under these conditions good prints are obtainable with copper, nickel or iron basis metals, using conventional color developers. Figure 25-6 shows time-current plots for chromium, copper, and iron in 0.5 *M* ammonium acetate at 1.5 volts using the same specimen areas. The rapid passivation of chromium is clearly evident. Table 25-3 summarizes test conditions for several coatings and basis metals

TABLE 25-3. POROSITY TESTS

Coating	*Basis Metal*	*Electrolyte*	*Applied Voltage, volts*
Au, Ag, Pt	Cu	0.5 M $NaC_2H_3O_2$ + 0.1 M $K_4Fe(CN)_6$	2
Sn, Cd, Zn	Fe	0.5 M $NH_4C_2H_3O_2$ + 0.1 M $K_4Fe(CN)_6$	3
Pb	Fe	0.5 M Na_2SO_4 + 0.1 M $K_4Fe(CN)_6$	3
Cr	Fe	0.5 M $NH_4C_2H_3O_2$ + 0.1 M $K_4Fe(CN)_6$	1.5
Sn, Ni, Pb	Cu	0.5 M Na_2SO_4 + 0.1 M $K_4Fe(CN)_6$	3
Cr	Cu	0.5 M $NH_4C_2H_3O_2$ + 0.1 M $K_4Fe(CN)_6$	1.5
Cr	Ni	0.5 M $NH_4C_2H_3O_2$ + Dimethylglyoxime	1.5

Printing of Structural Patterns.—A uniform solution potential may not exist over a metal surface, even though that metal is relatively pure. Varying orientation of crystal grains, strains, and disordering of the crystal lattice produced by mechanical distortion or cold working give rise to areas of small potential difference when immersed in an

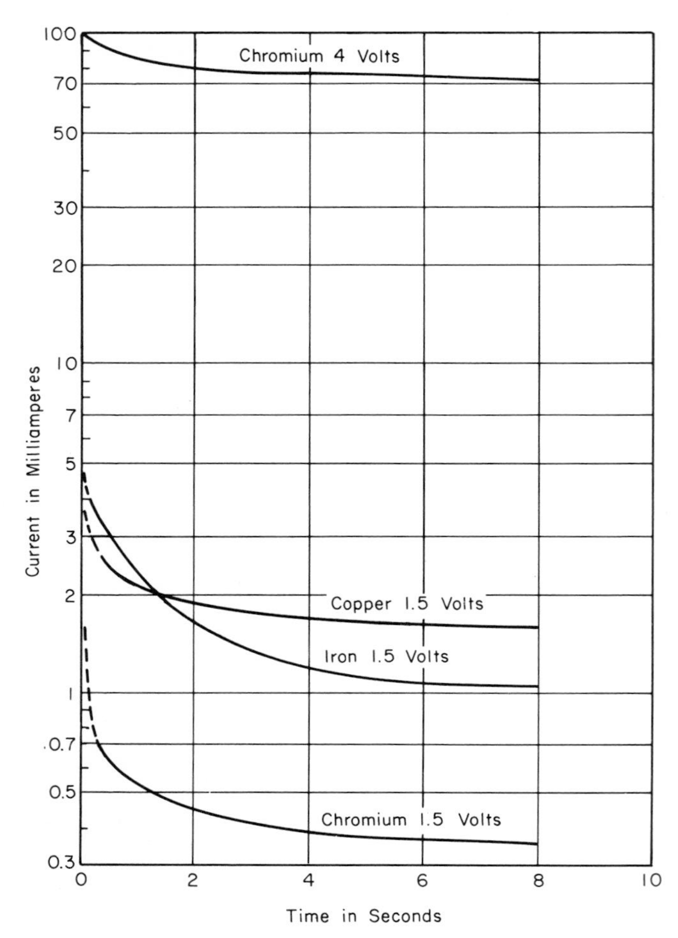

Fig. 25-6. Time-current Plots for Chromium, Copper, and Iron in 0.5 *M* Ammonium Acetate Electrolyte.

electrolyte. The selective attack in metallographic etching depends on these differences. In multiphase alloys, where the component crystal grains are different in composition, such differences in solution potential may be greater. Steels containing various carbides and other alloy components fall into this category. It is often possible to prepare electrographs showing the grosser structures of such metals, provided the applied voltage is held low enough to avoid masking the small potential differences. Glazunov, Ammerman, Hruska, and Jimena, Bernal, and Ibarz have all described the electrographic printing of cast iron and steel to show macrographic conditions such as slag inclusions, blow holes, piped conditions, fibrosity, etc.[12]

In making structure prints, the specimen surface is rough-finished on No. 400 aloxite paper followed by polishing in the conventional manner. The degree of polish will depend on the features to be printed, coarser structures requiring relatively little. The surface is etched to remove the disordered polishing layer which would behave as an equipotential surface, masking the underlying structures. The etchant will depend on the metal and can be found by referring to handbooks on metallography. For ferrous metals, iodine-potassium iodide or 5 percent alocholic nitric acid can be used. Suggested conditions: 0.1 *M* potassium ferrocyanide electrolyte at 1.4 volts, 10–30 seconds. Iron, at this voltage dissolves mostly as ferrous ion, hence will give little color in the print. Immersion in hydrogen peroxide solution, however, will develop the print to the full blue color. Examples of structure prints are shown in Fig. 25-7, *a* and *b*.

Transfer Between Metal Surfaces.—Frequently there is need to obtain evidence of transfer of metal from one surface to another. Such need may arise in studies of sliding friction or of electrical contact phenomena. In forensic practice, such transfer may provide evidence that a tool or instrument has been used to inflict damage, for example, that a certain cutter was used to sever a copper conductor.

Electrographic prints may provide a permanent record of the extent and the pattern of the transferred metal. The technique presents no problems not already discussed. The use of direct printing and the most sensitive reactions are naturally indicated, and the applied voltage should be sufficient to positively polarize the suspected metal when it is on a more positive surface (*i.e.*, copper on iron). Figure 25-7*g* shows frictional traces made by silver contactors sliding on a rotating bronze disc. Bowden,[13] in his studies of sliding friction, has made similar usage of electrography.

Inclusions.—The mapping of inclusions and segregations in a metal surface is another use for electrography. Here again, the selection of the printing conditions and an appropriate reaction to render the inclusion visible against the containing metal surface presents no new problems. It is suggested that these conditions be established first by the use of known specimens. Hunter, Churchill, and Mears[14] prepared such specimens by forcing known particles into various metals. From these they established their printing procedures. Copper or iron in aluminum, zinc, or nickel can be printed directly with ferrocyanide. Copper in iron can be printed with sodium diethyldithiocarbamate in 0.5 *M* sodium tartrate made slightly ammoniacal. Sulfide inclusions in iron also can be printed, with the specimen made cathodic against lead carbonate paper in a sodium carbonate electrolyte at 2–3 volts. A veiling sheet should be placed between the specimen and the lead carbonate paper. (See the section, "Anions-Corrosion Films," below.)

Conducting Minerals.—Minerals such as sulfides, arsenides, and antimonides are sufficiently conductive to be printed electrographically, yielding either an anion or cation, depending on the specimen polarity. Space does not permit elaboration, but the reader may find a summary of such techniques in the article published by Hiller.[15] Other references appear in the bibliography at the end of the chapter.

Anions-Corrosion Films.—The electro-transfer process may be employed to release anions from relatively insoluble combinations occurring in tarnish and corrosion films. The specimen is made cathodic, under which condition reduction of the film takes place.

[12] See the bibliography following the chapter, items 30, 31, 32, and 33, for specific works by these writers.

[13] Bowden, E., and Moore, A., Nature, **155,** 451, 1945.

[14] Hunter, Churchill, and Mears, Metal Progress, **42,** 1070, 1942.

[15] Hiller, T., Schweitz. Mineral. Petrog. Mitt., **17,** 88, 1937.

In this way, the sulfide ion, from heavy metal sulfides, the chloride and sulfate ions, from their insoluble basic combinations, may be detected and printed electrographically, and the necessity for bringing such insoluble materials into solution by more tedious chemical methods is eliminated.

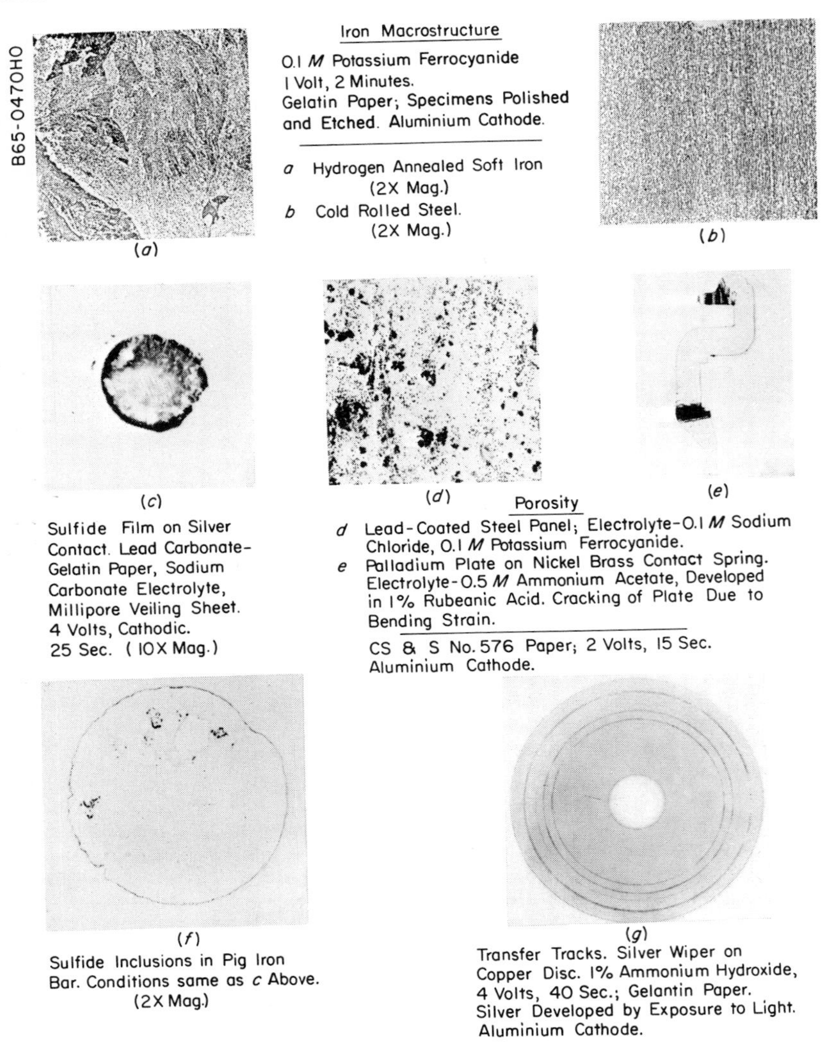

FIG. 25-7. Typical Electrographs.

The electrographic print may be useful, for the manner in which a corrosion product is distributed over a metal surface may provide clues as to how the attack was brought about. The corrosive agent may have reached the surface as a fine spray or fog; it may have been transferred by contact with fingers or other media; it may have been present in deposited dusts or it may have resulted from a gaseous agent. In the latter case, air flow patterns may be revealed.

For sulfides, lead carbonate paper is used,[16] with a sodium carbonate electrolyte. For sulfates, barium rhodizonate paper is used with ammonium acetate electrolyte. Chloride ion is indicated by the bleaching of red silver chromate paper. Because of its sensitivity to pH changes, a buffered electrolyte such as magnesium acetate should be used.

In making these tests, one difficulty may arise from the physical transfer of reduced metal to the print. Also, in the cases of lead carbonate and silver chromate papers, reduction of lead or silver may take place at the specimen surface. These effects may be avoided by interposing a thin "veiling" sheet in the pad between the specimen and the printing surface. For this purpose, it has been found that a porous membrane filter ("Millipore") is an excellent material which holds loss of print detail to a minimum. Printing time should not be prolonged; 10–20 ma./cm.^{2} for 20 seconds is suggested.

QUANTITATIVE APPLICATIONS

With the possibility of measuring the transferred metal coulometrically, it would seem logical to look to more quantitative uses of the electrospot method. To date, however, work in this direction has been limited to semiquantitative estimations of components of certain favorably constituted alloys. There are understandable reasons for this slow progress. A limiting one is the need for a satisfactory method of measuring the density of the spot obtained. Most of the published methods depend on a comparison with a series of known spots. With fixed reagents such as dimethylglyoxime or zinc sulfide and a favorable density range, spots may be thus evaluated to about ± 10 percent (Yagoda[17] and Clarke and Hermance[18]). It is also likely, as mentioned in the section, "Current, Time, and Voltage," (page 504), that measurement of the dissolved metal as a function of $I \times t$ will be complicated by the changing value of I during the transfer. The pad resistance usually increases with changes in the electrolyte concentration and composition and the formation of precipitated products. These effects can be partly overcome by judicious selection of electrolyte and pad material and by use of sensitive reactions requiring a minimum of transfer; precise measurement would require some method of integration. A recording milliammeter here is helpful, but what is really needed is a millicoulometer. To our knowledge, such an instrument is not available.

Perhaps the most serious difficulty in any general quantitative extension of the method is the fact that only when the alloy is a solid solution, presenting an equipotential surface, will its components dissolve in the precise proportions present in the alloy. Increasing the anode potential, using more dilute electrolyte and thicker pad to give the needed resistance, may offset somewhat the grain potential differences in multiphase alloys. Other difficulties may arise, however, as the decomposition potential of the electrolyte is exceeded, for then the solution efficiency falls off making coulometric measurements meaningless.

Everything considered, it appears that at present the electrospot method may find use for roughly estimating certain alloy components where these estimations serve to classify the alloy. Glazunov and Krivohlavy[19] have published a rather theoretical paper dealing with such a special application in the determination of nickel in nickel-iron alloys. Here they are favored by an alloy which is a solid solution of metals having almost

[16] Gelatin paper soaked 10 minutes in 0.5 *M* lead acetate, dried, then soaked 10 minutes in 1.0 M sodium carbonate.

[17] Yagoda, H., Mikrochemie, **24,** 117, 1938.

[18] Clarke, B. L., and Hermance, H., Ind. Eng. Chem., Anal. Ed., **10,** 591, 1938.

[19] Glazunov, A., and Krivohlavy, J., Z. Physik. Chem., **A161,** 373, 1932.

the same atomic weight, close together in the electromotive series, and for which sensitive and specific reactions are available.

One arrangement which may provide control of some of the variables is to print the two specimens to be compared in series in the same press. Transfer areas are made identical by using discs of pad material punched from a die. In this way $\frac{I \times t}{A}$ and the pressure will be the same for both known and unknown specimens.

A further discussion of this and other aspects of quantitative electrospot testing is given by Hermance and Wadlow in W. G. Berl's Physical Methods in Chemical Analysis.[20]

SELECTED BIBLIOGRAPHY

General and Apparatus

1. Fritz, H., Z. Anal. Chem., **78,** 418, 1929.
2. Glazunov, A., Chimie & Industrie, Spec. No., 425, 1929.
3. Hermance, H., and Wadlow, H., "Electrography," in W. G. Berl, Ed., Physical Methods in Chemical Analysis, Academic Press, New York, 1951. Apparatus, techniques, and applications.
4. Miller, H. and Friedl, E. B., "Developments in Electrographic Printing," Plating, **47,** No. 5,521, 1960. Possible errors and polarization effects. Method for pore magnification for counting purposes in porosity tests. Reagents for Al, Cr, Co, Cu, Fe, Ni, Sn.
5. Galitzine, N., and Ashley, S. E., "Examination of Plated Objects," ASTM Spec. No. 98, June 28, 1949. Discussion of electrodes and media including cellophane.
6. Monk, P. R., "Development of Electrographic Analysis with Special Reference to Recent British Apparatus," Analyst, **78,** 141, 1953. Laboratory equipment and a small portable unit for field spot testing. Use of NaF to suppress Fe in alloy testing. Tests for Mo, Zn, Cd, Co.
7. Langer, A., "Electrographic Arrangement for the Direct Observation of the Printing Process," Microchemical J., **1,** 101, 1957. Conducting Nesa glass as cathode for direct observation and photography.
8. Grassely, G., "Laboratory Equipment for Electrographic Examinations," Acta Mineral. Petrog. Univ. Szeged., **10,** 19, 1957.
9. Berges, L. S., "Recent Advances in Ring-Oven Techniques," Inform. de Quimica Analitica, Madrid, **5,** 138, 1959 (CA, **54,** 7414). Sampling by electrographic techniques and separation by ring-oven methods with spot test detection.
10. Longo, R. E., and Segura, R., "Electrography," Public. del Instit. de Investig. Microquim., Univ. Nac. del Litoral, Rosario, Argentina, **14,** 133, 1950 (CA, **46,** 6525).

Porosity and Discontinuities

11. Glazunov, A., and Jenicek, L., "The Electrographic Method and Its Use for Testing Coats of Varnish," Korrosion u. Metallschutz, **16,** No. 10, 341, 1940. Varnish films on iron.
12. Shaw, W. E., and Moore, E. T., "Pore Size in Protective Films by Electrographic Printing, Ind. Eng. Chem., Anal. Ed., **19,** 777, 1947. Paint and other protective coatings on iron.
13. Brenner, A., Plating and Finishing Guide Book, 14th Ed., Metal Industries Publishing Co., New York, 1945, p. 173. Porosity of nickel plated parts.
14. Glazunov, A., and Teindl, J., "Electrographic Determination of the Porosity of Metal Coatings," Metallwaren Ind. u. Galvano-Tech., **33,** 371, 1935. Test for gold and porosity of metal coatings on tin and iron.
15. Koehler, W. A., and Burford, R., Trans. Electrochem. Soc., **70,** 387, 1936. Porosity of zinc coating on iron.
16. Hermance, H., "The Electrographic Detection and Mapping of Discontinuities in Lead-Coated Copper Sheet," Report to ASTM Comm. B-2, Sub. VI, March, 1951. Includes discussion of pore clogging by successive printing.
17. Kronstein, M., "New Uses of Electrographic Printing for Coating Control," Chimie

[20] Academic Press, New York, 1951.

des Peintures, **13**, 151, 1950. Paint and varnish films on iron, copper, cadmium, aluminum.

18. Hunter, M., Churchill, J., and Mears, R., "Electrographic Methods of Surface Analysis," Metal Progress, **42**, 1070, 1942. Inclusions, with special consideration of polarization effects.
19. Noonan, H., "Electrographic Determination of Porosity in Metallic Coatings," Research Report No. 12, Burndy Corp. Research Div., November, 1964.

Identification of Metals and Alloys

20. Glazunov, A., Chimie & Industrie, Spec. Nos. 247, 1930; 332, 1932. Fe, Ag, Ni, Co, Cu, Bi, Zn, Pb, Cd, Sn, Sb.
21. Arnold, E., Chem. Listy, **27**, 73, 1933.
22. Jirkovsky, R., Chem. Listy, **25**, 254, 1931. Nickel and cobalt in steels.
23. Calamari, J., Hubata, R., and Roth, R. B., "Rapid Detection of Gold by the Electrographic Method," Ind. Eng. Chem., Anal. Ed., **14**, 535, 1942; "Detection of Molybdenum in Steels," Ind. Eng. Chem., Anal. Ed., **15**, 71, 1943.
24. Levy, M., "Electrographic Analysis for Identifying High Temperature Alloys," Iron Age, **164**, 98, 1949. Cr, Ni, Co, Mo, W, Ti, Fe in Inconel, Hastelloy B, Stellite 6.
25. Lewis, A., and Evans, D. R., "Rapid Identification of Metal Finishes," ASTM Spec. No. 98, June 28, 1949. Zn, Cd, Pb, Ni, Ag, Sn, Cr plated parts.
26. Fitzer, Erich, "Electrographic Rapid Identification of Alloy Steels and Alloys of Ferrous Metals," Arch. f. Eisenhuttenwesen, **25**, 321, 1954 (CA, **48**, 13533). Systematic testing for Cr, Co, Ni, Mn, Mo, W, Ti, Si, Fe, Cu.
27. Wawrzyczek, W., "Electrography in Analytical Chemistry," Chemia Analityczna, Warsaw, **4**, 891, 1959 (CA, **55**, 20773, 1961). Simultaneous detection of Co-Fe; Ni-Fe; Sn-Fe; Sn-Ni; Ni-Co; Fe-Ni-Co; Co-Sn; qual. for pyrrhotite and galena.
28. Clark, G. C. and Hale, E. E., "Identification of Alloys and Stainless Steel by Electrographic Methods," Analyst, **78**, 145, 1953. Cu, Ni, Fe, Mo, Ti, Cr. Suggests paper chromatography separations.
29. Hughes, H. D., "Electrography," Metal Industry, **66**, No. 11, 169, 1945.

Metal Structures

30. Glazunov, A., Oesterr. Chem. Ztg., **41**, 217, 1938.
31. Ammerman, E., Stahl u. Eisen, **51**, 207, 1931.
32. Hruska, J. H., Heat Treating and Forging, 1034, Nov. 1931.
33. Jimena, E., Bernal, J., and Ibarz, J., Anales soc. espan. fis. y quim., **30**, 655, 1932. Structural irregularities as slag inclusions, blow holes fibrosity, flow structure in cast iron and steels.

Semiquantitative Estimations

34. Glazunov, A., and Krivohlavy, J., "Quantitative Estimation of Nickel in Nickel Steel by the Electrographic Method," Z. f. physik. Chem., **A161**, 373, 1932.
35. Glazunov, A., and Drescher, E., "Lead in Lead-Tin Alloys by the Electrographic Method," Congr. chim. ind., Compt. rend. 17 eme Congr., pt. 2, 1937.
36. Garino, M., and Catto, R., "Rapid Determination of Small Quantities of Bismuth in Copper," Chimica e Industria, Milan, **17**, No. 4, 218, 1935.
37. Yagoda, H., Mikrochemie, **24**, 117, 1938.
38. Clarke, B. L., and Hermance, H., Ind. Eng. Chem., Anal. Ed., **10**, 591, 1938.
39. Stephen, W., "The Use of the Weisz Ring Oven in Electrographic Analysis," Mikrochimica Acta, **10**, 1531, 1956. Ring oven techniques for testing copper, nickel, and iron alloys.
40. Shibara, Yai, "Electrographic Determination of Copper in Brass and Nickel in Stainless Steel," Bunseki Kagaku, Univ. Tokyo, **11**, 664, 1962; "Electrographic Determination of Iron in Ferrous Alloys and Manganese in Manganese Alloys," Bunseki Kagaku, **12**, 283, 1963 (CA, **59**, 453).
41. Nall, W., and Scholey, R., "A Non-Destructive Microchemical Method of Sorting Steels," Metallurgia, **54**, 97, 1956. Tests for Mn, Ni, Co, Mo.
42. Jaluvka, J., "Electrographic Colorimetry," Chemie, Prague, **10**, 631, 1958. Printing conditions detailed. Only homogeneous alloys. (CA, **53**, 21363)

Minerals

43. Jirkovsky, R., Bansky Svet Bd. XI, Heft 2-3, 1932.
44. Wenger, P., Gutzeit, G., and Hiller, T., Compt. rend. soc. phys. hist. nat. Geneve, **51**, 63, 1934.
45. Hiller, T., Schweitz. Mineral. Petrog. Mitt., **17**, 88, 1937.
46. Yushko, S. A., Bull. acad. sci. U.R.S.S. Ser. geol., No. 3, 137, 1939.
47. Williams, D., and Nakhala, F. M., Bull. Inst. Mining. Met., No. 533, 257, 1951.
48. Dimitriu, A., and Goldhaar, I., Rev. Chim. Bucharest, **13**, 745, 1962 (CA, **59**, 1061).

49. Chernet, J., and Pierrot, R., Bull. Soc. Franc. Mineral. Cristal., **77,** 611, 1954.
50. Grassely, G., Acta Univ. Szegediensis, Hungary, Acta Mineral. Petrog., **6,** 47, 1952 (CA, **48,** 1891).
51. Hosking, K. F. G., Mining Magazine, London, **94,** 335, 1956.
52. Galopin, R., Schweitz. Mineral. Petrog. Mitt., **16,** 1, 1936.
53. Gutzeit, G., Gysin, M., and Galopin, R., Compt. rend. soc. phys. hist. nat. Geneve, **51,** 53, 1934.

Special Applications

54. Yagoda, H., "Contact and Electrographic Printing in Biological Materials," Ind. Eng. Chem., Anal. Ed., **15,** 135, 1943.
55. Shibara, Yai, "Local Patterns Analysis of K, PO_4 and Amino Acids in Plant Tissue by Migration Electrography," Bunseki Kagaku, **12,** 649, 1963.
56. Bowden, E., and Moore, A., Nature, **155,** 451, 1945.

Chapter 26

ELECTROMETRIC METHODS OF pH DETERMINATION

By Roger G. Bates
National Bureau of Standards,
Washington, D. C.

The great majority of pH measurements are made by electrometric procedures. The solution whose pH is to be determined is placed in a cell assembly consisting of two suitable electrodes. The voltage of this cell is then measured, usually by an instrument called a pH meter. This voltage or electromotive force (e.m.f.) is converted to a pH number by a formula relating it to the e.m.f. furnished by a standard reference solution of assigned pH. The definition of pH, electrodes for pH cells, and pH instrumentation will be discussed in that order.

MEANING OF pH

The quantity termed pH was originally defined in a fundamental way.[1] Sørensen intended that the pH should be a means of expressing the hydrogen ion concentration of a particular medium, thus pH = $-\log c_{\mathrm{H}}$. He proposed that experimental pH numbers be determined by measuring the e.m.f. (E) of a cell consisting of a hydrogen electrode and a calomel reference electrode separated by a liquid junction of concentrated potassium chloride solution. Essentially the same procedure is in use today, except that the versatile glass electrode has largely replaced the hydrogen electrode as the hydrogen ion indicator.

With the passage of time it became evident that the e.m.f. of the Sørensen cell did not respond in a simple way to hydrogen ion concentration, and, thus, the pH numbers obtained from this cell were not an exact measure of $-\log c_{\mathrm{H}}$ in the unknown solution. Indeed, they bore no exact simple relationship to either the concentration or activity of the hydrogen ions in these mixtures, but were influenced to some extent by other ions present. This experimental defect has its origin in the fact that all of the ions in the solution diffuse independently across the interface between the solution and the potassium chloride bridge, and, therefore, contribute to the liquid-junction potential at that point.

THE OPERATIONAL pH SCALE

Reproducibility is thus the prime consideration in the standardization of pH measurements. The interpretation of the pH numbers obtained in terms of the fundamental thermodynamic properties of the hydrogen ion in these solutions must perforce be of

[1] Sørensen, S. P. L., Biochem. Z., **21,** 131, 201, 1909; Compt. Rend. Trav. Lab. Carlsberg, **8,** 1, 1909.

secondary importance, and should be attempted only under restricted experimental conditions. The operational definition of pH now adopted almost universally is based on two assumptions, both of which are incapable of exact realization. These are: a) invariance of the liquid-junction potential when a standard reference solution is replaced by the unknown whose pH is to be measured; and b) the availability of standard reference solutions whose assigned pH values are an exact measure of $-\log a_{\mathrm{H}}$, where a represents the thermodynamic activity. The operational formula is as follows:

$$\mathrm{pH}(X) = \mathrm{pH}(S) + \frac{E_X - E_S}{(RT \ln 10)/F} \tag{1}$$

where R, T, and F are, respectively, the gas constant, the temperature on the Kelvin scale, and the faraday.

This definition of pH is evidently of considerable generality. It permits the determination of pH numbers for any medium in which the pH cell gives a steady reproducible e.m.f. Only a small fraction of these media, however, will be sufficiently ideally constituted to justify the interpretation of the experimental pH numbers in terms of the properties of the hydrogen ions therein. No interpretation should be attempted unless there is good reason to believe that the liquid-junction potential remains fairly constant when the standard solution is replaced by the unknown. In practice, this means that the "ideally constituted" unknowns shall be aqueous solutions of simple salts of total concentration not in excess of 0.2 M, and that the pH shall lie between 2.5 and 11.5.

STANDARD REFERENCE VALUES

The operational definition suggests that the measured pH of the unknown (X) and that of the standard (S) will fall on the same activity scale under the most favorable conditions. The standard reference values established at the National Bureau of Standards for five primary standards are listed in Table 26-1.[2] These values represent $-\log a_{\mathrm{H}}$ in the respective solutions, where a_{H} is a conventional or defined hydrogen ion activity. They were calculated from the e.m.f. of cells without liquid junction with the aid of the formula

$$\mathrm{pH}(S) = -\log (a_{\mathrm{H}}\gamma_{\mathrm{Cl}}) + \log \gamma_{\mathrm{Cl}} = -\log (a_{\mathrm{H}}\gamma_{\mathrm{Cl}}) - \frac{A\sqrt{I}}{1 + 1.5\sqrt{I}}, \tag{2}$$

which is based upon a conventional definition of γ_{Cl}, the activity coefficient of chloride ion.[3] In Eq. (2), A is the Debye-Hückel slope constant (0.511 at 25°C.) and I is the ionic strength.

HYDROGEN ION RESPONSIVE ELECTRODES

The hydrogen gas electrode is the primary standard for pH measurements. The purity of the hydrogen ion response of other, secondary electrodes is affirmed by comparison of their changes of potential upon change of pH with that displayed by the hydrogen electrode. Most pH measurements in practice, however, are made with the glass electrode, the applicability of which is far broader than that of the hydrogen electrode. In specialized situations, the quinhydrone and antimony electrodes also are useful indicators of hydrogen ion. The characteristics and limitations of these electrodes

[2] Bates, R. G., J. Res. Natl. Bur. Std., **66A,** 179, 1962.
[3] Bates, R. G., and Guggenheim, E. A., Pure Appl. Chem., **1,** 163, 1960.

TABLE 26-1. STANDARD pH VALUES, pH(*S*)

t, °C.	Tartrate (satd.)	Phthalate (0.05 *m*)	Phosphate (1:1)	Phosphate (1:3.5)	Borax 0.01 *m*
0	—	4.003	6.984	7.534	9.464
5	—	3.999	6.951	7.500	9.395
10	—	3.998	6.923	7.472	9.332
15	—	3.999	6.900	7.448	9.276
20	—	4.002	6.881	7.429	9.225
25	3.557	4.008	6.865	7.413	9.180
30	3.552	4.015	6.853	7.400	9.139
35	3.549	4.024	6.844	7.389	9.102
38	3.548	4.030	6.840	7.384	9.081
40	3.547	4.035	6.838	7.380	9.068
45	3.547	4.047	6.834	7.373	9.038
50	3.549	4.060	6.833	7.367	9.011
55	3.554	4.075	6.834	—	8.985
60	3.560	4.091	6.836	—	8.962
70	3.580	4.126	6.845	—	8.921
80	3.609	4.164	6.859	—	8.885
90	3.650	4.205	6.877	—	8.850
95	3.674	4.227	6.886	—	8.833

Compositions (m = molal):

Tartrate—Potassium hydrogen tartrate, saturated at 25°C.

Phthalate—Potassium hydrogen phthalate, 0.05 m (10.12 g., air weight, in 1 liter of solution at 25°C.).

Phosphate (1:1)—Potassium dihydrogen phosphate, 0.025 m, disodium hydrogen phosphate, 0.025 m (3.388 g. KH_2PO_4 and 3.533 g. Na_2HPO_4, air weights, in 1 liter of solution at 25°C.).

Phosphate (1:3.5)—Potassium dihydrogen phosphate, 0.008695 m, disodium hydrogen phosphate, 0.03043 m (1.179 g. KH_2PO_4 and 4.302 g. Na_2HPO_4, air weights, in 1 liter of solution at 25°C.).

Borax—Sodium tetraborate (borax), 0.01 m (3.80 g., air weight, $Na_2B_4O_7 \cdot 10H_2O$ in 1 liter of solution at 25°C.).

will be considered separately. For further details, the reader is referred to two recent monographs on pH measurements.[4,5]

Hydrogen Electrode.—The hydrogen gas electrode consists of a piece of platinum or other noble metal which has been activated in such a way that it is able to catalyze readily the fundamental electrode process, $H_2(g) = 2H^+ + 2e$. The most suitable activation is achieved by coating the platinum surface lightly with platinum black. In some instances, notably when the solution contains organic substances reducible by hydrogen in contact with finely divided platinum, a bright platinum electrode or a

[4] Mattock, G., pH Measurement and Titration, The Macmillan Co., New York, 1961.
[5] Bates, R. G., Determination of pH, John Wiley and Sons, New York, 1964.

piece of platinum mechanically activated may be advantageous.[6] Palladium electrodes coated lightly with palladium black are also useful under these circumstances.

For the proper operation of the hydrogen electrode, very pure hydrogen gas is essential, and all traces of air must be excluded from the electrode compartment. Complete saturation of the solution with hydrogen is necessary, and, therefore, equilibrium may not be reached for 15 to 45 minutes. The electrode does not behave well in unbuffered solutions. Oxidizing agents must be absent, as must lead and mercury ions and salts of the noble metals.

Quinhydrone Electrode.—When one wishes to avoid elaborate and expensive measuring equipment, such as is required to measure accurately the e.m.f. of cells containing highly resistant glass electrodes, the quinhydrone electrode may be a suitable choice. This electrode consists of a piece of bright platinum or gold in contact with a solution containing an excess of solid quinhydrone, a slightly soluble equimolecular compound or benzoquinone and hydroquinone. A good grade of commercial quinhydrone is usually satisfactory.

The quinhydrone electrode comes to equilibrium in 1 to 5 minutes, and its response over the pH range 0 to 8 is very near the theoretical $(RT\ln 10)/F$ volts per pH unit. Hence, operational pH values in this range can be determined by the usual formula, Eq. (1). For greatest accuracy, the inert electrode should be cleaned carefully with hot chromic acid and washed with water and absolute alcohol; the solution should likewise be freed of air.

The quinhydrone electrode can be used in solutions of many organic substances (aromatic acids and unsaturated aliphatic acids, for example) which are reduced by the platinum hydrogen electrode. It is likewise less sensitive than the hydrogen electrode to the presence of oxidizing agents, and the simplicity of its construction is an important point in its favor. Among its disadvantages and limitations must be mentioned its restricted pH range and the salt error. The importance of the salt error, however, has often been overemphasized; it rarely exceeds 0.06 unit when salt is added in 1 *M* concentration. The departure of the electrode above pH 8 has been attributed to oxidation of hydroquinone in alkaline solutions and to acidic dissociation of hydroquinone.

Antimony Electrode.—The antimony electrode is simple to construct. Its electrical resistance, like that of the hydrogen and quinhydrone electrodes, is low in many of its common forms, and elaborate measuring equipment is, therefore, unnecessary. It comes to equilibrium rapidly and responds quickly to changes of pH. Oxygen need not be carefully excluded from solutions in which the antimony electrode is to be used.

A convenient semimicro form of antimony electrode is made by drawing molten metal into a narrow glass tube.[7] The exposed surface is renewed from time to time by polishing with an abrasive cloth, removing a small amount of metal and the glass wall surrounding it. Antimony cast in air is covered with a surface coating of oxide, and the pH response of the electrode is doubtless to be attributed to the existence of a metal–metal oxide couple.

The antimony electrode can be used with some success over the range pH 0 to 11. Its chief limitations are a defective response and some lack of reversibility. For best results, its pH response should be calibrated at several points over the range of use, and even then errors as large as 0.1 unit may be incurred. Oxidizing and reducing agents cause some interference, and the electrode is very sensitive to traces of copper and to the ions of hydroxy acids, such as citrates and tartrates. For these reasons, the electrode

[6] Hills, G. J., and Ives, D. J. G., Chapter 2 in Reference Electrodes, D. J. G. Ives and G. J. Janz, Eds., Academic Press, New York, 1961.

[7] I. Levin, Chemist-Analyst, **41,** 89, 1952.

is most useful for titrations and for industrial control operations where a highly accurate estimate of the pH is not necessary.

Glass Electrode.—The glass electrode is highly versatile and is by far the most useful of the hydrogen ion responsive electrodes for practical measurements of pH. It has a very fast, almost instantaneous, response in buffered solutions, although equilibrium is achieved more slowly in unbuffered media. It is the only one of the common hydrogen ion responsive electrodes that is substantially unaffected by the presence of oxidizing agents. Furthermore, it responds well in most mixed solvents containing at least a few percent of water, and even in many completely anhydrous media without pronounced dehydrating properties. In addition, it responds in a nearly theoretical manner to deuterium ion in heavy water.

The faults of the glass electrode are few. Among the most prominent may be mentioned the high resistance of the glass membrane, which commonly runs from 10 to 500 megohms. Measurement of the e.m.f. of pH cells utilizing a glass electrode is, therefore, not as simple as the measurement of low-resistance cells and, until recently, not as accurate. Most glass electrodes available today respond in a nearly theoretical manner to changes of pH in the range 0 to 12 or even higher. There is, however, some impairment of the response at very low and at very high pH. These departures are known as the "acid error" and the "alkaline error," respectively.

Figure 26-1 is a diagram of a typical glass electrode of the immersion type. The pH-sensitive tip of the electrode consists of a small bulb or hemisphere of a special glass fused to a stem of ordinary pH-insensitive glass. A shielded lead passes through the stem and terminates in a small internal reference electrode within the bulb. This electrode in turn dips into the internal reference solution with which the inner surface of the pH-sensitive tip is bathed.

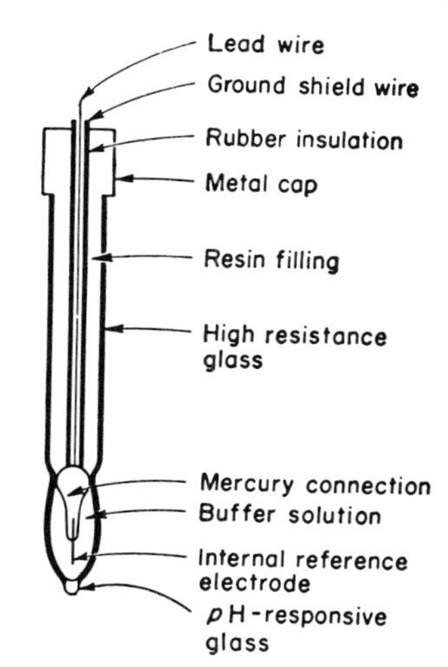

Fig. 26-1. Glass Electrode. (Reprinted from Willard, Merritt, and Dean, Instrumental Methods of Analysis, 4th Ed., 1965, D. Van Nostrand Co.)

A variety of inner electrodes and solutions is used. These are chosen to minimize the effect of temperature fluctuations on the e.m.f. of the cell as a whole and to regulate in a suitable way the pH at which the cell e.m.f. becomes zero. Internal reference electrodes of the following types are used in commercial glass electrodes: silver–silver chloride, mercury-calomel, thallium amalgam–thallous chloride, and mercury on platinum. A solution of mercurous perchlorate and perchloric acid is suitable for use with the mercury electrode, and buffered chloride solutions are used in conjunction with the electrodes reversible to chloride ion.

The properties of the glass electrode—its electrical resistance, its pH response, and the magnitude of the acid and alkaline errors, as well as the durability and longevity of the glass bulb—are markedly dependent on the composition of the pH-sensitive tip. The first widely used pH-sensitive glass, known as Corning 015, was a soda-lime glass whose composition (72.2 mole % SiO_2, 6.4% CaO, and 21.4% Na_2O) corresponds to the eutectic composition of the ternary system SiO_2, CaO, Na_2O. The chief fault of

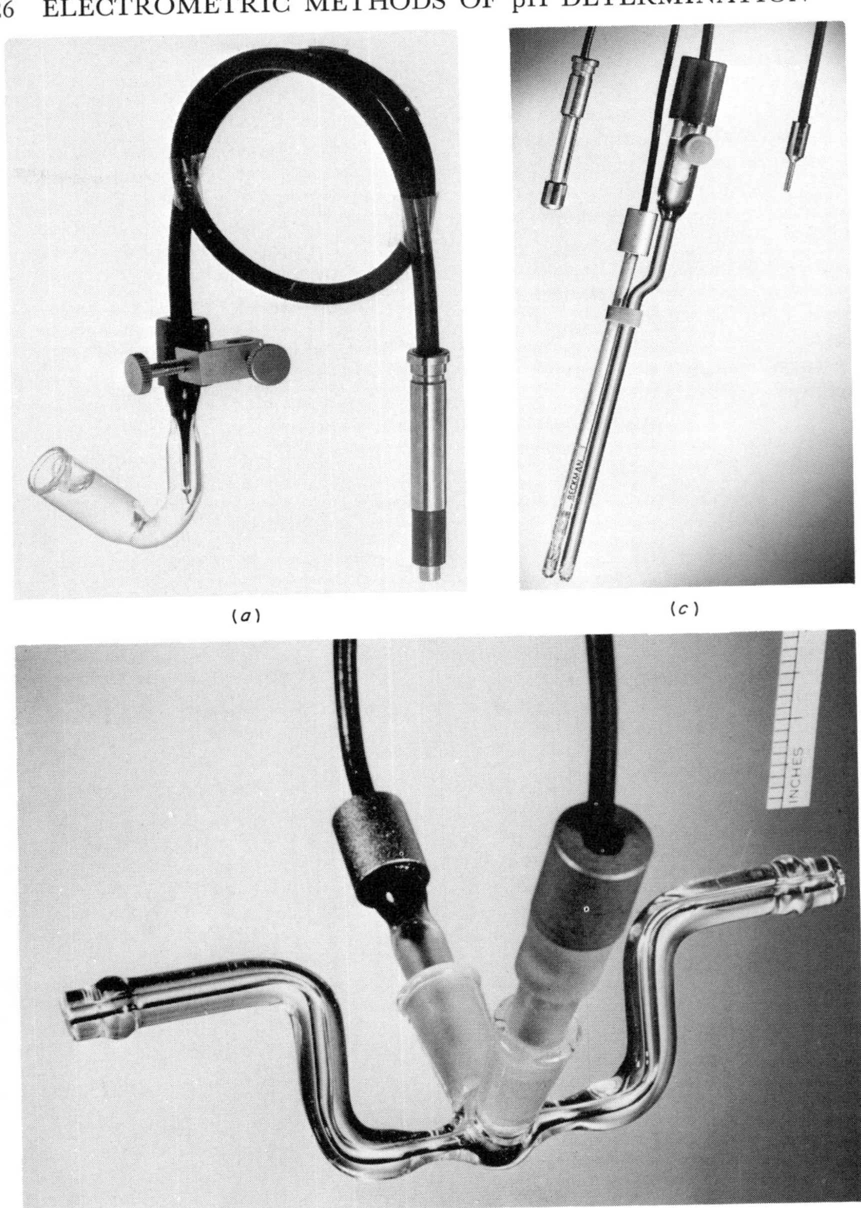

FIG. 26-2. Special Types of Glass Electrodes and Cell Assemblies: *A*, One-drop Assembly; *B*, Flow Assembly; *C*, Probe Assembly. (Courtesy Beckman Instruments, Inc.)

electrodes fabricated from this glass is a marked error in solutions containing sodium ion in quantity at a pH exceeding 10.

Changes in the composition of the glass, notably the substitution of Li_2O for Na_2O, have effected a considerable reduction in the alkaline error. The presence of small amounts of larger ions such as lanthanum, cesium, and barium is effective in reducing the sodium ion error still further, and commercial glass electrodes with negligible errors at pH values of 13 or above are obtainable. Even when the alkaline error is appreciable, accurate results can sometimes be obtained through application of corrections furnished by the manufacturer. When the correction exceeds 0.5 pH unit, however, the potential of the electrode usually drifts noticeably, and accurate results cannot be obtained.

The alkaline error causes the measured pH to be too low, and an error of opposite sign is observed in concentrated solutions of the strong acids. The onset of this acid error occurs at such low pH values that departures of this sort are of less concern than those observed at the high end of the pH scale. The mechanism of the acid error is not yet completely understood, but there is evidence that the departure is associated with penetration of acid anions or molecular acid into the surface of the glass. By contrast, the alkaline error appears to mark the development of a partial response to cations, for example sodium.

The chemical resistance and the electrical resistance of electrode glasses vary in the same way with changes of temperature, and both are profoundly affected by temperature changes. For this reason electrodes intended expressly for pH measurements at low temperatures may have a very short life at elevated temperatures. Conversely, an electrode designed for use at high temperatures may have too high an electrical resistance to be useful at low temperatures. Some manufacturers have solved this problem by providing electrodes designed for use within certain restricted temperature ranges.

Glass electrodes are fabricated in many different sizes and shapes for special uses. Some special forms of commercial glass electrodes and cell assemblies are shown in Fig. 26-2.

REFERENCE ELECTRODES

To complete the circuit for the measurement of the surface potential of the glass electrode, a reference electrode and salt bridge are used. The most common arrangement is a calomel electrode in a concentrated, often saturated, solution of potassium chloride, which also serves as a bridge solution between the electrode and the unknown solution. The silver–silver chloride electrode and the thallium amalgam–thallous chloride electrode are also employed, while in special applications, the bridge solution may contain ammonium nitrate, potassium nitrate, and even sodium chloride.

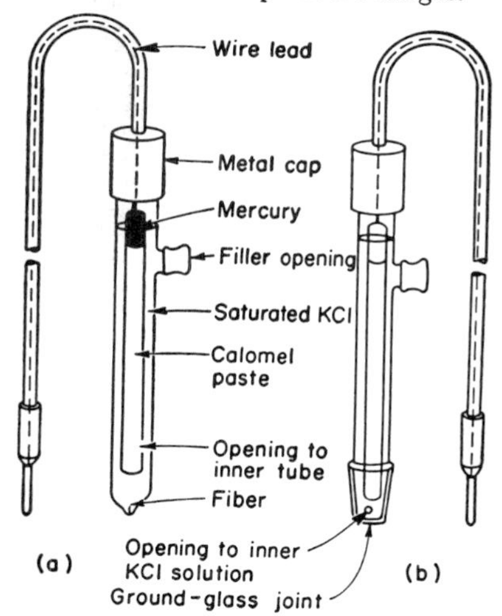

FIG. 26-3. Reference Electrodes: *a*, Commercial Type with Fiber Contact; *b*, Commercial Type with Ground-glass Joint.

Two common forms of calomel reference electrode and salt bridge, both of the immersion type, are shown in Fig. 26-3. These electrodes consist of mercury in contact with a paste of mercurous chloride in saturated potassium chloride solution. They differ in the manner by which the electrode is brought into electrical contact with the solution whose pH is to be determined. The electrode shown at (a) has a narrow hole at its lower end. This aperture is partially closed by an asbestos or linen fiber which permits the solution of potassium chloride to flow at a very slow rate into the unknown solution. In the electrode labeled (b), contact with the solution is established by an ungreased ground-glass joint. In other reference electrodes, the junction is formed at a porous ceramic plug or a loose-fitting plunger.

It is sometimes advantageous to prepare calomel electrodes of designs and shapes other than those obtainable commercially, or possibly of higher reproducibility. Instructions for the preparation of reproducible calomel electrodes have been given by Hills and Ives.[8] Due to the instability of calomel, reference electrodes of this type should not be used for long periods of time at temperatures above 80°C. Combination electrodes, with the glass and calomel reference electrodes in a single stem, are very convenient and are coming into common use.

The silver–silver chloride electrode immersed in a concentrated solution of potassium chloride is also a convenient reference element. In its smaller forms it usually consists of a silver wire coated with silver chloride by electrolysis or by immersion in the fused salt. It may also consist of a platinum wire on which both the silver and the silver chloride have been formed by electrolysis. Silver chloride is, however, appreciably soluble in strong solutions of potassium chloride; hence the potassium chloride used in the cell compartment should be saturated with precipitated silver chloride. Although this is not difficult to do in the laboratory, it is possible to obtain a solution saturated with both potassium chloride and silver chloride from commercial sources. A silver–silver chloride reference electrode is stable at 100°C.

A reference electrode consisting of a 40 percent thallium amalgam in contact with crystalline thallous chloride in a saturated solution of potassium chloride is coming into use. This reference electrode is said to be suitable for pH measurements at temperatures considerably above 100°C.

pH INSTRUMENTATION

The electrical resistance of hydrogen, quinhydrone, and antimony electrodes is low, in general, as is that of most reference electrodes. Hence, the e.m.f. of pH cells consisting of these electrodes can be measured with adequate accuracy by the compensation principle, using potentiometers of the low-resistance variety calibrated with a standard cell. This is by far the simplest and most accurate method when it can be used. If the cell contains a glass electrode, however, or if the reference electrode is of unusually small size, too little current can be drawn from the cell to give the visible deflection of the galvanometer needed to establish the point of balance. This is also the case when the reference electrode provides only a very narrow channel at the point where the liquid junction is formed, and when the crystallization of potassium chloride effectively blocks this passage.

When a glass electrode is part of the pH cell, electronic amplifiers must be used to measure accurately the e.m.f. under conditions of very feeble current drain. The pH meter is essentially an electronic voltmeter of requisite sensitivity and stability which provides a scale calibrated directly in pH units in addition to, or instead of, one calibrated to read volts.

Commercial pH meters may be classified broadly into two types, the *null-detector type* and the *direct-reading type*. The first is a direct extension of the potentiometric circuit

[8] Hills, G. J., and Ives, D. J. G., in D. J. G. Ives and G. J. Janz, Eds., Reference Electrodes, Academic Press, New York, 1961, Chapter 3.

used in the low-resistance measurement. The small "off-balance" current is amplified by suitable circuitry to the point that galvanometer deflections are easily observed. The direct-reading type furnishes an indication of the pH on a deflection meter calibrated to read in pH units. It is more readily adapted to recorder operation than is the potentiometric type. Meters of this design usually utilize negative feedback principles to achieve an output that varies in nearly linear fashion with the input voltage. Nevertheless, errors in scale-length calibration may reduce the accuracy below that obtainable with a meter of the null-detector type.

In the early pH meters, the output of the direct-coupled amplifiers used was influenced seriously by variations in both the zero point and in the amplifier gain. Errors of the former type result from variations in the emission of the electrometer tube, from changes in the battery voltages, or from fluctuations in the power supply. Improvements came through the development of improved power sources, from better circuitry, and from better electrometer tubes. Balanced amplifiers have also been used successfully, and in one type of meter an automatic correction for zero drift is made once each second.

Probably the most significant advance in pH instrumentation in recent years has been the introduction of the frequency-conversion amplifier utilizing either a chopper or a vibrating capacitor. These devices produce a pulsating signal of constant frequency whose amplitude is modulated by the e.m.f. of the pH cell. The resulting a.c. voltage is amplified by a stable a.c. amplifier. The output is then rectified in order to supply the stabilizing feedback potential and to operate a. d.c meter and, if desired, a recorder. Figure 26-4 illustrates in a simplified way the application of the vibrating reed elec-

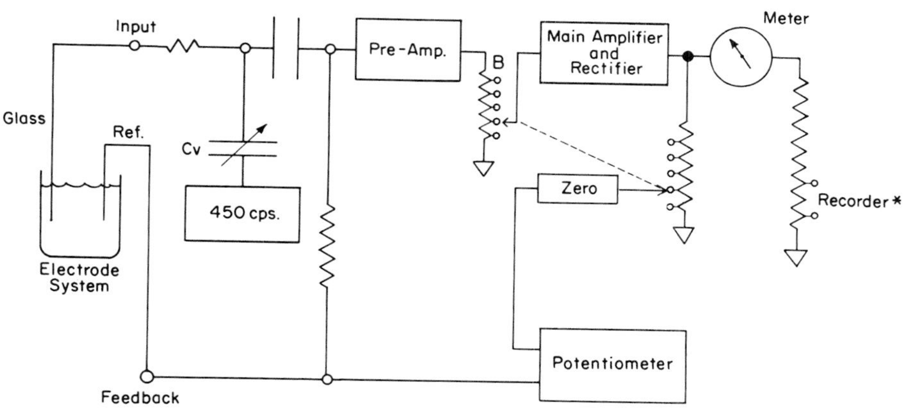

FIG. 26-4. Circuit for pH Measurement with the Cary 31 Vibrating Reed Electrometer. (Courtesy Applied Physics Corp.)

trometer to pH measurement, utilizing a potentiometric circuit. The vibrating reed is indicated at C_V.

Choppers and dynamic capacitors are also easily incorporated in direct-reading meters. They can provide a sensitivity of from 0.001 to 0.003 unit in the measurement of pH numbers. Furthermore, the zero point often does not vary by more than 0.002 or 0.003 unit during a 24-hour period.

The appropriate conversion of a difference of e.m.f. to a difference of pH is accomplished automatically by setting the "temperature compensator" of the pH meter to the proper value representing the temperature of the electrode system and the solution in the pH cell. Serious errors may result when the temperature of the standard reference solution and that of the unknown are different and when a temperature gradient through the cell exists.

A truly effective temperature compensation would provide corrections not only for the temperature variation of the pH/e.m.f. slope—that is, $(RT\ln 10)/F$ in Eq. (1)—but also for changes in the standard potential of the cell. When the variation of the standard potential is nearly linear with temperature, the plots of e.m.f. *vs.* pH at different temperatures all intersect in a point known as the "isopotential pH." [9] This simple relationship has led some manufacturers to provide automatic compensation for alteration of the standard potential of the pH cell with temperature. This feature may be of considerable value in industrial measurements where control of the temperature of the pH cell is not always possible.

pH MEASUREMENT TECHNIQUES

The measurement of pH is essentially the determination of a difference of pH between a standard and an unknown solution, both of which are at the same temperature. The most suitable electrodes should be chosen, and corrections should be applied where necessary.

Standardization of the pH Cell.—The pH meter should be standardized routinely with two solutions the pH values of which bracket, if possible, the pH of the unknowns to be determined (see Table 26-1). The standards with which the instrument is adjusted, however, should have pH values between 2.5 and 11.5 at room temperature. They should be warmed or cooled as necessary to match within 2°C. the temperature of the unknowns.

Wash the electrodes and sample cup carefully with distilled water and dry gently with clean absorbent tissue. Immerse the electrodes in the first standard solution and set the temperature compensator of the instrument to the temperature of the solutions whose pH is to be measured. Following the manufacturer's instructions, bring the instrument to balance and adjust the standardization control until the meter is again balanced at the known pH of the standard at the appropriate temperature as given in Table 26-1. Repeat the procedure with successive portions of the first standard until replacement of the solution causes no change in the position of balance. Wash the electrodes (the wash water should have a temperature not greatly different from that of the solutions to be measured) and dry as before.

Repeat this entire procedure with the second standard solution, reading the pH of the solution without changing the position of the standardization control. Replace the solution and repeat the measurement until successive readings agree within ± 0.02 pH unit. The glass electrode and measuring assembly are judged to be operating satisfactorily if the reading of the second buffer agrees within 0.02 unit with the appropriate value given in the table. It is advisable to make a final check with one of the buffers at the conclusion of a series of measurements.

Test Solutions.—The procedure for measuring the pH of unknowns is the same in every respect as that outlined for the second standard solution. Successive measurements on buffered solutions should agree to 0.02 unit or better; with water or poorly buffered solutions values agreeing no better than ± 0.1 unit may have to be accepted. It must be remembered that the extraction of the alkaline components of the relatively soluble pH-sensitive glasses can raise the pH of poorly buffered solutions by appreciable amounts

[9] Bates, R. G., Determination of pH, John Wiley and Sons, New York, 1964, pp. 364–368.

in a period of a few minutes. The effect is particularly pronounced when the volume of test solution is small and the electrode is of large area. Similarly, it may be necessary to protect poorly buffered solutions from carbon dioxide of the air during the period of measurement. Flow cells (see Fig. 26-2) are often advantageous for the measurement of the pH of water and slightly buffered solutions.

Precision and Accuracy.—Under the most favorable conditions, the best pH meters and assemblies are capable of furnishing pH numbers *precise* to 0.001 unit. The precision of the measurements on which the standard reference values are based is of the same order, but uncertainties in the electrochemical constants and the application of the convention lead to an estimate that these values are *accurate* to ±0.005 unit.[10] The accuracy of the pH values obtained for unknown or test solutions is further reduced by inconsistencies in the establishment of a standard experimental scale. These result from the unavoidable differences in the liquid-junction potential of the same pH cell when different primary standards are used. It has been found, for example, that the inconsistencies among the two phosphate standards, the phthalate standard, and the borax standard are only a few thousandths of a unit at 25°C., but at 40°C., a difference slightly greater than 0.01 unit may exist.[11] For these reasons, the accuracy of experimental pH numbers can be considered to be greater than 0.01 unit only under unusually favorable conditions.

Interpretation of pH Measurements.—When the composition and pH of the test solution match closely those of the primary standards, one may justifiably use the pH as an index of the properties of hydrogen ions in the solution or of the state of a chemical equilibrium of interest. The measured pH is then considered to be $-\log a_{\mathrm{H}}$, where a_{H} is the conventional activity defined in the manner described in an earlier section of this chapter.

Mean activity coefficients are measurable, at least in principle. Hence, the adoption of a convention for the activity coefficient of a single ionic species, for example that of chloride as embodied in the last term of Eq. (2), is sufficient to fix the numerical values of the activity coefficients of other ions as well.

In general, this procedure, though logical, is both laborious and time consuming at best, and is rarely justified by the uncertain character of the measured pH itself. When the ionic strength is less than 0.1, reasonably satisfactory results can be obtained if the activity coefficients of all univalent ions are taken to be equal to γ_{Cl} (Eq. (2)) and those of ions (i) of more than a single charge (z) are expressed in terms of γ_{Cl} through the valence relationships of the Debye-Hückel limiting law, namely $\gamma_i = (\gamma_{\mathrm{Cl}})^{z^2}$.

The following example illustrates the procedure:

The acid HA^- is titrated with sodium hydroxide and the pH is recorded at regular intervals along the titration curve. How can pK_2 for the acid be obtained?

The molar concentrations of NaHA and Na_2A at each point on the titration curve are designated c_1 and c_2, respectively. From the mass law and the simplified convention, the following relationship is derived:

$$\mathrm{pK}_2 = \mathrm{pH} - \log \frac{c_2 + [\mathrm{H}^+] - [\mathrm{OH}^-]}{c_1 - [\mathrm{H}^+] + [\mathrm{OH}^-]} + \frac{3(0.511)\sqrt{I}}{1 + 1.5\sqrt{I}}$$

A more complex expression must be used when the two dissociation steps for the acid H_2A "overlap" to an appreciable extent. The treatment of the activity coefficients is, however, the same.

[10] Bates, R. G., J. Res. Natl. Bur. Std., **66A,** 179, 1962.
[11] Bates, R. G., Determination of pH, John Wiley and Sons, New York, 1964, p. 87.

APPLICATIONS IN THE ANALYSIS OF SPECIAL MATERIALS

A procedure for the determination of the pH of water is given on page 2462, Volume IIB of Standard Methods of Chemical Analysis. A method for the determination of the pH of carbon black in rubber analysis is given in Chapter 59, Volume III of this reference.

Chapter 27

MASS SPECTROMETRY

By R. S. Gohlke
Eastern Research Laboratory
The Dow Chemical Co.
Wayland, Massachusetts

PRINCIPLES OF METHOD

Mass spectrometry may be described as a technique for converting molecules into ions and ion fragments. The mass distribution and relative abundance of the ionic products produced is recorded and provides the *mass spectrum*, which is a unique fingerprint representing the molecule from which it was formed. In the hands of the amateur interpreter—a bench chemist, perhaps—the mass spectrum provides exact molecular formulas and molecular weights rapidly. In the hands of the professional mass spectrometrist, the mass spectrum becomes perhaps the most powerful single tool available for the characterization and complete determination of molecular structure, although the latter can be accomplished only rarely at the present time.

Certain aspects of mass spectrometry are fundamental to the method as we now know it and can be enumerated as follows:

1. *The Sample.*—*If organic, the sample must have an obtainable vapor pressure of at least* 10^{-7} *mm.Hg.* In general, the higher the vapor pressure, the more easily is the mass spectrum obtained.

2. *Ions.*—*Ions must be prepared from the sample molecules.* In the instruments usually encountered by or available to the chemist, ionization is effected by electron bombardment of the sample vapor. The electrons possess sufficient energy (commonly 50–100 electron volts) to induce the rupture of any bond which might be present in the molecule.

3. *Positive Ions.*—*The positive ions are mass analyzed.* The positive ions are used because they are usually more abundant than the also-formed negative ions by a factor of 10^2 to 10^4. Ion mass analysis is accomplished by injecting the positive ions into a magnetic field where they will describe a circular path whose radius is determined by their mass/charge ratio. Since the singly-charged ions predominate, it is common to use the word "mass" when referring to an ion, rather than the more correct "mass/charge ratio or m/e." This convention is employed in this chapter.

The mass spectrum is magnetically scanned by varying the magnetic field in a precise manner, thereby causing the mass-separated ion beams to impinge upon a collector electrode in sequential order of their mass. The ions are usually bent through an angle of 60°, 90°, or 180°. A diagram for a typical mass spectrometer utilizing magnetic scanning is shown in Fig. 27-1.

It is also common to employ electrostatic scanning, in which the magnetic field strength is held constant and the energy of the injected ions is varied in a controlled manner.

Mass analysis can also be accomplished by injecting the ions into a linear drift region[1]

[1] Wiley, W. C., McLaren, I. H., Review of Scientific Instruments, **26,** 1150, 1955.

which is free of all electric and magnetic fields. The velocity of the ions is proportional to their mass and a useable mass separation is after the ions have flown for a distance of 30 cm. or more. Figure 27-2 provides a schematic representation of a time-of-flight mass spectrometer.

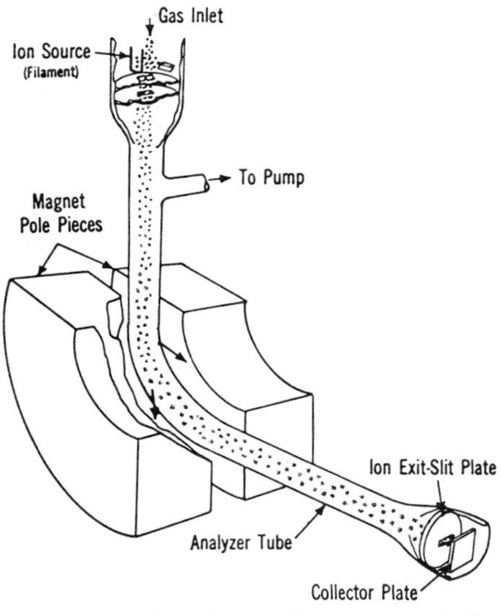

FIG. 27-1. Typical Mass Spectrometer Utilizing Magnetic Scanning.

4. *The Mass Spectrum.*—*The mass spectrum is recorded.* The mass spectrum itself usually consists of a roll of chart paper of varying length depending upon the length of the mass range scanned. Galvanometers and photosensitive paper or common pen and ink recorders are employed to produce the record with the choice being governed by the rapidity with which one wishes to scan the spectrum. In some instruments the mass spectral recording is produced by allowing the mass-separated ion beams to strike the emulsion of a glass photographic plate placed within the vacuum system of the mass spectrometer. Subsequent photographic development of the plate provides a permanent recording of the mass spectrum. A "strip-chart" recording may be prepared, if desired, from the photographic plate by passing it through a recording densitometer.

In some instances, it is most convenient to record the mass spectrum on magnetic tape for subsequent use. Occasionally it is desirable to photograph the mass spectrum as it appears upon an oscilloscope screen.

There is no single "best way" of recording mass spectra since the method of choice depends somewhat upon the application.

INSTRUMENTAL CHOICE

The discussion under this heading is restricted to those mass spectrometers which have sufficient capability to provide useable information of a fairly broad type to the chemist.

Since most mass spectrometers are still located in centralized analytical laboratories, the decision as to which of several mass spectrometers can be most fruitfully applied to a chemist's analytical problem is usually made by the analyst. Before the chemist submits his sample, though, there are several instrumental performance specifications which he should know and understand. Probably the most important specification of the mass spectrometer is its resolution which is a measure of the instrument's capability of separating ions of adjacent mass. Resolution is given as a number which means that ions of *less* mass than this number are completely separated from their neighbors while adjacent ions of greater mass begin to overlap to an increasingly severe extent as the mass increases.

Thus, if an instrument's resolution is 400, it means that ions of mass 400 and 401 and all adjacent ions of lower mass would be completely resolved from one another. Useable resolution of adjacent masses is usually retained to approximately twice the resolution figure. In this example, mass 800 and 801, although mutually interfering, could still provide useful information in some instances. Mass spectrometers useful for structure determination can have a resolution figure which might be as low as 200 or could be in excess of 40,000. Since spectral scanning time and interpretational difficulty invariably increases markedly as the resolution goes up, the chemist should be aware that his sample will probably be run at the lowest resolution consistent with the type of data desired.

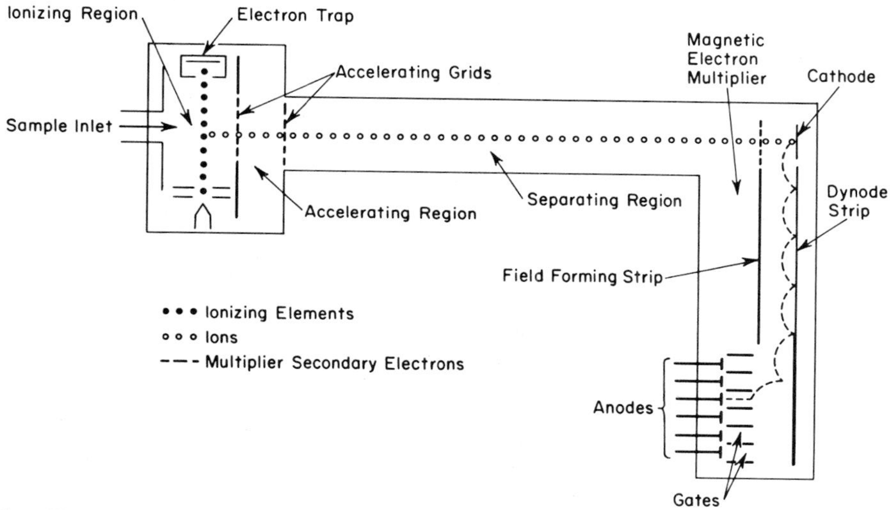

Fig. 27-2. Schematic of a Time-of-Flight Mass Spectrometer. (Courtesy Bendix Corp., Cincinnati, Ohio.)

Another fact of which the chemist should be aware is that heat will probably be applied to his sample in order to obtain sufficient vapor pressure for the mass spectrometer. In order to avoid the complicating effects of thermal decomposition, it is essential that the sample be run at as low a temperature as possible. This can vary widely. Some instruments are equipped with sophisticated inlet systems which permit a mass spectrum to be obtained at a temperature as low as 150°C. below the sample's *melting point*.[2] Other inlet systems can require that the sample be heated nearly to its atmospheric *boiling point* before good spectra can be obtained.

APPLICATIONS

Determination of Nominal Molecular Weight.—The mass spectrometer is unsurpassed by any other method for the determination of molecular weights. The procedure is simply to measure the mass at which the ion corresponding to the molecule (molecular ion, parent peak, *M*) occurs. In general, the data are accurate to the whole number nearest the true molecular weight of the compound. For example, the molecular weight of cholesterol (386.35) would be given by the mass spectrometer as 386. Nominal molecular weights can be obtained in this manner over the mass range extending from

[2] Gohlke, R. S., Anal. Chem., **31**, 535, 1959.

mass 1 to approximately the mass number given by twice the instrument's resolution. For example, a mass spectrometer which has a resolution of 200 can provide useable nominal molecular weight values to approximately mass 400. The sample *need not be highly purified* in order to perform this determination, and, indeed, the chemist's raw reaction product is usually quite useable. If the sample is a complex mixture, there is, of course, the possibility that a molecular ion and a fragment ion from another compound will have the same mass. There are numerous techniques known to the mass spectrometrist which almost always allow him to differentiate between the two types of ions, and to identify the molecular ion with certainty. The calculations require a few minutes to perform and can be done by untrained personnel.

Limitations.—Some compounds do not provide an ion at the molecular weight and in this circumstance the technique is not applicable. Most perhalogenated aliphatic, long chain ($\approx > C_{10}$) aliphatic, or aliphatic compounds which contain three or more heteroatoms do not provide molecular ions, and in these cases nominal molecular weight data are best obtained by some other method.

Determination of Partial Molecular Formula.—If a molecule contains any number of chlorine, bromine, silicon, or sulfur atoms, this fact is immediately apparent from the mass spectrum. The number of such atoms can be rapidly deduced with almost no chance for error. The number of carbon atoms present can also usually be rapidly estimated to ± 1 atom. Almost all metals can be recognized by inspection. Theoretically, the number of oxygen and nitrogen atoms can also be determined, but in practice the values obtained are often unreliable. A determination of partial molecular formula depends upon the fact that most of the atoms commonly encountered by the chemist are polyisotopic. Since the mass spectrometer sorts ions according to their actual mass, an examination of the mass *distribution* of the molecular ion will provide accurate information as to the atomic composition of that ion. For example, since all organic compounds contain a small amount (about 1.1 percent per carbon atom) of naturally occurring C^{13}, the mass spectrometer will provide ions at M corresponding to those molecules which contain no C^{13} and ions at $M + 1$ corresponding to those which do contain C^{13}. The simple ratio of the intensity of the M and $M + 1$ ion peaks will then provide the number of carbon atoms present in the molecule. It should be emphasized that for those cases in which more than two isotopes occur or where the concentration of the second most abundant isotope exceeds approximately 2 percent, the partial molecular formulas are obtained with almost no chance for error.

Limitations.—The method cannot be used to determine the number of atoms of a monoisotopic element. If the element is polyisotopic to a small extent, the method is difficult to use. Borderline results are obtained if the second most abundant isotope is present to an extent of 0.3 to 0.8 percent. If the degree of polyisotopism is small (C, N, O), the method is sensitive to impurities which might occur accidentally at the same mass as that of the isotope used for the determination.

Exact Molecular Formula Determination.—Mass spectrometers are rapidly becoming available which have sufficiently high resolving power to permit the precise formula of a molecule to be computed from a single measurement of the exact mass of the molecular ion. For example, acetophenone (C_8H_8O; Mol. wt. = 120.157), ethyl toluene (C_9H_{12}; Mol. wt. = 120.094), benzamidine ($C_7H_8N_2$; Mol. wt. = 120.069) and purine ($C_5H_4N_4$; Mol. wt. = 120.044) have an identical nominal molecular weight of 120. However, if the exact molecular weight of an otherwise unidentified material were precisely measured by the mass spectrometer as being 120.044, all molecular formulas except $C_5H_4N_4$ are positively excluded from further consideration. Hence, if a mass spectrometer of high resolving power is available, the fact that many molecules have the same nominal molecular weight is of relatively little concern to the analyst.

Limitations.—There are no limitations, except that the techniques for determining the exact mass are difficult or laborious to use unless electronic data handling equipment is readily available.

Structure Determination.—The distribution of ions—molecular and fragment—as represented by the mass spectrum provides a tool of enormous potential in the determination of molecular structure. It should be pointed out, however, that our present knowledge of molecular fragmentation processes is so incomplete, and the complete mass spectrum is so complex that it is not possible to determine the exact structure of any molecule (of molecular weight greater than perhaps 150) by using the mass spectrometer only. In any total structure determination, the mass spectrometer will usually play an indispensable role, but the additional evidence provided about the molecule by such methods as infrared spectroscopy and nuclear magnetic resonance spectroscopy is absolutely necessary.

The mass spectrum of 1-phenyl-5-ethylbarbituric acid is shown in Fig. 27-3. The reader is invited to attempt to derive this structure from the spectrum knowing *only*

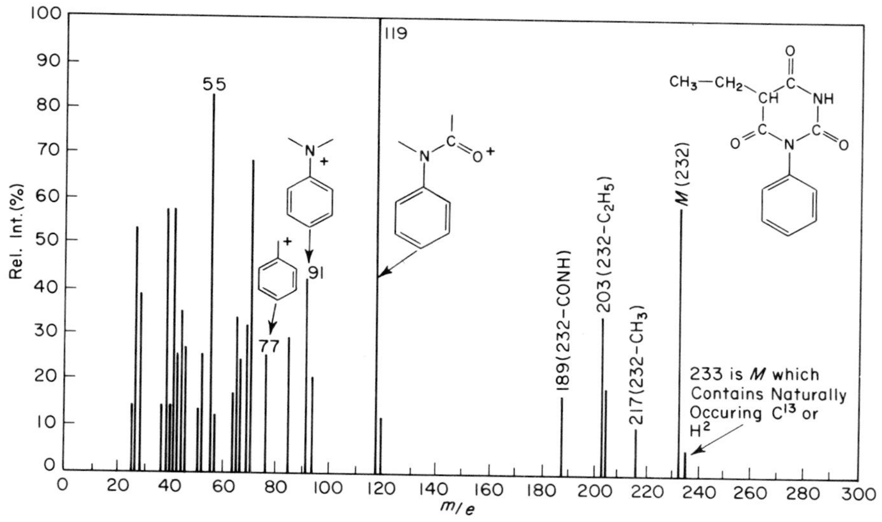

FIG. 27-3. Mass Spectrum of 1-Phenyl-5-ethylbarbituric Acid.

that the molecular weight is 232 and that the molecule contains 12 carbon atoms. If, however, the specific structure mentioned is suspected, it is relatively simple to assign likely identifications to most of the ions which appear.

The mass spectrum of 1-phenyl-5-ethylbarbituric acid is shown (Fig. 27-3) with possible identification of the ions most useful for attempts at structure determination. It should be pointed out that the absolute intensity of the ions is proportional to the number of molecules present. Hence, quantitative analytical determinations of mixtures can be performed by measuring the intensity of an ion fragment unique to a specific structure. For example, if this sample contained 1-phenyl-5-propylbarbituric acid as an impurity, an ion at m/e 246 would appear, and the ratio of m/e 232 to m/e 246 would provide an accurate measure (with suitable calibration factors) of the relative amount of each species. Under favorable circumstances 20–30 components can be determined.

Great strides have been made in the last few years in correlating mass spectra with molecular structure, and the interested reader can only be referred to the number of excellent books which discuss this particular subject more fully.[3,4,5,6,7]

Mass Spectrometric Thermal Analysis.—The products of thermal decomposition from any material may be studied rapidly and directly by placing a small amount (~1 μg) of the sample within a furnace located inside the ion source of the mass spectrometer.[8] If the mass spectrometer is capable of scanning a complete spectrum rapidly (seconds) it is possible to heat the sample at a known rate and to observe and record the volatile decomposition products as they occur. This technique is particularly useful in determining the decomposition products of high polymers and inorganic materials. It is also of value in detecting small amounts of volatile material in a nonvolatile matrix. Examples of the latter might include such diverse investigations as a search for petroleum in shale or the direct examination of a thin-layer chromatogram "spot" for the presence of an organic material. Foodstuffs such as grain and meat may be examined for the presence of volatile insecticides or drugs with this technique.

Limitations.—The samples examined by this technique must be rather nonvolatile since they are pumped to approximately 10^{-5} mm.Hg prior to introduction to the mass spectrometer.

MASS SPECTROMETRY—GAS CHROMATOGRAPHY COMBINATION

The direct combination of fast scanning mass spectrometers with gas chromatography instrumentation provides a tool of enormous analytical power since mass spectra are obtained of the gas chromatographic fractions as they leave the column.[2,9] In this manner, the identification of all major and most minor components in the chromatogram may be accomplished. Packed or capillary columns may be utilized as the situation requires.

Limitations.—Successful use of this technique requires persons highly skilled in the art of interpreting mass spectra, since they are usually (or often) of poor quality due to column substrate contamination. Then too, the spectrum is obtained on a sample which is continuously changing in concentration, which complicates the interpretation greatly. There are electronic means of eliminating the spectral intensity dependence upon concentration, but these are not particularly satisfactory.

SAMPLE REQUIREMENTS FOR THE MASS SPECTROMETER

1. ***Gases.***—1 cubic centimer at STP is the usual requirement for ease in handling.
2. ***Liquids.***—At least 1 microliter is usually preferred, again to provide handling ease.
3. ***Solids.***—1 milligram. Solid samples as small as 10^{-8} grams can provide good spectra if an inert bulking material is present.

[3] Beynon, J. H., Mass Spectrometry and its Applications to Organic Chemistry, Elsevier, Amsterdam, 1960.
[4] Biemann, K., Mass Spectrometry—Organic Chemical Applications, McGraw-Hill, New York, 1962.
[5] Budzikiewicz, H., Djerassi, C., Williams, D. H., Interpretations of Mass Spectra of Organic Compounds, Holden-Day, San Francisco, 1964.
[6] Budzikiewicz, H., Djerassi, C., Williams, D. H., Structure Elucidation of Natural Products by Mass Spectrometry, Volume I: Alkaloids, Volume II: Steroids, Terpenoids, Sugars, and Miscellaneous Classes, Holden-Day, San Francisco, 1964.
[7] McLafferty, F. W., Mass Spectrometry of Organic Ions, Academic Press, New York, 1963.
[8] Gohlke, R. S., Chem. and Ind., 946, 1963.
[9] Ryhage, R., Anal. Chem., **36,** 759, 1964.

GENERAL COMMENTS

The time required to obtain one complete mass spectrum can range from 0.1 millisecond to several hours depending upon the type of data required and the instrumentation available. In general, for most samples, 10 to 30 minutes is required to obtain the spectrum and to prepare the mass spectrometer for the next sample. The length of time required to interpret the data obtained varies, of course, with the skill of the analyst but usually ranges from a few minutes for a simple molecular weight or empirical formula determination to many hours for attempts at structure determination.

APPLICATIONS IN THE ANALYSIS OF SPECIAL MATERIALS

A number of determinations using mass spectrometry have been included in other chapters of Standard Methods of Chemical Analysis. These are:

1. Chapter 51, Volume III, Organic Functional Groups.
   a. Analysis of methyl- and phenylchlorosilane solutions
2. Chapter 52, Volume III, Gases, and Chapter 35, Volume IIB, Fuel Gases and Related Products, page 1531.
   a. The following substances in gases are determinable with the mass spectrometer:

Argon	Isobutane
Benzene	Methane
Butadiene	Naphthalene
Butane	Neon
Butenes	Nitrogen
Carbon dioxide	Oxygen
Carbon disulfide	Pentane
Carbon monoxide	Pentene
Ethane	Propane
Ethene	Propene
Helium	Styrene
Hexane	Sulfur dioxide
Hydrogen	Toluene
Hydrogen sulfide	Xylene

3. Chapter 57, Volume III, Petroleum and Petroleum Products.
   a. Characterization of olefinic hydrocarbon in petroleum
   b. Characterization of aromatic fractions in petroleum
   c. Identification of individual hydrocarbons in gasoline and higher-boiling mixtures
   d. Determination of the following substances:

Acetylene	Ethene
Argon	Hydrogen
Butadiene	Hydrogen sulfide
Butane	Isobutane
Butenes	Methane
Carbon dioxide	Nitrogen
Carbon disulfide	Oxygen
Carbon monoxide	Propane
Carbonyl sulfide	Propene
Ethane	

4. Chapter 58, Volume III, Plastics.
   a. Determination of pyrolysis products of plastics
5. Chapter 59, Volume III, Rubber and Rubber Products.
   a. Quantitative determination of composition of ethylene-propylene copolymers
   b. Polymer identification in rubber analysis
6. Chapter 60, Volume III, Semiconductors.
   a. Determination of impurities in semiconductors
7. Chapter 61, Volume III, Soaps and Synthetic Detergents.
   a. Examination of alkylates prior to sulfonation in detergent industry
   b. Determination of branched chain and linear alkylates in detergent industry
8. Chapter 64, Volume III, Determination of Water.
   a. Determination of water in gases or volatile liquids

Chapter **28**

RADIOISOTOPES IN ANALYTICAL CHEMISTRY

By George W. Leddicotte
Associate Professor of Nuclear Engineering and Radiology
University of Missouri
Columbia, Missouri

INTRODUCTION

Any scientific effort, whether it is fundamental research in biology or the development of better process controls for industrial requirements, begins and ends with the need for an analytical method. As a result, progress in science must be related to the specificity and the sensitivity of the analytical method and the ease with which it can be applied to the scientific problem. An analytical method is no better than the tools available to it, and too few of the many methods that have become available have contributed significantly to the advancement of science.

The invention and the use of the analytical balance and the microscope probably have contributed more to scientific advancement than any other tool or instrument. However, within recent years, research and development efforts in nuclear energy have provided tools and techniques that are equally as important as the analytical balance and the microscope. In particular, the discovery and the production of artificially radioactive isotopes and their use as tracer atoms have led to the development of analytical methods that are much more specific and sensitive and more easily applied than other analytical methods. The information that follows presents generally the technology that has already been derived and applied to problems in the physical sciences, biology, chemistry, and other areas.

THE NATURE OF RADIOACTIVITY

RADIOACTIVE DISINTEGRATION PROCESSES

The phenomenon of radioactivity results from the transformation of the nucleus of an atom into another nucleus. When the relationship between the number of neutrons and protons in the nucleus is favorable, the nucleus is in a stable state. The introduction of some change to this relationship results in an unfavorable balance in the number of neutrons and protons, and the nucleus undergoes a spontaneous disintegration or radioactive decay. Almost all nuclei found in nature are stable (notable exceptions are the naturally occurring radioactive nuclei) and can undergo a transmutation to radioactive nuclides by bombarding them with sources of nuclear particles, *viz.*, neutrons, protons, deuterons, and alpha particles. As any of these nuclear particles interacts with a stable nucleus, the product nucleus is left in an excited state and reaches a stable state only through the emission of one or more of several types of radiation.[1] These disintegration processes may occur in one of the following ways or as a combination of these ways:

Alpha-particle Emission. – An alpha-particle is the nucleus of the helium atom; it has a mass of four atomic units and a positive charge of two units. The energy of alpha-particles varies from 3 to 8 M.e.V., but owing to their large mass, they have a range of only a few centimeters in air and a fraction of a millimeter in solid materials. Radioisotopes emitting alpha-particles are usually found among both the naturally and artificially occurring heavy elements and their decay chains.

Beta-particle Emission. Beta-particles are electrons. They have a mass of 1/1850 of an atomic mass unit, and have a negative charge. They are easily scattered or rejected by other electrons because of their small mass and this negative charge. Beta-particles emitted in a radioactive disintegration process have a continuous spectrum of energies; the spectrum is a single peaked curve of characteristic shape that can have an energy range up to 2000 mg./cm^2., or about 1 cm. in aluminum. Beta-particle emitters occur either as members of the decay chains of the naturally radioactive heavy elements, as fission products, or as materials activated by nuclear particle bombardments, *e.g.*, neutrons.

Positron Emission.—All positrons are beta-particles of unit positive charge. They decay by a mass-energy annihilation process (annihilation radiation) to produce photons having an energy of 0.51 M.e.V. (the rest mass of an electron). Two such photons arise from the destruction of each positron.

Electron Capture (EC or K-capture).—This capture process involves the conversion of a nuclear proton to a neutron by capture of an orbital electron from the K orbit. This change is accompanied by the emission of x-rays.

Isomeric Transition (IT).—Sometimes the radioactive disintegration process creates a metastable nucleus which changes to an isomer (*i.e.*, a nuclide with the same atomic and mass numbers) with the excess energy being emitted in the form of a gamma-ray. An isomeric transition may also result from the ejection of a planetary electron. This process is known as an *internal conversion* of gamma radiations. The ejected electrons are called conversion electrons, and they have an intensity relative to that of the gamma photons. Gamma-rays and x-rays have no charge or mass, and are very penetrating. They are slowed down by both elastic and inelastic scattering processes which lead to the production of electrons which can be used to detect the radiations. About 75 percent of the radionuclides that disintegrate by the emission of either alpha-particles, negatrons and positrons, or by electron capture, emit gamma radiations as they decay.

FUNDAMENTAL UNITS OF RADIATION ENERGY

The energy of a nuclear radiation is measured as an *electron volt*, e.v., which is the energy acquired by an electron accelerated through a potential difference of 1 volt. Radiation energies can range from *kiloelectron volts*, k.e.V., to *million electron volts*, M.e.V. Alpha-, gamma-, and x-radiations have discrete energies while negatrons and positrons have a continuous distribution of kinetic energies that have an end point, or maximum energy, characteristic of the radionuclide, which is usually designated as E_{max}.

THE DECAY AND GROWTH OF A RADIOELEMENT

When any nuclear species decays in a simple process, the nucleus disintegrates immediately or at some later time. Since the behavior of a single atom cannot be forecast, the average behavior of a number of atoms must be used to describe the

[1] Friedlander, G., Kennedy, J. W., and Miller, J. M., Nuclear and Radiochemistry, 2nd Ed., John Wiley, New York, 1964.

process. Thus, the decay law states that the rate of decay is proportional to the number of atoms present. The law can be expressed mathematically as

$$\frac{dN}{dt} = -\lambda N \tag{1}$$

where: N is the number of radioactive atoms present; and
λ is the *proportionality* or *decay constant*.
The decay constant is different for each radionuclide.

Equation (1) describes an instant decay rate; in most decay measurements, however, knowledge of the number of radioactive atoms, N, or radioactive disintegrations, A, taking place in a described unit of time is required. This can be mathematically expressed by rearranging Eq. (1)

$$\frac{dN}{N} = -\lambda dt$$

and integrating for N or A, so that

$$\log_e N = -\lambda t + c \tag{2}$$

$$\text{when } t = 0,\ N = N_0,$$
$$\text{so that } c = \log_e N_0,$$

$$\text{and } \log N = -\lambda t + \log N_0 \tag{3}$$

$$\text{then } N = N_0\, e^{-\lambda t}$$
$$\text{or } A = A_0 c^{-\lambda t}$$

Since the decay constant λ is related to the half-life $t_{1/2}$, which is defined as the time required for the number of atoms (or the measured radioactivity) present to decay to half that number, Eq. (3) becomes

$$\frac{N_0}{2} = N_0\, e^{-\lambda t}$$

Half the atoms will have decayed when $e^{-\lambda t} = \frac{1}{2}$. The time at which this occurs is termed the half-life, T, which becomes $= \frac{0.693}{\lambda}$, when expressed as a logarithmic function to the base 10, so that

$$\frac{N_0}{2} = N_0\, e^{-\frac{0.693t}{T}} \tag{4}$$

where: N = number of radioactive atoms, or activity, after time t;
N_0 = the initial number of radioactive atoms, or activity;
λ = the decay constant = $0.693/T$; and
T = half-life.

Some radionuclides decay to daughter radionuclides. In these instances, the original species is called the parent, and the number of radioactive atoms, N, or the disintegration rate, A, of the daughter radionuclide is given as

$$N_2 = \frac{\lambda_2 N_{1O}}{\lambda_2 - \lambda_1}\,(e^{-\lambda_1 T} - e^{-\lambda_2 t}) + N_{2O}\, e^{-\lambda_2 t} \tag{5}$$

where: N_2 = the number of radioactive atoms of the daughter radionuclide;
λ_1, λ_2 = parent and daughter decay constants; and
N_{1O}, N_{2O} = initial activity of parent and daughter.

If the parent is much longer-lived than the daughter, the equation simplifies to

$$N_2 = N_1(1 - e^{-\lambda_2 t}) + N_{20}\, e^{-\lambda_2 t} \tag{6}$$

The term, $1 - e^{-\lambda t}$, is sometimes called the growth, or saturation factor. When a daughter radionuclide is produced at a constant rate from a long-lived parent or as the product of bombarding stable nuclei with nuclear particles, the saturation factor is the ratio of the radioactivity produced at a given time t to that which would be produced in a very long time of decay or bombardment. As $e^{-\lambda t}$ approaches unity, an equilibrium is approached. The relation between these quantities and the half-life is summarized in Table 28-1.

TABLE 28-1. GROWTH AND DECAY OF A RADIOELEMENT IN TERMS OF HALF-LIVES

Number of Half-Lives	*Radioactivity Growth as a Fraction of the Equilibrium Value*	*Radioactivity Decay in Terms of Fraction Remaining*
0.5	0.293	0.707
1	0.500	0.500
2	0.750	0.250
3	0.875	0.125
4	0.938	0.0625
5	0.969	0.0313
6	0.984	0.0156
7	0.992	0.0078
8	0.996	0.0039
9	0.998	0.0020
10	0.999	0.0010

RADIOCHEMISTRY UNITS

The number of disintegrations that a radionuclide emits in a given period of time is a measure of its activity. The basic unit is the *curie*, C, or that quantity of radioactivity equivalent to 3.70×10^{10} disintegrations per second (d/s). In tracer applications of radioisotopes, it is most common to use quantities of activity that are decimal fractions of a curie, *e.g.*, 1 *millicurie* (mC.), 3.7×10^7 d/s; or 1 *microcurie* (μC.), 3.7×10^4 d/s.

Since the quantity of radioactive isotope used in a tracer experiment is small, the amount used in an experiment, or recovered as a result of a chemical processing of the added tracer and the test material, the amount present per unit weight of total element is known as the *specific activity*. This is usually expressed in curies or millicuries per gram.

THE MEASUREMENT OF RADIOACTIVITY

The devices available for radioactivity measurements will vary with the types of radiations emitted by the radioisotope and the kinds of radioactive material.[2,3,4,5,6] Ionization

[2] Price, W. J., Nuclear Radiation Detection, McGraw-Hill, New York, 1958.
[3] Bell, P. R., and Hayes, F. N., Liquid Scintillation Counting, Pergamon Press, New York, 1958.
[4] Metrology of Radionuclides, International Atomic Energy Agency, Vienna, 1960.
[5] Measurement and Standards of Radioactivity, NAS-NRC Publication 573, 1958.
[6] O'Kelley, G. D., Detection and Measurement of Nuclear Radiation, NAS-NRC Nuclear Science, Series NAS-NS-3105, 1962.

chambers are used for gases; Geiger-Müller and proportional counters for solids; liquid scintillation counters for liquids and solutions; and solid crystal or semiconductor detector scintillation counters for liquids and solids emitting high-energy radiations. Each device can be adapted to detect and measure radioactive material in another state, *e.g.*, solids can be assayed in an ionization chamber.

The radiations interact with the detector of the counter to produce a signal. This function in each type of counter can be generally described as follows:

Ionization Chamber.—In an ionization chamber, the radioactive gas produces ions by collisions with the gas molecules. These ions are collected on electrodes at a relatively low potential to produce a current that is amplified by a vibrating reed electrometer to be read on a galvanometer. The current product is a measure of the average rate of ion production, and, therefore, the radioactivity of the gas. Ionization chambers are used to measure gamma- and x-ray (EC) radiations.

Geiger-Müller Counter.—In Geiger-Müller and proportional counters, the radiations emitted by a solid sample cause ionization in the gas with which the counter is filled. These ions are multiplied several thousands of times when a high voltage is applied to the electrodes. Ultimately, when the potential is discharged, the discharge is registered as a single event on a scaling device. These types of counters measure each β- or γ-ray entering the counter. In a proportional counter, the magnitude of the discharge is proportional to the energy of the entering radiation. Proportional counters, having a thin-window or a 2π geometry (internal source, 50 percent), are used to measure alpha radiations.

Liquid Scintillation Counter.—In liquid scintillation counting, the radioactive material is intimately mixed in a solution of an organic compound that has the property of emitting flashes of light on interaction with radiation. The light produced is seen by a multiplier phototube, which releases electrons that are amplified and registered on a scaling device. Each light pulse as it discharges corresponds to the disintegration of a radioactive atom, and its intensity is proportional to the energy of the ray emitted. Liquid scintillation counters are most effectively used in the measurement of alpha and very weak beta radiations (such as those of H^3 and C^{14}).

Solid Crystal Scintillation and Semiconductor Counters.—A solid crystal scintillation counter operates on the same principle as a liquid scintillation counter, except that the radiation strikes the crystal (usually sodium iodide, containing traces of thallium). The crystal has the property of emitting flashes of light corresponding to the radiation which strikes it. In a semiconductor counter, the radiations supply energy to a semiconductor material (*e.g.*, silicon) to produce free electrons. The freed electrons move randomly through the crystal lattice in much the same way as the molecules in a gas. When the electrons break away they leave vacancies or "holes." As other electrons move in to fill up the holes, other holes are created, and, when a voltage is applied across the crystal, the electrons and holes drift throughout the lattice with some order to produce a current that is proportional to the energy of the radiation striking the detector. Solid crystal counters are routinely used to measure α-, β-, γ- and x-radiations. Semiconductor counters are most often used to detect and measure α-radiations.

ANALYSIS OF MIXTURES OF RADIONUCLIDES

The characteristic half-lives and radiation types and energies have been used to some advantage in analyzing mixtures of radionuclides.[7,8] The absorption of beta radiations

[7] Overman, R. T., and Clark, H. M., Radioisotope Techniques, McGraw-Hill, New York, 1960.

[8] Reynolds, S. A., Record Chemical Progress, Kresge-Hooker Science Library, **16,** 99–119, 1955.

in aluminum have also been used to analyze mixtures of beta-emitting radionuclides.[1,7,8] However, spectrometric techniques are generally more useful than the absorption method. Mixtures of alpha-emitting radionuclides have been analyzed by spectrometers equipped with a gridded ionization chamber[2] or a semiconductor detector.[9] Scintillation spectrometers equipped with organic phosphors have been used to measure mixtures of beta-emitting radionuclides.[2] Liquid scintillators and scintillation spectrometers have also been used to measure beta-emitting mixtures.[3] Proportional counters have been used to analyze mixtures of electron-capture radionuclides by measuring the x-rays associated with their decay.[4]

GAMMA-RAY SCINTILLATION SPECTROMETRY

Since many radionuclides decay with gamma radiations, many measurements are being made by gamma-ray scintillation spectrometry.[6,10,11] Usually a crystal detector, such as a sodium iodide crystal, is connected to a spectrometer. As described above, the gamma-rays interact with the crystal to produce light pulses which are converted to electrical pulses by a multiplier phototube. The pulse height analyzer of the spectrometer sorts out the gamma-rays of various energies. From this operation, a spectrum of the radionuclide's gamma-rays can be obtained as the *photopeak* of full-energy pulses and the continuum of lower-energy pulses associated with the decay of the radionuclide.[10, 11] The photopeak, or photopeaks, in a gamma-ray spectrum can be used to identify and quantitatively measure the radionuclide. Heath[11] provides detailed information on the method of determining the efficiency of a sodium iodide detector for a given gamma-ray energy in order to measure it quantitatively. Mixtures of gamma-emitting radionuclides can be analyzed since the spectra are additive. Techniques for "stripping-off" the spectrum of each component and the ultimate processing of the data by a computer-integrated approach have been described recently.[12]

ERRORS AND STATISTICS IN MEASURING RADIOACTIVITY

In organizing a tracer experiment, it must be remembered that the radioactivity assay is to be made with some type of detector and a scaling or count rate-meter. The results of the measurement will be recorded in terms of the *count rate* of the sample, *i.e.*, the number of counts accumulated by the instrument in unit time and expressed as *counts per minute* (c.p.m.) or *counts per second* (c.p.s.). The conversion of a count rate into a meaningful expression of the amount of radioactive isotope is dependent upon (1) a statistical treatment of the reliability, or accuracy, of the observed count rate; (2) correcting the observed count rate for such factors as the efficiency and background of the counter; and (3) expressing the corrected count rate in terms of suitable units. Since the nature of the radioactive disintegration process is random, the accuracy achieved in any measurement is dependent on the actual magnitude of the count rate and the time taken to make the observation. Methods for the statistical treatment of radioactivity data have been described by Price,[2] Overman and Clark,[7] Kuyper,[13] and Jaffey.[14]

In most experiments, a single determination of the count rate would be made. How-

[9] Chetham-Strode, A. S., Tarrant, R., and Silva, H., IRE Trans. Nuclear Sci. NS-8, No. 1, 59, 1961.

[10] Crouthamel, C., Ed., Applied Gamma-ray Spectrometry, Pergamon Press, New York, 1960.

[11] Heath, R. L., "Scintillation Spectrometry, Gamma-ray Spectrum Catalogue," AEC Research and Development Report TID-4500, Volumes 1 and 2, August, 1964.

[12] O'Kelley, G. D., Ed., "Applications of Computers to Nuclear and Radiochemistry," NAS-NRC, Nuclear Science Series, NAS-NS-3107, 1963.

[13] Kuyper, A. C., J. Chem. Ed., **36,** 128, 1959.

[14] Jaffey, A. H., Nucleonics, **18,** No. 11, 180, 1960.

ever, if additional counts under the same conditions were made, the observed data would fluctuate in a statistically predictable manner and when plotted as a frequency distribution would approximate a Gaussian distribution. Thus, the chances of the total count n of a single measurement in a series of determinations being within given limits of the mean value of all the determinations are expressed in terms of a single parameter, the *standard deviation*. If one determination is made, then the standard deviation σ in the total count n is

$$\sigma = \sqrt{n} \tag{7}$$

The probability that the result found falls within $\pm 1\sigma$, $\pm 2\sigma$, and $\pm 3\sigma$ of the true value are respectively 68.3, 95.4, and 99.7%. The standard deviation of the counting rate R, *i.e.*, the counts per unit time t can be calculated to be

$$\sigma_R = \sqrt{\frac{R}{t}} \tag{8}$$

for the 68.3 percent confidence interval. The standard deviation, σ_{av}, of the average of several rates having similar deviations is

$$\sigma_{av} = \frac{\sigma}{\sqrt{N}} \tag{9}$$

where σ = the standard deviation of a single measurement, and N = the number of determinations.

The background radioactivity, natural or otherwise, of the counter and its environment sometimes needs to be considered in making the measurement. If the count rate of the radioactivity to be measured is low, then the net rate of the source can be calculated by

$$\sigma_s = \sqrt{\frac{R_T + R_b}{t_T + t_b}} \tag{10}$$

where: σ_s = the standard deviation in the net counting rate;
R_T = the total rate including background;
R_b = background count rate; and
t_T and t_b = the time intervals used respectively to count the source and the background of the counter.

When the source is reasonably active, the background needs to be determined only once. However, the background count interval should be long enough to make σ_b much smaller than σ_s so that the background can be ignored and Eq. (8) can be used.

In addition to the random errors in counting the radioactive source, systematic errors may result from faults in the counting equipment. Information on the treatment of the statistics involved in determining such errors as nonstatistical counter behavior, equilibrium time, coincidence corrections, detector efficiency, and random pulses in the counter circuits has been given by Kohl, *et al.*[15]

THE USE OF RADIOISOTOPES IN TRACER CHEMISTRY

A radioactive isotope of an element behaves identically with the stable isotopes of the given element in all chemical processes. It labels, without question, the particular atoms

[15] Kohl, J., Zentner, R. D., and Lukens, H. R., Radioisotope Application Engineering, D. Van Nostrand, Princeton, 1961, pp. 146–179.

to be traced regardless of what may happen to the atoms in any complicated system. The specificity and the sensitivity of detection of radioactive isotopes is extremely good; less than 100,000 atoms (about 10^{-18} g.) can often be detected. Table 28-2 lists the sensitivity of detection of some of the more important radioelements.

TABLE 28-2. DETECTION SENSITIVITIES OF SOME OF THE RADIOELEMENTS

Species	*Limits (g.)*
C^{14}	5.2×10^{-12}
P^{32}	4.5×10^{-14}
Ca^{45}	7.0×10^{-11}
Fe^{59}	3.6×10^{-10}
Co^{60}	9.0×10^{-13}
I^{131}	1.0×10^{-16}
Tl^{208}	7.5×10^{-20}
Pb^{212}	1.5×10^{-17}

A distinct advantage in the use of radioisotopes is the ability to detect ionizing radiation through substantial thicknesses of material. This sometimes makes it possible to use nondestructive testing in any analysis of a material.

Over 900 radioisotopes of the 102 elements in the periodic table have been characterized. Table 28-3 lists some of the important radionuclides available for analytical chemistry uses. All of these are commercially available at reasonable prices. Some companies, such as Nuclear Materials and Engineering at Apollo, Pa., also provide quantities of radioisotopes small enough to make it practical to use them without a specific United States Atomic Energy Commission By-Product Use License. Table 28-4 lists these products.

SELECTING A RADIOISOTOPE

Some elements have one or more radioactive species of varying half-lives that can be used in a tracer experiment. The selection of a tracer is then dependent primarily upon the duration of the experiment and the repeated use of the tracer. If the species is short-lived, *e.g.*, 24 hours or less, adjustments in each succeeding experiment must be made to compensate for the rapid radioactive decay. Similarly, a correction may have to be made for a longer-lived species' decay if the experiment is of long duration.

Radioactive tracers may either be "carrier free," *i.e.*, they have been produced by a nuclear reaction on some other elemental species (P^{32}, for example, which is produced by bombarding S^{32} with 2.3 M.e.V. neutrons) or they may contain some amount of the stable element (*e.g.*, Sb^{121}, As^{75}, Mn^{55}, etc.). The tracers should not only be free of other radioactive species but should be chemically pure so that a minimal amount of interference will be experienced from these sources during the experiment.

A radiotracer cannot be completed readily if an insufficient amount of radioactivity is obtained at the end of the experiment. An arbitrary rule is that the amount should be from 5 to 20 times greater than the experimentally determined background of the counter. Usually there is a large dilution of the amount of radiotracer added to the experiment. Kohl, *et al.*,[15] give some criteria for selecting the amount of tracer to be used in an experiment.

Any experimenter using a radiotracer must recognize that radioactivity can sometimes cause the material being analyzed to decompose. These radiation effects as well

TABLE 28-3. SOME IMPORTANT RADIONUCLIDES FOR ANALYTICAL CHEMISTRY USES

Element	*Isotope*	*Half-Life*	*Mode of Decay*	*Principal Radiation Energies, M.e.V.*	
				Particle	*Gamma*
Antimony	Sb-124	60 d	β^-, γ	0.63, 2.39	0.60, 1.71
Argon	Ar-41	109 m	β^-, γ	1.25	1.30
Arsenic	As-76	26.5 h	β^-, γ	2.41, 2.97	0.56, 1.2
Barium	Ba-139	85 m	β^-, γ	0.8, 2.23	0.16, 0.30
Bromine	Br-82	35.9 h	β^-, γ	0.44	0.55, 1.47
Calcium	Ca-45	164 d	β^-	0.25	—
Carbon	C-14	5600 y	β^-	0.16	—
Cesium	Cs-134	2.3 y	β^-, γ	0.66	0.61, 0.8
	Cs-137	30 y	β^-, γ	0.5, 1.2	0.66
Chlorine	Cl-36	3.1×10^5 y	β^-	0.7	
	Cl-38	37 m	β^-, γ	4.8, 1.1	2.15, 1.60
Chromium	Cr-51	27.8 d	EC, γ	—	0.323
Cobalt	Co-60	5.25 y	β^-, γ	0.31	1.17, 1.33
Copper	Cu-64	12.8 h	EC, β^-, $\beta^+(\gamma)$	0.6	0.51, 1.34
Gold	Au-198	2.70 d	β^-, γ	0.96	0.411
Iodine	I-131	8.04 d	β^-, γ	0.61	0.36, 0.64
	I-128	25.0 m	β^-, γ	1.7, 2.1	0.45
Iridium	Ir-192	74.4 d	β^-, γ	0.7, 0.5	0.31, 0.47
Iron	Fe-55	2.94 y	EC	—	—
	Fe-59	45 d	β^-, γ	0.46, 0.27	1.10, 1.29
Krypton	Kr-85	10.6 y	β^-, γ	0.67	0.54
Magnesium	Mg-28	21.4 h	β^-, γ	0.46	1.35, 0.95, 0.40
Manganese	Mn-54	291 d	EC, γ	—	0.84
	Mn-56	2.58 h	β^-, γ	2.8, 1.0, 0.7	0.85, 1.81, 2.1
Molybdenum	Mo-99	68 h	β^-, γ	1.2, 0.4	0.74
Nickel	Ni-65	2.56 h	β^-, γ	2.10, 0.6	1.13, 1.49, 0.37
Phosphorus	P-32	14.3 d	β^-	1.7	—
Potassium	K-42	12.5 h	β^-, γ	3.5, 2.0	1.53
Scandium	Sc-46	84 d	β^-, γ	0.36	0.89
Silicon	Si-31	2.6 h	$\beta^-, (\gamma)$	1.5	1.26
Sodium	Na-22	2.6 y	β^+, EC, γ	0.54	0.51, 1.27
	Na-24	15 h	β^-, γ	1.39	1.37, 2.76
Strontium	Sr-87	2.9 h	IT	—	0.39
	Sr-90	28 y	β^-	0.54	—
Sulfur	S-35	87.1 d	β^-	0.17	—
Tantalum	Ta-182	111 d	β^-, γ	0.90, 0.6	0.30, 0.97, 0.88
Thallium	Tl-204	3.56 y	β^-, EC	0.77	—
Thulium	Tm-170	127 d	β^-, γ	0.97, 0.88	0.084
Tin	Sn-121	27 h	β^-	0.4	—
Tritium	H-3	12.26	β^-	0.018	—
Tungsten	W-187	24.1 h	β^-, γ	0.6, 1.3	0.69, 0.48, 0.13
Xenon	Xe-133	5.27 d	β^-, γ	0.34	0.081
Yttrium	Y-90	64 h	β^-	2.3	—
Zinc	Zn-65	245 d	EC, $\beta^+\gamma$	0.325	1.11, 0.51

TABLE 28-4. RADIONUCLIDE QUANTITIES AVAILABLE WITHOUT SPECIFIC U.S.A.E.C. LICENSE[a]

Radionuclide	*Not as a Sealed Source (microcuries)*	*As a Sealed Source (microcuries)*
Antimony (Sb 124)	1	10
Arsenic 76 (As 76)	10	10
Arsenic 77 (As 77)	10	10
Barium 140—Lanthanum 140 (BaLa 140)	1	10
Beryllium (Be 7)	50	50
Cadmium 109—Silver 109 (CdAg 109)	10	10
Calcium 45 (Ca 45)	10	10
Carbon 14 (C 14)	50	50
Cerium 144—Praseodymium 144 (CePr 144)	1	10
Cesium 137—Barium 137 (CsBa 137)	1	10
Chlorine 36 (Cl 36)	1	10
Chromium 51 (Cr 51)	50	50
Cobalt 60 (Co 60)	1	10
Copper 64 (Cu 64)	50	50
Europium 154 (Eu 154)	1	10
Fluorine 18	50	50
Gallium 72 (Ga 72)	10	10
Germanium 71 (Ge 71)	50	50
Gold 198 (Au 198)	10	10
Gold 199 (Au 199)	10	10
Hydrogen 3 (Tritium) (H 3)	250	250
Indium 114 (In 114)	1	10
Iodine 131 (I 131)	10	10
Iridium 192 (Ir 192)	10	10
Iron 55 (Fe 55)	50	50
Iron 59 (Fe 59)	1	10
Lanthanum 140 (La 140)	10	10
Manganese 54 (Mn 54)	1	10
Manganese 56 (Mn 56)	50	50
Molybdenum 99 (Mo 99)	10	10
Nickel 59 (Ni 59)	1	10
Nickel 63 (Ni 63)	1	10
Niobium 95 (Nb 95)	10	10
Palladium 109 (Pd 109)	10	10
Palladium 103—Rhodium 103 (PdRh 103)	50	50
Phosphorus 32 (P 32)	10	10
Polonium 210 (Po 210)	0.1	1
Potassium 42 (K 42)	10	10
Praseodymium 143 (Pr 143)	10	10
Promethium 147 (Pm 147)	10	10
Rhenium 186 (Re 186)	10	10
Rhodium 105 (Rh 105)	10	10
Rubidium 86 (Rb 86)	10	10
Ruthenium 106—Rhodium 106 (RuRh 106)	1	10

[a] As reported by Nuclear Materials and Engineering, Apollo, Pa.

TABLE 28-4 (cont.)

Radionuclide	Not as a Sealed Source (microcuries)	As a Sealed Source (microcuries)
Samarium 153 (Sm 153)	10	10
Scandium 46 (Sc 46)	1	10
Silver 105 (Ag 105)	1	10
Silver 111 (Ag 111)	10	10
Sodium 22 (Na 22)	10	10
Sodium 24 (Na 24)	10	10
Strontium 89 (Sr 89)	1	10
Strontium 90—Yttrium 90 (SrY 90)	0.1	1
Sulfur 35 (S 35)	50	50
Tantalum 182 (Ta 182)	10	10
Technetium 96 (Tc 96)	1	10
Technetium 99 (Tc 99)	1	10
Tellurium 127 (Te 127)	10	10
Tellurium 129 (Te 129)	1	10
Thallium 204 (Tl 204)	50	50
Tin 113 (Sn 113)	10	10
Tungsten 185 (W 185)	10	10
Vanadium 48 (V 48)	1	10
Yttrium 90 (Y 90)	1	10
Yttrium 91 (Y 91)	1	10
Zinc 65 (Zn 65)	10	10

as such other factors as isotope effects, chemical states, and adsorption mechanisms are discussed more fully by such authors as Overman and Clark[7] and Kohl, *et al.*[15]

ANALYTICAL APPLICATIONS OF RADIOISOTOPES

The first analytical application of a radioisotope was recorded by Hevesy in 1923.[16] In these experiments, he used ThB(Pb^{212}) to study the absorption of lead from aqueous solutions by vegetation. Since that time many radioisotope applications have been made in basic and applied research and in service requirements in all branches of science. These applications can be categorized as being measurements of natural and added radioactivity and activation analysis. The general techniques followed in using radioisotopes in such applications are described below. For comprehensive lists of the analytical applications of radioisotopes, the reader is referred to the recent reviews prepared by Leddicotte[17,18] and Reynolds and Leddicotte[19] for this information.

THE MEASUREMENT OF NATURAL RADIOACTIVITY

A few of the elements contain naturally radioactive isotopes, and since some of these elements have long half-lives, the isotopic concentration remains constant. In effect, the radioactivity is relative to the weight of the element or compound, so that a measurement of the radioactivity is a measure of the quantity of the element present in the sample

[16] Hevesy, G., Z. anal. Chem., **88,** 1, 1932.
[17] Leddicotte, G. W., Anal. Chem., **34,** 143R–171R, 1962.
[18] Leddicotte, G. W., Anal. Chem., **36,** 419R–453R, 1964.
[19] Reynolds, S. A., and Leddicotte, G. W., Nucleonics, **21,** No. 8, 128–142, 1963.

material. All of the natural radioactivities can be analyzed for either by alpha or gamma detectors. Potassium, rubidium, samarium, lutecium, rhenium, francium, thorium, and uranium can be analyzed in this way.[17,18,19]

THE MEASUREMENT OF ADDED RADIOACTIVITY

Added tracers have been used as described in the following paragraphs.

In Carrier Techniques.—This is a qualitative tool used to identify the chemical form of small amounts of radioactive labeled materials. The method followed involves the addition of unlabeled material in the same chemical form (as a carrier) to a solution of the radioactivity and then isolating it in a pure state, followed by a determination of the radioactivity of the compound isolated. If the isolated compound is radioactive, then it is certain that the unknown and the added carrier are identical. This is a relatively simple technique that is used frequently to test the separation of one elemental species from another, and it has found much use in the field of analytical radiochemistry, an area of application that is much more fully covered by Reynolds.[8]

As Radioactive Reagents.—If an element is labeled with a radioisotope and the radioactivity is determined per unit weight, and if this specific radioactivity remains constant throughout the experiment, then the radioactivity observed is directly proportional to the quantity of the element involved. This type of experimentation has been used to determine solubilities, co-precipitation, in elemental analysis, and in the separation of one species from another. For example, I^{131} has been used in a radioactive isotopically labeled reagent to determine small amounts of silver ion in solution. There are many applications of this technique,[19] which is more commonly known as the *radiometric method* of analysis. For examples of these applications, see Tables 28-5, 28-6, 28-7, 28-8, and 28-9.

Isotope Dilution.—The basic principle involved in the isotope dilution method is to measure the change in the isotopic composition of the added tracer. The method involves the addition of a tracer material (element or compound) of known specific activity (*viz.*, counts per minute per milligram) to the test sample. Some fraction of the material to be determined is recovered and its weight and radioactivity are measured. The basic equation[20,21] for isotope dilution is

$$W_u = W_f\left(\frac{A_0}{A_f}\right) - W_0 \tag{11}$$

where: W_u = the unknown weight of material in the sample;
W_f = the weight of the material recovered;
W_0 = the weight of material added with the tracer;
A_0 = the amount of radioactivity added; and
A_f = the amount of radioactivity recovered.

If W_0 is insignificant compared to W_u, Eq. 11 becomes

$$W_u = W_f\left(\frac{A_0}{A_f}\right) \tag{12}$$

This is the simplest form of isotope dilution. Lambie[22] reports that more precise results can be obtained by measuring the radioactivity of the unreacted fraction rather than measuring the radioactivity of the dissolved fraction.

[20] Rosenblum, C., Nucleonics, **14,** No. 5, 58, 1956.
[21] Rosenblum, C., Anal. Chem., **29,** 1740, 1959.
[22] Lambie, D. A., Analyst, **84,** 173, 1959.

TABLE 28-5. RADIOREAGENT METHODS: ELEMENTS

Element	*Tracer*	*Application*	*References*[a]
Aluminum	P^{32}	Pptn. as $P^*O_4^{\equiv}$	3, 38
Arsenic	Ag^{110m}	Pptn. as $Ag_2{}^*TlAsO_4$	4
Beryllium	Co^{60}	Pptn. with $[Co^*(NH_3)_6]Cl_3$	7
	P^{32}	Pptn. in paper as phosphate	39
Bismuth	Co^{60}	Pptn. with $[Co^*(NH_3)_6]Cl_3$	7
	I^{131}	Pptn. with I^{*-}	14
Bromine	Ag^{110m}	Detn. of bromide	8
Calcium	P^{32}	Pptn. with $HP^*O_4^{=}$	6
	Pb^{212}	Pptn. with xs oxatate	15
Carbon	Ag^{110m}	Detn. of cyanide	9, 35
Cerium	P^{32}	Pptn. as $P^*O_4^{\equiv}$	38
Chlorine	Ag^{110m}	Pptn. as Ag^*Cl	8, 9, 13, 34, 39
	Hg^{203}	Pptn. as $Hg_2{}^*Cl_2$	9
Chromium	Ag^{110m}	Pptn. of $Ag_2{}^*CrO_4$	9
Copper	I^{131}	Pptn. of $[Cu(C_6H_8N_2)_2]HgI_4{}^*$	20
Fluorine	Ca^{45}	Pptn. of Ca^*F_2	9
	Ta^{182}	Detn. of fluoride	25
Hydrogen	H^3	Detn. of hydrogen in Al	11
Indium	P^{32}	Pptn. of In P^*O_4	38
Iodine	Ag^{110m}	Pptn. of Ag^*I	8, 9
	I^{131}	$IO_3^- + xs\ I^{*-}$ and measure I_2	28
	Tl^{204}	Pptn. of Tl^*I	30
Lanthanum	P^{32}	Pptn. of LaP^*O_4	38
Lead	P^{32}	Paper chromatog., developed by $P^*O_4^{\equiv}$	40, 41, 42
	S^{35}	Pptn. of PbS^*O_4	9
Lithium	Pb^{212}	Li + xs H_3PO_4; Pptn. + xs H_2SO_4 + xs Pb^{*++}	16
Magnesium	P^{32}	Pptn. with $P^*O_4^{\equiv}$	3, 6, 23, 39
Molybdenum	Ag^{110m}	Pptn. as $Ag_2{}^*MoO_4$	12
Phosphorus	Ca^{45}	Detn. of $PO_4^{\equiv}$ in water	33
	Co^{60}	Detn. of P in foods, detergents and manure	1
	I^{131}	Paper chromatog, developed by Ag, treated with KI^*	43
	Ag^{110m}	Pptn. of $Ag_2{}^*TlPO_4$	4
Potassium	Co^{60}	Pptn. as $K_2Ag[Co^*(NO_2)_6]$	29
		Pptn. with $Na_3[Co^*(NO_2)_6]$	18
		Pptn. as $K_2Na[Co^*(NO_2)_6]$	21, 22
	I^{131}	Paper chromatog. of I^{*-}	31
Scandium	Co^{60}	Pptn. of $[Co^*(NH_3)_6]ScF_6$	37
Silver	I^{131}	Pptn. of AgI^*	
		$Be(OH)_2$ collector	14
		Zirconium phosphate collector	27
		$Fe(OH)_3$ carrier	36
		Detn. of Ag in film	2
Sodium	I^{131}	Paper chromatog. of I^{*-}	31
Sulfur	Ba^{140}	Pptn. of Ba^*SO_4 with xs Ba^*	10
	S^{35}, Ag^{110m}	Detn. of polythionates	32
Thallium	Co^{60}	Pptn. of $[Co^*(NH_3)_6]TlCl_6$	17
	I^{128}	Pptn. as TlI^*	26
Thorium	P^{32}	Pptn. with xs $P_2{}^*O_7{}^{-4}$	24
		Pptn. with $P_2{}^*O_7{}^{-4}$, Ag carrier	19
Tungsten	Co^{60}	Pptn. of Co^*WO_4	5
Vanadium	Ag^{110m}	Pptn. of Ag^*VO_3	12
Zinc	P^{32}	Pptn. with $P^*O_4^{\equiv}$	3
Zirconium	P^{32}	Pptn. with $P^*O_4^{\equiv}$	38

[a] Numbers refer to the following works:

1. Adam, L., Isotopen Technik, **2,** No. 2, 46, 1962.
2. Ballard, A. E., Stevens, G. W. W., and Zuehlke, C. W., PSA Journal, **18B,** 27, 1952.
3. Barcia-Goyanes, C., and Serrano, Sanchez E., Bol. Radiactiv., **24,** 34, 1951.

TABLE 28-5 (cont.)

4. Barcia-Goyanes, C., Serrano, Sanchez E., and Gomis, C., Bol. Radiactiv., **26,** 37, 1954.
5. Bradhurst, D. H., Coller, B. A. W., and Duncan, J. F., J. Inorg. Nuclear Chem., **4,** 379, 1957.
6. Brown, C. T., *et al.*, BMI-1415, 1960.
7. Dema, I., Gainar, I., and Nascutiu, T., Rev. Chim. (Bucharest), **11,** 291, 1960.
8. Driscoll, W. J., AECU-4471, 1959.
9. Driscoll, W. D., and Huff, E. A., Exploration of Radiometric Methods, Report No. 2, AECU-4417, 1959.
10. Eisler, S. L., Metal Finishing, **50,** 71, 1952.
11. Foster, L. M., Nucleonics, **21,** No. 4, 63, 1963.
12. Govaerts, J., and Barcia-Goyanes, C., Anal. Chim. Acta, **6,** 121, 1952; Nature, **168,** 198, 1951.
13. Hein, R. E., and McFarland, R. H., J. Chem. Educ., **33,** 33, 1956.
14. Herman, Z., Coll. Czech. Chem. Commun., **26,** 1925, 1961.
15. Ishibashi, M., and Kishi, H., Nippon Kagaku Zasshi, **59,** 702, 1938.
16. Ishibashi, M., and Kishi, H., Nippon Kagaku Zasshi, **59,** 698, 1938.
17. Ishimori, T., Bull. Chem. Soc. Japan, **26,** 336, 1953.
18. Ishimori, T., and Takashima, Y., Bull. Chem. Soc. Japan, **26,** 481, 1953.
19. Kar, K. R., and Sawhney, B. C., J. Sci. Ind. Research (India), **17B,** 365, 1958; **18B,** 39, 1959; **19B,** 401, 1960.
20. Kiseleva, N. A., Megorskaya, I. B., and Rozova, M. I., Zavod. Lab., **22,** 1291, 1956.
21. Korenman, I. M., *et al.*, Trudy Khim. i Khim. Tekhnol., **94,** 1959.
22. Korenman, I. M., Sheyanova, F. R., and Giasunova, Z. I., Zavod. Lab., **21,** 774, 1955.
23. Mizuike, A., Nakajima, T., and Hirano, S., Bunseki Kagaku, **7,** 588, 1958.
24. Moeller, T., and Schweitzer, G. K., Anal. Chem., **20,** 1201, 1948.
25. Moore, F. L., Anal. Chem., **35,** 1032, 1963.
26. Moureu, H., Chovin, P., and Daudel, R., Compt. Rend., **219,** 127, 1944.
27. Purkayastha, B. C., and Vernecker, V. R. P., J. Indian Chem. Soc., **34,** 487, 1957.
28. Raben, M. S., Anal. Chem., **22,** 480, 1950.
29. Serrano, Sanchez E., and Lopez, Santos, J., Inf. Quim. Anal., **7,** 43, 1953; Bol. Radiactiv., **24,** 49, 1951.
30. Sarsunova, M., Majer, J., and Tolgyessy, J., Ceskosl. Farm. **8,** 567, 1959.
31. Schiller, P., and Tolgyessy, J., Chem. Zvesti, **11,** 508, 1957.
32. Schoon, N. H., Acta Chem. Scand., **14,** 2009, 1960.
33. Scott, B. F., and Driscoll, W. J., Nucleonics, **19,** No. 6, 49, 1961.
34. Shatalova, A. A., and Meerov, G. I., Biokhimiya, **25,** 769, 1960.
35. Straub, G., Csapo, Z., Acta Chim. Acad. Sci. Hung., **26,** 267, 1961 (Ger).
36. Süe, P., Bull. Soc. Chim. France, 102, 1946.
37. Takashima, Y., Nippon Kagaku Zasshi, **79,** 246, 1958.
38. Tananaev, I. V., and Efremova, A. M., Izvest. Akad. Nauk SSSR, 5, 1955.
39. Thackray, M., Nature, **190,** 434, 1961.
40. Van Erkelens, P. C., Anal. Chim. Acta, **25,** 570, 1961.
41. Van Erkelens, P. C., Anal. Chim. Acta, **26,** 32, 1962.
42. Van Erkelens, P. C., Anal. Chim. Acta, **26,** 46, 1962.
43. Zubrzycki, Z. J., Budzynski, A. Z., and Campbell, I. G., Talanta, **2,** 164, 1959.

Rosenblum[20,23] has reported on the use of a *reverse isotope* method. In this approach, the material to be determined is already associated with a radioactive tracer, the amount of which can be determined by adding a known weight of inactive material. However, for this method to be effective, the specific radioactivity of the material in the sample must be known. A method of *double isotope dilution* analysis has also been described by Christian.[24] The principal advantages in using isotope dilution methods are their speed, sensitivity, and the possibility of making nonquantitative separations. Exchange between the radioactive and inactive species can be obtained through the use of such chemical treatments as boiling with acids, oxidation and/or reduction, complexing agents, etc.

[23] Rosenblum, C., Chem. Revs., **16,** 99, 1935.

[24] Christian, J. E., Radioactivity for Pharmaceutical and Allied Research Laboratories, Academic Press, New York, 1960, pp. 49–62.

TABLE 28-6. RADIOREAGENT METHODS: ORGANIC COMPOUNDS

Compound	*Tracer*	*Application*	*References*[a]
Alkaloids	P^{32}	Paper Chromatog., developed by P^{32}-molybdophosphates	13
Amino acids	I^{131}	With I^{131}-pipsyl chloride	7, 8
Carboxyl group	Ca^{45}	Detn. in cellulose	6
	Co^{60}	Detn. in cellulose	12
Estrogens	I^{131}	With I^{131}-pipsyl chloride	9
Fatty acids	Co^{60}	Paper chromatog. developed with Co^{60}	11
	I^{131}	Paper chromatog. use AgI^{131}	18
Fatty acids (unsat.)	I^{131}	Paper chromatog., iodination	2
β-Galactosidase	C^{14}	With C^{14}-*o*-nitrophenyl-β-D-galactoside	10
Hemoglobin	C^{14}	In blood satd. with $C^{14}O$	14
Linseed Oil—Iodine No.	I^{131}	With NaI^{131}-$NaIO_3$	1
α-Nitroso-β-naphthol	Co^{69}	Pptn. as Co^{60} complex	17
Pyrimidines	I^{131} or S^{35}	With pipsyl chloride	3
Salicylic acid	I^{131}	With $I^{131}Cl$	15
Steroid alcohols	C^{14}	With C^{14}-Ac_2O	5
Urea	C^{14}	Pptn. with C^{14}-xanthhydrol	4, 16

[a] Numbers refer to the following works:

1. Abdel-Wahab, M. F., and El-Kinawi, S. A., Z. anal. Chem. **180,** 420, 1961.
2. Budzynski, A. Z., Zubrzycki, Z. J., and Campbell, I. G., Nature, **182,** 178, 1958.
3. Fresco, J. R., and Warner, R. C., J. Biol. Chem., **215,** 751, 1955.
4. Herbain, M., and Bertin, D., Bull. Soc. Chim. Biol., **41,** 621, 1959.
5. Hollander, V. P., and Vinecour, J., Anal. Chem., **30,** 1429, 1958.
6. Hostomsky, J., Tolgyessy, J., and Krivan, V., Chem. Zvesti, **14,** 290, 1960.
7. Keston, A. S., *et al.*, J. Am. Chem. Soc., **63,** 1390, 1946; **71,** 249, 1949.
8. Keston, A. S., Udenfriend, S., and Levy, M., J. Am. Chem. Soc., **69,** 3151, 1947; **72,** 748, 1950.
9. Leegwater, D. C., Nature **128,** 916, 1956.
10. Noll, H., and Orlando, J., Anal. Biochem., **2,** 205, 1961.
11. Otto, R., Isotopentechnik, **1,** 184, 1961; Atompraxis, **7,** 209, 1961.
12. Rochas, P., Bussiere, R., and Gavet, L., Compt. Rend., **248,** 3436, 1959.
13. Sarsunova, M., and Tolgyessy, J., J. Majer, Pharm. Acta Helv., **35,** 221, 1960.
14. Shatalova, A. A., Meerov, G. I., and Savinskii, Ya. R., Biokhimiya, **25,** 577, 1960.
15. Swartz, H. A., and Christian, J. E., J. Am. Pharm. Assoc., Sci. Ed., **47,** 701, 1958.
16. Velluz, L., *et al.*, Compt. Rend., **246,** 3071, 1958.
17. Weiss, H. V., and Lai, M. G., USNRDL-TR-440, 1960.
18. Zubrzycki, Z. J., Budzynski, A. Z., and Campbell, I. G., Talanta, **2,** 164, 1959.

Examples of the analytical applications of isotope dilution are given in Tables 28-10 and 28-11.

ACTIVATION ANALYSIS

The most frequently used radioisotope application is the method of *activation analysis.* Originally introduced and defined by Boyd,[25] the method has been well documented by others.[17,18,19,26,27]

[25] Boyd, G. E., Anal. Chem., **21,** 335, 1949.
[26] Leddicotte, G. W., and Reynolds, S. A., Nucleonics, **8,** No. 3, 62, 1951.
[27] Brooksbank, W. A., Leddicotte, G. W., and Mahlman, H. A., J. Phys. Chem., **57,** 815, 1953.

TABLE 28-7. RADIOMETRIC METHODS: ELEMENTS

Element	*Tracer*	*Application*	*References*[a]
Antimony	Sb^{124}	Distribution in steel	23
Arsenic	As^{78}	Distribution in steel	23
Bismuth	Bi^{210}	Detn. in biological materials	13
Calcium	Ca^{45}	Soly. in $SiHCl_3$	49
Carbon	C^{14}	Detn. in steel	60
Cerium	Ce^{144}	Distribution in steel	15, 16
Cesium	Cs^{134}	Soly. of chloride in organic liqs.	36
Chlorine	Cl^{36}	Depos. on Cr electrode	43
Chromium	Cr^{51}	Detn. in feces	5
Copper	Cu^{64}	Detn. of vapor pressure	46, 47
Gold	Au^{198}	Detn. of vapor pressure	46, 47
		Distribution in gallium arsenide	39
Hydrogen	H^3	Soly. of H_2O in hydrocarbons	4, 37
		Soly. and detn. of H_2O in oil	9
		Detn. of H_2O in varnish films	10
Iodine	I^{131}	Copptn. of I^- with oxides	54
		Adsorpt. on clays	61
		Detn. in feces	5
Iron	Fe^{59}	Soly. in $SiHCl_3$	40
		Electrolytic sepn. of FeO	41
		Detn. in feces	5
Lanthanum	La^{140}	Copptn. with $Th(C_2O_4)_2$	38
Lead	Pb^{210}	Soly. of $PbCrO_4$ and PbS	29
		Detn. in biol. material	13
	Pb^{212}	Copptn. with Ag and Tl	1
		Retention by filters	34
	I^{131}	Soly. of PbI_2	18
Manganese	Mn^{52}	Anodic depos. with PbO_2	8
	Mn^{54}	Copptn. with Sn compds.	27
Mercury	Hg^{197m}	Detn. of Hg vapor in air	24, 33
Neodymium	Pm^{147}	Soly. of $Nd_2(C_2O_4)_3$	6
Phosphorus	P^{32}	Adsorpt. on clays	61
		Copptn. with $PbMoO_4$	28
		Detn. in biol. material	12
		Detn. in slag	48
		Detn. in slag and steel	59
		Detn. in steel	22, 31
		Phosphate in fused salt	53
		Detn. of vapor pressure	17
Plutonium	Pu^{239}	Detn. in process water	21
Potassium	K^{42}	Copptn. with Mg	30
Radium	Ra^{224}	Detn. in natural water	11, 32, 35
Ruthenium	Ru^{106}	Soly. of $Ru(OH)_4$	7
Scandium	Sc^{46}	Adsorpt. on various materials	50
		Copptn. with $Ce(IO_3)_4$	40
Silver	Ag^{110m}	Copptn. with Tl, Pb	1
		Exchange capacity of clays	42
		Soly. of chloride in organic liquids	36

TABLE 28-7 (cont.)

Element	*Tracer*	*Application*	*References*[a]
		Detn. of vapor pressure	46, 47
	Ag^{111}	Anodic deposition with PbO_2	8
Sodium	Na^{24}	Copptn. with Mg	30
		Detn. in fused salt	53
		Penetration in glass	58
Strontium	Sr^{90}	Adsorption studies	2, 19, 20, 56
		Copptn. with $BaSO_4$	26
		Detn. in fused salt	53
		Exchange capacity of clays	42
Sulfur	S^{35}	Adsorpt. of sulfate	51
		Combined S in rubber	57
		Detn. in steel	60
		Distribution in steel	14, 15, 16
		Sulfate adsorption by cation columns	50
		Sulfate in fused salt	53
Tellurium	$Te^{127,129}$	Copptn. with Sb	52
Thallium	Tl^{204}	Copptn. with Ag, Pb	1
		Copptn. with AgCl	25
Thorium	Th^{234}	Size of ThO_2 particles	55
Tin	Sn^{113}	Distribution in steel	23
Tungsten	W^{185}	Soly. of $BaWO_4$	62
	W^{187}	Cinchonine pptn.	45
Yttrium	Y^{90}	Detn. in fused salt	53
		Exchange capacity of clays	42
Zinc	Zn^{65}	Copptn. with $Cr(OH)_3$	3
		Copptn. with $Cr(OH)_3$ and $Fe(OH)_3$	44

[a] Numbers refer to the following works:

1. Alimarin, I. P., and Sirotina, I. A., Zhur. Neorg. Khim., **3,** 1709, 1958.
2. Ames, L. L., Rept. HW-SA-2364, December 1961, Hanford Atomic Products Operations, Richland, Wash.
3. Babko, A. K., and Shtokalo, M. I., Zavod. Lab., **21,** 767, 1955.
4. Black, C., *et al.*, J. Chem. Phys., **16,** 537, 1948.
5. Bonnet, J. D., Hightower, N. C., Petrany, Z., and Sommer, A. W., Am. J. Digest. Diseases, **6,** 520, 1961; Nucl. Sci. Abstr., **17,** 15894, 1963.
6. Bradley, A., and Peterson, H. T., Jr., J. Chem. Educ., **37,** 398, 1960.
7. Brandstet, R. J., Krivanek, M., and Vrestal, J., Coll. Czech. Chem. Commun., **26,** 2596, 1961.
8. Byrne, J. T., and Rogers, L. B., J. Electrochem. Soc., **103,** 442, 1956.
9. Cameron, J. F., Boyce, I. S., and Glaister, R. M., Brit. J. Appl. Phys., **10,** 463, 1959.
10. Calkins, G. D., *et al.*, Nucleonics, **13,** No. 2, 76, 1955.
11. Chaikin, P. I., and Golubev, N. V., Radiokhimiya, **5,** 397, 1963.
12. Chiewitz, O., and Hevesy, G., Nature, **136,** 754, 1935.
13. Christiansen, I. A., Hevesy, G., and Lomholt, S., Compt. Rend., **178,** 1324, 1923; **179,** 291, 1924.
14. Cochran, A. A., and Jensen, J. W., U. S. Bureau of Mines, Rept. of Investigation No. 6122, 1962.
15. Cochran, A. A., and Miller, V. R., U. S. Bureau of Mines, Report of Investigation No. 6256, 1963.
16. Cochran, A. A., and Miller, V. R., J. of Metals, **914,** December 1963.
17. Dainton, F. S., and Kimberly, H. M., Trans. Faraday Soc., **46,** 912, 1950.
18. Duncan, J. F., J. Inorg. Nuclear Chem. **11,** 161, 1959.
19. Egorov, Y. V., Krylov, E. I., and Tkachenko, E. V., Radiokhimiya, **3,** 654, 1961.

Table 28-7 (cont.)

20. Egorov, Y. V., and Krylov, E. I., Radiokhimiya, **5,** 211, 1963.
21. Elliot, F., and Pearon, G. W., Nucleonics, **21,** No. 5, 78, 1963.
22. Fodor, J., Acta Chim. Acad. Sci. Hung., **19,** 13, 1959.
23. Gomiscek, S., Nova Proizvodnja, **11,** 273, 1960.
24. Goodman, C., Irvine, J. W., Jr., and Horan, C., J. Ind. Hyg. Toxicol. **25,** 275, 1943.
25. Gordon, L., Peterson, J. I., and Burtt, B. P., Anal. Chem., **27,** 1770, 1955.
26. Gordon, L., Reimer, C. C., and Burtt, B. P., Anal. Chem., **26,** 842, 1954.
27. Gordon, L., Teicher, H., and Burtt, B. P., Anal. Chem., **26,** 992, 1954.
28. Heslop, R. B., and Kirby, R., Analyst, **86,** 134, 1961.
29. Hevesy, G., and Paneth, F., Z. anorg. Chem., **82,** 323, 1913.
30. Heyn, A. H. A., and Finston, H. L., Anal. Chem., **32,** 328, 1960.
31. Hill, J. E., U. S. Patent 2,365,553, 1944.
32. Hurst, J. B., and Lovaas, A., Intern. Symposium Natural Radiation Environment, Houston, Texas, April 1963, CONF-16-1, 1963.
33. Irvine, J. W., Jr., and Goodman, C., J. Appl. Phys., **14,** 496, 1943.
34. Ishibashi, M., and Kishi, H., Nippon Kagaku Zasshi, **57,** 1031, 1936.
35. Ivanova, K. S., Radiokhimiya, **3,** 348, 1961.
36. Izmailov, N. A., and Chernyi, V. S., Zhur. Fiz. Khim. **34,** 127, 1960.
37. Joris, G., and Taylor, H., J. Chem. Phys., **16,** 45, 1948.
38. Kall, H. L., Coprecipitation studies with thorium oxalate as carrier, dissertation, Syracuse University, 1955, Dissertation Abs., **15,** 2403, 1955.
39. Kern, W., J. Electrochem. Soc., **109,** 60, 1962.
40. Kimura, K., Natsume, H., and Suzuki, Y., Bunseki Kagaku, **6,** 719, 1957.
41. Kohn, A., Chim. Anal., **44,** 425, 1962.
42. Lieser, K. H., Z. anorg. u. allgem. Chem., **304,** 207, 1960.
43. Maksimchuck, V. P., and Rosenfel'd, I. L., Doklad. Akad. Nauk SSSR, **131,** 354, 1960.
44. Mashima, M., Bunseki Kagaku, **5,** 324, 1956.
45. Merz, E., Z. anal. Chem., **191,** 416, 1962.
46. Nesmeyanov, A. N., *et al.*, Zhur. Fiz. Khim., **33,** 342, 1959.
47. Nesmeyanov, A. N., Smakhtin, L. A., and Lebeedev, V. I., Zhur. Fiz. Khim., **33,** 599, 1959.
48. Osipov, A. I., *et al.*, Zavod. Lab., **21,** 391, 1955.
49. Petrov, D. A., Vlasova, I. V., and Zimina, G. V., Zhur. Neorg. Khim., **4,** 2500, 1959.
50. Sass, R. L., and Eisler, S. L., Plating, **41,** 497, 1954.
51. Schweitzer, G. K., and Bomar, M. R., J. Am. Chem. Soc., **77,** 4528, 1955.
52. Seaborg, G. T., Chem. Rev., **27,** 199, 1940.
53. Süe, P., Pauly, J., and Mouaille, A., Compt. Rend., **244,** 1212, 1957.
54. Sugawara, K., Koyama, T., and Terada, K., Coprecipitation of iodide ions by some metallic oxides, in Radioisotopes in Scientific Research, Vol. 2, Pergamon Press, New York, 1958, p. 681.
55. Takeda, T., Suzuki, I., and Kimura, K., Nippon Genshiryoku Gakkaishi, **2,** 122, 1960.
56. Takizawa, M., Proceedings of 5th Japan Conference on Radioisotopes, Tokyo, May 21–23, 1963; Japan Atomic Industrial Forum, Inc., Tokyo, 1963.
57. Tarasova, Z. N., Kaplunov, M. Ya., and Dogadkin, B. A., Zavod. Lab., **21,** 396, 1955.
58. Trebge, E., and Fischer, R., Silikat Tech., **10,** 351, 1959.
69. Winkler, T. B., and Chipman, J., Am. Inst. Mining Met. Engrs., Tec. Pub. 1987, 1946.
60. Wuttkowski, H., Giesserei Praxis, **17,** 343, 1961.
61. Zaduban, M., Jaderna Energie, **9,** No. 4, 114, 1963.
62. Zimakov, I. E., Zavod. Lab., **25,** 133, 1959.

Although an activation analysis may be initiated by bombarding a sample with either neutrons, deuterons, protons, or alpha particles, only those analyses involving bombardments with thermal neutrons will be discussed, since most of the experiments recorded in the literature (see footnotes 17 and 18 for many of these) have used the method of *neutron activation analysis*. However, it should be noted that the same basic principles of the method will apply if other nuclear particle reactions are used. Most of the reactions used in neutron activation analysis involve neutron capture. These reactions are all similar to the reaction used for the determination of sodium in a sample material:

$$_{11}Na^{23} + _{0}n^{1} \rightarrow _{11}Na^{24} + \gamma \tag{13}$$

TABLE 28-8. RADIOMETRIC METHODS: ORGANIC COMPOUNDS

Compound	*Tracer*	*Application*	*References*[a]
Aerosol	S^{35}	Concn. at liquid surfaces	3
DDT	Mn^{52}	Detn. after spraying	4
DDT, DDE	C^{14}	Solvent extrn.	6
Detergent ($C_{18}H_{37}SO_4Na$)	S^{35}	Concn. at liquid surfaces	1
Monosaccharides and polyols	I^{131}	Paper chromatog., use AgI*	2
Serum albumin	I^{131}	Adsorpt. on glass	7
Surfactants	C^{14}	Adsorpt. studies	8
Tri-*n*-butyl phosphate	P^{32}	Soly. and distribution	5

[a] Numbers refer to the following works:

1. Aniansson, G., and Lamm, O., Nature, **165**, 357, 1950.
2. Beer, J. Z., Talanta, **8**, 809, 1961.
3. Dixon, J. K., *et al.*, Nature, **163**, 845, 1949.
4. Irvine, J. W., Jr., Anal. Chem., **21**, 364, 1949.
5. Kennedy, J., and Grimley, S. S., Radiometric studies with phosphorus-32 labelled tri-*n*-butly phosphate, AERE-CE/R-1283–1284, 1953.
6. Perry, A. S., Jensen, J. A., and Pearce, G. W., J. Agr. Food Chem., **3**, 1008, 1955.
7. Reed, G. W., and Rossall, R. E., Radioisotopes in Scientific Research, Vol. 2, Pergamon Press, New York, 1958, p. 502.
8. Seaman, W., and Roberts, G. L., Anal. Chem., **33**, 414, 1961.

TABLE 28-9. RADIOMETRIC TITRATIONS

Element	*Tracer*	*Application*	*References*[a]
Bromine	Ag^{105}	Detn. of Br^- with Ag^{*+}	18
	Ag^{110m}	Detn. Cl^-, Br^-, I^- in a mixture	12
Cadmium	Cd^{115m}	Extrn. with dithizone	15
	Fe^{59}	Detn. with $K_4Fe^*(CN)_6$	10
Calcium	Ag^{110m}	With EDTA and Ag* indicator	5
Carbon	Ag^{110m}	Detn. of CN^- and $C_2O_4^=$	3, 27
Chlorine	Ag^{105}	Detn. of Cl^- with Ag^{*+}	18
	Ag^{110m}	Detn. of Cl^-, Br^-, I^- in a mixture	12
		Detn. of Cl^- with Ag^{*+}	21, 29
Cobalt	Co^{60}	Detn. with $K_4Fe(CN)_6$	8
		$[Co^*Py_4]^{++}+NH_4SCN$, $CHCl_3$ extrn.	11
		Pptn. of $[CoPy_4](SCN)_2$	20
		With EDTA	25
Copper	Ag^{110m}	With EDTA, Ag^*IO_3 indicator	6
	Cd^{115m}	Dithizone extrn., Cd^{*++} indicator	15
	H^3	Labeled org. reagent	2
	Fe^{59}	With $K_4Fe^*(CN)_6$	28
	I^{131}	Copper(I) with KI*	30
	Zn^{65}	With $K_4Fe(CN)_6$, Zn^{*++} indicator	16
Iodine	Ag^{110m}	Cl^-, Br^-, I^- in a mixture	12
		Detn. of IO_3^-	3
Lead	Ag^{110m}	With K_2CrO_4, Ag^{*+} indicator	3
	Fe^{59}	With $K_4Fe^*(CN)_6$	28
	Tl^{204}	With K_2CrO_4, Tl* indicator	17
Magnesium	Ag^{110m}	With EDTA, Ag^{*+} indicator	5, 20
	P^{32}	With $Na_2HP^*O_4$	19, 23
Mercury	Hg^{203}	Dithizone extrn.	7, 13, 24
	Zn^{65}	Dithizone extrn. with Zn^{*++}	14, 15

TABLE 28-9 (cont.)

Element	*Tracer*	*Application*	*References*[a]
Nickel	Co^{60}	Pptn. of $[Ni(Co^*)Py_4](SCN)_2$	20
Palladium	I^{131}	Palladium(II) with KI*	30
Phosphorus	P^{32}	Detn. of $P^*O_4^{\equiv}$ with Mg^{++}	19
Silver	Ag^{110m}	With HCl	22
	Ag^{105}	With Cl^-	18
	Fe^{59}	With $K_4Fe^*(CN)_6$	28
	I^{131}	With KI*	30
	P^{32}	With $Na_2HP^*O_4$	19
Strontium	Ag^{110m}	With EDTA, Ag^{*+} indicator	5
Sulfur	S^{35}	Sulfate with Ba^{++}	21
Thallium	Tl^{204}	With tetraphenylboron	26
		With I^- and $CrO_4^=$	1, 17
Tungsten	Co^{60}	Pptn. of Co^*WO_4	4
Zinc	Ag^{110m}	With EDTA, Ag^{*+} indicator	9
	Co^{60}	Dithizone extrn.	7
	Fe^{59}	With $K_4Fe^*(CN)_6$	10, 28
	Zn^{65}	Dithizone extrn.	13, 14, 15
		With $K_4Fe(CN)_6$	16
Zirconium	P^{32}	With $Na_2HP^*O_4$	1

[a] Numbers refer to the following works:

1. Alimarin, I. P., *et al.*, Intern. J. App. Radiation Isotopes, **2,** 117, 1957.
2. Aylward, G. H., *et al.*, J. Inorg. Nuclear Chem., **16,** 350, 1961; Chem. and Ind., **20,** 560, 1960.
3. Bebesel, P., and Sirbu, I., Rev. Chim. (Bucharest), **11,** 288, 1960.
4. Bradhurst, D. H., Coller, B. A. W., and Duncan, J. F., J. Inorg. Nuclear Chem., **4,** 379, 1957.
5. Braun, T., *et al.*, Zhur. Anal. Khim., **14,** 542, 1959.
6. Braun, T., Maxim, I., and Galateanu, I., Nature, **182,** 936, 1958.
7. Duncan, J. F., and Thomas, F. G., J. Inorg. Nuclear Chem., **4,** 376, 1957.
8. Eristavi, D. I., Brouchek, F. I., and Tsivtsivadze, T. A., Zhur. Anal. Khim., **14,** 631, 1959.
9. Galateanu, I., Maxim, I., and Braun, T., Z. anal. Chem., **172,** 274, 1960.
10. Gibalo, I. M., and Byr'ko, V. M., Zavod. Lab., **24,** 281, 1958.
11. Ionescu, S., and Grigorescu-Sabau, C., in Proceedings of the 2nd U. S. International Conference on the Peaceful Uses of Atomic Energy, Vol. 28, p. 148 (United Nations, Genèva, 1958.
12. Kimura, K., and Kametani, F., Bunseki Kagaku, **10,** 1293, 1961.
13. Korenman, I. M., J. Anal. Chem., USSR, **12,** 43, 1957.
14. Korenman, I. M., *et al.*, Zhur. Anal. Khim., **12,** 48, 1957.
15. Korenman, I. M., *et al.*, Trudy Khim. i Khim. Tekhnol., 109, 1958.
16. Korenman, I. M., *et al.*, Zavod. Lab., **22,** 1143, 1956.
17. Korenman, I. M., Sheyanova, F. R., and Mulyanov, P. V., Trudy Khim. i Khim. Tekhnol., 118, 1958.
18. Langer, A., Anal. Chem., **22,** 1288, 1950.
19. Langer, A., J. Phys. Chem., **45,** 639, 1941.
20. Maxim, I., Braun, T., and Galateanu, I., J. Inorg. Nuclear Chem., **10,** 166, 1959.
21. Moeller, D. W., Terrill, J. G., Jr., and Seal, M. S., in Proceedings of the Int. Conference on the Peaceful Uses of Atomic Energy, Vol. 15, p. 49, United Nations, New York, 1956.
22. Plotnikov, V. I., Zavod. Lab., **24,** 927, 1958.
23. Polevaya, N. I., Chernova, N. N., and Mirkins, S. L., Inform. Sbornik Vsesoyuz. Nauch Giol. Inst., 119, 1955.
24. Ruzicka, J., and Stary, J., Talanta, **8,** 535, 1961.
25. Schumacher, E., and Friedli, W., Helv. Chim. Acta, **43,** 1013, 1960.
26. Sirotina, A., and Alimarin, I. P., Zhur. Anal. Khim., **12,** 367, 1957.

TABLE 28-9 (cont.)

27. Straub, G., and Csapo, Z., Acta Chim. Acad. Sci. Hung., **26**, 267, 1961.
28. Tolgyessy, G., Magyar Kem. Foly., **65**, 149, 1959.
29. Tolgyessy, J., and Sajter, V., Acta Chim. Acad. Sci. Hung., **26**, 179, 1961.
30. Tolgyessy, G., and Schiller, P., Magyar Kem. Foly., **63**, 269, 1957.

TABLE 28-10. ISOTOPE DILUTION: ELEMENTS

Element	*Tracer*	*Application*	*References*[a]
Antimony	Sb^{124}	Extrn. detn. in lead	72
Arsenic	As^{76}	Detn. in zinc	18
Barium	Ba^{142}	Detn. in phosphors	64
Calcium	Ca^{45}	Detn. in phosphors	64
		Detn. in ion exchanges	44
		Diffusible Ca in soils	5
		Pptn. as oxalate	56
		Pptn. of nitrate	38
Carbon	C^{14}	Detn. of alkaline earths	9
		Detn. of C in blood	71
Cerium	Ce^{141}	Ion exchange sepn. of Ce-Pr	28
	Ce^{144}	Color detn.	19
Chlorine	Cl^{36}	Detn. of ClO_4^- in sea water	32
		Detn. of Cl^- in biol. materials	13
		Pptn. of AgCl*	33
Chromium	Cr^{51}	Detn. in blood	69
		Sepn. of Cr	7
Cobalt	Co^{60}	Color detn.	57, 66
		Detn. in blood	27
		Electrodeposition	54
		Pptn. as NH_4CoPO_4	36
		Extrn. and color detn.	47
Copper	Cu^{64}	Detn. in soln.	53
Fluorine	F^{18}	Adsorpt. by glass	21, 35
Hafnium	Hf^{181}	Detn. in Zr	2, 24
		Detn. in ZrO_2—HfO_2	16
Hydrogen	H^3	Active H by $LiAlH_4$*	10, 11
		Detn. in metals	17
Iodine	I^{131}	Detn. in blood	69
		AgI* pptn.	45
Iron	Fe^{59}	Detn. of Fe	43, 60
		Ion exchange sepn.	59
Lead	Pb^{210}	Detn. in minerals	37, 65
Mercury	Hg^{203}	Detn. of $HgCl_2$ in graphite	42
Molybdenum	Mo^{99}	Detn. in steel	23
Neptunium	Np^{239}	Detn. of Np^{237}	67
Niobium	Nb^{95}	Detn. mixed with Ta	26
		Pptn. and extrn.	1
Phosphorus	P^{32}	Color detn.	31
		Detn. in rocks	49
		Detn. in uranium compds.	41
		Detn. of phosphate in soils	6, 55

TABLE 28-10 (cont.)

Element	*Tracer*	*Application*	*References*[a]
		Detn. of phosphate in other compds.	22
		Detn. of polyphosphates in mixtures	46
		Pptn. of ammonium phosphomolybdate	4
Potassium	K^{42}	Detn. in Na and Li salts	61
		Detn. in phosphors	64
Selenium	Se^{75}	Color detn.	34
Silver	Ag^{110m}	Coulom. detn.	51
		Electrodeposition	52
Sodium	Na^{24}	Detn. in body	19
		Exchangeable Na in body	50
Strontium	Sr^{89}	Pptn. of nitrate	38
	Sr^{90}	Detn. in phosphors	64
	Sr^{85}	Detn. of Sr^{90}	25
Sulfur	S^{35}	Pptn. as BaS^*O_4	14, 15, 56
		Detn. of S in rubber	30
Tantalum	Ta^{182}	Detn. in presence of Nb	3, 26
		Pptn. and extrn.	1
Thorium	Th^{230}	Sepn. and α-spect.	29
	Th^{234}	Detn. in granites	48
Uranium	U^{237}	Detn. using α-nitroso-β-naphthol	68
		Extrn. and fluo. detn.	70
	$Th^{232,228}$	Indirect sepn. and α-spect.	29
Vanadium	V^{48}	Detn. in steel, amperometric titration	39
Zinc	Zn^{65}	Detn. in Co-Zn mixtures	12
		Detn. in Ga metal	40
		Dithizone extrn.	58
		Electrodeposition	62
		Sepn. as ferricyanide	63
		Sepn. and electrodeposition	8

[a] Numbers refer to the following works:

1. Alimarin, I. P., and Bilimovich, G. N., Coll. Czech. Chem. Commun., **26,** 255, 1961.
2. Amano, H., Sci. Repts. Research Insts., Tohoku Univ., **11,** Ser. A, 383, 1959.
3. Amano, H., Sci. Repts. Research Insts., Tohoku Univ., **11,** Ser. A, 360, 1959.
4. Arriaga e Cunha, J. M., and Baptista, J., in Proceedings, 2nd Internation Conference on the Peaceful Uses of Atomic Energy, Vol. 28, p. 654, United Nations, Geneva, 1958.
5. Barbier, G., and Tyszkiewicz, E., Compt. Rend., **236,** 2105, 1953.
6. Barbier, G., and Tyszkiewicz, E., Compt. Rend. **238,** 1733, 1954.
7. Begeermann, K., Z. anal. Chem., **191,** 346–339, 1962.
8. Bleshinskii, S. V., and Nagaeva, A. G., Izvest. Akad. Nauk Kirz. SSR, **2,** 51, 1960.
9. Chiriboga, J., Anal. Chem., **34,** 1843, 1962.
10. Chleck, D. J., *et al.*, Intern. J. Appl. Radiation Isotopes, **7,** 182, 1960.
11. Chleck, D. J., *et al.*, AECU-4493, 1959.
12. Collee, L'Analyse Selective du Zine et du Cobalt par Double Marquage Radioactif et Spectrometrie du Rayonnement Gamma, Monographie No. 8, Inst. Interuniv. Sci. Nucl., Brussels, 1959.
13. Cotlove, E., Anal. Chem., **35,** 95, 1963.
14. Driscoll, W. J., and Huff, E. A., Exploration of Radiometric Methods, Report No. 2, AECU-4417, 1959.
15. Eisler, Plating, **39,** 1019, 1952.
16. Elinson, S. V., Determination and Analysis of Rare Elements, Vinogradov, A. P., Ed., Publishing House of the Academy of Sciences, Moscow, 1961, p. 303.
17. Evans, C., and Herrington, J., Radioisotopes in the Physical Sciences and Industry,

TABLE 28-10 (cont.)

Copenhagen, Internation Atomic Energy Agency, Vienna, Vol. II, p. 309, 1962.
18. Foldzinska, A., and Malinowski, J., Nukleonika, **7,** 153, 1962.
19. Forbes, G. B., and Perley, A., Estimation of Total-body Sodium by Isotopic Dilution, AECU-1448, p. 1520, 1951.
20. Freedman, A. J., and Hume, D. N., Anal. Chem., **22,** 932, 1950.
21. Fremlin, J. H., Hardwick, J. L., and Suthers, J., Nature, **180,** 1179, 1957.
22. Gauthier, P., Bull. Soc. Chim. France, 981, 1955.
23. Geldhof, M. L., Eeckhaut, J., and Cornand, P., Bull. Soc. Chim. Belges, **65,** 706, 1956.
24. Getoff, N., Atompraxis, **5,** 472, 1959.
25. Gilat, J., J. Inorg. Nucl. Chem., **16,** 147, 1960.
26. Grandjean, Ph., Lerch, P., and Monnier, R., Helv. Chim. Acta, **43,** 838, 1960.
27. Haerdi, W., *et al.*, Helv. Chim. Acta, **43,** 869, 1960.
28. Harris, D., and Tompkins, E., J. Am. Chem. Soc., **69,** 2792, 1947.
29. Howard, L. E., Nucleonics, **16,** 112, 1958.
30. Ikeda, S., and Kanbara, S., Nippon Kagaku Zasshi, **75,** 1308, 1954.
31. Ishibara, Y., and Taguchi, Y., Bunseki Kagaku, **6,** 724, 1957.
32. Johannesson, J. K., Anal. Chem., **34,** 1111, 1962.
33. Johannesson, J. K., Analyst, **86,** 72, 1961.
34. Kelleher, W. J., and Johnson, M. J., Anal. Chem., **33,** 1429, 1961.
35. Kudahl, J. N., Fremlin, J. H., and Hardwick, J. L., Radioisotopes in the Physical Sciences and Industry, Copenhagen, International Atomic Energy Agency, Vienna, Vol. 2, p. 317, 1962.
36. Lambie, D. A., Analyst, **84,** 173, 1959.
37. Ledent, D., Piciotto, E., and Poulaert, G., Bull. Soc. Belge Geol. Pal. Hydr., **65,** 233, 1956.
38. Leliaert, G., and Eeckhaut, J., Anal. Chim. Acta, **16,** 311, 1957.
39. Leliaert, G., Hoste, J., and Eeckhaut, J., Talanta, **1,** 369, 1958.
40. Lerch, P., and Kreienbuhl, L., Chimia (Zurich), **15,** 518, 1961.
41. Lima, F. W., and Atalla, L. T., An. Acad. Bras., C **33** (2), 149, 1961; Anal. Abstr., **9,** 4647, 1962.
42. Maute, R. L., Benson, R. H., Hodgsum, J. D., and Beasecken, D. R., Anal. Chem., **34,** 553, 1962.
43. Mencis, I., and Sweet, T. R., Anal. Chem., **35,** 1904, 1963.
44. Mikheev, N. B., Zhur. Anal. Khim., **14,** 735, 1959.
45. Purkayastha, B. C., and Vernecker, V. R. P., J. Indian Chem. Soc., **34,** 487, 1957.
46. Quimby, O. T., Mabis, A. J., and Lampe, H. W., Anal. Chem., **26,** 661, 1954.
47. Ralph, W. D., Jr., Sweet, T. R., and Mencis, I., Anal. Chem., **34,** 92, 1962.
48. Reynolds, S. A., Talanta, **10,** 611, 1963.
49. Rijkheer, J., J. S. Afr. Chem. Inst., **13,** 1, 1960.
50. Robinson, C. V., Arons, W. L., and Solomon, A. K., J. Clin. Invest., **34,** 134, 1955.
51. Ruzicka, J., Coll. Czech. Chem. Commun., **25,** 199, 1960.
52. Ruzicka, J., and Benes, P., Coll. Czech. Chem. Commun., **26,** 1784, 1961.
53. Ruzicka, J., and Stary, J., Talanta, **9,** 617, 1962.
54. Salyer, D., and Sweet, T. R., Anal. Chem., **28,** 61, 1956; **29,** 2, 1957.
55. Sapetti, C., Ann. Sper. Agrar. (Rome), **13,** 99, 1959.
56. Sarsunova, M., Tolgyessy, J., and Majer, J., Ceskosl. Farm., **9,** 68, 1960.
57. Sporek, K. F., Anal. Chem., **33,** 754, 1961.
58. Stary, J., and Ruzicka, J., Talanta, **8,** 296, 1961.
59. Stary, J., and Ruzicka, J., Talanta, **8,** 775, 1961.
60. Stary, J., Ruzicka, J., and Salamon, M., Talanta, **10,** 375, 1963.
61. Süe, P., Bull. Soc. Chim. France, ser. 5, **14,** 405, 1947; Nature, **157,** 622, 1946.
62. Theurer, K., and Sweet, T. R., Anal. Chem., **25,** 119, 1953.
63. Tolgyessy, J., Sarsunova, M., and Majer, J., Ceskosl. Farm., **8,** 565, 1959.
64. Toperczer, J., Z. Anal. Chem., **180,** 265, 1961.
65. Von Buttlar, H., Naturwissenschaften, **42,** 90, 1955.
66. Vogel, J., Monnier, D., and Haerdi, W., Anal. Chim. Acta, **24,** 55, 1961.
67. Wahl, A. C., and Seaborg, G. T., Phys. Rev., **73,** 940, 1948.
68. Weiss, H. V., Lai, M. G., and Gillespie, A., Anal. Chim. Acta, **25,** 550, 1961; also USNRDL-TR-496, 1960.
69. Williams, J. A., and Williams, J. B., Nucleonics, **20,** No. 11, 63, 1962.
70. Wilson, J. D., *et al.*, Anal. Chim. Acta, **23,** 505, 1960.
71. Winteringham, F. P. W., and Disney, L. W., Nature, **195,** 1303, 1962.
72. Zimakov, I. E., and Rozhavskii, G. S., Trudy Komiss. Anal. Khim., **9,** 231, 1958.

TABLE 28-11. ISOTOPE DILUTION: ORGANIC COMPOUNDS

Compound	*Tracer*	*Application*	*References*[a]
Acids	C^{14}	In irradiated benzoic acid	5
Alcohols	C^{14}	Chromat. on SiO_2	6
Amino acids	C^{14}	Chromat. sepn.	17
Benzylpenicillin	C^{14}	C^{14}-compd. hydrol. to $C_6H_5—CH_2—COOH$	1
Cobalamines	Co^{60}	Detn. in mixts.	2
Corticosterone	C^{14}	Detn. in plasma, fluo.	12
Ethyl ether	C^{14}	In org. mixts.	4
Glucose and gentobiose	C^{14}	With C^{14} diluents	14
Insulin	I^{131}	Detn. in serum	10
Penicillins	S^{35}	Detn. in broth	7
Serum albumin	S^{35}	Pptn. and extrn.	9
Sucrose	C^{14}	Detn. in sugar beets	8
Thyroxine	I^{131}	In protein mixts.	13
Vitamine B_{12}	Co^{60}	Detn. in vitamin mixts.	3, 16
Vitamin D	P^{32}	Detn. in vitamin mixts.	11, 15

[a] Numbers refer to the following works:

1. Ashton, G. C., and Foster, M. C., Analyst, **80,** 123, 1955.
2. Bruening, C. F., *et al.*, J. An. Pharm. Assoc. Sci. Ed., **46,** 66, 1957.
3. Bacher, F. A., Boley, A. E., and Shonk, C. E., Anal. Chem., **26,** 1146, 1954.
4. Burtle, J. G., and Ryan, J. P., Anal. Chem., **27,** 1215, 1955.
5. Danno, A., Isotopes and Radiation (Japan), **3,** 496, 1961.
6. Efremov, V. Ya., Neiman, M. B., and Panfilov, V. N., Trudy Komiss. Anal. Khim. Akad. Nauk SSSR, **9,** 361, 1958.
7. Gordon, M., Virgona, A. J., and Numerof, P., Anal. Chem., **26,** 1209, 1954.
8. Hoerning, H., and Hirschmueller, H., Zeit. f. Zuckerind., **9,** 499, 1959.
9. Hradec, J., Chem. Listy, **52,** 2015, 1958.
10. Kallee, E., Klin. Wochschr., **32,** 508, 1954.
11. Numerof, P., *et al.*, J. Nutrition, **55,** 13, 1955.
12. Peterson, R. E., J. Biol. Chem., **225,** 25, 1957.
13. Reineka, E. P., J. Dairy Sci., **37,** 1227, 1954.
14. Sowden, J. C., and Spriggs, A. S., J. Am. Chem. Soc., **76,** 3539, 1954.
15. Snyder, R. H., Eisner, H. J., and Steenback, H., J. Nutrition, **45,** 305, 1951.
16. U. S. Pharmacopeia XV, Sup. 1, p. 21, 1956.
17. Wada, T., J. Agr. Chem. Soc. Japan, **30,** 229, 1956; **31,** 743, 1957.

The product, Na^{24}, decays with a half-life of 15 hours and is a beta-gamma emitter. At least 70 of the elements can be activated by thermal neutron capture reactions; Table 28-12 lists the principal radioactive products of these reactions.

When a radioisotope is produced in a given element by a nuclear particle bombardment, its activity can be calculated from the equation

$$A = N\sigma f(1 - e^{-\lambda t}) \tag{14}$$

where: A = radioactivity, disintegrations per second;
N = the number of target atoms in the sample;
σ = the atomic activation cross section for the nuclear particle reaction (10^{-24} cm.^{2});
f = the nuclear particle flux (particles/cm.^{2} sec.); and
λ = the decay constant of the radioisotope produced.

Equation (14) can be rearranged in terms of the weight of the element required to produce a predetermined amount of radioactivity in a given time interval:

$$W = \frac{AM}{(6.02 \times 10^{23})\sigma f S} \tag{15}$$

where: W = the weight of the element, g.;
M = the atomic weight; and
$S = 1 - e^{-\lambda t}$, or the growth factor.

An activation analysis can be completed in one of two ways: either by an *absolute* method, or by a *comparator* method. Equation (15) is the basis of the absolute method, which involves the bombardment of a sample for a definite time interval at a known flux, after which the absolute radioactivity of the element of interest is determined. Then, the weight of element is calculated from knowledge of the reaction's cross section and the half-life of the radioisotope. The absolute method is sometimes limited in obtaining accurate and precise data because it is not easy to measure the flux accurately, and the cross sections and half-lives are not known precisely for many elements. The comparator method is more simple and more accurate. In this method, a known amount of the element to be determined is bombarded simultaneously with the test sample and is processed after its activation in the same manner as the test sample. Since all of the terms in Eq. (15), except those for W and A, are the same for both the comparator and the test sample, then a simplified equation can result:

$$\frac{W \text{ in test sample}}{W \text{ in comparator}} = \frac{A \text{ in test sample}}{A \text{ in comparator}} \tag{16}$$

Corrections for chemical yield (if a radiochemical separation is made), radioactive decay, and sample weights must be considered in Eq. (16).

Procedure of Analysis.—An activation analysis follows a procedure similar to that shown in Fig. 28-1. In almost all analyses, the sample materials are not treated before the bombardment, but are placed directly into the bombardment capsule or container. The length of bombardment interval is usually determined by the half-life of the radionuclide used for the element of interest and the flux of nuclear particles.

The post-bombardment processing of the activated sample may follow either a nondestructive assay of the radioactivity in the sample (gamma-ray scintillation spectrometry is used most often for this) or a chemical processing of the sample prior to the radioactivity assay. Techniques involving either precipitation, electrodeposition, solvent extraction, and ion exchange or some combination of these form the basis of the radiochemical separation techniques used in activation analysis.

Although the beta radiations emitted by the radioisotope after its isolation can be measured, gamma-ray scintillation spectrometry is used most often in the radioactivity measurements. Table 28-13 lists the gamma-rays (in order of their increasing energy) of the various radioisotopes used in the neutron activation analysis method.

Sensitivity.—The most important advantage of activation analysis is that it is usually more sensitive for many elements than other analytical methods. Neutron activation analysis sensitivities are at least 1 to 2 orders of magnitude greater than any other method. From Eqs. (14) and (15), it can be seen that the sensitivity for a given element depends directly upon the activation cross section and the flux available, and is an inverse function of the half-life of the radioisotope produced. In practice, sensitivity has been defined as the weight of the element in micrograms required to produce 40 disintegrations per second, d.p.s., when bombarded in a known flux for some time interval.

TABLE 28-12. NEUTRON-INDUCED RADIONUCLIDES

Element	*<1m*	*1–10m*	*10–60m*	*1–10h*	*10–24h*	*1–10d*	*10–100d*	*100d–1y*	*1–10y*	*>10y*
Aluminum		Al^{28}			$(Na^{24})^a$					
Antimony						Sb^{122}	Sb^{124}			
Arsenic						As^{76}				
Barium		Ba^{137m}		Ba^{139}						
Bromine						Br^{82}				
Cadmium			Cd^{111mm}			Cd^{115}	Cd^{115m}			
Calcium		Ca^{49}				Ca^{47}				
Cerium						Ce^{143}	Ce^{141}			
Cesium				Cs^{134m}					Cs^{134}	
Chlorine			Cl^{38}							
Chromium							Cr^{51}			
Cobalt			Co^{60m}						Co^{60}	
Copper		Cu^{66}			Cu^{64}					
Dysprosium		Dy^{165m}		Dy^{165}						
Erbium				Er^{171}						
Europium				Eu^{152}						

Fluorine	F^{20}			(F^{18})						
Gadolinium		Gd^{161}			Gd^{159}					
Gallium					Ga^{72}					
Germanium				Ge^{75}	Ge^{77}		Ge^{71}			
Gold						Au^{198}				
Hafnium	Hf^{179}			Hf^{180m}			Hf^{181}			
Holmium						Ho^{166}				
Indium			In^{116m}							
Iodine			I^{128}							
Iridium					Ir^{194}		Ir^{192}			
Iron				(Mn^{56})			Fe^{59}	(Mn^{54})		
Lanthanum						La^{140}				
Lead				Pb^{204m}						
Lutetium				Lu^{176m}		Lu^{177}				
Magnesium		Mg^{27}			(Na^{24})					
Manganese				Mn^{56}						
Mercury					Hg^{197mm}	Hg^{197}				
Molybdenum			Mo^{101}			Mo^{99}				

TABLE 28-12 (cont.)

Element	*<1m*	*1–10m*	*10–60m*	*1–10h*	*10–24h*	*1–10d*	*10–100d*	*100d–1y*	*1–10y*	*>10y*
Neodymium							Nd^{147}			
Nickel				Ni^{65}			(Co^{58})			
Niobium		Nb^{94m}								
Osmium						Os^{193}	Os^{191}			
Palladium					Pd^{109}					
Potassium					K^{42}					
Platinum				Pt^{197m}	Pt^{197}	Pt^{195m}				
Praeseodymium					Pr^{142}					
Rhenium					Re^{188}	Re^{186}				
Rhodium	Rh^{104}	Rh^{104m}								
Rubidium							Rb^{86}			
Ruthenium						Ru^{97}				
Samarium			Sm^{155}			Sm^{153}				
Scandium	Sc^{46m}						Sc^{46}			
Selenium	Se^{77m}							Se^{75}		
Silicon				Si^{31}						
Silver	Ag^{110}	Ag^{108}						Ag^{110m}		

Sodium					Na^{24}					
Strontium				Sr^{87m}						
Sulfur		S^{37}					S^{35}			
Tantalum			Ta^{182m}					Ta^{182}		
Tellurium			Te^{131}			Te^{131m}				
Terbium							Tb^{160}			
Thallium		Tl^{206}							Tl^{204}	
Thorium			Th^{235}				(Pa^{233})			
Thulium								Tm^{170}		
Tin		Sn^{125}				Sn^{125}				
Titanium		Ti^{51}				(Sc^{48})	(Sc^{46})			
Tungsten						W^{187}				
Uranium			U^{239}			(Np^{239})				
Vanadium		V^{52}								
Ytterbium				Yb^{177}		Yb^{175}				
Zinc					Zn^{69m}			Zn^{65}		
Zirconium					Zr^{97}		Zr^{95} (Nb^{95})			

[a] All radioisotopes enclosed in parentheses are sometimes used to determine element of interest; they may be product of fast neutron reactions or a daughter activity of (n,γ) induced parent radioisotope.

TABLE 28-13. GAMMA-RAY ENERGIES OF NEUTRON-INDUCED RADIONUCLIDES

γ Energy	*<1m*	*1–10m*	*10–60m*	*1–10h*	*10–24h*	*1–10d*	*10–100d*	*100d–1y*	*1–10y*	*>10y*
<0.02 M.e.V.				Cs^{134m}		Mo^{99}				
0.02–0.04 M.e.V.	Rh^{104}			Hf^{180m}		Pt^{195m}				
0.04–0.06 M.e.V.		Gd^{161} Nb^{94m} Rh^{104m}	Co^{60m}		Gd^{159} Ge^{77}	Ce^{143} Mo^{99}	Os^{191}			
0.06–0.08 M.e.V.		Gd^{161}	U^{239}		Ge^{77} Pt^{197}	Ho^{166} Hg^{197} Sm^{153} W^{187}		Se^{75} Ta^{182}		
0.08–0.10 M.e.V.			Mo^{101} Th^{233}	Dy^{165} Hf^{180} Lu^{176m}	Pd^{109}	Pt^{195m}	Nd^{147} Tb^{160}			
0.1–0.20 M.e.V.	Hf^{179m} Rh^{104}	Dy^{165m} Gd^{161}	In^{116m} Mo^{101} Sm^{155}	Ba^{139} Cs^{134m} Er^{171} Eu^{152} Ge^{75} Nd^{147} Si^{31} Yb^{177}	Hg^{197m} Pt^{197} Pr^{142} Re^{188}	Ca^{47} Mo^{99} Lu^{177} Hg^{197} Np^{239} Os^{193} Re^{186} Sm^{155} Te^{131m} W^{187} Yb^{175}	Sb^{124} Ce^{141} Hf^{181}	Ag^{110m}		

TABLE 28-13 (cont.)

γ *Energy*	< *1m*	*1–10m*	*10–60m*	*1–10h*	*10–24h*	*1–10d*	*10–100d*	*100d–1y*	*1–10y*	> *10y*
0.2–0.4 M.e.V.	Hf^{179m}	Gd^{161} Sn^{125} Ti^{51}	Cd^{111mm} Pt^{197}	Dy^{165} Er^{171} Eu^{152} Ge^{75} Hf^{180m} Ni^{65} Pb^{204m} Sr^{87m}	Gd^{159} Ge^{77} Ir^{194} Hg^{197mm}	Sb^{122} Cd^{115} Ca^{47} Ce^{143} La^{140} Lu^{177} Mo^{99} Np^{239} Os^{193} Ru^{97} Yb^{175}	Cr^{51} Hf^{181} Ir^{192} Nd^{147} Pa^{233}		Te^{204}	
0.4–0.6 M.e.V.		Gd^{161} Ag^{108}	In^{116m} I^{128}	Er^{171} F^{18} Ge^{75} Hf^{180m} Si^{31}	Cu^{64} Ge^{77} Re^{188} Zn^{69m}	Sb^{122} As^{76} Br^{82} Cd^{115} Ce^{143} Au^{198} La^{140} Os^{193} Sm^{155} W^{187}	Cd^{115m} Hf^{181} Ir^{192} Nd^{147}	Se^{75}		
0.6–0.8 M.e.V.	Ag^{110}	Ba^{137m} Ag^{108}	Te^{131} Th^{233}	Dy^{165}	Ga^{72} Zr^{97}	Br^{82} Au^{198} Mo^{99}	Sb^{124} Co^{38} Hf^{181} Ir^{192} Nb^{95} W^{187} Zr^{95}		Cs^{134}	

TABLE 28-13 (cont.)

γ *Energy*	*<1m*	*1–10m*	*10–60m*	*1–10h*	*10–24h*	*1–10d*	*10–100d*	*100d–1y*	*1–10y*	*>10y*
0.8–1.0 M.e.V.	Rh^{104} Ag^{110}	Mg^{27} Nb^{94m} Ti^{51}	I^{128} Mo^{101} Pb^{204m}	Mn^{56}	Ga^{72} Re^{188}	Br^{82} Ca^{47} La^{140} Sc^{48}	Cd^{115m} Sc^{46} Tb^{160}	Mn^{54} Tm^{170}		
1.0–1.2 M.e.V.	F^{20}	Cu^{66} Mg^{27}	In^{116m}	Ba^{139} Ni^{65}	Ga^{72} Ge^{77}	As^{76} Br^{82} Au^{198} Sc^{48}	Ir^{192} Rb^{86} Sc^{46} Fe^{59}	Zn^{65}	Co^{60}	
1.2–1.4 M.e.V.			In^{116m}	Si^{31}	Cu^{64} Ga^{72} Re^{188} Na^{24}	Br^{82} Ca^{47} Ho^{166} Sc^{48}	Fe^{59} Cd^{115m}	Ta^{182}	Co^{60}	
1.4–1.9 M.e.V.		Al^{28} V^{52}	In^{116m} Ta^{182m} Cl^{38}	Mn^{56} Ni^{65}	Ge^{77} Ga^{72} Ir^{194} K^{42} Pr^{142}	As^{76} Ho^{166} La^{140}	Sb^{124}	Ag^{110m}		
1.9–2.5 M.e.V.			In^{116m} Cl^{38}		Ga^{72} Ir^{194}	As^{76} Sn^{125}	Sb^{124}			
>2.5 M.e.V.		Ca^{49} S^{37}		Mn^{56}	Ga^{72} Na^{24}				Co^{60}	

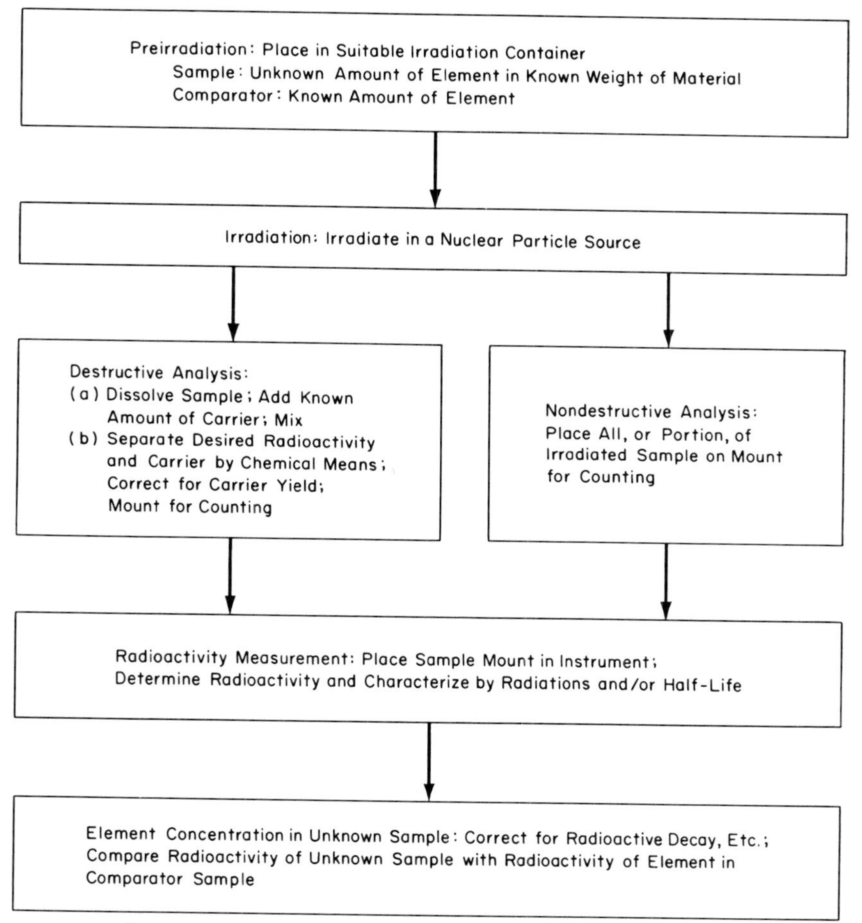

FIG. 28-1. A Typical Procedure for Radioactivation Analysis.

Table 28-14 reports the detection limits in micrograms calculated for irradiation periods, in a neutron flux, of 30 minutes and 1 week at a flux of 10^{13} neutrons/cm.^{2} sec.

Applications.—Neutron activation analysis has been used to determine any of the elements shown in Table 28-14 in a wide variety of sample materials. Many of the elemental methods being used have been applied routinely to assay samples from all branches of science. Although activation analysis has been used principally in requirements for minor and trace elements, it is sometimes used to assay sample materials for major constituents. The reviews by Leddicotte[17,18] reference many of these applications. Activation analyses are offered as a service, at a nominal cost by such laboratories as those of the Nuclear Research Center, Union Carbide Corp., Tuxedo, N. Y., and General Atomics, San Diego, Calif. These laboratories customarily state that the accu-

TABLE 28-14. NEUTRON ACTIVATION ANALYSIS; CALCULATED LIMITS OF DETECTION

Element	*Detection Limits, μg.*[a] Δt_i = *1 w*	Δt_i = *30 m*
Aluminum	0.0009	0.0009
Antimony	0.0003	0.007
Arsenic	0.0001	0.008
Barium	0.004	0.02
Bismuth	0.2	30.
Bromine	0.0002	0.0002
Cadmium	0.003	0.2
Calcium	0.2	0.2
Cerium	0.01	0.9
Cesium	0.0003	0.03
Chlorine	0.002	0.004
Chromium	0.004	1.
Cobalt	0.00002	0.00003
Copper	0.0004	0.005
Dysprosium	0.000004	0.000005
Erbium	0.002	0.04
Europium	0.000002	0.00004
Gadolinium	0.002	0.006
Gallium	0.0003	0.01
Germanium	0.007	0.03
Gold	0.00002	0.002
Hafnium	0.004	0.03
Holmium	0.00002	0.002
Indium	0.000005	0.00002
Iodine	0.0002	0.0004
Iridium	0.000006	0.000006
Iron	2.	400.
Lanthanum	0.0002	0.002
Lead	6.	60.
Lutetium	0.00003	0.0004
Manganese	0.00003	0.0002
Magnesium	0.06	0.06
Mercury	0.002	0.05
Molybdenum	0.007	0.04
Neodymium	0.005	0.03
Nickel	0.03	0.2
Niobium	0.0006	0.0006
Osmium	0.002	0.2
Palladium	0.0003	0.01
Phosphorus	0.004	4.
Platinum	0.005	0.009
Potassium	0.003	0.2
Praseodymium	0.00009	0.005
Rhenium	0.00003	0.002
Rhodium	0.000005	0.000005
Rubidium	0.006	0.02
Ruthenium	0.006	0.08
Samarium	0.00002	0.004
Scandium	0.0003	0.0003
Selenium	0.0003	0.0003
Silicon	0.06	0.5
Silver	0.00003	0.00003
Sodium	0.0003	0.02
Sulfur	0.4	20.
Strontium	0.006	0.08
Tantalum	0.002	0.06
Tellurium	0.005	0.02
Terbium	0.0008	0.01
Thallium	0.02	0.02
Thorium	0.0002	0.0004
Thulium	0.0003	0.08
Tin	0.07	0.07
Titanium	0.05	0.05
Tungsten	0.0002	0.009
Uranium	0.0006	0.002
Vanadium	0.00008	0.00008
Ytterbium	0.0002	0.01
Yttrium	0.0006	0.09
Zinc	0.003	20.006
Zirconium	0.4	20.

[a] Based on calculations involving the production and measurement of 40 disintegrations per second of radioactivity when a 1-g. test sample is irradiated in a neutron flux (neutrons cm.0^{-2} sec. 0^{-1}) of 10^{13} in a time period Δt_i.

racy of the analysis is 10 percent; however, it is often better than this, approaching 1 percent in favorable circumstances.

Typical examples of these applications are given in the reviews cited above, and in Table 28-15.

TABLE 28-15. ACTIVATION ANALYSIS

Element	*Determined in*	*References*[a]
Aluminum	Graphite	117, 133
	Metals	51
	Rocks and minerals	44, 62, 136
	Sea sediments	78, 82
Antimony	Blood	21
	Metals	1, 83, 133
	Silicon	54, 75
	Selenium	88
	Steel	59
Arsenic	Biological materials	35, 50, 148
	Nonmetals	54, 67, 71, 73, 88, 117
	Steel	140
Beryllium	Ores and minerals	47, 128, 129, 130, 131
Boron	Minerals	128, 129, 130, 131
	Steel	96
Bismuth	Steel	59
Bromine	Food	28, 60, 142
Cadmium	Biological materials	14, 21
Calcium	Biological materials	21, 91, 140
	Steel	59
Carbon	Metals	2
	Steel	87
Cesium	Biological materials	21
	Rocks	25
Chlorine	Biological materials	91, 140
Chromium	Gallium arsenide	81
	Metals	92, 133
	Rocks	27
	Steel	12, 13, 59
Cobalt	Metals	29, 76, 92, 97, 133
	Steel	59, 133, 139
Copper	Biological materials	14, 16, 21, 22, 56, 72, 91, 112, 140
	Diamonds	98, 99
	Gallium arsenide-zinc sulfide	20, 80, 81, 132
	Metals	82, 92, 94
	Rocks and minerals	39, 57
	Silicon and selenium	33, 75, 88, 120
Fluorine	Minerals	126, 127
	Teflon	157
Gallium	Aluminum	82
	Rocks and minerals	26, 74
	Silicon and phosphorus	73, 75
Gold	Alloys	68, 116, 121
	Biological materials	14, 66, 134
	Gallium arsenide	81
	Minerals	93
	Silicon	75, 120

TABLE 28-15 (cont.)

Element	*Determined in*	*References*[a]
Hafnium	Rocks	109
	Zirconium	49, 65, 77, 133, 161
Iodine	Biological materials	23, 36, 37, 45, 46, 79, 104, 156, 160
Iron	Beryllium	92
	Blood	21
	Lead	11
Magnesium	Blood	16
	Sea sediments	78
Manganese	Biological materials	14, 16, 21, 22, 72, 91, 147
	Quartz	39
	Sea water	138
	Steel	59, 139
Mercury	Biological materials	22, 36, 37, 149, 151
	Water	34
Molybdenum	Rocks	63, 64
	Sea water	53
	Steel	12, 13, 59
Nickel	Sea sediments	78
	Steel	59
Niobium	Ores	84
Oxygen	Biological materials	152
	Gallium arsenide	9
	Metals	6, 10, 30, 43, 44, 52, 86, 87, 95, 105, 153, 154, 155, 158
	Polymers	31
	Rocks	159
Phosphorus	Alloys	17
	Biological materials	21, 110, 113
	Food	85, 89
	Steel	19, 59
Potassium	Blood	125
	Minerals	63
Rare earths	Graphite	55
	Soil	144
Selenium	Feeds and plant products	69, 90
	Fertilizers	18
	Sulfur	118
Silicon	Beryllium	92
	Gallium arsenide	58
	Sea sediments	78
Silver	Photographic emulsions	107
	Steel	59
	Sulfides	101, 102, 103, 119
Sodium	Biological materials	15, 21, 91, 125, 141
	Metals and alloys	40, 92, 135
	Sea water	70
	Solutions	5, 7

TABLE 28-15 (cont.)

Element	*Determined in*	*References*[a]
Strontium	Biological materials	14, 21, 106, 146, 150
Sulfur	Steel	19, 59
	Water	114, 162
Tantalum	Alloys	38
	Rocks and minerals	63, 64, 84, 85
	Steel	85
Thorium	Rocks and minerals	32, 100, 108
	Solutions	3
Tungsten	Rocks	63
	Sea water	53
	Steel	115
Uranium	Biological materials	42
	Graphite	24
	Metals	11, 42, 145
	Rocks and minerals	4, 41, 48, 108
	Solutions	3, 111
Vanadium	Aluminum	137
	Graphite	117
	Petroleum	8
	Sea water	53
	Steel	61
Zinc	Blood	21
	Gallium arsenide	58
	Ores	122, 123, 124
	Sea water	138
Zirconium	Meteorites	143

[a] Numbers refer to the following works:

1. Adams, F., and Hoste, J., Talanta, **9,** 827, 1962.
2. Albert, P., Modern Trends in Activation Analysis, Texas A and M College, College Station, Texas, December 15–16, 1962, p. 78.
3. Amiel, S., Anal. Chem., **34,** 1683, 1962.
4. Amiel, S., Atomwirtschaft, **7,** 217, 1962.
5. Amiel, S., and Peisach, M., Israel At. Energy Comm. Rept. IA-799, February 1963.
6. Amiel, S., and Peisach, M., Anal. Chem., **35,** 323, 1963.
7. Amiel, S., and Peisach, M., Anal. Chem., **35,** 1072, 1963.
8. Aoki, F., and Okada, M., Tokyo Kogyo, Shikensho Hokoku, **58,** 49, 1963; Nucl. Sci. Abstr., **17,** 21647, 1963.
9. Bailey, R. F., and Ross, D. A., Anal. Chem., **35,** 791, 1963.
10. Bate, L. C., Nucleonics, **21,** No. 7, 72, 1963.
11. Benson, P. A., Holland, W. D., and Smith, R. H., Anal. Chem., **34,** 1113, 1962.
12. Benson, P. A., and Gleit, C. E., Anal. Chem., **35,** 1029, 1963.
13. Benson, P. A., and Gleit, C. E., J. Am. Nucl. Soc., Annual Meeting, Salt Lake City, June 1963, CONF-39-6, 1963.
14. Bergman, R., and Soeremark, R., Nucl. Med., **3,** 175, 1963.
15. Bergstrom, J., Scand. J. Clin. Lab. Invest., **14,** Suppl. 68, 1962; Nucl. Sci. Abstr., **17,** 37051, 1963.
16. Bethard, W. F., Schmitt, R. A., and Olehy, D. A., General Atomic Division, General Dynamics Corp., San Diego, Calif., Rept. GA-2803, January 3, 1962.
17. Blackburn, R., and Peters, B. F. G., Anal. Chem., **35,** 10, 1963.
18. Bowen, H. J. M., and Cawse, P. A., Analyst, **88,** 721, 1963.
19. Bouten, P., and Hoste, J., Anal. Chim. Acta, **27,** 315, 1963.

TABLE 28-15 (cont.)

20. Brosen, I., and Franke, K. H., Z. Physik, **172,** 520, 1963.
21. Bruenger, F. W., Atherton, D. R., and Stover, B. J., Health Physics, **9,** 232, 1963.
22. Bryant, J., Intern. J. Appl. Radiation Isotopes, **13,** 273, 1962.
23. Bryant, F. J., Chem. Ind. (London), 1228, 1962.
24. Buchanan, J. D., General Dynamics Corp., San Diego, Calif., Rept. GA-2211, Jan. 18, 1962.
25. Butler, J. R., and Thompson, A. J., Geochim. Cosmochim. Acta, **26,** 1349, 1962.
26. Cali, J. P., Weiner, J. R., and Connor, J. J., Nature, **199,** 1081, 1963.
27. Carr, M. H., and Turekian, H. H., Geochim. Cosmochim. Acta, **26,** 411, 1962.
28. Castro, C. E., and Schmitt, R. A., J. Agr. Food Chem., **10,** 236, 1962.
29. Cattaneo, F., Germagnoli, E., and Schiavini, G., Energia Nucleare (Milan), **9,** No. 8, 467, 1962.
30. Cerrai, E., and Gadda, F., Energia Nucleare (Milan), **9,** No. 8, 467, 1962.
31. Chepel, L. V., and Viting, B. I., Zhur. Anal. Khim., **18,** 865, 1963.
32. Cherdyntsey, V. V., Shmonin, L. I., and Ostapenko, V. F., Sb. Nauchn. Rabot Kafedry Optiki i Kafedry Experim. Fiz. Kazakhsk Univ., No. 2, 13, 1960; Nucl. Sci. Abstr., **17,** 30493, 1963.
33. Chiba, M., Trans. Nat. Inst. Met. (Japan), **4,** 143, 1962.
34. Choi, S. S., and Tuck, D. G., J. Chem. Soc., 4080, 1962; Nucl. Sci. Abstr., **17,**44 51, 1963.
35. Christell, R., and Sjostrand, B., Acta Chem. Scand., **16,** 2123, 1960.
36. Comar, D., Comm. Energie Atomique, France, Rept. CEA-2095, 1963.
37. Comar, D., LePoec, C., Joly, M., and Kellershohn, C., Bull. Soc. Chim. France, **56,** No. 1, 56, 1962.
38. Corth, R., Anal. Chem., **34,** 1607, 1962.
39. Czamanske, G. K., Roedder, E., and Burns, C. F., Science, **140,** 401, 1963.
40. Das, H. A., Atomenergie Haar, Toepassingen, **4,** 295, 1962; Nucl. Sci. Abstr., **17,** 14171, 1963.
41. Das, M. S., TID-18304, November 1962.
42. Decat, D., Van Zanten, B., and Leliaeret, G., Anal. Chem., **35,** 845, 1963.
43. Demildt, A. C., Microneutron Analysis for Oxygen in Actinide Metals, Lawrence Rad. Lab., University of California, Berkeley, Rept. UCRL-10324, July 19, 1962.
44. Demildt, A. C., Anal. Chem., **35,** 1228, 1963.
45. Dimitriadou, A., Turner, P. C. R., and Fraser, T. R., Nature, **197,** 446, 1963.
46. Dimitriadou, A., Turner, P. C. R., and Fraser, T. R., Nature, **198,** 576, 1963.
47. Dumensil, P., Inds. Atomiques, **5,** 61, 1961.
48. Dyer, F. F., Emery, J. F., and Leddicotte, G. W., Oak Ridge National Lab., Rept. ORNL-3342, 1962.
49. Einfeld, K., Ruppert, E., and Tornau, R., Atomwirtschaft, **7,** 312–16, 1962.
50. Fergusson, A. G., Dewar, W. A., Derblay, P. R., Lenihan, J. M. A., and Smith, H., Proc. XIIth Intern. Congress of Dermatology, Washington, 1962.
51. Fournet, L., Deschamps, N., and Albert, P., Compt. Rend., **254,** 1640, 1962.
52. Fujii, I., Muto, H., Ogawa, K., and Tani, A., Nippon Genshiryoku Gakkaishi, **5,** 455, 1963.
53. Fukai, R., and Meinke, W. W., Limnol. Oceanog., **7,** 186, 1962.
54. Gebauhr, W., Kerntechnik, **4,** 323, 1962.
55. Gebauhr, W., and Martin, J., Nukleonika, **4,** 9, 1962.
56. Gitter, S., Amiel, S., Gilat, G., Sonnino, T., and Welwart, Y., Nature, **197,** 383, 1963.
57. Gorski, L., Nukleonika, **8,** 421, 1963.
58. Green, D. T., Heslop, J. A. B., and Whitley, J. E., Analyst, **88,** 522, 1963.
59. Gruverman, I. J., and Henninger, W. A., Anal. Chem., **34,** 1680, 1962.
60. Guinn, V. P., and Potter, J. C., J. Agr. Food Chem., **10,** 232, 1962.
61. Haerdi, W., Martin, E., and Monnier, D., Helv. Chim. Acta, **46,** 1572, 1963.
62. Haffner, J. W., Am. Nucl. Soc. 9th Annual Mtg., Salt Lake City, June 1963, CONF-39-75, 1963.
63. Hamaguchi, H., Kuroda, R., Shimizu, T., Sugisita, R., Tsukahara, I., and Yamamoto, R., J. At. Energy Soc. Japan, **3,** 800, 1961; Nucl. Sci. Abstr., **16,** 1712, 1962.
64. Hamaguchi, H., Kuroda, R., Shimizu, T., Tsukahara, I., and Yamamoto, R., Geochim. Cosmochim. Acta, **26,** 503, 1962.
65. Hecker, R., and Herr, W., Nukleonika, **4,** 19, 1962.
66. Helby, P., and Rygard, J., Acta Rheumatol. Scand., **8,** 222, 1962; Nucl. Sci. Abstr., **17,** 21621, 1963.
67. Hermsen, J., and VanDuuren, K., U. S. Patent 3,056,059, September 25, 1962.

TABLE 28-15 (cont.)

68. Hirayama, T., Nitto, M., Haraoka, T., and Hamada, K., Radioisotopes (Tokyo), **11,** 265, 1962.
69. Hogue, D. E., Proctor, J. F., Warner, R. G., and Looski, J. K., J. Animal Science, **21,** No. 1, 25, 1962.
70. Hori, R., Radioisotopes (Tokyo), **12,** 115, 1963.
71. Ishibashi, M., Fujinaga, T., and Koyama, M., Nippon Kagaku Zasshi, **82,** 185, 1961; Nucl. Sci. Abstr., **17,** 23451, 1963.
72. Jacobson, A., Brar, S., Fields, T., Fels, I. G., Kaplan, E., Gustafson, P., and Oester, Y. T., J. Nucl. Med., **2,** 289, 1961.
73. Jakowlew, J. W., and Sterlinski, S., Nukleonika, **7,** 141, 1962.
74. Jaskolska, H., and Minczewski, J., Acta Chim. Acad. Sci. Hung., **32,** 9, 1962.
75. Kalinin, A. I., Kuznetsov, R. A., and Moiseev, V. V., Radiokhimiya, **4,** 575, 1962.
76. Kamemoto, Y., and Yamagishi, S., Nippon Genshiryoku Gakkaishi, **4,** 866, 1962.
77. Kamemoto, Y., and Yamagishi, S., Nippon Kagaku Zasshi, **84,** 291, 1963.
78. Kehler, P., and Monaghan, R., TID-18125, November, 1962.
79. Kellershohn, C., Comar, D., and Le Poec, C., Intern. J. Appl. Radiation Isotopes, **12,** 87, 1961.
80. Kern, W., J. Electrochem. Soc., **109,** 700, 1962.
81. Kern, W., Radio Corp. of America, Publication No. ST-2461, Semiconductor Products, 1963.
82. Kiesl, W., Bilstein, H., and Hecht, F., Radiochimica Acta, **1,** 123, 1963.
83. Killick, R. A., and Morris, D. F. C., Talanta, **9,** 879, 1962.
84. Kim, C. K., Intern. At. Energy Agency, Preprint SM-32/32, Vienna, 1962.
85. Kim, C. K., and Meinke, W. W., Anal. Chem., **35,** 2135, 1963.
86. Kobayashi, H., Proc. 5th Japan Conf. Radioisotopes, Tokyo, May 21–23, 1963, Japan Atomic Industrial Forum, Inc., Tokyo, 1963.
87. Kobayashi, M., and Sawai, T., Tokyo Metropolitan Isotopes Center Ann. Rept., **1,** 25, 1962; Nucl. Sci. Abstr., **17,** 35663, 1963.
88. Koch, H., and Hoch, B., Kerntechnik, **5,** 248, 1963.
89. Koch, R. C., and Roesmer, J., J. Food Sci., **27,** 309, 1962.
90. Kramer, H. H., Molinski, V. J., Wahl, W. W., and Stier, P. M., NYO-10171, Sept. 1962.
91. Kruger, P., and Gruverman, I. J. Intern. J. Appl. Rad. Isotopes, **13,** 106, 1962.
92. Laverlochere, J., and May, S., Bull. Soc. Chim. France, **3,** 457, 1963.
93. Lbov, A. A., and Naumov, I. I., Zavod. Lab., **28,** 1475, 1962.
94. Leliaeret, G., and Decat, D., Intern. J. Appl. Radiation Isotopes, **12,** 63, 1961.
95. Leonhardt, W., Kernenergie, **5,** 166, 1962.
96. Levitin, V. V., Bull. Nauchn. Tekhn. Inform. Ukr. Nauchn. Dokl. Inst. Metal, **8,** 78, 1960; Nucl. Sci. Abstr., **17,** 21627, 1963.
97. Lieser, K. H., Elias, H., and Sorg, F., Z. Anal. Chem., **191,** 104, 1962.
98. Lightowlers, E. C., Anal. Chem., **34,** 1398, 1962.
99. Lightowlers, E. C., Anal. Chem., **35,** 1285, 1963.
100. Lovering, J. F., and Mongan, J. W., Nature, **199,** 479, 1963.
101. Lux, F., Radiochimica Acta, **1,** No. 1, 20, 1962.
102. Lyon, W. S., ORNL-3397, 1962, pp. 71–112.
103. Maeck, W. J., Kussy, M. E., and Rein, J. E., Anal. Chem., **35,** 2086, 1963.
104. Manney, T. R., and La Roche, G., UCRL 9897, 1961, pp. 27–30.
105. Markowitz, S. S., and Mahony, J. D., Anal. Chem., **34,** 329, 1962.
106. Matsumura, Y., and Fugino, R., J. Biochem. (Tokyo), **49,** 561, 1961.
107. Mercer, T. T., and Golden, R., Health Phys., **9,** 187, 1963.
108. Morgan, J. W., and Lovering, J. F., Anal. Chim. Acta, **28,** 405, 1963.
109. Morris, D. F. C., and Slater, D. N., Geochim. Cosmochim. Acta, **27,** 285, 1963.
110. Nakayama, F., and Blomstrand, R., Acta Chem. Scand., **15,** 1595, 1961; Nucl. Sci. Abstr., **16,** 7489, 1962.
111. Nikolae, M., Acad. Rep. Populare Romine Ref. Phys., **6,** 127, 1961; Nucl. Sci. Abstr., **16,** 6373, 1962.
112. Nixon, G. S., and Smith, H., Dental Res., **41,** 101362.
113. Odeblad, E., and Malmfors, K. G., Acta Isotopica, **1,** 127, 1961; Nucl. Sci. Abstr., **17,** 21620, 1963.
114. Okada, M., Intern. J. Appl. Radiation Isotopes, **13,** 53, 1962.
115. Okada, M., Nature, **196,** 1088, 1962.
116. Okada, M., Nature, **197,** 278, 1963.

TABLE 28-15 (cont.)

117. Okada, M., Tokyo Kogyo Shikensho Hohoku, **58,** 7, 1963.
118. Okada, M., Tokyo Kogyo Shikensho Hohoku, **58,** 11, 1963.
119. Okada, M., Tokyo Kogyo Shikensho Hohoku, **58,** 54, 1963.
120. Ordogh, M., and Upor-Juancz, V., Acad. Sci. Hung., **26,** 253, 1961.
121. Perey, M., Goldsztaub, S., and Baltzinger, C., Acad. Sciences (Paris), C. R. **255** (7), 1174, 1962.
122. Pierce, T. B., and Peck, P. F., Analyst, **87,** 369, 1962.
123. Pierce, T. B., and Peck, P. F., Analyst, **88,** 217, 1963.
124. Pierce, T. B., and Peck, P. F., Analyst, **88,** 603, 1963.
125. Pijck, J., and Hoste, J., Clin. Chem. Acta, **7,** 5, 1962.
126. Plaksin, I. N., Belyakov, M. A., Rentyrgin, V. L., and Starchik, L. P., Dokl. Akad. Nauk SSSR, **139** (2), 424, 1961.
127. Plaksin, I. N., Belyakov, M. A., and Starchik, L. P., Dokl. Akad. Nauk SSSR, **141,** 921, 1961.
128. Plaksin, I. N., Belyakov, M. A., and Starchik, L. P., At. Energ., **13,** 374, 1962.
129. Plaksin, I. N., Belyakov, M. A., and Starchik, L. P., Dokl. Akad. Nauk SSSR, **142,** 374, 1962.
130. Plaksin, I. N., and Smirnov, V. N., Izvest. Akad. Nauk SSSR, Otdel. Tekh. Nau, Met i Toplivo, No. 4, 118, 1961; Nucl. Sci. Abstr., **16,** 3249, 1962.
131. Plaksin, I. N., Smirnov, V. N., and Starchik, L. P., At. Energy Akad. Nauk Uz, SSR, **2,** 193, 1960; Nucl. Sci. Abstr., **17,** 10570, 1963.
132. Potter, R. M., Aven, M., and Kastner, J., J. Electrochem. Soc., **109,** 1154, 1962.
133. Rakovic, M., Jaderna Energia, **8,** 127, 1962.
134. Rakovic, M., Atompraxis, **9,** 177, 1963.
135. Reuland, R. J., and Voigt, A. F., Anal. Chem., **35,** 1263, 1963.
136. Rhodes, D. F., and Mott, W. E., Anal. Chem., **34,** 1507, 1962.
137. Riebartsch, K., Control of Qualitative Semimicro Separation Processes with Regard to Behavior of Rare Earths Using Radioisotopes (Thesis), Berlin, Technische Universitat, NP-12726, 1962.
138. Rona, E., Hood, D. W., Muse, L., and Buglio, R., Limnol. Oceanog., **7** (2), 201–6, 1962.
139. Rozen, A. M., Khorkhorina, L., Karpacheva, S. M., and Agashkina, G. D., Radiokhimiya, **4,** 591, 1962.
140. Samsahl, K., and Soeremark, R., Aktiebolaget Atomenergi, Stockholm, Rept. AE-61, December 1961.
141. Sanders, F. W., and Auxier, J. A., Health Phys., **8,** 371, 1962.
142. Schmitt, R. A., and Zweig, G. J., Agr. Food Chem., **10,** 481–4, 1962.
143. Setser, J. L., TID-19179, 1963.
144. Shibuya, M., and Nakai, T., Proceedings of 5th Japan Conference on Radioisotopes, Tokyo, May 21–23; Japan Industrial Forum, Inc., Tokyo, 1963.
145. Smales, A. A., Mapper, I., and Seyfang, A. P., Anal. Chim. Acta, **25,** 287, 1961.
146. Smith, H., "Activation Analysis, " Proceedings of British Association of Forensic Medicine, Edinburgh, 1962.
147. Smith, H., Anal. Chem., **34,** 190, 1962.
148. Smith, H., J. Forensic Med., **9,** 143, 1962.
149. Smith, H., Anal. Chem., **35,** 635, 1963.
150. Smith Anal. Chem., **35,** 749, 1963.
151. Smith, H., Forshufvud, S., and Wassen, A., Nature, **194,** 725, 1962.
152. Solberg, D. E., Wethington, J., and Parkinson, T. F., Nature, **197,** 611, 1963.
153. Steele, E. L., and Meinke, W. W., Proceedings of 1961 International Conference on Modern Trends in Activation Analysis, College Station, Texas, 1961, p. 161–5; Nucl. Sci. Abstr., **17,** 4479, 1963.
154. Steele, E. L., and Meinke, W. W., TID-14083, 1961.
155. Steele, E. L., and Meinke, W. W., Anal. Chem., **34,** 185, 1962.
156. Studier, M. H., *et al.*, ANL-6577, 1962.
157. Van Zanten, B., Decat, D., and Leliaeret, G., Intern. J. Appl. Radiation Isotopes, **14,** 105, 1963.
158. Veal, D., and Cook, C. F., Anal. Chem., **34,** 178, 1962.
159. Volborth, A., and Banta, H. E., Anal. Chem., **35,** 2203, 1963.
160. Wagner, H. N., Nelp, W. B., and Dowling, J. H., J. Clin. Invest., **40,** 1984, 1961.
161. Walker, F. W., KAPL-M-FW-4, December 21, 1961.
162. Wayman, C. H., Anal. Chem., **35,** 768, 1963.

APPLICATIONS IN THE ANALYSIS OF SPECIAL MATERIALS

A number of radiochemical methods have been described for the analysis of special materials. These appear in other chapters of Standard Methods of Chemical Analysis as follows:

I. Radiometric Methods.
  1. Chapter 58, Volume III, Plastics.
     a. Liquid scintillation counter used in preparing polymer standards for infrared spectrometric methods
  2. Chapter 59, Volume III, Rubber and Rubber Products.
     a. Dispersion methods in rubber analysis
     b. Determination of the composition of ethylene-propylene copolymers
     c. Determination of dispersion of fillers in rubbers
     d. Determination of solubility of sulfur in rubber
  3. Chapter 47, Volume IIB, Vitamins.
     a. Determination of Vitamin B_{12}, page 2372.
  4. Chapter 63, Volume III, Water Analysis.
     a. Radioactive barium in water
     b. Radium in water
     c. Radium-226 in water
     d. Radioactive strontium in water
     e. Strontium-90 in water

     Chapter 48, Volume IIB, Water Analysis.
     a. Radioactivity of water, page 2470.
  5. Chapter 64, Volume III, Water Determination.
     a. Water in fuels and cement slurries
     b. Water in hydrocarbons
     c. Water in soil

II. Activation Analysis.
  1. Chapter 43, Volume III, Alloys: Iron, Steel, Ferro-alloys, and Related Products.
     a. Determination of oxygen in the analysis of steel and steel-making materials
  2. Chapter 44, Volume III, Alloys: Nonferrous.
     a. Determination of oxygen in nonferrous metals and alloys
  3. Chapter 57, Volume III, Petroleum and Petroleum Products.
     a. Petroleum analysis
  4. Chapter 60, Volume III, Semiconductors.
     a. Antimony
     b. Arsenic
     c. Bismuth
     d. Cobalt
     e. Copper
     f. Gallium
     g. Gold
     h. Indium

III. Isotope Dilution.
  1. Chapter 44, Volume III, Alloys: Nonferrous.
     a. Hydrogen in nonferrous metals and alloys
     b. Oxygen in nonferrous metals and alloys
     c. Nitrogen in nonferrous metals and alloys

Chapter 29

MAGNETIC SUSCEPTIBILITY

By L. N. Mulay
Associate Professor, Materials Research Laboratory
The Pennsylvania State University
University Park, Pennsylvania

INTRODUCTION

The measurements of magnetic susceptibility and the magnetic moment derived therefrom are widely used by the chemist in structural interpretations and in determining the concentrations of certain types of species. These magnetic quantities can be defined only in terms of certain basic concepts, which are given below. Some aspects of measuring techniques and applications will be described later. For further details, the reader should refer to the author's publications and other selected references listed in the bibliography at the end of the chapter.

BASIC CONCEPTS AND DEFINITIONS[1]

Magnetic Dipole.—A magnetic dipole is a macroscopic or microscopic magnetic system, in which the north and south poles of a magnet, equal and opposite in character, are separated by a short but definite distance. A magnetic dipole tends to orient itself parallel to an applied magnetic field in the same way that an electric dipole behaves in an electric field.

Unit Pole.—Unlike an electric charge of either sign (+ or −), a single magnetic pole (north or south) cannot be isolated. However, the purely fictitious concept of a unit pole helps to develop other useful quantitative aspects of magnetism. A unit pole may be defined as one which repels an equal and similar pole, placed 1 cm. away *in vacuo*, with a force of 1 dyne. The force between two poles is governed by Coulomb's law.

Pole Strength.—The strength (the attractive or repulsive power) of a magnet is measured by the number of unit poles to which each pole of the magnet is equivalent.

Intensity or Strength of a Magnetic Field.—If a unit pole is placed at a fixed point *in vacuo* in a magnetic field, it is acted upon by a force which is taken as a measure of the intensity or strength of the magnetic field. It follows from the preceding definitions that unit magnetic intensity exists at a point where the force on a unit pole is 1 dyne. This unit magnetic intensity was formerly called the Gauss and is so called even today by many manufacturers and users of magnets. According to the recommendations of the International Conference on Physics, London, 1934, the term Oersted is used instead. Some writers use the abbreviation oe. A smaller unit, the gamma (γ), is equivalent to 10^{-5} Oersted.

Magnetic field intensity or the magnetizing force is measured by the space rate of

[1] Reproduced with permission from L. N. Mulay, "Magnetic Susceptibility," in L. Meites, Ed., Handbook of Analytical Chemistry, McGraw-Hill, N. Y., 1963.

variation of magnetic potential. This unit is designated as the Gilbert per cm. and is the same as the Oersted.

Magnetic Flux or Flux Density.—This is defined in terms of the lines of force of a magnet. A line of force is the free path that would be traced by a unit pole in a magnetic field because of the forces acting on it. The number of lines of force per $cm.^2$ is taken to be numerically equal to the strength or intensity of the field at any point. The total number of lines of force emanating from the (north) pole face of a magnet is called the total magnetic flux; the number of lines of force per unit area is called the flux density. The unit of flux generally used for theoretical purposes is the Maxwell, which is defined as the flux through 1 $cm.^2$ normal to a field of 1 Oersted. The "line," which is equivalent to the Maxwell, is also used, as is the Weber, which is equivalent to 10^8 Maxwells.

Magnetic Moment.—This is a term that is probably most widely known to chemists but one whose physical significance is least understood. Like the "moment of a force," the magnetic moment refers to the turning effect produced under certain conditions. When a magnetic dipole is placed in a magnetic field, it experiences a turning effect, which is proportional to a specific character termed the magnetic moment. If a field of strength H acts on a dipole N-S of length l and strength m, the N and S poles of the dipole will experience forces equal to $+mH$ and $-mH$, respectively. These two equal and opposite forces constitute a couple whose turning moment M is given by

$$
\begin{aligned}
M &= \text{force} \times \text{distance} \\
&= mH \times l \sin \theta \\
&= \mu H \sin \theta
\end{aligned}
$$

where θ is the angle between the magnetic dipole and the direction of the applied field. Thus, the quantity $\mu(=ml)$ defines the magnetic moment and serves as a measure of the turning effect. It is expressed in dyne-cm./Oersted or ergs/Oersted. Although no practical unit for magnetic moment has been formulated, experiments with the basic electrical and magnetic properties of fundamental particles have revealed the existence of a fundamental unit of magnetic moment, the Bohr magneton. This is just as real a quantity as the charge of an electron, and may be placed among the "universal constants." Often abbreviated "BM" or given the symbol μ_B, this is equal to $eh/4\pi mc$,

where: e is the charge of the electron;
m is the mass of the electron;
h is Planck's constant; and
c is the velocity of light.

Introducing the values of these quantities gives $\mu_B = 9.27 \times 10^{21}$ ergs/Oersted. In early work the "Weiss magneton" was used; 1 Bohr magneton is equivalent to 4.97 Weiss magnetons.

Coulomb's Law and Magnetic Permeability.—Magnetic permeability is best understood in terms of Coulomb's law for magnetic attraction, which is treated in the same manner as electrical attraction.

If two poles of strength m_1 and m_2 are separated by a distance of r cm., the force between them is given by the inverse square law:

$$\text{force} = Km_1m_2/r^2$$

where K is a constant of proportionality. North and south poles are denoted by positive and negative signs, respectively; hence, a positive value of the force corresponds to a repulsion, and a negative value to an attraction. With $K = 1$, this equation is strictly true for vacuum and approximately so for air. However, in many media the force between magnetic poles is quite different than *in vacuo*. Therefore, the concept of permeability is introduced to measure the extent to which a medium is permeable to the magnetic (lines of) force. Thus,

$$\text{force} = m_1 m_2 / r^2 \mu$$

where μ is the magnetic permeability of the medium in which the poles are located. (Note that the symbol μ is used for both permeability and the magnetic moment.) For a vacuum, μ is taken to be unity, and this equation furnishes the definition of a unit magnetic pole stated above. The value of μ serves as a constant of proportionality depending on the nature of the medium and on the units used to express distance, force, etc. It may be noted that, in an analogous situation in electrostatics, one employs a constant K', termed the specific inductive capacity or the dielectric constant, to express the force between two electric charges q_1 and q_2 placed r cm. apart; in this case, force $= q_1 q_2 / K' r^2$.

Intensity of Magnetization.—The amount of pole strength induced over unit area represents intensity of magnetization. Thus,

$$I = m/A$$

where m is the induced pole strength over a total area of A cm.² An alternative definition is obtained by multiplying both numerator and denominator by the distance l; this gives

$$I = ml/Al = \mu/\text{volume}$$

or magnetic moment per unit volume.

Gauss's Law and Magnetic Induction.—According to the definition of field intensity, in a field of unit strength one line of force must pass through every cm. area of one square centimeter. If one considers a sphere of 1-cm. radius (4π cm.² surface area) enclosing a unit pole at its center, it follows that 4π unit lines of force emanate from a unit pole. Gauss's law states that the total magnetic induction over a closed surface is 4π times the amount of pole enclosed. Hence, for a pole m, $4\pi m$ Maxwells emanate from its surface.

A bar of unmagnetized material will become magnetized when placed in a uniform magnetic field. Consider a unit surface A within the material at right angles to the direction of the applied field H. If I is the intensity of magnetization induced, there will be $4\pi I$ unit lines of force across the unit surface. In addition, there will be H lines of force of the applied magnetic field superimposed on the induced magnetization. Therefore, the magnetic induction B, representing the total number of lines of force across the unit surface, is given by

$$B = 4\pi I + H$$

With a vacuum in place of the magnetic material, one would have simply $B = H$, because the magnetic permeability of vacuum is taken as 1. It also follows that, for a magnetic material of permeability μ, the magnetic induction B will be given by

$$B = \mu H$$

The c.g.s.m. (cm.-g.-sec. magnetic) unit of magnetic induction of flux density is the Gauss; because of the dimensionless character of permeability, μ, B, and H have the same dimensions in the electromagnetic system. As stated before, it is customary to express H in Oersteds.

Electronic and Nuclear Magnetic Susceptibility.—The magnetic susceptibility (defined below) observed in bulk matter represents the contributions from both the electrons and nuclei within the system (atoms, ions, molecules, and free radicals). However, the contributions of the nuclei to the susceptibility ($\sim 10^{-10}$ c.g.s. units) are negligible in comparison with those of the electrons, and, therefore, the term "magnetic susceptibility" is usually taken to represent only the electronic property, since this results from the spin and orbital momenta of electrons. However, some authors prefer the term "electronic susceptibility" to distinguish it from "nuclear susceptibility." The latter is usually encountered in discussions of nuclear magnetic resonance absorption spectroscopy, where the emphasis is naturally on the magnetic properties of nuclei.

Magnetic Susceptibility.—The intensity of magnetization I induced at any point in a body is proportional to the strength of the applied field H:

$$I = \kappa H \text{ (or } \kappa = I/H)$$

where κ is a constant of proportionality depending on the material of the body. It is called the magnetic susceptibility per unit volume, and may be defined qualitatively as the extent to which a material is susceptible to induced magnetization. For an isotropic body the susceptibility is the same in all directions. However, for anisotropic crystals, the susceptibilities along the three principal magnetic axes are different, and measurements on their powder samples give the average of the three values.

Magnetic susceptibility is obviously related to magnetic permeability, and the following relationships may be derived.

As was shown before,

$$B = \mu H = 4\pi I + H$$

Therefore,

$$\mu = 4\pi I/H + 1 = 4\pi\kappa + 1$$

or

$$\kappa = (\mu - 1)/4\pi$$

It should be noted that, since κ is a ratio of the intensity of magnetization, I, to the intensity of the applied field, H, the susceptibility κ should strictly be a dimensionless quantity if I and H are expressed in the same units. However, magnetic susceptibility is still expressed in terms of "c.g.s. units" (or "c.g.s. e.m.u." units), more as a matter of convention than of scientific thought. This is so because there are uncertainties in both the measurement and the units of magnetic permeability which have led to confusion over whether or not B and H are quantities of the same kind. In order to simplify matters, the convention of expressing susceptibility in "c.g.s. units" will be followed here.

Mass (or Specific), Atomic, and Molar Susceptibilities.—If ρ is the density of a material, then the susceptibility for 1 cm.^{3} (or ρ g.) is equal to the volume susceptibility κ. Hence, the susceptibility per gram of the material, called the mass or specific susceptibility χ, is given by

$$\chi = \kappa/\rho$$

The atomic susceptibility χ_A and the molar susceptibility χ_M are simply defined as the susceptibility per gram-atom and per gram-mole, respectively. Hence

$$\chi_A = \chi_x \text{ atomic weight}$$
$$\chi_M = \chi_x \text{ molecular weight}$$

The "ionic susceptibility" is similarly defined as the susceptibility per gram-ion.

The magnetic susceptibilities are occasionally expressed in units of the rationalized Georgi system based on the m.k.s. (meter-kilogram-second) system. For volume susceptibility κ, the ratio of units is

$$\text{Georgi/c.g.s.} = 4\pi$$

TABLE 29-1. COMMON TYPES OF MAGNETIC BEHAVIOR[a,b,c]

Type	Effect of External Field on Substance	Examples	Comments on Origin	Magnitude of Specific Susceptibility, χ, at 20°C.	Dependence of Susceptibility on: Temperature	Dependence of Susceptibility on: Field
Diamagnetism	Feeble repulsion $I < H$	Most inorganic compounds, except those containing ions of transition elements; organic compounds except free radicals; certain compositions like stainless steel, special Cu-Ni alloys (*e.g.*, 5-cent coin).	Caused by orbital motion of electron(s). Hence, it is a universal property. Most perceptible when all electrons are "paired" that is, when they have no permanent "spin" moment.	Negative and very small ($\sim 1 \times 10^{-6}$)	None theoretically. Small dependence, attributable to change in state of aggregation of system with temp.	None
Paramagnetism	Attraction $I > H$	Salts and certain complexes of transition elements; "odd" electron molecules like NO_2; O_2; free radicals such as triphenylmethyl.	Caused by spin and (usually) orbital momentum of (unpaired) electrons. The system contains permanent magnetic dipoles (moments) with no interaction.	Positive and small ($\sim 1000 \times 10^{-6}$). Sufficiently large to mask the underlying diamagnetism	$\chi \propto \frac{1}{T}$ (Curie law) or $\chi \propto \frac{1}{T + \theta}$ (Curie-Weiss law)	None
Ferromagnetism	Intense attraction $I \gg H$	Metals like iron, cobalt, nickel, and their alloys; γ-Fe_2O_3.	Caused by "domains" or lattice of particles containing electrons with parallel spins. Positive interaction among dipoles	Positive and very large ($\sim 1 \times 10^{3}$)	Complex. Beyond a certain temp. (Curie point), magnetization, σ, drops and shows paramagnetic behavior.	Described by hysteresis curves.
Collective or superparamagnetism.[d] (Behavior intermediate between para- and ferromagnetism).	Attraction $I > H$	Catalyst in which fine particles of nickel, etc. are dispersed in silica or alumina.	Particles too small to constitute "domains," but exhibit positive "exchange effects" between dipoles.	Positive and very large ($\sim 1 \times 10^{2}$)	$\chi \propto \frac{1}{T + \theta}$ (Curie-Weiss law)	χ increases with fields. "Saturation" is difficult. Generally σ is linear with H/T.

[a] Mulay, L. N., "Analytical Applications of Magnetic Susceptibility," in Kolthoff and Elving, Eds., Treatise on Analytical Chemistry, Vol. IV, Part I, Chapter 38, Interscience Publishers, New York, 1963, pp. 1751–1883.
[b] Mulay, L. N., Anal. Chem., **34**, 343R, 1962.
[c] Nyholm, R. S., J. Inorganic Nucl. Chem., **8**, 402, 1958.
[d] Selwood, P. W., Adsorption and Collective Paramagnetism, Academic Press, New York, 1962.

For the mass susceptibility, the Georgi system employs density in units of kg./m.[2]; thus the ratio Georgi/c.g.s. = $4\pi \times 10^{-3}$.

Types of Magnetic Behaviors.—Table 29-1 summarizes the origins and characteristics of diamagnetic, paramagnetic, and ferromagnetic behavior, and lists some substances in which these are observed. Similar information for some special types of magnetic behavior is given in Table 29-2.

ADDITIVITY RELATIONSHIPS

Mixtures and Solutions.—The mass (or specific) susceptibility χ of a mixture or solution of n components having susceptibilities $\chi_1, \chi_2, \ldots, \chi_n$ and weight fractions $P_1, P_2, \ldots, P_n$ is given by Wiedemann's additivity law:

$$\chi = P_1\chi_1 + P_2\chi_2 + \cdots + P_n\chi_n$$

This is obeyed quite closely by mechanical mixtures and solutions of diamagnetic substances, in which generally little or no interaction takes place either between molecules or ions of the components or between these and the solvent. However, caution must be exercised in deducing the susceptibility of a solute from that of its solution.

Additivity of Atomic Susceptibilities in (Organic) Molecules.—According to Pascal the molecular susceptibility χ_M of a compound can be expressed by

$$\chi_M = \sum_i N_i\chi_i + \lambda$$

where: N_i is the number of atoms of the ith element in each molecule of the compound;
- χ_i is the atomic susceptibility of that element (typical values of χ_i are listed in Table 29-3); and
- λ is a constitutive correction constant depending on the nature of the chemical bonds between the atoms.

Typical values of λ for certain types of bonds and ligands are listed in Table 29-4.

The following calculation, for diphenylpentadienone, illustrates the use of these parameters.

$$C_6H_5\overset{\alpha}{-}C(=O)-\overset{\alpha}{C}H=\overset{\beta}{C}H-\overset{\gamma}{C}H=\overset{\delta}{C}H\overset{\epsilon}{-}C_6H_5 \qquad (C_{17}H_{14}O)$$

$$\begin{aligned}\chi_M &= 17\chi_C + 14\chi_H + \chi_{0,\text{ketone}} + 2\lambda_{C=C} + 2\lambda_{\text{benzene}} + \lambda_{C_{\alpha}{}^4} + \lambda_{C_{\alpha}{}^3} + \lambda_{C_{\beta}{}^3} + \lambda_{C_{\gamma}{}^3} \\ &\quad + \lambda_{C_{\delta}{}^3} + \lambda_{C_{\epsilon}{}^4} \\ &= [(17 \times -6.00) + (14 \times -2.93) + 1.73 + (2 \times 5.5) + (2 \times -1.41) + (-1.54) \\ &\quad + (-1.3) + (-0.5) + (-1.3) + (-1.3) + (-1.54)] \times 10^{-6} \\ &= -140.59 \times 10^{-6}\end{aligned}$$

The experimental molar susceptibility for dephenylpentadienone is -140.5×10^{-6}.

Additivity of Ionic Susceptibilities.—For salts, it is assumed that $\chi_M = \chi_{\text{cation}} + \chi_{\text{anion}}$. The susceptibility constants for many ions are given in the references under Table 29-4.

THEORETICAL CALCULATIONS OF MAGNETIC SUSCEPTIBILITY

There are presented below a number of fundamental equations relating to magnetic susceptibility. For derivations and details, please see especially Bibliography items (1), (4), (6), (7), (10), (29), (30), (31), and (32).

TABLE 29-2. SPECIAL TYPES OF MAGNETIC BEHAVIOR[a,b,c]

Type	Effect of External Field on Substance	Example	Origin	Magnitude of Specific Susceptibility at 20 °C.	Dependence of Susceptibility on Temperature
Temperature-independent (Van Vleck) paramagnetism	Feeble attraction	$KMnO_4$, Co(III) ammines	Atom with upper state separated from ground state by energy interval large compared to kT. System has no permanent magnetic moment.	Positive and very small ($\sim 1 \times 10^{-6}$)	None
Pauli (free-electron) Paramagnetism	Feeble attraction	Metallic K and Na (vapors)	Paramagnetism of an "electron gas."	Positive and very small ($\sim 1 \times 10^{-5}$)	Very slight, generally for vapors $\chi \propto \frac{1}{T}$ (Curie law)
Antiferromagnetism	Feeble attraction	$KNiF_3$, MnSe, Ti_2O_3, ferrites	Two lattices of particles having electron spins in one lattice antiparallel to those in another lattice. Negative interaction among magnetic dipoles.	Positive and very small (1×10^{-7} to 1×10^{-3})	Complex. Up to a critical temp. (antiferromagnetic Curie point or Neél temp.), magnetization increases with temp. then decreases
Ferrimagnetism	Feeble attraction	$FeCr_2O_4$	Interpenetrating lattices with unequal numbers of electrons with antiparallel spins. Simultaneous unequal + and − interaction among dipoles.	Positive and small ($\sim 1 \times 10^{-5}$)	Positive dependence
Metamagnetism. (May be regarded as a special case of antiferromagnetism with low Neél temp.) It shows field-strength dependence	Feeble attraction	$NiCl_2$ or $CoCl_2$ at liquid H_2 temp.	Parallel or antiparallel alignment of moment in domains.	Positive and small ($\sim 1 \times 10^{-5}$)	Positive dependence

[a] Mulay, L. N., "Analytical Applications of Magnetic Susceptibility," in Kolthoff and Elving, Eds., Treatise on Analytical Chemistry, Vol. IV, Part I, Chapter 38, Interscience Publishers, New York, 1963, pp. 1751–1883.

TABLE 29-3. TYPICAL VALUES OF ATOMIC SUSCEPTIBILITY CONSTANTS[a]

Atom	$\chi(\times 10^{-6})$	Atom	$\chi(\times 10^{-6})$
Ag	−31.0	I	−44.6
B	−7.00	N: Open chain	−5.57
		Closed chain (ring)	−4.61
Bi	−192.0		
		O: Alcohol or ether	−4.61
Br	−30.6	Aldehyde or ketone	+1.73
		Carboxylic = 0 in esters and acids	−3.36
C	−6.00		
		3 O atoms in acid anhydrides	−11.23
Cl	−20.1		
F	− 6.3	P	−26.30

[a] For a complete listing of these values see the following references:

Mulay, L. N., "Analytical Applications of Magnetic Susceptibility," in Kolthoff and Elving, Eds., Treatise on Analytical Chemistry, Vol. IV, Part I, Chapter 38, Interscience Publishers, New York, 1963, pp. 1751–1883.
Mulay, L. N., "Measurement of Magnetic Susceptibility and Related Quantities," in L. Meites, Ed., Handbook of Analytical Chemistry, McGraw-Hill, New York, 1963.
Foex, G., Gorter, C. J., and Smits, L. J., Tables de Constantes Selectionnées Diamagnetisme et Paramagnetisme, Masson et Cie, Paris, 1957.

(1) Langevin's Equation for Diamagnetism.[2]

$$\chi_A = -Ne^2/6mc^2 \Sigma \overline{r^2} = -2.832 \times 10^{10} \Sigma \overline{r^2}$$

where $\Sigma \overline{r^2}$ is the sum of the mean square radii of various orbits in an atom. Other values have their usual significance (see references under Table 29-4). Values for $\overline{r^2}$ may be calculated by using (semi-empirical) equations developed by Slater[3] and modified by others.[4] This equation is strictly applicable to mononuclear systems.

(2) Van Vleck's Equation for Diamagnetism.[5]

$$\chi_A = -\frac{Ne^2}{6mc^2}\left\{\frac{h^2}{4\pi^2 ze^2 m}\right\}^2 \left[\frac{5}{2}n^4 l(l+1) - \frac{3}{2}n^2 l(l+1) + \frac{1}{2}n^2\right]$$

where n and l are the principal and subordinate quantum numbers, respectively, and z is the atomic number. h is Planck's constant of action, and other terms have their usual significance.

(3) Langevin's Equation for Molar Paramagnetism.[2]

$$\chi_M = N\mu^2/3kT$$

where: N is Avogadro's number;
μ is the permanent moment;
k is Boltzmann's constant; and
T is the absolute temperature.

[2] Langevin, P., J. Phys., **4,** 678, 1905.
[3] Slater, J. C., Phys. Rev., **32,** 349, 1928; **36,** 57, 1930.
[4] Stoner, E. C., Magnetism and Atomic Structure, 1926; Magnetism and Matter, 1934, Methuen and Co., Ltd., London.
[5] Van Vleck, J. H., The Theory of Electric and Magnetic Susceptibilities, Oxford University Press, London, 1932.

TABLE 29-4. TYPICAL VALUES OF CONSTITUTIVE CORRECTION CONSTANTS (λ) FOR GROUPS AND LIGANDS[a]

Group	$\lambda(\times 10^{-6})$
C=C, ethylenic linkage	+5.5
C=C—C=C, diethylenic linkage	+10.6
CH_2=CH—CH_2—, allyl group	+4.5
C≡C, acetylenic linkage	+0.8
Ar—C≡C—Ar	+2.30
C in one aromatic ring (*e.g.*, benzene)	−0.24
C in two aromatic rings (*e.g.*, naphthalene)	−3.1
C in three aromatic rings (*e.g.*, pyrene)	−4.0
—C—Br, monobromo derivative	−4.1
Br—C—C—Br, dibromo derivative	+6.24
—C—Cl, monochloro derivative	+3.1
—C—I, monoiodo derivative	+4.1
C bound to other C atoms with 3 bonds and in α, γ, δ, or ε position with respect to a carbonyl group	−1.3
C bound to other C atoms with 4 bonds and in α, γ, δ, or ε position with respect to a carbonyl group	−1.54
C bound to other C atoms with 3 or 4 bonds and in β position with respect to a carbonyl group	−0.5

[a] For a complete listing of these values see the following references:

Mulay, L. N., "Analytical Applications of Magnetic Susceptibility," in Kolthoff and Elving, Eds., Treatise on Analytical Chemistry, Vol. IV, Part I, Chapter 38, Interscience Publishers, New York, 1963, pp. 1751–1883.
Mulay, L. N., "Measurement of Magnetic Susceptibility and Related Quantities," in L. Meites, Ed., Handbook of Analytical Chemistry, McGraw-Hill, New York, 1963.
Foex, G., Gorter, C. J., and Smits, L. J., Tables de Constantes Selectionnées Diamagnetisme et Paramagnetisme, Masson et Cie, Paris, 1957.

This equation ignores the underlying diamagnetism of paramagnetic susceptibility, and also the temperature-independent paramagnetism observable in certain cases.

(*4*) *Van Vleck's Equation for Paramagnetism.*[5]

$$\chi_M = (N\beta^2\mu_{B^2}/3kT) + N\alpha$$

where: μ_B is the low-frequency part of the magnetic moment expressed in Bohr magnetons, β.

$\beta = 0.927 \times 10^{-20}$ erg/Oersted;
N is Avogadro's number;
k is Boltzmann's constant; and
T is the absolute temperature.

The term $N\alpha$ represents the combined temperature-independent contribution of the high-frequency elements of the paramagnetic moment and of the underlying diamagnetism.

The values of μ and α depend on the splitting of energy levels, measured in terms of kT. Three different cases are considered.[6,7]

[6] Van Vleck, J. H., The Theory of Electric and Magnetic Susceptibilities, Oxford University Press, London, 1932.
[7] Bates, L. F., Modern Magnetism, Cambridge University Press, 1961.

(a) Multiplet intervals large compared to kT (applicable to most rare earth ions):

$$\chi_M = \frac{Ng^2\beta^2 J(J+1)}{3kT} + \frac{N\beta^2}{6(2J+1)}\left[\frac{F(J+1)}{h\nu(J+1;J)} - \frac{F(J)}{h\nu(J+1;J)}\right]$$

$$F(J) = \frac{[(S+L+1)^2 - J^2][J^2 - (S-L)^2]}{J}$$

where: J is the vector sum of the spin moment S and the angular momentum L;
g is the Landé splitting factor;
h is Planck's constant; and
ν is the frequency separation of energy levels.

(b) Multiplet intervals small compared to kT (applicable to ions of transition elements):

$$\chi_M = \frac{N\beta^2}{3kT}[4S(S+1) + L(L+1)] - \frac{Ne^2}{6mc^2}\Sigma\,\overline{r^2}$$

The high-frequency elements of the paramagnetic moment are absent (*i.e.*, $N\alpha = 0$). The second term, representing the underlying diamagnetism, is very small and may be ignored.

The magnetic moment μ, expressed in Bohr magnetons on the basis of the classical theory, may be calculated from

$$\mu = g\sqrt{J(J+1)}$$

where J is the resultant angular momentum, which is a vector sum of L and S.

For atoms in the S-spectroscopic state, $L = 0$; the magnetic moment is entirely due to the electron spins, so that $J = S$ and $g = 2$, giving

$$\mu = 2\sqrt{S(S+1)} = \sqrt{2S(2S+2)} = \sqrt{n(n+2)}$$

Here S, the total spin momentum for n unpaired electrons, is given by n times the spin momentum for each electron, which is $\frac{1}{2}$ quantum unit.

(c) Multiplet intervals comparable to kT (particularly applicable to the ions of samarium and europium):

$$\chi_M = N \sum_{J=L-S}^{L+S} \frac{\{[g_J{}^2\beta^2 J(J+1)/3kT] + \alpha_J\}(2J+1)e^{-W_J{}^0/kT}}{\Sigma\,(2J+1)e^{-W_J{}^0/kT}}$$

In this special case, the effect of the quantum number J is comparable to kT, and it is necessary to consider that the system, containing N atoms, is made of groups of atoms N_{J_1}, N_{J_2}, etc., with different values for J. The distribution of atoms among various groups is governed by the Boltzmann temperature factor and is proportional to $(2J+1)e^{-W_J/kT}$, where W_J is the energy of precession.

Tables 29-5 and 29-6 list the Bohr Magneton numbers for typical paramagnetic ions.

EXPERIMENTAL TECHNIQUES

These have been described in detail by the author (items 13, 15, and 16 in the bibliography). A summary of important aspects of these techniques is given in Table 29-7. In the author's opinion, the Faraday helical spring method provides the most versatile technique, not only for measuring magnetic susceptibility, but also for a quantitative *in situ* type of studies on adsorption, thermogravimetry, and for studying changes in

TABLE 29-5. BOHR MAGNETON NUMBERS FOR IONS OF FIRST TRANSITION GROUP[a]

Ion	Number of 3d Electrons	Term	Calculated $\mu_{eff.} = \sqrt{n(n+2)})$	Observed $\mu_{eff.}$
Sc^{+++}, Ti^{4+}, V^{5+}	0	$^1S_0$	0.00	0.0
Ti^{3+}, V^{4+}	1	$^2D_{3/2}$	1.73	1.77–1.79
V^{+++}	2	$^3F_2$	2.83	2.76–2.85
V^{++}, Cr^{+++}, Mn^{4+}	3	$^4F_{3/2}$	3.87	3.68–4.00
Cr^{++}, Mn^{+++}	4	$^5D_0$	4.90	4.80–5.06
Mn^{++}, Fe^{+++}	5	$^6S_{5/2}$	5.92	5.2–6.0
Fe^{++}	6	$^5D_4$	4.90	5.0–5.5
Co^{++}	7	$^4F_{9/2}$	3.87	4.4–5.2
Ni^{++}	8	$^3F_4$	2.83	2.9–3.4
Cu^{++}	9	$^2D_{5/2}$	1.73	1.8–2.2
Cu^{+}, Zn^{++}	10	$^1S_0$	0.00	0.0

[a] Reproduced, with permission, from P. W., Selwood, Magnetochemistry, Interscience Publishers, New York, 1956, p. 159.

TABLE 29-6. THEORETICAL EFFECTIVE BOHR MAGNETON NUMBERS FOR TRIPOSITIVE RARE EARTH IONS[a]

Ion	Number of 4f electrons	Terms	$\mu_{eff.}$, Theoretical
La^{+++}	0	^1S	0.00
Ce^{+++}	1	$^2F_{5/2}$	2.56
Pr^{+++}	2	$^3H_4$	3.62
Nd^{+++}	3	$^4I_{9/2}$	3.68
Pm^{+++}	4	$^5I_4$	2.83
Sm^{+++}	5	$^6H_{5/2}$	1.55–1.65
Eu^{+++}	6	$^7F_0$	3.40–3.51
Gd^{+++}	7	$^8S_{7/2}$	7.94
Tb^{+++}	8	$^7F_6$	9.7
Dy^{+++}	9	$^6H_{15/2}$	10.6
Ho^{+++}	10	$^5I_8$	10.6
Er^{+++}	11	$^4I_{15/2}$	9.6
Tm^{+++}	12	$^3H_6$	7.6
Yb^{+++}	13	$^2F_{7/2}$	4.5
Lu^{+++}	14	^1S	0.00

[a] Theoretical values of $\mu_{eff.}$ are taken, with permission, from J. H. Van Vleck, The Theory of Electric and Magnetic Susceptibilities, Oxford University Press, London, 1932, and, with Frank, Phys. Rev., **34,** 1494, 1625, 1929.

TABLE 29-7. SUMMARY OF IMPORTANT ASPECTS OF METHODS OF MEASURING MAGNETIC SUSCEPTIBILITIES

Method	General Field Requirements	Applicable to	Physical Nature of Sample	Approximate Minimum and Convenient Size of Sample	Accuracy	Temperature Control
Gouy	Uniform field. Recommended and easily available range with electromagnets is 3000 to 15,000 Oersteds. Permanent magnets up to 5000 Oersteds.	Dia- and paramagnetics only.	Powdered solids, pure liquids, and solutions (adaptable for measuring of a gas surrounding a known sample).	0.5 g. solids 5 ml. liquids (macroscale) Few mg. or μg. can be handled in special apparatus.	Generally $\pm 1\%$ may be improved to $\pm 0.1\%$. (Separate density measurement required; accuracy depends on packing.)	Is possible over a wide range. From liq He or liq H_2 temps to several hundred degrees may be obtained.
Quincke	Uniform field. Recommended and easily available range with electromagnets is 3000 to 15,000 Oersteds. Permanent magnets up to 5000 Oersteds.	Dia- and paramagnetics only.	Pure liquids and solutions. (Adaptable for measuring x of a gas above the meniscus of a known liquid.)	app. 5 ml.	Generally $\pm 0.1\%$	Limited range depending on f.p. or b.p. of system.
Rankine	Low fields 15 to 100 Oersteds.	Dia- and paramagnetics only.	Pure liquids and solutions. (Adaptable to flow system and gases).	app. 2 ml.	Generally $\pm 0.1\%$	Same as above.
Faraday	Field strength range same as for Gouy balance, but giving nonuniform field with a constant field gradient.	Dia-, para- and ferromagnetic materials.	Generally useful for powdered solids (liquids may be handled in special containers).	Few mg. (microtechniques are also available).	$\pm 0.1\%$	Temperature control is possible over a wide range (same as stated for Gouy technique).
Induction Methods (a.c. including R.F. and d.c.)	External fields not required except in a study of ferromagnetics.	Generally to dia- and paramagnetics. Ferromagnetics may be studied in special apparatus.	Solids and liquids.	0.5 g. solids 5 ml. liquids	Accuracy generally better than $\pm 0.1\%$ but depends on dielectric characteristics.	Temperature control over a wide range is rather difficult with the R.F. method, but is adaptable in other inductance methods.

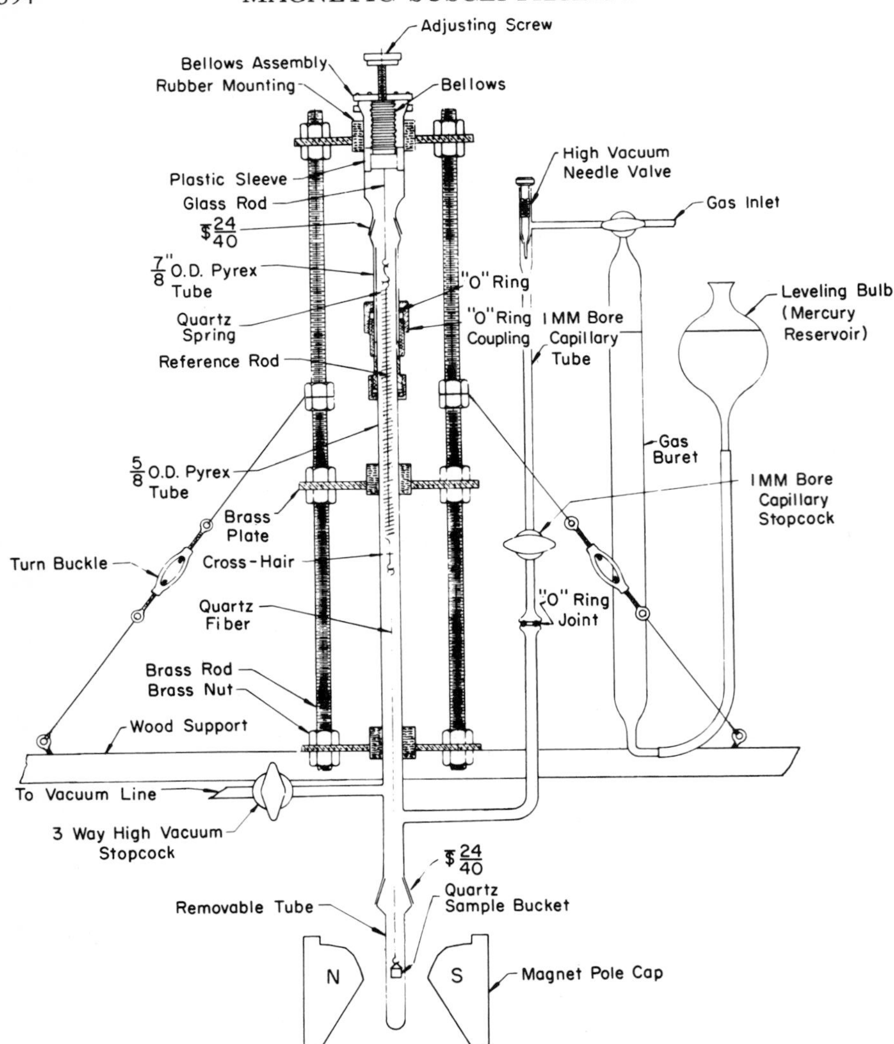

Fig. 29-1. Faraday Type Helical Spring Microbalance. Designed for Studies of Magnetic Susceptibility, Magneto-adsorption and Thermomagnetic Analysis. (Courtesy Anal. Chem., **36,** 2383, 1964.)

magnetic susceptibility occurring during these processes. These studies may be classified as magneto-adsorption and thermomagnetic analysis, and they constitute a wide variety of applications.

Figure 29-1 shows the construction of a Faraday balance specially designed for these studies.[8] The details of construction, operation, and some applications have been de-

[8] Mulay, L. N., and Keys, L. K., Anal. Chem., **36,** 2383, 1964.

scribed separately by this author.[8,9,10] It will suffice to point out here that in this method the sample is placed in a uniform region of the magnetic field gradient $H\frac{dH}{dx}$, and the magnetic force f acting on the sample is measured by observing the change in its weight when the electromagnet is turned on. The force is measured in terms of the 'deflection' of the cross-hair on the quartz spring and may be expressed in some arbitrary units. By measuring the deflection d_r for a sample of known susceptibility, χ_r and mass m_r, and comparing this with the deflection d_s for a sample of mass m_s, its susceptibility χ_s is calculated from the equation

$$\chi_s = \frac{d_s \times m_r \times x_r}{d_r \times m_s}$$

SOME RECENT APPLICATIONS OF MAGNETIC SUSCEPTIBILITY

Several analytical applications of magnetic susceptibility have been described during 1962 to 1964 (see Bibliography, items (13), (14), (15), and (16). Recently the apparatus described in the preceding section was used by this author for studying the adsorption of oxygen on gamma-alumina with special reference to the possibility of formation of polymeric species like O_4.[11]

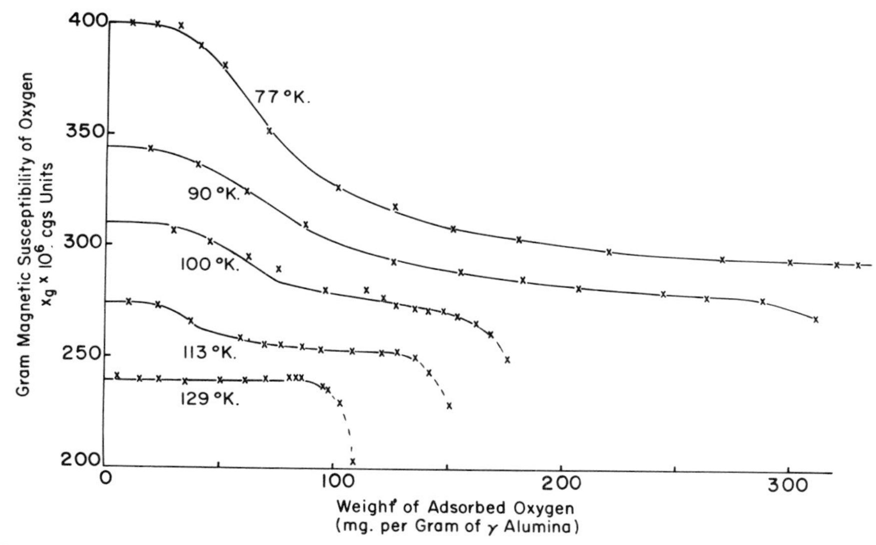

FIG. 29-2. Magnetic Susceptibility of Oxygen as a Function of Amount Adsorbed. (Reproduced from J. Am. Chem. Soc., **86,** 4489, 1964. Copyright 1964 by the American Chemical Society and reproduced by permission of the copyright owner.)

Figure 29-2 shows a plot of magnetic susceptibility of oxygen *vs.* the amount of oxygen adsorbed. In reality this represents a combination of curves obtained for (a) amount of

[9] Mulay, L. N., "Analytical Applications of Magnetic Susceptibility," in Kolthoff and Elving, Eds., Treatise on Analytical Chemistry, Vol. IV, Part I, Chapter 38, Interscience Publishers, New York, pp. 1751–1883, 1963.

[10] Mulay, L. N., Anal. Chem., **34,** 343R, 1962.

[11] Mulay, L. N., and Keys, L. K., J. Am. Chem. Soc., **86,** 4489, 1964; **87,** 1192, 1965.

oxygen *vs.* pressure, and (b) magnetic susceptibility of oxygen as a function of pressure. As shown in Fig. 29-2, the temperature was held constant during one susceptibility run; thus measurements were made at five different temperatures. The decrease in susceptibility was attributed to the formation of O_4 species (in the singlet and/or triplet state) from O_2, which has two unpaired electrons. From this, valuable information such as the heat of dimerization for O_4 in the adsorbed (quasi-liquid) phase, physical heats of adsorption for O_2 and O_4 species, etc. were obtained.

The apparatus was also used to demonstrate the thermomagnetic analysis[8] of $CuSO_4 \cdot 5H_2O \rightarrow CuSO_4 \cdot H_2O + 4H_2O$ in which changes in magnetic susceptibility occur due not only to the loss of four molecules of water, but also to decrease in the paramagnetic susceptibility of copper(II) ion.

SELECTED BIBLIOGRAPHY

(1) Bates, L. F., Modern Magnetism, Cambridge University Press, 1961.
(2) Bozorth, R. M., Ferromagnetism, D. Van Nostrand Co., Inc., Princeton, N. J., 1951.
(3) Bozorth, R. M., Van Vleck, J. H., *et al.*, Magnetic Properties of Metals and Alloys, American Society for Metals, Cleveland, 1959.
(4) Figgis, B. N., and Lewis, J., "The Magnetochemistry of Complex Compounds," in Modern Coordination Chemistry, J. Lewis and R. G. Wilkins, Eds., Interscience Publishers, New York, 1960.
(5) Figgis, B. N., and Lewis, J., "Magnetochemistry of Coordination Compounds," in Progress in Inorganic Chemistry; F. A. Cotton, Ed., Interscience Publishers, New York, 1964.
(6) Foex, G., Gorter, C. J., and Smits, L. J., Tables de Constantes Selectionnees Diamagnetisme et Paramagnetisme, Masson et Cie, Paris, 1957.
(7) Griffith, J. S., The Theory of Transition Metal Ions, Cambridge University Press, 1961.
(8) Hutchison, C. A., Jr., "Magnetic Susceptibilities," in Determination of Organic Structures by Physical Methods; E. A. Braude and F. C. Nachod, Eds., Academic Press, Inc., New York, 1955.
(9) Kittel, C., Introduction to Solid State Physics, John Wiley, New York, 1960.
(10) Langevin, P., J. Phys., **4,** 678, 1905.
(11) McGuire, T. R., "The Measurement of Magnetic Susceptibility," in Methods of Experimental Physics, Vol. 6, K. Lark-Horovitz and V. A. Johnson, Eds., Academic Press, New York, 1959.
(12) Michaelis, L., "Determination of Magnetic Susceptibility," in Techniques of Organic Chemistry; A. Weisseberger, Ed., Vol. I, Part II, Interscience Publishers, New York, 1949.
(13) Mulay, L. N., "Analytical Applications of Magnetic Susceptibility"; Chapter 38, in Vol. IV, Part I, Treatise on Analytical Chemistry; Kolthoff and Elving, Eds., Interscience Publishers, New York, 1963, pp. 1751–1883.
(14) Mulay, L. N., "Measurement of Magnetic Susceptibility and Related Quantities," Section 7 in Handbook of Analytical Chemistry; L. Meites, Ed., McGraw-Hill, New York, 1963. This gives complete tables for atomic susceptibility constants, etc.
(15) Mulay, L. N., and Mulay, I. L., Anal. Chem., **36,** 404R, 1964. This lists several additional references in the general area of magnetism.
(16) Mulay, L. N., Anal. Chem., **34,** 343R, 1962.
(17) Mulay, L. N., Proc. Ind. Acad. Sci., **34A,** 245, 1951.
(18) Mulay, L. N., and Fox, Mary E., J. Chem. Phys., **38,** 760, 1962.
(19) Mulay, L. N., and Haverbusch, Martha, Rev. Sci. Instr., **35,** 756, 1964.
(20) Mulay, L. N., and Keys, L. K., Anal. Chem., **36,** 2383, 1964.
(21) Mulay, L. N., and Keys, L. K., J. Am. Chem. Soc., **86,** 4489, 1964; **87,** 1192, 1965.
(22) Mulay, L. N., and Naylor, Mary C., in Advances in Coordination Chemistry, Proc. of the 6th Int. Conf. Coord. Chem. (1961), S. Kirschner, Ed., Macmillan Company, New York, 1961, pp. 520–533.
(23) Mulay, L. N., and Selwood, P. W., J. Am. Chem. Soc., **77,** 2693, 1955.
(24) Nyholm, R. S., J. Inorganic Nucl. Chem., **8,** 402, 1958.
(25) Pacault, A., Hoarau, J., and Marchand, A., "Recent Aspects of Diamagnetism," in Advances in Chemical Physics; I. Prigogine, Ed., Interscience Publishers, New York, 1961.

(26) Pacault, A., Rev. Sci., **84,** 169, 1946.
(27) Selwood, P. W., Adsorption and Collective Paramagnetism, Academic Press, New York, 1962.
(28) Selwood, P. W., Magnetochemistry, Interscience Publishers, New York, 1956.
(29) Slater, J. C., Phys. Rev., **32,** 349, 1928; **36,** 57, 1930.
(30) Stoner, E. C., Magnetism and Matter, 1934; Magnetism and Atomic Structure, 1926, Methnen and Co., Ltd., London.
(31) Van Vleck, J. H., The Theory of Electric and Magnetic Susceptibilities, Oxford University Press, London, 1932.
(32) Van Vleck, J. H., and Frank, Phys. Rev., **34,** 1494, 1625, 1929.

Chapter 30

NUCLEAR MAGNETIC RESONANCE SPECTROMETRY

By Harlan Foster
Central Research Department
E. I. du Pont de Nemours and Company
Wilmington, Delaware

INTRODUCTION

Nuclear magnetic resonance (NMR), the newest of the spectrometric disciplines, has developed a remarkably wide range of applications in the short time it has been known, due largely to the early availability of commercial instruments. A number of books and other extensive treatments of NMR are available.[1–5] This chapter will be confined to what is known as the high resolution aspect of the field, particularly as it is applied to problems of structure determination and to qualitative and quantitative analysis. Reference will be made only incidentally to many other facets of the subject such as the study of physico-chemical problems which depend on rate processes. The discussion will be largely devoted to the spectrometry of protons, the nucleus to which the most numerous and profitable applications have been made.

To be available for study by nuclear magnetic resonance a nucleus must possess angular momentum and an associated magnetic moment. The most important nuclei falling in this category are H^1, F^{19}, P^{31}, and B^{11}. In principle C^{13}, N^{14}, O^{17}, and Sn^{119}, among others, possess the needed properties but for such reasons as low isotopic abundance, and poor inherent sensitivity they are of marginal importance. Most other nuclei either do not have the required properties or are of low technical interest. The hydrogen nucleus or proton with a spin of $\frac{1}{2}$ will be used for the presentation of the origin of nuclear resonance.

A correct presentation of the theory of nuclear magnetic resonance must be based on quantum mechanics. The following highly simplified exposition avoids this approach and is intended only to give a newcomer to the field some feeling that the effect has a physical reality. Treatments of varying degrees of completeness are cited in footnotes throughout the chapter.

[1] Gutowsky, H. S., in Weissberger, A., Ed., Techniques of Organic Chemistry, 3rd Ed., Vol. 1, Part IV, Interscience, New York, 1960.
[2] Jackman, L. M., Applications of Nuclear Magnetic Resonance Spectroscopy in Organic Chemistry, Pergamon Press, London, 1959.
[3] Pople, J. A., Schneider, W. G., and Bernstein, H. J., High Resolution Nuclear Magnetic Resonance, McGraw-Hill, New York, 1959.
[4] Roberts, J. D., An Introduction to the Analysis of Spin-Spin Splitting in Nuclear Magnetic Resonance, Benjamin, 1961.
[5] Varian Associates, High Resolution NMR Spectra Catalog, Vol. 1, 1962; Vol. 2, 1963. Varian Associates, Palo Alto, Calif.

ORIGIN OF NMR SPECTRA

A nucleus which has the required properties of angular momentum and magnetic moment together with a charge may act as a small bar magnet and orient itself in a magnetic field H_o. The number of possible orientations depends upon the spin I and is equal to $(2I + 1)$. The energy characteristic of each orientation is $E = I\mu H_o$ where μ is the component of the magnetic moment in the direction of the magnetic field. For protons $I = \frac{1}{2}$ and there are two orientations, parallel and antiparallel to the field, characterized by the energies $E_1 = +\frac{1}{2}\mu H_o$ and $E_2 = -\frac{1}{2}\mu H_o$. If the nucleus can be induced to change from the orientation of lower energy to that of higher energy then the required work is

$$\Delta E = E_1 - E_2$$
$$= \mu H_o$$

Applying the Bohr frequency relation $\Delta E = h\nu$ one derives the basic NMR equation

$$\nu = \frac{\mu H_o}{h}$$

If then a nucleus of moment μ be placed in a magnetic field H_o and an oscillating field H_1 of frequency γ be applied perpendicular to H_o the system can absorb energy from the rf-field and transitions will be induced between the lower and the higher levels. For spins other than $\frac{1}{2}$ there are additional orientations, and the form of the basic NMR equation undergoes obvious changes.

The supply of excess nuclei in the lower energy level is very small (*ca.* 7 in 10^6). If no additional factors intervened, this supply of nuclei would be exhausted very shortly, the system would be saturated, and there would be no further absorption of energy. In fact, the process is a radiationless one, but some of the nuclei can relax back by losing thermal energy to the environment and can, thereby, constantly replenish the supply if the power level of the oscillating field is not too high. This process is characterized by the spin-lattice relaxation time T_1. There is an additional relaxation mechanism whereby energy is interchanged between spins but there is no net loss from the system. This is characterized by the spin-spin relaxation time T_2. Both govern the lifetime of the excited state and thereby may influence the line width through the uncertainty principle

$$\Delta E \cdot \Delta t = h/2\pi$$

With the nuclei most commonly encountered in high resolution work T_1 and T_2 are sufficiently long to make instrumental factors largely controlling of line width. In the so-called broad-line NMR of solids there is additional broadening from dipole-dipole interactions of neighbors which have the effect of creating an inhomogeneous magnetic field at the nucleus. In the high resolution spectrometry of liquids or high density gases tumbling motion largely averages the dipolar interactions to zero.

INSTRUMENTATION

A simplified theoretical foundation having been given, it is now in order to devote some attention to the instrumental requirements for observing the effect. Conceptually these requirements are simple. It is possible, as will be seen from the basic equation, to operate at a constant frequency ν and vary the magnetic field H_o until the resonance condition is realized. Alternately, the field may be held constant and the frequency varied through resonance. The first procedure is usually followed because more difficult problems are presented in making the several necessary variable frequency components track together for the second case. Spectrometers may be further divided into absorption or induction types. In the first a bridge circuit is commonly used to detect the absorption of radiofrequency (rf.) energy from a coil surrounding the sample. In the induction type two coils at right angles are used. Energy is absorbed from the transmitter coils to orient the nuclei. This orientation process induces a voltage in the receiver coils. For

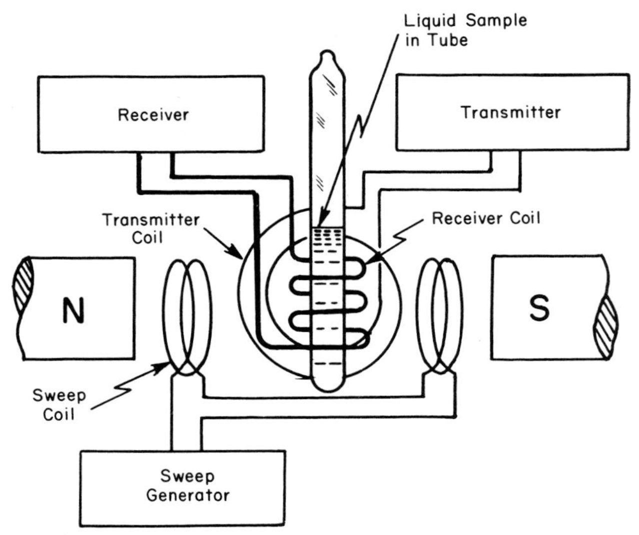

Fig. 30-1. Essential Components of Double Coil NMR Spectrometer.

either type of spectrometer, shown diagramatically in Fig. 30-1, the requirements are broadly for:

1. A magnet to supply the principal part of the field H_o. This may be either an electromagnet or permanent magnet. The required high field and homogeneity are the controlling criteria.
2. A sweep circuit consisting of a set of Helmholtz coils which superimpose on the main field of the magnet the additional field required to bring the total to the resonance condition.
3. A transmitter to supply the rf. energy of frequency γ.
4. A detector-amplifier circuit to pick up and amplify the resonance signal.
5. A probe which primarily serves to hold the sample between the pole pieces. Commonly, it also carries the coils of the sweep, transmitter, and receiver circuits.
6. Devices for observing and/or recording the signal and which track with the sweep circuit.

While the instrumental requirements for high resolution work are simple in principle they are stringent in practice. The NMR effect is a tiny perturbation in the total system involving approximately 1 in 10^5 of the pertinent nuclei. Currently, most work with protons is done at a frequency of 60×10^6 cps. and a field of 14,094 gauss. Increasingly, frequencies of 100×10^6 cps. and fields of 23,490 gauss are being used. In either case measurements are made to less than a cycle and the corresponding fraction of a milli-gauss. Thus the regulation of both the frequency and field must be of the order of one in

10^8–10^9 for protons. Requirements for other nuclei are only slightly less demanding. To attain this regulation the necessary stabilization gear such as control loop circuitry is as much a part of the spectrometer as the basic components indicated above.

No further discussion of instrumentation is justified here. Gutowsky discusses the subject in some detail.[1] NMR being a relatively new field, the equipment is being modified and improved constantly and new suppliers are entering the market. Operating instructions are supplied with different instruments.

In taking an NMR spectrum the sample is placed in the probe which is accurately positioned between the pole pieces at the point of maximum homogeneity for the field H_o. The sample is bathed in energy of the proper frequency while additional field is supplied by the sweep coils until the resonance condition is attained. This condition is sensed in the detector circuit and the amplified signal fed to the observing and recording stations.

The spectrum which is obtained contains three types of information, all of which are illustrated in the spectrum of diethyl malonate shown in Fig. 30-2. There are principal

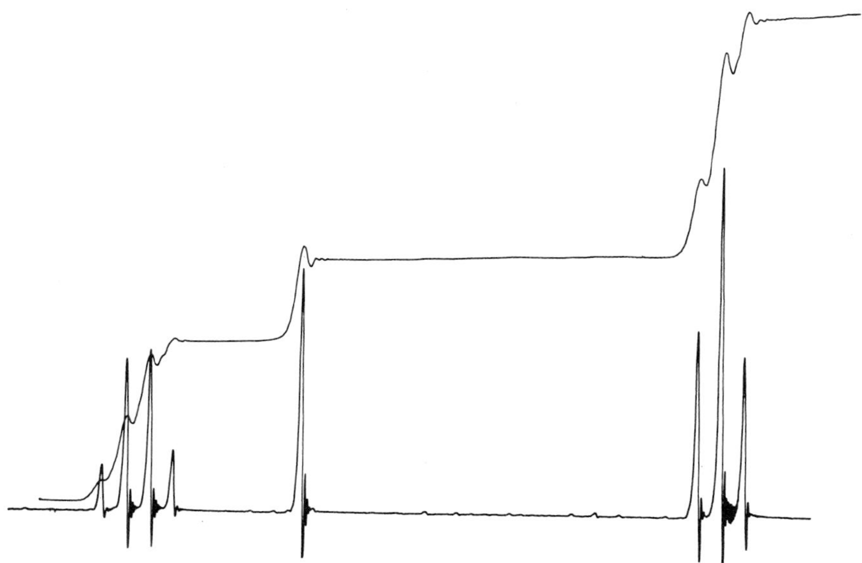

Fig. 30-2. Proton NMR Spectrum of Diethyl Malonate With Integral Curve. From Left to Right the Principal Peaks are Assigned to —CH_2CH$_3$, OC—CH_2—CO and —CH$_2CH_3$ Respectively.

peaks at three positions, two of which show additional fine structure and the three are in the intensity ratios 2:1:3. The chemical shift or position of the line gives information on the molecular environment of the nuclei from which it arises. The chemical shifts of nuclei in different molecules are similar if the molecular magnetic environments are similar. Fine structure in the peaks may tell much about the spatial relationships of the nuclei and the nature of near neighbors, particularly their number. The intensity of the lines tells directly the relative number of magnetically active nuclei undergoing the different chemical shifts. Much of the remainder of this chapter is devoted to a more detailed discussion of these spectral features.

CHARACTERISTICS OF SPECTRUM

Chemical Shifts.—The foregoing basic NMR equation

$$\nu = \frac{\mu H_o}{h}$$

would imply that all protons would resonate at the same field and frequency. In actual fact protons which are differently situated in a molecule may be magnetically nonequivalent and come successively into resonance as the field is changed by the sweep coils, and it is to these differences in the positions of resonance that the analytical utility of NMR is primarily due. These differences are called chemical shifts. The theory of chemical shifts is very unsatisfactory and sophisticated treatments frequently seem to be based more on mathematical convenience than physical reality. For present purposes the chemical shifts will be regarded as arising largely from two sources, the electronegativity of near neighbors and molecular magnetic anisotropy of the groups present. The electrons moving near a proton, being charged, create their own magnetic field, which, by Lenz Law, should oppose the applied field. Therefore, the applied field, H_{app}, of the magnet must be greater than H_{eff}, the effective field at the nucleus, in order to attain the resonance condition. Just how great the difference will be will depend upon the electronegativity of the neighbors which act to pull the nearby shielding electrons from around the proton. The more strongly the electrons are pulled away the less the protons are shielded and the proton goes into resonance at a lower field. If a near neighbor is electron-repelling then the shielding electronic magnetic field is more effective, so that H_{app} must be greater in order to achieve a given H_{eff} at the proton and the chemical shift moves to higher field. The molecular magnetic anisotropy arises from the circulation of electrons through the molecule, such as about a π-bond. This electronic motion creates a field which may act with or against the applied field, depending primarily on molecular geometry. It is the field due to π-electron ring currents acting with the applied field which causes aromatic protons to resonate at a much lower field than ethylenic protons. Magnetic anisotropy of the carbonyl bond contributes heavily to shifting an aldehyde proton to a very low field. With acetylenic protons the effect is opposite. Electronegativity contributions tend to be roughly additive; anisotropy effects are not so, due to their strongly geometric characteristics. There are other factors affecting the chemical shifts such as fields from associated molecules and solvents, but they are usually minor compared to the two factors discussed.

An NMR spectrum is obtained as a plot of the band intensities as the ordinate *vs.* the changing magnetic field as the abscissa. The abscissa is usually graduated in the equivalent frequency, however, and the shifts appear as cycles per second (cps.). There are additional conventions to be followed. It is impractical to express NMR shifts in absolute frequencies or fields, and they are measured relative to some standard. It is also desirable to express the shifts in dimensionless units which are independent of the magnitude of the field and frequency. This enables workers using instruments with different characteristics to get the same answers. What is perhaps the most used method expresses the chemical shift, δ, in parts per million from some reference so that it takes the form

$$\delta_{\text{p.p.m.}} = \frac{H_s - H_r}{H_r} \times 10^6$$

where H_s and H_r refer to the field at resonance of the sample and the reference. Because of the linear relationship between field and frequency this may take the equivalent form

$$\delta_{\text{p.p.m.}} = \frac{\nu_s - \nu_r}{\nu_r} \times 10^6$$

where ν_s and ν_r refer to the sample and reference resonance frequencies. Tetramethylsilane is currently the reference of choice except where conditions such as immiscibility preclude its use. Other materials which give single strong sharp peaks may be used but water, benzene, and acetone should be avoided if possible as they are subject to strong solvent effects.

A standard but less popular convention than the above expresses the chemical shift as a τ-value. Tetramethylsilane is used as the reference and τ-values are simply related to δ by

$$\tau = 10 - \delta_{\text{p.p.m.}}$$

For accurate τ values the shift is obtained by extrapolation to infinite dilution.

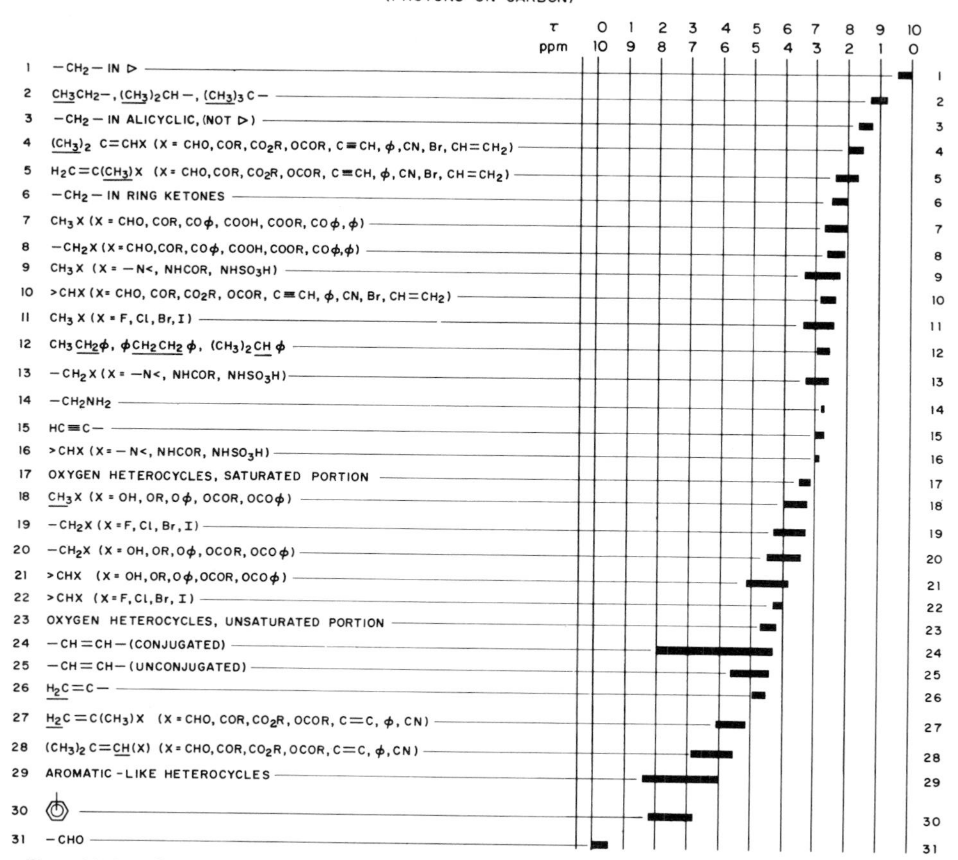

FIG. 30-3. Correlation of Chemical Shifts With Some Typical Structures Containing Protons Bonded To Carbon. (Adapted from a chart due to Dr. Erno Mohacsi.)

When possible the reference should be used as an internal standard by adding it to the sample. If there are problems of miscibility with tetramethylsilane (TMS) another internal reference such as cylohexane, dioxane, or chloroform may be used and a shift correction applied. Alternatively one may use external referencing wherein the reference is contained in a capillary tube inserted in the sample. The same procedure may be used if one wishes to avoid contamination of the sample with an internal reference. Unless forced by circumstances, one should avoid external referencing.

Control loops which tie transmitter frequency and magnetic field together make it possible to take directly calibrated spectra. When a spectrometer not so equipped is being used the spectra are best calibrated by a side-band technique. Here audio-sidebands are generated off the strong reference peak with a variable oscillator. The sidebands are made to coincide with the peak being measured and the frequency read directly off the oscillator or off a counter. As an alternate procedure a modulation pattern may be set up and the resonance peaks calibrated by interpolation.

A correlation chart for different types of protons is given in Fig. 30-3. This and any similar chart should be taken as indicative rather than as compelling. The occasional NMR user may employ a correlation chart for guidance, but would probably do better to look at the spectra of some closely related compounds if possible. One who intends to make relatively steady application of NMR may wish to prepare his own chart, mentally or actually by charting, from spectra such as those in the Varian Spectral Catalogs.[5]

In Fig. 30-4 is given the range of chemical shifts for some groups containing labile

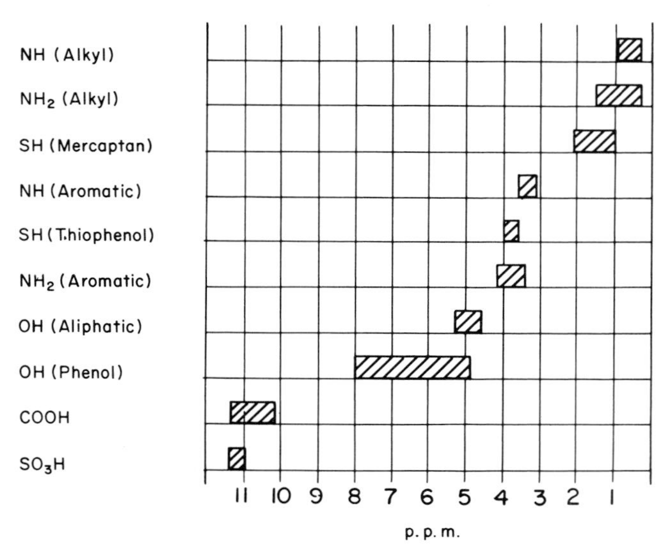

FIG. 30-4. Correlation of Chemical Shifts With Some Groups Containing Active Protons.

protons. Because the protons of these groups are subject to temperature effects and exchange phenomena to be discussed the information on this chart should be used even more cautiously than that of Fig. 30-3.

The data of Fig. 30-5 indicate the approximate relative effect of different groups in bringing about low field shifts in nearby protons. This table may be useful in estimating the expected position of resonance in a new compound.

Spin-Spin Coupling.—In addition to the chemical shifts NMR spectra may show further character arising from interactions transmitted by the intervening electrons between nonequivalent nuclei. The oriented spin of a nucleus gives an adjacent electron an opposite orientation. This orienting effect is transmitted down the chain and may ultimately reach a second nucleus. The spin orientations are characterized by different energies, and so create multiplets in the chemically shifted peaks. The components of the multiplets are separated by a coupling constant J. The effect is a reciprocal one, and if nucleus A splits nucleus B then B splits A and the value of J is the same for both. This coupling falls off rapidly as the number of intervening bonds increases. Propagation through multiple bonds is stronger than through single ones. Typical values to be expected for proton-proton, spin-spin couplings in some typical bonding situations are given in Fig. 30-6.

The rigorous analysis of spin-spin multiplets is a problem in quantum mechanics which increases rapidly in complexity as the number of nonequivalent nuclei is made greater. Fortunately, approximations can be made and a first order approach is adequate for many spectra. Spectra which are obviously not first order are frequently close enough to be so treated. The first order approximation may be illustrated by an analysis of the ethyl group spectrum.

Approximate Shielding Constants

Group	Effect on CH p.p.m. to Lower Field
R–C(=O)–O–	3.1
HO–	2.6
Cl–	2.5
RO–	2.4
Br–	2.3
PHENYL–	1.8
I–	1.8
CN–	1.7
R–C(=O)–	1.7
RS–	1.6
R_2N–C(=O)–	1.6
R_2N–	1.6
RO–C(=O)–	1.6
C≡C–	1.4
C=C–	1.3
CF_3–	1.1
CH_3–	0.5

FIG. 30-5. Approximate Effect of Various Groups in Shifting a Proton on an Adjacent Carbon to a Lower Field.

The spins associated with the two methylene protons have the following configurations ↑↑, ↑↓, ↓↑, ↓↓. Each of the configurations is equally probable, and has a certain energy associated with it. The two sets with oppositely directed spins are equivalent. There are, therefore, four pertubations of the methyl by the methylene, two of which are degenerate, giving rise to a triplet of component intensity ratios 1:2:1. Similarly, the spins of the methyl can be set up as

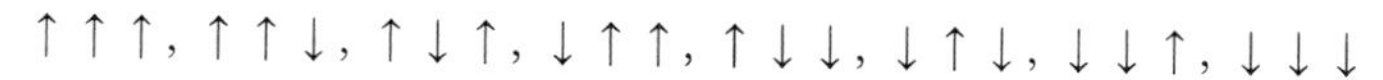

Here are two states with no equivalent sets and two made up of three equivalent sets each. Thus, the methyl splits the methylene into a quartet of relative intensity ratios 1:3:3:1 and the generalized ethyl spectrum has the form

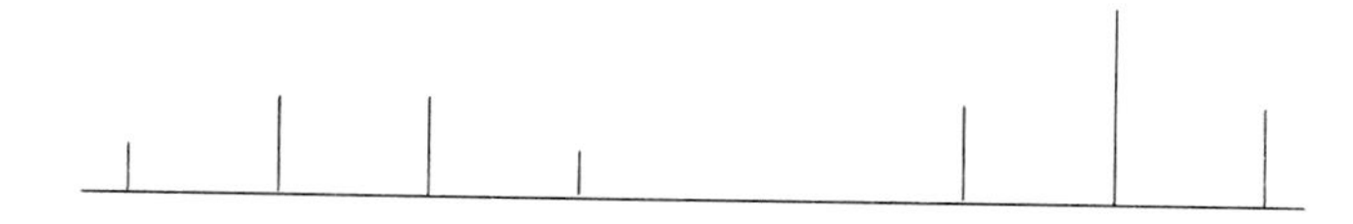

This simple approach permits the following rules for multiplicity and intensity to be deduced. If n is the number of nuclei creating the multiplet and I is the spin quantum number of that nucleus ($\frac{1}{2}$ for H^1) then the multiplicity is $(2nI + 1)$ and the relative intensities are the coefficients of the expansion of $(1 + x)^n$.

Proton-Proton Spin Coupling Constants

	Range	Usual Value
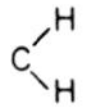	0–30	12–15
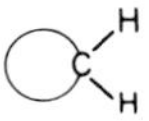	0–20	
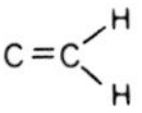	0–3.5	
CH–CH	2–9	6–9
CH–CH=C	4–10	
C=CH–CH=C	10–13	
CH–CH–C(–)=O	1–3	
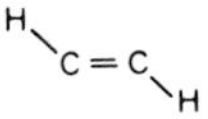	11–18	
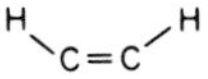	6–14	
CH=CH–C=O	15	
CH–OH	4–7	5
CH=C–CH	0.5–2	
CH≡C–CH	2–3	
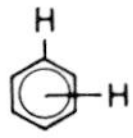	o 7–10 m 2–3 p 0–1.5	

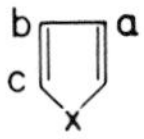	X = O	N	S
ab	3.2–3.8	2.8–3.7	3.5–3.9
bc	1.8–2.0	2.0–2.6	4.7–6.0
ac	0.7–0.9	1.4–2.1	1.4–1.8

	Range	Usual Value
aa	6–16	8–9
ae	0–6	2–3
ee	0–6	2–3

FIG. 30-6. Correlation of Some Coupling Constants With Structure.

Departures from simple first order are shown in various ways such as deviations from the predicted intensities and the presence of additional peaks. Fortunately, from an empirical study of the spectra of known materials published in the literature, it is possible to learn to recognize many of the higher order pattern without going through a complete analysis. These higher order pattern appear as the chemical shift differences and the coupling constants between groups approach the same order of magnitude. The ratio of these quantities is the parameter which governs the exact form of the spectrum.

A convenient notation has been developed to designate various general pattern types and the molecular situations which will give them. It is based on a correlation of chemical shifts with the alphabet. If nonequivalent nuclei have a small shift difference between themselves they will be designated by letters of the alphabet close together such as AB. If there is a moderate difference the description might be AM while a large difference could be noted as AX. Subscripts denote the number of each type of nuclei. Ethyl fluoride would thus be described as A_2B_3X. Magnetically inactive nuclei are not considered.

One higher order pattern is of such frequent occurrence as to demand some further treatment, even in this elementary discussion. This is called the AB pattern and most commonly arises in molecular situations of unsymmetrical substitution coupled with restricted rotation as in

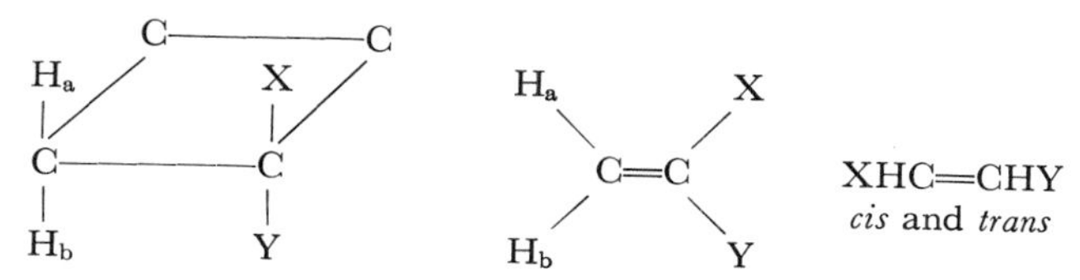

Here the chemical shift difference and the coupling constant between nonequivalent nuclei will frequently be of the same order of magnitude. In such a case one obtains, not two simple doublets but instead, a pattern of the generalized form

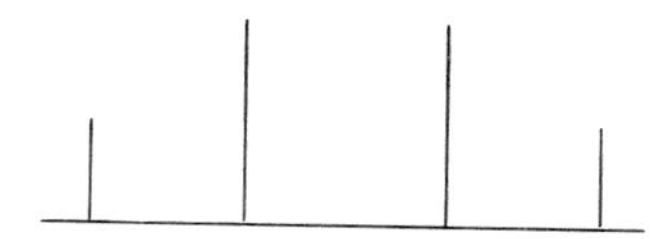

Depending upon the ratio of δ to J_{AB} the form may vary from

to

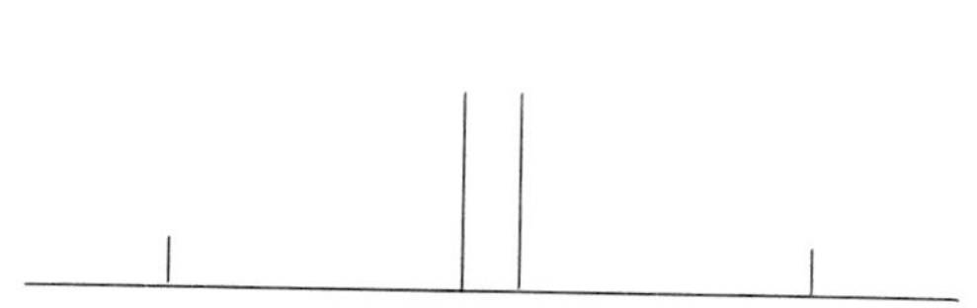

Certain A_2B_2 cases, such as some para-substituted benzenes, may give a pattern of this same appearance.

It must be pointed out that a given peak may be split more than once if there is more than one type of magnetically nonequivalent nucleus sufficiently close.

Intensity.—In contradistinction to other electromagnetic spectrometries, NMR is not characterized by inherently strong and weak bands such as the strong carbonyl band of infrared. The relative intensities of the several peaks in the spectrum of a given sample are directly proportional to the number of protons of each type present. Further, currently available electronic integration makes measurement of the intensities generally easy and accurate.

EXAMPLES

The application of nuclear magnetic resonance to the proof of structures can be made most clear by consideration of examples. Immediately following a relatively simple and a moderately complex molecule and the associated spectra are discussed.

Trans-*Crotonaldehyde*.—The complete spectrum of *trans*-crotonaldehyde together with the designation of the various protons is given in Fig. 30-7. The assignment of the

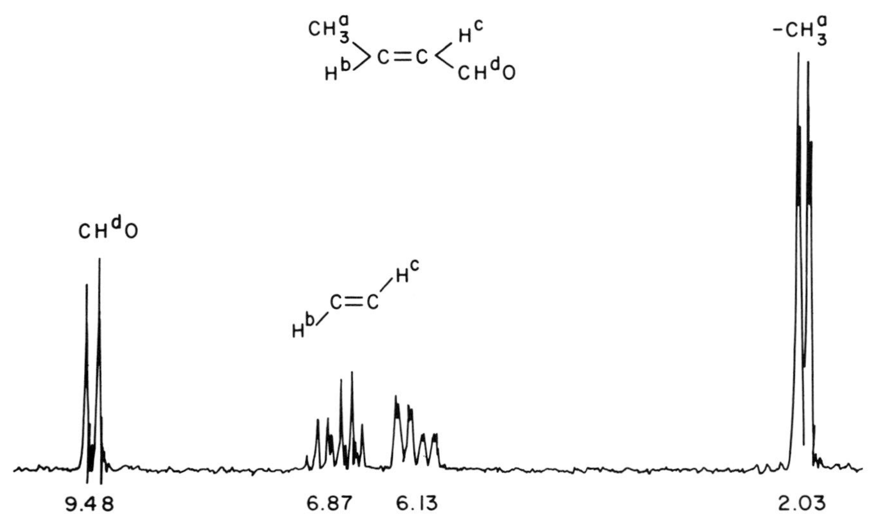

FIG. 30-7. Proton NMR Spectrum of *trans*-Crotonaldehyde.

carbonyl proton H^d at 9.48 p.p.m. is straightforward. This peak is split 8 cps. to a doublet by the nearest ethylenic proton H^c. A methyl on a double bond is consistent with the peak at 2.03 p.p.m. This peak is split twice by spin coupling; initially 7 cps. by H^b, and then 1.8 cps. by H^c. This assignment of the splittings is based on proximity. The complex center portion of the spectrum arises from the unsaturated protons. The lines centered at 6.87 p.p.m. are assigned to H^b, and those centered at 6.13 p.p.m. to H^c. In Fig. 30-8 an expanded presentation of this portion of the spectrum is given in which the details of the fine structure are apparent. At first glance this might appear to be an inexplicable tangle. In actual fact the analysis is very direct. The splitting diagram of Fig. 30-9 shows the genesis of the pattern. The chemical shift difference between H^b and H^c is only 0.64 p.p.m. or 38.4 cps. at 60 Mcps., while the coupling constant between the two is 15.5 cps. Since the two values are close to each other they give rise to the basic AB pattern previously discussed. The two lines ascribed to H^b are then split to quartets by the adjacent methyl (H^a). There is some overlap of the quartets. The two lines arising from H^c are split to doublets by the adjacent aldehyde proton (H^a). The four resulting lines are then split to moderately resolved quartets by the more distant methyl. Unfortunately not all patterns can be explained so simply.

The assignment of H^b as the low field component of the AB pattern is contrary to what would be expected from the two-dimensional formula of *trans*-crotonaldehyde. Reference to the shielding parameters of Fig. 30-5 shows that the presence of the carbonyl on the same carbon would be expected to put H^c at the low field. However, if an accurate three-dimensional model is constructed it will be seen that H^b is actually much closer to the carbonyl than H^c and the powerful across-space electron withdrawing effect of the oxygen strongly deshields H^b.

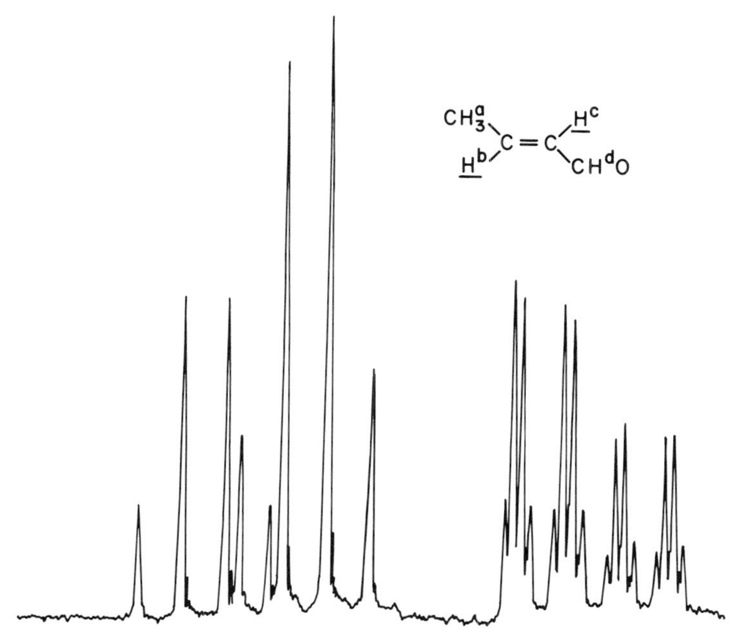

FIG. 30-8. NMR Spectrum for Unsaturated Protons of *trans*-Crotonaldehyde.

1,3,3,6-Tetramethyl-1-(3-bromo-4-methyl-5-methoxyphenyl)-7-bromo-5-methoxyindan.—Nuclear magnetic resonance was used to assist in deciding whether structure I or II below corresponded to a synthetic product. The proton NMR spectrum obtained is

CH$_3$ CH$_3$ / Br H / CH$_3$ OCH$_3$ / CH$_3$O CH$_3$ / H Br / CH$_3$ CH$_3$

I

OCH$_3$ CH$_3$ / CH$_3$ H Br OCH$_3$ / CH$_3$ / Br H / H / H$_2$ CH$_3$ / CH$_3$

II

shown in Fig. 30-10. This is consistent only with II. The group of low field peaks are aromatic in origin. The singlet at 6.78 p.p.m. belongs to the single proton of ring A adjacent to the methoxyl group. The doublet at 6.67 p.p.m. is assigned to the proton of ring B adjacent to the methoxyl while that at 7.14 p.p.m. comes from the proton *ortho* to the bromine. The mutual splitting of *ca.* 1.6 cps. is consistent with *meta* orientation to each other. At 3.94 and 3.74 p.p.m. are the peaks for two slightly dissimilar aromatic methoxyls. The incompletely resolved peak centered at 2.29 p.p.m. results from an overlap of two almost identical aromatic methyls and the single tertiary methyl on the

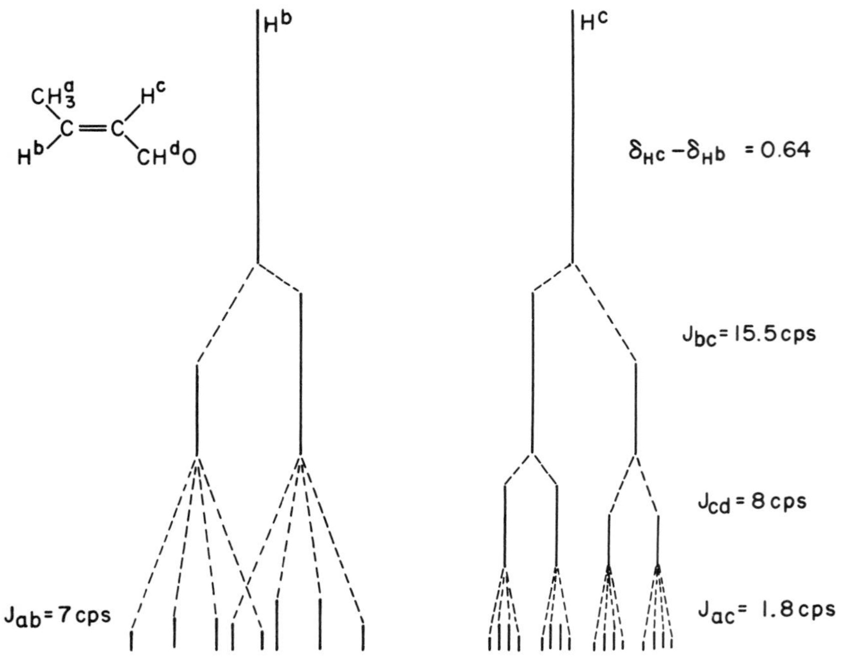

FIG. 30-9. Splitting Pattern for NMR Spectrum of Unsaturated Protons of *trans*-Crotonaldehyde.

cyclopentane ring. At 1.87 p.p.m. is the resonance of the alicyclic —CH_2—. The two tertiary *gem*-methyls of the ring give the peaks at 1.22 and 1.35 p.p.m. Their nonequivalence is the result of the expected nonplanarity in the molecule as a whole. This results in the methyls not being in identical environments.

With one exception none of the foregoing assignments call for any explanation. Some accounting must be given for the appearance of the single tertiary methyl resonance with that of the aromatic methyls rather than with that of the two *gem*-methyls. This is probably due to the previously mentioned ring current effect of the benzene ring producing a low field shift in properly oriented neighbors. The effect is considerable here because there are two rings to produce it.

Had structure I been correct a much simpler spectrum should result. If a prediction may be risked, there would have been four unsplit peaks in the intensity ratios 2:6:6:12 at approximately 6.8, 3.8, 2.3, and 1.3 p.p.m.

INTEGRATION AND QUANTITATIVE ANALYSIS

Integration is most commonly used to determine the ratio of different kinds of magnetically nonequivalent protons in a sample by measuring the relative intensities of the

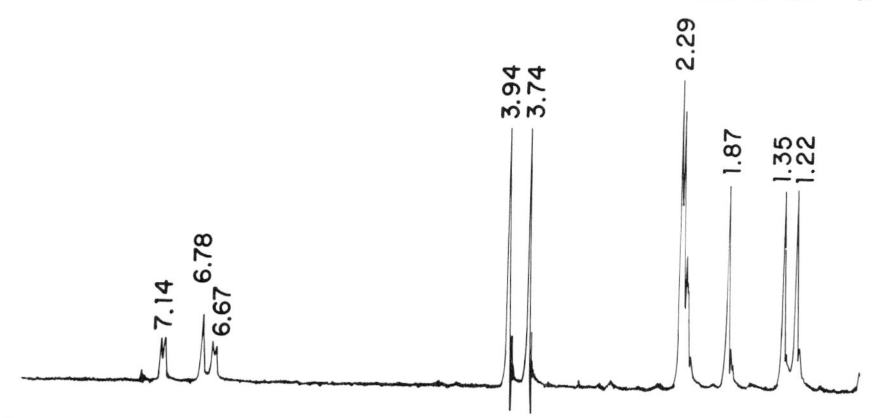

Fig. 30-10. Proton NMR Spectrum of a Substituted Indan. (Sample provided by Prof. R. H. Eastman, Stanford University. A spectrum on this compound has been published previously by Varian Associates, but the earlier spectrum is not as sharply resolved as the one here because it was taken on an instrument whose performance did not match that of current ones. The spectrum gave the same information, however.)

associated peaks. The same sample is used for this purpose and for taking the spectrum. In Fig. 30-2, the integration of the spectrum of diethyl malonate was shown. The ratio of the intensities of the peaks is the ratio of the distances between plateaus of the integration curve. If one peak can be assigned unequivocally both as to type and number of protons present then the number of protons of other types can be immediately deduced. Perhaps the greatest difficulty encountered in the application of electronic integration is overlap of resonance peaks, either complete or partial. The total proton count can be determined, but accurate breakdown by types is impossible because of lack of a clean break between the integral plateaus.

Integration may also be used for the determination of total hydrogen. The technique is based on comparison of the total integrated signal of the unknown with the signal of a standard reference. There are several different ways of setting up the comparison. Most obviously the sample solution may be made up with a known amount of standard present and the signal intensities compared. The standard may be the solvent. In this procedure the reference and sample signal must not overlap, the reference line should be a singlet if possible, and the intensities of the reference and sample signals should be as close to the same as possible to permit the most accurate comparison. In an alternative procedure sample tubes are precalibrated with knowns such as quantitatively prepared solutions of cyclohexane in carbon tetrachloride. The unknown is then run in the calibrated tubes using the same instrument settings. Obviously too much time must not elapse between the calibration and sample run, otherwise instrument performance may change. A further alternative employs a set of sealed standards with which one brackets the integral of the unknown. In both alternative procedures overlap is not a problem because the unknown and reference integrals are obtained separately. Otherwise they are less desirable than the first procedure because they involve sample interchange.

In any of the quantitative procedures the standard of spectrometer operation must be high. Saturation of the signals from the use of too much power must be avoided. Electronic integrators use phase sensitive detection and the balance and phasing must be properly adjusted else spurious signals of either sign may enter to vitiate the results. Accuracies of the order of 2 percent are obtainable.

THE SAMPLE

In high resolution NMR the sample must be a liquid. It may be either a neat sample, a suitable solution, or a melt if the melting point is not too high (150°–250°C. depending on the installation). Because they often give better spectra, solutions are frequently preferred even when pure liquid samples are available.

Solvents for NMR should have high solvent power and give no resonance which overlaps that of the sample. This may or may not require freedom from the nucleus being observed. For proton work carbon tetrachloride, carbon disulfide, and deuterated solvents commend themselves. The most generally useful and available of the latter materials are deuterated chloroform, acetone, acetonitrile, dimethyl sulfoxide, benzene and water. These solvents are still very expensive but are becoming less so. On occasions one may use several solvents, each of which interferes in a different part of the spectrum, and thereby permits an interference free spectrum to be synthesized. If the solvents selected give widely separated sharp peaks this approach is quite practical. Chloroform, benzene, cyclohexane, dioxane, and tetramethylsilane have the required characteristics.

The amount of material which may be required for a satisfactory NMR sample may vary by as much as two orders of magnitude. Very small quantities are required if the proton content is high, all protons are magnetically equivalent, there is no splitting, and the lines are inherently narrow. A Varian A-60 spectrometer will detect a 0.016 molar concentration of proton in a single line of less than 0.6 cps. natural line width with resolution adjusted to 0.6 cps. full line width at half amplitude. If there is broadening, the nuclear content is low and is present in several nonequivalent types, each undergoing considerable splitting, the amount of material required will be very much greater.

The usual NMR sample is cylindrical in shape in a 5-mm. O.D. tube. With cylindrical samples there may be end effects which distort the signal unless there is appreciable length of sample both above and below the receiver coil. With spherical samples this end effect is absent and considerably less volume is needed. Spherically-shaped microcells are commerically available of only 25 microliters capacity.

If one is using a type of spectrometer in which the inserts can be changed then sample tubes up to 15 mm. O.D. may be used to enhance weak signals because of the improved filling factor. The expected gain may not be realized, however, because there may be severe loss of resolution. It is difficult to maintain a satisfactory magnetic field homogeneity over this large volume.

COMPLICATING FACTORS

Overlap.—A serious problem in NMR is overlap. A study of any of the several chemical shift charts which have been compiled will show that the possibility and probability of overlap is very great. The total spread of proton chemical shifts is quite narrow and the ranges of various types of groups extend into each other. Unfortunately, one can rarely do much about the problem. Integration may be of great assistance in demonstrating the presence of overlap, but the problem of disentangling the resonance lines, particularly to assess fine structure, will remain. If one is fortunate enough to have available facilities for operating a spectrometer at two considerably different frequencies, and the peaks do not overlap on centers, it may be possible to obtain spectra which allow the overlap to be disentangled. Chemical shifts are linerally frequency dependent and an ambiguous overlap at one frequency may become something interpretable at another. A principal reason for constantly attempting to build NMR spectrometers operating at higher and higher frequencies is the possibility of increasing the shifts and thereby reducing overlap. Occasionally selective solvent effects may give the same result but there are no reliable guides for selecting the solvents to be used. Coupling constants are frequency independent.

Hydrogen Bonding.—If the structure of the sample molecule is such that strong hydrogen bonding takes place, then the proton involved will have a chemical shift to a considerably lower field than would otherwise be expected. For instance, in salicylaldehyde, where there is extremely strong chelation between the two *ortho* substituents, the hydroxyl resonance is found at 11.00 p.p.m. below tetramethylsilane, while in the *para* isomer where chelation is not possible the hydroxyl resonance comes at a more normal 6.6 p.p.m. In both compounds the aldehyde proton show no unusual shift. The same effect of a low field shift may be observed, but somewhat diminished, when the hydrogen bonding is intermolecular as in acids and alcohols. The significant difference is that intermolecular bonding is highly sensitive to breaking of the bonds by dilution or heating. In this way a proton so bonded can be shifted to progressively higher field. Intramolecular bonding is relatively immune to such influences.

Exchange.—When two molecular species are present, both of which carry labile protons which may exchange with each other, there may be complications appearing in the spectrum the nature of which depends upon the velocity of the exchange. If the velocity is very low, then the peaks of each type of labile proton will be seen at the usual position and of almost normal appearance except for possibly some broadening. As the exchange speeds up the peaks broaden still further and move toward each other. When the rate becomes somewhat greater than the chemical shift between them the peaks coalesce. Further increase in the rate only sharpens up the line. The final position of the common resonance lies at a point between those of the pure components and closely proportional to the respective mole fractions. Exchange may also destroy spin-spin coupling because the coupling cannot be transmitted through the constantly breaking and reforming bonds. With certain types of mixtures, such as a carboxylic acid contaminated with a little water, this exchange phenomenon may result in a spectrum quite different from the one expected. It is not necessary for the exchanging protons to be in different molecules. Hydroxyacetic acid, for example, does not show the three peaks of —CH_2—, —OH, and —COOH, but rather the —CH_2— peak and a common line for the exchanging —OH and —COOH.

While exchange is a possible complication and source of ambiguity in a spectrum, it may also have interpretative utility. For example, addition of a small amount of an acid may permit assignment of an otherwise questionable hydroxyl peak by the manifestation of exchange. Catalyzed exchange with deuterium oxide may be used to remove a labile proton from a molecule as water with corresponding changes in the spectrum. It may be used in rate studies by observing the changes in the exchanging materials as a function of temperature and concentration, for example.

Other factors in addition to concentration and temperature may influence exchange. It may be inhibited sterically. An otherwise exchangeable proton may be tied up by chelation. The rate of exchange may be too slow for the coalescence described to take place and spectra of intermediate character will be obtained. Some protons, such as the —SH of mercaptans, which might be expected to exchange readily frequently behave contrariwise. No topic discussed in this short presentation of NMR has been more oversimplified than that of exchange and the interested reader should seek more complete discussions.[1,2,3]

Solvent Effects.—In addition to the action of solvents in exchange phenomena and in hydrogen bonding, there are other definite, if difficultly classifiable, solvent effects which may modify chemical shifts. It is possible for striking changes in the spectrum to result. The presence of solvent effects is the principal reason that shift values should be determined at infinite dilution. The effect is not eliminated thereby, but it is standardized. Shifts of the order of 100 cps. may be experienced on occasions with different solvents and this factor should always be considered, particularly when comparing spectra which should be identical but are not so. It will be remembered that second order spectra depend upon the ratio of the chemical shifts to the coupling constants. Because coupling constants are largely independent of solvents, this ratio may be considerably changed with resultant changes in the second order spectra.

Solvents which are particularly suspect include acetone, benzene, dioxane, and acetonitrile. Deuteration does not seem to change this effect. Chloroform is intermediate in its action. Cyclohexane, carbon tetrachloride, and tetramethylsilane are generally well-behaved. Carbon disulfide usually has little effect on proton spectra, but may strongly influence those of fluorine.

NUCLEI OTHER THAN PROTONS

The foregoing discussion has been based almost entirely on the hydrogen nucleus. By far the greater part of the significant work in NMR has been done with protons, but valuable results have been obtained with other nuclei which require operation with different frequencies and fields. Otherwise, the principles of operation and interpretation previously outlined apply. Attention here will be confined to indicating some sources of more extensive information, in particular, chemical shifts as related to structure. Brame[6] and Konstantinov[7] have published correlation charts for F^{19} shifts. Muller and Carr[8] have tabulated the data for a variety of fluorine containing compounds. An extensive summary of the application of NMR to phosphorus chemistry has been recently published by Jones and Katritzky.[9] Lauterbur[10] has summarized published data on C^{13}, B^{11}, P^{31}, and a number of other nuclei of lesser interest. The book of Fluck[11] covers applications to inorganic chemistry thoroughly.

LIMITATIONS

As with every other technique, NMR has its limitations. Perhaps the most serious is the limited number of nuclei which may be usefully studied. In principle a large number of nuclei possess the required nuclear properties. But in practice low isotopic abundance, low inherent sensitivity, quadrupolar moments, and other factors reduce the applicable species considerably. H^1, F^{19}, B^{11}, and P^{31} are the only nuclei widely used in NMR studies. C^{13}, O^{17}, Sn^{119}, and N^{14} are right on the edge of general utility.

The technique is limited to liquid samples and if the material of interest is not ordinarily a liquid it must be capable of solution in a suitable solvent or of melting at a temperature of not over about 250°C. The limitation then becomes one of finding a suitable solvent.

Fairly large samples, compared to other spectroscopic disciplines, are required. This problem is being met by the use of microcells and improved spectrometer performance.

[6] Brame, E. G., Jr., Anal. Chem., **34,** 591, 1962.
[7] Konstantinov, Y. S., Proc. Acad. Sci. (U.S.S.R.), Phys. Chem., **134,** 915, 1960.
[8] Muller, N., and Carr, D. T., J. Phys. Chem., **67**, 112, 1963.
[9] Jones, R. A. Y., and Katritzky, A. R., Angew. Chem., **74,** 60, 1962; *Ibid*, Int'l. Ed., **1,** 33, 1962.
[10] Lauterbur, P. C., in Nachod, F. C., and Phillips, W. D., Eds., Determination of Organic Structures by Physical Methods, Vol. 2, Academic Press, New York, 1962.
[11] Fluck, E., Die Kernmagnetische Resonanz und ihre Anwendung in der Anorganische Chemie, Springer Verlag, Berlin, Göttingen, Heidelberg, 1963.

There is some compensation in the fact that NMR is in truth nondestructive. Not only is the sample conserved, but recovery presents no problem.

As with any physical technique one may at times obtain a result that he cannot interpret.

APPLICATIONS IN THE ANALYSIS OF SPECIAL MATERIALS

Nuclear magnetic resonance methods have been used in a number of procedures described in other chapter of Standard Methods of Chemical Analysis. These are:

1. Chapter 48, Volume III, Natural Fats.
   a. Oil content of oilseeds
   b. Solid fat content of fats
2. Chapter 51, Volume III, Organic Functional Groups.
   a. Determination of molecular structure
   b. Average molecular weight of natural fats
   c. Determination of unsaturation of natural fats
   d. Quantitative analysis of aspirin, phenacetin, and caffeine mixtures.
3. Chapter 54, Volume III, Paint, Varnish, and Lacquer.
   a. Determination of organic substances (polymers and polyesters) used in paints, varnishes, and lacquers
4. Chapter 57, Volume III, Petroleum and Petroleum Products.
   a. Characterization of aromatic fractions in petroleum analysis
   b. Measurement of branching chains in hydrocarbon structures
   c. Characterization of saturated hydrocarbons in petroleum
5. Chapter 58, Volume III, Plastics.
   a. Structure of polymers
   b. Ratio of methylmethacrylate to ethylacrylate units in copolymers
6. Chapter 59, Volume III, Rubber and Rubber Products.
   a. Determination of structural composition
   b. Determination of structural characteristics of butadieneisoprene copolymers.
7. Chapter 64, Volume III, Determination of Water.
   a. Determination of water in
      Chicle
      Corn syrup
      Cotton
      Egg albumin
      Paperboard pulp
      Pectin
      Potato
      Starch and starch suspensions
      Sucrose
      Vegetables
      Wheat and wheat products
      Wood

Chapter 31

ELECTRON SPIN RESONANCE

By Allen J. Bard
Department of Chemistry
The University of Texas
Austin, Texas

PRINCIPLES

Electron spin resonance (ESR) spectroscopy[1] is based on transitions between energy levels produced by the action of a magnetic field on an unpaired electron. The following somewhat oversimplified discussion of the principles of ESR should be sufficient for analytical applications. Excellent, detailed discussions of the theory of ESR are available in the literature (see the selected bibliography following this chapter).

THE SPIN RESONANCE PHENOMENON

The basic principles of ESR are identical to those of nuclear magnetic resonance (Chapter 30), although the applications and the instrumentation of the technique are quite different. An electron may be pictured as a spinning, negatively-charged, particle. By virtue of its charge and spin, an electron then behaves as a bar magnet (just as a loop of wire carrying a current produces a magnetic field) and can interact with an external magnetic field. The magnetism of an electron can be expressed by saying that an electron has a *magnetic moment*, μ, which is proportional to e/m, where e is the charge on the electron and m is its mass. The magnitude of the magnetic moment of a free electron is β, the Bohr magneton, and has a value of 9.2732×10^{-21} erg per gauss. Because an electron is an atomic particle, its momentum and energy are governed by quantum mechanical considerations. Each electron is assigned a spin quantum number s which is either $+\frac{1}{2}$ or $-\frac{1}{2}$ denoting that there are only two possible orientations of an electron in a magnetic field. The magnetic moment of any electron can be written in a more general form as

$$\mu = -g\beta s \tag{1}$$

where g, called the *spectroscopic splitting factor* (or the *g-factor* or *gyromagnetic ratio*) is a factor which is a function of the environment of the electron. For a free electron g would be 2 (more precisely 2.00229 because of relativity effects), so that the magnetic moment would be essentially β. In a group of free electrons each electron is a magnetic dipole of magnitude β (erg/gauss). When these electrons are placed in a magnetic field, measured in gauss, the electrons will have their energy changed by a certain number of ergs, given by

$$E = \mu H = -g\beta s H = \pm\tfrac{1}{2}(g\beta H) \tag{2}$$

[1] Also called by the synonymous terms: electron paramagnetic resonance (EPR); and electron magnetic resonance (EMR) spectroscopy.

where H is the magnetic field strength. Those of spin $+\frac{1}{2}$ (pointing in the direction of the magnetic field) will decrease in energy by an amount $\frac{1}{2}(g\beta H)$, while those with

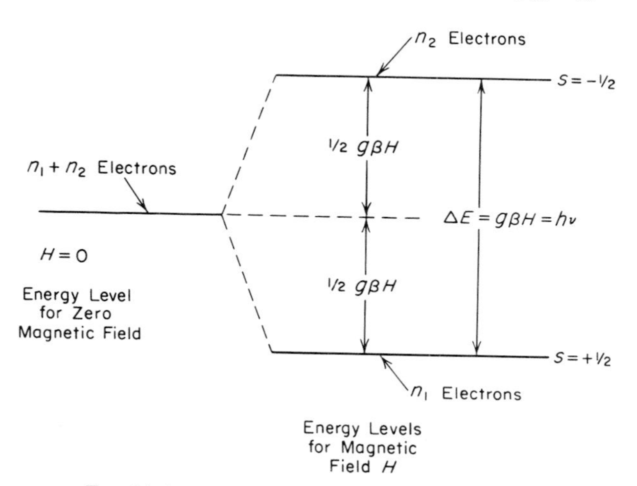

FIG. 31-1. Energy Levels in ESR Spectroscopy.

spin $-\frac{1}{2}$ (pointing opposite to the field) will increase in energy by a like amount, so that the difference in energy in between the two levels is (Fig. 31-1)

$$\Delta E = g\beta H \tag{3}$$

Just as in other spectroscopic experiments, there is an electromagnetic radiation frequency associated with this energy level difference which satisfies the equation

$$\Delta E = h\nu = g\beta H \tag{4}$$

which will cause transitions between these energy levels. In distinction to other types of spectroscopy, in which the energy levels are essentially fixed, in ESR spectroscopy the splitting in energy levels, and, therefore, the frequency capable of causing transitions between these levels, is a function of the magnetic field strength, H. Putting in values for the constants in Eq. (4) yields a value for ν of 2.8026 Mc. (megacycles per second)/gauss.

It may be fruitful to consider where ESR spectroscopy lies in comparison to other forms of spectroscopy (see Fig. 31-2). For a magnetic field strength of 3300 gauss (a field strength which is commonly employed, and which requires a good sized electromagnet), the energy level difference due to electron spin is 6.1×10^{-17} ergs (or about 1.5×10^{-24} calories) and ν is 9.2 Gc. (gigacycles, or 10^9 cycles, per second). This frequency lies in the microwave region of the electromagnetic radiation spectrum (Fig. 31-2), so that the instrumentation used will involve radar-type components: wave guides, microwave cavities, and klystrons. Note that identical considerations hold for proton magnetic resonance, but because the hydrogen nucleus is about 1800 times heavier than the electron, and its g-value is about 5.585 for NMR at 3300 gauss, ν would be a radio wave of about 14 Mc. Since the magnetic moment of the proton is about 650 times smaller than that of the electron, the energy level separation for protons would be about 650 times smaller than that for electrons, at the same magnetic field intensity. Because ΔE is relatively small for ESR in comparison to visible or infrared spectroscopy, differences in behavior other than a different frequency of the transition are also noted. The relative population of two energy levels separated by an energy difference ΔE is governed by the Boltzmann equation:

$$\frac{n_2}{n_1} = e^{-\Delta E/kT} \tag{5}$$

(where k is the Boltzmann constant, 1.38×10^{-16} erg/°K., and T is the temperature). For a ΔE of 6.1×10^{-17} ergs (corresponding to a magnetic field of 3300 gauss) the

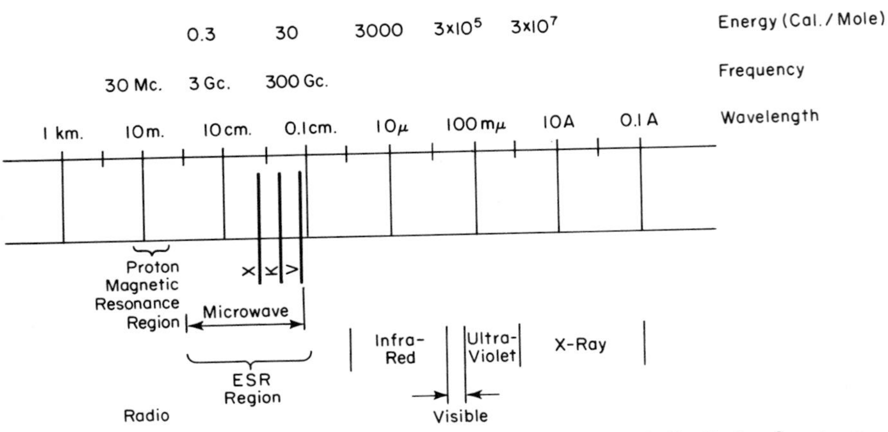

FIG. 31-2. Location of ESR Spectroscopy in the Electromagnetic Radiation Spectrum.

relative population of the two energy levels is 0.9984 at room temperature, so that for every 1000 electrons in the low energy state (pointing in the direction of the magnetic field), 998 are in the high energy state (because of thermal agitation, pointing opposite to the magnetic field).[2] The net absorption of radiation and hence the sensitivity depends upon the difference in the relative populations n_1 and n_2, so that working at a magnetic field strength of 3300 gauss will give a higher sensitivity than working at lower field strengths (other factors being assumed equal). The field strengths and relative populations for spectrometers operating a different frequencies are given in Table 31-1.

Because the relative populations of the energy levels are so near being equal, it is sometimes possible to produce a sufficient rate of transitions to cause the population of the higher energy state to be equal to that of the lower one. This phenomena, known as *saturation*, depends upon the intensity of the microwave radiation and upon the time required for a molecule in the upper level to fall back to the lower level. This time, related to the *spin-lattice relaxation time*, is a measure of the interaction of the unpaired electron with the molecules or its environment (the lattice). When saturation occurs, the signal level decreases and the signal broadens.

An alternate classical picture of the spin resonance phenomenon based on precession of a rotating magnet can also be given and leads to essentially the same result.

[2] Note that for spectroscopy in the visible region at room temperature the number of atoms in an excited state compared to that in the ground state is so small as to be statistically meaningless (calculated to be 10^{-22} or smaller).

TABLE 31-1.

Nominal ν	Wavelength	H (gauss)	ΔE (ergs)	n_2/n_1	Sensitivity[a] (unpaired spins)	Typical Commercial Spectrometer[b]
340 Mc.		120	2.25×10^{-18}	0.999946	$10^{14}\ \Delta H$	Alpha AL340SY Electrospec 200
9.5 Gc. (X-Band)	3 cm.	3400	6.3×10^{-17}	0.9985	$10^{11}\ \Delta H$	Varian V-4502 Alpha ALX-10 Strandlabs 601 A/X JES-P-10
35 Gc. (K-Band)	0.9 cm.	12,500	2.3×10^{-16}	0.9944	$5 \times 10^{9}\ \Delta H$	Varian V-4503 Strandlabs 601-A/K_A JES-3BX
70 Gc. (V-Band)	4 mm.	25,000	4.6×10^{-16}	0.989	?	?

[a] Approximate, as quoted by manufacturers. ΔH is half-width of absorption line. Sensitivity depends upon method of detection, noise in circuit, band-width, and other factors (see text).
[b] Manufacturers:
Alpha Scientific Laboratories, Inc., Berkeley, Cal.
Elion Instruments, Burlington, N. J.
Japan Electron Optics Laboratory Co., Medford, Mass.
Strandlabs, Inc., Cambridge, Mass.
Varian Associates, Palo Alto, Cal.

THE BASIC ESR EXPERIMENT

A very simple instrument for carrying out ESR spectroscopy at microwave frequencies and, for comparison, the familiar spectrometer operating in the visible region are shown in Fig. 31-3. The source of the 9.5 Gc. (or the so-called r.f.) radiation is a klystron. The microwaves are conducted to the sample through a waveguide. The sample, contained

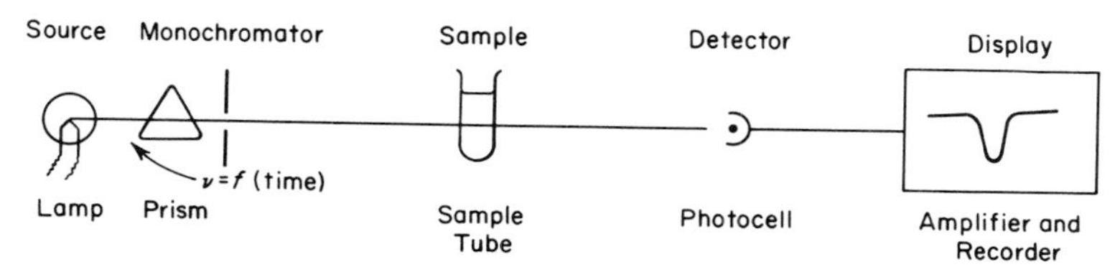

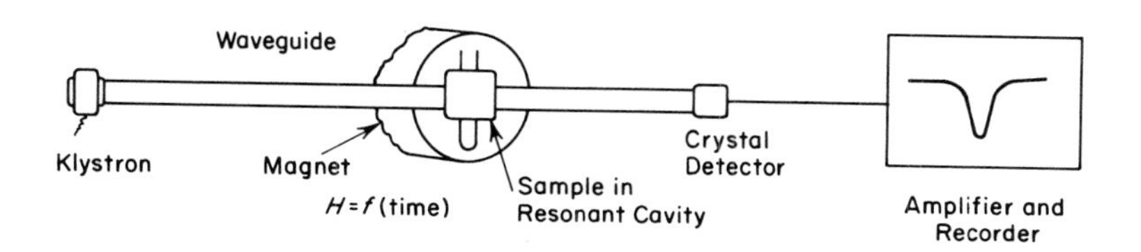

FIG. 31-3. Comparison Between an Optical Spectrometer and a Simple Transmission ESR Spectrometer.

in a sample tube, is held in a microwave cavity between the poles of a magnet operating in the region of 3400 gauss. The detector is a crystal diode which produces a d.c. output proportional to the level of r.f. power falling on it. The d.c. from the crystal is displayed on a recorder or oscilloscope. While it would be possible to operate analogously to visible spectrometry, by holding the magnetic field fixed and varying the frequency of the klystron, in practice it is much easier to hold the klystron frequency fixed and vary the magnetic field. At a fixed klystron frequency there is a certain value of the field strength which satisfies Eq. (4). At this value of H, transitions are induced from the lower to the upper energy level, and microwave energy is absorbed by the sample. The microwave energy falling on the crystal is then smaller, and the d.c. output from the crystal as a function of H, shows the absorption band.

Although this method of operation of a ESR spectrometer is possible, it is not usually used because of its poor sensitivity and poor signal-to-noise ratio. Various modifications involving modulation of the magnetic field and lock-in (phase-sensitive) or superheterodyne detection give higher sensitivity and are used in most commercial instruments. These are described in the sections on instrumentation.

APPLICATION OF ESR MEASUREMENTS

ESR measurements require that an odd (unpaired) electron occur in the substance of interest. The following classes of substances are those which have been investigated:

TABLE 31-2. TRANSITION GROUPS AND THE ELECTRONIC CONFIGURATION OF THE NEUTRAL ATOMS IN THE GROUND STATE[a]

Iron Group		*Palladium Group*		*Platinum Group*	
Sc	$3d\,4s^2$	Y	$4d\,5s^2$	Lu	$5d\,6s^2$
Ti	$3d^2 4s^2$	Zr	$4d^2 5s^2$	Hf	$5d^2 6s^2$
V	$3d^3 4s^2$	Nb	$4d^4 5s$	Ta	$5d^3 6s^2$
Cr	$3d^5 4s$	Mo	$4d^5 5s$	W	$5d^4 6s^2$
Mn	$3d^5 4s^2$	Tc	$4d^5 5s^2$	Re	$5d^5 6s^2$
Fe	$3d^6 4s^2$	Ru	$4d^7 5s$	Os	$5d^6 6s^2$
Co	$3d^7 4s^2$	Rh	$4d^8 5s$	Ir	$5d^7 6s^2$
Ni	$3d^8 4s^2$	Pd	$4d^{10}$	Pt	$5d^9 6s$
Cu	$3d^{10} 4s$	Ag	$4d^{10} 5s$	Au	$5d^{10} 6s$
Zn	$3d^{10} 4s^2$	Cd	$4d^{10} 5s^2$	Hg	$5d^{10} 6s^2$

Rare Earth Group		*Actinide Group*	
La	$5d\,6s^2$	Ac	$6d\,7s^2$
Ce	$4f\,5d\,6s^2$?	Th	$6d^2 7s^2$
Pr	$4f^3 6s^2$	Pa	$6d^3 7s^2$?
Nd	$4f^4 6s^2$	U	$5f^3 6d\,7s^2$
Pm	$4f^5 6s^2$	Np	
Sm	$4f^6 6s^2$	Pu	$5f^6 7s^2$
Eu	$4f^7 6s^2$	Am	$5f^7 7s^2$
Gd	$4f^7 5d\,6s^2$	Cm	
Tb	$4f^8 5d\,6s^2$	Bk	
Dy	$4f^{10} 6s^2$	Cf	
Ho		Es	
Er		Fm	
Tm	$4f^{13} 6s^2$		
Yb	$4f^{14} 6s^2$		

[a] See "Selected Bibliography," item 3.

1. ***Free Radicals.***—Free radicals occur as transient intermediates in chemical reactions and as more-or-less stable species produced by chemical, photochemical, electrochemical, or other means. Most of the applications of ESR to chemical problems have centered upon the identification and measurement of free radicals.

2. ***Transition Elements.***—Paramagnetic salts of the transition elements listed in Table 31-2 contain unpaired electrons in their *d*- or *f*-shells. Spectra of some oxidation states of these are obtained either in the solid state or in solution.

3. ***Miscellaneous.***—Several other groups of substances show ESR spectra, although few of these are of direct analytical interest. Carbonaceous materials, such as carbon blacks and graphite, show evidence of unpaired electrons, thought to be associated with broken bonds in condensed carbon rings. Signals also originate in structural defects in crystals (F and V centers), triplet states, and in electrons in semiconductors (cyclotron resonance).

INSTRUMENTATION

An understanding of ESR instrumentation requires a general knowledge of the operation of microwave and other spectrometer components. A brief description of these will be given and the design of a typical commercial instrument, the Varian V-4502 spectrometer, will be described. Detailed discussions of the design of ESR spectrometers can be found in the references.

SPECTROMETER COMPONENTS

Klystrons.—The source of the radiation ν is a klystron tube operating in the X-band (3 cm.) region at about 9 Gc. The klystron can be tuned over the range of about ± 0.5 Gc. by a control which varies the dimensions of a resonant cavity inside the tube. The output frequency is also a function of the resonator and reflector voltages fed to the klystron by a power supply. It is generally stabilized against temperature fluctuations by immersion in an oil bath or by forced air cooling, and it is usually held at a fixed frequency by a feed-back, automatic frequency control (AFC), circuit. The power output of klystrons used in ESR spectrometers is generally about 300 milliwatts.

Wave Guide.—The microwave radiation is conveyed to the sample and crystal by a wave guide, a hollow, rectangular, brass tube, 0.9 in. by 0.4 in. (Fig. 31-4).

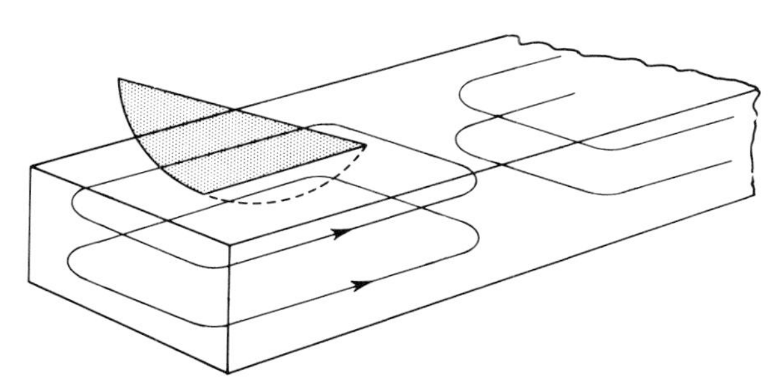

Fig. 31-4. Wave Guide With a Variable Attenuator.

Attenuators.—The power propagated down the wave guide can be continuously decreased by inserting a variable attenuator consisting of a piece of resistive material into the wave guide. By the use of this attenuator, the power at the sample may be varied from the full power of the klystron to one attenuated by a factor of 100 or more.

Isolators.—Reflection of microwave power back into the klystron is prevented by an isolator (also called a microwave gyrator). This isolator is a strip of ferrite material which passes microwaves in one direction only, and helps to stabilize the klystron frequency. It is also sometimes used in other points in the microwave system.

Cavities.—The sample is contained in a resonant cavity in which a standing wave is set up. The cavity is analogous to a tuned circuit (*e.g.*, a parallel *L-C* combination) used at lower frequencies. A measure of quality of the cavity is its Q or "Q-factor," which is defined as

$$Q = \frac{\text{Energy stored in cavity}}{\text{Energy lost}} \tag{6}$$

The sensitivity of a spectrometer is directly proportional to this value of Q. The standing wave is composed of both magnetic and electric fields at right angles to each other. Two frequently used cavities are the rectangular TE_{102} cavity and the cylindrical TE_{011} cavity (Fig. 31-5). Since the component of interest is the magnetic field, which interacts

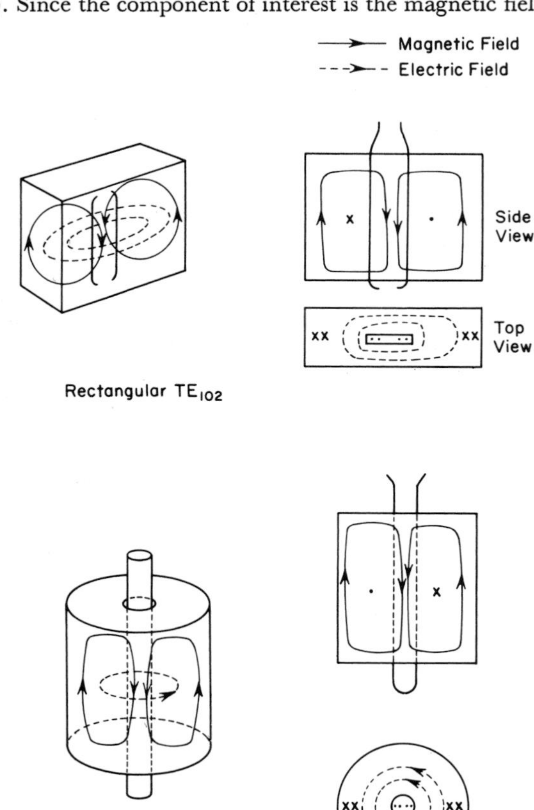

Fig. 31-5. Resonant Cavities, and the Magnetic and Electric Fields of the Standing Microwaves.

with the sample to cause spin resonance, the sample is placed where the intensity of the magnetic field is at its highest. The electric field, however, also interacts with the sample, and if the sample has a high dielectric constant (*i.e.*, is "lossy") the Q of the cavity may be drastically decreased. Therefore, the sample is usually located in the cavity in a position of maximum r.f. magnetic field and minimum r.f. electric field. Flat cells with a thickness of about 0.25 mm. (sample volume of 0.05 ml.) are often used with rectangular cavities. Tubing of a 3–5 mm. i.d. with a sample of volume of about 0.15–0.5 ml. can be used with samples which are not lossy. Other variations on the basic cavity design include rotatable cavities for studying anisotropic effects in single crystal and solid sample studies, and dual cavities for simultaneous spectroscopic observation of a sample and a standard. Slots can be machined into the walls of the cavity without appreciably degrading the cavity Q-factor to allow simultaneous ultraviolet or visible light irradiation of the sample.

Couplers and Matching Screws.—Components in the microwave assembly may be coupled together by a variety of methods. Frequently irises or slots of various sizes are used. For example the resonant cavity may attach to the wave guide with a standard-sized flange, and be coupled by an iris. Matching of wave guide elements (analogous to impedance matching in conventional circuits) is accomplished using screws or stubs which can be positioned in the wave guide or across the coupling iris.

Crystal Detectors and Holders.—The detector of the microwave radiation is usually a silicon crystal detector which converts the r.f. radiation to d.c. An appreciable amount of noise is generated in a crystal detector; the magnitude of this noise decreases with increasing frequency of the output signal. Therefore, the signal is usually modulated at a high frequency (6 kc. to 100 kc.) to decrease this source of noise. Superheterodyne detection methods can also be used to alleviate the crystal noise problem. Selection of the crystal diode used can often provide one with lower noise characteristics than another.

Magic-T's and Hybrid Rings.—Rather than employ a detection technique which requires the observation of a small decrease in a large zero signal, which prevents very high amplification, a bridge arrangement is sometimes used. Microwave bridges (which are analogous to impedance bridges in conventional circuits) can be of the "magic-T" or "hybrid ring" variety. A magic-T bridge is shown in Fig. 31-6. Power entering arm A

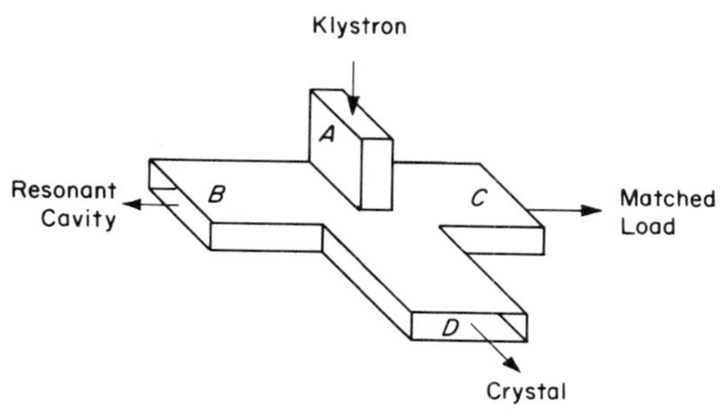

FIG. 31-6. Magic-T Bridge.

will divide between arms B and C if the impedances of B and C are the same, so that no power will enter arm D. Under these conditions the bridge is said to be balanced. If the impedance of arm B changes, say because a resonant cavity coupled to the end arm B changes its Q because of the occurrence of ESR absorption by a sample in it, the bridge becomes unbalanced and some microwave power enters into arm D, containing the crystal detector. In this way the ESR absorption occurs as an increase of a small signal rather than as a decrease in a large one.

Magnets.—An electromagnet capable of producing fields of at least 5000 gauss is required for ESR. The homogeneity of the field for solution studies should be about 50 milligauss over the ESR sample region. The ESR spectrum is recorded by slowly varying the magnetic field through the resonance condition by sweeping the current supplied to the magnet by the power supply; this sweep is generally accomplished with a variable speed motor drive. Both the magnet and the power supply may require water cooling. The magnetic field is regulated by using a feedback circuit to sense changes in the magnet current and correct for these changes. An alternate approach involves the use of a field strength sensor (*e.g.*, a Hall probe) which generates the signal which is controlled (the Varian Associates Fieldial System).

Modulation Coils.—The modulation of the signal at a frequency consistent with good signal-to-noise ratios in the crystal detector is accomplished by a small alternating variation of the magnetic field. This variation is produced by supplying an a.c. signal to modulation coils oriented with respect to the sample in the same direction as the magnetic field. For low frequency modulation (400 cycles per second or less) the coils can be mounted outside the cavity and even on the magnet pole pieces. Higher modulation frequencies (1 kc. or more) cannot penetrate metal effectively, and either the modulation coils must be mounted inside the resonant cavity or cavities constructed of a nonmetallic material (*e.g.*, quartz with a thin silvered plating) must be employed.

Display Devices.—A cathode ray oscilloscope is used to adjust the spectrometer and sometimes to observe the signal. Usually the signal is recorded with a strip-chart or X-Y recorder..

ESR SPECTROMETERS

The most widely used commercial ESR spectrometers are probably those made by Varian Associates. A simplified block diagram of the Varian V-4502 spectrometer is shown in Fig. 31-7, and a photograph of a typical ESR system is shown in Fig. 31-8.

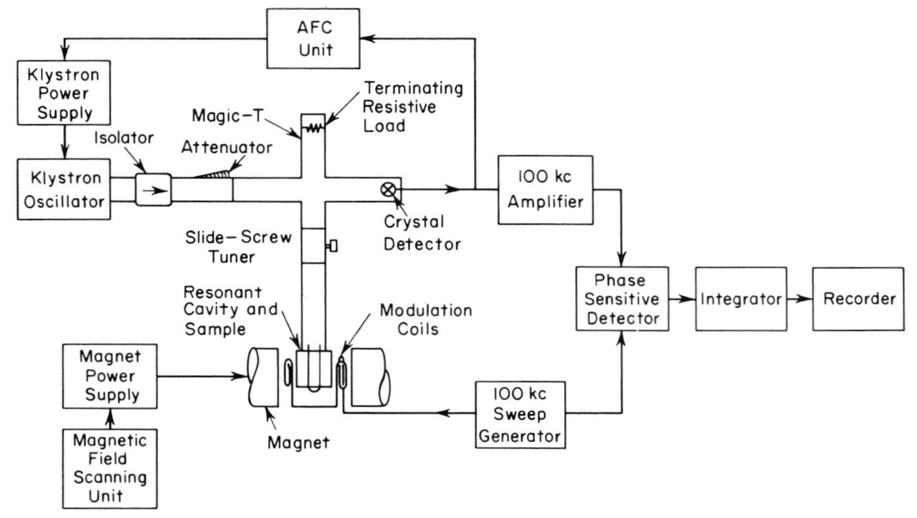

Fig. 31-7. Block Diagram of a Reflection ESR Spectrometer Incorporating 100 kc. Modulation and Phase Sensitive Detection. The Varian Associates V-4502 Spectrometer.

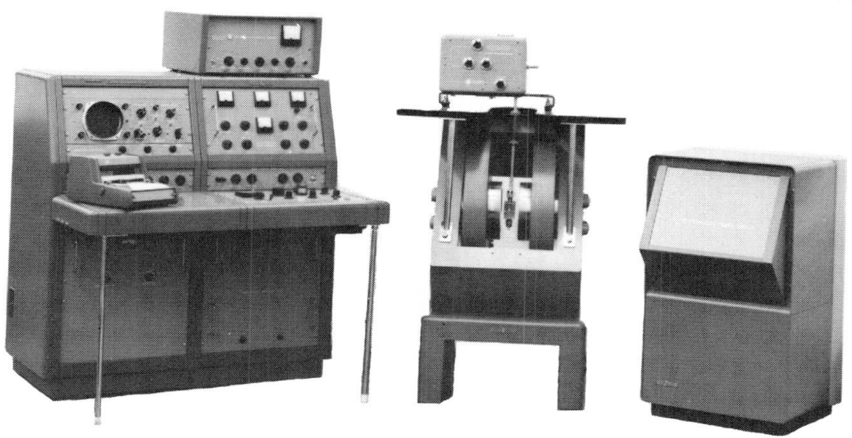

FIG. 31-8. Photograph of a Typical Commercial ESR Spectrometer. The Varian Associates V-4502-11 EPR Spectrometer, with Associated Magnet and Power Supply. (Courtesy Varian Associates.)

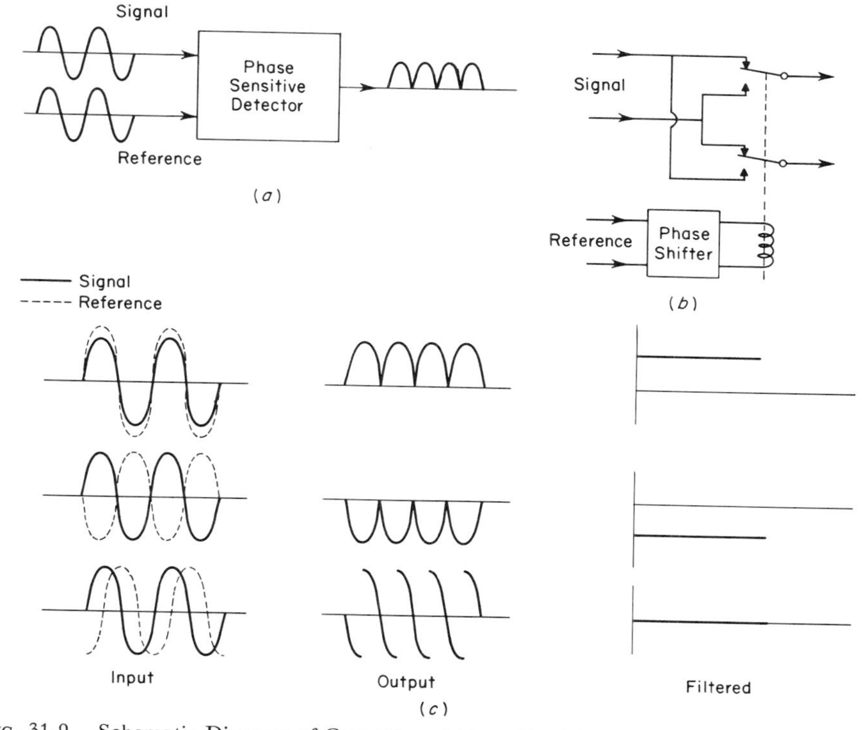

FIG. 31-9. Schematic Diagram of Operation of Phase Sensitive Detector. *a*. General Block Diagram; *b*. Schematic Operation of a Chopper-Type Detector. The Reference Signal Controls the Position of the Contacts and the ESR Signal Is Fed to the Upper Channel; *c*. Output from Detector for Different Phases between Signal and Reference.

Most of the components have already been described. The klystron provides r.f. power which divides equally between the resistive arm and the cavity in the magic-T bridge. The cavity is coupled to the bridge with an adjustable iris, and the bridge is balanced using a slide-screw tuner. A slight unbalance of the bridge is desirable, so that some power reaches the crystal even without ESR absorption in the cavity. This small zero-signal bias allows the crystal to operate in a linear and more sensitive region. To decrease crystal noise the microwave signal is modulated at 100 kc. by sinusoidally sweeping the magnetic field at this frequency by means of modulating coils within the cavity. The signal is demodulated using a phase sensitive detector, filtered, and presented on a recorder. The action of the phase sensitive detector is shown in Fig. 31-9. The signal of interest coming from the crystal and a reference signal obtained from the oscillator powering the modulation coils are fed into the detector, and a pulsating d.c. is obtained whose polarity depends upon the phase between the signal and the reference. The behavior of the phase sensitive detector for different phases is illustrated by a chopper-type demodulator, although for demodulation at 100 kc. electronic diodes are actually

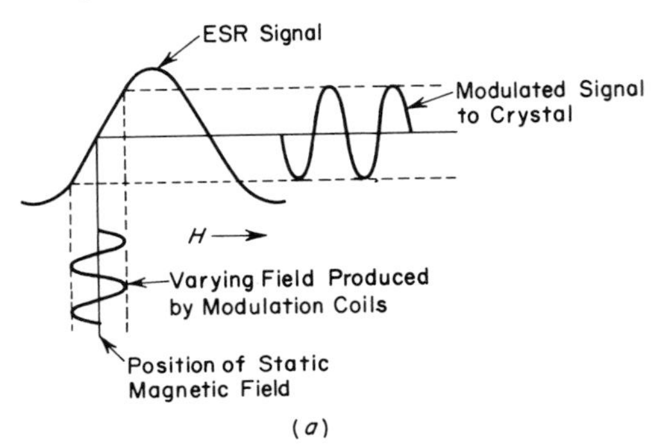

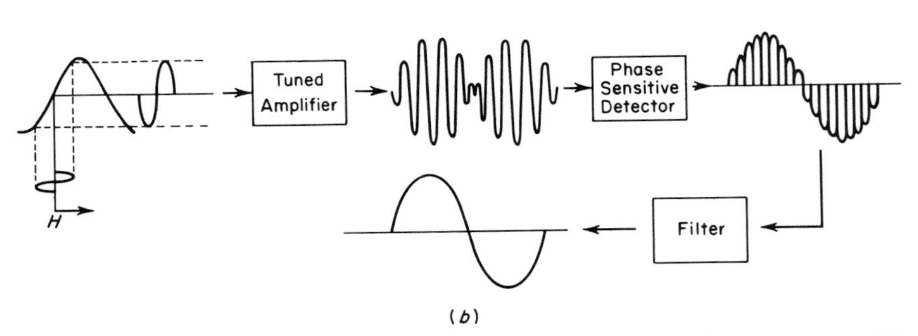

Fig. 31-10. Flow of ESR Signal through Detection Portion of the Spectrometer. *a*. Effect of Modulation on the Signal; *b*. Flow of Modulated Signal through the Tuned Amplifier, Detector and Filter, Resulting in a First-derivative Presentation.

employed in the instrument. The modulation of the resonance signal and its flow through the spectrometer is shown in Fig. 31-10. Because of the method of detection, the output presentation approaches the first derivative of the absorption curve. The spectrometer also contains an automatic frequency control circuit which maintains the klystron frequency at the resonant frequency of the cavity. Details of the operation of the spectrometer and circuitry can be found in literature by Varian Associates (see item 7 in "Selected Bibliography").

Other commercial microwave spectrometers in the U.S. are offered by Strandlabs, Inc. (Cambridge, Mass.) and Alpha Scientific Laboratories, Inc. (Berkeley, Calif.). The Strandlabs instrument operates with 6 kc. signal modulation and uses a different microwave bridge design and a high-Q cavity. The Alpha Scientific instrument utilizes 100 kc. modulation and a slow-wave structure sample receptacle instead of a resonant cavity. Spectrometers operating at lower r.f. frequencies are offered by Alpha Scientific, operating at 340 Mc., and Elion Instruments, operating at 10, 30, 60, 90, 200, and 1000 Mc. (see "Selected Bibliography," item 3). Many workers have built their own equipment for ESR spectrometry (see "Selected Bibliography," items 4 and 5). Listings of commercial suppliers of ESR equipment and accessories are available.[3]

CONSIDERATIONS IN ANALYSIS BY ESR

HYPERFINE INTERACTION AND QUALITATIVE ANALYSIS

Well-resolved ESR spectra of many substances contain hyperfine structure. This hyperfine structure allows the identification of the paramagnetic substance in many cases, and can also provide information about the environment of the molecule and the distribution of the electron density within the molecule. A brief discussion of the origin and interpretation of this hyperfine splitting follows.

The resonance frequency of an electron depends upon the magnetic field at the electron. Previously the applied magnetic field was assumed to be the field at the electron. Actually the electron is affected by both the applied magnetic field, H_o, and any local fields due to the magnetic fields of nuclei, or other effects, H_{local}, so that Eq. (4) may be written

$$h\nu = g\beta(H_o + H_{local}) \tag{7}$$

The effect of the magnetic moments of nuclei on the ESR spectrum is called *hyperfine interaction*, and leads to a splitting of the ESR line (hyperfine structure). Consider a hydrogen atom, composed of an unpaired electron associated with a proton. Since the proton is a charged spinning particle with a nuclear spin, I, of $\frac{1}{2}$, it has a magnetic moment, and the electron will be affected by the magnetic field of the proton as well as that of the applied magnetic field. The relative orientation of the nuclear magnetic moment and the electron magnetic moment causes a splitting of the original two levels to four levels (Fig. 31-11). Only two transitions are found between these states, because the nuclear moment remains fixed during electronic transitions, so that transitions occur only between $I = +\frac{1}{2}$ or $I = -\frac{1}{2}$ states (*i.e.*, the selection rule for the transition is $\Delta M_I = 0$). The result is a splitting of the original line into a doublet. Another way of visualizing the resulting spectrum is as follows. When the proton points in the same direction as the applied field, the electron finds the appropriate resonance H at a lower value of H_o. When the proton magnetic moment opposes the field, a higher value of H_o is needed for resonance. The magnitude of the splitting, usually given in gauss, is called the *hyperfine coupling constant*, a. For the hydrogen atom a_H is about 508 gauss. In general, a single nucleus of spin I, will cause a splitting into $(2I + 1)$ lines, so that interaction with a single nitrogen nucleus (N^{14}, $I = 1$) will cause a splitting into three lines, and unpaired electrons in manganese(II) (Mn^{55}, $I = \frac{5}{2}$) interacts with the nucleus to form

[3] Science, **142,** 720, 1963; Anal. Chem., **36,** No. 5 65BG, 104BG, 1964.

a six-line spectrum. Many common nuclei, such as carbon-12 and oxygen-16 have zero spin and do not interact with the electron.

For a system with the unpaired electron interacting with two equivalent protons a similar analysis shows that formation of a triplet occurs with relative intensities 1:2:1

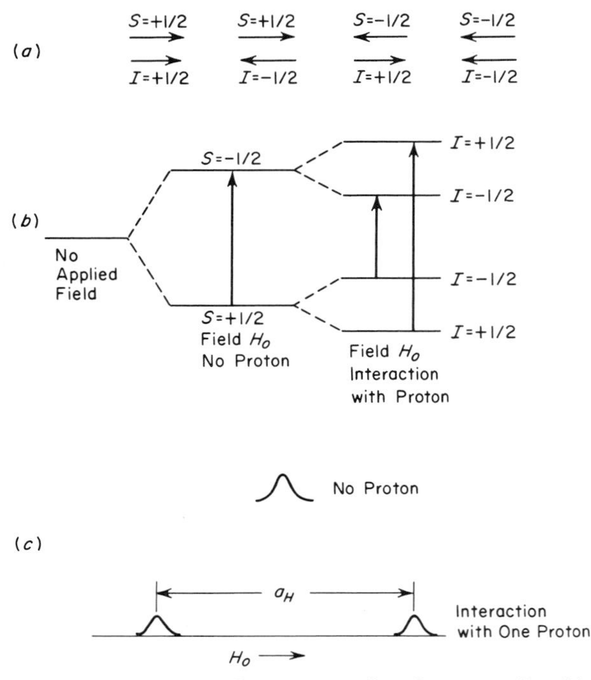

FIG. 31-11. Interaction of Unpaired Electron with One Proton. *a*. Possible Orientations of Electron and Nuclear Magnetic Moments; *b*. Splitting of Energy Levels; *c*. Splitting of Spectral Line.

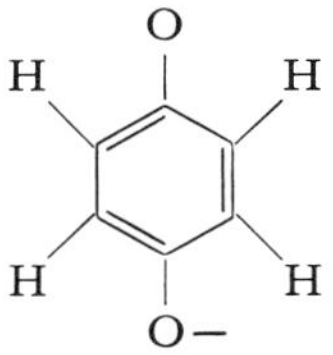

(Fig. 31-12). The two protons may either both oppose or both act in the direction of the magnetic field, causing the two extreme lines, or they may act in opposite directions from one another, essentially cancelling their effect on the electron, resulting in the line located at the same position as the unperturbed line. Since this latter condition can occur in either of twc ways, this center line is twice as intense as the two extreme lines. Continuing an analysis in this way results in the general conclusion that n equivalent protons cause a splitting into $n + 1$ lines; the relative intensities of these lines follow the binomial expansion. For example the *p*-benzosemiquinone ion, has four equivalent protons, so that its ESR spectrum shows five lines with relative intensities of 1:4:6:4:1, and a coupling constant of 2.4 gauss.[4] For the general case of n equivalent nuclei of spin I, the resulting spectrum involves $(2nI + 1)$ lines. For example, two equivalent N^{14} nuclei produce a five-line spectrum.

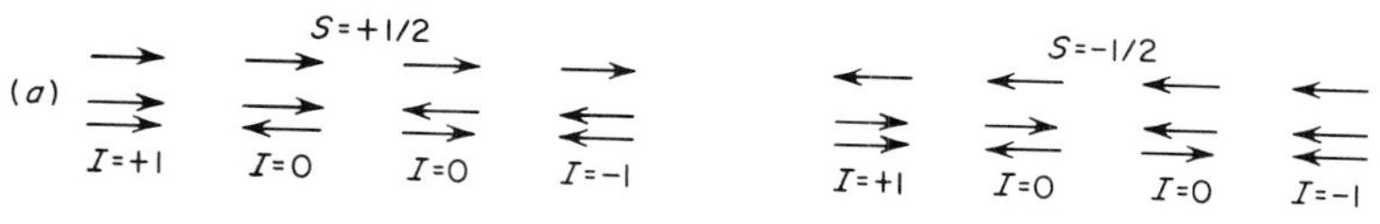

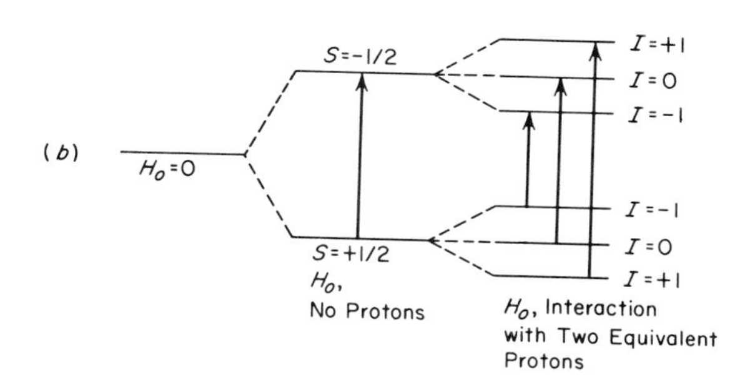

Fig. 31-12. Interaction of Unpaired Electron With Two Equivalent Protons.

For nonequivalent nuclei, each will interact with the electron with a different coupling constant to produce a hyperfine splitting. For example, if the electron interacts with one proton (H_1) with a coupling constant a_1, and another (H_2) with a coupling constant a_2, assuming a_1 is much larger than a_2, a doublet due to the interaction of H_1, split into a doublet due to H_2 will result (Fig. 31-13*a*). Similarly the interaction of two equivalent hydrogens with a second pair of equivalent hydrogens results in a triplet of triplets for very different coupling constants (Fig. 31-13*b*). However, as the values of the coupling constants approach one another in magnitude, the spectra may differ from the above simple behavior (Fig. 31-13*c*). The hyperfine splittings and coupling constants can be useful in identifying species. However, one should note that the magnitude of the coupling constants are sometimes a function of solvent, particularly nitrogen coupling constants.[5] Also ion-pair formation between radicals and metal-ions can often change hyperfine splittings.[6] Further details on the interpretation of ESR spectra and to the

[4] Ventkataraman, B., and Fraenkel, G. K., J. Am. Chem. Soc., **77**, 2707, 1955.

[5] Gendell, J., Fred, J. H., and Fraenkel, G. K., J. Chem. Phys., **37**, 2832, 1962; Stone, E. W., and Maki, A. H., *ibid.*, **36**, 1944, 1962; Chambers, J. Q., Layloff, T., and Adams, R. N., J. Phys. Chem., **68**, 661, 1963.

[6] Maki, A. H., and Geske, D. H., J. Chem. Phys., **33**, 825, 1960; Ward, R. L., *ibid.*, **32**, 410, 1960.

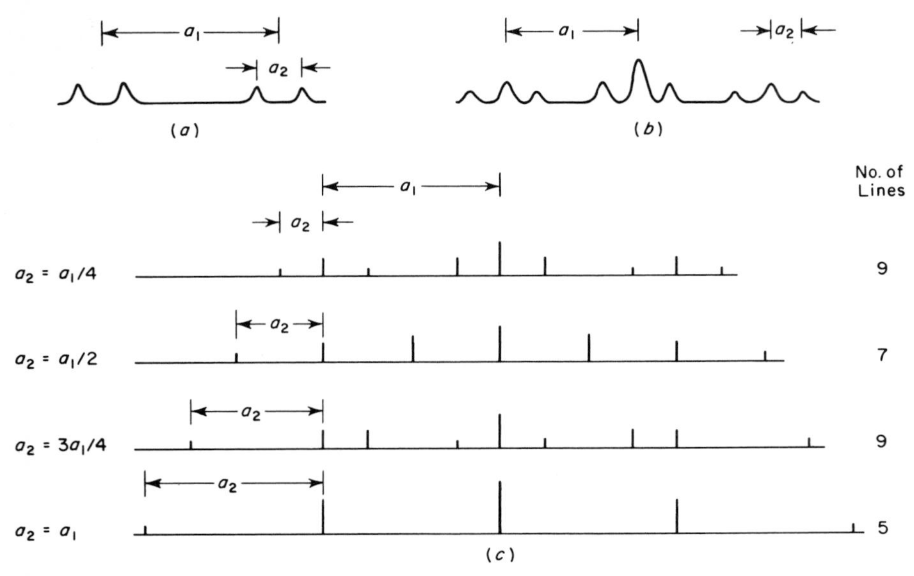

FIG. 31-13. A Spectra due to Interaction of Unpaired Electron with: *a*. Two Nonequivalent Protons; *b*. Two Nonequivalent Sets of Two Equivalent Protons; and *c*. Variation of Spectra for Interaction of Two Sets of Equivalent Pairs of Protons for Different Values of the Coupling Constants a_1 and a_2.

application of these spectra to electron density determinations are found in the bibliography, items 1, 5, and 6.

QUANTITATIVE ANALYSIS

Measurement of Intensities.—The overall absorption of a sample is basically obtained by integration under the absorption curve, where $f(x)$

$$\text{concentration} \propto \text{intensity} \propto \int_{-\infty}^{+\infty} f(x)\, dx \tag{8}$$

is the absorption curve. When a first derivative presentation $[f'(x)]$ is obtained, a double integration is required; the curve must first be integrated to obtain the absorption curve, and this must then be integrated to obtain the intensity. This double integration can be performed electronically, by using stabilized operational amplifiers in the integrator configuration, for example, or graphically. A graphical double integration can be avoided and a single integration alone can be performed by using the relation

$$\int_{-\infty}^{+\infty} f(x)\, dx = \int_{-\infty}^{+\infty} xf'(x)\, dx \tag{9}$$

In many applications where line widths are constant, calibration curves can be obtained by simply using the peak heights as a measure of intensity, rather than the peak areas.

Calibration and Standards.—The integrated intensity is usually related to the concentration of the paramagnetic species by comparison with a standard. Theoretically, an absolute calculation of the number of unpaired spins within the cavity can be made, but in practice this calculation requires knowledge of the intensity of microwave power in the cavity, the cavity Q, the signal amplifier gain, the crystal conversion gain, and the filling factor f, which is proportional to the ratio of the volume of the sample divided by the volume of the cavity. Because of the difficulty of determining these parameters, and their inaccuracy, comparison of the intensity of the signal with that of a standard is usually performed.

Unlike visible spectroscopy, where the intensity of the absorption is different for each substance, in ESR spectrometry the intensity is proportional to the number of unpaired spins in the sample, no matter what the sample is (subject to some important limitations discussed below). Therefore, the determination of the number of unpaired spins may be made by comparing the sample intensity to a standard of different composition. Some standards which have been suggested include:

(1) Standard solutions or mixtures of the substance being determined. When these are available, as in the determination of manganese(II) or vanadium(IV), these would represent the best kind of standards.

(2) Standards containing a known number of unpaired spins. These include solid samples or solutions of stable free radicals, such as diphenylpicrylhydrazyl (DPPH) (available from Eastman Organic Chemicals) or peroxylamine disulphonate. DPPH, which is frequently used, has a molecular weight of 394 and contains 1.53×10^{21} unpaired spins per gram. A crystal of $CuSO_4 \cdot 5H_2O$ has also been used.

(3) Secondary standards such as powdered charcoal diluted in KCl,[7] charred dextrose,[8] or synthetic ruby[9] can be employed. In general, standards should be stable and have line widths close to that of the sample. Accuracy will be higher if the spin concentration in the standard is close to that of the sample.

A larger source of difficulty is in substitution of the standard for the sample in the spectrometer. The following are some of the sources of error in comparison of standard and sample.[7] The filling factors f must be the same, so that the volume of the standard in the r.f. field must be the same as that of the sample. The spectrometer adjustments must be the same for standard and sample; hence, the dielectric losses in both sample and standard must be the same so that the cavity Q remains constant. The size of the sample tubes and the wall thicknesses must be identical. The cavity match, crystal leakage current, amplifier gains, and r.f. power must be the same.

Difficulties with actual physical interchange of standard and sample can be avoided by several techniques. An internal standard mixed with the unknown (provided their signals are well separated) could be used. Using a synthetic ruby attached in the cavity in an out-of-the-way location, so that both the sample and ruby resonance can be observed at the same time, removes the hazards of changes in spectrometer and matching during the comparison.[9] The g-value of the ruby resonance is anisotropic, so that the ruby signal can be shifted away from the sample signal by proper orientation of the ruby. Another approach is to use a dual cavity technique. A dual sample cavity is composed of two cavities fastened together, each with its own modulation coils and detection system. The cavities are modulated at different frequencies (*e.g.*, 100 kc. for one and 400 c. for the other) and the two signals are separated in tuned circuits and separately detected and displayed. Using an unknown sample in one cavity and a standard sample in the other then is analogous to operation of a dual channel optical spectrometer. A dual sample cavity is available from Varian Associates.

[7] Instruction Manual for V-4502 Spectrometer Systems, Varian Associates, Palo Alto, California.

[8] Hoskins, R. H., and Pastor, R. C., J. Appl. Phys., **31,** 1506, 1960.

[9] Singer, L. S., *ibid.*, **30,** 1463, 1959.

Sensitivity.—The sensitivity of ESR spectrometers has been discussed by Ingram (see bibliography item 5) and Feher.[10] In general the sensitivity is proportional to the Q-factor of the cavity, f, the filling factor, and the r.f. power, and is inversely proportional to temperature, ΔH, the line width, and the bandwidth of the detector system. A limiting factor is generally the noise level in the spectrometer due to crystal noise and klystron noise. Ingram gives the following expression for the ultimate room temperature sensitivity of practical X-band systems

$$N_{O min} = \frac{10^{11}\Delta H}{\tau^{1/2}} \tag{10}$$

where $N_{O min}$ is the minimum number of detectable spins, ΔH is the line width, and τ is the time constant of the detecting system, which, incidentally, is inversely proportional to the bandwidth. The sensitivity of some commercial spectrometers was given in Table 31-1. For a sample with a very small dielectric loss, this would correspond to a concentration in the order of 10^{-9} M. For aqueous solutions, 10^{-7} M probably represents a reasonable lower limit. The signal-to-noise ratio in an ESR signal can be improved by using a computer-of-average-transients (CAT). This device essentially converts the signal to digital form and stores this information in a magnetic core memory. In repetitive scans the noise tends to average out (as the square root of the number of scans) and the signal builds up. Improvement of sensitivity by a factor of ten (for 100 repetitive scans) should be attainable.[11]

APPLICATIONS

The scope of application of ESR spectrometry to analysis is somewhat limited by the requirement that the substance being analyzed contains unpaired electrons. A few methods for transition metals and free radicals have been reported. The widest use for ESR in organic chemistry has been in the analysis of free radicals produced by chemical reactions or irradiation. These studies were usually associated with kinetic measurements or involved only qualitative identification of the radicals. However, nonparamagnetic organic substances can be determined by a technique which converts them quantitatively or at a constant yield into free radicals which are then observed by ESR spectrometry. Techniques for producing free radicals include pyrolysis, adsorption on alumina or zeolites, photolytic methods, and reduction or oxidation by chemical or electrolytic means. Classes of compounds which might be studied by this kind of technique include aromatic hydrocarbons, ketones, quinones, amines, and phenols.

ANALYSIS OF METALS

Analysis of Vanadium in Petroleum Oils.—Vanadium(IV), found in the p.p.m. range in petroleum oils, leads to corrosion effects in combustion engines and furnaces using petroleum oil fuels, and alters the catalytic cracking of the petroleum during processing. The analysis of vanadium by ESR spectroscopy in such samples has been investigated by several groups[12,13,14] and has been shown to be a rapid and convenient method of analysis. Vanadium(IV) yields an eight-line spectrum due to the interaction of an unpaired $3d$ electron with a nucleus ($I = \frac{7}{2}$). In highly viscous media, due to the anisotropy of the g-value, splitting into a greater number of lines occurs. A typical

[10] Feher, G., Bell System Tech. J., **36,** 499, 1957.
[11] Allen, L. C., and Johnson, L. F., J. Am. Chem. Soc., **85,** 2668, 1963.
[12] Saracero, A. J., Fanale, D. T., and Coggeshall, N. D., Anal. Chem., **33,** 500, 1961.
[13] Roberts, E. M., Rutledge, R. L., and Wehner, A. P., *ibid.*, p. 1879.
[14] Ulbert, K., Coll. Czech. Chem. Commun., **27,** 1438, 1962.

analyses[12] involves using identical precision bore tubes of 3 mm. i.d. and using vanadyl etioporphyrin(I) dissolved in heavy oil distillate as a standard. Ulbert[14] used a ruby internal standard. A discussion of temperature and viscosity of effects in these measurements has also been given.[13] The intensity measurements were made by measuring the peak-to-peak height on the first derivative recording of a given hyperfine line. Peak height measurement, rather than double integration, can be used as long as line widths and shapes remain constant. Quantities of vanadium in the 0.1 to 50 p.p.m. range were determined with results checking to within ±20 percent in most cases with analysis performed by alternate methods. No other constituents of oil interfered.

ORGANIC ANALYSIS

Analysis of Polynuclear Hydrocarbons.—The determination of anthracene, perylene, dimethylanthracene, and naphthacene by conversion to radical cations and determination by ESR spectrometry has been described.[15] When benzene or carbon disulfide solutions of these hydrocarbons are treated with an activated silica-alumina catalyst, they are quantitatively converted to the radicals and adsorbed on the surface of the catalyst. The procedure involves adding the polynuclear hydrocarbon sample in benzene or carbon disulfide and activated catalyst to 6 mm. uniform bore tubes and measuring the peak heights. The standard deviation of a series of measurements of samples in the 10 μg. range was about 5 percent. Benzene, naphthalene, and other hydrocarbons which do not form radicals at the catalyst surface did not interfere.

ANALYSIS BASED ON REACTION RATES AND RELAXATION TIMES

Determination of Oxygen.—A method for determining oxygen based upon the decrease in relaxation time of a stable free radical has been proposed.[16] The method is based upon observing the variation of the peak height of a free radical signal with increasing r.f. power and with different concentrations of oxygen present. The radical used, which was not clearly specified but which originated in a commercial terphenyl coolant used in an organic moderated and cooled reactor, had a long spin-lattice relaxation time, so that the ESR signal saturated easily. With increasing microwave power on the sample the signal height *decreased* in the absence of oxygen, because the upper energy level was being populated rapidly enough to cause it to become as equally populated as the lower level. On addition of oxygen, the relaxation time was decreased, and the peak height behavior with varying r.f. power changed. At 740 mm. of oxygen, the signal was the same as that characteristic of a radical which does not saturate at the microwave powers available in the instrument. The method is said to be useful at dissolved oxygen concentrations down to 10^{-5} *M*.

Determination of Hydroperoxides.—A method for analyzing solutions of *tert*-butyl hydroperoxide, cumene hydroperoxide, peracetic acid, and *meta*-chloroperbenzoic acid, based on the reaction of these with diphenylpicrylhydrazyl (DPPH) and the measurement of the rate of this reaction using an ESR spectrometer has been suggested.[17] The method is based on measuring either the change in the DPPH spectrum or the spectrum due to the appearance of a new species, as a function of time. The calculation of the hydroperoxide concentration is based on the measured rate of the reaction. The author suggests that mixtures of hydroperoxides might be distinguishable on the basis of different reaction rates. The reaction between DPPH and hydroperoxides does not

[15] Flockhart, B. D., and Pink, R. C., Anal. Chim. Acta, **9,** 931, 1962.
[16] Ingalls, R. B., and Pearson, G. A., Anal. Chim. Acta, **25,** 566, 1961.
[17] Ueda, H., Anal. Chem., **35,** 2213, 1963.

appear to be well defined however. Although analytical results are not given, the useful concentration range of hydroperoxides is probably about 10–100 *mM*.

CONTINUOUS PROCESS ANALYZERS

Vanadium Analyzer.—A continuous analyzer for vanadium in oil, based upon the same principles as the batch method previously discussed, has been devised.[18] A diagram of the apparatus is shown in Fig. 31-14. Most of the apparatus is the same as that in

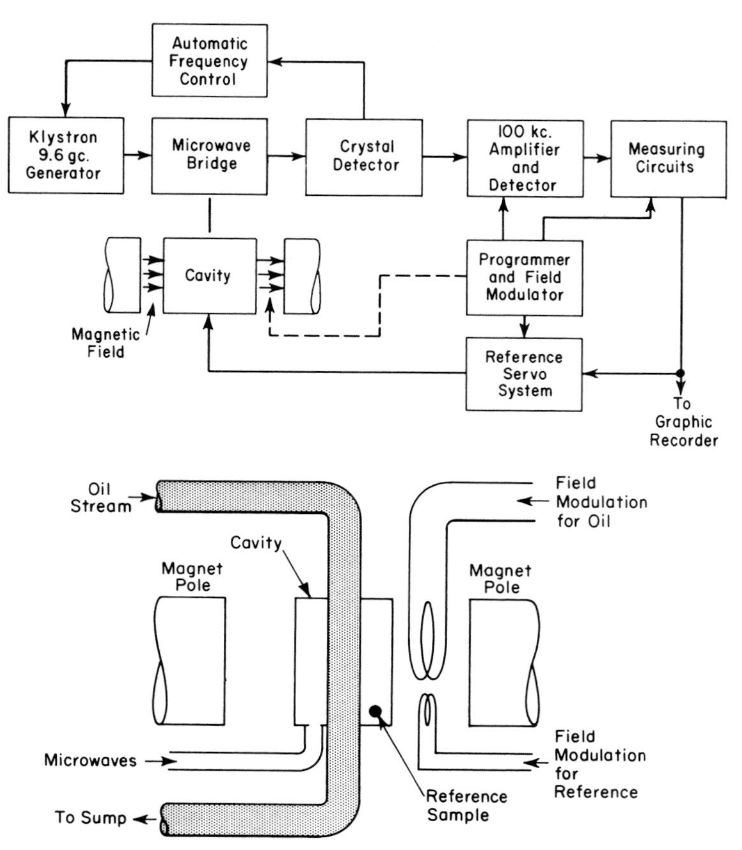

FIG. 31-14. *a.* Block Diagram of ESR Vanadium Monitor. *b.* Functional Diagram of Cavity in Vanadium Monitor. (Reprinted with permission from Nelson, F. A., J. Instrument Soc. Am., **11,** 55–59, 1964; based on paper given at 18th ISA Instrument-Automation Conf., Sept. 1963.)

the usual microwave spectrometer; the sample of oil passes through a 6-mm. i.d. tube in the resonant cavity. To take care of changes in temperature, microwave power, etc.,

[18] Nelson, F. A., 18th Annual ISA Conference, Chicago, Ill., Sept. 1963, Preprint No. 31.3.63. Coggeshall, N. D., Nelson, F. A., Doolen, O. K., and Baker, G. A., 28 Midyear Meeting of Am. Pet. Inst. Div. of Refining, Philadelphia, Pa., May 1963. Donaldson, R. E., Murphy, J. R., McBride, W. R., and Stony, D. O., *ibid.*

which might alter the calibration, a reference sample is included in the spectrometer, modulated with a second pair of modulation coils. The phasing is adjusted so that the signal from the reference opposes the vanadium output signal, and the modulation amplitude on the reference is adjusted so that the reference signal just cancels the vanadium signal. The magnitude of the modulation at the reference signal is controlled by a servomotor driving a potentiometer to maintain a zero output signal. The position of this potentiometer is recorded and is proportional to the vanadium concentration in the oil.

Catalyst Contamination Monitoring.—Elion[19] described an analyzer based on a lower frequency spectrometer (Electrospec 200). The analyzer used sequencial sampling and was used to measure and control the catalyst in a fluid catalytic cracker of petroleum.

Since microwave ESR systems including a magnet are more costly than many other types of analytical instrumentation, their most widespread applications will probably be in areas where other analytical systems will not work. Because it is a very selective method, chemical separations before the analysis are frequently not required, and very rapid analyses can be made. Furthermore, ESR measurements are made without destroying or even changing the sample being analyzed. These latter two considerations may make ESR a good technique for continuous process analysis. Its high sensitivity and ability to analyze substances in the solid state may also make the technique useful for trace analysis.

SELECTED BIBLIOGRAPHY

1. Bersohn, R., Roberson, R. Z., Chapters 9 and 10 in Determination of Organic Structures by Physical Methods, Vol. II, F. C. Nachod and W. D. Phillips, Eds., Academic Press, 1962.
2. Blois, M. S., *et al.*, Free Radicals in Biological Systems, Academic Press, 1961.
3. Elion, H. A., and Shapiro, L., Chapter 2 in Progress in Nuclear Energy, Ser. IX, Analytical Chemistry, Vol. 2, C. E. Crouthamel, Ed., Pergamon Press, 1962.
4. Fraenkel, G. K., Chapter 42 in Physical Methods of Organic Chemistry, A. Weissberger, Ed., Interscience Publishers, 1960.
5. Ingram, D. J. E., Free Radicals, as Studied by Electron Spin Resonance, Butterworths, London, 1958.
6. Symons, M. C. R., in Advances in Physical Organic Chemistry, V. Gold, Ed., Vol. 1, p. 284, Academic Press, 1963.
7. Varian Staff, NMR and EPR Spectroscopy, Pergamon Press, 1960.
8. Wertz, J. E., Chem. Rev., **55,** 829, 1955.

[19] Elion, H. A., ISA Paper No. 83 NY60, September 29, 1960; 20th Annual Convention of Society for Nondestructive Testing, Philadelphia, Pa., October, 1960. See also "Selected Bibliography," item 3.

Chapter 32

THERMOMETRIC TITRIMETRY

By Wesley W. Wendlandt
Texas Technological College
Lubbock, Texas

INTRODUCTION

In contrast with the other *thermal methods* discussed in the following three chapters, in which some physical parameter of a system is continuously monitored as a function of temperature, thermometric titrimetry involves the measurement of the temperature change of a system as a function of time or volume of titrant. This technique consists of the detection and measurement of the change in temperature of a solution as the titrant is added to it, under as near adiabatic conditions as possible. Experimentally, the titrant is added from a constant delivery buret into the titrate (solution to be titrated) which is contained in an insulated container such as a Dewar flask. The resultant temperature-volume (or time) curve thus obtained is similar to other titration curves, *e.g.*, acid-base, in that the end point of the reaction can be readily ascertained. Since all reactions involve a detectable endothermic or exothermic enthalpy change, the technique has potentially wide application in analytical chemistry, especially in those cases where other more common methods are not applicable.

Perhaps the first description of this technique was by Bell and Cowell[1] who applied it to the titration of citric acid with ammonia. Further work by Dutoit and Grobet[2] demonstrated the utility of the method for acid-base, complexation, and precipitation titrations. Other early workers studied the titration of a soluble sulfate with barium chloride,[3] a soluble chloride with silver nitrate,[4] various oxidation and reduction reactions,[5] and various complexation and precipitation reactions by Indian investigators.[6] Because of the relatively crude apparatus employed by these early investigators, the data obtained were susceptible to a number of unavoidable errors. These errors were minimized when Linde, Rogers, and Hume[7] introduced a virtually automatic titration system. It was at this point that modern thermometric titrimetry came into existence. References to many of the excellent papers and reviews to this modern work are given in the bibliography at the end of the chapter.

Several idealized thermometric titration curves for an exothermic reaction are given in Fig. 32-1. A titration curve in which the titrant and the titrate are at the same initial temperature is illustrated in (a). The actual titration is preceded by a blank run, *CD*, in which no titrant is added to the titrate. At *D*, titrant is added, causing the temperature

[1] Bell, J. M., and Cowell, C. F., J. Am. Chem. Soc., **35,** 49, 1913.
[2] Dutoit, P., and Grobet, E., J. chim. phys., **19,** 324, 1922.
[3] Dean, P. M., and Watts, O. O., J. Am. Chem. Soc., **46,** 855, 1924.
[4] Dean, P. M., and Newcombe, E., *Ibid.*, **47,** 64, 1925.
[5] Mayr, C., and Fisch, J., Z. anal. chem., **76,** 718, 1929.
[6] Bhattacharya, A. B., and Gaur, H. C., J. Indian Chem. Soc., **24,** 487, 1947; and many others.
[7] Linde, H. W., Rogers, L. B., and Hume, D. N., Anal. Chem., **25,** 404, 1953.

of the titrate to rise rapidly, reaching a maximum value at E. Beyond E, additional titrant causes no further change in the temperature of the titrate, hence, the horizontal excess reagent line, EF. The temperature rise of the titrate (and titration vessel), ΔT, is obtained by determining the vertical distance between the excess reagent line, ED',

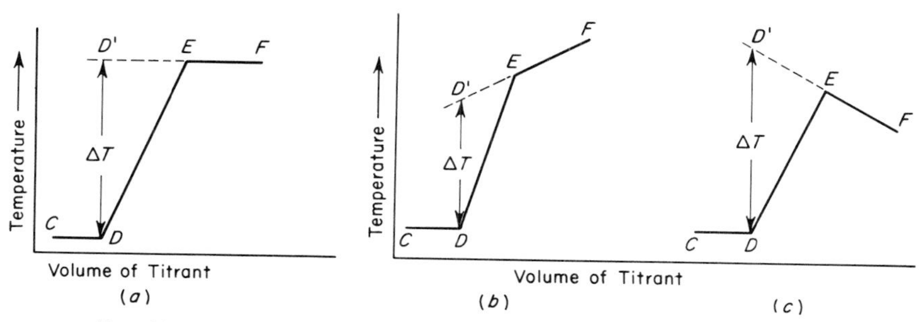

FIG. 32-1. Thermometric Curves for an Exothermic Reaction (Ideal).

and CD. In curve (b), the conditions of the titration were identical to those of (a) except that the titrant was at a higher temperature than the titrate, hence, the sloping excess reagent line, EF. For curve (c), conditions were also identical to the above except that the titrant was at a lower temperature than the titrate. The excess reagent line, EF, thus slopes in an opposite direction to that of curve (b). For an endothermic reaction, the curves would be identical to the above except that the temperature changes would be in an opposite direction.

To aid in the determination of the exact end point of the titration, other means of representing the titration curve have been described. These curve representations are illustrated in Fig. 32-2. In curve (a), using the same terminology as in Fig. 32-1, the first derivative of the titration curve, dT/dv, is plotted against volume of titrant.[8] In this curve, and in all of the following curves in Fig. 32-2, E is the end point region of the curve. In curve (b), the second derivative of the titration curve, d^2T/dv^2, is plotted against volume of titrant,[8] and in curve (c), using a twin thermistor bridge which records the temperature difference between T (titrate plus titrant) and T_{blank} (pure solvent plus titrant), T-T_{blank} is plotted against the volume of titrant.[9]

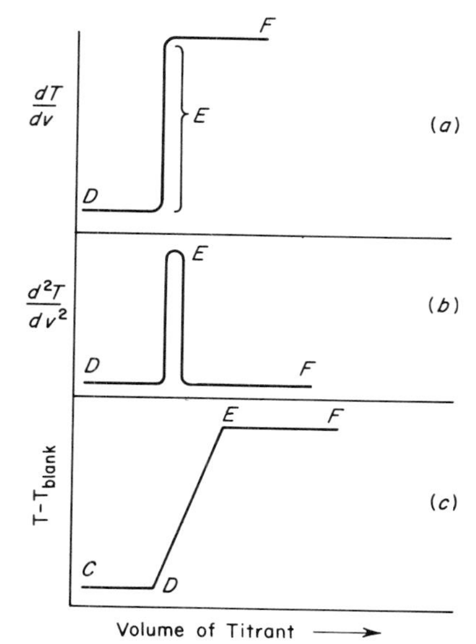

FIG. 32-2. Various Representations of Thermometric Titration Curves (Ideal).

[8] Zenchelsky, S. T., and Segatto, P. R., Anal. Chem., **29**, 1856, 1957.
[9] Tyson, B. C., McCurdy, W. H., and Bricker, C. E., Anal. Chem., **32**, 1640, 1961.

Contrary to potentiometric titrations of various types which depend solely on equilibrium constants, and, hence, the free energy of the reaction, ΔF°, or

$$-\Delta F^\circ = RT \ln K \quad (1)$$

thermometric titrations depend only on the heat of reaction, ΔH, or

$$\Delta H = \Delta F + T\Delta S \quad (2)$$

Thus, a thermometric titration may be feasible when all "free energy" methods may fail. The change in temperature, ΔT, of the titration of, say, an acid and a base, is dependent on the heat of neutralization of the system, according to the equation

$$\Delta T = \frac{N_m \Delta H_a}{Q} \quad (3)$$

where N_m represents the number of moles of water formed by the neutralization, ΔH_a is the molar heat of neutralization, and Q is the heat capacity of the system. In practice, ΔH_a and Q are constant throughout the titration so that ΔT is proportional to N_m.

Jordan[10] has calculated that to attain an accuracy of better than ± 1 percent in the titration of weak acids, the acid must have a $K_a = 1.0 \times 10^{-10}$. An even more general index has been defined[10] which is called the *enthalpimetric sensitivity index*, *ESI*, and is defined in terms of the equation

$$P_n = |C_{\min} \Delta H^\circ| \quad (4)$$

where $C_{\min}$ denotes the minimum concentration, in millimoles per liter, with which a determination can be carried out with a given accuracy indicated by the subscript n. The *ESI*, P_n, is expressed in calories per liter, and is dependent solely on the characteristics of the titration apparatus. For example, the minimum concentration which can be determined, of a monoprotic acid ($\Delta H_a = 13$ kcal. per mole), to an accuracy of 1 percent is about 3 millimole per liter. The *ESI* is then evaluated as

$$P_{1\%} = 40 \text{ cal. per liter.} \quad (5)$$

Using Eq. (3), if the ΔH_a and Q values are known, the number of moles of product, N_m, can be calculated from ΔT. In solution dilute enough to use the approximation

$$\Delta H \approx \Delta H^\circ \quad (6)$$

quantitative determinations in the order of ± 5 percent in the millimolar concentration range have been reported.[10]

INSTRUMENTATION

A block diagram of the apparatus used in thermometric titrations is given in Fig. 32-3. The apparatus consists basically of: a motor driven automatic buret; an adiabatic titration cell; a thermistor and Wheatstone bridge circuit; and a strip-chart recorder. The Wheatstone bridge circuit for the thermistor is given in Fig. 32-4. A number of modifications of this basic apparatus design have been described, such as the use of a constant delivery buret instead of the motor-driven type,[7] or a twin-thermistor (one located in a blank solution of the solvent) bridge instead of the single thermistor tem-

[10] Jordan, J., Record of Chemical Prog., **19,** 193, 1958.

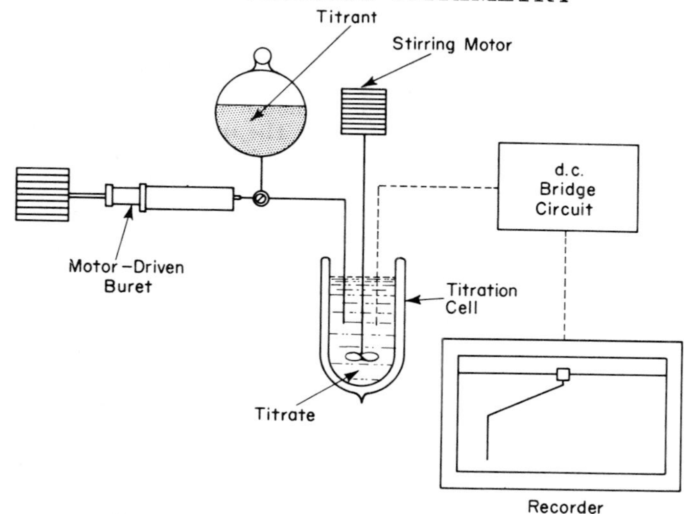

FIG. 32-3. Thermometric Titration Apparatus.

perature detector,[9] and so on. A high temperature titration apparatus for titration in fused salts media has also been described.[11]

The physical parameters of the instruments vary widely from apparatus to apparatus. The flow rate of the buret depends upon the size of the syringe employed, although

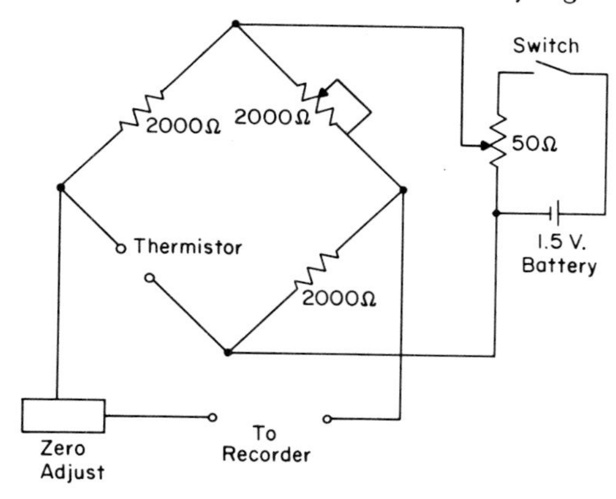

FIG. 32-4. Thermistor Wheatstone Bridge Circuit. (Adapted with permission from Jordan, J., Record of Chemical Progress, **19**, 193, 1958.)

flow rates from 0.1 to 1.0 ml. per min. are generally used. The magnitude of the temperature changes is, of course, dependent on the volume of the titration vessel (Q), the thermistor sensitivity, the bridge circuit, and the recorder sensitivity. Since tem-

[11] Jordan, J., Meier, J., Billingham, E. J., and Pendergast, J., Anal. Chem., **31**, 1439, 1959; *Ibid.*, **32**, 651, 1960.

perature changes in the course of a titration range between 0.01° and 0.2°C., the accuracy of the temperature measurement must be of the order of 10^{-4}°C.

The experimental procedure used by Jordan[10] is as follows. The 50-ml. samples of titrate were allowed to come to temperature equilibrium for at least 20 minutes in the Dewar titration vessel, maintained at 25±1°C. The titrant concentration was about 100 times that of the titrate, the latter of which was 0.01 *M* or less. The titrate solution was then titrated with the titrant, after a "blank" (no addition of titrant) run of about 2 minutes duration. The blank runs are important and were used to test the adiabaticity of the system. The titration end point was evaluated by accurately measuring the distance on the time (or volume) axis by projection from points *D* and *E* in Fig. 32-1a. Heats of reaction could be evaluated by determining the distance, *D* to *D'*, and the appropriate titration apparatus constant, *Q*.

APPLICATIONS

The applications of this technique include the determination of the concentration of an unknown substance, determination of reaction stoichiometry, and the determination of the thermodynamic quantities, ΔH, ΔF, and ΔS. The first application is perhaps the most useful to the analytical chemist and is generally applicable to an analysis especially when other methods fail. For example, it has been shown that even thick slurries can be titrated in this manner.[7] Likewise, weak acids can also be readily titrated by this technique. In general, the technique is applicable to the following types of reac-

TABLE 32-1. THERMOMETRIC TITRATION OF ACIDS AND BASES IN AQUEOUS SOLUTION

Titrate	*Titrant*	*Precision and Accuracy*
NaOH	HCl	0.11[a,b]
NH_3	HCl	0.56[b]
H_3PO_4	NaOH	2.8[b]
2nd H^+	NaOH	2.1[b]
3rd H^+	NaOH	0.85[b]
H_3BO_3	NaOH	0.38[b]
C_5H_5N	HCl	4.7[b]
$OH^- + CO_3^{2-}$	HCl	0.84[b]
Ethylenediamine		
overall	HCl	0.1[c]
1st NH_2	HCl	1.7[c]
2nd NH_2	HCl	2.0[c]
Ethanolamine	HCl	0.9[c]
Alanine	NaOH	±2[d,e]
Glutamic acid	NaOH	±2[e]
H_3PO_4 + HCl	NaOH	—[f]
Monochloroacetic acid	NaOH	±1[g]
Trichloroacetic acid	NaOH	±1[g]

[a] σ values.
[b] Linde, H. W., Rogers, L. B., and Hume, D. N., Anal. Chem., **25**, 404, 1953.
[c] Tyson, B. C., McCurdy, W. A., and Bricker, C. E., Anal. Chem., **32**, 1640, 1961.
[d] Accuracy values, in percent.
[e] Chatterji, K. K., and Ghosh, A. K., J. Indian Chem. Soc., **34**, 407, 1957.
[f] Paris, R., and Robert, J., Compt. rend., **223**, 1135, 1946.
[g] Jordan, J., and Dumbaugh, W. H., Anal. Chem., **31**, 210, 1959.

tions with the following precision and accuracy (percent): (a) acid-base, 0.2 to 1; (b) oxidation-reduction, 0.5 to 2; (c) complexation, 0.1 to 1; (d) precipitation, 0.3 to 1. The precision and accuracy of the measurements depend largely on the ΔH° of the reaction involved.

Acid-Base Titrations.—Although a large number of acids and bases have been titrated by the use of this technique, only a partial listing is given in Table 32-1. The most important potentialities and limitations of acid-base thermometric titrations are due to the fact that the heats of neutralization of various acids differ by only 50 percent or less.

Precipitation Titrations.—The formation of a slightly soluble substance, AB, can be followed nicely by the technique of thermometric titrations. The heat of reaction, ΔH, evolved or absorbed by the equation

$$A^{+}(\text{aq}) + B^{-}(\text{aq}) \rightarrow AB(s) \pm \Delta H$$

is generally of a large enough magnitude so that a suitable titration curve is obtained. A partial listing of some compounds which have been studied in this manner is given in Table 32-2.

TABLE 32-2. THERMOMETRIC TITRATION OF PRECIPITATION REACTIONS IN AQUEOUS SOLUTION

Titrate	*Titrant*	*Precipitate*	*Precision and Accuracy, %*
Ca^{++}	$(NH_4)_2C_2O_4$	CaC_2O_4	1[a]
Ag^+	HCl	$AgCl$	0.3[b]
$CaCl_2$	$(NH_4)_2C_2O_4$	CaC_2O_4	[c]
$SrCl_2$	$(NH_4)_2C_2O_4$	SrC_2O_4	[c]
$Hg(NO_3)_2$	$(NH_4)_2C_2O_4$	HgC_2O_4	[c]
Pb^{2+}	$H_2C_2O_4$	PbC_2O_4	[c]
$HgCl_2$	KI	HgI_2	[d]
$NiSO_4$	KCN	$Ni(CN)_2$	[d]
$Zn(NO_3)_2$	KCN	$Zn(CN)_2$	[d]

[a] Jordan, J., and Billingham, E. J., Anal. Chem., **33,** 120, 1961.
[b] Linde, H. W., Rogers, L. B., and Hume, D. N., Anal. Chem., **25,** 404, 1953.
[c] Mayr, C., and Fisch, J., Z. anal. Chem., ***76,*** 718, 1929.
[d] Mondain-Monval, P., and Paris, R., Compt. rend., **198,** 1154, 1934.

Complexation Reactions.—Thermometric titrations have been used extensively to study complexation reactions. However, there is considerable doubt concerning the reliability and accuracy of much of the early work, mainly because of errors due to dilution, stirring, and the time constant of the temperature detection device. A partial listing of some complexation reactions that have been studied by thermometric titrations is given in Table 32-3.

Oxidation-Reduction Reactions.—Compared to the number of studies on the preceding types of reactions, little work has been done on oxidation-reduction reactions. A partial listing of some redox reactions that have been studied by thermometric titrations is given in Table 32-4.

Nonaqueous Titrations.—A number of thermometric titrations have been carried out in nonaqueous solvents. Studies include tin(IV) chloride titrated with dioxane in

TABLE 32-3. COMPLEXATION REACTIONS STUDIED BY THERMOMETRIC TITRATIONS

Titrate	*Titrant*	*Complex Formed*	*Precision and Accuracy, %*
Pb^{2+}	$EDTA^{4-}$	$Pb(EDTA)^{2-}$	1[a]
Cd^{2+}	$EDTA^{4-}$	$Cd(EDTA)^{2-}$	0.4[a]
Cu^{2+}	$EDTA^{4-}$	$Cu(EDTA)^{2-}$	0.3[a]
Ni^{2+}	$EDTA^{4-}$	$Ni(EDTA)^{2-}$	0.5[a]
Ca^{2+}	$EDTA^{4-}$	$Ca(EDTA)^{2-}$	1[a]
Zn^{2+}	$EDTA^{4-}$	$Zn(EDTA)^{2-}$	0.8[a]
Co^{2+}	$EDTA^{4-}$	$Co(EDTA)^{2-}$	0.1[a]
Mg^{2+}	$EDTA^{4-}$	$Mg(EDTA)^{2-}$	0.5[a]
$HgCl_2$	KI	K_2HgI_4	[b]
$Zn(NO_3)_2$	KCN	$K_2Zn(CN)_4$	[b]
$NiSO_4$	KCN	$K_2Ni(CN)_4$	[b]
Zn^{2+}	Na_2 tartrate	ZnT, $[ZnT]^{2-}$	[c]
Zn^{2+}	Na_3 citrate	Zn cit^-	[c]

[a] Jordan, J., and Alleman, T. G., Anal. Chem. **29,** 9, 1957.
[b] Mondain-Monval, P., and Paris, R., Compt. rend., **198,** 1154, 1934.
[c] Jordan, J., and Ben-Yair, M. P., Arkiv for Kemi, **11,** 239, 1956.

TABLE 32-4. REDOX (ELECTRON TRANSFER) REACTIONS STUDIED BY THERMOMETRIC TITRATION

Titrate	*Titrant*	*Precision and Accuracy, %*
Fe^{2+}	Ce^{4+}	1[a]
	$Cr_2O_7^{2-}$	0.5[a]
	MnO_4^-	1[a]
$Fe(CN)_6^{4-}$	Ce^{4+}	1[a]
Ti^{3+}	Ce^{4+}	2[a]
H_2O_2	Ce^{4+}	3.7[b]
$(-CH_2NH_3)_2SO_4 \cdot FeSO_4 \cdot 4H_2O$	Ce^{4+}	1[b]
$H_2C_2O_4$	MnO_4^-	[c]
$Fe(CN)_6^{4-}$	MnO_4^-	[c]
$KBrO_3$	H_3AsO_3	[c]
NaOCl	H_3AsO_3	[c]

[a] Jordan, J., and Ewing, G. J., Bull. Chem. Thermodynamics, **3,** A-13, pp. 7–8, 1960.
[b] Tyson, B. C., McCurdy, W. H., and Bricker, C. E., Anal. Chem., **33,** 1640, 1961.
[c] Mayr, C., and Fisch, J., Z. anal. chem., **76,** 718, 1929.

benzene, carbon tetrachloride, nitrobenzene, and chloroform[12] A $SnCl_4$: dioxane complex with a 1:1 stoichiometry was formed. A similar study was concerned with the titration of tin(IV) chloride with various Lewis bases in benzene.[13] The thermometric titration of a number of amines with hydrobromic acid in acetonitrile has been reported.[14] Jordan *et a*.[11] studied the thermometric titration of potassium chloride with silver nitrate at 158°C. in a lithium nitrate-potassium nitrate melt.

[12] Zenchelsky, S. T., Periale, J., and Cobb, J. C., Anal. Chem., **28,** 67, 1956.
[13] Cioffi, F. J., and Zenchelsky, S. T., J. Phys. Chem., **67,** 357, 1963.
[14] Forman, E. J., and Hume, D. N., J. Phys. Chem., **63,** 1949, 1959.

SELECTED BIBLIOGRAPHY

Jordan, J., and Ewing, G. J., Handbook of Analytical Chemistry, L. Meites, Ed., McGraw-Hill Co., New York, 1963, Sect. 8, pp. 3–7.
Jordan, J., J. Chem. Educ., **40,** A5, 1963.
Jordan, J., Rec. of Chemical Prog., **19,** 193, 1958.
Jordan, J., Chimia, **17,** 101, 1963.
Wendlandt, W. W., Thermal Methods of Analysis, Interscience, New York, 1964.
Zenchelsky, S. T., Anal. Chem., **32,** 289R, 1960.

Chapter 33

THERMAL ANALYSIS

By Wesley W. Wendlandt
Texas Technological College
Lubbock, Texas

INTRODUCTION

The purity of organic and inorganic compounds can be determined by a number of techniques ranging from simple physical methods of boiling and melting point determinations to more sophisticated instrumental methods such as mass spectrometry or absorption spectroscopy. A method offering perhaps the widest potential for the determination of the purity of a substance is thermal analysis (also called cryoscopic determination of purity). This technique is applicable to all substances which are sufficiently stable at their melting points, and permits the determination of the total quantity of contaminant not soluble in the solid phase. It is a nonspecific technique in that there is no differentiation of the impurities that are present; only the total amount is determined in the analysis.

Thermal analysis (not to be confused with differential thermal analysis) may be defined as a method for the determination of the amount of impurity in a substance from an analysis of the temperature-time or temperature-heat content curve, of the material covering its melting range. The basic equation employed is

$$N_0 = K(T_0 - T) \tag{1}$$

in which $K = \frac{100\,\Delta H_f}{RT_0^2}$ = cryoscopic constant, mole percent per °C., and where N_0 is the mole percent impurity, T_0 is the absolute freezing point of the major component when 100 percent pure, T is the absolute temperature of the freezing point equilibrium, ΔH_f is the heat of fusion of the pure component, and R is the gas constant.

A more sophisticated and exact equation, in which the purity of a substance is related to its freezing point, is

$$\log_{10} P = 2.000 - \frac{A}{2.303}(T_0 - T) - \frac{AB}{2.303}(T_0 - T)^2$$

in which $B = \frac{1}{T_0} - \frac{\Delta C_{p0}}{2\Delta H_f}$. The other terms in the equation have the same meaning as previously described. In those analyses where P is greater than 90 percent, the third term of Eq. (2) is generally dropped. It should be noted that the expression is only valid for an ideal solution.

There are two basic methods used to determine the temperature-time or temperature-heat content curves of a substance. They are:

(a) static or calorimetric methods in which an adiabatic calorimeter is employed;
(b) dynamic or thermometric (not to be confused with thermometric titrations) in

which heat evolution or absorption occurs continuously and preferably at a constant rate.

A third method, which is not as widely used as the above, is the differential temperature method described by Handley[1] and Herington.[2] A precision differential thermal analysis apparatus is employed to obtain a differential temperature curve instead of a temperature-time curve.

A typical melting curve of a substance containing varying amounts of impurity is given in Fig. 33-1. In curve (*A*), the lowest amount of impurity is present, while curve (*C*) represents the maximum amount of impurity present. As can be seen, the constant temperature region of the curve shifts to lower values as the amount of impurity increases, while the deviation from the steep-rising early part of the curve also shifts to lower temperatures.

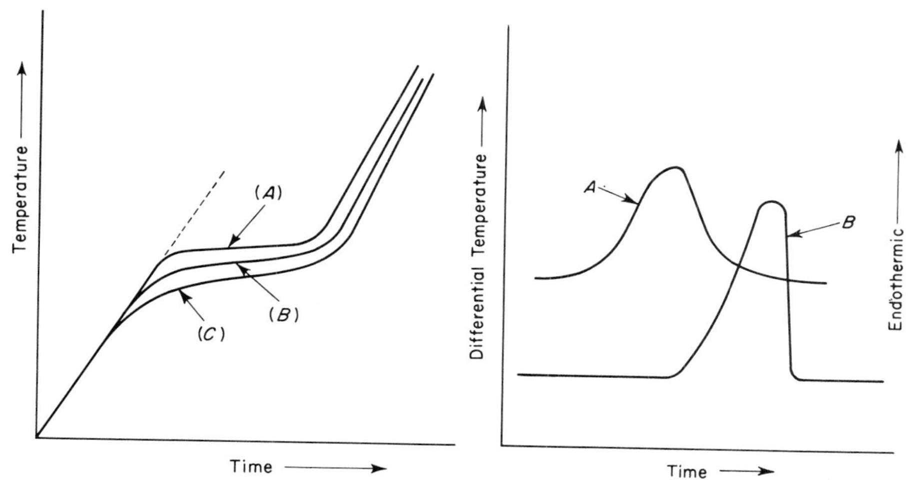

FIG. 33-1. Melting Point Curves of Various Mixtures Containing Different Amounts of an Impurity.

FIG. 33-2. Differential Temperature-Time Curves.

A typical differential melting curve is given in Fig. 33-2. Curve (*B*) is the differential curve for the compound with the highest purity. It should be noted that the sample of lowest purity, curve (*A*), began to melt first (deviation from base line, $\Delta T = 0$), and also reaches its maximum temperature sooner than the highest purity sample. The lower the purity, the less the peak height of the curve, and also the more sudden is the deviation from the base line.

APPARATUS

For thermal analysis by the static method, a precision adiabatic calorimeter is required. Since such an instrument requires a large amount of expensive auxiliary equipment, it will not be discussed here.

In the case of the dynamic method, two different methods are used to maintain a

[1] Handley, R., Anal. Chim. Acta, **17,** 115, 1957.
[2] Herington, E. F. G., Anal. Chim. Acta, **17,** 15, 1957.

constant thermal head between the sample and its surroundings. They are: (a) by a constant wall apparatus; and (b) by an adapted wall apparatus. The former maintains a constant temperature between the wall of the sample container and the sample, while in the latter, constant heat supply to the sample is also maintained when the sample is surrounded by a mantle. The wall temperature is continuously adapted to the temperature of the sample in such a way that the difference between both temperatures remains constant. The various constant and adapted wall apparatuses have been summarized by Smit.[3]

A constant wall apparatus is used mainly for the determination of cooling or freezing curves and not for heating or melting curves. This is because when heat is transported to the sample, the outer wall of the apparatus, and thus the isolating mantle, must be at a temperature much higher than when heat must be transported from the sample.[3] Since the insulating power of the vacuum jacket decreases rapidly at increasing temperatures, due to radiation, the thermal head for heating a sample at a permissible rate will be lower than the opposite thermal head for cooling the sample at the same rate. Depending upon the temperature range employed, the wall of the adapted wall apparatus consists of a glass bulb immersed in a liquid bath or thick cylindrical mantle made of metal. The temperature of the bath or of the metal is adapted to the temperature of the sample so that the difference between the two temperatures remains constant. The temperature difference is usually about 2°C. and the rate of heating of the sample is quite low, about 0.1 to 0.3°C. per min.

A simple, constant wall apparatus is illustrated in Fig. 33-3. The container is a vacuum jacket (Dewar flask) in which equilibrium of temperature in the sample is provided by the mechanical stirrer. This type of apparatus does not permit reliable temperature measurements in the range where the majority of the sample is solid. Indeed, accurate temperature measurements are restricted to the range of 80–100% liquid. The size of the sample for an apparatus of this type may range from 10 to 50 g. Sample temperature is determined by a sensitive thermometer, thermopile, or resistance thermometer, depending upon the accuracy and precision required in the measurements.

An adapted wall apparatus is illustrated in Fig. 33-4, and has previously been described by Carleton[4] and Smit.[5] The enclosure of the sample is in the form of a thin, uniform film surrounding the bulb of a 0.1°C. graduated mercury thermometer. The thermometer is positioned, by means of a bored cork, into a glass tube drawn to the proper dimensions in the portion surrounding the thermometer bulb. To reduce the effects of temperature fluctuations, the sample tube is jacketed by a slightly larger tube retained by a plastic ring. The entire assembly is placed in a 300-ml., round-bottomed flask, in such a position that the thermometer bulb is at the approximate center of the flask. The flask is immersed to the neck in a suitable heating bath which is provided with a stirrer, thermostat, and thermometer. The volume of sample required for a determination is much less than that of the constant wall apparatus, namely, only about 0.3 ml. The temperature of the outside bath is heated at a rate of about 0.3°C. per 100 seconds or per minute.

A somewhat more elaborate apparatus of the above type (also called *thin film* type) has been described by Smit and Kateman[6,7] and is illustrated in Fig. 33-5. The apparatus may be manually operated[7] or adapted to completely automatic control.[6]

The calorimeter consists of an aluminum cylindrical block[4] enclosed by an aluminum

[3] Smit, W. M., Z. Electrochem., **66,** 779, 1962.
[4] Carleton, L. T., Anal. Chem., **27,** 845, 1955.
[5] Smit, W. M., Chem. Weekblad, **36,** 750, 1939.
[6] Smit, W. M., and Kateman, G., Anal. Chim. Acta, **17,** 161, 1957.
[7] Smit, W. M., Rec. trav. chim., **75,** 1309, 1956.

cover. A hole in the cover permits the introduction of the glass sample holder.[5] The apparatus contains two thermometers, one inserted in the sample holder, the other in the thermometer well.[7] The cylindrical block is surrounded by a heating element[3] which consists of a Constantan heating element insulated by glass wool and asbestos paper.

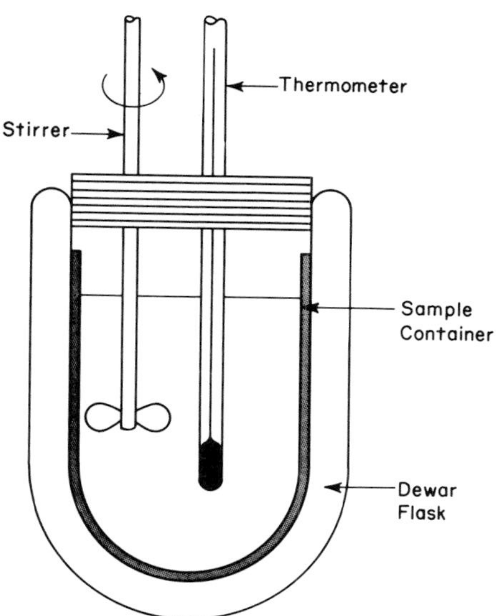

FIG. 33-3. Constant Wall Apparatus for Thermal Analysis.

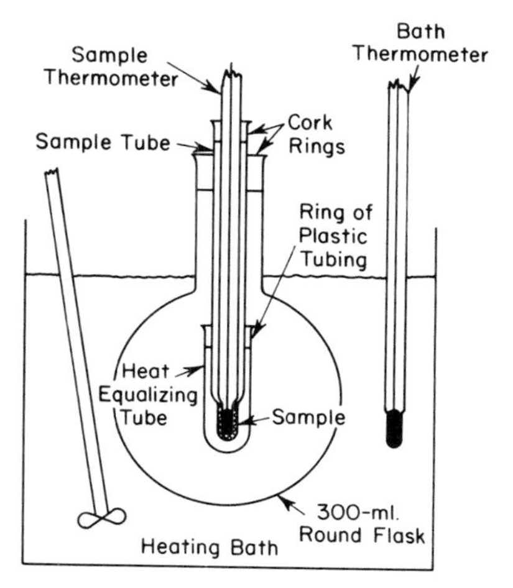

FIG. 33-4. Adapted Wall Apparatus of Carleton. (Reprinted from Analytical Chemistry, **27**, 845, 1955. Copyright 1955 by the American Chemical Society and reprinted by permission of the copyright owner.)

The block and heating element is contained in a cylindrical aluminum jacket and suspended in a Dewar flask[1] by means of support rods, attached to the cover[6] of the flask.

The amount of sample required for a measurement is about 0.5 g. or less. The level of the molten sample has to be about 2 mm. above the top of the thermometer bulb. Trapped air bubbles can be removed by gentle tapping of the sample holder. Details on the automatic operation of the auxiliary equipment have been presented.[6]

APPLICATIONS

It is evident that thermal analysis provides a convenient technique for the determination of the purity of a number of organic and inorganic compounds. However, it is used only in the case of high purity compounds, >99 mole percent composition of the main component, to greatest advantage. It should be noted that Aston[8] has stated that the melting curve (freezing curve) is not always a reliable criterion of purity. Reliable standard samples are needed to check the reliability of this method for purity determination in certain representative cases. It should also be noted that the purity values determined by static methods are systematically lower than those determined on the same sample by dynamic methods. An extremely careful study by Glasgow *et al.*[9] on

[8] Aston, J. G., Anal. Chim. Acta, **17**, 173, 1957.
[9] Glasgow, A. R., *et al.*, Anal. Chim. Acta, **17**, 54, 1957.

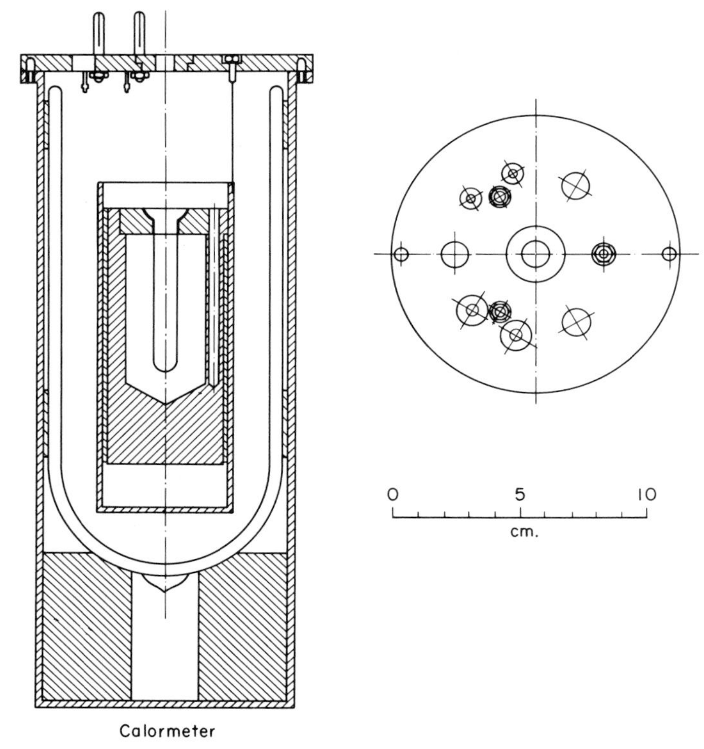

FIG. 33-5. Calorimeter for Thermal Analysis. (After Smit and Kateman; courtesy Analytica Chimica Acta.)

a sample of very pure benzene contaminated by known amounts of *n*-heptane showed that the discrepancy between the two methods is not as large as was formerly obtained. The results of this study are given in Table 33-1. It is suggested that the difference in values may be due to chemi-sorbed water as a source of contamination.

TABLE 33-1. COMPARISON OF THE RESULTS OBTAINED FROM STATIC AND DYNAMIC METHODS

Sample	*Purity, mole %*		
	Computed from Contamination	*Dynamic*	*Static*
A	100[a]	99.994 ± 0.002	99.9937 ± 0.0010
B	99.9964	99.970 ± 0.004	99.958 ± 0.005
C	99.9610	99.940 ± 0.002	99.947 ± 0.005

[a] The "pure" sample was assumed to be pure beyond the sensitivity of the methods of analysis employed.

In the comparative method of purity determination, the amount of contaminant present in the sample can be obtained by determining the freezing curve of the original sample and also the curve of the original sample plus a known amount of contaminant. Using this method, Handley[1] determined the purity of a benzene sample. The results of this investigation are given in Table 33-2. As can be seen, the agreement between added and calculated impurities values is quite good.

TABLE 33-2. COMPARATIVE METHOD OF PURITY DETERMINATION

Sample	*Impurity Present*	*Mole, % Added Impurity*	*Calculated Impurity*
A	0.005 ± 0.002	0.0	0.002
B	0.005 ± 0.002	0.055	0.065
C	0.005 ± 0.002	0.11	0.12
D	0.005 ± 0.002	0.23	0.28

The errors, limitations, and other factors affecting the results obtained in thermal analysis have been previously discussed.[10,11] The former discussed the qualitative considerations concerning the rates of phase transitions, rates of diffusion, and the temperature differences occurring with the "thin film" method. The latter were concerned with the limitations of the calorimetric (static) method. In general, the following recommendations should be followed when using this technique:[10]

(1) When a static method is used, each period of heat supply should be followed by a period of "adiabatic conditions" of sufficient length so as to approach equilibrium to a desired extent.
(2) For the dynamic method, heating curves are preferred to cooling curves.
(3) Before starting the measurement of a heating curve, the sample should be kept at a temperature slightly below the initial melting point for at least 1 hour.
(4) The stirring method for determining heating curves is not recommended.
(5) The rate of heating of samples with small heats of fusion should be as low as practical.
(6) Subject each curve to an internal check and also select a reliable part of the curve for purity determination.

With all of the above sources of error and limitations, thermal analysis has several incomparable advantages. Being a physical method, it may be applied without any knowledge of the chemical properties of the main components or the contaminants of the sample. It is sensitive, although not equally sensitive, to all types of contaminants.

A cryoscopic method for the determination of water in foods is described in Chapter 50, Foods.

SELECTED BIBLIOGRAPHY

Best, R. J., "Cryoscopic Evaluation of Purity," in Handbook of Analytical Chemistry, L. Meites, Ed., McGraw-Hill Book Co., Inc., New York, 1963, Section 8-1.
Smit, W. M., Thermal Analysis, Elsevier Press, Amsterdam, 1959.
Wendlandt, W. W., Thermal Methods of Analysis, Interscience Publishers, New York, 1964.

[10] Smit, W. M., Anal. Chim. Acta, **17,** 23, 1957.
[11] McCullough, J. P., and Waddington, G., Anal. Chim. Acta, **17,** 80, 1957.

Chapter 34

DIFFERENTIAL THERMAL ANALYSIS

By Wesley W. Wendlandt
Texas Technological College
Lubbock, Texas

INTRODUCTION

In the classic paper entitled "De l'action de la chaleur sur les argiles," Le Chatelier[1] described a new technique for the study of clays and minerals by an examination of their temperature-time curves as the substances were heated to elevated temperatures. Roberts-Austen[2] suggested that instead of a single thermocouple, a two-thermocouple system be employed. One thermocouple was placed in the sample, the other in a reference block in the furnace. Thus, the differential temperature, which was more sensitive to small temperature changes of the sample, was recorded as a function of time or temperature. Burgess[3] further discussed the merits of the differential thermocouple arrangement as well as other functions such as $d(\Delta T)$ *vs.* T, and so on.

The early use of this technique was in the identification of clays, minerals, metals, and ceramic materials.[4,5,6,7,8,9] Only fairly recently has this technique been employed extensively to problems of chemical interest. A bibliography of some of the more important references is given at the end of this chapter.

The thermal technique of *differential thermal analysis* (also known as thermography) is one in which the heat effects, associated with chemical and physical changes of a substance, are recorded as a function of temperature or time as the substance is heated at a linear rate. The thermal effects may be either endothermic or exothermic, and are caused by such physical phenomena as fusion, crystalline structure inversions, vaporization, boiling, sublimation, destruction of the crystal lattice, and others. Still other enthalpic effects are caused by chemical reactions such as dissociation or decomposition, dehydration, oxidation and reduction, direct combination, displacement, and so forth. Most of the above transitions or reactions produce endothermic heat effects except those of oxidation and some decomposition reactions, and certain crystalline structure inversions, all of which give exothermic heat effects.

The thermal effects associated with the preceding physical and chemical changes are measured by a differential method in that the sample temperature is continuously compared against the temperature of a thermally inert reference material. This tem-

[1] Le Chatelier, H., Bull. soc. franc. mineral, **10,** 204, 1887.
[2] Roberts-Austen, W. C., Proc. Inst. Mech. Engs., p. 35, 1899; Metallographist, **2,** 186, 1899.
[3] Burgess, G. K., U. S. Bur. Standards, Bull. **5,** 199, 1908–1909.
[4] Norton, F. H., J. Am. Ceram., Soc., **22,** 54, 1939.
[5] Grim, R. E., Ann. N. Y. Acad. Sci., **53,** 1031, 1951.
[6] Berkelhamer, L. H., U. S. Bur. Mines, Rept. Invest., **R13762,** 1942.
[7] Kerr, P. F., and Kulp, J. L., Am. Mineralogist, **33,** 387, 1948.
[8] Kauffman, A. J., and Dilling, E. D., Econ. Geol., **45,** 222, 1950.
[9] Foldvari-Vogl, M., Acta Geological, **5,** 1, 1958.

perature difference, or differential temperature, ΔT, is recorded as a function of reference material temperature (or furnace temperature) or time, assuming that the furnace temperature rise is linear with respect to time. Experimentally, this technique is quite simple to carry out in the laboratory. A furnace is employed which contains a sample holder or sample block, the latter of which has two identical and symmetrically located chambers. Each chamber contains a centered thermocouple or other temperature detection device (thermistor, resistance thermometer, or thermopile). The sample is placed in one chamber and a reference material, such as α-aluminum oxide, α-Al_2O_3, is placed in the other chamber. The furnace and sample block temperature are then increased at a linear rate, and the temperature difference between the sample and reference is continuously measured or recorded against the furnace or reference material temperature.

If the temperature of the sample and the differential temperature are compared with each other, as a function of time, the curves in Fig. 34-1 are obtained. At A on the

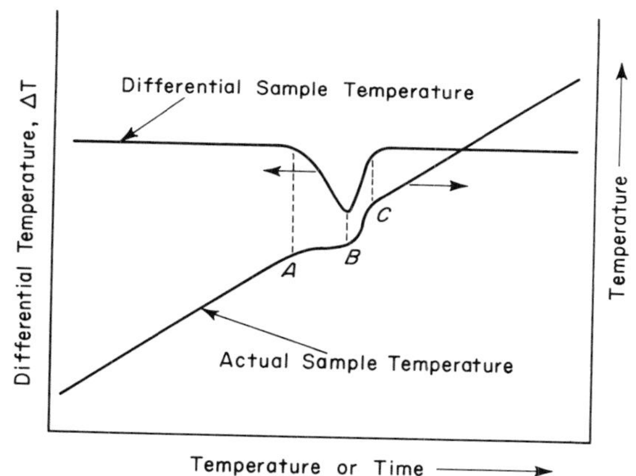

FIG. 34-1. Comparison Between Sample Temperature and Differential Temperature.

curve, it is assumed, the sample undergoes some type of an endothermic transition. As can be seen on the sample temperature curve, the sample temperature is no longer linear with respect to time, but lags the furnace temperature due to the absorption of heat. The reaction is about completed at B and the sample temperature increases, catching up with the furnace temperature again at C. In the case of the differential temperature curve, the sample and reference material temperature differ (ideally) during the actual transition which began at A. This results in a peak in the curve, the maximum of which occurs at about B. Beyond B, the curve returns to the base line, $\Delta T = 0$, due to the equalization of sample and reference temperatures. The differential temperature curve, as can be seen from Fig. 34-1, contains a more pronounced peak than the sample temperature curve, hence, is a more sensitive method for the detection of sample thermal transitions. Although only an endothermic transition is illustrated here, the curve deviations would be in an opposite, inverted position for an exothermic transition.

The importance of differential thermal analysis (DTA) to analytical chemistry lies in the characterization of a substance by its ΔT curve. Each substance will, in general, give a curve whose number, shape, and position of the various endothermic and exothermic peaks, serve as a means of qualitative identification of the substance. Since the area enclosed by the peaks (in reference to the base line) is roughly proportional to the heat of the thermal transition involved, DTA is useful for the semiquantitative or, in some cases, quantitative determination of the heat of reaction. Also, because the heat of reaction is proportional to the amount of reacting substance, the technique can be used to evaluate quantitatively the amount of substance present if the former is known. One of the serious defects of DTA is the empirical nature of the resulting curve due to the experimental conditions employed. The curve is highly sensitive to such variables as ambient atmosphere, heating rate, sample size, sample packing, and so forth. These variables are discussed later in this chapter.

THEORY

The theoretical interpretation of the DTA curve, on the basis of heat transfer equations, has been the subject of a number of studies. All of these theories relate, in some manner, the area enclosed by the curve peak to the various parameters of the sample and the apparatus. Since the derivation of each of these theories is beyond the scope of this discussion,[7,10,11,12] only one final result will be given here.[12]

For a sample block constructed from a metal such as nickel, in which the sample holder geometry is a cylinder, Boersma derived the following equation for the peak area:

$$\int_{t_1}^{t_2} \theta \, dt = qa^2/4\lambda \tag{1}$$

where t_1 and t_2 are the times at the beginning and end of the peak, q is the heat of transformation per unit volume, θ is the differential temperature, a is the radius of the sample chamber, and λ is the thermal conductivity of the sample.

According to the above equation, the sample is: (a) a producer of heat; and (b) a heat measuring resistance in which the flow of heat develops a temperature difference to be measured. To separate these two functions, the use of metal sample and reference cups in which the temperature difference was measured from outside of the sample and reference materials was recommended.[12] The peak area will then depend only on the sample heat of transformation and the calibration factor of the instrument. Thus, the heat of reaction, ΔH, is equal to

$$\Delta H = \frac{\psi}{m} \int_{t_1}^{t_2} \theta \, dt \tag{2}$$

where ψ is an experimental determined constant, and m is the sample mass. From a knowledge of ψ for a particular apparatus, the heat of reaction or transformation can be evaluated. The method is, at best, only an approximation, and only semiquantitative results are obtained.

INSTRUMENTATION

A typical DTA apparatus, as illustrated schematically in Fig. 34-2, consists of the following components: furnace or other heating device; sample holder; microvolt or millivolt d.c. amplifier; differential temperature detectors; furnace temperature controller; recorder; and furnace atmosphere control system. There are a number of

[10] Speil, S., Berkelhamer, L. H., Pask, J. A., and Davis, B., U. S. Bur. Mines, Tech. Paper, 664, 1945.

[11] Vold, M. J., Anal. Chem., **21,** 683, 1949.

[12] Boersma, S. L., J. Am. Ceram. Soc., **38,** 281, 1955.

modifications of this basic design but they all measure and record ΔT as a function of temperature or time.

Various containers have been employed to contain the sample and reference materials. They have been constructed in a variety of shapes and dimensions using such materials as alumina, boro-silicate glass, Vycor glass, fused quartz, zirconia, beryllia, stainless steel, nickel, platinum, Inconel, silver, aluminum and other metals, graphite, and the sample itself. Obviously, the choice of construction material depends upon the temperature range to be studied as well as the nature of the sample. The sample should not react with the container during the pyrolysis. Several of the more common types

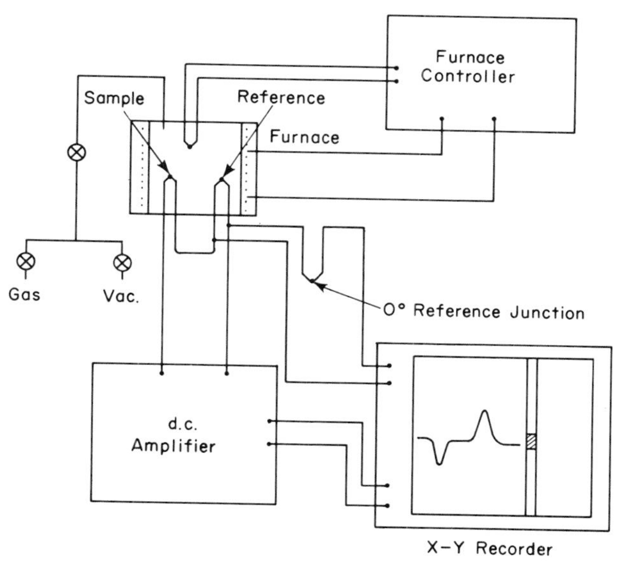

FIG. 34-2. Typical DTA Apparatus (Schematic).

of sample holders are illustrated in Fig. 34-3. Multiple sample holders have also been described, capable of studying three, four, five, or six samples simultaneously. The convenience of this type of sample holder is readily apparent when a large number of samples are to be studied.

The choice of a temperature detection device is again dependent on the maximum temperature desired, the chemical reactivity of the sample, and the sensitivity of the d.c. amplifier and recording equipment. The most commonly used device is the thermocouple although thermopiles, thermistors, and various resistance elements have been employed. Thermocouples have been constructed from Chromel *vs.* Alumel, copper *vs.* platinum-10 or 13% rhodium, and others. For high temperature studies, up to 1500°C., the platinum couple is recommended; for fairly low temperatures, up to 300°C., the copper couple may be used. A satisfactory general purpose thermocouple is Chromel-Alumel, which may be used up to about 1100°C. Thermistors may be employed, with certain advantages, only up to about 300°C.

The choice of furnace geometry and heating element depends upon the temperature range desired. Furnaces have been described which cover the range from −190° to 2800°C.; they may be heated by a resistance element, infrared radiation, high frequency

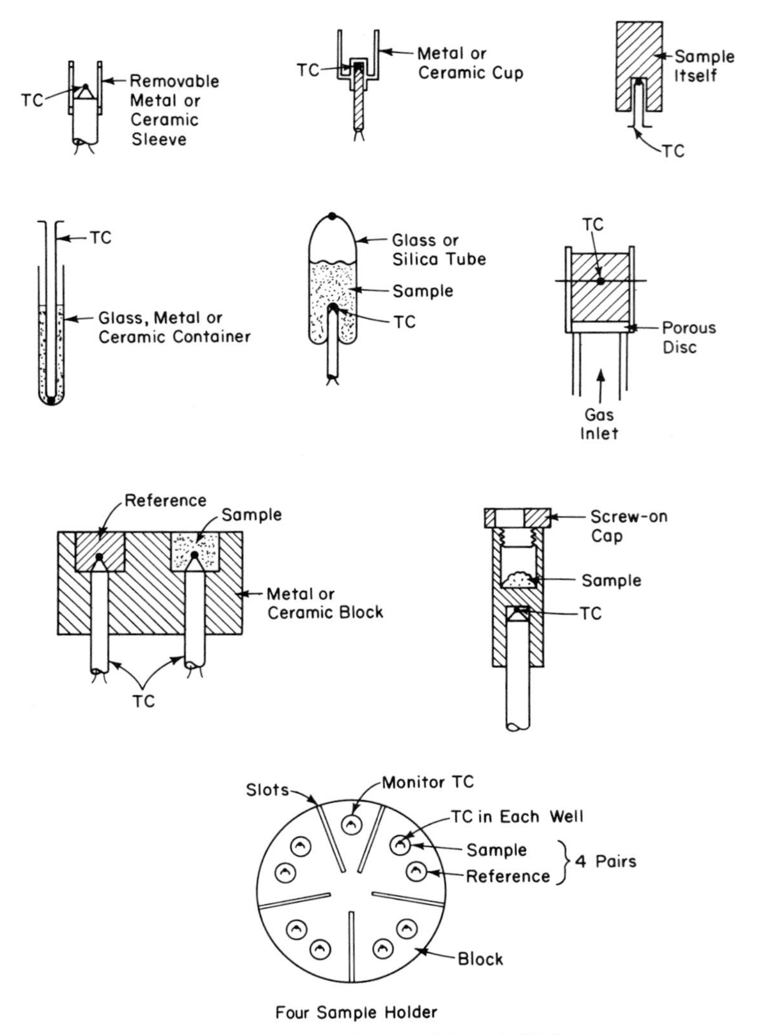

Fig. 34-3. Various Types of Sample Holders.

r.f. oscillation, or by a coil of tubing through which a heated or cooled liquid or gas is circulated. Resistance elements are perhaps the most commonly employed; they include such materials as Nichrome, Kanthal, platinum, rhodium, Globar, molybdenum, tungsten, and others. Furnaces have been designed to operate in a high vacuum or in static or dynamic atmospheres of various gases.

The temperature rise of the furnace is controlled by either increasing the voltage through the heater element by a motor-driven variable transformer or by a thermocouple-actuated feed-back type of controller. Heating rates from 0.1° to 300°C. per minute have been employed, although the most commonly used rate is 10° to 15°C.

per minute. It is important that the heating rate be linear with time as any sudden change may appear on the ΔT curve as a spurious peak.

A good low-noise-level d.c. amplifier is required for a DTA apparatus unless thermopiles or thermistors are employed as the ΔT detectors. Since sample sizes may range in weight from one to several hundred milligrams, the ΔT voltages, as detected by the thermocouples, are of the order of microvolts. These microvolt signals are amplified and recorded, generally, on a millivolt recorder; hence, an amplification of about one thousand is required. The amplifier must be linear in response and should be as electronically stable as possible. Low electronic stability will result in undue base-line drift of the curve.

The amplified ΔT signals are recorded as a function of temperature or time on a strip-chart potentiometric or galvanometric recorder or an X-Y recorder. Again, the requirements of a good recorder are that it be free from electronic noise, possess good electronic and mechanical stability, and have a response which is linear to the incoming signal. Other types of recorders which have been employed are X_1-X_2 *vs.* time, or multipoint instruments of various types.

FACTORS AFFECTING RESULTS

The DTA curve of a substance is not as strictly reproducible as, say, its infrared spectrum or x-ray diffraction pattern. Different instruments located in different laboratories will not, in general, yield identical DTA curves. The reasons for this are manifold, but they can be divided into those caused by the instrument and those dependent on the sample characteristics. The instrumental factors include furnace atmosphere, size and shape of the furnace, sample holder material, sample holder geometry, wire and bead size of the thermocouple junction, heating rate, speed and response of recording equipment, and thermocouple location in the sample chamber. Factors which depend on the sample characteristics are particle size, thermal conductivity, heat capacity, packing density, swelling or shrinkage of sample, amount of sample, effect of diluent, and degree of crystallinity. Each of these factors plays an important role in determining the overall shape of the curve peaks as well as their positions in relation to the temperature axis. Thus, it is easy to understand the empirical nature of the DTA curve. A correlation cannot easily be made between, say, peak maxima temperature and the thermal stability of a compound. However, for DTA curves obtained on the same instrument, a rough correlation can at times be made if identical conditions of pyrolysis were employed on each sample. No attempt will be made here to elucidate these many variables as they are described in detail elsewhere.

The basic assumption for quantitative DTA studies is that the area enclosed by the curve peak be proportional to the heat of reaction. Many studies have been concerned about this; one of the more thorough studies was by Wittels.[13] He found that using calcite samples ranging in weight from 0.30 to 3.00 mg., the peak areas obeyed a linear relationship to the sample weight. In another study,[14] he related the curve peak area with heating rate and sample mass by the relationship

$$\Delta H = \frac{A}{\tan\left(\frac{\ln R(R - C)}{m}\right)}$$

where R is the heating rate, A is the peak area, and m and C are constants. The best

[13] Wittels, M., Am. Mineralogist, **36,** 615, 1951.
[14] Wittels, M., *Ibid.*, **36,** 760, 1951.

response of the instrument was obtained at a heating rate of 30°C. per minute, but it fell off rapidly below 15°C. per minute. Conversely, if the heat of reaction, ΔH, is known, the amount of sample can be determined in a mixture by the measurement of the peak area. This presumes, of course, that there are no disturbing side reactions with the diluent which would alter the peak area.

APPLICATIONS

The application of DTA to problems in analytical chemistry covers a broad area and includes its use as a control or routine tool for comparing similar but not identical materials. As a control technique,[15] it can be used to distinguish between raw materials quickly and easily in those cases where the treatment of the material must be modified if slight changes in the material are encountered. As a comparison technique, DTA may be used in some cases to examine materials that yield anomalous results by other methods. As already mentioned, if the ΔH of the peak forming reaction is known, DTA can be used to determine the composition of mixtures containing this component. Perhaps the most important use of DTA is that of the identification of various compounds or mixtures of compounds by an examination of their ΔT curve. One does not always obtain unequivocal results by this method, and must resort to thermogravimetry, gas evolution analysis, analysis of the reaction products, x-ray diffraction, or the like for supplementary information. DTA curves have thus been used to identify polymers, lubricating greases, fats and oils, coordination compounds, carbohydrates, amino acids and proteins, metal salt hydrates, metal and nonmetal oxides, coal and lignite, wood and related substances, natural products, various organic compounds, and other materials. Little or no information is available concerning the detection limits of a specific component in a mixture, since these limits can vary so widely. The limits depend not only on the heat of reaction of the component but also on the sensitivity of the recording equipment and other apparatus components.

Only a few illustrative examples can be given here; for further information, the bibliography should be consulted.

Determination of Moisture Content of Powdered Substances.—Using the dynamic gas flow technique, Stone developed a rapid analytical method for the determination of the moisture content of a "nearly dry" powdered substance.[16] The sample was placed in the DTA sample holder at room temperature and at atmospheric pressure. On evacuation of the sample chamber at a fixed rate, the DTA curve peak began at the point (time) where the external water vapor pressure was less than the partial pressure of the water vapor pressure of the sample. From the peak height, using a suitable calibration curve, the amount of moisture in the sample was determined.

Linear Polymer Content of Polyethylene.—The linear polymer content of polyethylene has been determined by a DTA method by Clampitt.[17] The DTA curves of several of the polyethylene blends are given in Fig. 34-4. The curve for the unannealed polyethylene sample had an endothermic peak with a peak maximum temperature (T_m) of 134°C., and also a small shoulder peak. On annealing this sample for 30 minutes at 120°C., the shoulder peak was resolved into two peaks, with T_m values of 115° and 124°C., respectively. For a pure high pressure polyethylene sample, only one peak was obtained with a T_m of 110°C., while for the pure linear polyethylene sample, a single peak was observed with a T_m of 135°C. The area under the 115°C. peak decreased as the amount of linear polymer increased while the area under the 134°C. peak increased.

[15] Garn, P. D., and Flaschen, S. S., Anal. Chem., **29,** 271, 1957.
[16] Stone, R. L., Anal. Chem., **32,** 1582, 1960.
[17] Clampitt, B. H., Anal. Chem., **35,** 577, 1963.

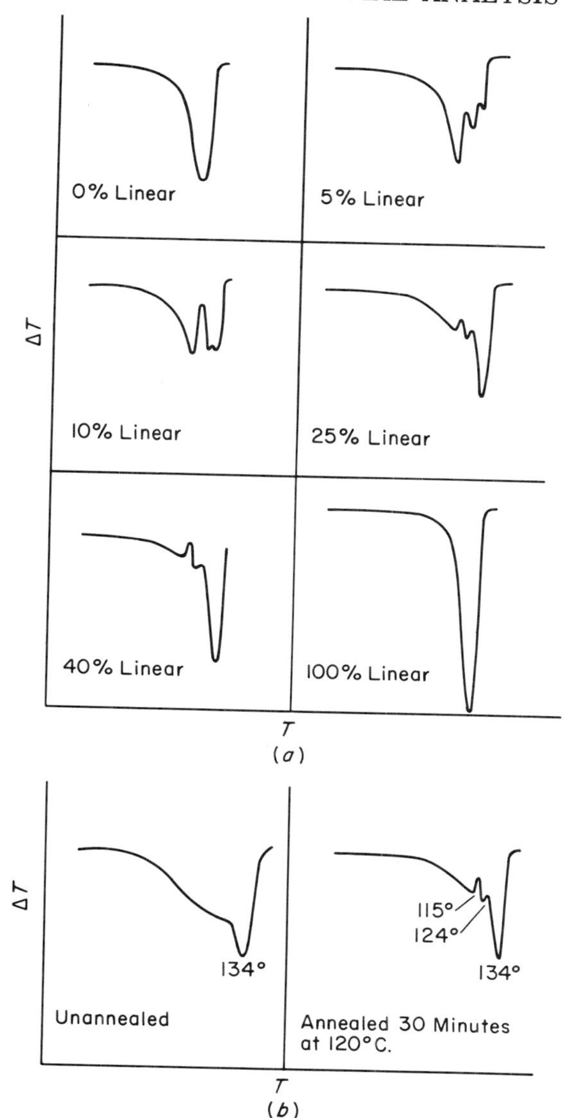

FIG. 34-4. (*a*) DTA Curves of Linear-High Pressure Polyethylene Blends. (*b*) Effect of Annealing on 25% Linear Blends. (Reprinted from Analytical Chemistry, **35**, 577, 1963. Copyright 1963 by the American Chemical Society and reprinted by permission of the copyright owner.)

Thus, it was concluded that the 115°C. peak decreased as the amount of linear polymer increased while the area under the 134°C. peak increased. If it is assumed that all of the linear polyethylene is crystallized, then using a proportionality constant and the area under the 134°C. peak, the amount of linear content of the sample was calculated.

It was found that using this method, fairly good agreement was obtained between the true blend composition and the calculated linear content. The melting points and degree of crystallinity of a number of polyolefins has also been studied by Ke.[18]

Effect of Radiation on Polymeric and Other Substances.—An interesting application of DTA was a study of the effect of radiation on polymeric and other substances by Murphy and Hill.[19] The DTA curves of biphenyl and irradiated biphenyl are given in Fig. 34-5. The nonirradiated sample curve contained two endothermic peaks which were caused by fusion (70°C.) and volatilization (175°C.) of the compound. The irradiated sample gave the first two peaks as well as an exothermic peak with a T_m of about 370°C. It was assumed that the 370°C. peak was caused by the air oxidation of

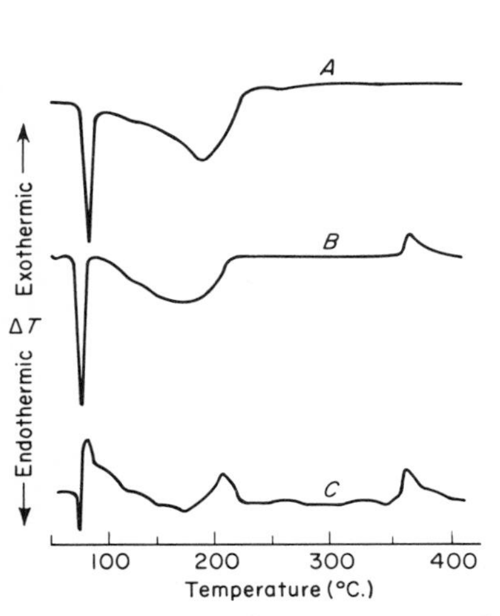

Fig. 34-5. DTA Curves of Biphenyl: *A*, Nonirradiated; *B*, Irradiated; *C*, Irradiated *vs.* Nonirradiated Samples. (Courtesy Nucleonics.)

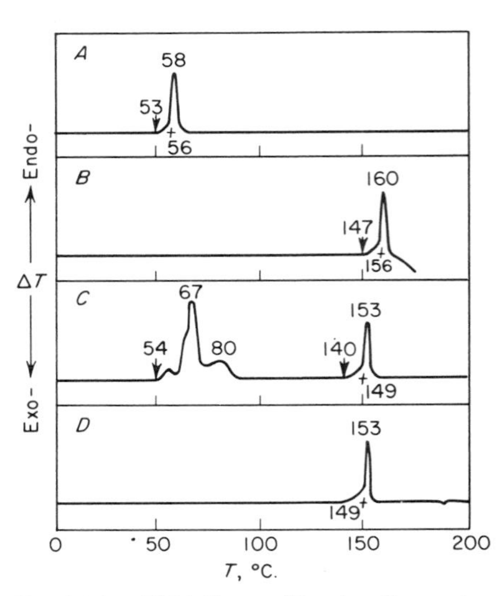

Fig. 34-6. DTA Curves Showing Formation of the *p*-Nitrophenylhydrazone of Acetone: *A*, Acetone; *B*, *p*-Nitrophenylhydrazine; *C*, Reaction Mixture of *A* and *B*; *D*, Rerun of Residue from *C*. (Reprinted from Analytical Chemistry, **34**, 1841, 1962. Copyright 1962 by the American Chemical Society and reprinted by permission of the copyright owner.)

the nonvolatile, radiation-induced biphenyl polymer remaining in the sample holder after volatilization of low-molecular weight materials. A lowering of the melting point of biphenyl was also caused by irradiation. It was observed that by proper choice of materials, on the basis of the relationship of peak area to radiation dose, DTA might be applied to dosimetry over a wide range of energy levels.

Derivatives of Organic Compounds.—The formation of derivatives of organic compounds in a DTA sample chamber has been described by Chiu.[20] Instead of employing the traditional method of preparing the derivative from sample and a reagent, Chiu

[18] Ke, B., J. Polymer Sci., **42,** 15, 1960.
[19] Murphy, C. B., and Hill, J. A., Nucleonics, **18,** 78, 1960.
[20] Chiu, J., Anal. Chem., **34,** 1841, 1962.

replaced it with a one-step process. The sample was heated with the reagent at a programmed heating rate in a selected atmosphere. The resulting DTA curve showed the derivative-forming reaction, the physical transitions of the sample or reagent in excess, and the transitions of the intermediates and products. The formation of the acetone hydrazone derivative with *p*-nitrophenylhydrazine is shown in Fig. 34-6. The curves for pure acetone, pure *p*-nitrophenylhydrazine, and a mixture of the two are given. The curve for the mixture gave a complex endothermic peak in the 54° to 80°C. temperature range which was attributed to the net result of evaporation of excess acetone, solution of *p*-nitrophenylhydrazine in acetone, and hydrazone formation. The fusion of the hydrazone was indicated by the endothermic peak with a T_m of 153°C. The reported melting point of the hydrazone derivative is 152°C. Similar results were obtained for the reactions between triethylamine and picric acid, and dextrose and propylamine. The method is said to be rapid and convenient.

Characterization of Rare Earth Chlorides.—DTA has been used to characterize the rare-earth chloride hydrates by Wendlandt and Bear.[21] The DTA curves of these compounds are presented in Fig. 34-7. On the basis of these curves, the compounds can be

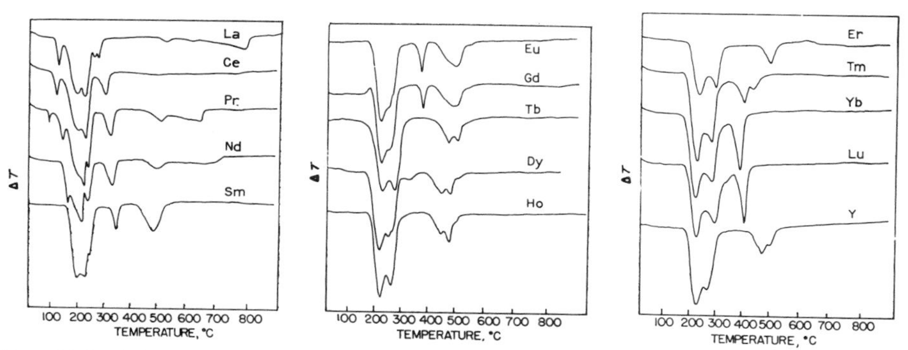

Fig. 34-7. DTA Curves of Rare-Earth Chloride Hydrates. (Courtesy Analytica Chimica Acta.)

placed into four groups, each of which is characterized by the presence or absence of certain endothermic peaks. In Group I, which includes lanthanum, cerium(III), praseodymium, and neodymium, there are one or two small endothermic peaks which precede the large endothermic dehydration peaks. Also observed in this group, with the exception of cerium(III), are the endothermic peaks in the 400° to 650°C. temperature range which are presumably due to oxychloride formation. In Group II, which includes samarium, europium, and gadolinium, the dehydration peaks consisted entirely of just one maximum. However, there were sharp endothermic peaks in the 160° to 180°C. temperature range and broad endothermic peaks in the 390° to 400°C. temperature range. The curves for the compounds in Group III—terbium, dysprosium, yttrium, holmium, erbium, and thulium, were characterized by the splitting of the dehydration into two peaks and also the splitting of the oxychloride formation peaks. In Group IV—ytterbium and lutetium, the splitting of the dehydration endothermic peak was observed but also new peaks appeared in the 310° to 325°C. temperature range.

[21] Wendlandt, W. W., and Bear, J. L., Anal. Chim. Acta, **21**, 439, 1959.

APPLICATIONS IN THE ANALYSIS OF SPECIAL MATERIALS

The following procedures have been included in other chapters of Standard Methods of Chemical Analysis:

1. Chapter 46, Volume III, Portland Cement.
   a. Determination of alite phase in cement clinkers
   b. Hydration of calcium hydroxide
   c. Studies of silicate phase
2. Chapter 48, Volume III, Natural Fats.
   a. Determination of fat crystallizing characteristics
   Chapter 33, Volume IIB, Natural Fats.
   a. Cooling curves in the physical characterization of fats
3. Chapter 54, Volume III, Paint, Varnish, and Lacquer.
   a. Determination of glass transition temperatures of polymers
   b. Characterization of a series of esters
   c. Characterization of polyesters
   d. Determination of curing of unsaturated polyesters
4. Chapter 57, Volume III, Petroleum and Petroleum Products.
   a. Analysis of high molecular weight fractions obtained by column chromatography
5. Chapter 58, Volume III, Plastics.
   a. DTA provides a method for studying physical and chemical transformations in polymers which are accompanied by thermal effects, such as polymerization or curing, crystallization, melting, oxidation, and thermal decomposition
   b. Characterization of polymers and polymer mixtures
   c. Glass transitions
   d. Degree of crystallinity
   e. Oxidative and thermal stability of polymers
6. Chapter 59, Volume III, Rubber and Rubber Products.
   a. Determination of internal structure of rubber
7. Chapter 64, Volume III, Determination of Water
   a. Determination of water in hydrates

SELECTED BIBLIOGRAPHY

Foldvari-Vogl, M., Acta Geological, **5,** 1, 1958.
Gordon, S., J. Chem. Educ., **40,** A87, 1963.
Kauffman, A. J., and Dilling, E. D., Econ. Geol., **45,** 222, 1950.
Kerr, P. F., and Kulp, J. L., Am. Mineralogist, **33,** 387, 1948.
Kissinger, H. E., and Newman, S. B., Differential Thermal Analysis in Analytical Chemistry of Polymers, G. M. Kline, Ed., Vol. XII, Part II, Interscience, New York, 1962.
Mackenzie, R. C., Ed., Differential Thermal Analysis of Clays, Central Press, Aberdeen, Scotland, 1957.
Murphy, C. B., Anal. Chem., **30,** 867, 1958; **32,** 168, 1960; **34,** 298R, 1962; Modern Plastics, 125, August, 1960.
Norton, F. H., J. Am. Ceram. Soc., **22,** 54, 1939.
Smothers, W. J., Chiang, Y., and Wilson, A., Bibliography of Differential Thermal Analysis, University of Arkansas, Fayetteville, Ark., 1951.
Smothers, W. J., and Chiang, Y., Differential Thermal Analysis: Theory and Practice, Chemical Publishing Co., New York, 1958.
Speil, S., Berkelhamer, L. H., Pask, J. A., and Davis, B., U. S. Bur. Mines, Tech. Paper **664,** 1945.
Wendlandt, W. W., "Differential Thermal Analysis," in Techniques of Inorganic Chemistry, Jonassen and Weisberger, Eds., Interscience, New York, 1963, Chapter 6.
Wendlandt, W. W., Thermal Methods of Analysis, Interscience, New York, 1964.

Chapter 35

THERMOGRAVIMETRIC ANALYSIS

By Wesley W. Wendlandt
Texas Technological College
Lubbock, Texas

INTRODUCTION

The drying and/or ignition temperatures of analytical precipitates is of great interest in inorganic gravimetric analysis. In the early years of analytical chemistry, practically all analytical precipitates were dried at 100° to 120°C., the usual temperature of the laboratory oven, or else ignited at "red heat," the undefinable temperature of the Meker gas burner or other type of burner. All this has changed, however, since the development of the modern recording thermobalance[1] and the classic studies of Duval and his co-workers.[2] From an examination of the weight-change *vs.* temperature curve of a substance, information can be obtained concerning the thermal stability and composition of the original material, the composition and thermal stability of intermediate compounds (if any), and the composition of the residue.

The technique of thermogravimetric analysis (TGA), or thermogravimetry, is concerned with an analysis of the sample weight-change curve. The sample is continuously weighed as it is heated at a constant, preferably linear rate. Although manual recording methods have been employed, by the use of an automatic recording thermobalance, a curve of weight-change of the sample *vs.* sample temperature can be obtained directly. The principle of the technique can be illustrated by the weight-loss curve in Fig. 35-1. Using the hypothetical compound, $MCO_3 \cdot 2H_2O$, it is seen that water is evolved beginning at *A*. The temperature at *A* is called the minimum weight-loss temperature. Although a great amount of exactness has been placed in this value by certain investigators, the value is quite empirical and dependent on a number of variables as will be discussed later. At *B*, a break is obtained in the curve at the stoichiometry approaching that of $MCO_3 \cdot H_2O$. However, since a definite weight-plateau was not obtained, this composition may be fortuitous. Further heating gives the anhydrous MCO_3 weight-level from *C* to *D*. From the usual practice, as described by Duval,[2] the drying temperature for MCO_3 would be placed somewhere between *C* and *D*. It should be pointed out that the values of *C* and *D* are dependent on the heating rate of the furnace; a slower heating rate will shift these temperatures to lower values. The sample, MCO_3, began to evolve carbon dioxide at *D*, giving the MO weight-level from *E* to *F*.

From the various regions in the curve, then, the thermal stabilities of the original sample, the intermediate compounds, and the final product can be ascertained. The curve is quantitative in that calculations can be made to determine the stoichiometry of the compound at any given temperature. In the simplicity of the method and the information obtained from a single measurement, lies the utility of the technique. How-

[1] Chevenard, P., Wache, S., and de la Tullaye, R., Bull. Soc. Chim. France, [5], **11**, 41, 1944.
[2] Duval, C., Inorganic Thermogravimetric Analysis, Elsevier, Amsterdam, First Ed., 1953; Second Ed., 1963.

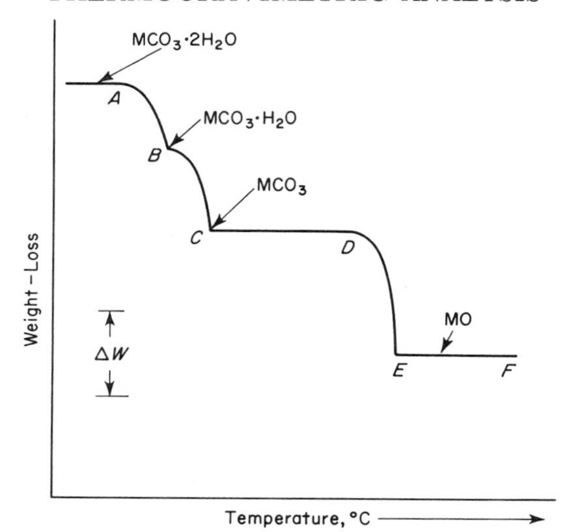

FIG. 35-1. Weight-Loss Curve of $MCO_3 \cdot 2H_2O$; Ambient Air Atmosphere.

ever, like most other laboratory techniques, complementary methods must be used at times in order to interpret the weight-change curve.

One of the useful contributions that the thermobalance has made to analytical chemistry has been the technique of automatic thermogravimetric analysis. The principle of this technique is discussed here using the curve illustrated in Fig. 35-2. For a single-component system, the base line of the thermobalance is first determined, as indicated by the dashed line *B*. The wet sample, *e.g.*, analytical precipitate, is then placed in the sample container. The sample is heated and the weight-change curve is recorded in the usual manner. From the horizontal weight-level, *DE*, the weight w_{DE} can be obtained,

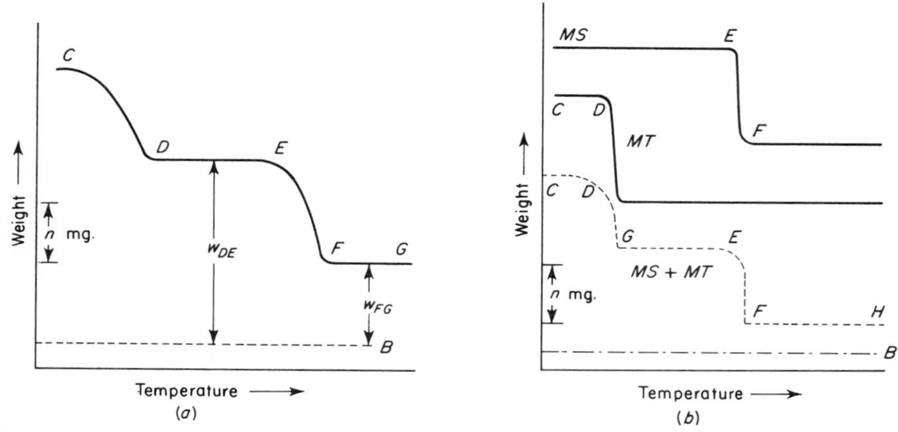

FIG. 35-2. Automatic Thermogravimetric Analysis: *a*, Single-Component System; *b*, Binary System.

and from weight-level FG, the weight w_{FG} is obtained. Since the weight-levels indicate that a definite compound stoichiometry has been attained, multiplication of w_{DE} and w_{FG} by the appropriate gravimetric factors gives the weight of metal ion present.

In the case of the binary mixture, the procedure is similar to the above. The weight-loss curves for pure MS and MT, and for a mixture of $MS + MT$, are given in Fig. 35-2b. In the curve for the mixture, horizontal weight-levels are obtained at the same temperatures as were found for the pure compounds. Thus, the amount of MT can be obtained in the mixture curve from BG; and the amount of MS present from EF. In one simple operation, then, the analysis of certain binary and ternary mixtures can be obtained rapidly and with reasonable accuracy.

INSTRUMENTATION

The principles of TGA require that the sample be continuously weighed as it is heated to elevated temperatures. The sample is continuously weighed by an instrument called a thermobalance. Many crude thermobalances have been described in the literature since Honda[3] first used the term to describe his instrument in 1915. Both manual and automatic-recording balances have been built, but for practical reasons, the latter type is preferred. It was first thought that almost any old, worn analytical balance could be converted into a thermobalance by the addition of a furnace and a sample holder suspended from one of the balance pans. Results obtained by an instrument such as this are certainly not very reliable. In the first place, any old, worn analytical balance should not be used for any precision weighing but should be discarded. Secondly, it is difficult to control the furnace atmosphere and the conditions of pyrolysis. And lastly, air convection currents, especially above 600°C., are an annoying source of error. Such an instrumentation arrangement is certainly not recommended. A modern thermobalance consists generally of the following components: a recording balance; a furnace; a furnace programmer or controller; and a recording device. Such a thermobalance is illustrated schematically in Fig. 35-3. Perhaps the most important component of the thermobalance is the recording balance. The requirements of a suitable recording balance are essentially those for a good quality analytical balance, namely, accuracy, reproducibility, sensitivity, capacity, rugged construction, and insensitivity to ambient temperature changes. The balance should have an adjustable range of weight change, a high degree of electronic and mechanical stability, be able to respond rapidly to changes in weight, and be relatively unaffected by vibration. From a practical viewpoint, the balance should be simple to operate and versatile so that it can be used for varied applications. A number of excellent reviews are available on recording balances and thermobalances.[2,4,5,6,7]

The requirements for the furnace are similar to those described for differential thermal analysis (see Chapter 34). Furnaces have been described which operate up to maximum temperatures of over 2000°C. The furnace must be constructed so as to allow easy access to the sample holder and also to cool down quickly after a run has been completed. A number of different sample holder geometries have been described.[2,8,9,10] Lukaszewski proposed that the sample holder be symmetrical and of minimal volume

[3] Honda, K., Sci. Repts. Tohoku Imp. Univ., **4**, 97, 1915.
[4] Gordon, S., and Campbell, C., Anal. Chem., **32**, 271R, 1960.
[5] Lewin, S. Z., J. Chem. Educ., **39**, A575, 1962.
[6] Lukaszewski, G. M., and Redfern, J. P., Lab. Practice, **10**, 552, 1961.
[7] Jacque, L., Guiochon, G., and Gendrel, P., Bull. soc. chim. France, **1961**, 1061.
[8] Garn, P. D., and Kessler, J. E., Anal. Chem., **32**, 1563, 1960.
[9] Garn, P. D., Anal. Chem., **33**, 1247, 1961.
[10] Lukaszewski, G. M., Nature, **194**, 959, 1962.

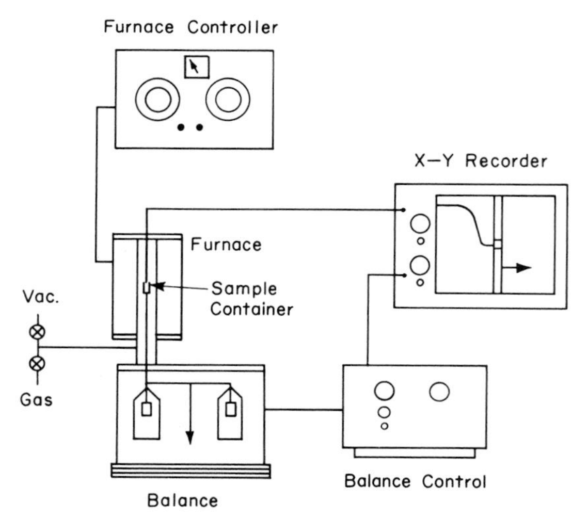

FIG. 35-3. A Modern Automatic-Recording Thermobalance (Schematic).

while the support assembly should be as small and as streamlined as possible. Garn and Kessler[8] recommended the use of a self-generated atmosphere sample holder. In such a holder, the sample is placed in a cylindrical shaped holder into which is inserted a loose fitting piston. In this manner, the evolved gases are in intimate contact with the sample during the pyrolysis and do not diffuse off rapidly into the furnace atmosphere. Duval[2] suggested that since the walls of the sample crucible are heated more strongly than the center, the use of a plate and a thin sample layer should be the best sample holder, whereas the high-walled crucible should be the worst. However, since certain samples swell or spatter when heated, the use of a crucible with high walls is necessary.

The weight-loss curve can be recorded on a potentiometric strip-chart recorder as a function of time; on an X_1-X_2 recorder, where the furnace temperature is also recorded as a function of time; or on an X-Y recorder, as a function of temperature. Various multipoint recorders have also been employed. The choice of a recording system depends upon the investigator. However, for reaction kinetics studies, a time-base recorder is preferred.

The furnace temperature programmers of controllers are of the same type as are used in differential thermal analysis. Various heating rates have been employed in TGA work, from 0.5 to several hundred degrees C. per minute. Generally, a heating rate of 5°C. per minute is preferred and it should be linear with respect to time. If at all possible, the temperature rise of the furnace should be recorded as a function of time since any change in the heating rate may adversely affect the weight-change curve.

Provision should be made for the use of controlled atmospheres in the furnace chamber. In many cases, the furnace may be flooded with an inert gas, or a dynamic gaseous atmosphere may be employed. Vacuum-recording balances are also available so that pyrolysis studies can be carried out at reduced as well as atmospheric pressures.

FACTORS AFFECTING RESULTS

With great similarity to DTA, the factors which affect the curve obtained in TGA can be divided into two groups: instrumental factors; and sample characteristics. The instrumental factors are: furnace heating rate; recording or chart speed; furnace atmosphere; geometry of sample holder and furnace; sensitivity of recording balance and recorder; and composition of sample container. The sample characteristics which affect the weight-loss curve are: amount of sample; solubility of evolved gases in sample; sample particle size; heat of decomposition reaction; sample packing; nature of the sample and sample thermal conductivity. Unfortunately, definitive studies are lacking on many of the above factors. Many of these factors are fixed by the type of thermobalance, such as sample holder geometry, recording speed, balance sensitivity, and so on, while it is difficult to reproduce some of the sample characteristics such as particle size, packing, and thermal conductivity (changes due to sintering and swelling). A more complete discussion of these factors and their effect on the weight-loss curve is given in the bibliography at the end of the chapter.

APPLICATIONS

With all of its limitations and sources of error, the technique of TGA is a useful one in analytical chemistry. It is difficult for the author to think of a modern analytical laboratory without a thermobalance. Palei *et al.*[11] and Duval[2] have summarized the uses of TGA to problems in analytical chemistry. They are:

(1) New weighing compositions in gravimetric analysis and the determination of their thermal stability ranges.
(2) Weighing substances which are unstable at ambient temperatures such as those which absorb carbon dioxide and water from the air.
(3) Determination of the composition of complex mixtures.
(4) Determination of the purity and thermal stability of analytical reagents, including primary and secondary standards.
(5) The systematic study of the properties of materials in relation to the methods used for their preparation.
(6) Automatic gravimetric analysis.
(7) Studying the behavior of materials in atmospheres of vacuum or various gases.
(8) The evaluation of various filtration techniques, such as ignition of filter paper and so on.
(9) Correction of errors in gravimetric analysis.
(10) The study of sublimation behavior of various substances.
(11) For deciding whether or not a precipitate should be dried or ignited.
(12) Discovery of new methods of separation and in gasometry.

Indeed, the technique has a great number of uses in other fields of chemistry as well.[4,6]

A comprehensive listing and discussion of the TGA curves of a large number of compounds of analytical interest has been published by Duval[2] and others, as given in the bibliography; only a few illustrative examples will be included here.

The thermal decomposition of the oxine (8-quinolinol, 8-hydroxyquinoline), ammonium, and quinolinium phosphomolybdates have been studied by TGA. For the drying and ignition temperature of ammonium phosphomolybdate, Dupuis and Duval[12] found that the precipitate had the composition, $(NH_4)_3PO_4(MoO_3)_{12} \cdot 2HNO_3 \cdot H_2O$. On heating, the precipitate lost water and nitric acid to yield a horizontal weight-plateau from 180° to 410°C. which corresponded to the composition, $(NH_4)_3PO_4(MoO_3)_{12}$. The

[11] Palei, P. N., Sentyurin, I. G., and Sklyarenko, I. S., Zhur. Anal. Khim., **12**, 329, 1957 (English translation).

[12] Dupuis, T., and Duval, C., Anal. Chim. Acta, **4**, 256, 1950.

author, using a different method of precipitation, obtained the weight-loss curve for the precipitate as shown in Fig. 35-4.[13] The air dried precipitate began to evolve loosely held water at 60°C., giving a horizontal weight-plateau from 160° to 415°C. which corresponded to the composition, $(NH_4)_2HP(Mo_3O_{10})_4 \cdot H_2O$. Above 415°C., addi-

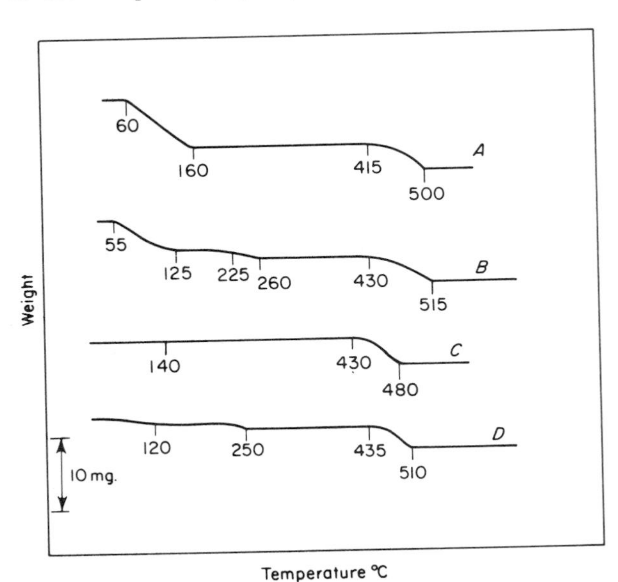

Fig. 35-4. Weight-Loss Curves of Ammonium Phosphomolybdate: *A*, HNO_3 Washed and Air Dried; *B*, NH_4NO_3 Washed and Air Dried; *C*, HNO_3 Washed and Oven Dried; *D*, NH_4NO_3 Washed and Oven Dried. (Courtesy Analytica Chimica Acta.)

tional weight-loss occurred to give the oxide level, $P_2O_5 \cdot 24MoO_3$, beginning at 500°C. The ammonium nitrate washed precipitate gave a similar weight-loss curve except for the loss of ammonium nitrate from 225° to 260°C. The horizontal weight-level from 260° to 430°C. corresponded to the composition, $(NH_4)_3[P(Mo_3O_{10})_4]$. Undoubtedly, the inherent disagreement between these two results can be attributed more accurately to the nature of the precipitation reaction rather than to the differences occurring in instrumentation.

A similar situation concerning drying and ignition temperatures was noted for oxine phosphomolybdate. Duval[14] first reported that a compound corresponding to the 2-hydrate was stable in the 176° to 225°C. temperature range. He later reported[15] that the 2-hydrate was stable in the temperature range of 236° to 268°C., and beyond 341°C., the compound began to decompose, giving the $P_2O_5 \cdot 24MoO_3$ weight-level beginning at 765°C. The author, with Brabson,[16] reported that the air dried precipitate began to lose weight at 60°C., as shown in Fig. 35-5. A horizontal weight-level was observed

[13] Wendlandt, W. W., Anal. Chim. Acta, **20**, 267, 1959.
[14] Duval, C., Inorganic Thermogravimetric Analysis, 1st Ed., Elsevier, Amsterdam, 1953, pp. 130, 132.
[15] Duval, C., Inorganic Thermogravimetric Analysis, 2nd Ed., Elsevier, Amsterdam, 1963, pp. 245–246.
[16] Wendlandt, W. W., and Brabson, J. A., Anal. Chem., **30**, 61, 1958.

from 85° to 285°C., which corresponded to the composition for the anhydrous compound, $3C_9H_7ON \cdot H_3(PMo_{12}O_{11})$. The air-dried precipitate agreed with the stoichiometry for the 2-hydrate. Above 285°C. the anhydrous compound began to decompose, giving a short weight-level from 335° to 375°C., whose composition approximated that of the mono-oxine compound, $C_9H_7ON \cdot H_3(PMo_{12}O_{40})$. The $P_2O_5 \cdot 24MoO_3$ weight-level began at about 470°C.

In continuing with this series of compounds, the author, with Hoffman,[17] studied the TGA of quinolinium phosphomolybdate. According to the weight-loss curve in Fig. 35-6, the compound began to lose weight starting at 107°C. A horizontal weight-level was observed from 155° to 370°C. which corresponded to the composition of the anhydrous compound, $(C_9H_7N)_3H_3PO_4 \cdot 12MoO_3$. Beyond 370°C., rapid decomposition took place, giving the $P_2O_5 \cdot 24MoO_3$ weight-level beginning at 500°C. To determine the optimum drying period for the precipitate, samples were studied at constant temperatures on the thermobalance. At 100°C., a horizontal curve obtained, indicating that the compound did not lose its hydrate-bound water nor did it decompose in any other manner. At 150°C., the hydrate water was lost in a very short time, giving a horizontal weight -level on further heating. At a still higher temperature, 200°C., the hydrate water was lost almost immediately, and there was no evidence of any further decomposition. From the isotherm curves, it can be concluded that the precipitate can be rendered anhydrous by drying at 150° or 200°C. for less than 15 minutes.

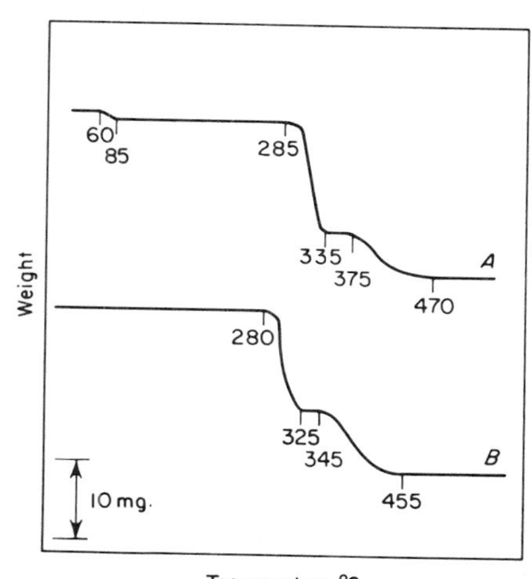

Fig. 35-5. Weight-Loss Curves of Oxine Phosphomolybdate: *A*, Air-Dried; *B*, Oven-Dried at 140°C. (Reprinted from Analytical Chemistry, **30**, 61, 1958. Copyright 1958 by the American Chemical Society and reprinted by permission of the copyright owner.)

Thermogravimetric methods described in other chapters of Standard Methods of Chemical Analysis are:

1. Chapter 58, Volume III, Plastics.
   a. Determination of energy of activation of thermal degradation of polymers
   b. Determination of thermal or oxidative stability of plastics
   c. For studying reactions occurring during thermal or oxidative degradation of plastics
2. Chapter 62, Volume III, Soils.
   a. Determination of carbonates
   b. Determination of hygroscopic water
   c. Determination of organic matter in soil
3. Chapter 64, Volume III, Determination of Water.
   a. Determination of water in various materials

[17] Wendlandt, W. W., and Hoffman, W. M., Anal. Chem., **32,** 1011, 1960.

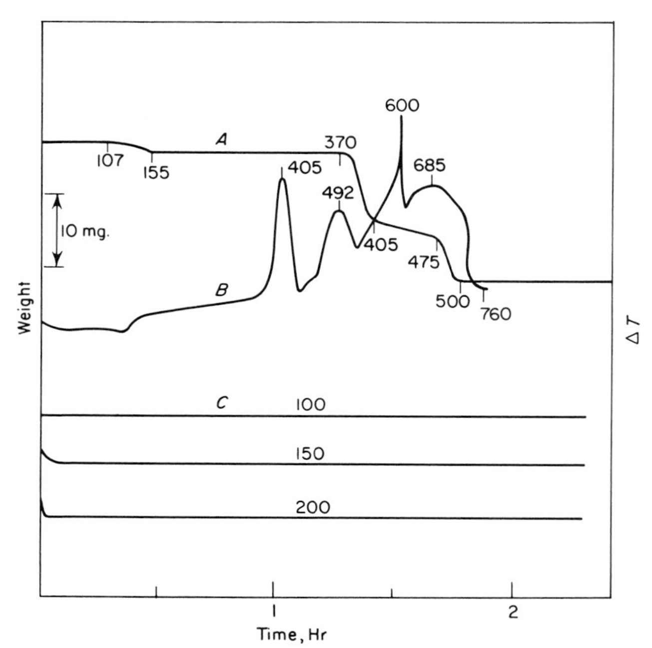

FIG. 35-6. Weight-Loss Curves of Quinolinium Phosphomolybdate: *A*, TGA Curve; *B*, DTA Curve; *C*, Isotherm Curves; All Temperatures in °C. (Reprinted from Analytical Chemistry, **32,** 1011, 1960. Copyright 1960 by the American Chemical Society and reprinted by permission of the copyright owner.)

BIBLIOGRAPHY

Duval, C., Inorganic Thermogravimetric Analysis, Elsevier, Amsterdam; 1st Ed., 1953; 2nd Ed., 1963.

Duval, C., Anal. Chem., **23,** 1271, 1951.

Wendlandt, W. W., Thermal Methods of Analysis, Interscience, New York, 1964.

Wendlandt, W. W., "Final Gravimetric Treatment," in Standard Methods of Chemical Analysis, F. J. Welcher, Ed., 6th Ed., Vol. 2, Part A, D. Van Nostrand Co., Princeton, N. J., 1963, pp. 243–253.

Chapter 36

CRITICAL SOLUTION TEMPERATURES

By Robert W. Fischer
Universität Graz
Institut für Pharmakognosie
Graz, Austria

and

Harald H. O. Schmid
University of Minnesota
The Hormel Institute
Austin, Minnesota

PHASE EQUILIBRIA OF TWO LIQUID COMPONENTS

When two liquids, which are not completely miscible, are brought in contact, they form two phases, each being the saturated solution of one component in the other. The two liquids in equilibrium are called *conjugate solutions*. Assuming a closed system of two components, three phases can exist in equilibrium—the two liquid phases and a vapor phase.

According to the Phase Rule of Gibbs,[1,2] such a system is univariant; at a given temperature the concentrations of the components in the two liquid phases, as well as the vapor pressure, must have definite values.

If the vapor is not taking part in the equilibrium, the system is bivariant unless the pressure is fixed. As the mutual solubilities of liquids usually are studied under atmospheric pressure, the compositions of the conjugate solutions are defined by the temperature only.

These compositions under constant total pressure are not quite the same as they would be under variable equilibrium pressure. But the differences are negligible unless either the constant external pressure or the vapor pressure is very great.[2]

CRITICAL SOLUTION TEMPERATURES

Upper Critical Solution Temperature.—In the majority of cases, a rise in temperature increases the mutual solubilities of the two components. A temperature may be reached at which the two liquids become completely soluble in each other. This temperature is known as the *upper critical solution temperature* (CST) or *consolute temperature*[3] of the system. At temperatures above the CST, the two-component system occurs as one homogeneous liquid phase.

The CST of two liquids is reached at a certain composition, the *critical composition* of the system. It may also be called the *consolute concentration* of the solution.[2]

[1] Gibbs, J. W., Collected Works, Longmans, Green & Co., Inc., New York, 1931.
[2] Findlay, A., The Phase Rule and Its Applications, 9th Ed., Dover Publications, Inc., New York, 1951.
[3] Glasstone, S., Textbook of Physical Chemistry, 2nd Ed., D. Van Nostrand Co., Inc., Princeton, N. J., 1946.

By plotting the compositions of the conjugate solutions *vs.* the temperature, various types of solubility diagrams may be obtained. The classical curve of the system, phenol-water, first studied by Alexejew,[4] is shown in Fig. 36-1.[5]

Figure 36-1 illustrates, on the left side of the diagram, the increasing amounts of phenol dissolved in water at rising temperatures. Similarly, the ratio of water dissolved

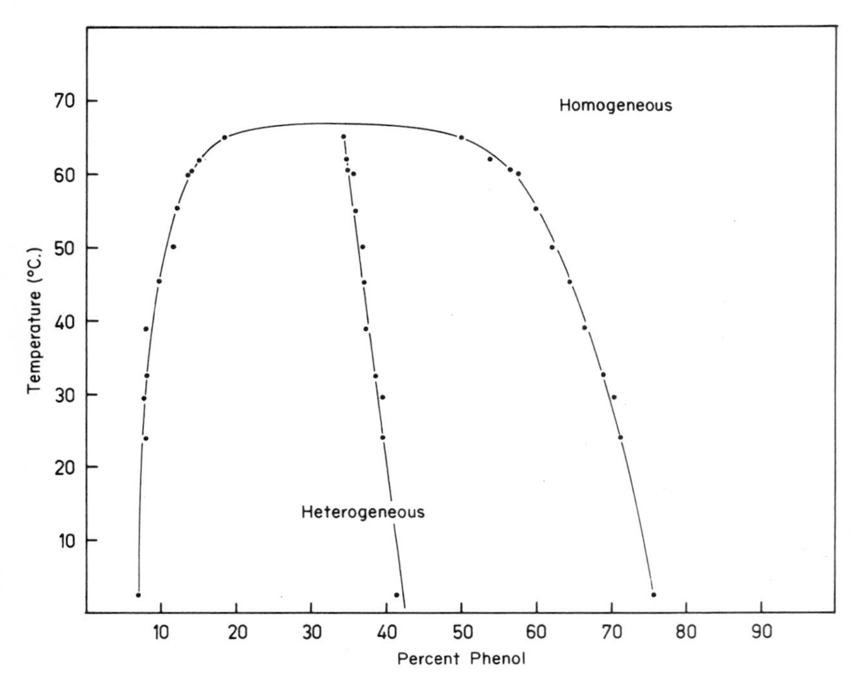

FIG. 36-1. Solubility Diagram of Phenol-Water According to Data Reported by Campbell and Campbell.[5]

in the "phenol-rich" layer of the two-component system is plotted on the right side of the diagram. The upper critical solution temperature is reached when both layers become identical at 66.8°C., the composition being 34.5 percent (by weight) phenol. Since the curve is very flat in the range of the CST, an accurate determination of the critical composition is difficult. Therefore, the mean values of the compositions of the two conjugate solutions may be plotted and thus a straight line may be obtained which, at the critical solution temperature, indicates the critical composition.[2,6] It has been shown, however, that the coexistence curve of aniline-cyclohexane has a finite horizontal top, which means that there is a range of compositions, all of which can be called "critical compositions."[7]

Lower Critical Solution Temperature.—In certain cases the mutual solubilities of the two components increase with *decreasing* temperature. Thus, a lower critical solution

[4] Alexejew, W., Ann. physik. Chem., **28,** 305, 1886.
[5] Campbell, A. N., and Campbell, A. J. R., J. Am. Chem. Soc., **59,** 2481, 1937.
[6] Rothmund, V., Z. physik. Chem., **26,** 433, 1898.
[7] Atack, D., and Rice, O. K., J. Chem. Phys., **22,** 582, 1954.

temperature (LCST), the temperature *below* which the two liquids are completely miscible, may be realized.

Systems behaving in this manner are uncommon. Most of them consist of a hydroxy-compound and an amine, or of a hydroxy-compound and a keto or ether grouping. Therefore, compound formation through hydrogen bonding has been assumed to explain the irregular behavior.[3] As an example, the well known solubility diagram of the system triethylamine-water[8] is shown in Fig. 36-2.[6]

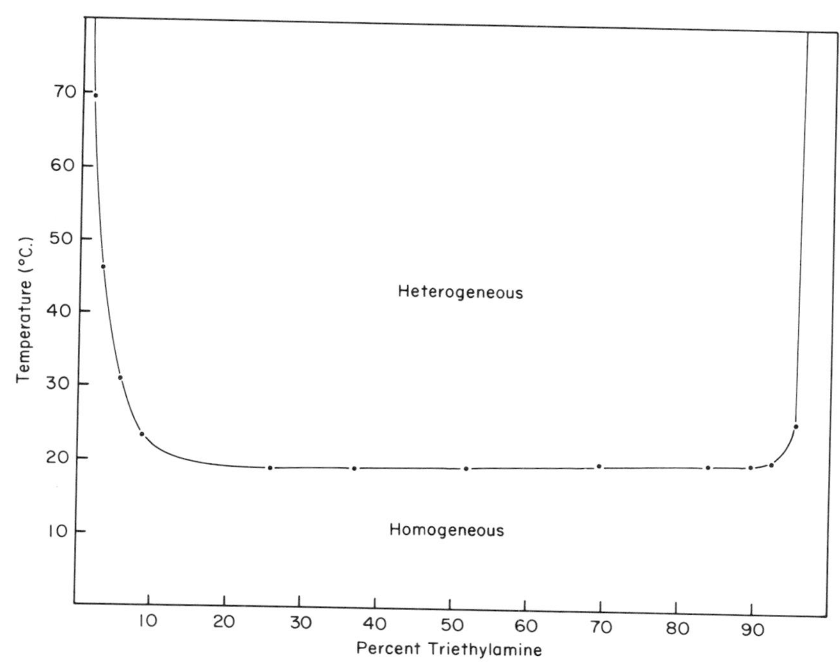

FIG. 36-2. Solubility Diagram of Triethylamine-Water According to Data Reported by Rothmund.[6]

The phase separation behavior of systems exhibiting upper and lower critical solution temperatures was also studied on a number of models in which the molecular interactions depend on the relative orientations of the molecules.[9]

The lower critical solution temperatures of liquid propane and other short-chain hydrocarbons with various high molecular weight aliphatic compounds have been utilized for their separation.[10,11]

In the temperature range above the lower critical solution temperature of a system, the mutual solubilities of the two phases decrease with increasing temperature, but not indefinitely. From a certain temperature on, the solubilities increase usually in the normal manner. Therefore, systems exhibiting a lower critical solution temperature should also have an upper critical solution temperature. The solubility curve in such

[8] Guthrie, F., Phil. Mag., **18,** 29, 1884.
[9] Barker, J. A., and Fock, W., Discussions Faraday Soc., **15,** 188, 1953.
[10] Hixson, A. W., and Hixson, A. N., Trans., Am. Inst. Chem. Engrs., **37,** 927, 1941.
[11] Bogash, R., and Hixson, A. N., Chem. Eng. Progress, **45,** 597, 1949.

a case would be closed, all points outside the curve representing a homogeneous liquid, and inside a heterogeneous system of two liquid phases. Curves of this type have been obtained for various pairs of liquids,[2,12] the first case to be established being the system nicotine-water.[13]

Solubility diagrams, such as those shown in Fig. 36-1 and Fig. 36-2, are not obtained with all pairs of partially miscible liquids. Any liquid, if cooled sufficiently, will solidify. The curve of partial solubility may thus be intersected by curves representing the stable existence of solid phases. Also, upon heating, the *critical temperature* of one of the two components may be reached; since this substance can then no longer exist as a liquid, equilibrium between two liquid phases becomes impossible.

Influences Upon Critical Solution Temperatures. **Pressure.** The compositions of the liquid phases in a two-component system are defined by the temperature only, if the pressure is kept constant or if the vapor phase is taking part in the equilibrium. Consequently, the critical solution temperatures as well as the critical compositions may vary with pressure.

Depending on the nature of the system, critical solution temperatures may be either raised or lowered by increase of pressure. The effect of pressure, however, is not great unless the pressure is very high. The CST of the system, phenol-water, for example, was found to be 66.09°C. at 10 atm., 66.78°C. at 200 atm., 68.39°C. at 600 atm., and 70.61°C. at 1000 atm.[14]

Additional Substances.—The mutual solubilities of two liquids may be increased or decreased to a marked extent by adding a foreign substance which dissolves in both or at least in one of the two components. In such a three-component system, which forms two liquid phases, there are two conjugate ternary solutions in equilibrium. The compositions of the ternary solutions depend not only on the amount and nature of the added substance, but also on the relative amounts of the two liquids. Hence, upper and lower critical solution temperatures of a two-component system, as well as the critical composition, may be altered significantly by adding a third component.

Detailed discussions of the phase relations of systems of three and more components and their critical solution phenomena are found in several monographs.[2,15,16]

Within the limits of this chapter it is useful to consider the solubility of an additional substance in each of the two liquids. If the solubility in the two liquids is very different, or if the substance is practically insoluble in one of the two components, an upper CST will be raised and a lower CST will be depressed.

However, if the solubility of the addendum in the two liquids is of the same order, the mutual solubility will be increased. Consequently, an upper CST will be lowered and a lower CST will be raised.[2]

Applicability of the Phenomenon.—1. Critical solution temperatures are widely used in screening possible solvents for selectivity between desired and undesired components. The difference in the CST values of different compounds with the same solvent is taken as a measure of the relative affinity or selectivity of the solvent.[17]

2. Organic compounds may be characterized in the liquid state by determining their CST values with suitable test substances. Both upper and lower critical solution

[12] Francis, A. W., Critical Solution Temperatures, No. 31, Advances in Chemistry Series, American Chemical Society, Washington, D. C., 1961.

[13] Hudson, C. S., Z. physik. Chem., **47,** 113, 1904.

[14] Timmermans, J., J. Chim. Phys., **20,** 491, 1923.

[15] Hildebrand, J. H., and Scott, R. L., The Solubility of Nonelectrolytes, 3rd Ed., Reinhold Publishing Corp., New York, 1950.

[16] Ricci, J. E., The Phase Rule and Heterogeneous Equilibrium, D. Van Nostrand Co., Inc., Princeton, N. J., 1951.

[17] Francis, A. W., Ind. Eng. Chem., **36,** 764, 1944.

temperatures are reproducible characteristics of the two liquids involved. Complex mixtures of compounds, *e.g.*, petroleum hydrocarbons[18] or naturally occurring lipids,[19] may be characterized, provided that none of their components react with the test substance or decompose upon heating.

3. Another use of CST determinations is the rapid analysis of binary mixtures, especially the determination of water present in organic solvents.[12,20] When the addition of a third substance to a heterogeneous liquid system exerts a significant change of the CST, this fact may be utilized for determining the relative amount of the additional component.

EXPERIMENTAL TECHNIQUES

SOLUBILITY STUDIES

Upper and lower critical solution temperatures may be obtained through solubility measurements,[21] which can be expressed in solubility diagrams such as those shown in Fig. 36-1 and Fig. 36-2. Three general methods may be employed:

In the *analytical* method, the two liquids are brought to equilibrium at a constant temperature; portions of the two conjugate solutions are analyzed; the measurements are repeated at different temperatures.

Most frequently the *synthetic* method is employed in which definite amounts of the components are weighed and sealed into a small glass tube. The temperature at which complete solubility is achieved is determined through heating and cooling processes.

The *thermostatic* method[22] is a combination of analytical and synthetic methods. In this procedure, different amounts of the two liquids are weighed into each of two special graduated vessels, and equilibrium is attained at a constant temperature. Then the volumes of the two liquids are read.

Generally, the upper CST of a system may be determined with practical precision by a simple procedure. The two liquids are placed in a test tube and are stirred with a thermometer while heating or cooling until the liquids just mix while heating, or just cloud on cooling. Measurements above the boiling point of one of the components may be obtained under equilibrium pressure by using sealed tubes. Refinements in the observation have been described.[23] Methods have been standardized for characterizing hydrocarbons[18] and fats.[19] A discussion of the practical approach of CST determinations and an extensive compilation of data have recently been published by Francis.[12]

Generally, most of the investigations published lack critical evaluations of the purities of the substances used. In addition, studies of highly purified compounds, which are chemically similar, are scarcely found in the literature. So far, the instrumentation requiring about 1 ml. of sample has restricted the analytical application of the phenomenon mainly to petroleum chemistry.[12] Results have not only been obtained by different techniques, but also with liquids of different degrees of purity. The comparison and evaluation of reported data, therefore, constitute a precarious effort.

However, the influences of molecular weights and functional groups of the compounds on their CST values have been recognized, and the difference in the solubility

[18] ASTM Method D611 and D1012, American Society for Testing and Materials, Philadelphia, Pa.

[19] AOCS Official Methods Cb4-35, American Oil Chemists' Society, 35 E. Wacker Drive, Chicago 1, Ill.

[20] Crismer, L., Bull. Soc. Chim. Belg., **18**, 18, 1904.

[21] Linke, F. W., in Standard Methods of Chemical Analysis, Frank J. Welcher, ed., 6th Ed., Vol. II, Part A, D. Van Nostrand Co., Inc., Princeton, N. J., 1963.

[22] Hill, A. E., J. Am. Chem. Soc., **45**, 1143, 1923.

[23] Brown, C. W., Ind. Eng. Chem., Anal. Ed., **18**, 739, 1946.

properties of aliphatic and aromatic compounds has been studied, especially with hydrocarbons.[17,24,25]

Two examples may demonstrate to what extent CST determinations permit distinctions to be made between similar compounds. The solubilities of equal volumes of various isomeric heptanes were determined with a number of solvents.[26] These data are listed in Table 36-1.

TABLE 36-1. COMPARISON OF SOLUTION TEMPERATURES OF SIX ISOMERIC HEPTANES WITH VARIOUS SOLVENTS[26]

	Solution Temperature (°C.)					
Solvent	2, 2-Dimethyl Pentane	2, 4-Dimethyl Pentane	2, 2, 3-Trimethyl Butane	2, 3-Dimethyl Pentane	2-Methyl Hexane	*n*-Heptane
Aniline	78.05	78.4	72.0	67.95	73.5	70.0
Benzyl alcohol	64.7	64.9	53.5	46.4	57.25	50.7
Diethyl phthalate	31.1	32.4	16.9	18.85	30.05	28.2
β-Phenyl ethyl alcohol	46.6	47.05	34.45	28.2	39.1	20.7
o-Toluidine	28.2	28.4	21.55	17.7	23.6	19.7
m-Toluidine	27.65	28.0	20.7	16.25	23.25	18.85
Phenyl acetate	11.55	11.7	5.55	4.05	8.9	7.45
Acetyl diethylamine	1.1	2.95	−11.95	—	—	6.25
Nitrobenzene	26.8	26.55	20.9	16.05	22.35	18.15
Benzonitrile	13.2	13.05	7.35	3.0	8.45	—
o-Bromophenol	3.85	3.15	−3.80	—	—	—
Benzyl benzoate	12.35	12.1	2.55	−3.65	4.45	−2.05

NOTE. Hydrocarbon content, 50 percent by volume. Accuracy of determination, 0.1°C.

Table 36-1 shows that the various liquids used are of different "sensitivity" for distinguishing between the isomeric heptanes. Diethyl phthalate exhibits the greatest difference and is, therefore, most suitable.

Critical solution temperatures of various phenols with water are listed in Table 36-2.[27] They demonstrate the possibility of distinguishing between aromatic isomers by their CST values.

THE "ANILINE POINT"

The aniline point is the temperature at which *equal volumes* of pure aniline and another liquid, usually a petroleum product, become miscible.[12] Thus, the problem of determining the critical composition of the pair of liquids is avoided. Although the CST of the system may be reached at a slightly higher temperature, the aniline point is frequently used instead. Relations between the aniline points of hydrocarbons and their

[24] Woodburn, H. M., Smith, K., and Tetewsky, H., Ind. Eng. Chem., **36,** 588, 1944.
[25] Francis, A. W., Ind. Eng. Chem., **36,** 1096, 1944.
[26] Miller, V. A., Anal. Chem., **17,** 5, 1945.
[27] Erichsen, L. V., Dobbert, E., Brennstoff-Chem., **36,** 338, 1955.

TABLE 36-2. CRITICAL SOLUTION TEMPERATURES OF VARIOUS PHENOLS WITH WATER[27]

	CST (°*C*.)
Phenol	68.3
p-Cresol	143.7
m-Cresol	148.0
o-Cresol	166.5
3, 4-Dimethylphenol	190.2
3, 5-Dimethylphenol	200.0
2, 3-Dimethylphenol	208.8
2, 4-Dimethylphenol	213.5
2, 5-Dimethylphenol	219.0
2, 6-Dimethylphenol	241.2
2, 4, 5-Trimethylphenol	244.2
2, 3, 5-Trimethylphenol	247.8
3-Methyl-5-ethylphenol	229.8
p-*n*-Propylphenol	221.1

other characteristics, such as boiling points and "octane numbers," have been investigated.[28] Similarly, the aniline points of fats and oils and their relations to other properties of these materials have been reported.[29]

Equipment for determining aniline points according to ASTM methods D611 and D1012 is available from Fisher Scientific Company (Cat. No. 13-394-25 and 13-394-50). The same company supplies an aniline point apparatus for automatic determinations (Cat. No. 13-394-100 V1).

THE MICRODETERMINATION OF CRITICAL SOLUTION TEMPERATURES

Upper and lower critical solution temperatures may easily be determined by sealing minute amounts of sample and test liquid into a capillary glass tubing, heating the latter on a hot stage, and observing the interface between the two liquids under a microscope. No weighing or measuring is necessary. The apparatus, the amounts of sample used, and the speed and accuracy of CST determinations by this method are similar to the microdetermination of melting points as described by Kofler.[30,31] This fact makes it a generally applicable procedure for testing the identity and purity of organic compounds. It may also be used for determining the composition of solutions and for characterizing complex mixtures.[32]

Equipment. **Microscope.**—The Reichert microscope model "RCH" [33] is especially de-

[28] Francis, A. W., Ind. Eng. Chem., **33**, 554, 1941.

[29] Kaufmann, H. P., and Thieme, J. G., Fette, Seifen, Anstrichmittel, **58**, 585, 1956.

[30] Kofler, L., and Kofler, A., Thermo-Mikro-Methoden zur Kennzeichnung Organischer Stoffe und Stoffgemische, Universitäts-Verlag Wagner, Innsbruck, 1954.

[31] McCrone, W. C., Fusion Methods in Chemical Microscopy, Interscience Publishers, Inc., New York, 1957.

[32] Fischer, R. W., in Microchemical Techniques, N. D. Cheronis, ed., Microchem. J., Symposium Vol. **2**, 977, 1962.

[33] C. Reichert, Optische Werke AG., Wien 17, Austria; U. S. Representative, William J. Hacker & Co., Inc., P.O. Box 646, West Caldwell, N. J.

signed for use in connection with a heating stage. It is equipped with an objective 10× and a Huyghenian eyepiece 10×, thus yielding a total magnification of 100×. However, any upright transmitted light microscope can be used provided the stage top contains two plug holes to accept clips for mounting a heating stage. The stage top should be all metal and nonrotary in order to resist higher temperatures.

Microheating Stage.—Suitable microheating stages are available from Reichert Optische Werke AG.[33] and A. H. Thomas Company.[34] These heating stages are equipped with exchangeable mercury in glass thermometers. The Reichert thermometers range from 20° to 230°C. and 120° to 350°C., whereas the Thomas thermometers have ranges from 30° to 230°C. and 60° to 350°C. A typical microscope equipped with heating stage and regulating transformer is shown in Fig. 36-3.

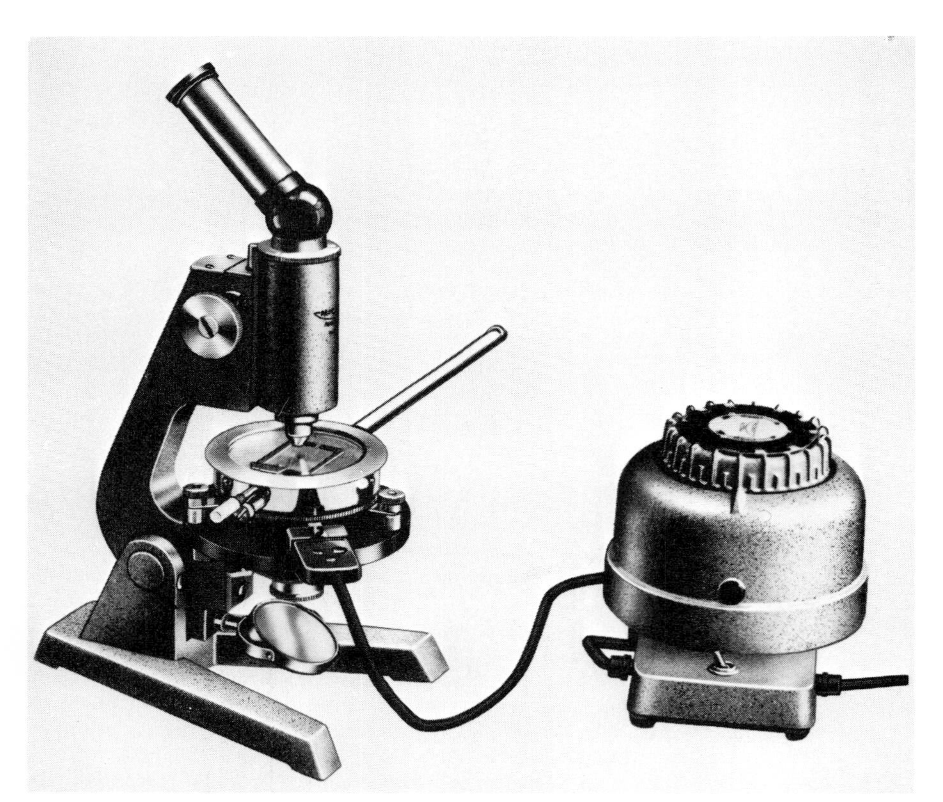

FIG. 36-3. Kofler Hot Stage with Microscope and Variable Transformer. (Reproduced with permission from C. Reichert, Optische Werke AG., Vienna, Austria.)

Slide and Capillaries.—A 38 × 26 × 1 mm. microscope slide may be adapted for holding the capillaries by gluing two glass strips (38 × 4 × 1 mm.) onto the slide, leaving a channel 0.5 mm. wide. Aluminum slides for inserting the capillaries are available from A. H. Thomas Company.

[34] A. H. Thomas Co., Vine Street at Third, Philadelphia 5, Pa.

Glass capillaries 0.2 to 0.3 mm. in inner diameter and 150 to 200 mm. long may be drawn from glass tubing about 7 mm. in diameter. They are also available from A. H. Thomas Company.

Procedure.—1. The test substance and the liquid sample are introduced into the capillary by dipping the capillary consecutively into both liquids. Each liquid may be drawn up to a height of about 7 to 10 mm. The ratio of the volumes is not important, because only a small volume on either side of the interface is involved in the mixing process. The capillary is then sealed with a microburner at both ends, the total length of the sealed capillary being 30 to 35 mm. It should contain no more than about half its volume of liquid to allow room for expansion. Care has to be taken in sealing the capillary to avoid the formation of glass clots at either end. The sealed ends should be slightly bent to the same side, as shown in Fig. 36-4, in order to secure proper contact between slide and capillary when the latter is inserted into the channel of the slide.

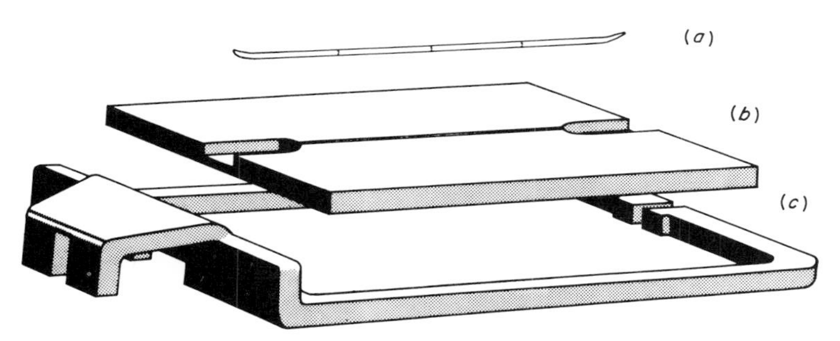

Fig. 36-4. (*a*) Sealed Capillary, Containing Sample and Test Substance. (*b*) Aluminum Slide. (*c*) Shifting Device of the Kofler Hot Stage.

Samples that are solid at room temperature are melted on a glass slide over a microburner. The melt is drawn up into the capillary which already contains the liquid test substance. Generally, the sample solidifies immediately after it has ascended, thus preventing proper sealing of the capillary. It is, therefore, liquefied again through contact with a hot glass strip while the capillary is sealed.[35]

If the two compounds in the capillary are separated by air, they are brought into contact by centrifugation. Before centrifuging, solids may be liquefied again by inserting the capillary into a centrifuge glass which contains water and heating above the melting point of the sample. Centrifuging is also employed to separate two liquids which form several segments in the capillary, because a number of interfaces migrating during the heating process could prevent exact observation of the CST. When working with substances that may react with each other, the sealed capillary is inserted with the heavier compound toward the bottom of the centrifuge glass to minimize contact of the two liquids while centrifuging.

2. The sealed capillary tubing is inserted into the channel of the microscope slide and heated on the stage. The interface between the two liquids is observed under the microscope. Although the components begin to dissolve in each other during the heating process, the interface remains visible as a meniscus. At the CST the meniscus disappears

[35] Schmid, H. H. O., Mangold, H. K., and Lundberg, W. O., J. Am. Oil Chemists Soc., **42,** 372, 1965.

with a characteristic movement, and upon cooling it reappears at the same temperature and at the same place in the capillary.

In some cases the refractive indexes of the two liquids become identical within a certain temperature range, making the interface invisible. However, upon further heating the interface will reappear.

Generally, the heating and cooling processes may be repeated several times by regulating the temperature of the heating stage. Identical temperature readings at the CST have to be obtained; otherwise, decomposition or reaction between the compounds may be assumed.

Test Substances.—The use of CST determinations as an analytical procedure requires standard test substances in order to obtain reproducible results. Valuable is the CST determination of the respective test substance with pure standard liquids, such as benzene, hexadecane, or water.[35,36] See Table 36-3.

The following requirements have to be considered when selecting a suitable test substance:

The substance should be available in high purity and it should be storable without the use of special precautions. It is of practical advantage when the test substance is a liquid at room temperature. Its solubility properties have to be reproducible at any specific temperature used.

With a certain sample the test substance should yield a CST in a range between the temperature of solidification and about 200°C. The refractive indexes of sample and test substance have to be different enough to make the interface visible. At the CST, total miscibility should occur instantly, to permit exact observations of the disappearing and reappearing interface.

For special applications, the test substance has to be sufficiently "sensitive" to distinguish between closely related compounds or to detect certain impurities.

TABLE 36-3. MUTUAL CRITICAL SOLUTIONS TEMPERATURES (°C) OF SOME TEST SUBSTANCES

	Water	*Ethylene Glycol*	*1,3-Butanediol*	*Nitromethane*	*Acetonitrile*	*Benzene*	*Cyclohexane*	*n-Octane*	*n-Hexadecane*
Water	—	b**	b	109	—2	a*	a	a	a
Ethylene glycol	b	—	b	39	—14.5	188	a	a	a
1,3-Butanediol	b	b	—	32.5	—11.5	78	165	203.5	a
Nitromethane	109	39	32.5	—	b	b	89	110.5	151
Acetonitrile	—2	—14.5	—11.5	b	—	b	75.5	92.5	144
Benzene	a	188	78	b	b	—	b	b	b
Cyclohexane	a	a	165	89	75.5	b	—	b	b
n-Octane	a	a	203.5	110.5	92.5	b	b	—	b
n-Hexadecane	a	a	a	151	144	b	b	b	—

*a Above experimental temperature range.
**b Below experimental temperature range or below m. p.

Nine test substances frequently used for CST determinations are listed in Table 36-3. Included are all CST values of these substances with each other. It has been shown

[36] Fischer, R., and Kartnig, T., Pharm. Zentralhalle., **98**, 366, 1959; C.A. 10586c, 1959.

that only four of them (water, ethylene glycol, acetic anhydride, and hexadecane) are sufficient to characterize a large variety of organic liquids by their CST values.[32]

APPLICATIONS OF THE MICROMETHOD

The technique can be applied essentially in the same way as other methods for determining critical solution temperatures. When only two compounds are present, the maximum of the solubility diagram is obtained, as the interface remains visible during the heating process until the temperature of total miscibility is reached. When testing systems of three or more components, the temperature readings at the CST may not in all cases correspond to those obtained with other techniques.[37]

Minute amounts of sample (0.5–2 μl.) are required for one determination. These amounts can easily be isolated and purified by chromatographic methods. After determination of the CST, the sample may be recovered from the capillary for further analysis.

The accuracy of the temperature readings is limited to the experimental error of ±0.5°C. of the instrument. Determinations of CST values above 200°C. are less reliable and less easily measured, because of possible decomposition of the sample or test substance. Temperature readings below room temperature are possible if cooling equipment is employed.[33,34]

CST values may be obtained in certain cases at temperatures below the melting point of the sample, when the sample can be prevented from solidifying in the presence of the test substance. Determinations of CST values are especially valuable for characterizing compounds which occur in various polymorphic modifications and, therefore, exhibit different melting points.

CHARACTERIZATION OF ORGANIC COMPOUNDS

Organic substances which are either liquid at room temperature or melt without decomposition may be characterized, and closely related compounds may be distinguished by their CST values with a suitable test substance.

The CST values of straight-chain aliphatic compounds with a certain test substance depend on the molecular weight, on the type and position of the functional group(s), and on the number and configuration of double bonds of the compound.[38]

Systematic studies on homologous series of aliphatic compounds established the microdetermination of their CST values as a convenient tool for distinguishing between them.[38,39]

***Acyclic Compounds.* Homologous Compounds.**—CST values of some saturated aliphatic compounds of various classes with nitromethane and acetonitrile are given in Table 36-4.

It was also observed that, within each series, all CST values fall on the same curve when plotted against the molecular weights, regardless of whether the carbon number of the respective compound is odd or even.[38] This fact makes predictions of CST values for compounds of a given homologous series possible.

The comparative use of different test substances yields further information about the identity of a compound. Complete miscibility or immiscibility over the entire experimental temperature range, or even reaction with a certain test substance, characterizes to some extent the compound being analyzed. The application of two test substances of similar solubility characteristics can provide additional information. For example,

[37] Gölles, F., Monatsh., **93**, 1019, 1962.
[38] Schmid, H. H. O., Mangold, H. K., and Lundberg, W. O., Microchem. J., 7, 287, 1963.
[39] Schmid, H. H. O., Mangold, H. K., and Lundberg, W. O., Microchem. J., 7, 297, 1963.

TABLE 36-4. CRITICAL SOLUTION TEMPERATURES OF SOME ALIPHATIC COMPOUNDS WITH NITROMETHANE AND ACETONITRILE[35]

	CST (°C.)		
	Nitromethane	*Acetonitrile*	*Difference*
Hydrocarbons			
n-Octane	110.5	92.5	18
n-Decane	122.5	107.5	15
n-Dodecane	132.5	121.5	11
n-Tetradecane	142	133.5	8.5
n-Hexadecane	151	144	7
n-Octadecane	159	154	5
Bromides			
n-Octyl bromide	38	17.5	20.5
n-Decyl bromide	63	45.5	17.5
n-Dodecyl bromide	82.5	69	13.5
n-Tetradecyl bromide	98	87.5	10.5
n-Hexadecyl bromide	111	104.5	6.5
n-Octadecyl bromide	123.5	120	3.5
Alcohols			
n-Decanol-1	57	23	34
n-Dodecanol-1	66	34.5	31.5
n-Tetradecanol-1	74	44.5	29.5
n-Hexadecanol-1	81.5	54.5	27
n-Octadecanol-1	89	64	25
n-Eicosanol-1	96.5	74	22.5
Acids			
n-Tetradecanoic acid	91.5	53.5	38
n-Hexadecanoic acid	104	68.5	35.5
n-Octadecanoic acid	113.5	81.5	32
n-Eicosanoic acid	121	91.5	29.5
n-Docosanoic acid	128	101	27
n-Tetracosanoic acid	134	109	25

within the various homologous series the CST values with both nitromethane and acetonitrile rise with increasing chain lengths of the compounds tested, but at a different rate. Besides the chain length, the difference between the CST of a compound with nitromethane and acetonitrile depends mainly upon its functional group[35] (see Table 36-4).

Positional Isomers.—The position of the functional group(s) in long-chain compounds exerts a marked effect upon the critical solution temperatures of these substances.[35,40] The CST values with nitromethane of isomeric dialkyl esters and ethers having a total carbon number of 18 are given as examples in Table 36-5.

Unsaturated Compounds.—Increasing degree of unsaturation per molecule results in a decrease of the CST values, the effects being additive in many cases. Generally, the influence of double bonds on the CST decreases with increasing molecular weights of the compounds tested. In Fig. 36-5, the CST values of various compounds with increasing degree of unsaturation are plotted against the total number of double bonds per molecule.[38,39]

Cyclic Compounds.—Isomeric straight-chain and branched-chain compounds usually

[40] Schmid, H. H. O., Mangold, H. K., and Lundberg, W. O., Microchem. J., **9**, 134, 1965.

TABLE 36-5. CRITICAL SOLUTION TEMPERATURES OF ISOMERIC ESTERS (MOL. WEIGHT, 284.5) AND ISOMERIC ETHERS (MOL. WEIGHT, 270.5) WITH NITROMETHANE[35]

	Ester	*CST (°C.)*	*Ether*	*CST (°C.)*
C_1-C_{17}	Methyl margarate	53.5	Methyl-heptadecyl	105
C_2-C_{16}	Ethyl palmitate	59.5	Ethyl-hexadecyl	112.5
C_4-C_{14}	Butyl myristate	65	Butyl-tetradecyl	119
C_6-C_{12}	Hexyl laurate	67.5	Hexyl-dodecyl	120.5
C_8-C_{10}	Octyl caprate	68	Octyl-decyl	120.5
C_{10}-C_8	Decyl caprylate	68		
C_{12}-C_6	Dodecyl caproate	66.5		
C_{14}-C_4	Tetradecyl butyrate	63.5		
C_{16}-C_2	Hexadecyl acetate	47.5		

can be distinguished by their CST values. Their alicyclic isomers also may exhibit different critical solution temperatures with a given test substance.[35]

Increasing chain lengths of the aliphatic moieties of cyclic compounds yield increasing CST values. This effect is similar to that observed with straight-chain aliphatic compounds. CST values of the cholesteryl esters of homologous and vinylogous fatty acids with nitromethane are given in Table 36-6. Similarly, relations between the amounts of "paraffinic carbon atoms" in cyclic hydrocarbons and their CST values with various test substances have been investigated by Francis.[25]

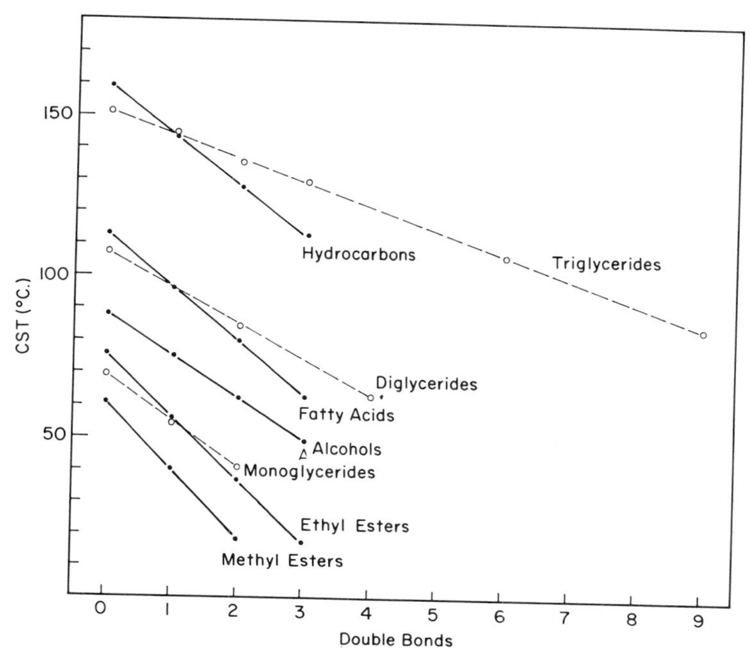

FIG. 36-5. Critical Solution Temperatures of Various Saturated and Unsaturated Compounds Containing Straight-chains of C_{18}, $C_{18:1}$, $C_{18:2}$, and $C_{18:3}$ with Nitromethane.[35]

TABLE 36-6. CRITICAL SOLUTION TEMPERATURES OF CHOLESTERYL ESTERS WITH NITROMETHANE[35]

Ester	*CST (°C.) (Nitromethane)*
Cholesteryl dodecanoate	168
Cholesteryl tetradecanoate	175
Cholesteryl hexadecanoate	181.5
Cholesteryl octadecanoate	187
Cholesteryl eicosanoate	192
Cholesteryl docosanoate	197.5
Cholesteryl octadecenoate	175
Cholesteryl octadecadienoate	166.5

The limitations of distinguishing between closely related cyclic compounds by their CST values have not yet been fully investigated. It may be assumed, however, that the micromethod can be applied in the same way as demonstrated on homologous and vinylogous series of aliphatic compounds. Some CST values of alicyclic and aromatic compounds with nitromethane and 1,3-butanediol are given in Table 36-7.

TABLE 36-7. CRITICAL SOLUTION TEMPERATURES OF SOME CYCLIC COMPOUNDS WITH NITROMETHANE AND 1,3-BUTANEDIOL

	CST (°C.)	
	Nitromethane	*1,3-Butanediol*
Cyclohexane	89	165
Methyl cyclohexane	94	175
Benzene	—[a]	78
Toluene	—	94.5
Ethyl benzene	—	110
n-Butyl benzene	—6	136.5

[a] Below experimental temperature range.

ANALYSIS OF LIQUID MIXTURES AND SOLUTIONS[36,41–46]

The microdetermination of critical solution temperatures offers a means for analyzing the concentration of compounds dissolved in one of the two liquids. For example, the percentage of water in organic solvents may be determined rapidly by its effect on the CST of the solvent with a suitable test substance.[42] Also, a number of aqueous solutions of organic and inorganic compounds may be analyzed with phenol and other test substances.[42,43]

The use of CST determinations for quantitative analysis is demonstrated in Fig. 36-6. Each substance is dissolved in water to concentrations of 0.5, 1, 2, 5 and 10 percent

[41] Fischer, R., and Karasek, L., Microchemie, **33,** 316, 1947.
[42] Fischer, R., Pinter, E., and Auer, H., Pharm. Zentralhalle., **99,** 299, 1960; C.A. 55: 900d, 1961.
[43] Fischer, R., and Horner, J., Microchim. Acta, **4,** 386, 1953.
[44] Fischer, R., and Kolmayr, F., Pharm. Zentralhalle., **94,** 8, 1955.
[45] Fischer, R., and Auer, H., Pharm. Zentralhalle., **96,** 497, 1957.
[46] Fischer, R., and Neupauer, E., Microchemie, **34,** 319, 1949.

by weight. CST values of these solutions are determined (*e.g.*, with phenol) and plotted against the respective concentrations.[43] The diagrams obtained are used to recognize the concentration of the respective solution, after determining its CST.

Other test substances frequently employed are primary and secondary *n*-butanol and adiponitrile.

Generally, the temperature readings are reproducible within the experimental error of the instrument (±0.5°C.). The effect of the additional substance on the CST is especially great at concentrations below 1 or 2 percent. High salt concentrations (10–20 percent) result in less reliable and reproducible temperature readings at the CST.[43]

CST values of mixtures of organic liquids, such as acetic acid–acetic anhydride or methanol-acetone,[42–44] with suitable test substances, may similarly be used for determining the relative amounts of the components. Mixtures of two substances which differ widely in their solubility properties, *e.g.*, ethanol-water, require a number of test substances to cover the whole range of possible compositions.[45]

Upper and lower critical solution temperatures have been determined by the micromethod for the systems β-picoline-water, α-picoline-water-sodium chloride,[43] and *s*[illegible]-*n*-butanol-water-oxalic acid.[42]

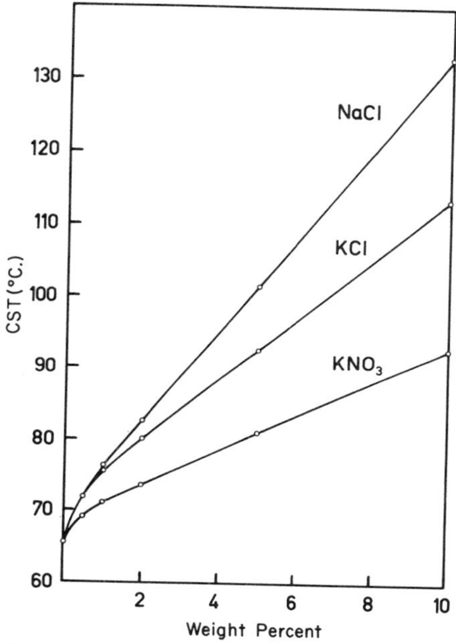

FIG. 36-6. Microcalibration Curves for Quantitative Analysis. CST Values of Water-Salt-Phenol Are Plotted *vs.* the Respective Concentrations of the Aqueous Solutions.

CHARACTERIZATION OF COMPLEX MIXTURES

The micromethod is applicable for determining upper critical solution temperatures of petroleum products with aniline. Even volatile and dark-colored samples may be characterized without difficulty. A number of other test substances suitable for distinguishing between individual hydrocarbons and also between hydrocarbon mixtures have been proposed.[47]

Also, CST values of fats and oils can be obtained by the micromethod.[43,48] Paraffin oil present as adulterant in commercial products may be determined quantitatively.[43] The various amounts of autoxidation products in fats affect the CST of the sample. Rancid fats generally yield lower CST values with polar test substances than the fresh products. In most cases, the CST values of deteriorated fats are not reproducible, as decreasing temperature readings are obtained when repeating the heating process with the same sample. The CST values of fatty raw material may be used in conjunction with other characteristics, such as iodine number or saponification number.[48] Suitable test

[47] Fischer, R., and Moser, H., Erdöl Kohle, **9,** 377, 1956.
[48] Fischer, R., and Kartnig, T., Fette, Seifen, Anstrichmittel, **60,** 904, 1958.

substances for fats and oils are nitromethane, acetonitrile, 1,3-butanediol, and ethylene glycol monoethyl ether.

Essential oils may be characterized by their CST values.[49,50] Samples of less than 1 mg. are taken directly from the plant tissue. In many cases, the amount of the major component of a complex mixture can be determined. For example, menthol and menthol esters have been determined in the oil of peppermint.[49]

DISCUSSION

The microdetermination of critical solution temperatures makes a well known phenomenon conveniently applicable through a simple, inexpensive, and accurate laboratory procedure. In general, this method may be applied in conjunction with other techniques for characterizing small amounts of sample, such as determinations of the melting points, eutectic melting points, boiling points, or refractive indexes.[30,31]

When characterizing organic compounds, the small amounts required allow previous purifications through chromatography and other small-scale techniques. Impurities may or may not alter the CST values of organic substances, depending upon their solubility properties.

CST determinations aid in assessing the compositions of fractions isolated from natural mixtures or synthetic preparations by crystallization, distillation, countercurrent distribution, and chromatographic methods.[35]

Standard properties of the liquids employed as test substances have to be maintained to achieve reproducible results. By considering an experimental error of ±0.5°C., however, small variations in the purities of the "pure" test substances are not recognizable.

It has to be considered also that studies of critical solution phenomena have been concerned mainly with hydrocarbons which are particularly unreactive compounds. A general application of the micromethod as an analytical procedure presupposes that chemical reactions are excluded. As a rule, reaction between the components, as well as decomposition, may be observed directly under the microscope. In such a case, reproducible critical solution temperatures are not obtained.

The full use of the phenomenon and the method described for identifying organic compounds are still limited by the lack of analytical tables. Critical solution temperatures are, however, predictable for many substances and may be estimated or calculated from other physical characteristics or from the CST values of closely related compounds.

SELECTED BIBLIOGRAPHY

General Discussions of Solubilities and Phase Equilibria

Findlay, A., Campbell, A. N., and Smith, N. O., The Phase Rule and Its Applications, 9th Ed., Dover Publications, Inc., New York, 1951.

Hildebrand, J. H., and Scott, R. L., The Solubility of Nonelectrolytes, 3rd Ed., Reinhold Publishing Corp., New York, 1950.

Ricci, J. E., The Phase Rule and Heterogeneous Equilibrium, D. Van Nostrand Co., Inc.; Princeton, N. J., 1951.

Compilations of Data

Francis, A. W., Critical Solution Temperatures, No. 31, Advances in Chemistry Series, American Chemical Society, Washington, D. C., 1961.

International Critical Tables, McGraw-Hill Book Co., Inc., New York, 1928.

Seidell, A., and Linke, W. F., Solubilities of Inorganic and Metal Organic Compounds, Solubilities of Organic Compounds, 3rd and 4th Eds. and Supplement, D. Van Nostrand Co., Inc., Princeton, N. J., 1940–1960.

Timmermans, J., The Physico-Chemical Constants of Binary Systems in Concentrated Solutions, Vols. I–IV, Interscience Publishers, Inc., New York, 1959–1960.

[49] Fischer, R., and Resch, H., Arzneimittel-Forsch., **5**, 137, 1955.

[50] Fischer, R., and Kartnig, T., Arzneimittel-Forsch., **7**, 365, 1957.

Chapter 37

ELECTROPHORESIS

By R. D. Strickland
Research Service
Veterans Administration Hospital
Albuquerque, New Mexico

INTRODUCTION

Any charged particle suspended between the poles of an electrical field tends to travel toward the pole that bears the charge opposite to its own. The rate at which it travels is conditioned by a number of factors, including the characteristics of the particle, the properties of the electrical field, and environmental factors, such as temperature, and the nature of the suspending medium. The mobility of a particle is approximately proportional to its charge:mass ratio. Thus an oxalate ion with two charges and a formula weight of 88.1 (charge ÷ mass = 0.0227) would be expected to move more rapidly than a stearate ion (1 ÷ 283.5 = 0.0035). Unfortunately this relationship is complicated by such factors as the molecular volume of the migrant, coordination of the migrant with molecules of solvent, and interference with migration by the supporting medium. Factors such as these make it impossible, with our present knowledge, to make accurate quantitative predictions of electrophoretic mobilities unless experimental data are available. It is true, nevertheless, that when a solution containing substances with different charge:mass ratios is acted upon by an electrical field, the components tend to separate by migrating at different rates. In this chapter the word *electrophoresis* will be used to mean any application of this principle without regard to whether the substances are colloidal or ionic, and without considering whether the purpose of the application is preparation, purification, or measurement.

The essential components of an apparatus for electrophoresis are shown diagrammatically in Fig. 37-1. The area upon which electrophoretic separations occur, called the *bed*, can be composed of any of a number of materials including gels, films, and powders. It is moistened with an electrolyte solution (usually a buffer). The ends of the bed are immersed in more of the electrolyte contained in two chambers designed to hold electrodes that are connected to a d.c. power supply. Provision is made for adjusting the electrolyte in the electrode chambers to equal levels so that siphoning action does not occur through the bed. The entire apparatus, excluding the power supply, is enclosed in an airtight chamber to prevent excessive evaporation of buffer. When a spot of sample mixture is applied to the bed and the power is turned on, those components of the mixture whose particles are charged will migrate toward the electrode having the opposite polarity.

Electrophoretic Mobilities.—The rate at which a particle moves under a controlled set of circumstances is reproducible, making it possible to calculate how far it will travel during an electrophoresis, once the necessary data have been accumulated. Let it be emphasized that mobilities can be established solely by experimentation, and that they are reproducible only when all conditions are controlled. Only voltage gradient and time of migration can be treated as variables if mobility calculations are to be valid. Variations in pH, temperature, ionic strength, medium, and the like, have not successfully been taken into account in mobility calculations. Knowing the mobilities of the components of a mixture enables one to predict the positions of the components after arbitrary time intervals or in response to varying field strengths. This is useful for locating and identifying components after separations have been obtained and for calculating the time necessary to effect complete separations.

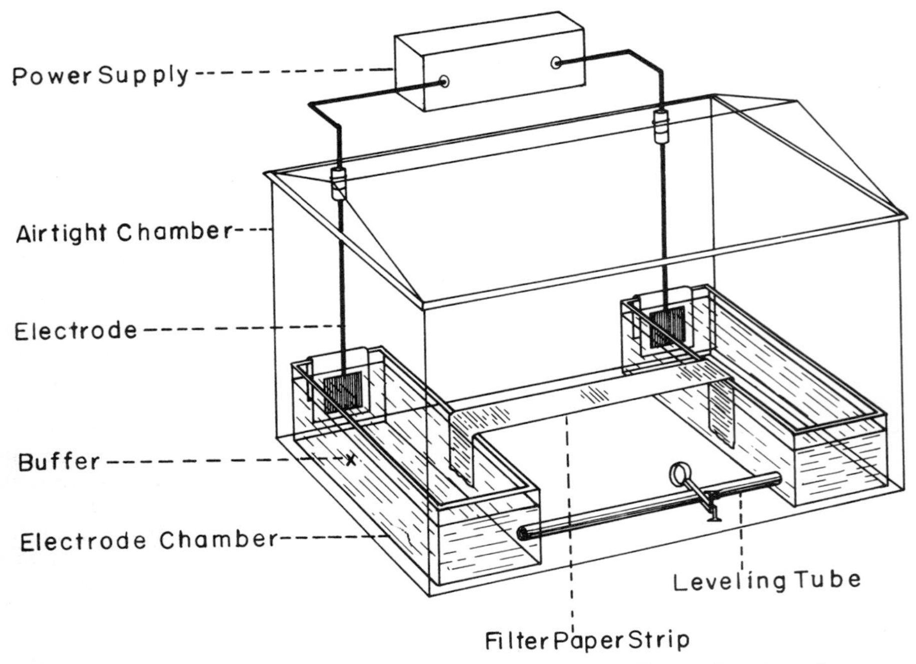

Fig. 37-1. The Essential Components of an Apparatus for Electrophoresis on Paper.

Conventionally, mobility is defined as the distance a particle will travel in a unit of time per unit of strength of an electrical field. Distance of travel is customarily stated in centimeters and time in seconds; field strength is expressed as the voltage gradient, in volts per centimeter, along the electrophoretic bed. From this it follows that the dimensions of mobility, u, are

$$\frac{\text{cm.}}{\text{sec.}} \div \frac{\text{volts}}{\text{cm.}}$$

which simplifies to

$$u = \frac{\text{cm.}^2}{\text{volts} \times \text{sec.}}$$

If this formula for mobility seems strange remember that it does not describe velocity but is instead a factor intended for use in calculating velocity under defined conditions in response to any given voltage gradient. To illustrate the use of this factor, let us calculate the distance, d_A, a particle of substance A will move in 1 hr. (3.6×10^3 sec.)

of time, t, in response to a voltage gradient, e, of 5 volts per cm., if $u_A = 4.0 \times 10^{-5}$. To do this we obtain the product of time, voltage gradient, and mobility:

$$d_A = teu_A \tag{1}$$

The units are included in the calculation to show that they cancel:

$$d_A = 3.6 \times 10^3 \text{ sec.} \times 5 \frac{\text{volts}}{\text{cm.}} \times 4.0 \times 10^{-5} \frac{\text{cm.}^2}{\text{volts} \times \text{sec.}} = 0.72 \text{ cm.}$$

To illustrate the method for estimating the time needed to obtain a separation, let us consider that substance A is mixed with substance B, with $u_B = 3.5 \times 10^{-5}$, and that the electrophoretic conditions remain as in the previous example. Ordinarily the zones spread out during electrophoresis; usually by the end of a run the zones are about 1 cm. wide. If this is true for the substances in our example, let us specify that the fronts of the two zones be 1.5 cm. apart to preclude the possibility of overlapping. An equation for calculating the times necessary to obtain any stated distance of separation of two substances can be derived from Equation (1). First subtract, algebraically, the solutions for d_A and d_B:

$$d_A - d_B = teu_A - teu_B$$

Then rearrange this expression into a solution for t:

$$t = \frac{d_A - d_B}{e(u_A - u_B)} \tag{2}$$

The required distance of separation, $d_A - d_B$, has been given as 1.5 cm. The values of u_A, u_B, and e also are known. Using these numbers in Equation (2) gives:

$$t = \frac{1.5}{5 \times (4.0 - 3.5) \times 10^{-5}} = 6 \times 10^4 \text{ sec. or } 16.7 \text{ hr.}$$

In these calculations, seconds have been used as the units of time in accordance with the convention. In view of the slow rate of electrophoretic migrations, minutes or hours are more appropriate time units. To emphasize this, the example used to illustrate the application of Equation (1) can be recalculated using hours for time units. The migration time of 3.6×10^3 sec. becomes 1 hr., and the mobility becomes 0.144; the calculation in these units now becomes:

$$d_A = 1 \text{ hr.} \times 5 \frac{\text{volts}}{\text{cm.}} \times 0.144 \frac{\text{cm.}^2}{\text{volts} \times \text{hr.}} = 0.72 \text{ cm.}$$

VARIETIES OF ELECTROPHORESIS

Free-solution Electrophoresis.—Much of the pioneering work with electrophoresis was done without stabilizing media. Picton and Linder[1] appear to have originated the method in 1892, but it was not fully developed until 1937 when Tiselius[2] described the apparatus and methodology for which he received the Nobel prize. In free-solution electrophoresis the samples are fractionated in a U-tube that has been filled with unstabilized buffer. Usually they are carefully injected into the bottom of the U-tube through a capillary tube sidearm. Careful thermal regulation and isolation from mechanical vibration are depended upon to prevent spreading of the sample by con-

[1] Picton, H., Linder, S. E., J. Chem. Soc., **61**, 148, 1892.
[2] Tiselius, A., Trans. Faraday Soc., **33**, 524, 1937.

vection currents. This regulation is difficult, so that free-solution apparatuses tend to be expensive; another factor that makes them costly is the elaborate optical system which is necessary for locating and measuring the fractions. The cost as well as the technical difficulties of maintaining a free-solution electrophoretic system have resulted in diminishing use of this method in favor of methods using stabilizing media. Nevertheless, it retains its popularity among workers interested in the theoretical aspects of electrophoresis, and it remains the reference method for measuring electrophoretic mobilities.

Moving Boundary Electrophoresis.—In free-solution electrophoresis the volume of the sample can be large, so long as the boundary, or leading edge, between the sample and the buffer is kept sharply defined. When such a preparation is subjected to electrophoresis, the boundary of each component retains its identity. The components advance at rates proportional to their differing mobilities, developing a pattern in which the components overlap to make sharply defined steplike contributions to the total solute concentration. Understanding of this is helped by visualizing each component within the tube as a separate cylinder of solute which migrates independently. At the beginning these cylinders are telescoped into each other so that they occupy the same region. As electrophoresis proceeds, the cylinders move at different rates, sliding out like the sections of a telescope. Each fraction remains as a well-defined cylinder, resulting in sharp changes in concentration at the points where successive fractions overlap. Since the refractive index of a solution changes in direct proportion to the concentration of solute, the boundaries of the fractions can be detected by scanning the tube with a refractometer. The concentration of each fraction can be calculated as a function of its contribution to the change in refractive index. Because measurements depend upon maintaining sharply defined boundaries while the fractions migrate, this kind of electrophoresis is frequently called *moving boundary electrophoresis*. This distinguishes it from *zone electrophoresis* in which the fractions separate completely into discrete zones. Such a distinction is artificial because, if moving boundary electrophoresis could be sufficiently prolonged without loss of resolution due to convection currents, the fractions would separate completely. The fundamental difference between the two methods is that zone electrophoresis makes use of an anticonvection medium, whereas moving boundary electrophoresis does not.

Density gradient electrophoresis[3] is a form of free-solution electrophoresis. In this modification, fractionations are accomplished in a vertical cylinder which is filled with electrolyte containing an electrophoretically inert solute, such as dextrose, sucrose, or dextran. The density of the solution is graded so that the specific gravity diminishes toward the top of the cylinder. A sample can be layered on this solution and its components forced to migrate against the density gradient. This arrangement serves to reduce convection currents, allowing complete separation of sample components to be obtained. If the solute used to produce the density gradient does not impede the progress of the migrants, mobility measurements using this technique agree with those obtained by free-solution electrophoresis.[4,5]

Zone Electrophoresis.—The separation of the fractions of a sample into discrete zones is desirable for both analytical and preparative purposes. Such separations are made possible by using a supporting medium to keep convection currents from distorting the electrophoretic pattern. Almost everything that conceivably could be used as a supporting medium has been tried. In addition to the media that are generally accepted as useful, such as filter paper, cellulose acetate strips, starch powder, cellulose powder,

[3] Svensson, H., and Valmet, E., Science Tools, **2,** 11, 1955.
[4] Aach, H. G., Z. Naturforsch., **18b,** 337, 1963.
[5] Manson, W., J. Electroanal. Chem., **3,** 203, 1962.

starch gel, agar gel, and synthetic gels, good results have recently been reported using ion-exchange paper and membranes, asbestos paper, rayon acetate cloth, glass fiber paper, silica powder, kieselguhr, glass microbeads, glass powder, silica gel, and agarose gel.[6,7] Ribeiro has listed more than thirty supporting substances and has attempted to give credit to the original users.[8]

The kind of supporting medium that is selected depends upon the task. Most analytical separations are made on strips of filter paper or cellulose acetate. These materials are easily obtained, easily manipulated, and give good resolution. They are sometimes unsuitable for dilute solutions or substances that are difficult to detect because they carry only small volumes of sample. Occasionally, when the sample or solvent would attack organic materials, glass fiber paper has been used. These materials, particularly paper, are widely used for routine clinical fractionation of the proteins in blood serum. With paper, the proteins in human blood serum separate easily into five fractions. By contrast, cellulose acetate is capable of resolving serum proteins into nine or more fractions. Since the diagnostic usefulness of extensive subfractionation has not yet become firmly established, paper continues to be the most widely used medium for clinical purposes.

When a high degree of resolution is desired, gels are recommended because they offer maximum stabilization against convection currents. Examples of this kind of medium include starch, agar, and synthetic gels. In addition to affording improved resolution, gels can be cast into thick beds with sample capacities up to 0.1 ml., which is several times larger than the capacity of paper strips. If gels were easy to manipulate, they would probably supersede paper for general use.

Immunoelectrophoresis is a technique whereby biological material is separated into fractions by electrophoresis and the fractions are allowed to react with immune serum following their diffusion through the electrophoretic bed. Since this combines two separative techniques (electrophoresis and diffusion) with a highly specific detection technique (precipitin reaction), it is possible to detect many more fractions in a proteinaceous mixture by immunoelectrophoresis than by conventional electrophoresis. Usually immunoelectrophoresis is accomplished in gels,[9] but good results have also been reported with cellulose acetate sheets. This valuable method is in the province of immunochemistry rather than analytical chemistry and is outside the scope of this chapter; a book describing the methodology of immunoelectrophoresis is available[10] and the subject has been reviewed extensively.[11–15]

Preparative Electrophoresis.—If the purpose of electrophoresis is to prepare a usable amount of purified substance rather than to fractionate for analytical reasons, the electrophoretic bed must have a large capacity. Capacity can be increased by making a thick bed of particulate material, such as starch powder, sand, glass wool, cotton, or filter paper pulp. Such beds are suitable for fractionations involving milliliter batches of sample if a high degree of resolution is not required. When the amount of material to be fractionated is too large to be handled conveniently on a batch basis, separations

[6] Strickland, R. D., Anal. Chem., **34,** 31R, 1962.
[7] Strickland, R. D., Anal. Chem., **36,** 80R, 1964.
[8] Ribeiro, L. P., Mitidieri, E., and Affonso, O. R., Paper Electrophoresis, a Review of Methods and Results, Elsevier Publishing Company, Amsterdam, 1961.
[9] Grabar, P., and Williams, C. A., Jr., Biochim. Biophys. Acta, **10,** 193, 1953.
[10] Grabar, P., and Burtin, P., Immuno-Electrophoretic Analysis, Elsevier Publishing Co., Amsterdam, 1964.
[11] Ballieux, R. E., Imhof. J. W., Stoop, J. W., and Niehaus, G. N., Ned. Tijdschr. Geneesk., **106,** 1531, 1962.
[12] Barcelo, R., Riopel, P., and Legresley, L. P., Union Med. Can., **90,** 1235, 1961.
[13] Mainardi, P. C., Minerva Pediat., **14,** 877, 1962.
[14] Noir, B., Ciencia Invest., **18,** 49, 1962.
[15] Poetschke, G., Progr. Med. Virol., **3,** 79, 1961.

can be made by *continuous electrophoresis*. To do this, provision must be made for introducing the sample in a steady stream and for removing the fractions as they separate. Most methods of continuous electrophoresis are based on the work of Svensson and Brattsten.[16]

INSTRUMENTATION

Power Supplies.—A controversy has arisen concerning the relative merits of power supplies regulated to give constant current *vs.* those regulated to give constant voltage.[8] The reason for this misunderstanding is that voltage is sometimes measured between the terminals of the power supply rather than between the ends of the electrophoretic bed. This practice gives an erroneous estimate of the voltage gradient within the bed because it includes the voltage used to overcome the resistance of the electrodes and electrode chambers, and this resistance varies because of electrolysis. If the voltage expended in the electrode chambers changes but the overall voltage does not, the voltage gradient within the bed must alter. If, however, the overall voltage is made to vary in a way that compensates for the varying resistance in the electrode chambers, then the voltage drop between the ends of the bed remains constant, as does the current flowing through it. Since current must be the same through every cross section of a circuit, it may be measured at any point between the power supply terminals. When current is constant and the resistance of the bed is not allowed to vary, the voltage gradient in the bed cannot change. Directions for constructing power supplies that compensate automatically for resistance variations in the electrode chambers have been published;[17,18] even for someone with no background in electronics, these power supplies are neither expensive nor difficult to make. If a power supply is being used that is not equipped to make compensating changes in response to variations in electrode chamber resistance, it is necessary that the electrodes be designed so that their resistance does not change appreciably owing to polarization, and that the buffer content of the electrode chambers be sufficient so that a negligible fraction of the buffer is consumed during an electrophoretic run. The method for calculating the amount of buffer needed will be discussed in the section entitled "Some Problems of Electrophoresis."

These considerations are important chiefly when knowledge of mobility is significant. The importance of voltage regulation and range has been overstressed, particularly in advertisements of commercial apparatuses. In practice great versatility is seldom useful because, once a working electrophoretic procedure has been established, the range of required voltage is usually small. For conventional electrophoresis the voltage gradient most likely to be used lies between 5 and 10 volts per cm.; this requires a power supply capable of developing between 50 and 150 volts. If separation alone is desired and no exact knowledge of mobilities is needed, almost any d.c. power supply, even a half-wave rectifier, will perform satisfactorily. With paper or cellulose acetate the current drain is less than 1 mA. per strip, so the power requirement is very low: For many purposes a number of dry cell batteries connected in series provide adequate voltage and will give several months of service before replacements become necessary.

Systems for *high-voltage electrophoresis* are often described in the literature.[19–25]

[16] Svensson, H., and Brattsten, I., Arkiv Kemi, **1,** 401, 1949.
[17] Proctor, C. M., Anal. Chem., **28,** 2032, 1956.
[18] Watt, D. D., Hannan, E. C., Iowa State J. Sci., **38** (1), 115, 1963.
[19] Bennett, J. P., and Boursnell, J. C., Biochim. Biophys. Acta, **63,** 382, 1962.
[20] Gross, D., J. Chromatog., **5,** 194, 1961.
[21] Murray, K., Biochim. Biophys. Acta, **59,** 211, 1962.
[22] Osborn, E. C., Clin. Chim. Acta, **6,** 743, 1961.
[23] Pasieka, A., Can. J. Biochem. Physiol., **39,** 1313, 1961.
[24] Rentsch, G., Biochem. Z., **335,** 69, 1961.
[25] Vahvaselka, E., Nature, **193,** 474, 1962.

Increasing the voltage gradient not only speeds fractionation but enhances the quality of resolution because the decreased running time minimizes the opportunity for diffusion of the fractions. High voltage is an arbitrary term; it is usually applied to the voltage gradients lying between 10 and 100 volts per cm. It should be remembered that the important consideration in electrophoresis is the voltage gradient in the bed rather than the voltage drop between the terminals of the power supply. One sometimes finds descriptions of "high-voltage apparatuses" in which the greater part of the voltage drop is in the electrode chambers or in wicks leading to the electrophoretic bed, rather than in the bed itself; such an apparatus introduces the problems of high-voltage electrophoresis without taking full advantage of the beneficial aspects of this technique. This concept of a high-voltage gradient should make it clear that separations using 150 volts between the ends of a 3-cm. bed are just as truly high-voltage electrophoresis as those using 3000 volts through a 60-cm. bed.

Electrophoretic Chambers.—The first consideration in selecting or constructing an electrophoretic chamber should be safety. The chamber should be made of insulating material and designed so that liquid spilling from the apparatus cannot create an electrical hazard. Most commercial chambers cannot be opened without disconnecting the power supply; it would be wise for persons constructing their own chambers to incorporate some such arrangement. The need for measuring the voltage drop between the ends of the electrophoretic bed instead of between the power-supply terminals has already been pointed out; this measurement can be made by placing the probes of a vacuum-tube voltmeter in contact with the bed at a measured distance from one another. To avoid the danger of making voltage measurements with the cover off the apparatus, platinum wires can be fastened to the members that support the bed and brought to terminals that communicate with the outside of the chamber. The terminals should be of the jack type, making it impossible to touch live wires with the fingers. By bringing the probes of the vacuum-tube voltmeter into contact with the terminals once the bed is in place, the voltage drop across the bed can be measured without opening the chamber.

A well-constructed apparatus must also include provision for preventing evaporation from the electrophoretic bed. This is usually accomplished by enclosing the bed and the electrode compartments in an airtight chamber. This provision is important because the production of heat during electrophoresis favors evaporation. The difficulties associated with the production of heat will be discussed in detail in the section entitled "Some Problems of Electrophoresis."

Another requirement is that provision be made for matching the liquid level in the electrode compartments. This can be accomplished by connecting the compartments by means of a tube that can be closed with a pinchcock when electrophoresis is in progress (Fig. 37-1). If the liquid levels do not match, a siphoning action occurs, and the flow of buffer can wash the sample away from the site of application.

If the bed is a strip or sheet, it must be suspended in a way that keeps it from sagging, else excessive buffer will accumulate at the low point and will cause serious distortion of the pattern. Ways to correct this defect have been devised. This author prefers his own system by which the strips are pulled taut with movable braces.[26] A slight sagging of the strip remains when this device is used, but it is not so great that the accumulation of liquid becomes a problem. In another apparatus a ridgepole system is used with the center of the strip supported by a rod to form a tent-like arrangement.[27] With this arrangement the sample is applied and the pattern developed along one sloping side. Difficulties inherent in this system include washing of the sample downward owing to

[26] Strickland, R. D., and Podleski, T. R., Am. J. Clin. Pathol., **28**, 385, 1957.
[27] Durrum, E. L., J. Am. Chem. Soc., **72**, 2943, 1950.

drainage from the apex, and drying at the apex from the same cause. This latter effect is serious if mobilities are to be measured, because such drying causes a nonlinear voltage gradient. Another objection to the ridgepole arrangement is that it requires a strip nearly twice as long as when the paper is suspended horizontally, and consequently a higher overall voltage is required to achieve a given voltage gradient; this makes it harder to control heat. Notwithstanding these difficulties, satisfactory separations can be obtained using an apparatus of this type.

Apparatuses have also been described in which the strips are supported on a rigid plate.[28] This obviates any problem with sagging, but the area of contact between the strip and the plate is inherently troublesome, since capillary action tends to pull buffer and with it the sample from the strip. This causes serious distortions of the electrophoretic pattern. Attempts have been made to control this by treating the plate with an anti-wetting agent, such as one of the silicones. Recently an apparatus has been devised that uses a bag inflated with coolant to exert pressure upon the strip.[29] This apparatus is designed for high-voltage electrophoresis and should be effective in this application because the short running time required minimizes the opportunity for the patterns to wash out of the strip by capillary action. Another rigid support that should be useful if capillary action can be controlled is an anodized aluminum plate.[20] The anodized surface is a good electrical insulator, and the metallic plate is additionally useful for carrying away heat generated by passage of current through the strip. It can even be drilled so that coolant can be circulated through it if desired. It has also been suggested that the strip be immersed in a tank of some liquid that is immiscible with the buffer.[30] The excellent cooling action obtainable from liquid-to-liquid contact, coupled with the inhibition of evaporation, make this approach seem very promising. Unfortunately, the mechanical difficulties of maintaining such a system are so great that it has not found much use. Another objection is that even though the buffer is immiscible with the liquid in which it is immersed, the samples may interact with it. Chlorobenzene, for example, has a detrimental effect upon the lipoproteins in human serum.

When a gel or powder is used, the bed can be cast directly into a trough running between the two electrode chambers.[31,32] With powders and gels there is less difficulty with loss of buffer and distortion of the pattern by capillary action, but evaporation leads to problems even more serious than those encountered with paper. The flow of liquid into the medium is through the ends of the bed; since this is necessarily a slow process with gels and since evaporation can occur over the entire surface of the bed, it is possible to dry out a portion of the gel completely. Covering the gel with a nonwettable plastic film such as Saran Wrap is useful in preventing evaporation. Inasmuch as gels and powders usually have a greater cross section than does a strip, more heat is generated and relatively less surface is available for dissipating it. This problem is intensified by the excellent anticonvective properties of gel. For this reason it will usually be found desirable to run electrophoresis in gel or powder beds at reduced temperatures. An ordinary refrigerator set at approximately 4°C. is very useful for this. The wires connecting the electrodes to the power supply can be brought out between the door and the refrigerator without damaging them because refrigerators are equipped with soft-rubber sealing gaskets.

Electrophoresis inevitably results in the destruction of buffer at the electrodes. Unless measures are taken to prevent it, diffusion and convection processes can carry

[28] Kunkel, H. G., and Tiselius, A., J. Gen. Physiol., **35,** 89, 1951.
[29] Bailey, S. W., and Hackman, R. H., J. Chromatog., **8,** 52, 1962.
[30] Consden, R., and Stanier, W. M., Nature, **170,** 1069, 1952.
[31] Kunkel, H. G., and Slater, R. J., Proc. Soc. Exptl. Biol. Med., **80,** 42, 1952.
[32] Strickland, R. D., Mack, P. A., Gurule, F. T., Podleski, T. R., Salome, O., and Childs, W. A., Anal. Chem., **31,** 1410, 1959.

decomposition products into the bed. Provision is usually made to minimize this by interposing electrically permeable barriers between the electrode chambers and the bed. Such barriers may be made of gel, filter paper, sponge, or other suitable material. The barriers should offer low resistance to the passage of electrical current, because the potential drop across the barrier serves no useful purpose and it increases the production of heat. A number of apparatuses have been described that provide for continual mixing and recycling of the buffer in the chambers to neutralize the decomposition products. None of these devices has found widespread use, probably because the value of the buffer does not justify the effort required to preserve it. During electrophoresis, when no provision is made for regenerating the buffer, the permissible time for an electrophoretic run is established by the amount of buffer in the chambers. This, in turn, establishes the size of the electrode chambers. The calculation of the volume of buffer needed will be discussed in the section on "Some Problems in Electrophoresis." Usually the electrode chambers of apparatuses for filter paper electrophoresis are constructed to contain approximately a liter of buffer in each chamber.

Electrodes.—A number of materials, including graphite rods, stainless steel, silver–silver chloride, and the noble metals, have been recommended for electrodes. Platinum is the best substance for this purpose because it does not deteriorate; electrodes once installed need never be replaced. Various forms of platinum electrodes have been devised, ranging from fine wires to sheets of foil. Fine wires are not very satisfactory because they are more subject to mechanical damage and harder to clean than foil. Excellent electrodes can be made by bonding sheets of very thin platinum foil to pieces of acrylic plastic.[26] Such electrodes are inexpensive because the platinum is thin, they present a large surface to the buffer, and they are easily cleaned because they are mechanically strong.

If electrodes are too small, they are apt to polarize by becoming covered with gas bubbles or other products of electrolysis. Small electrodes can also limit the amount of current that can flow between them. Attempts to overcome this limitation by immersing the electrodes in cellophane bags containing concentrated solutions of nonbuffering salts are to be discouraged; this practice creates an undesirable osmotic gradient and also results in unwanted ions being introduced into the bed by electrical transference.

Apparatus for Continuous Electrophoresis.—When large volumes must be handled it becomes desirable to use a continuous-flow system; this requires apparatus of a different design. Most such apparatuses are constructed in accordance with a principle suggested by Svensson and Brattsten;[16] the apparatus of Durrum[33] is best known, but numerous other designs have been proposed.[34,35,36,37,38,39,40,41,42]

The essential parts of a continuous electrophoresis apparatus are shown diagrammatically in Fig. 37-2. A sheet of filter paper is usually used as a supporting medium, although apparatuses have been described that use beds of particulate material; it is even possible to use free solution by allowing a thin film of buffer to flow uniformly over a sloping plate.[43] Any of these forms of the apparatus is commercially available. Whatever the medium, buffer is made to run over the bed at a uniform rate, while the material to

[33] Durrum, E. L., J. Colloid. Sci., **6**, 274, 1951.
[34] Bighi, C., Ann. Univ. Ferrara Sez., **2**, Suppl. No. 1, 1, 1961.
[35] Brattsten, I., Arkiv Kemi, **8**, 347, 1955.
[36] Hoermann, H., and Fujii, T., Z. Physiol. Chem., **328**, 65, 1962.
[37] Karler, A., Anal. Chem., **31**, 848, 1959.
[38] Leister, C. I., Jr., and Kirk, P. L., J. Forensic Med., **8**, 42, 1961.
[39] Lewis, J. H., and Marchant, W. R., J. Clin. Invest., **38**, 1924, 1959.
[40] Pucar, Z., and Konrad-Jakovac, Z., J. Chromatog., **9**, 106, 1962.
[41] Siefert, G., Arzneimittel-Forsch., **10**, 1024, 1960.
[42] Wallace, A. L. C., and Ferguson, K. A., J. Chromatog., **4**, 233, 1960.
[43] Barrollier, J., Watzka, E., and Gibian, H., Z. Naturforsch., **13b**, 754, 1958.

be fractionated is applied in a small stream that flows in a thin line across the bed in the same direction as the buffer. When voltage is applied to the electrodes, the fractions migrate laterally at differential rates while the flow of buffer carries them downward. The pathway of each individual fraction describes the vector of these two forces, causing the electrophoretic pattern to take the form of a fan, with fractions coming out of the bed at different points as indicated in the drawing. This form of electrophoresis is called "curtain electrophoresis" because separations are accomplished in a sheet or curtain of buffer.

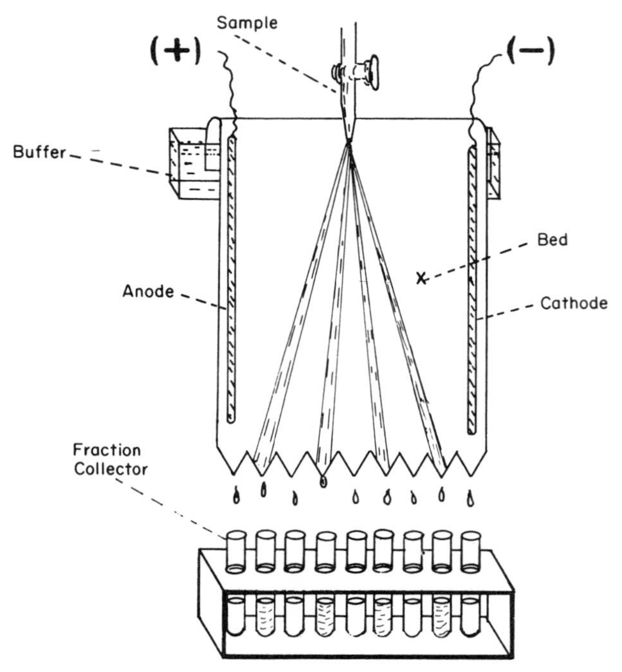

Fig. 37-2. A Diagram Illustrating the Principle of Continuous Electrophoresis. As buffer siphons down the bed it carries the sample with it. Differential electrophoretic mobility causes the fractions to stream along divergent pathways.

A continuous electrophoresis apparatus of this kind requires a permeable bed through which the liquid can flow. Gels are too dense for continuous electrophoresis. Regulating the flow of liquid through the bed so that it is steady and not turbulent is difficult. The fluid fronts of buffer and sample should advance at rates that are perfectly matched. If they do not, the resulting turbulence at the site of application interferes seriously with resolution. The large cross section of the bed increases the power requirement and consequently the problems with electrolysis; this makes it necessary to provide for continuous replacement of the buffer in the electrode chambers. The most economical system for this purpose combines the buffer pumped from the two chambers in order to restore the pH, and then recycles it. In such apparatuses, power leakage through the pumping circuit can be prevented by means of a reciprocating valve or some other device to interrupt the electrical continuity of the stream. Precautions must be taken to control the additional electrical hazard engendered by pumping buffer solution that is in contact with the electrodes.

SOME PROBLEMS OF ELECTROPHORESIS

Electrolysis.—Electrophoresis is accompanied by electrolysis which causes microscopic bubbles to accumulate on the electrodes. Since electrical contact with the buffer is lost where a bubble occurs, the resistance of an electrode gradually builds up until, by coalescing, the bubbles become large enough to break away from the surface, thereby restoring contact with the buffer. When the electrode areas are large, the variations in resistance caused by formation and breaking away of bubbles are negligible because only a fraction of the total area is obscured at any given time. With small electrodes, however, this fluctuation of resistance becomes important because almost the entire surface can become covered before the bubbles become large enough to break away. Although such fluctuations in resistance must cause particles to migrate at erratic rates, the effect is visible only as an apparent reduction in mobility.

Another kind of resistance change at the electrodes occurs when one of the products of buffer decomposition is sparingly soluble. An example of this is the plating out of diethylbarbituric acid on the anode when veronal buffer is used. This forms an insulating coat over the electrode which requires an increasing fraction of available voltage to overcome electrode resistance, with resultant diminution in the voltage gradient within the electrophoretic bed. As a result, electrophoretic migration becomes progressively slower and ultimately ceases. This form of resistance change unnecessarily limits the useful duration of an electrophoretic run.

Even if the electrode products are soluble, the transfer of the anions and cations into opposite electrode chambers results in a gradual divergence of the pH in the chambers; the buffer at the cathode becomes progressively more alkaline, while that at the anode becomes more acidic. This effect, even with appropriate barriers, can eventually extend itself into the electrophoretic bed as a progressive change in pH which affects the mobility of the migrants. It is erroneous to think that the change in pH of the bed is a passive one owing to diffusion of the buffer decomposition products back from the electrode chambers into the bed. To understand what actually happens, it is desirable to consider the electrode reactions. Let us take as an example the case where the buffering substance is the salt of a weak acid and a strong base. Sodium diethylbarbiturate is typical. The cations move from the anode chamber through the bed to the cathode, where they are reduced momentarily to the metallic element:

$$Na^+ + e^- \rightarrow Na^0$$

This reacts with water to form hydrogen gas, which bubbles away from the electrode, and sodium hydroxide:

$$Na^0 + H_2O \rightarrow Na^+ + OH^- + \tfrac{1}{2}H_2$$

When this reaction occurs, the cathode chamber acquires hydroxide anion in addition to the barbiturate anion, and the proportion of hydroxide increases steadily as electrolytic decomposition continues. Since the OH^- has the same charge as the barbiturate anion, it moves in the same way through the bed toward the anode. This results in the bed *as a whole* becoming more alkaline, an effect that increases as the fluid in the cathode chamber becomes more alkaline. With the example being used, the charge:mass ratio of OH^- is more than ten times that of the barbiturate anion. This means that amounts of OH^- disproportionately large in comparison to its concentration in the cathode chamber will travel through the bed. The reaction at the anode does little to counteract this situation.

Here the barbiturate anion moves to the electrode and loses its electron to become, momentarily, a free radical.

$$A^- \rightarrow A^0 + e^-$$

This reacts with water to form oxygen, which bubbles off at the anode, and diethylbarbituric acid:

$$2A^0 + H_2O \rightarrow 2HA + \tfrac{1}{2}O_2$$

(The letter A in these equations symbolizes the diethylbarbituric acid group.) This acid is weakly ionized, so only a few hydrogen ions are free to move into the electrophoretic bed. The net effect of this is that during an electrophoretic run there is a tendency for the pH of the bed to become *uniformly* more alkaline, and not alkaline at one end and acid at the other as might be expected on an intuitive basis.

These bad effects of electrolysis can be held to a minimum by continuous replacement of the buffer in the electrode chambers, but this is seldom done because of the expense and the technical difficulties of providing a pumping system. The permissible time for a run cannot be increased by increasing the strength of the buffer, because the rate of decomposition is proportional to the amount of current that is passed, and strong solutions are proportionately more conductive than weak ones, so that, for a given voltage gradient, the same *fraction* of buffer will be decomposed regardless of its concentration. However, the effects can be adequately controlled by providing a sufficient *volume* of buffer in the electrode chambers. If effective anticonvection barriers are present between the electrodes and the bed, at least 1 percent of the buffering capacity can be lost through electrolysis without affecting the electrophoretic pattern to a noticeable degree.

The quantity of electricity consumed during a run determines the volume of buffer required. This varies with the situation, but is calculable by means of Faraday's law. The *faraday*, that is, the amount of electricity required to decompose one gram-equivalent weight of a compound, is 96,500 coulombs; for electrophoretic calculations it is convenient to express this in different units as 26,806 mA.-hr. With these units, the amount of substance that will be decomposed expressed in gram-equivalents, X, is proportional to the product of the current in milliamperes, I, and the time in hours, T, so that the gram-equivalents of buffering substance that will be decomposed by any given current during any time of run can be calculated:

$$X = \frac{IT}{26{,}806}$$

Since a 100-fold excess of buffer is required, the gram-equivalents of buffering substance, Y, that should be present in the electrode chambers is:

$$Y = 100X = \frac{100IT}{26{,}806}$$

This simplifies to: $Y = 0.0037IT$ gram-equivalents. The gram-equivalents of substance in a solution are calculated by multiplying the volume, V, in liters by the normality, N, of the solution. Since Y equivalents are required, $V = Y/N$ liters of solution will be needed. Combining this with the previous equation gives

$$V = \frac{0.0037IT}{N}$$

As an example of the application of this equation, let us assume that the buffer is 0.1 N sodium diethylbarbiturate, that with the voltate gradient being used 5 mA. of current have been found to flow, and further that the time required for separation will be 8 hours.

From these data it can be calculated that the volume of buffer needed for this operation is

$$V = \frac{0.0037 \times 5 \times 8}{0.1} = 1.48 \text{ liters}$$

Such exactness is meaningless. The run will require 1.5 liters of buffer divided evenly between the electrode chambers. It should be noted that the constant 0.0037 applies to any electrophoretic situation; therefore, if the milliamperes of current required for electrophoresis, the hours required to accomplish it, and the normality of the buffer are known, the computation of the volume of buffer needed is easy.

These specifications are intended only as a guide. If it were permissible to decompose as much as 10 percent of the buffer, and if the run required only an hour with the current flow limited to 1 mA., only about 4 ml. of 0.1 N buffer, barely enough to wet a paper strip, would be needed. This last calculation is not a reduction to absurdity. It is included to help the reader realize that for limited short-run separations, particularly with nonamphoteric substances, it is sometimes possible to obtain good results by using an apparatus no more complicated than a strip of filter paper, moistened with buffer, and laid across two electrodes of platinum wire. This minimal apparatus should be protected from drying out by an airtight cover.

It is common practice to conserve buffer by mixing and reusing the contents of the electrode chambers after an electrophoretic run, or by reversing the polarity of the electrodes during alternate runs. There is no serious objection to this practice if measurements of conductivity and pH are used to make certain that the buffer is still good.

Ionic Strength.—The activity coefficients of ionic substances in solution are influenced by the concentration of the solution and by the valences (electrical charges) of the ions. Using elementary considerations, Lewis and Randall[44] have defined this effect mathematically, introducing a measure of effective concentration that they have named *ionic strength*, the symbol for which is μ. If c_i represents the molal concentration of each ion and z_i the charge of each ion, ionic strength is defined as

$$\mu = \tfrac{1}{2} c_i z_i^2$$

As examples, a 0.1 molal solution of NaCl has the ionic strength

$$\mu = \tfrac{1}{2}[(0.1 \times 1^2) + (0.1 \times 1^2)] = 0.1$$

whereas a 0.1 molal solution of $CuSO_4$ has the ionic strength

$$\mu = \tfrac{1}{2}[(0.1 \times 2^2) + (0.1 \times 2^2)] = 0.4$$

and a 0.1 molal solution of $Al_2(SO_4)_3$ has the ionic strength

$$\mu = \tfrac{1}{2}[(0.2 \times 3^2) + (0.3 \times 2^2)] = 1.5$$

When the solution is a buffer, the weakly ionized component makes virtually no contribution to the ionic strength of the solution. As a result, when the pH of a buffer solution changes, the ionic strength must also change, even though the combined molality of the buffer pair remains unchanged; therefore the pH must be taken into account when the ionic strength of a buffer is calculated.

To clarify this statement, let us calculate the ionic strength of a 0.1 M NaH_2PO_4–Na_2HPO_4 buffer at two pH values, say 7.6 and 6.6. This solution is dilute, so molarity can be assumed to be equal to molality without introducing significant error.

Let the dissociation constant for the reaction $H_2PO_4^- \rightleftarrows H^+ + HPO_4^=$ be written

[44] Lewis, G. N., and Randall, M., J. Am. Chem. Soc., **43,** 1112, 1921.

$$\frac{[H^+][HPO_4^{=}]}{[H_2PO_4^-]} = 7.5 \times 10^{-8}$$

This equation can be rearranged to

$$\frac{[HPO_4^{=}]}{[H_2PO_4^-]} = \frac{7.5 \times 10^{-8}}{[H^+]}$$

From this it can be seen that the ratio of $[HPO_4^{=}]$ to $[H_2PO_4^-]$ can be calculated for any pH. By our specification, the combined molarity of these two ions is 0.1; let the molarity of $HPO_4^{=}$ be X. Then the molarity of $H_2PO_4^-$ is necessarily $0.1 - X$. If this is true, then

$$\frac{X}{0.1 - X} = \frac{7.5 \times 10^{-8}}{[H^+]}$$

At pH 7.6, $[H^+] = 10^{-7.6} = 2.5 \times 10^{-8}$, and

$$\frac{X}{0.1 - X} = \frac{7.5 \times 10^{-8}}{2.5 \times 10^{-8}} = 3.0$$

Solving for X gives 0.075, which is the molarity of $HPO_4^{=}$; the molarity of $H_2PO_4^-$, then, is 0.025. The molarity of sodium ion is 0.050 (from Na_2HPO_4) plus 0.025 (from NaH_2PO_4), or 0.075 total.

Calculating the ionic strength gives

$$\mu = \tfrac{1}{2}[(0.075 \times 1^2) + (0.075 \times 2^2) + (0.025 \times 1^2)] = 0.200$$

Following the same calculation sequence, it can be shown that the ionic strength at pH 6.6 is 0.104; this is about half the strength at the higher pH.

It is sometimes desirable to measure electrophoretic behavior of a substance at different pH values while maintaining the same ionic strength. This can be accomplished by adding enough neutral salt to the solution to make up for the diminution in the ionic strength of the buffer owing to change in pH, and it is done when isoelectric points are being measured. Directions have been published for making buffers at different pH's up to the same ionic strength.[45,46]

In spite of the inconvenience involved in calculating ionic strength, this parameter is universally used by electrophoreticists, because it is related not only to the conductivity of the buffer but to such other important physical properties as osmotic pressure, refractive index, and vapor pressure. Ionic strength has important effects upon the solubility of macromolecules; many proteins become insoluble when ionic strength is too low or too high. There is also a relationship between electrophoretic mobility and the ionic strength of the buffer, the mobility being approximately proportional to the reciprocal of the square root of the ionic strength; this has been demonstrated experimentally.[47] Since mobility increases with diminishing ionic strength, it is often possible to shorten the time required for electrophoretic separations by using a dilute buffer. It is also desirable to keep ionic strength low because conductivity, and consequently power consumption, is a function of ionic strength. This means that the use of buffers with low ionic strength helps to minimize both the production of heat and the quantity of electrode products formed.

[45] Coch-Frugoni, J. A., Gazz. Chim. Ital., **87,** 403, 1957.
[46] Elving, P. J., Markowitz, J. M., and Rosenthal, I., Anal. Chem., **28,** 1179, 1956.
[47] McDonald, H. J., Ionography, Electrophoresis in Stabilized Media, The Year Book Publishers, Inc., Chicago, 1955.

It should not be assumed from the illustrations that have been given that the computation of ionic strength is always a simple matter. When a buffer has a complex composition, for example "Tris" buffer (see Table 37-1 given subsequently), the ionic strength ceases to be calculable because of the difficulties of establishing the concentrations and charges of the ionized particles. This deficiency can be compensated for by measuring the conductivity.

pH and Other Chemical Characteristics.—The pH of a buffer greatly affects electrophoretic mobility, particularly when the sample is a weak acid or base, because the pH establishes its degree of ionization. If the sample substance is amphoteric, as is the case with proteins, the direction of migration depends upon whether the buffer pH is above or below the isoelectric point of the sample. It is frequently possible to improve the quality of separations by finding the optimum pH value. An example of this is seen in electrophoretic separations of the amino acids. Inasmuch as most of these exist as zwitterions in the pH range between 6 and 8, electrophoretic separations using buffers in this range are unsatisfactory. As would be expected, better separations can be obtained using either strongly alkaline or strongly acid buffers. Most papers reporting successful separations of these substances have suggested very acid buffers.[48–55]

The optimum pH range for separating proteins is narrow; the best results have been obtained between pH 8.6 and pH 9.2. The number of substances capable of good buffering action in this pH region is limited. The ideal substance for buffering to pH 8.6 would exist half as the acid and half as the salt at this pH, which would require a dissociation constant of 2.5×10^{-9}. The rarity of suitable substances is pointed up by the fact that diethylbarbituric acid ($k_a = 1.6 \times 10^{-8}$) and boric acid ($k_a = 6.4 \times 10^{-10}$) are both frequently used, even though their dissociation constants are far from ideal. Even tris (hydroxymethyl)aminomethane (commonly known as "Tris") ($k_b = 1.2 \times 10^{-7}$) is not ideal; the ideal buffering base would have a $k_b = 4 \times 10^{-6}$. Of substances that might be suitable on the basis of their dissociation constants, some are insufficiently soluble (*p*-toluidine), some react with the sample material (phenol), and some have objectionable characteristics such as offensive odor (pyridine). These considerations make it clear that the discovery of a substance with suitable buffering properties is an event of considerable importance.

Proteins are extraordinarily sensitive to chemical influences. Other substances are more stable, so that the possibilities for improving separations by varying the buffer are greatly extended.

Although cations generally can be separated in dilute solutions of some weak acid, it is possible, when a refractory supporting medium such as asbestos paper is used, to accomplish separations in fused salts.[56–59] Such dramatically extreme conditions are exceptional. Ordinarily strongly alkaline or acid solutions are to be avoided because

[48] Atfield, G. N., and Morris, C. J. O. R., Biochem. J., **81,** 606, 1961.
[49] Biserte, G., Plaquet-Schoonaert, T., Boulanger, P., and Paysant, P., J. Chromatog., **3,** 25, 1960.
[50] Cook, E. R., and Lascombe, M., J. Chromatog., **35,** 75, 1960.
[51] Gross, D., Nature, **184,** 1298, 1959.
[52] Jirgl, V., Experientia, **15,** 235, 1959.
[53] Naughton, M. A., and Hagopian, H., Anal. Biochem., **3,** 276, 1962.
[54] Scherr, G. H., Anal. Chem., **34,** 777, 1962.
[55] Werum, L. N., Gordon, H. T., and Thornburg, W., J. Chromatog., **3,** 125, 1960.
[56] Alberti, G., Grassini, G., and Truco, R., J. Electroanal. Chem., **3,** 283, 1962.
[57] Arniker, H. J., Ann. Phys., **4,** 1291, 1959.
[58] Arniker, H. J., and Chemla, M., Radioisotopes Sci. Research, Proc. Intern. Conf., Paris, 1957, **2,** 421, 1958.
[59] Lunden, A., Z. Naturforsch., **14a,** 801, 1959.

of their deleterious effects upon the supporting medium. It is usually better to try electrophoresis in the intermediate pH range using complexing agents, such as lactic,[60–62] tartaric,[63,64] or citric [65,66] acids, to ensure solubility. Procedures for separating polyvalent cations, including those of the lanthanide and actinide series, have generally made use of complexing agents. See the works of Pucar and Konrad-Jakovac,[40] Hoyle and West,[67] Lancina,[68] Majunder and Singh,[69,70,71] Shvedov and Stephanov,[72] Strain, Binder, Evans, Frame, and Hines,[73] and Wenger, Janstein, and Kapetanidis.[74]

Among the anionic substances, the halides can be separated at almost any pH, since they form fully ionized neutral salts; but other anions require pH regulation, particularly the anions of weakly ionized or polybasic acids. Since different degrees of ionization can exist with such substances, a pH that permits two ionization states to exist in equilibrium will result in spreading of the zones owing to the different rates of migration of the two ionization states. In such cases, spreading of the zone rather than separation of the two ionization states occurs, because as fast as the particles differing in charge are separated by electrophoretic action the particles of each group undergo the changes necessary to re-establish equilibrium. From these considerations, it is clear why most procedures for separating anions require alkaline solutions, such as sodium carbonate[75] or sodium hydroxide.[76,77] The same reasoning makes it evident that such weakly ionized bases as amines[78] and alkaloids[79–82] should be separated at low pH values.

The general considerations discussed here for weakly ionized inorganic substances apply with equal force to separations of weakly acidic organic substances, such as carboxylic acids[83,84] and phenols[85,86]; these are best separated at high pH's. Certain organic substances have no charge at any pH, but form electrophoretically mobile complexes with substances that do have a charge. The sugars and polyalcohols form such complexes in the pH range between 9 and 10 with a number of anions, including

[60] Sato, T. R., Diamond, H., Norris, W. P., and Strain, H. H., J. Am. Chem. Soc., **74,** 6154, 1952.
[61] Sato, T. R., Norris, W. P., and Strain, H. H., Anal. Chem., **24,** 776, 1952.
[62] Sato, T. R., Norris, W. P., and Strain, H. H., Anal. Chem., **26,** 267, 1954.
[63] Maki, M., Japan Analyst, **3,** 393, 1954.
[64] Yasunaga, S., and Shimomura, O., J. Pharm. Soc. Japan, **74,** 66, 1954.
[65] Lederer, M., Compt. rend., **236,** 200, 1953.
[66] Lederer, M., J. Chromatog., **1,** 86, 1958.
[67] Hoyle, W., and West, T. S., Talanta, **3,** 47, 1959.
[68] Lancina, M. H., J. Chromatog., **2,** 438, 1959.
[69] Majunder, A. K., and Singh, B. R., Anal. Chim. Acta, **18,** 220, 1958.
[70] Majunder, A. K., and Singh, B. R., Anal. Chim. Acta, **18**, 224, 1958.
[71] Majunder, A. K., and Singh, B. R., Anal. Chim. Acta, **20,** 275, 1959.
[72] Shvedov, V. P., and Stephanov, A. V., Radiokhimiya, **1,** 112, 1959.
[73] Strain, H. H., Binder, J. F., Evans, G. H., Frame, H. D., Jr., and Hines, J. J., Anal. Chem., **33,** 527, 1961.
[74] Wenger, P. E., Janstein, W. V., and Kapetanidis, I., Mikrochim. Ichoanal. Acta, 97, **1963.**
[75] Belling, G. B., and Underdown, R. E., Anal. Chim. Acta, **22,** 203, 1960.
[76] Grassini, G., and Lederer, M., J. Chromatog., **2,** 326, 1959.
[77] Grassini, G., and Ossicini, L., J. Chromatog., **7,** 351, 1962.
[78] Lahdevirta, J., Raina, A., and Heikel, T., Scand. J. Clin. Lab. Invest., **9,** 345, 1957.
[79] Burma, D. P., Naturwissenschaften, **41,** 19, 1954.
[80] Casinovi, G. C., Lederer, M., and Marini-Bettolo, G. B., Gazz. Chim. Ital., **86,** 342, 1956.
[81] Marini-Bettolo, G. B., and Casinovi, G. C., J. Chromatog., **1,** 411, 1958.
[82] Wagner, G., Pharmazie, **10,** 470, 1955.
[83] Barnett, A. J. G., and Smith, D. K., Nature, **174,** 659, 1954.
[84] Perila, O., Acta Chem. Scand., **9,** 1231, 1955.
[85] Meikle, R. W., Nature, **196,** 61, 1962.
[86] Michl, H., Monatsh. Chem., **83,** 737, 1952.

borate,[87–91] molybdate,[92] and arsenite.[93] Such complexes are usually unstable and can be separated only if the complexing agent is present in the buffer in large excess so that mass action maintains the compounds in the complexed condition.

Electroosmosis.—During electrophoresis there is often a flow of water under the influence of the voltage gradient. This phenomenon is called *electroosmosis*. The rate of this flow is influenced by the species and concentration of ionic solutes in the water. The molecular basis for this phenomenon should be understood.

An ion in aqueous solution becomes hydrated, that is to say, associated with the molecules of water in its vicinity. This occurs because water molecules are dipolar, so that the portions of adjacent water molecules bearing a charge opposite to that of an ion are held to the ion. The oppositely charged portions of the water molecules that are held in this way present a charged surface which, in turn, attracts, and to some extent holds, another layer of water molecules. This arrangement has been described by Helmholtz as the *electrical double layer*, a concept that is discussed at length in textbooks of physical chemistry. The term "double layer" is misleading because the formation of successive polarized shells of molecules continues outward for a number of molecular radii, with the arrangement of the molecules becoming less orderly as the field effect of the central ion becomes attenuated by distance. When the hydrated ions are subjected to a voltage gradient, they migrate to the appropriate electrodes, carrying with them their associated water.[94] It is possible for hundreds or even thousands of solvent molecules to be dragged along by each migrating ion, and therefore the electroosmotic flow can become an important factor in electrophoretic procedures. The opposing flows caused by cations and anions seldom compensate, because the ions differ in the amounts of water that they can carry with them. Inasmuch as cations usually carry more water than anions, the net flow of liquid is almost always toward the cathode. Whatever the direction of electroosmotic flow, it causes a passive displacement of the entire sample with respect to the electrophoretic bed exactly as a river carries a log downstream. Since all fractions of a sample are carried along together by electroosmotic flow, the motion has no desirable effect upon the quality of fractionation; indeed, when measurement of mobility becomes important, it is necessary to make corrections for this motion by observing the displacement of some uncharged solute.[28]

When molecules of a polar solvent are in contact with a wettable surface, the polar groups on the molecules that form the surface build up fixed layers of solvent in the same way as has been described for dissolved ions. This bound water, along with water held mechanically in folds and cul-de-sacs of the supporting medium, forms a stationary phase of solvent that extracts portions of a sample from solvent moving past the surface by electroosmosis. This effect is useful in chromatography, but it is undesirable in electrophoresis because the presence of portions of a fraction in both the stationary and the moving phases of the solvent leads to trailing. This is not the only cause of trailing; another cause will be discussed under "Heat." The displacement of samples by electroosmotic flow is determined to some extent by the species of supporting medium; Bermes and McDonald[95] have shown, for example, that the electroosmotic displacement is greater in glass fiber paper than it is in cellulose paper.

[87] Bourne, E. J., Hutson, D. H., and Weigel, H., Chem. & Ind. (London), **1960,** 1111.
[88] Consden, R., and Stanier, W. M., Nature, **169,** 783, 1952.
[89] Gross, D., Nature, **172,** 908, 1953.
[90] Jaenicke, L., Naturwissenschaften, **39,** 86, 1952.
[91] Lindgren, B. O., Acta Chem. Scand., **12,** 447, 1958.
[92] Bourne, E. J., Hutson, D. H., and Weigel, H., Chem. & Ind. (London), **1959,** 1047.
[93] Thorn, W., and Busch, E. W., Biochem. Z., **333,** 252, 1960.
[94] Darmois, E., Compt. rend., (Acad. Sci.) **227,** 339, 1948.
[95] Bermes, E. W., Jr., and McDonald, H. J., Biochim. Biophys. Acta, **20,** 416, 1956.

Interaction with Supporting Media.—Electrophoretic migration is slower in stabilizing media than it is in free solution. This is to be expected, because the presence of supporting material in the pathway of migration of a particle would impede its progress. Collisions of a migrating particle with the supporting medium could result in a momentary dead stop, ricocheting, or entrapment in a cul-de-sac or narrowing fissure. Progress might also be delayed by chemical forces, such as coordination or the formation of bonds with ionic side chains. Such impediments would have different effects upon different kinds of migrating particles owing to differences in molecular volume and shape and in the sign and magnitude of their charges. It would be difficult to assign useful numerical values to any one of these properties, and, since mobilities in stabilizing media are the resultant of interactions among all of them, attempts to correlate the mobilities in various media with those found in free solution are not apt to be generally useful.

If the supporting medium has ionic side chains (for example, sulfate groups in agar or carboxylate groups in paper), these can interact with the particles being separated by electrophoresis. Ionic side chains are usually undesirable because they produce trailing, with portions of the fractions being held back by binding to the side chains. However, advantage has been taken of this effect by using ion-exchange substances as supporting media. These have enough binding capacity to hold the entire sample in combination with the side chains; in this condition, since the bonds formed with the bed are capable of dissociation, electrophoretic movement of the zones can still occur, although mobilities are reduced. At the same time, movements of the sample due to electroosmosis, convection, and diffusion are inhibited.

Most protein molecules have a number of ionic side chains, some of them positive and some negative. The direction of migration depends upon the net charge: a molecule with six negative side chains and five positive side chains would be expected to migrate toward the anode. Since macromolecules potentially can have multiple charges of both signs, ionic side chains of either charge on the stabilizing medium can affect their mobilities. Attempts to remove this interference by removing or inactivating the side chains on the media have been numerous. The sulfate side chains of agar, for example, have been inactivated by treating the agar with barium,[96] and more recently agar has been processed to make a sulfate-free product called agarose.[97,98] Directions have also been published for altering the charge on filter paper.[99]

Heat.—The unavoidable electrical heating that accompanies electrophoresis has a number of adverse effects. In free-solution electrophoresis, heat causes convection currents that can disrupt the electrophoretic pattern. Supporting media are intended to prevent this by impeding liquid flow. Unfortunately, preventing liquid flow increases the difficulty of heat disposal; the bad effects of heat are most evident in gel beds, where convection is virtually eliminated.

There is a tendency for the bed to lose heat to the environment by evaporation, which can occur from all surfaces of the bed; replacement of the evaporating solvent, however, can occur only by liquid flow from the reservoirs at the ends of the bed. As a result, there is a flow of liquid from both ends of the bed toward the center. Concentration of salts at the midpoint of the bed causes a diminished voltage gradient in this region, which greatly reduces the rate of electromigration. In addition to this, it is difficult for

[96] Houtsmuller, A. J., Protides Biol. Fluids, Proc. Colloq., **10,** 149, 1962 (pub. 1963).
[97] Ghetie, V., and Motet-Grigoras, D., Acad. Rep. Populare Romine, Studii Cercetari Biochim., **5,** 409, 1962.
[98] Hjerten, S., Biochim. Biophys. Acta, **62,** 445, 1962.
[99] Jermyn, M. A., and Thomas, R., Nature, 728, 172, 1953.

fractions to progress beyond this area because of the opposing flow of solvent. It is possible for these effects to be of sufficient magnitude to recombine fractions already separated. The flow of buffer from both ends toward the center of the bed in response to evaporative effects is distinct from electroosmosis, with which it is sometimes confused. Evaporation from gels presents a particularly serious problem because liquid is apt to be lost more rapidly than it is replaced. When this happens there can be a regional drying of the bed so severe that the flow of electrical current is interrupted. With gels, evaporation can be prevented by covering their surfaces with a moistureproof film such as Saran Wrap or by forming the bed inside a tube. Probably the use of a film is preferable because, if a gel is enclosed in a rigid tube, heating causes it to expand so that the ends extrude and may break off, particularly if the bed is allowed to cool.

When the bed is of thin material, such as cellulose acetate or paper, heat production is less than for thick beds and heat dissipation is easier. At low voltage gradients, it is usually possible to control evaporation sufficiently by enclosing the strips in an airtight chamber; the atmosphere surrounding the strips then is saturated with solvent vapor. Even in an airtight chamber there is some evaporation from a suspended strip because the electrical current keeps it at a temperature above that of the surrounding atmosphere. A strip having a rectangular cross section has four surfaces from which evaporation can occur. A molecule of liquid at the edge of the strip has a chance to evaporate from any of three surfaces, whereas a molecule at the center can escape through only two surfaces. As a result there is an increased rate of evaporation from the edges that causes the buffering salt to be concentrated in these regions.

This effect is not limited to the edges; the compensatory effects of diffusion and solvent flow result in a concentration gradient that diminishes toward the center of the paper. It has been mentioned that mobility decreases with increasing ionic strength. This effect becomes visible in an electrophoretic pattern when edge evaporation has occurred. Migration is slower at the edges than it is in the center of the strip, and thus each zone assumes the shape of a V pointing in the direction of migration. V-shaped fractions are difficult to measure quantitatively, particularly with a densitometer, because the trailing edges of the V's may dovetail.

In gels, similar V-shaped patterns occur even when there is no possibility of evaporation. This is because the absence of convection in gels results in a heated region along the longitudinal axis of the bed with cooler regions at the periphery. Since mobility increases with heat, the central portion of each zone migrates in advance of its edges. When beds are thick, as is the case with preparative beds made of powder, this uneven temperature distribution causes the fractions to migrate as a set of nested hollow cones. Since the base of each cone encircles the apex of the cone following it, a cross section taken from the bed will contain both fractions, even when the fractions are entirely separated. If this form of overlapping could be avoided, powder beds would give resolution of a quality equal to that seen in filter paper.

It sometimes happens that the cover of the apparatus is not airtight. Even a pinhole-sized leak can cause serious distortion of the pattern. The nature of the distortion from this cause is characteristic: because the evaporation is unilateral, samples shift toward one side of the strips; the greatest distortion of the pattern will be at the point closest to the leak. Where the problem exists, it can often be solved by sealing the leak with electricians' plastic tape.

Heat produced within the apparatus is not the only source of pattern distortion caused by temperature. This author has several times been consulted concerning one-sided distortions of patterns obtained in various apparatuses, and has traced them to the positioning of the apparatus with respect to a heat source, such as a steam radiator.

The samples closest to the radiator will sometimes move almost twice as rapidly as those on the opposite side of the apparatus. This effect can be detected when the apparatus is as far as 5 ft. away from the heat source.

The appearance of a pattern is also affected by the increase in diffusion rate that accompanies elevation of temperature: the zones spread out, causing a loss in resolution of the fractions.

The undesirable effects of heat are not limited to distortion of the electrophoretic pattern. The chemical composition of biological materials can be significantly altered by heat. The biological activities of some enzymes and hormones are destroyed at temperatures only a few degrees above those at which they normally exist.

Some of the problems relating to heat, particularly this denaturation of samples, can be solved by performing electrophoresis at reduced temperatures. There is a limit to the degree of cooling that is permissible; electrophoretic separations cannot be made in frozen buffer. Four degrees centigrade, a temperature easily maintained in an ordinary refrigerator, is a suitable temperature for electrophoresis. Fractionation at reduced temperatures is rewarded by improved resolution due to the reduction of diffusion. It must be borne in mind, however, that there is a general depression of activity when temperature is reduced, so that not only diffusion but electrophoretic mobility and degree of ionization of a sample diminish; there is also a change in pH and ionic strength of the buffer. Because all these factors have their effects upon electrophoretic separation, it is important that operating temperature be stated in descriptions of electrophoretic methods and results. If the apparatus is refrigerated, drops of condensate may form on the sides and top of the box. When these break away and fall onto the bed, the pattern acquires a rain-spotted appearance. This difficulty can be corrected by placing a sloping cover over the bed area to act as a watershed.

Diffusion.—It is usually unprofitable to attempt to improve resolution by prolonging an electrophoresis: the wider separation of fractions that can be obtained is counteracted by their spreading as a result of the increased time during which diffusion can occur. If heat can be controlled, it is better to increase the distance between fractions by increasing the voltage gradient: this minimizes the time necessary for a run and consequently minimizes the broadening of zones by diffusion.

PRINCIPLES OF ELECTROPHORETIC TECHNIQUE

The techniques underlying electrophoretic methods are so similar that it is worthwhile to discuss them first in a general way without regard to the material being fractionated. Since filter paper is the medium most frequently used, a detailed description of general technique will be included under this heading. Those variations of technique that are apposite when other media are used will be discussed under the appropriate designations.

Filter Paper Electrophoresis.—The apparatus should be set up on a level surface and the electrode chambers filled with buffer. The liquid level in the two chambers must be equalized; otherwise siphoning action across the bed will displace and distort the electrophoretic pattern.

Since the quality of separations depends upon minimizing the distorting effects of fluid shift, it is advisable to use a technique that equilibrates the fluid in the filter paper before applying the sample. First the paper strip is wetted by dipping it in buffer; then it is freed of excess buffer by laying it out on a sheet of filter paper. Following this the strip is positioned in the apparatus without delay and allowed to stand for an hour or so with the cover of the apparatus in place. It is not permissible to place the dry strip on the apparatus and allow it to wet itself by capillary action. When this is done, the chromatographic effect allows the solvent front to travel faster than the solutes, causing an uneven distribution of buffering substances along the paper. Another reason for wetting the paper before suspending it is to eliminate sagging. A strip that is taut when dry sags after wetting.

For good resolution the sample should be applied in a small well-defined area. One of the most satisfactory applicators is the end of a glass microscope slide with its corners beveled by rubbing on sandpaper. A sample that must be measured can be applied to the end of the slide from a micropipet, as shown in Fig. 37-3a. The drop of sample is

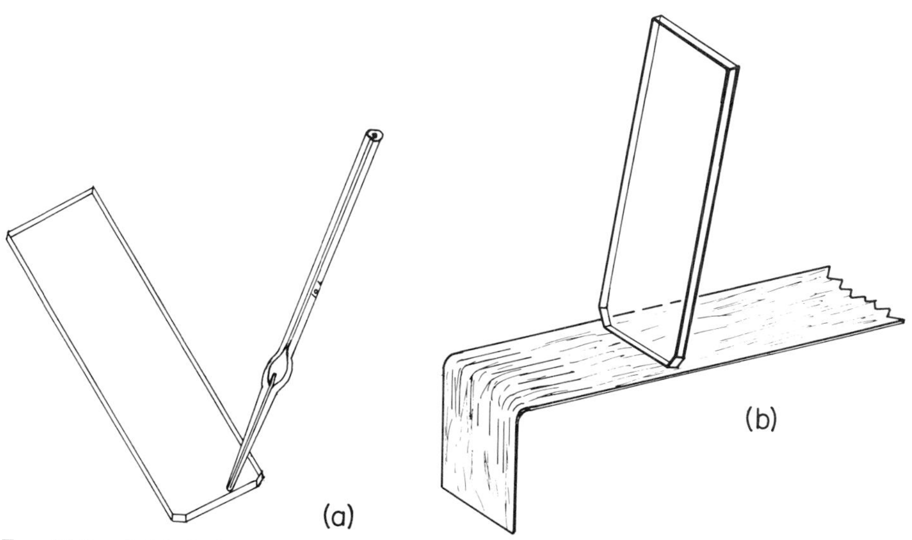

FIG. 37-3. A Method for Applying Samples to a Paper Strip. The use of a microscope slide with beveled corners allows the sample to be applied as a neat rectangle.

spread evenly along the edge of the slide. When the edge of the slide is brought into contact with the strip, the blotting action of the paper causes the sample to transfer (Fig. 37-3b). Some workers prefer to pipet the sample directly onto the paper. The pipet is then used in the manner of a pen to apply the sample in a thin line at right angles to the direction of migration. With practice this can be done evenly. Occasionally samples have been applied to the paper by soaking small rectangles of filter paper in the sample and placing them on the strip. This is unsatisfactory because the sample does not transfer completely to the bed; trailing occurs if the rectangle is left in place.

Many kinds of filter paper can be used for electrophoresis. This subject has been reviewed.[100] Papers that are commonly used include Schleicher & Schull 2043A and B; Whatman 1, 2, and 3; Eaton-Dikeman 301-85, 320, and 652; and Munktells 20/50. These papers are suitable for making fractionations of samples up to 20 μl. in volume. For larger volumes, an extra-thick paper, such as Whatman 3MM or 31 E.T., can be used. The additional thickness will support samples as large as 60 μl. in volume. Very thick paper is inconvenient to use because of its stiffness and because the additional weight gives it a tendency to sag. Often large samples can be better fractionated on a wide sheet of thin paper, such as Whatman 1. This paper can be bought in sheets $18\frac{1}{4} \times 22\frac{1}{2}$ in. in size and cut to the desired dimensions. When the materials being used

[100] Hartley, B. S., Biochem. J., **80**, 36p, 1961.

would react adversely with ordinary paper, a paper made from fibers of borosilicate glass, such as Whatman GF/B, may be used.

The voltage to be applied and the time required for fractionation vary widely, depending upon the sample. The worker must experiment to find the conditions best suited to his own purpose.

Once samples have been fractionated it is usually possible to locate the components by spot-test techniques. Proteins are customarily demonstrated by staining, enzymes by their specific activities, ions by color reactions,[101] and amino acids by ninhydrin.[102] Materials can often be detected and measured by their fluorescence under ultraviolet light[103,104] or by ultraviolet absorption.[105–107] Radioactive materials can be detected by autoradiography or by scanning.[108–111]

Filter paper has been used for *two-dimensional electrophoresis*. In this technique, separation is made on a sheet rather than a strip; then, following a change of buffer, the plane of the sheet is rotated through 90° and further separation is brought about by electrophoresis at right angles to the original direction of migration.[112–114] This technique is analogous to two-dimensional chromatography, but it has not been as successful because it is difficult to remove and replace buffers and because large paper beds are difficult to support and to cool. An alternative to two-dimensional electrophoresis is to perform one-directional electrophoresis and, following isolation and reconcentration of the fractions, to submit them individually to electrophoresis under changed conditions. Combining electrophoresis with chromatography is often successful; in this technique electrophoresis is used for fractionating the sample along one axis of the paper, and the fractions are subfractionated along the other axis by chromatography.

Electrophoresis on Cellulose Acetate.—The resolutions obtainable with cellulose acetate are better than those obtainable on paper because it is more homogeneous, stabilizes fluids more efficiently, and is relatively free of surface charges.[115–121] Another advantage is that cellulose acetate can be made transparent for densitometry by treating it with a plasticizing agent.[122–124] The techniques for its use are not greatly different

[101] Feigl, F., Spot Tests in Inorganic Analysis, Elsevier Publishing Co., Amsterdam, 1958.
[102] Heilmann, J., Barollier, J., and Watzke, E., Z. Physiol. Chem., **309,** 219, 1957.
[103] Fidanza, F., and Cioffi, L A., Boll. Soc. Ital. Biol. Sper., **35,** 1901, 1959.
[104] Franq, J. C., Eyquem, A., and Grabar, P., Rev. Franc. Études Clin. Biol., **4,** 821, 1959.
[105] Edstrom, J. E., J. Biophys. Biochem. Cytol., **8,** 39, 1960.
[106] Hale, A. J., and Renwick, J. H., Biochem. J., **80,** 49p, 1961.
[107] Ressler, N., Springgate, R., and Kaufman, J., J. Chromatog., **6,** 409, 1961.
[108] Foss, O. P., Scand. J. Clin. Lab. Invest., **10,** 418, 1958.
[109] Foss, O. P., Scand. J. Clin. Lab. Invest., **11,** 169, 1959.
[110] Hochwald, G. M., and Thorbecke, G. J., Protides Biol. Fluids, Proc. Colloq., **10,** 316, 1962 (pub. 1963).
[111] Sirlin, J. L., and Edstrom, J. E., Nature, **197,** 89, 1963.
[112] Peeters, H., and Vuylsteke, P., Chem. Weekblad, **55,** 703, 1959.
[113] Rey, J., Mayer, M. A., Deysson, A., Frezal, J., and Lamy, M., Rev. Franc. Études Clin. Biol., **7,** 877, 1962.
[114] Rothman, F., and Higa, A., Anal. Biochem., **3,** 173, 1962.
[115] Afonso, E., Clin. Chim. Acta, **7,** 545, 1962.
[116] Barrolier, J., J. Chromatog., **4,** 99, 1960.
[117] Korotzer, J. L., Bergquist, L. M., and Searcy, R. L., Am. J. Med. Technol., **27,** 197, 1961.
[118] Maier, K. H., and Voggel, K., Z. anal. Chem., **186,** 257, 1962.
[119] Mullan, F. A., Hancock, D. M., and Neill, D. W., Nature, **194,** 149, 1963.
[120] Nanto, V., Acta Chem. Scand., **17** (3), 857, 1963.
[121] Pieper, J., Klin. Wochschr., **39,** 1293, 1961.
[122] Albert-Recht, F., Clin. Chim. Acta, **4,** 627, 1959.
[123] Grunbaum, B. W., Fessel, W. J., and Piel, C. F., Anal. Chem., **32,** 860, 1961.
[124] Grunbaum, B. W., Kirk, P. L., and Atchley, W. A., Anal. Chem., **32,** 1361, 1960.

from those for paper.[125–127] Cellulose acetate has a smaller sample capacity than paper; 5 μl. of sample constitutes a heavy load.

Electrophoresis in Gels.—When gels are used as media the bed is formed by casting the gel in a trough or tube that forms a bridge between the electrode chambers. As far as results are concerned, it matters very little whether the bed is vertical or horizontal, but apparatuses of both forms have been described.[19,21,22,128–130] Whatever the design of the apparatus, provision should be made for measuring voltage gradients within the bed. When tubing is used to cast the gel, glass tubing is usually chosen; the trough form is often constructed from acrylic plastic. A glass tube is easily cooled by enclosing it in a condenser jacket. In contrast, acrylic plastic conducts heat much less readily than glass and it tends to flex under hydrostatic pressure, with disastrous effects upon the bed; probably this substance will be superseded by one with more desirable properties, such as anodized aluminum. Electrical contact between the chambers and the bed can be achieved by wicks, but when the antidiffusion barriers in the electrode chambers are of gel, it is better to cast the bed so that it is continuous with these.[32] Gels may swell by imbibing liquid or they may shrink by expelling it (syneresis). When the bed is enclosed in a rigid tube, changes in volume cause variations in length that endanger the physical and electrical continuity of the bed; in an open trough, a volume change causes only inconsequential variations in the thickness of the bed.

Techniques for preparing gels vary with the matrix, but in all cases the liquid used is the buffer to be used during electrophoresis. The chief difference between synthetic and natural gels is that the synthetic gels form by polymerization in the bed, whereas the natural gels are already polymers that are poured while hot and allowed to set by cooling. A number of independent reports have confirmed the usefulness of synthetic (polyacrylamide) gels, [131–135] and describe the techniques required for their use.[136–141] The best resolutions that have been obtained by electrophoresis were achieved using starch gel,[142] but the preparation of beds using this medium is difficult. For starch gel techniques the reader is referred to papers by Smithies[143–145] who first used the medium, and to other articles.[128,146–148] Agar is a popular medium[32,130] even though it lacks

[125] Brackenridge, C. J., Anal. Chem., **32,** 1353, 1357, 1960.
[126] Brackenridge, C. J., Anal. Chem., **32,** 1359, 1960.
[127] Friedman, H. S., Clin. Chim. Acta, **6,** 775, 1961.
[128] Cunningham, A. W. B., and Magnusson, O., J. Chromatog., **5,** 90, 1961.
[129] Raymond, S., Clin. Chem., **8,** 455, 1962.
[130] Wieme, R. J., Clin. Chim. Acta, **4,** 317, 1959.
[131] Antoine, B., Rev. Franc. Études Clin. Biol., **7,** 612, 1962.
[132] Hermans, P. E., Beetham, W. P., Jr., McGuckin, W. F., and McKenzie, B. F., Proc. Staff Meetings Mayo Clinic, **37,** 311, 1962.
[133] Jongkind, J. F., Wisse, J. H., and Bloemendal, H., Protides Biol. Fluids, Proc. Colloq., **10,** 77, 1962 (pub. 1963).
[134] McAllister, H. C., Jr., Wan, Y. C., and Irvin, J. L., Anal. Biochem., **5,** 321, 1963.
[135] Paleus, S., and Porath, J., Acta Chem. Scand., **17,** 57, 1963.
[136] Ott, H., Protides Biol. Fluids, Proc. Colloq., **10,** 305, 1962 (pub. 1963).
[137] Raymond, S., and Nakamichi, M., Anal. Biochem., **3,** 23, 1962.
[138] Raymond, S., and Nakamichi, M., and Aurell, B., Nature, **195,** 697, 1962.
[139] Reisfeld, R. A., Lewis, U. J., and Williams, D. E., Nature, **195,** 281, 1962.
[140] Sogami, M., and Foster, H. F., J. Biol. Chem., **237,** 2514, 1962.
[141] Wieme, R. J., Protides Biol. Fluids, Proc. Colloq., **10,** 309, 1962 (pub. 1963).
[142] Johnson, T., and Barrett, O'N., Jr., J. Lab. Clin. Med., **57,** 961, 1961.
[143] Smithies, O., Arch. Biochem. Biophys. Suppl., **1,** 125, 1962.
[144] Smithies, O., Biochem. J., **61,** 629, 1955.
[145] Smithies, O., Biochem. J., **71,** 585, 1959.
[146] Aresu, R., and Monti, G., Rass. Fisiopatol. Clin. Terap. (Pisa), **33,** 1210, 1961.
[147] Harris, H., Penington, D. G., and Robson, E. B., Biochem. J., **74,** 44p, 1960.
[148] Krans, H. M. J., Eijk, H. G. van, and Westenbrink, H. G. K., Biochim. Biophys. Acta, **65,** 166, 1962.

the resolving power of starch gel. Of all the gels it is the easiest to use in forming a bed, partly because it is fluid in a convenient temperature range, and partly because of its relatively great mechanical strength in the solid state. This mechanical strength is also an asset in manipulating the completed electrophoregram, which with most gels is easily damaged during the process of staining and sample recovery. An agar electrophoregram can be prepared for scanning with a densitometer, or for storing, by soaking it in 5 percent glycerin and then allowing it to dry. The glycerin, which acts as a plasticizing agent, causes the dried strip to resemble a piece of cellophane.

Loading beds constructed of gel present special problems because introducing the sample can interrupt the continuity of the gel. Most workers load the bed by excavating small holes in it and pouring the sample into these holes. Others absorb the sample on small pieces of filter paper and press them into the gel or cast the gel around them. With agar, excellent results can be obtained by cutting small blocks of the gel and soaking them in sample solution until they have equilibrated. These blocks are then placed in position and the bed is poured around them. Unfortunately, this technique is not applicable to starch gel, which must be poured while it is so hot that a protein sample would be denatured. Whatever technique is used for applying the sample to the gel bed, great care should be exercised to be sure that no opportunity occurs for a surface through which the sample must pass to dry even slightly. If a gel is allowed to stand in the open air for a few minutes, drying out of its surface causes formation of a thin skin that is impermeable to large molecules. Injecting a sample into a gel is not recommended because, instead of blending into the bed, the sample liquid splits the gel. When the bed is formed in a tube, sample loading is especially difficult. It is desirable to have gel on both sides of the sample even if migration is expected to occur only in one direction, to prevent spillage of the sample. One method involves partially filling the tube with gel and allowing it to set, adding the sample mixed with gel and allowing this to set, and then filling the rest of the tube with gel. It is nearly impossible to accomplish this without streaking the sample along the sides of the tube, even when special pipets are used. One method of sample introduction involves soaking a bit of filter paper in sample and pressing it into the gel through a port in the side of the tube. This approach gives good results even though it is somewhat inconvenient.

Electrophoresis in tubes is sometimes called *disc electrophoresis* because of the shape assumed by the fractions as they migrate in the cylindrical bed.

It is harder to detect and measure substances in gels than in paper because of the greater difficulty of bringing reagents into contact with the samples. When proteins, for example, are detected by staining, it takes time for the dye to permeate the gel and more time to wash out the excess dye. There are techniques for removing excess dye rapidly by electrical means.[149,150] For quantitative measurements of proteins in gels, staining is not even as reliable as it is in filter paper because one can never be sure that a dye has penetrated the gel sufficiently to stain all of a fraction. A number of methods other than staining can be used for measuring proteins in gels, including direct gravimetry, nitrogen determination, and ultraviolet absorption.[32,151] When it is desired to locate fractions without damaging the electrophoregram, a print can be made by using electromigration to transfer a portion of the fractions to paper to which tests can be applied.[152] Such a contact print can be used as a map for locating fractions in the gel so that they can be excised and eluted into an appropriate solvent. Elution is made

[149] Ferris, T. G., Easterling, R. E., and Budd, R. E., Am. J. Clin. Pathol., **38,** 383, 1962.
[150] Ferris, T. G., Easterling, R. E., and Budd, R. E., Am. J. Clin. Pathol., **39,** 193, 1963.
[151] Strickland, R. D., Mack, P. A., Podleski, T. R., and Childs, W. A., Anal. Chem., **32,** 199, 1960.
[152] Johns, E. W., J. Chromatog., **5,** 91, 1961.

easier if the gel is first disintegrated by forcing it through a sieve. If heat is not destructive to the sample, it is sometimes possible to remove fractions by melting the sections of gel in hot solvent.

Electrophoresis in Powders.—A wide range of powdery and granular materials can be used as supporting media, as has already been indicated in the general discussion of "Zone Electrophoresis." The reader is referred to reviews[6,7] and books[8] on electrophoresis for references to specific substances that have been used.

The powders used should have granules of fairly uniform size. Particles that are too large impede electromigration, whereas particles approaching colloidal size will themselves undergo electromigration. The range of particle size that is customarily used lies between 50 and 250 μ. Particles can be classified by sieving to remove coarse particles and by repeated sedimentation to remove fine ones.

Powder beds are formed by making a slurry of the powder in buffer, pouring it into a form, and allowing it to settle. When the excess liquid is drained or blotted out, the bed is suitably firm and remains sufficiently moist for electrophoresis.

The bed is loaded by scooping out a narrow slot and packing it with a paste formed by mixing the sample with some of the powder. The surface of a powder bed must be covered with plastic film to prevent evaporation.

A number of articles have described apparatuses especially constructed for use with powders.[153–155]

Contact prints can be made from powder beds by pressing a piece of filter paper to the moist surface; detectable amounts of the fractions flow into the paper by capillary action. Because of the tendency of the fractions to migrate as cones, it is desirable to section the bed sagittally and make the print from the surface thus exposed. Fractions can also be located by sectioning the bed serially and testing the individual blocks thus obtained; this is the technique that is most widely used, even though it does nothing to compensate for the cone-like shape of the fractions. Fractions are easily removed from the sections by shaking them up in an appropriate solvent and then removing the powder by centrifugation. When the fractions are proteins, it is a simple matter to estimate them nondestructively by ultraviolet spectrophotometry.

One form of powder electrophoresis is *thin-layer electrophoresis*[156] in which the powder is deposited in a thin layer on a plate, usually of glass. Here the advantages of powder electrophoresis are combined with those of paper electrophoresis. Since fine-grained powders can be used, a homogeneous bed can be obtained that has resolving power superior to paper; at the same time, fractions can be excavated with a spatula, suspended in solvent, and separated by centrifugation as with powder. Alternatively, the electrophoregrams can be preserved by treating the plates with a fixative. Most of the techniques for manipulating these beds are borrowed from those of thin-layer chromatography.[157]

APPLICATIONS OF ELECTROPHORESIS

The electrophoretic method is extraordinarily versatile. Insofar as substances are soluble and have charges, or can be made soluble and given charges either by ionization or by attaching charged substances to them, they become suitable subjects for electrophoretic operations. The method has become indispensable to biochemists, who have found it useful for fractionating an astonishing variety of biological materials.

153 deWet, W. J., and Pretorius, V., Anal. Chem., **32,** 169, 1960.
154 Esposito, C. G., Anal. Chem., **33** (10), 103A, 1961 (Abstract).
155 Grob, R. L., Mercer, D., Gribben, T., and Wells, J., J. Chromatog., **3,** 545, 1960.
156 Honneger, C. G., Helv. Chim. Acta, **44,** 173, 1961.
157 Heftmann, E., ed., Chromatography, Reinhold Publishing Corp., New York, 1961.

Perhaps the greatest usefulness of the method has been in clinical diagnosis, for analyzing serum, urine, spinal fluid, gastric juice, and other body fluids. References to such applications are too numerous to include individually in a chapter of this length. Recent applications can be found in reviews,[6,7] and the body of the literature concerning clinical applications has been admirably summarized by Ribeiro.[8] Clinical interest has centered around the electrophoresis of serum on filter paper. This form of fractionation has virtually superseded the classical methods for diagnostic serum protein fractionation, and most clinical laboratories now have apparatuses for filter-paper electrophoresis. Certain diagnostically important electrophoretic applications—for example, the detection of abnormal hemoglobins as an aid to diagnosing the hereditary anemias,[158]—cannot easily be done with filter paper, and consequently an increasing number of clinical laboratories are acquiring facilities for electrophoresis in gels or on cellulose acetate film. Inasmuch as usually only a little ingenuity is needed to adapt a filter paper apparatus for use with gels or cellulose acetate, it is likely that these media also will shortly be in general clinical use.

A further refinement of the electrophoretic technique that has already been mentioned, immunoelectrophoresis, is finding increasing clinical application in addition to its usefulness for fundamental research in immunology. This technique is outstanding for demonstrating that proteins from different sources are identical, for determining the origins of small amounts of biological material, and for demonstrating phylogenetic relationships.

Separation of Serum Proteins on Filter Paper.—The fractionation of serum proteins on filter paper will be discussed here as a typical electrophoretic procedure. It will be assumed that the reader is familiar with the material discussed previously in this chapter.

The characteristic apparatus will have electrode chambers spaced 15 cm. apart and will be equipped with a device to support up to six 1-in. strips of filter paper between them. The apparatus is equipped with a d.c. power supply that is continuously variable between zero and 250 volts; this is sufficient to provide the requisite 75-volt potential difference between the ends of the bed. The volume of buffer in each electrode chamber will be approximately 1 liter, which is enough for an overnight run. The levels of the buffer in the chambers must be equalized.

The three best known buffers available for serum protein electrophoresis are *diethylbarbiturate*, also called *veronal* or *barbital*, buffer[27]; the "*Tris*" buffer of Aronsson and Gronwall[159]; and *borate* buffer.[160] The compositions of all three are given in Table 37-1. "Tris" buffer is much the most expensive of the three and should be used only when the quality of the supporting medium justifies it; the fractionation it gives on ordinary filter paper is not discernibly better than that obtained with diethylbarbiturate buffer.

The paper should be examined for such imperfections as grease, spots, torn edges, and the like, because even minor defects can seriously impair the quality of a pattern. The strips are usually cut about 30 cm. long to allow length for dipping into the electrode chambers; the length varies with the apparatus being used. The strips are prepared by dipping them in a container of buffer until they are thoroughly wet, and then are blotted free of excess buffer by laying them out on a large sheet of filter paper, care being taken to avoid creasing them. The strips are then smoothed into place on the apparatus with their ends dipping into the electrode chambers, and the apparatus is sealed airtight and allowed to stand for an hour or more in the environment in which the run will actually occur. This allows the bed to equilibrate by giving the liquid sufficient time to distribute itself evenly throughout the paper.

[158] Gratzer, W. B., and Allison, A. C., Biol. Rev. Cambridge Phil. Soc., **35** (4), 459, 1960.
[159] Aronsson, T., and Gronwall, A., Science Tools, **5** (2), 21, 1958.
[160] Consden, R., and Powell, M. N., J. Clin. Pathol., **8**, 150, 1955.

TABLE 37-1.

Name	Amounts per Liter of Solution		Characteristics
Barbital or Veronal	Sodium diethylbarbiturate Diethylbarbituric acid	20.60 g. 2.80 g.	Ionic strength 0.100 pH 8.6
	Sodium diethylbarbiturate Diethylbarbituric acid	15.45 g. 2.76 g.	Ionic strength 0.075 pH 8.6
	Sodium diethylbarbiturate Diethylbarbituric acid	10.30 g. 1.84 g.	Ionic strength 0.050 pH 8.6
Borate	Sodium hydroxide Orthoboric acid	1.77 g. 9.62 g.	Ionic strength 0.044 pH 8.6
"Tris"	Tris(hydroxymethyl)aminomethane Ethylenediaminetetraacetic acid Orthoboric acid	60.50 g. 6.00 g. 4.60 g.	pH 8.9 Conductivity 3.0 millimho

In alkaline buffer, serum proteins migrate toward the positive pole. Albumin migrates in advance of the other fractions, with α_1-, α_2-, β-, and γ-globulins following in succession. This pattern of migration requires that the sample be applied at a point on the bed distant from the anode. The procedure for applying the sample to the paper has already been described in detail. Once the samples have been applied, the apparatus is sealed carefully to prevent air leaks and the power supply is turned on and adjusted to give the desired voltage gradient. It has been mentioned that when diethylbarbiturate is being used there is a tendency for diethylbarbituric acid to plate out on the anode, thereby changing the electrical characteristics of the system. Detection of this effect does not require uncovering the apparatus; the increased resistance of an electrode can be detected by the accompanying decrease in current flow or, if the power supply is of the constant-current type, by the rise in applied voltage.

Within limits, separations can be improved by prolonging the time of runs, but the area of the spots on the paper increases at a rate approximately proportional to the duration of the run, so that even though the distance between the centers of the fractions is increased, only a small improvement in resolution is obtained. From this it follows that the time of run depends largely on the inclination of the operator. Excellent, sharply defined separations of serum proteins into five fractions, each the width of a broad pencil mark, within a span of 2 cm., can be obtained by an hour's run; extending the run to 16 hr. will usually yield a pattern approximately 12 cm. long with five fractions appearing as spots ranging in width from 1 to 2 cm. There is some advantage in obtaining the long diffuse pattern if the stained strip is to be subjected to densitometry, because most commercial densitometers are designed to accommodate patterns of this approximate size.

When a run has been completed, the fractions must be located and measured. With proteins this is usually done by staining. One may either dry the strip and fix the protein to the paper before staining it, or one may stain the moist strip directly by incorporating a protein precipitant in the staining solution. The latter method is easier and more rapid, and when it is properly done there is no danger of significant loss of sample by washing the precipitated protein from the strip. Fixing the protein on the dried strip (which is often done by heating in an oven) not only affects the staining properties of the protein, but does not ensure that the fractions are made insoluble. Many dyes have been suggested for staining proteins.[6,7] For simple detection, any of them are adequate, but not all are equally good for quantitative measurement. The method of quantitative measurement by staining is based on the assumption that all protein fractions have equal affinities for the dye. Under this assumption, colorimetric measurements of the bound dyes make it possible to compute the percentage contribution of each fraction to the whole sample by dividing the absorbance of each component by the sum of the absorbances of all the components. Unfortunately, the assumption is only approximately true. The protein fractions differ in their affinities for any given dye, as has been demonstrated repeatedly. The use of correction factors has only limited value, since staining properties of a given fraction can vary from sample to sample. In spite of this serious objection to the use of dyes, their popularity as a measuring method continues unabated. This is due in part to the fact that results are reasonably consistent for a given technique and therefore diagnostically useful for clinical purposes, and in part to the fact that such measurements can be made easily even when only primitive equipment is available.

Staining is accomplished by soaking the strips in a dye. The usual solvent for the dye is a mixture consisting of 4.5 parts of water, 4.5 parts of methanol, and 1 part of acetic acid. The stain is made by dissolving 2 g. of the dye in a liter of the solvent. Suitable dyes include Amido Black 10B,[161,162] Ponceau 2R,[26] and Brilliant Green S.F.[163] Bromophenol Blue[27] has also been used successfully, but the technique for its use is more difficult and the results obtained with it are in no way superior to those obtained with other dyes. Trichloracetic acid to the amount of 5 percent by weight is sometimes added to the dye mixture to assist in precipitating the proteins, but this has doubtful value. Comparative and evaluative studies of the various stains have been numerous,[164–168] as have investigations of the optimum conditions for staining.[126,169] If the strip is dried before being dipped in the dye, staining requires about 10 min. A half hour should be allowed for staining wet strips because of the additional time required for the dye solution to displace the water. It is desirable that the strips hang freely without being folded or in contact with one another or with the sides of the staining vessel. One way in which this can be accomplished is by using a tall battery jar full of staining solution and allowing the strips to hang down into it. A convenient rack can easily be made by bending a piece of plastic-insulated #3 electrical wire into an appropriate shape and fastening one end of the strip to it with a plastic clothespin. When the staining is completed, the background stain in the paper can be removed by immersing the strip in a series of washing tanks filled with the solvent used for the dye, and allowing it to hang approximately 15 min. in each tank. Destaining is complete when all excess dye has been removed from the strip and only the pattern appears to be colored; this usually requires three washings.

Once the strip has been dried by hanging it in the open air or in a warm oven, it is ready for quantitative measurements. This can be done by scanning the strip with a densitometer. For densitometry it is possible to render the strip translucent by impregnating it with an oil. The results obtained by densitometry are no better than

161 Grassmann, W., and Hannig, K., Angew. Chem., **62,** 170, 1950.
162 Grassmann, W., and Hannig, K., Naturwissenschaften, **37,** 496, 1950.
163 Rideout, L. A., and Prichard, R. W., Science, **121,** 374, 1955.
164 Besson, S., and Barrier, J., Bull. Soc. Pharm. Nancy, **43,** 5, 1959.
165 Meulemans, O., Clin. Chim. Acta, **5,** 615, 1960.
166 Sarkar, B. C. R., J. Sci. Ind. Res. (India), **20,** 239, 1961.
167 Strickland, R. D., Podleski, T. R., Gurule, F. T., Freeman, M. L., and Childs, W. A., Anal. Chem., **31,** 1408, 1959.
168 Walsh, J. R., Humoller, F. L., and Dunn, A. L., J. Lab. Clin. Med., **46,** 772, 1955.
169 Selman, G. G., J. Chromatog., **3,** 531, 1960.

those that can be obtained by colorimetry. For colorimetry, the dye must be extracted from the paper and its absorption measured at an appropriate wavelength. Most protein stains are acid dyes and can be extracted from the paper into 0.1 *M* sodium hydroxide. This can be done conveniently by cutting the fractions from the electrophoregram and placing them in 15-ml. centrifuge tubes. When the bits of paper are immersed in measured amounts of 0.1 *M* sodium hydroxide (5 ml. each for the globulin fractions and 10 ml. for the more concentrated albumin) and allowed to stand for approximately 20 min., with occasional shaking, the dye is completely extracted from the paper. If the paper disintegrates during this process it can easily be separated by centrifugation. The amount of dye from each fraction can then be measured colorimetrically. Even when no background dye is visible in the strip, it is advisable to extract a measured section of paper that contains no protein. Measuring the dye in this extract makes it possible to correct for background dye.

Sometimes it is desired to measure or detect special kinds of proteins, such as lipoproteins, glycoproteins, or enzymes.

Lipoproteins can be detected by staining the strip with a fat-soluble dye such as Oil Red O or one of the Sudan dyes. The dye solvent used for making the stain is usually ethanol, and the solution for washing away excess dye is half ethanol and half water. When duplicate strips are made and one is stained with the fat stain while the other is stained with ordinary protein stain, comparison of the strips makes it possible to identify the protein fractions to which lipids are bound. Colorimetric estimation of the lipids by dye absorption is often described in the literature.[170–177] Such measurements are only semiquantitative. Lipoproteins can also be measured by direct spectrophotometry[107] or by fluorescence.[103] The general subject of staining lipoproteins has been discussed in detail by Ribeiro.[8]

Glycoproteins are usually detected and measured by using some modification of the Schiff Reaction.[178–180] This requires that the carbohydrates be oxidized, usually with periodic acid, to polyaldehydes which react with Schiff's reagent (fuchsin decolorized with sulfurous acid) to restore the fuchsin's color by binding the sulfite. The periodic acid-Schiff reaction detects only the neutral glycoproteins; acid mucopolysaccharides can be stained with Alcian Blue 8 GS[181] and with Toluidine Blue (a basic dye);[182,183] Acriflavin,[184] Alcian Blue,[185] and Azocarmine[186] can also be used to stain mucopolysaccharides.

Enzymes can be located by sectioning the paper strip and testing the activity of each section with respect to specific substrates. Comparison with an electrophoregram stained for proteins in the conventional way gives some idea of the mobilities of the enzyme

[170] Ashworth, U. S., and Chaudry, M. A., J. Dairy Sci., **45**, 952, 1962.
[171] Barritt, D. W., Biochem. J., **57**, xxxv, 1954.
[172] Groulade, J., and Olliver, C., Ann. Biol. Clin. (Paris), **18**, 577, 1960.
[173] Hirsch, A., and Cattaneo, C., Klin. Wochschr., **34**, 581, 1956.
[174] Meier, W., Verhandl. Deut. Ges. Pathol., **42**, 421, 1959.
[175] Raynaud, R., d'Eshougues, J. R., Pasquet, P., and DiGiovanni, S., Ann. Biol. Clin. (Paris), **11**, 377, 1953.
[176] Ribeiro, L. P., and McDonald, H. J., J. Chromatog., **10**, 443, 1963.
[177] Zakelj, A., and Gros, M., Clin. Chim. Acta, **5**, 947, 1960.
[178] Duijn, P. van, J. Histochem. Cytochem., **9**, 234, 1961.
[179] Hotchkiss, R. D., Arch. Biochem., **16**, 131, 1948.
[180] Koiw, E., and Gronwall, A., Scand. J. Clin. Lab. Invest., **4**, 244, 1952.
[181] Buscarini, L., and Ezechieli, S., Boll. Ist. Sierterap., Milan, **38**, 156, 1959.
[182] Benhamou, E., Amouch, P., and Chemla, E., Presse Med., **61**, 1725, 1953.
[183] Benhamou, E., Pugliese, J., Chiche, J. C., and Amouch, P., Presse Med., **62**, 650, 1954.
[184] Takeuchi, J., Stain Technol., **36**, 159, 1961.
[185] Foster, T. S., and Pearce, R. H., Can. J. Biochem. Physiol., **39**, 1771, 1961.
[186] Emmrich, R., and Urbaszek, W., Z. Inn. Med. Ihre Grenzg., **17**, 801, 1962.

constituents of a serum. A number of recent papers have described methods for detecting and measuring enzymes.[106,187–193]

Separation of Inorganic Substances.—The general procedure for any electrophoresis will resemble very closely that which has just been described for separating serum proteins. Usually knowledge of the chemistry of the substances involved will be the source of ideas for promoting separations. Such properties as amphoterism, the ability to form complexes, and differences in valence state[194] can all be used for this purpose. As examples, zinc is amphoteric and migrates as the cation in acid solution or as an anion (zincate) in alkali[64]; cobalt(II) is cationic when complexed with chloride, but antimony(III) and aluminum(III) are anionic.[195] The resolving ability of electrophoresis for inorganic ions is remarkable. The alkali metals,[196] the Group IIA cations,[71] the rare earths,[68,72] and even isotopes[197–199] can be separated. Some of the conditions for separation of inorganic substances have already been discussed in the section on "pH and Other Chemical Characteristics." In general, inorganic substances have larger charge:mass ratios than organic chemicals and biochemicals. At the same time the volumes of inorganic ions are relatively small, and thus the barrier effect of stabilizing media is less important than with macromolecules. On the other hand, inorganic ions are more likely to interact chemically with the medium. In recent years a large number of spot tests involving organic reagents for detecting and identifying inorganic substances have been developed. Feigl has collected these in a useful volume.[101] A great many of the tests described in his book can be used without modification for detecting and measuring the zones in the electrophoregrams of inorganic substances. A second volume by the same author deals with spot tests for organic substances.[200]

The following methods using electrophoresis are described in other chapters of Standard Methods of Chemical Analysis:

1. Chapter 47, Volume III, Instrumental Methods in Clinical Medicine.
   a. Separation of proteins
2. Chapter 63, Volume III, Water Analysis.
   a. Used in the study of chemical coagulation of water
   b. Coagulation of turbidity
   c. Removal of color

CONCLUSION

This chapter is intended to describe the principles underlying electrophoresis, and to point out essential methodology with emphasis on that which ordinarily must be learned by experience. Specific electrophoretic applications and discussions of theory have been

[187] Boyd, J. W., Biochem. J., **81,** 39p, 1961.
[188] Burman, D., Am. J. Clin. Pathol., **37,** 134, 1962.
[189] Karcher, D., Sande, M. van, Lowenthal, A., Helm, H. J. van der, and Wieme, R. J., Protides Biol. Fluids, Proc. Colloq., **10,** 339, 1962 (Pub. 1963).
[190] Laursen, T., Scand. J. Clin. Lab. Invest., **14,** 152, 1962.
[191] Vincent, D., and Segonzac, G., Compt. rend. Soc. Biol., **155,** 927, 1961.
[192] Vincent, D., and Segonzac, G., Compt. rend. Soc. Biol., **156,** 2133, 1962.
[193] Wieme, R. J., Sande, M. van, Karcher, D., Lowenthal, A., and Helm, H. J., van der, Clin. Chim. Acta, **7,** 750, 1962.
[194] Bighi, C., Ann. Univ. Ferrara Sez., **5,** No. 1, 57, 1954–60.
[195] Lederer, M., Research, **4,** 371, 1951.
[196] Tuckerman, M. M., and Strain, H. H., Anal. Chem., **32,** 695, 1960.
[197] Adloff, J. P., and Bacher, M., J. Chromatog., **9,** 231, 1962.
[198] Oss, C. J. van, and Beyrard-Benchemoul, N. R., Brit. Patent 826,278, Dec. 31, 1959.
[199] Shukla, S. K., and Adloff, J. P., J. Chromatog., **8,** 501, 1962.
[200] Feigl, F., Spot Tests in Organic Analysis, Elsevier Publishing Co., Amsterdam, 1958.

included only when they are helpful in understanding the practical aspects of electrophoresis.

The extremely wide range of organic and biochemical applications that have gone completely unmentioned include investigations of hormones, vitamins, nucleoproteins and nucleotides, toxins, and metabolic products such as porphyrins. Substances of pharmacological interest such as carcinogens and antibiotics, and substances of commercial interest such as agricultural and dairy products, have also been neglected. All of these subjects and numerous others are reviewed biennially in a series of articles that appear in the Fundamental Analytical Review section of *Analytical Chemistry*.[6,7] These reviews not only list significant experimental papers published during each two-year review period, but also make note of other pertinent reviews and textbooks. Previous to 1962 the electrophoresis review was included in the general review of chromatography.[201]

[201] Strain, H. H., Anal. Chem., **32,** 3R, 1960.

Chapter 38

GAS CHROMATOGRAPHY

By S. Dal Nogare

Plastics Department
E. I. du Pont de Nemours and Co., Inc.
Wilmington, Delaware

In a period of slightly more than twelve years, gas chromatography has become perhaps the most used instrumental technique of modern times. In the United States alone, it is estimated that there are about 10,000 chromatographs in use[1] and this number is increasing steadily. It is the purpose of this chapter to discuss the elementary theory and some experimental aspects of gas chromatography so that the beginner may gain an appreciation of this technique.

GENERAL BACKGROUND

This separation method is the invention of A. J. P. Martin and A. T. James. Gas chromatography was originally suggested in 1941 by Martin and Synge in a paper which described liquid-liquid chromatography.[2] At the end of this paper, the authors noted that the moving phase could be a gas as well as a liquid. No one took up this suggestion until Martin and James, confronted with the problem of separating a wide range of fatty acids and amines, acted on the early idea and implemented what is now generally called gas-liquid chromatography.[3] Since then, the acceptance and application of this technique has been so widespread that numerous articles, reviews, and books have been written on many aspects of theory and application.

Throughout this chapter, reference will be made to the book by Dal Nogare and Juvet[4] which covers many facets of gas chromatography and contains details which are beyond the scope of the present treatment.

The chromatographic technique requires that a solute undergo distribution between two phases, one of them fixed (stationary phase) and the other one moving (mobile phase). It is the mobile phase which translates the solute down the column until it eventually emerges from the end of the column separated from other solutes which elute earlier or later. Gas chromatography, which will frequently be designated GC in this chapter, is the generic name for the technique of chromatography in which the moving phase is a gas. In the older forms of chromatography, the moving phase was a liquid. The fixed phase in all important chromatographic techniques is either a solid, a liquid, or a combination of both. Thus, in GC we have gas-solid (GSC), gas-liquid (GLC) chromatography, and liquid-modified GSC.

[1] Sanfranski, L. W., and Dal Nogare, S., C & E News, **39,** 102–113, June 26, 1961, and 76–83, July 3, 1961.
[2] Martin, A. J. P., and Synge, R. L. M., Biochem. J., **35,** 1358, 1941.
[3] James, A. T., and Martin, A. J. P., Biochem. J., **50,** 679, 1952.
[4] Dal Nogare, S., and Juvet, R. S., Gas-Liquid Chromatography, John Wiley and Sons, Inc., New York, 1962.

DESCRIPTION OF CHROMATOGRAPHIC PROCESS

A schematic presentation of the chromatographic process (GLC) is shown in Fig. 38-1. In this case, the stationary liquid phase is immobilized as a thin film on a finely divided solid support such as Celite, crushed firebrick, glass beads, or even the inner wall of a small diameter tube. If the column is filled with the liquid-covered finely divided solid, it is called a *packed* column. If the wall of a small diameter tube is coated with the liquid, it is called an *open tubular* or *capillary* column. In some of the latest techniques, the inner wall of the open tubular columns has been coated with a finely divided solid support, so that the difference between the two main types of GC columns is becoming less distinct.

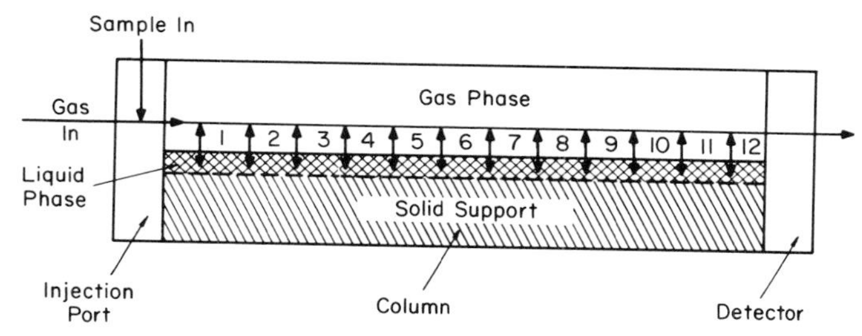

FIG. 38-1. Schematic Representation of the Chromatographic Process.

Referring again to Fig. 38-1, the mobile gas phase is continuously moving over the stationary liquid phase. When a sample of solute vapor is introduced into the gas stream at the head of the column, it is swept into the column and undergoes distribution between the gas and liquid phases in a more or less steplike manner indicated by the arrows. The behavior of a solute in such a partition process is most conveniently defined by a dimensionless factor called the *partition ratio*, k. The partition ratio is simply the ratio of the amount of solute in the stationary phase to the amount of solute in the mobile phase:

$$k = \frac{\text{amount of solute in liquid phase}}{\text{amount of solute in gas phase}} \tag{1}$$

and for our purposes, k will be assumed constant throughout the column. The partition ratio is also related to the *time* a solute spends in each of the phases:

$$k = \frac{\text{time in the liquid phase}}{\text{time in the gas phase}} \tag{2}$$

Obviously, the greater the total amount of liquid phase in the column, the more solute will dissolve in it and the greater will be the partition ratio by Equation (1). Similarly, an increase in the amount of liquid phase results in increased residence time in that phase, and the partition ratio increases, Equation (2). As noted above, the gas phase simply serves to move the solute down the column between excursions into the liquid phase. Consequently, *all* solutes spend the *same time in the gas phase* in any particular column. This is an important fact to remember.

From the above discussion, it is apparent that the partition ratio depends on

1. The particular solute
2. The particular liquid phase (solvent)

3. The amount of liquid phase
4. The temperature

Consequently, a partition ratio will exist for each column, solute, and temperature; and in order to reproduce the behavior of a particular solute, almost every experimental factor must be carefully reproduced.

BASIC APPARATUS

The basic apparatus required in order to perform gas chromatographic separations is quite simple, in sharp contrast to some of the highly sophisticated commercial equipment. It is a well established fact that the fineness of separation is not a strong function of either the price or the number of switches, dials, and knobs which can be incorporated on the outside of a box. This comment is intended to encourage the novice to assemble his own equipment for his own specific needs. As a result, he will garner a strong appreciation of the principles of gas chromatography and an understanding of the critical apparatus aspects.

Elements of a gas chromatograph are shown in Fig. 38-2. One needs a supply of *carrier gas* usually available in compressed form in a cylinder fitted with a suitable pressure

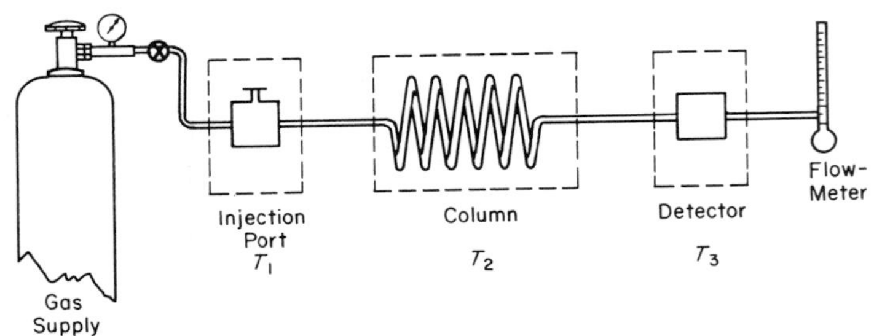

Fig. 38-2. Schematic Gas Chromatograph; T_1, T_2, T_3 Are Temperatures Which Usually Are Different and Controlled.

reducing valve. This carrier gas is conducted from the cylinder to a *sample injection port*. Since solutes to be chromatographed must be in the vapor phase, the injection port is heated to a temperature, T_1, which will ensure rapid vaporization but not thermal degradation of the solute. Liquid and gas samples are almost always injected by syringe through a silicone rubber diaphragm in the injection port. The solute vapor mixes nearly instantaneously with the flowing carrier gas and is swept into the *column*. The column is the heart of the chromatograph. It is here that the different solutes in the vaporized samples are separated from each other by virtue of their different interaction with the column packing. The column also must be maintained at a selected temperature, T_2, which determines the time for the passage of the solutes, and also determines, to a degree, the resolution and efficiency obtained with the particular column. As the solutes emerge individually from the end of the column, they enter the *detector*. This device supplies a signal corresponding to the amount of solute leaving the column. This signal also serves to indicate the time or volume to the peak maximum (see Fig. 38-3) which is characteristic for the particular experimental conditions being employed. It is essential to control the detector temperature to prevent condensation. Finally, the carrier gas is passed into a flow meter where the flow rate is determined. This step is necessary if one is to reproduce a particular flow condition which has been found best for the resolution of a mixture. The detector signal is supplied to a suitable automatic recording device, such as a recording potentiometer, where it is recorded on a chart driven at a constant rate. The resulting record is a signal-time plot, such as Fig. 38-3c, which may then be used to evaluate the identity of the components and their concentrations.

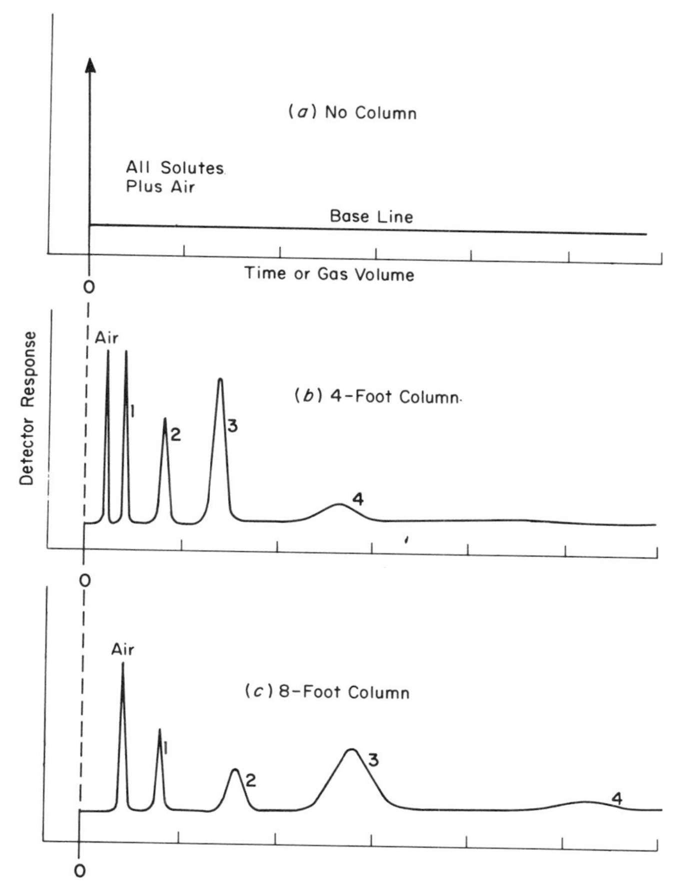

FIG. 38-3. Chromatograms Illustrating the Effect of Column Length on Peak Position, Height, and Width.

As Fig. 38-3c shows, the usual detector supplies a signal proportional to the concentration of the solute in the carrier gas as it leaves the column. A detector arrangement which provides such a signal is called a *differential* type detector, and the curves in Fig. 38-3 accurately represent the distribution process as it occurred during the residence time of the solutes in the column. These bell-shaped curves have an area which corresponds to the amount of each solute present in the original mixture as it was introduced into the sample injection port. Consequently, all that is required to perform a *quantitative* analysis is to measure the area of each peak and convert this to mass of sample by multiplying the peak area by a sensitivity factor for that solute. Of course, this implies that one knows what the solutes in the sample are. Gas chromatography is only a *separation* method, and without previous calibration it cannot provide identification. To achieve this *qualitative* analysis function, one must determine the retention time or volume of a known pure standard. Then, when an unknown appears at that time of volume *under the same experimental conditions*, the certainty of identification is quite high. Alternatively, one may collect the individual solutes in a cold trap as they emerge from the column and subject them to independent instrumental analysis by infrared or mass spectrometry.

It is evident from Fig. 38-3 that solute 3 has the largest area and solute 4 the smallest. It is reasonably certain that 3 is the major component and that 4 is the minor component.

Note that in Fig. 38-3a, all the solutes emerge as a single spike since they have simply been vaporized into the detector without a column. In Fig. 38-3b, a 4-ft. column has been introduced and the four sample components are reasonably well separated. By doubling the column length, we further improve the resolution of the peaks. However, increasing the column length also increases the time the solutes spend in the column, with the result that the peaks which initially were very high and extremely narrow (Fig. 38-3a) progressively become shorter and broader. If excessive column lengths are used, the peaks may become so squat as to be difficult to distinguish from the base line. This tendency is especially evident with minor components, such as solute 4.

The elution time or volume for air is an important quantity since it closely corresponds to the gas space in the column. This value is frequently used to obtain absolute and relative retention data for solute characterization, as discussed below.

ABSOLUTE RETENTION

We can use the *partition ratio*, k, discussed above, as the point of departure for calculating the *retention volume*, V_R^0, or retention time, t_R, which is required to describe the chromatographic behavior of a solute. Conversely, if V_R^0 or t_R is expressed in sufficiently reduced terms, such information can be used to identify the solute in unknown mixtures. This is one of the valuable uses for gas chromatography. In Fig. 38-4, we have a typical

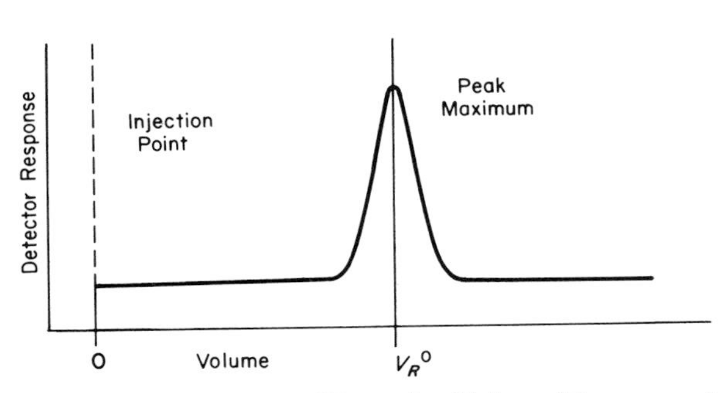

FIG. 38-4. Illustration of Retention Volume Measurement.

chromatographic peak having a characteristic retention volume which is measured from the point of sample injection. Experimentally, the retention volume is calculated from the product of the retention time, t_R, and gas flow rate at the column outlet adjusted to the column temperature, F_c. An additional correction factor, j, is applied in order to correct the gas volume for compressibility in the column. Thus,

$$V_R^0 = t_R \cdot F_c \cdot j \tag{3}$$

where

$$j = \frac{3}{2} \cdot \frac{[(p_i/p_0)^2 - 1]}{[(p_i/p_0)^3 - 1]} \tag{4}$$

V_R^0 has the significance of being the volume of mobile phase required to elute one-half of the solute from the column if the mobile phase (gas) were *not compressible*. It is necessary to know the column inlet gas pressure, p_i, and the column outlet gas pressure, p_0, to make this calculation.

It can be seen from Fig. 38-4 that one-half the solute is in the column at the point corresponding to V_R^0 and one-half the solute has been eluted in the volume, V_R^0. The one-half portion of solute remaining in the column is distributed between the gas space in the column, V_M, and the volume of liquid phase, V_L. We also know that the solute in the column is distributed between V_M and V_L in the proportions required by the partition coefficient, k. Thus, letting c_L and c_M be the concentrations of solute in the liquid and gas phase, respectively,

$$k = \frac{c_L \times V_L}{c_M \times V_M} = K \cdot \frac{V_L}{V_M} \tag{5}$$

The factor, $K = c_L/c_M$, is the *partition coefficient* and, unlike k, it is independent of the amount of liquid phase in the column. It is dependent only on the solute, solvent, and temperature. Taking the ratio of the amount of solute that remains *in* the column to that which has *eluted* from the column, we get

$$\frac{0.5}{0.5} = 1 = \frac{(c_M \times V_M) + (c_L \times V_L)}{(c_M \times V_R^0)} = \frac{V_M + KV_L}{V_R^0}$$

and

$$V_R^0 = V_M + KV_L \tag{6}$$

Equation (6) is the fundamental retention equation required for all chromatographic processes which have two immiscible phases corresponding to V_M and V_L and a partition equilibrium factor corresponding to K.

SPECIFIC RETENTION

Only rarely does an experimenter determine absolute retention by Equations (3) and (6), since V_R^0 is specific for a single column having specific V_M and V_L values. It is preferable to describe retention in some reduced, specific form so that anyone can, by inserting his particular column parameters, calculate the experimental retention volume or time he may expect. Such a quantity in gas chromatography is called the specific retention volume, V_g, and it is defined from the above terms as

$$V_g = \frac{V_R^0 - V_M}{W_L} \cdot \frac{273}{T_c} = \frac{j \cdot F_c \cdot (t_R - t_A)}{W_L} \cdot \frac{273}{T_c} \tag{7}$$

where W_L is the weight of liquid phase in the column, T_c is the absolute column temperature, and t_A is retention time for a nonretained solute such as air. V_g is equal to the volume of gas at 0°C. required to elute one-half of a specified solute from a column which contains one gram of a specified liquid phase and contains no gas space. Whenever standard retention data is to be cited, V_g values should be used. From Equation (7), it is apparent that the gas space in the column, V_M, is given experimentally by

$$V_M = jF_c t_a \tag{8}$$

Another useful relation which may be derived from the retention equations involves the partition coefficient, K. By the use of Equations (5) and (6), remembering that $W_L = V_L \cdot \rho_L$, where ρ_L is the density of the liquid phase, we obtain

$$V_g = \frac{K}{\rho_L}$$

and

$$K = V_g \cdot \rho_L \qquad (9)$$

Equation (9) is a useful relationship to remember, since the partition coefficient is a fundamental quantity related to a number of important solution parameters.

RELATIVE RETENTION

The calculation of absolute retention volumes, $V_R{}^0$ and V_g (Equations (3) and (7)), requires the use of experimental quantities, t_R, t_A, F_c, T_c, W_L, and the calculated compressibility correction, j, which is a function of inlet and outlet column pressure. It would be desirable to eliminate the need to know the precise values of these quantities and yet be able to express a retention behavior in such a way as to be useful and reproducible by anyone who wants to repeat the work. Such a simple treatment of retention is called the *relative retention*, α, because it is the retention of a specified solute relative to that of a specified standard solute on the same column at the same temperature. Thus,

$$\alpha = \frac{t_{R1} - t_A}{t_{R2} - t_A} = \frac{V_{R1}^0 - V_M}{V_{R2}^0 - V_M} = \frac{V_{g1}}{V_{g2}} \neq \frac{V_{R1}^0}{V_{R2}^0} \qquad (10)$$

Note that α is *not* equal to the ratio of $V_R{}^0$ values because these contain the gas volume of the column (V_M), whereas the other ratios given in Equation (10) are corrected for the gas volume. Whenever a relative retention is cited, it should be accompanied by information on the solute, liquid phase, temperature, and standard solute. If the absolute retention for the standard solute is calculated by Equation (3) or (7), the absolute retention of any solute referred to this standard at the same temperature and liquid phase is simply

$$V_R{}^0 \text{ (solute)} = \alpha \cdot V_R{}^0 \text{ (standard)}$$

or

$$V_g \text{ (solute)} = \alpha \cdot V_g \text{ (standard)} \qquad (11)$$

or

$$(t_R - t_A) \text{ solute} = \alpha \cdot (t_R - t_A) \text{ standard}$$

COLUMN EFFICIENCY

In distillation practice and in countercurrent distribution (both important separation methods), it is conventional to discuss efficiency in terms of the *number of theoretical plates*, N. This same concept has been widely adopted also for gas chromatography. Usually, the greater N, the greater is the separating power of the system. This quantity is calculated from a chromatographic peak, as shown in Fig. 38-5. The dimensions given in the figure are simply substituted into the following equation

$$N = 16 \left(\frac{x}{y}\right)^2 \qquad (12)$$

It is important that the dotted lines on the slopes of the peak be superimposed on the straight portion of the peak sides; *i.e.*, they are the tangents to the peak. The peak width, y, is equal to 4σ (σ = standard deviation). Both x and y must be measured in the same units, usually cm. or inches, measured directly on the chromatogram.

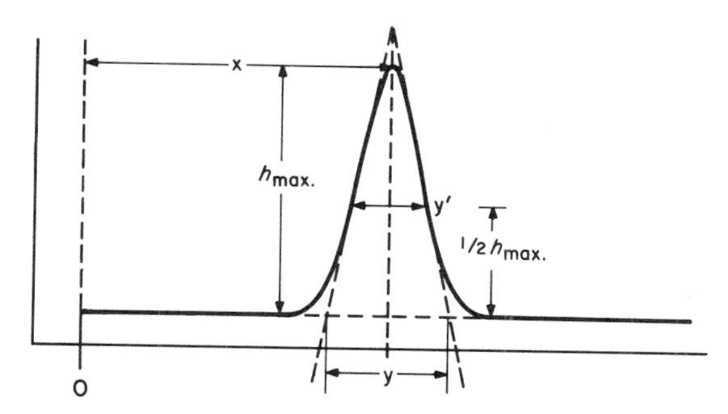

FIG. 38-5. Peak Dimensions Required for the Measurement of Column Efficiency.

Various experimenters have suggested variants of Equation (12). One of the most widely accepted is

$$N = 5.54\left(\frac{x}{y'}\right)^2 \tag{13}$$

where y' is the width at one-half the peak height as measured from the base line (see Fig. 38-5). Using this method for N, the need to construct tangents to the peak slopes is eliminated and accuracy is considerably improved.

A second way of expressing efficiency is in terms of a linear quantity, H, the *height equivalent to a theoretical plate* (often written H.E.T.P.). Since N is the *number* of theoretical plates in the particular column length, H is given by

$$H = \frac{L}{N} \tag{14}$$

L, the column length, is almost invariably given in cm. so that H is also in cm.

With H as the measure of column performance, it can be shown that at least four mechanisms in the column account for the magnitude of H. First, it is necessary to recognize that H is a measure of peak width relative to column length; *i.e.*, the width, $y = 4\sigma$, is developed while the solute travels the column length, L, in time, t_R. All solutes passing through the same column travel the same length and develop a width *in the column* of l, corresponding to σ in the *eluted* peak. Thus,

$$N = 16\left(\frac{x}{y}\right)^2 = \left(\frac{x}{\sigma}\right)^2 = \left(\frac{L}{l}\right)^2 \tag{15}$$

and the theoretical plate height is then

$$H = \frac{L}{N} = L \cdot \left(\frac{l}{L}\right)^2 = \frac{l^2}{L} \tag{16}$$

We can assume that the various mechanisms occurring in the column contribute to l^2, the *peak variance*, so that

$$l^2 = l_1^2 + l_2^2 + l_3^2 \cdots + l_n^2$$

and

$$H = \frac{l^2}{L} = \frac{l_1^2}{L} + \frac{l_2^2}{L} + \frac{l_3^2}{L} \cdots + \frac{l_n^2}{L}$$

where the subscripts serve to identify the different mechanisms. Most of the factors contributing to peak spreading are velocity dependent. The four most widely accepted mechanisms contributing to peak spreading are:

1. ***Multiple path term,*** A, due to imperfect (nonuniform) packing. This factor is absent in capillary columns. In a uniformly packed column with uniform support particles, this factor is very small. It is not dependent on the carrier gas velocity.

2. ***Longitudinal diffusion,*** B/u, which provides a measure of how much the initially narrow solute band has spread in the gas phase by the time it is eluted. Thus, the less time the solute spends in the column (proportional to $1/u$, where u = carrier gas velocity) the less the magnitude of this term. Note that peaks 1–4 in Fig. 38-3b are narrower than the same peaks in Fig. 38-3c because they have spent less time in the gas phase of the shorter column.

3. ***Liquid phase mass transfer resistance,*** $C_l u$, which represents the variation in transfer times the solute requires to go in and out of the liquid phase. Spreading due to this cause increases with velocity, since the system simply gets farther away from transfer equilibrium the faster the carrier gas moves with respect to the liquid phase. This term increases rapidly as the liquid phase is increased beyond 10 percent on the usual diatomaceous solid supports.

4. ***Gas phase mass transfer resistance,*** $C_g u$, which, analogous with the $C_l u$ term above, represents the spread of transfer times in the gas phase. This term also is proportional to velocity. It is generally smaller than the liquid phase term. With 0–10 percent liquid phase, it may be larger than the C_l term.

The above factors can be summed up to give the total plate height,

$$H = A + \frac{B}{u} + C_l u + C_g u \tag{17}$$

This equation is frequently referred to as the *van Deemter* equation. The significance of the terms in Equation (17) (except the $C_g u$ term) was discussed by Keulemans and Kwantes[5] and by Dal Nogare and Juvet.[4] A plot of Equation (17) is shown in Fig. 38-6. It is apparent that efficiency (H) becomes very poor (H very large) as the velocity is made either very small or very large. A curve, such as Fig. 38-6, is obtained for *each solute* that is introduced into a column, and for each solute the column will exhibit a maximum efficiency, H_{min}, at an optimum velocity, u_{opt}. Consequently, when a mixture is introduced into a column, the carrier gas velocity will be ideal for only *one solute*. In actuality, the minimum in the H-u curve is quite broad for the usual 10–20 percent liquid phase column. As a result, a single velocity setting will be optimum, or near optimum, for several closely spaced solutes. This is a fortunate situation, inasmuch as the experimenter may then set the flow rate to that which is optimum for the most difficult solute pair in his sample.

It can be shown[6] by differentiating Equation (17) to get the optimum velocity ($dH/du = 0$) that

[5] Keulemans, A. I. M., and Kwantes, A., Vapour Phase Chromatography, D. H., Desty, ed., Academic Press, Inc., New York, 1958, p. 15.

[6] Said, A. S., J. Gas Chromatography, **1,** No. 6, 20, 1963.

$$H_{\min} = A + 2d_p[f(B, C_l, C_g)] \tag{18}$$

where d_p is the average diameter of the solid support particles in the packed column. As a result, the smaller the diameter of the support particle the more efficient the column. In fact, it was shown experimentally that $H_{\min}$ values should lie between two

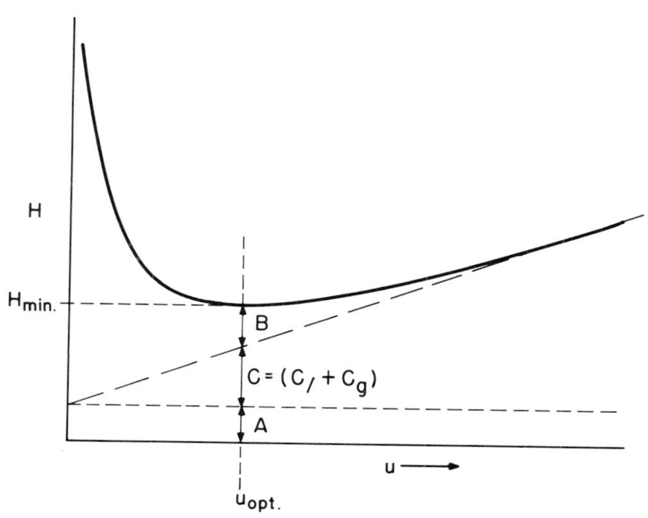

FIG. 38-6. *H-u* Plot Showing the Dependence of Efficiency on Gas Velocity and the Contribution Due to the Van Deemter Terms.

and three particle diameters with uniformly packed columns in apparatus where the dead volume (and the *A* term) is negligible.[7]

It might appear from Equation (18) that the only requirement for an infinitely efficient column is to use an infinitely small diameter solid support. Actually, the practical limitation of pressure drop across the column must be considered, since this increases rapidly with the reciprocal of the particle diameter squared. It can be shown from the Kozeny-Carman equation for gas flow in a packed tube that

$$\Delta p = \frac{\bar{u} \cdot \eta \cdot L}{d_p^2} \cdot C \tag{19}$$

where: Δp = the pressure drop across the column ($p_{\text{in}} - p_{\text{out}}$),
η = the gas viscosity and is temperature dependent,
L = the column length,
$\bar{u}$ = the average gas velocity, and
C = a geometry constant.

From Equation (19) it can be concluded that reducing the particle diameter from 500 μ (0.5 mm.) to 100 μ (0.1 mm.) will increase the pressure drop by a factor of 25 if the velocity is maintained constant.

[7] Dal Nogare, S., and Chiu, J., Anal. Chem., **34,** 890, 1962.

RESOLUTION

One must be careful to distinguish between column efficiency (N or H), separation ($V_{R2}^0 - V_{R1}^0$ or $t_{R2} - t_{R1}$), and resolution which is the degree to which *peak areas* are separated from each other. Column efficiency refers only to the dimensions of a single chromatographic peak. Separation is the distance, volume, or time between two peak maxima. Resolution must then refer to both peak width ($\sqrt{H}$) and the separation between peak areas in distance, volume, or time. This can be seen by comparing Figs.

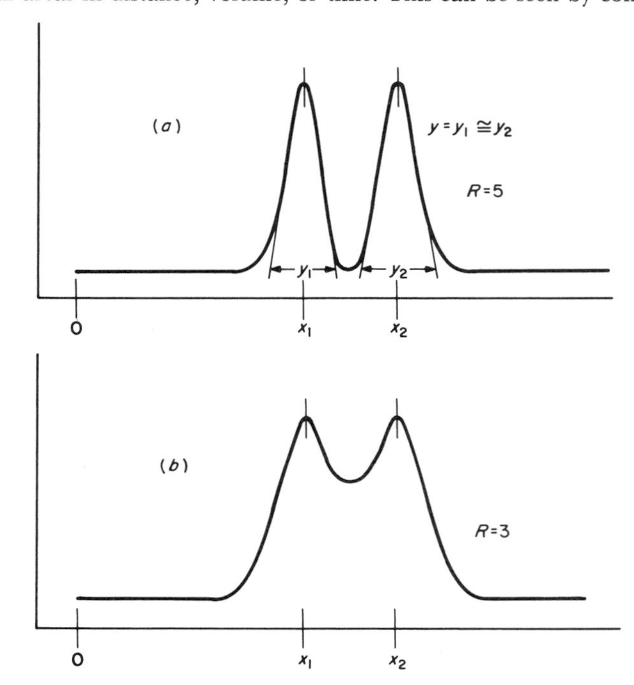

Fig. 38-7. Demonstration of Resolution.

38-7a and 38-7b, where x's are identical but widths are different. A simple and effective definition of resolution, R, which applies *only* to equal-area peaks is given by

$$R = \frac{x_2 - x_1}{\sigma} = 4\left[\frac{x_2 - x_1}{y}\right] \tag{20}$$

where R is in terms of the number of standard deviations (peak width) by which two peak maxima at x_2 and x_1 are separated (see Fig. 38-7). A resolution of $R = 4$ is essentially complete separation (97.8 percent) of peak areas.

It is an easy matter to show with the help of Equations (6), (12), and (20) that

$$R = \sqrt{\frac{L}{H}}\left[1 - \frac{\beta + K_1}{\beta + K_2}\right] \tag{21}$$

where β is the column characteristic, *i.e.*, the ratio of gas space to liquid space in the column, V_M/V_L, and K_2, K_1 are the partition coefficients for the two solutes. According to Equation (21), in columns of high β, solutes of small K (short retention) would be difficult to separate since the quantity in brackets would be near zero. Consequently, for high-temperature separations (where K's are made small), columns with high percent liquid phase, small β, are most effective. With solutes that are considerably retained (high K values or low temperature), β values can be increased without substantial resolution penalty. Since high β implies low percent liquid phase, these columns will be fast and solutes will be rapidly eluted. Table 38-1 shows the relative effect of varying β and K on resolution.

TABLE 38-1.

K_2	K_1	β	*Percent Liquid Phase*[a]	*N Required for R = 4*
200	100	5	~25	18
200	100	100	~ 3	64
2	1	5	~25	550
2	1	100	~ 3	160,000

[a] On typical diatomaceous support.

Another way to look at resolution is in terms of the number of theoretical plates required to effect a particular resolution. This is given in the last column of Table 38-1 and can be obtained from Equation (21) by rearrangement to give for essentially complete resolution ($R = 4$):

$$N = 16\left(\frac{\beta + K_2}{\Delta K}\right)^2 \qquad (22)$$

Thus, N theoretical plates are required to separate any two peaks that are a fixed distance apart (ΔK) and retained to a degree shown by K_2 on a column characterized by β. The curves in Fig. 38-8 show this relationship clearly. It should be borne in mind that capillary columns and glass bead columns, because of their low capacity (specific surface area) for liquid phase, are high β columns. Diatomaceous supports such as Celite, firebrick, Chromosorb, Sil-O-Cel, etc., are high surface supports; and columns packed with these materials can contain relatively large volumes of liquid phase and, therefore, exhibit small β's.

The generalized case for resolution of *unequal-area* peaks has been derived by Glueckauf[8] and corrected by Said.[6]

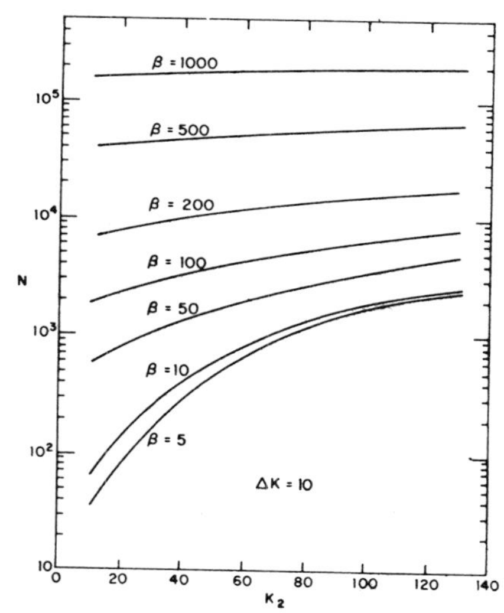

FIG. 38-8. Number of Theoretical Plates, N, Required for Quantitative Resolution for Columns of Different β Values and Different Retention, K_2.

TEMPERATURE DEPENDENCE OF RETENTION

Temperature is one of the important parameters which the experimenter can control to improve and/or accelerate a chromatogram. With easy separations, the temperature

[8] Glueckauf, E., Trans. Faraday Soc., **51**, 1955, 34.

may be adjusted upward to gain the advantage of speed and, conversely, a downward adjustment of temperature leads to prolonged retention but usually improved resolution.

Normally, gas chromatography is carried out in an isothermal mode, *i.e.*, the temperature of the column is adjusted and maintained constant. It is important, then, to understand the influence of temperature on retention and resolution. It will be recalled from the preceding section that the *absolute retention volume* is given by

$$V_R^0 = V_M + KV_L \tag{23}$$

and that the *specific retention volume* is

$$V_g = \frac{V_R^0 - V_M}{\rho \cdot V_L} = \frac{K}{\rho} \tag{24}$$

Now, the partition coefficient exhibits a temperature dependence derivable from the Clausius-Clapeyron equation and given by

$$\log K = -\frac{\Delta H}{2.3RT} + c \tag{25}$$

An equivalent expression can be gotten by Equation (24) to yield

$$\log V_g = -\frac{\Delta H}{2.3RT} + c' \tag{26}$$

in which H = the pertinent heat (ideally, the heat of vaporization),
R = the gas law constant,
T = the absolute temperature (°C. + 273), and
c' = a constant which contains, among other things, the density of the liquid phase.

Equation (26) gives a fairly good linear plot in most cases and can, for convenience, be written as a three-constant equation of the so-called Antoine type

$$\log V_g = -\frac{A}{(t + B)} + C \tag{27}$$

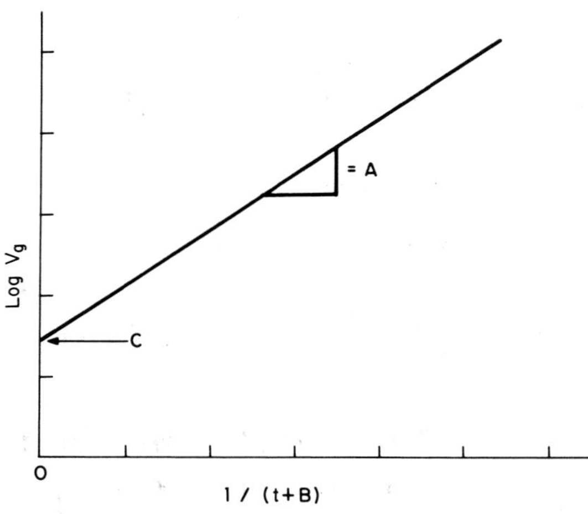

FIG. 38-9. Retention-Temperature Plot Showing the Terms of the Antoine Equation.

The negative sign implies a plot of slope, $-A$; but since ΔH in Equation (25) is usually negative, the observed slope is positive. B in Equation (27) is an adjustable quantity which is added to t, temperature in degrees centigrade, to provide the best straight-line plot. Its value is around 273. C is a constant representing the intercept of this plot on the log V_g axis. Figure 38-9 illustrates the relationship of these terms. Note that the slope, A, varies with the nature of the solute and liquid phase. It is, therefore, a measure of the degree of interaction. The same solute on different liquid phases will yield different values of A, B, and C, as will different solutes on the same liquid phase. The larger A, the greater is the change in retention for a given change in temperature. An important advantage of Equation (27) is that the temperature dependence of any number of solutes or any number of liquid phases may be concisely defined with three constants for each combination. This makes data generally useful and reproducible from laboratory to laboratory.

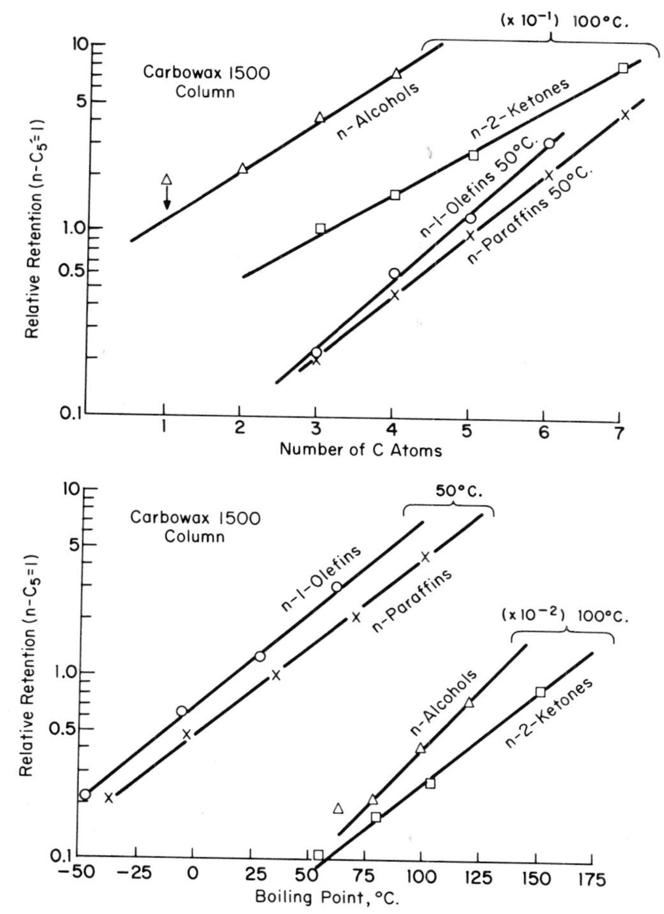

FIG. 38-10. Plots of Relative Retention (Log Scale) *vs.* Number of Carbon Atoms and Boiling Point for Several Homologous Series.

Equation (26) contains the heat of solution, ΔH, which is closely related to the heat of vaporization. This, in turn, determines the boiling point of a particular solute; and, from the regular variation of boiling point with carbon number in a homologous series, we can construct useful *family plots*, as shown in Fig. 38-10.

PROGRAMMED TEMPERATURE OPERATION

It is apparent from Fig. 38-10 that if one had a mixture containing solutes covering a wide range of boiling points, the low-boiling components would be quickly eluted while the higher boiling components would require excessive waiting time (note the log retention scale). This effect can be seen in Fig. 38-11b. Note how well resolved the late components are relative to the early homologs. Another result of isothermal opera-

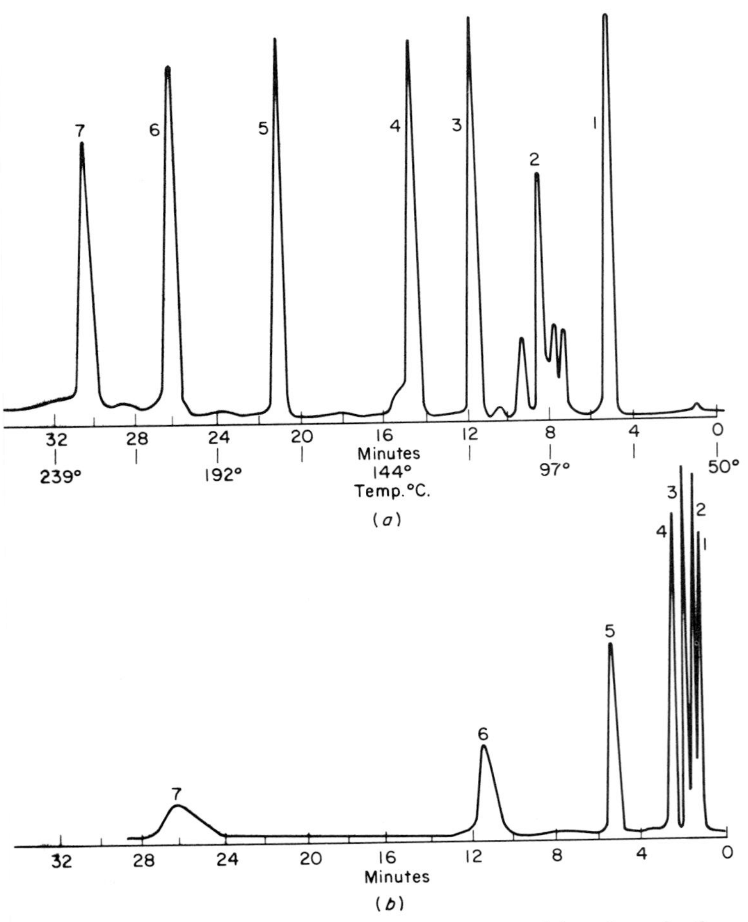

FIG. 38-11. A Programmed Temperature Chromatogram (a) and an Isothermal Chromatogram (b). The Same Mixture of Hydrocarbons Was Chromatographed in Each Case.

tion is that the peak height decreases inversely with retention, and peak width increases directly with retention. Thus, early peaks are spikelike, whereas late peaks are low and broad. Eventually, peaks become so low that detector sensitivity is not sufficient to distinguish between peak and base line.

One means for eliminating some of the problems is to employ temperature programming of the column. In the simplest case, the column temperature is increased linearly with time. However, the temperature rise may take any desired form and may even be interrupted with isothermal intervals for specific purposes. The result of linearly heating a chromatographic column is shown in Fig. 38-11a. Note how the peaks are uniformly spaced and how resolution is approximately constant along the entire length of the chromatogram. Furthermore, peak width and height are not markedly dependent on retention and the peak shapes are relatively uniform. By simply altering the heating rate, the duration of the chromatogram may be controlled.

The exact description of the retention time of solutes under programmed temperature conditions is quite difficult to solve.[9] Recently, Giddings[10] has proposed a simplified picture which well illustrates the action of temperature programming and allows a reasonable estimate of *retention temperature* from isothermal data only.

It might be inferred from the chromatograms in Fig. 38-11 that resolution is improved by temperature programming. Actually, it can be shown that the best resolution is obtained by operating isothermally at the starting temperature, although retention times quickly become excessive. In fact, retention is proportional to $1/\sqrt{R_h}$, and quadrupling the heating rate reduces resolution by one-half. The best mode of operation under programmed temperature conditions is the slowest possible heating rate consistent with the desired resolution and completion time. With some commercial apparatus (such as the Beckman Thermo-Trac), a temperature program may literally be written so that in uncritical regions heating rates may be increased to save time; in other regions the rate may be set to zero (isothermal) to achieve the best possible resolution.

APPLICATIONS OF GAS CHROMATOGRAPHY

Only a brief summary of some prominent areas in which GC has found extensive application will be cited here. The references cited have been selected mainly from the 1963 literature to reflect the breadth and flexibility of GC rather than the importance of the application. The reader should bear in mind that the general principles of resolution, retentions, and efficiency, as discussed earlier, will apply in any case. What is often unique in applications of GC is the instrumentation modifications adapted to the specific end and the manner in which the sample is treated before, during, and after chromatography. Each of the following headings contains a few comments on the general approach to the particular application. The cited literature contains more details for those readers who wish to pursue the topic further.

Petroleum.—The field of analysis of petroleum and derived products and chemicals is awesome to contemplate, and GC has found extensive application to many analytical studies. Included among these are analyses of crude petroleum fractions, gasolines, waxes, reformates, LPG, sulfur and nitrogen compounds, catalysts, and unsaturation. Buzon[11] and Gambrill[12] have recently reviewed this area, and Martin[13] has provided

[9] Dal Nogare, S., and Juvet, R. S., Gas-Liquid Chromatography, John Wiley and Sons, Inc., New York, 1962, p. 325.

[10] Giddings, J. Calvin, Facts and Methods, **3**, No. 2, Summer, 1962.

[11] Buzon, J., Bull. Soc. Chim. France, No. 3, 526, 1963.

[12] Gambrill, C. M., Anal. Chem., **35**, 111R, 1963.

[13] Martin, R. L., Gas Chromatography, Fowler, ed., Academic Press, Inc., New York, 1963, p. 127.

an interesting picture of GC in a petroleum research laboratory. As is invariably the case, auxiliary techniques of many kinds, both chemical and instrumental, have been used to augment the separation effected by GC. The use of the urea adduct to effect an initial separation of *n*- from branched hydrocarbons results in the simplified chromatogram obtained by Desty[14] and shown in Fig. 38-12.

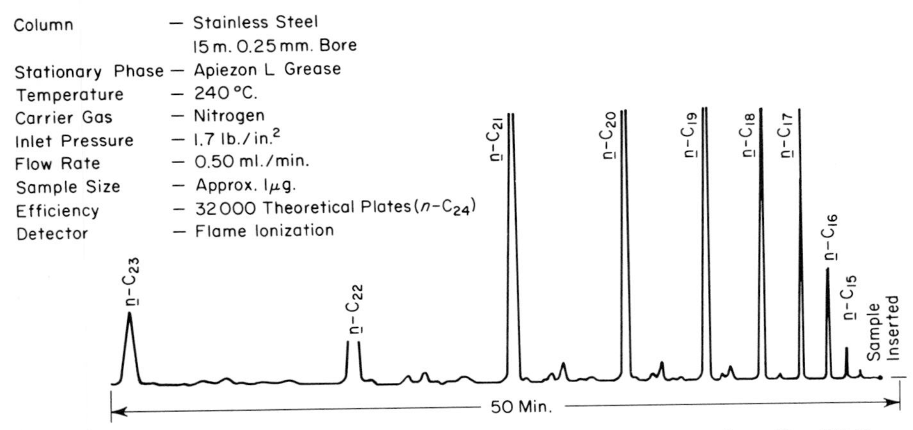

FIG. 38-12. Chromatogram of *n*-Paraffins Isolated as Urea Adducts from Gas Oil.[11]

Gas chromatography has been used to separate petroleum hydrocarbons into components as a preliminary to their identification by infrared and ultraviolet spectrometry, mass spectrometry, and nuclear magnetic resonance (see Chapter 57, Petroleum and Petroleum Products).

Food.—Work in this area has been characterized by the use of ultrasensitive detectors, since many studies have centered around the trace components which account for the odor and flavor of foods. Such devices are based on flame ionization, electron capture, electron mobility, and other electronic phenomena. Detector sensitivities are of the order of 10^{-12} g. per cc. of carrier gas, and they are well suited to sampling environments over crushed fruit, milk, coffee, bread, etc. Where the detector is not sufficiently sensitive, some form of concentration technique is often employed. This may take the form of a recycling trap, a pre-column, or a cold trap through which a large volume of the flavor or odor containing matrix is processed.

Because of the complexity of food components, very efficient columns are frequently used. These may be long capillary or packed columns used in conjunction with sensitive detectors. A recent review article by Borker and Sloman[15] provides many references to current GC techniques used in the study of foods. As an example of the information obtainable by GC, the work of Oaks *et al.*[16] with garlic head space gas and extract using dual channel detection is interesting. The combination of flame ionization and electron capture detectors in parallel provides a dual chromatogram, Fig. 38-13, one corresponding to almost every species eluted, the other only to those that show a substantial ability to capture electrons. The ratio of responses provides a means for char-

[14] Desty, D. H., Trans. Soc. Inst. Tech., **15,** 81, 1963.
[15] Borker, E., and Sloman, K. G., Anal. Chem., **35,** 62R, 1963.
[16] Oaks, D. M., *et al.*, Anal. Chem., **36,** 1560, 1964.

acterizing the solutes. In this way considerable information can be obtained about the nature of the flavor components. Other combination detectors also may be used.

Methods have been described for the determination of residual solvents in spice oleoresins and for pesticides in foods in Chapter 50, Volume III, Foods.

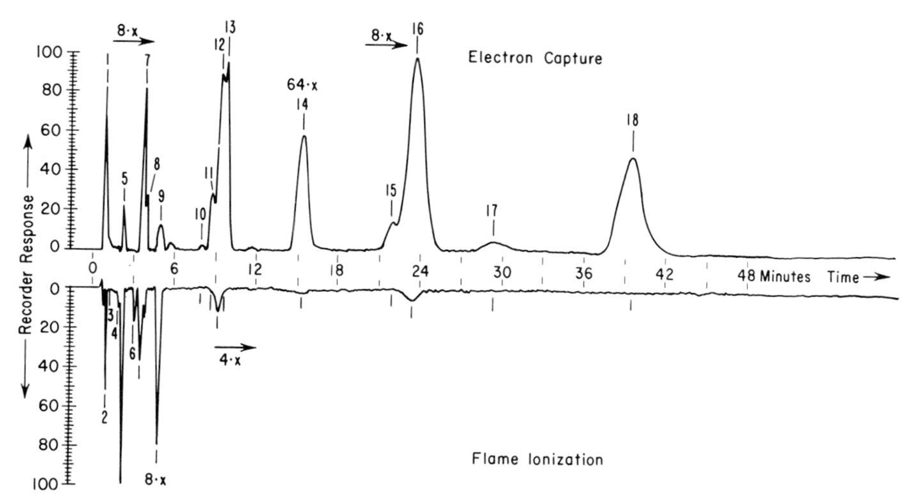

FIG. 38-13. Dual-channel Chromatogram of Garlic Head Space Gas.[13]

Biochemical and Clinical.—Under this heading we can consider those applications involving body components of all types. Especially active are the areas of fatty acid and steroid analysis. Because these materials are high boiling and not entirely thermally stable, derivatives are commonly prepared. In the case of the fatty acids, methyl esters and, in the case of steroids, acetates or trifluoroacetates are commonly prepared. The great complexity of these natural mixtures requires that highly specialized columns and preliminary extraction procedures be employed. These are well noted in several articles dealing with fatty acids.[17,18] A review of fatty acids pertinent to food studies is contained in the Borker and Sloman review.[15]

Steroids have been exhaustively discussed by Vanden Heuvel and Horning in a recent review.[19] Figure 38-14 shows the separation of a group of related cholesterol compounds on a silicone rubber gum (F-60) column at 235°C. Such separations were considered next to impossible only a few years ago. Applications of GC to clinical problems have been treated by Kingsley,[20] and Burchfield and Storrs have published a book on biochemical GC.[21]

The following methods are described in Chapter 47, Instrumental Methods in Clinical Medicine:

[17] Ettre *et al.*, Application Rpt. No. GC-AP-001, Perkin-Elmer Corp., Norwalk, Conn.
[18] Horning, E. C., *et al.*, J. Lipid Research, **5**, 20, 1964.
[19] Vanden Heuvel, W. J. A., and Horning, E. C., in Biomedical Applications of Gas Chromatography, H. A. Szymanski, ed., Plenum Press, New York, 1964.
[20] Kingsley, G. R., Anal. Chem., **35**, 11R, 1963.
[21] Burchfield, H. P., and Storrs, E. E., Biochemical Applications of GC, Academic Press, Inc., New York, 1962.

a. Blood gases
b. Estrogens
c. Homovanillic acid and vanilmandelic acid
d. Hydroxycorticosteroids
e. 17-Ketosteroids
f. Pregnanediol

Herbicides, Pesticides.—In order to measure the extremely small quantities of these control agents present on the surface of crops and in animal tissue, extremely sensitive

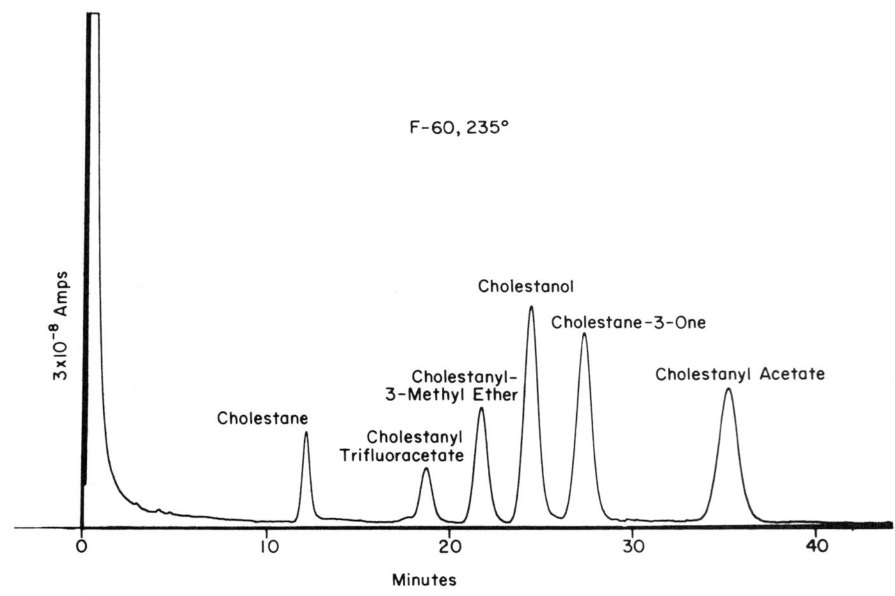

FIG. 38-14. Resolution of Various Cholesterol Derivatives on an F-60 (DC Siloxane Polymer) Column. (Reproduced with permission from W. J. A. Vanden Heuvel and E. C. Horning, in Biomedical Applications of Gas Chromatography, H. A. Szymanski, ed., Plenum Press, New York, 1964.)

detectors must be used. It is a fortunate circumstance that the most effective pesticides are halogenated compounds which can be measured with excellent quantitative results by microcoulometric methods after pyrolysis of the GC column effluent.[22] Preparation of the sample requires some care, particularly if the pesticide is to be measured in animal tissue. One of the newest detectors is based on the ability of electronegative molecules to associate with electrons. This electron capture detector is particularly effective in detecting polynuclear aromatics, halogenated compounds, and other molecules with conjugated systems. Pesticides also are effectively detected with this device as shown in Fig. 38-15 from the work of Cieplinski.[23] A recent review by Westlake[24] may be consulted for additional details of the problems and possibilities encountered in this field.

Methods described in Chapter 56, on the analysis of pesticides, are:

[22] Coulson, D. M., *et al.*, J. Agr. Food Chem., **8**, 399, 1960.
[23] Cieplinski, E. W., Applications Rpt. No. GC-AP-005, Perkin-Elmer Corp., Norwalk, Conn.
[24] Westlake, W. E., Anal. Chem., **35**, 105R, 1963.

a. Analysis of pesticide residues
b. Determination of organophosphates in pesticides

Pharmaceuticals.—Some idea of the large number of drugs and their diverse classifications can be obtained from the review by Brownell *et al.*,[25] which includes a list of techniques for their detection and measurement. GC is increasingly being used in the

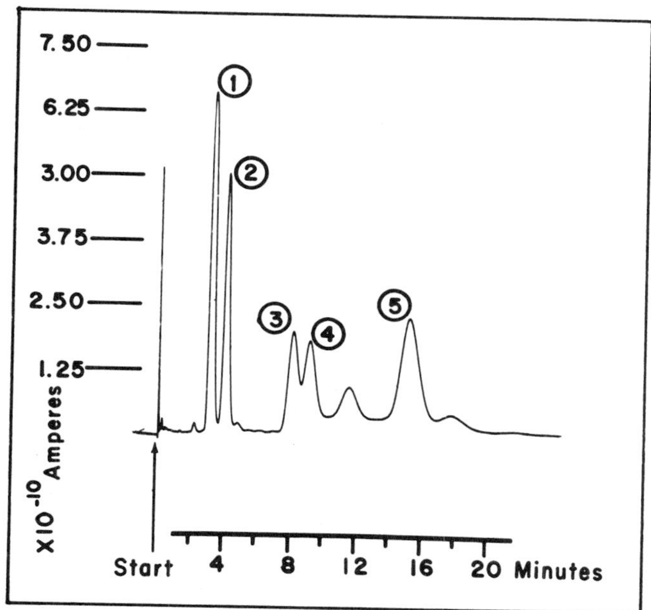

FIG. 38-15. Chromatogram of Pesticide Mixture; 1 = Heptachlor, 2 = Aldrin, 3 = Dieldrin, 4 = Endrin, and 5 = DDT. Each component is present at the 10^{-9} g. level. This separation was carried out at 175°C. on an SE-30 (silicone rubber gum) column.

pharmaceutical area not only to assay drugs, but to determine their fate in the body and to detect them for legal purposes.[26]

Cosmetics and Perfumes.—The composition of various cosmetics, the quality of ingredients and the components of subtle fragrances are all amenable to study by GC. In fact, the characterization of essences is a real challenge to both the chemist and the chromatograph. Some aspects of this area have been noted in the publications by Wheatley[27] and Seher.[28]

Protective Coatings.—The volatile components of paints and even the relatively nonvolatile components have been identified and measured by GC. The identity of solvents is a relatively simple matter. Nonvolatile materials, such as the alkyd resins, must either be saponified or pyrolyzed for identification purposes. Such techniques are well illustrated in the references cited by Swann *et al.* in their review.[29]

The following methods are described in Chapter 37, Volume IIB of Standard Methods of Chemical Analysis:

[25] Brownell *et al.*, Anal. Chem., **35**, 143R, 1963.
[26] Parker, K. D., Anal. Chem., **35**, 356, 1963.
[27] Wheatley, V. R., Am. Perfumer Cosmet., **78**, 27, 32, 1963.
[28] Seher, A., J. Soc. Cosmetic Chemists, **13**, 385, 1962.
[29] Swann *et al.*, Anal. Chem., **35**, 35R, 1963.

a. Analysis of solvents, page 1703
b. Identification and determination of fatty acids of oils, page 1647

The following additional methods are described in Chapter 54 of Volume III, Paint, Varnish, and Lacquer:

a. Analysis of solvents
b. For qualitative analysis of alkyd and acrylic resins and some other coating binders
c. Determination of styrene monomer
d. Determination of vinyltoluene
e. Determination of toluenediisocyanate
f. Determination of latex
g. Determination of formaldehyde and phenol in phenol-formaldehyde resins

Plastics.—The application of GC to plastics, intermediates, plasticizers, etc., involves all aspects of the GC technique. This is exemplified by the paper of Cobler *et al.*[30] In this field strong emphasis is placed upon the characterization of polymers by pyrolysis followed by GC analysis of the pyrolyzate. The technique has been refined so that artifacts induced by older, static pyrolysis methods are eliminated. This is achieved by a process in which the pyrolyzate is swept into the chromatograph the instant it is formed.

The following gas chromatographic methods have been described in Chapter 41, Volume IIB, Plastics:

a. Identification of plastics, page 2041
b. Determination of esters in acrylic copolymers, page 2093
c. Determination of long-chain alcohol esters in acrylic copolymers, page 2097
d. Determination of styrene monomers in styrene plastics, page 2058
e. Determination of vinylacetate in its copolymers, page 2077

The following procedures are given in Chapter 58, Volume III, Plastics.

a. Identification of plastics
b. Determination of additives
c. Determination of high-boiling esters in polymer extracts
d. Determination of styrene monomer in styrene polymers

Organic Functional Groups.[31]—The following methods have been described in Chapter 51, Volume III, Organic Functional Groups:

a. Analysis of a C_{10}–C_{18} aliphatic hydrocarbon mixture
b. Analysis of a mixture of oxygenated solvents (methanol, ethanol, acetone, tetrahydrofuran, and dioxane)
c. Analysis of a mixture of nitrogen-containing compounds (ethylenediamine, diethylenetriamine, glyconitrile, aminoacetonitrile, and piperazine)
d. Analysis of a 1, 4-dichloro-2-butyne and 1, 2, 4-trichloro-2-butene

Gases.[32]—Methods for the analysis of gases are given in Chapter 35, Volume IIB Fuel Gases (page 1534), and also in Chapter 52, Volume III.

Coal Tar Products.—Sauerland[33] has described a method for the analysis of coal tar products, using gas chromatography.

Fertilizers.—Schall[34] has used gas chromatography in the analysis of fertilizers.

Alcoholic Beverages.—Bober and Haddaway[35] have used gas chromatography in the analysis of alcoholic beverages.

[30] Cobler, J., *et al.*, Soc. Plastics Engrs. Trans., **2,** 145, 1962.
[31] Ma, T. S., and Gutterson, M., Microchem. J., **6,** 409, 1962.
[32] Kienitz, H., Z. anal. Chem., **192,** 160, 1962.
[33] Sauerland, H. D., Brennstoff-Chem., **44,** 37, 1963.
[34] Schall, E. D., Anal. Chem., **35,** 58R, 1963.
[35] Bober, A., and Haddaway, L. W., J. Gas Chromatography, **1,** 8, 1963.

Air Pollutants.—A method for the determination of hydrocarbons in air pollution studies is given in Chapter 42, Volume III.

Natural Fats.—A method for the determination of fatty acids in natural fats is given in Chapter 33, Volume IIB, Natural Fats (page 1475) and in Chapter 48 of Volume III.

Rubber and Rubber Products.—The following methods are given in Chapter 59, Volume III, Rubber and Rubber Products:

a. Identification of substances in rubber analysis
b. Determination of copolymer composition
c. Determination of amine antioxidants

Soaps and Synthetic Detergents.—The following methods are given in Chapter 61, Volume III, Soaps and Synthetic Detergents:

a. Determination of ethyl alcohol in liquid detergents
b. Determination of fatty acids

Water Analysis.—The following methods are given in Chapter 63, Volume III, Water Analysis:

a. Pesticides in water
b. Silvex, an aquatic herbicide

Water Determination.—The use of gas chromatography for the determination of water in the following: butane gas, creams, emulsions, ointments, and pastes, is discussed in Chapter 64, Volume III, Determination of Water.

For those who wish access to a convenient source of the GC literature, the compilation of Preston is recommended.[36] An impressive compilation of GC data from the literature has been made by Lewis and published as a reference work by ASTM.[37]

[36] Preston, S., Comprehensive Bibliography and Index to GC Literature, to be published 1965.

[37] Lewis, J. S., Compilation of GC Data, ASTM Special Technical Publication No. 343, 1963.

Chapter 39

THIN-LAYER CHROMATOGRAPHY

By Donald C. Malins
Bureau of Commercial Fisheries
Technological Laboratory
U. S. Fish and Wildlife Service
Seattle, Washington

and

Helmut K. Mangold
University of Minnesota
The Hormel Institute
Austin, Minnesota

INTRODUCTION

Chromatography using thin layers of adsorbents on glass plates (Thin-Layer Chromatography, TLC) had its genesis in 1938 when Izmaĭlov and Shraĭber published the paper "A Drop Chromatographic Method of Analysis and Its Utilization in Pharmacy." [1] More than a decade elapsed, however, before this technique was further developed by Meinhard and Hall,[2] Kirchner, Miller, and Keller,[3] Mottier,[4] and Reitsema.[5] Although the contributions of these workers suggested that the new technique held great promise for the analysis of complex mixtures, it received little attention until Stahl[6] perfected the method. He developed equipment and standardized adsorbents for the preparation of uniform layers on glass plates. In addition, Stahl demonstrated the potential usefulness of thin-layer chromatography for the fractionation of a wide range of substances.

This chapter will discuss the practical aspects of thin-layer chromatography, and will present a few examples of the application of this technique to the solution of some difficult analytical problems. Detailed descriptions of specialized applications can be found in several more comprehensive texts which are listed in the bibliography at the end of this chapter.

FEATURES AND APPLICABILITY OF THIN-LAYER CHROMATOGRAPHY

It should be realized that thin-layer chromatography constitutes a special *technique* and that all chromatographic *principles* functioning in solid-liquid and liquid-liquid *systems* can be utilized. Adsorption chromatography is most widely practiced, but ion-exchange, partition, and reversed-phase partition can also be applied in the thin-layer

[1] Izmaĭlov, N. A., and Shraĭber, M. S., Farmatsiya (Sofia), **1938,** No. 3, 1.
[2] Meinhard, J. E., and Hall, N. F., Anal. Chem., **21,** 185, 1949.
[3] Kirchner, J. G., Miller, J. M., and Keller, G. J., Anal. Chem., **23,** 420, 1951.
[4] Mottier, M., Mitt. Gebiete Lebensm. Hyg., **43,** 118, 1952.
[5] Reitsema, R. H., Anal. Chem., **26,** 960, 1954.
[6] Stahl, E., Chemiker-Ztg., **82,** 323, 1958.

technique. The various systems, techniques and principles of chromatography are listed in Table 39-1.

TABLE 39-1. SYSTEMS, TECHNIQUES, AND PRINCIPLES OF CHROMATOGRAPHY[7]

Stationary Phase	Mobile Phase	Techniques	Physical Principles
Solid	Liquid	Column, thin-layer, and paper chromatography	Adsorption, ion exchange, gel filtration, and others
Liquid	Liquid	Column, thin-layer, and paper chromatography	Partition, reversed-phase partition
Solid	Gaseous	Gas-solid chromatography	Adsorption
Liquid	Gaseous	Gas-liquid chromatography	Partition, reversed-phase partition

The choice of the chromatographic principle is determined by the chemical nature of the compounds to be resolved and by the desired pattern of fractionation. Table 39-2 presents a survey of experimental conditions suitable for separating a great variety of compounds.

The fact that two or more principles of chromatography can be applied consecutively, on one plate, is of great value. Other reasons for the popularity of thin-layer chromatography are: (a) the low cost of the equipment used; (b) the simplicity of the method; (c) its speed; (d) the sharpness of separation; and (e) the sensitivity of detection of the fractions on the plate. In adsorption-TLC, the high capacity of the layer is especially appreciated.

Thin-layer chromatography constitutes a versatile tool which can be utilized not only for resolving a complex mixture on an analytical scale and for characterizing its components, but also for isolating fractions in amounts sufficient for further applications.

OUTLINE OF GENERAL PROCEDURES

The practical procedures of the TLC technique are as follows:

A glass plate is coated with a loose powder or, better, with a slurry of an adsorbent or another finely ground material. Slurries will adhere to the surface of the plate, after drying, as a thin layer. (Coated glass plates, plastic sheets, and aluminum foils are also commercially available.)

The unknown substance and reference materials, dissolved in water or an organic solvent, are applied in a row of spots, 1 to 2 cm. from the edge of the plate or sheet, using a microsyringe, a micropipet, or a capillary.

The chromatoplate is placed in a vessel containing developing solvent. Rapid equilibration with vapors of solvent is achieved by lining one or all sides of the tank with filter paper that extends into the solvent. The jar is closed with a lid. As the solvent rises through the layer by capillary action, the sample is resolved into fractions.

The plate (or sheet) is withdrawn after the solvent front has migrated about three-fourths of the length of the plate, and the various fractions are revealed on the layer, usually by spraying with a reagent solution.

[7] Maier, R., and Mangold, H. K., in Advances in Analytical Chemistry and Instrumentation, C. N. Reilley, Ed., Vol. 3, Interscience and John Wiley, New York, 1964, p. 369.

TABLE 39-2. CHOICE OF EXPERIMENTAL CONDITIONS

Substances to Be Fractionated	Main Chromatographic Principle Functioning	Capacity of a Standard Plate (20/20-cm., layer 0.25 mm. thick) Developing Time (10 cm.)	Pattern of Separation Achieved	Typical Layers and Solvents
Hydrophobic neutral and ionic material, such as hydrocarbons and other petroleum products; fats and waxes; essential oils; carotenoids; fat-soluble vitamins, alkaloids, and dyes; insecticides.	Adsorption	50–100 mg. <30 min.	Fractionation according to classes of compounds having different types and/or numbers of functional groups per molecule.	Silica Gel G; Hexane-diethyl ether-acetic acid, 90:10:1, v/v/v (see also Tables 39-4 and 39-5)
	Adsorption. Formation of π-complexes of unsaturated compounds (with silver nitrate)	10–50 mg. <30 min.	(Fractionation according to classes) and separation of classes into groups of compounds having the same number of double bonds. Separation of *cis*- from *trans*-unsaturated compounds.	Silica Gel G containing 5% (w/w) of silver nitrate; Chloroform (see also Table 39-5)
	Reversed-phase Partition	1–5 mg. 30–60 min.	(Fractionation according to classes) and resolution of classes into individual compounds according to molecular weight *and* degree of unsaturation. Saturated compounds may overlap with unsaturated constituents.	Kieselguhr G impregnated with paraffin oil (5% in diethyl ether); Chloroform-methanol-water, 75:25:5, v/v/v (see also Tables 39-10 and 39-11)
Phenolic and quinoid compounds, such as tannins, coumarins, flavone glycosides, many antioxidants. Aromatic nitro compounds, DNP-amino acids, sulfonic acids, and their amides.	"Polyamide-Chromatography"	10–50 mg. 1–2 hr.	Separation into groups of compounds having the same number and positions of hydrophilic functional groups.	Polyamide TLC; Ethanol-water, 50:50, v/v (see also Tables 39-12 and 39-13)
Hydrophilic neutral compounds such as carbohydrates, glycosides, water-soluble vitamins, sterols, alkaloids, and dyes. Also some ionic compounds, especially those forming zwitter-ions, *e.g.*, amino acids and peptides, detergents.	Partition	1–5 mg. 30–60 min.	(Fractionation according to classes) and resolution of classes into constituent compounds according to molecular weight.	Cellulose MN 300; Butanol-acetic acid-water, 40:10:50, v/v/v (see also Tables 39-8 and 39-9)
	Molecular Sieve Processes ("Gel filtration")	1–10 mg. several hours	Fractionation of macromolecules according to molecular weights.	Sephadex G-25, fine; Aqueous sodium phosphate buffer, pH7 (see also Tables 39-14 and 39-15)
Hydrophilic ionic compounds such as short-chain acids, sugar phosphates, amino acids, nucleotides, detergents.	Ion-exchange	5–10 mg. <30 min.	Separation according to the net charges of the constituent compounds.	Polyethyleneimine Cellulose; Aqueous Lithium Chloride solutions (see also Tables 39-6 and 39-7)
	Thin-layer Electrophoresis			

APPARATUS AND TECHNIQUES

Coating of glass plates can be achieved by spreading, pouring, dipping, or spraying. Most uniform layers are obtained by the spreading technique. A number of devices for applying thin layers of adsorbents and other materials to glass plates are obtainable from commercial houses, or may be made from simple laboratory equipment. Furthermore, a host of coating materials are available that are specially made for the thin-layer chromatography of a wide variety of products.

Several procedures for the coating of glass plates by spreading with a special applicator are described here. Directions for making chromatoplates without the use of a spreader are also given.

PREPARATION OF CHROMATOPLATES WITH AN APPLICATOR

Table 39-3 lists several types of commercially available spreaders for the preparation of uniform layers of coating materials on glass and other surfaces. The addresses of the suppliers are given.

TABLE 39-3. COMMERCIALLY AVAILABLE APPLICATORS FOR PRECOATED PLATES

Applicators for the preparation of layers 0.25 mm. in thickness	
Stahl's original applicator (see Fig. 39-1)	7[a]
"Chromatofilm Spreader"	15
Applicators for the preparation of layers 0.25–2 mm. in thickness	
Stahl's "Model II S" (see Figs. 39-2 and 39-3)	7
"Variable Thickness Chromatofilm Spreader"	15
Mutter and Hofstetter's original applicator (see Fig. 39-5)	4
Models similar to that of Mutter and Hofstetter	3, 11, 14, 16
Applicator with "Unoplan" leveling device	18
Motorized applicators	4, 5, 7, 9
Applicator for the preparation of gradient layers	
"GM-Applicator" according to Stahl (see Fig. 39-4)	7
Simple leveling devices and spray guns	
Plexiglas applicator	2
"Utility model"	7
Spreading rod	1, 17
Applicator for coating ridged plates	7
Special spray gun	10
Aerosol packages of adsorbent suspensions	13
Precoated glass plates and sheets	
Coated microscope slides	6, 13
Coated glass plates	6
Coated plastic sheets	6, 8
Coated aluminum foil	12

[a] Numbers refer to the following list of suppliers:
1. Aimer Products, Ltd., 56–58 Rochester Place, London N.W.1, England.
2. Applied Science Laboratories, Inc., P. O. Box 140, State College, Pennsylvania.
3. Baird & Tatlock (London), Ltd., Chadwell Heath, Essex, England.
4. Camag A. G., Muttenz B. L., Homburger Str. 24, Switzerland. U. S. Representatives: A. H. Thomas Company, Vine Street at Third, Philadelphia 5, Pennsylvania; and

TABLE 39-3 (cont.)

Microchemical Specialties Co., 1825 Eastshore Highway, Berkeley 10, California. Representative in England: Griffin & George, Ltd., Chromatography Division, Ealing Road, Alperton, Middlesex.
5. Chemetron, 28, Via Sangallo, Milano, Italy.
6. Custom Service Chemicals, New Castle, Delaware.
7. C. Desaga, G.m.b.H., Heidelberg, Hauptstr. 60, Germany. U. S. Representative: C. A. Brinkmann and Co., Inc., Cantiague Rd., Westbury, L. I., New York. Representative in England: Camlab (Glass), Ltd., Milton Rd., Cambridge.
8. Eastman Kodak Co., Rochester 3, New York. Representative in England: Kodak Limited, Research Chemicals Sales Division, Kirkby, Liverpool.
9. C. Erba S.p.A., 24, Via Imbonati, Milano, Italy.
10. Hormuth & Vetter, Heidelberg 1, Postfach 750, Germany. Representative in England: The Northern Media Supply, Ltd., 11 and 12 Blanket Row, Hull.
11. Kensington Scientific Corp., 1717 Fifth Street, Berkeley 10, California.
12. Macherey, Nagel & Co., Düren-Rhld., Germany. U. S. Representative: C. A. Brinkmann and Co., Inc. (see 7 above). Representative in England: Camlab (Glass), Ltd. (see 7 above).
13. Mann Research Laboratories, Inc., 136 Liberty Street, New York 6, New York.
14. G. Pleuger S. A., 511, Turnhoutsebaan, Wijnegem, Belgium. Representative in England: Townson & Mercer, Ltd., Beddington Lane, Croydon, Surrey.
15. Research Specialties Co., 200 S. Garrard Blvd., Richmond, California.
16. T. J. Sas & Son, Ltd., 23 Upper Brook Street, London W.1, England.
17. Serva Entwicklungslabor, Heidelberg, Römerstr. 118, Germany. U. S. Representative: Gallard-Schlesinger, Chemical Manufacturing Corp., 580 Mineola Ave., Carle Place, L. I., New York.
18. Shandon Scientific Co., 65 Pound Lane, London N.W.10, England. U. S. Representative: Colab Laboratories, Inc., Chicago Heights, Illinois.

The basic equipment designed by Stahl is used most widely. It consists, for the most part, of a carefully machined applicator and a plastic spreading board. By the use of this equipment, smooth layers, about 0.25 mm. in thickness, can be prepared on glass plates measuring 5 × 20 × 0.4 cm., 10 × 20 × 0.4 cm., 20 × 20 × 0.4 cm. and 40 × 20 × 0.4 cm. Square plates of the size 20 × 20 cm. are employed most frequently.

A technique for the preparation of microchromatoplates with Stahl's applicator has

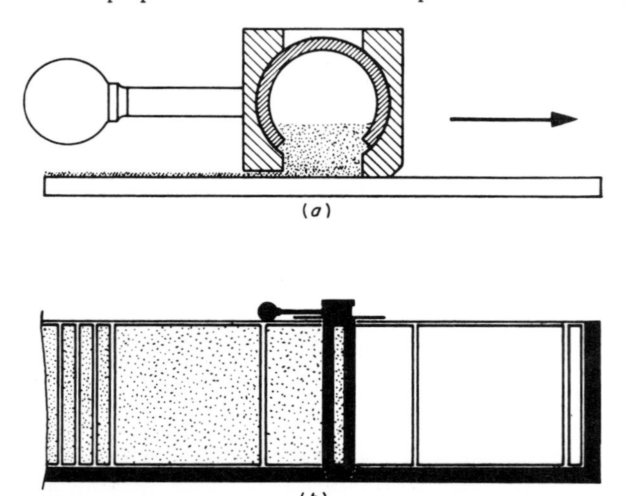

FIG. 39-1. Cross-cut of Stahl's Original Applicator, *a*; Applicator on the Spreading Board *b*.

been described.[8] It is possible to coat at one time 75 microscope slides, 76 × 26 × 1 mm., or 30 plates measuring 66 × 66 × 1 mm.

A more versatile applicator, Stahl's "Model S II," permits the preparation of layers 0.25 to 2 mm. thick. Relatively large amounts of sample can be fractionated on "thick" layers.

Figures 39-1, 39-2, and 39-3 show the design of Stahl's applicators, and demonstrate their use.

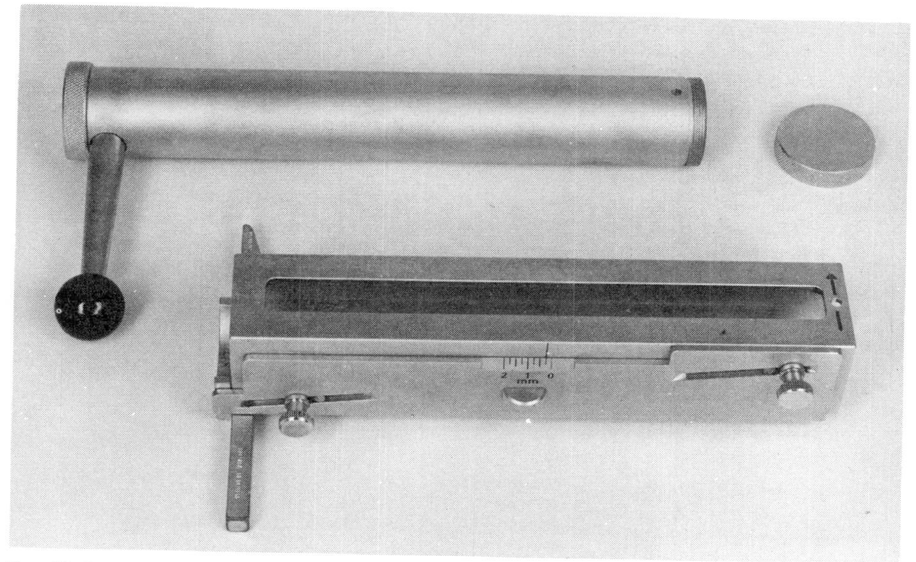

Fig. 39-2. Stahl's Applicator "Model SII," for the Preparation of Layers up to 2 mm. Thick.

Procedure for Coating Glass Plates with Stahl's Applicators.—The applicator designed by Stahl consists of three parts (Fig. 39-2). The slurry of coating material is held in a rotatable round metal cylinder which fits into the bore of a heavy metal block (Figs. 39-1*a* and 39-2). A screw cap closes the open cylinder and holds it in place. When the cylinder is rotated about its axis by 180°, the slurry flows out through an adjustable exit slit at the lower face of the block (Fig. 39-1).

A plastic "spreading board" with retaining rims along a short and a long side (Fig. 39-1*b*) is placed on a laboratory bench. The long edge faces the worker; the short rim is at his right. A glass plate, 5 × 20 cm., 5 plates, 20 × 20 cm., and another plate, 5 × 20 cm., all uniformly 0.4 cm. thick, are placed in a row on the spreading board. The plates must be free of greasy spots. Sliding of the plates can be prevented by sticking each of them down on the board with a drop of water. The empty applicator is moved across the row of plates, from left to right, to make sure that the plates are well aligned. Then, the applicator is filled with a slurry of the coating material and placed on the small plate at the left. The lever is turned 180° to the "open" position to permit the slurry to run out of the slit as the applicator is moved in a slow and steady motion across the row of glass plates on the board (Figs. 39-1*b* and 39-3). When the small plate at the right end has been reached, the lever is turned back again to prevent remaining

[8] Hofmann, A. F., Anal. Biochem., **3**, 145, 1962.

slurry from running out. The layers thus produced should be uniform in appearance in both reflected and transmitted light.

If adsorbents containing plaster of Paris are used, the entire operation, from the addition of water to the adsorbent until the spreading of the thin layers, must be finished in about 4 minutes before the slurry hardens.

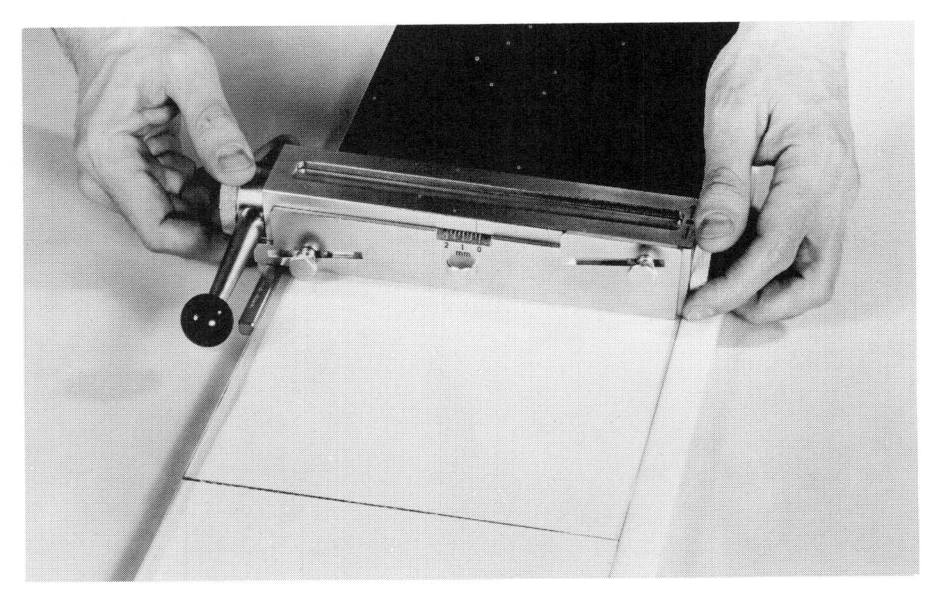

Fig. 39-3. Use of Stahl's Applicator "Model SII."

Simplified versions of the original Stahl applicator have become commercially available (Table 39-3). Automatic devices based on Stahl's apparatus are also on the market.

A spreader which permits coating of plates with layers of continuously changing composition has been devised by Stahl.[9] Chromatoplates coated with "gradient layers" are useful, *e.g.*, for comparing the chromatographic behavior of a sample on different adsorbents or mixtures of adsorbents, under otherwise identical conditions. The "GM-Applicator" of Stahl is shown in Fig. 39-4.

Procedure for Coating Glass Plates with Stahl's "GM-Applicator."—The GM-applicator (G = gradient, M = mixer) (Fig. 39-4) is similar in design to Stahl's Model SII. However, the rotatable open cylinder is divided into about 30 cells by a series of round discs, which are separated by spacers and mounted on a shaft. These small cells are filled with two coating materials, each at a different ratio. This is achieved in the following way: the lever of the cylinder is turned so that the top of the applicator is closed. A "divider box" which contains a diagonal partition is closely fitted on top of the applicator. Two slurries of different composition are filled, one in each of the two compartments. Both compartments should be filled evenly and to the same level. The partition of the divider box is carefully removed and the lever is turned to fill the cells in the cylinder with the two slurries, each in a different proportion. The contents of each of the cells are mixed by rotating the shaft in the cylinder for 30 seconds in

[9] Stahl, E., Angew. Chem., Intl. Ed., **3,** 784, 1964.

both directions by means of a cogwheel drive. The divider box is now removed, the exit slot of the applicator is closed and the cylinder is turned to the starting position. The mixing process is now repeated, as described above. The lever of the cylinder is turned until only a slit on top remains open. This position can easily be sensed when

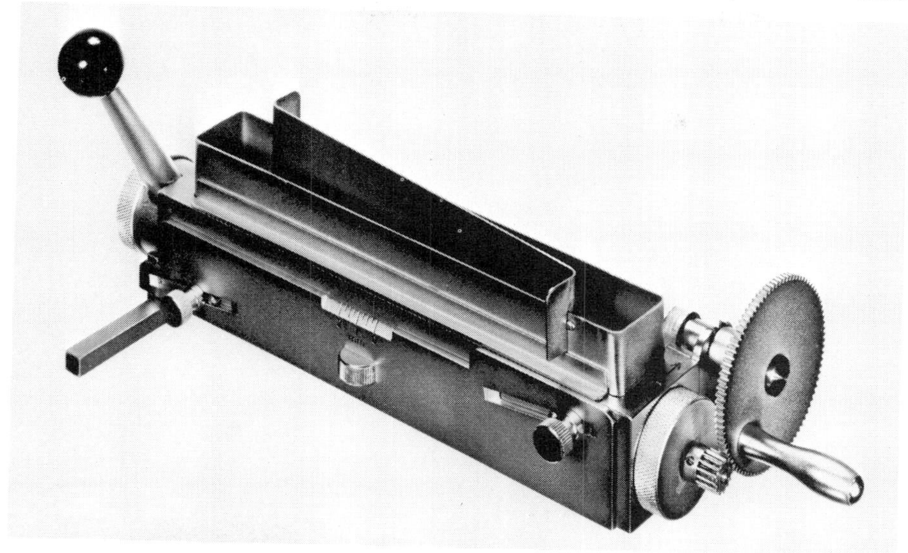

FIG. 39-4. "GM-Applicator" According to Stahl for the Preparation of Gradient Layers.

a built-in detent ball is reached. The exit slot is now raised to a level of 0.35 mm. and the applicator is moved across the row of plates.

Stahl gave three examples of pairs of coating slurries:

Kieselguhr-Silica Gel.

(a) 20 g. Kieselguhr G (Merck) is slurried with 45 ml. of water.

(b) 18 g. Silica Gel HF_{254} (Merck) is slurried with 45 ml. of water.

Alkaline Silica Gel-Acidic Silica Gel.

(a) 20 g. Silica Gel G. (Merck) is slurried with 45 ml. of 0.1 *N* potassium hydroxide solution.

(b) 20 g. Silica Gel G. (Merck) is slurried with 45 ml. of 0.1 *N* phosphoric acid solution.

Basic Alumina-Acidic Alumina.

(a) 35 g. aluminum oxide, basic (Woelm) and 3.5 g. plaster of Paris are slurried with 45 ml. of water.

(b) 35 g. aluminum oxide, acidic (Woelm) and 3.5 g. plaster of Paris are slurried with 45 ml. of water.

Pairs of coating materials used for the preparation of gradient layers must be of identical grain size.

Some applications of the comparatively new method of chromatography on gradient layers will be discussed later in the chapter.

An applicator designed by Mutter and Hofstetter[10] is shown in Fig. 39-5. It can be used for the preparation of chromatoplates of the sizes 10 × 20 cm. and 20 × 20 cm. by slowly passing a row of plates under a stationary reservoir or hopper containing a slurry of coating material.

Procedure for Coating Glass Plates with the Applicator of Mutter and Hofstetter.—The applicator (Fig. 39-5) consists of a base plate of metal. A chamber serving

FIG. 39-5. Applicator According to Mutter and Hofstetter.

as reservoir for the slurry to be applied is formed by two vertical side plates which are mounted on the base plate, and two gate plates which fit loosely into slots of the side plates. A glass plate is placed under this chamber, with the leading edge protruding beyond the exit gate. The entrance gate rests on the glass plate, whereas the lower edge of the exit gate is adjusted, by thumbscrews, to a level that determines the desired layer thickness. The chamber is filled with a slurry of coating material, and a second glass plate is used to push the first plate through the trough. The second plate is pushed by a third one, and so on.

Several spreaders similar to that of Mutter and Hofstetter have become available (Table 39-3). Motorized and mechanized models are being offered by several manufacturers.

Very simple and inexpensive spreaders have been used for the preparation of thin layers on glass plates, and several designs are commercially available (Table 39-3). Plexiglas applicators are recommendable for use in high school and laboratory courses.[11] Plastic spreaders of this type have distinct advantages over most metal applicators when slurries containing corrosive chemicals, such as silver nitrate, are employed.

Several authors have given detailed instruction for the building of inexpensive spreaders.[12,13,14]

COATING OF PLATES WITHOUT THE USE OF AN APPLICATOR

Simple procedures for coating standard-size plates and microscope slides by spreading, pouring, dipping, and spraying are described here.

[10] Mutter, K., and Hofstetter, J., unpublished material.
[11] Malins, D. C., and Wekell, J. C., J. Chem. Educ., **40,** 531, 1963.
[12] Wollish, E. G., Schmall, M., and Hawrylyshyn, M., Anal. Chem., **33,** 1138, 1961.
[13] Machata, G., Microchim. Acta, 709, 1960.
[14] Gamp, A., Studer, P., Linde, H., and Meyer, K., Experientia, **18,** 292, 1962.

Procedure for Coating Glass Plates by Spreading.[15]—One strip or several layers of strips of surgical adhesive tape, $\frac{1}{2}$ in. wide, are glued to two opposite edges of a row of plates and onto the support. A slurry of coating material is poured on the first plate and a thick glass rod is used to spread this slurry over the plates. The rod should be held in such a manner that the thumbs ride along the taped edges of the plates; it should not roll but glide on the surface of the tapes. As long as the slurry has not yet hardened, it is possible to draw a clean rod over the surface again to smooth out any imperfections in the layer. After the layers have been air-dried for about 10 minutes, the tape is carefully removed and the plates are processed in the usual way.

Procedure for Coating Glass Plates by Pouring.[16]—Silica gel without a binder is shaken in a closed flask with ethyl acetate, 1:3, w/v. The slurry is evenly distributed on a glass plate by slightly tipping the plate to and fro, without touching its edges. The chromatoplate can be used after having been air-dried for 15 minutes.

Procedure for Coating Microscope Slides by Dipping.[17]—Thirty-five g. of Silica Gel G and 100 ml. of chloroform-methanol, 2:1, v/v, are slurried by shaking in a stoppered bottle for several minutes. Two thoroughly cleaned microscope slides are then sandwiched together and dipped into the adsorbent suspension. After a few seconds, the slides are slowly withdrawn and allowed to drain by resting them with their lower edges upon the rim of the bottle. The two slides are separated as soon as the solvent is evaporated. Adsorbent adhering to the edges and inside surfaces of the soaked slides is scraped off, the slides are briefly exposed to steam, and dried for 1 to 3 minutes on a wire gauze which is kept about 1 cm. above the surface of an electric hot plate (<200°C.).

Procedure for Coating Glass Plates and Slides by Spraying.[18]—A slurry of 15 g. silica gel (325-mesh) in 35 ml. of water is sprayed onto glass plates with an ordinary laboratory spray gun using an air pressure of 1.0–1.2 p.s.i. Slurries of silica gel are also available in aerosol packages.[19] This coating procedure should only be applied in a well ventilated hood!

PRECOATED PLATES AND SHEETS

Several firms offer glass plates coated with adsorbents or other materials (Table 39-3). Plastic sheets and aluminum foil coated with silicic acid are also available.

The inherent advantage of thin-layer chromatography is that it employs granular rather than fibrous media, thereby minimizing lateral flow of the fractions. It should be borne in mind that supports for thin layers should be nonfibrous and impervious to the liquid phase: adsorbent-impregnated (cellulose) paper and glass fiber sheets do not yield separations as sharp as those afforded by thin layers of adsorbent on glass.

CHROMATOJARS AND ACCESSORY EQUIPMENT

Figure 39-6 shows a typical jar for developing chromatoplates. For chromatography in an atmosphere of an inert gas, this jar can be equipped with a lid having a gas inlet and outlet.[20] A different design of a jar for chromatography under controlled conditions has been described.[21] A jacketed jar[22] can be used, in connection with a ther-

[15] Lees, T. M., and DeMuria, P. J., J. Chromatog., **8**, 108, 1962.
[16] Hörhammer, L., Wagner, H., and Bittner, G., Deut. Apotheker Ztg., **14**, 41, 1962.
[17] Peifer, J. J., Microchim. Acta, 529, 1962.
[18] Bekersky, I., Anal. Chem., **35**, 261, 1963.
[19] Mann Research Laboratories, Inc., 136 Liberty St., New York 6, N. Y.
[20] C. Desaga, G. m. b. H., Heidelberg, Hauptstr. 60, Germany. U. S. representative: C. A. Brinkmann and Co., Inc., Cantiague Rd., Westbury, L. I., N. Y. Representative in England: Camlab (Glass), Ltd., Milton Road, Cambridge.
[21] Geiss, F., Schlitt, H., Ritter, F. J., and Weimar, W. M., J. Chromatog., **12**, 469, 1963.
[22] Stahl, E., Angew. Chem., Intl. Ed., **3**, 784, 1964.

mostat, for chromatography at constant temperatures. A commercial model, the "Kryobox," [23] is depicted in Fig. 39-7.

Fig. 39-6. A Typical Jar for Developing Chromatoplates.

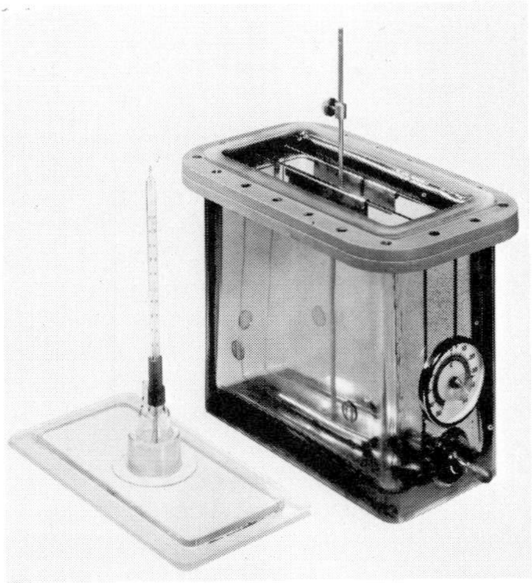

Fig. 39-7. "Kryobox" for Thin-layer Chromatography at Low Temperatures.

Two types of "sandwich chambers" are shown in Figs. 39-8 and 39-9. The "S-chamber" according to Stahl (Fig. 39-8) consists of a glass plate, 20 × 20 cm. or 40 × 20 cm. which is framed along three edges with thin glass strips. This plate is used to cover a chromatoplate of the same size. The narrow chamber thus formed is held together by two clamps. The chromatoplate is developed by placing the glass plates, with the open side down, in a horizontal stainless steel tube which contains 15 to 20 ml. of developing solvent (for a 20 × 20 mm. plate). Figure 39-8 shows a commercial model[24] of the S-chamber. A simplified version is also being offered.[25]

The "BN-chamber," according to Brenner and Niederwieser,[26] permits developing a chromatoplate at different temperatures and in an inert atmosphere. This can be done either continuously, in an ascending, descending, or horizontal manner. A commercial model of the BN-chamber is shown in Fig. 39-9.

Devices for developing chromatoplates with a solvent of continuously changing composition (gradient elution) have been described by several authors.[27,28]

Microchromatoplates are conveniently developed in baby food jars or in glass beakers covered with aluminum foil.

[23] C. Desaga, G.m.b.H., Heidelberg, Hauptstr. 60, Germany. U. S. representative: C. A. Brinkmann and Co., Inc., Cantiague Rd., Westbury, L. I., N. Y. Representative in England: Camlab (Glass), Ltd., Milton Road, Cambridge.

[24] C. Desaga, G.m.b.H. (same as 23).

[25] Camag A. G., Muttenz B. L., Homburger Str. 24, Switzerland. U. S. representatives: Microchemical Specialties Co., 1825 Eastshore Hwy., Berkeley 10, Calif., A. H. Thomas Co., Vine St. at Third, Philadelphia 5, Pa. Representative in England: Griffin & George, Ltd., Chromatography Division, Ealing Road, Alperton, Middlesex.

[26] Brenner, M., and Niederwieser, A., Experientia, **15,** 237, 1961.

[27] Wieland, Th., Lüben, G., and Determann, H., Experientia, **18,** 430, 1962.

[28] Rybicka, S. M., Chem. and Ind. (London), 308, 1962.

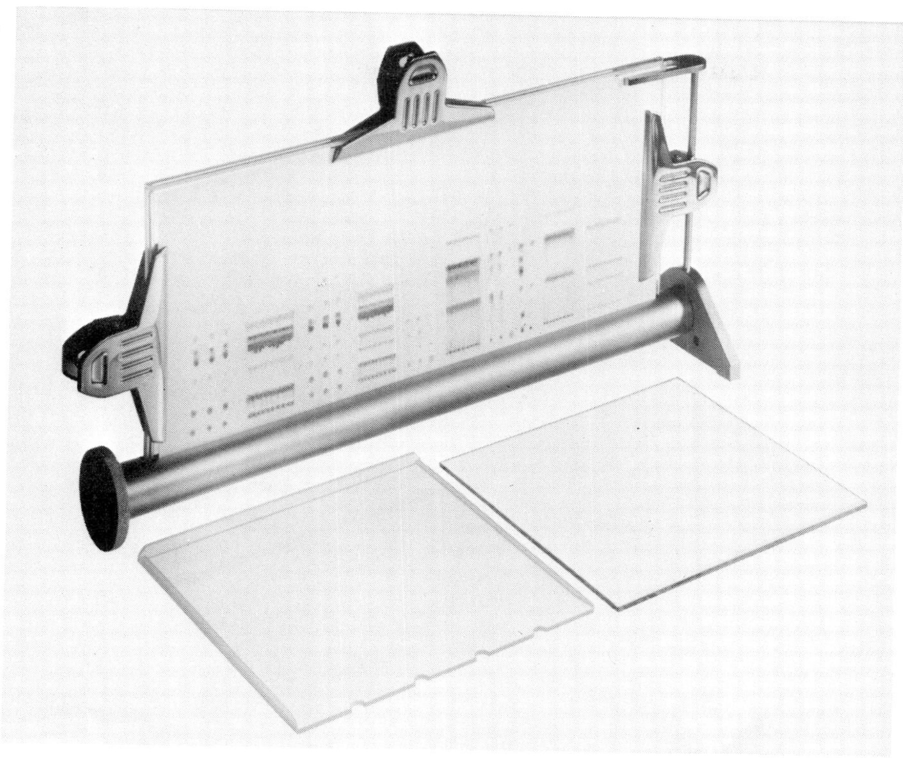

FIG. 39-8. S-Chamber for Developing One Plate, 40 × 20 cm.

APPLICATION OF THE SAMPLE AND DEVELOPMENT OF THE PLATE

Application of Sample.—In analytical thin-layer chromatography, 0.1–1 percent solutions of the samples are applied to the plates with glass capillaries, micropipets,[29] or microsyringes.[30] The solutions are applied as single spots in a row along one side of the plate, about 2 cm. from the edge. The spots should not spread more than 0.5 cm. during application. This can be achieved by spotting the solutions in small portions in a stream of nitrogen. Between 10 and 20 samples can be chromatographed side-by-side on a plate measuring 20 × 20 cm.

It is advantageous to chromatograph a sample to be analyzed in different amounts, *e.g.*, 1, 5, 10, and 50 μg. on one plate. The main components are best recognized in the small sample, whereas minor constituents may become apparent in the large sample.

The maximum amount of sample that can be applied in one spot depends on the thickness of the layer and on the principle of chromatography employed. If adsorbent

[29] Micropipets can be purchased from companies distributing equipment for chromatography (see Table 39-3).

[30] Hamilton Company, Inc., P. O. Box 307, Whittier, Calif. Most suppliers of chromatography equipment carry Hamilton syringes.

layers, 0.25 mm. thick, are used, 50–500 μg. of mixtures of lipophilic substances can be fractionated. In partition and reversed-phase partition chromatography, however, the amount of sample should be kept between 1 and 50 μg. per spot.

Transparent templates that can be used to cover and protect the layer during spotting of sample solutions are available from several companies.[31,32,33]

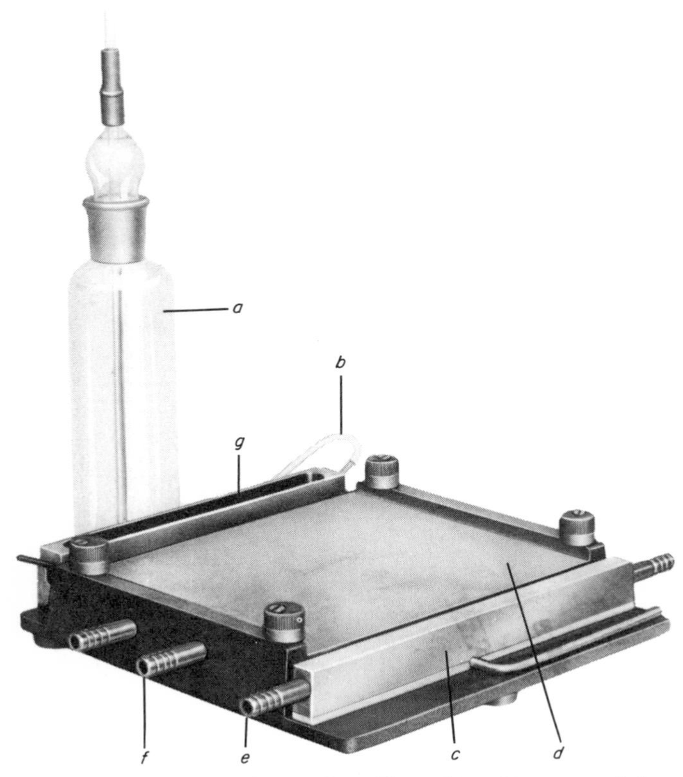

Fig. 39-9. BN-Chamber for Developing One Plate, 20 × 20 cm.: *a*, Solvent Reservoir; *b*, Solvent Supply Tube; *c*, Heating Block; *d*, Cooling Block; *e*, Heating Connections; *f*, Cold Water Connections; *g*, Solvent Trough.

A flat plastic box that permits the application of sensitive samples in an inert atmosphere and under a cover that absorbs UV. light is available commercially.[34]

[31] Camag A. G., Muttenz B. L., Homburger Str. 24, Switzerland. U. S. representatives: Microchemical Specialties Co., 1825 Eastshore Hwy., Berkeley 10, Calif., A. H. Thomas Co., Vine St. at Third, Philadelphia 5, Pa. Representative in England: Griffin & George, Ltd., Chromatography Division, Ealing Road, Alperton, Middlesex.

[32] C. Desaga, G. m. b. H., Heidelberg, Hauptstr. 60, Germany. U. S. representative: C. A. Brinkmann and Co., Inc., Cantiague Rd., Westbury, L. I., N. Y. Representative in England: Camlab (Glass), Ltd., Milton Road, Cambridge.

[33] Research Specialties Co., 200 S. Garrard Blvd., Richmond, Calif.

[34] C. Desaga, G. m. b. H., Heidelberg, Hauptstr. 60, Germany. U. S. representative: C. A. Brinkmann and Co., Inc., Cantiague Rd., Westbury, L. I., N. Y. Representative in England: Camlab (Glass), Ltd., Milton Road, Cambridge.

Special precision microsyringes have to be employed for quantitative analysis (see p. 770). The spotting techniques used in preparative thin-layer chromatography are described below (see p. 775).

Before developing a chromatoplate, coating material adhering to the edges should be scraped off to assure an even rate of migration of the solvent over the entire width of the layer. Thin-layer chromatograms usually are developed at room temperature (or 20°C.) by placing them on edge in a jar containing a 0.5- to 1-cm. layer of solvent. After covering the jar with an air-tight lid, the developing solvent travels up the length of the plate. Several chromatoplates may be simultaneously developed in one jar. Satisfactory separations often are obtained after the solvent has traveled about 10 cm.

The insides of the jars may be lined with filter paper which acts as a wick and thus saturates the atmosphere in the jars with solvent vapors. Chromatography in a "saturated atmosphere" yields straight solvent fronts. The developing time is shortened by about one-third and the Rf are appreciably less than in unlined tanks. However, the separations achieved usually are not as sharp as those obtained in plain jars.

Typical chromatojars are shown in Figs. 39-6 and 39-7. Both the S-chamber (Fig. 39-8) and the BN-chamber (Fig. 39-9) provide a saturated atmosphere without a lining of filter paper.

Chromatography at temperatures above or below room temperature can yield improved separations.[35,36] The BN-chamber is quite suitable for chromatographing at "high" temperatures, whereas the "Kryobox" (Fig. 39-7) can be used at temperatures from −50 to +50°C.

Development of Plate.—Chromatoplates usually are developed once, with a single solvent, by either horizontal, ascending, or descending elution.

Horizontal Development.—Horizontal development can be employed with adhering thin layers, it is mandatory when working with loose layers. Radial development, *i.e.*, circular thin-layer chromatography, is also done on horizontal chromatoplates. The sample is placed in the center of the plate and developed either by slowly dripping solvent onto it from a pipet or by supplying solvent from a reservoir through a wick.

Vertical Development.—Vertical development, usually ascending, is practiced most widely. In the majority of applications, the plate is developed once, but more discrete separations can be effected by the following modifications:

Multiple Development.—Multiple development is developing repeatedly with the same solvent and in the same direction.

Stepwise Development.—Stepwise development is developing consecutively and in the same direction, with two different solvents. One of the solvents is run to a height of 15–18 cm. and the other to 10–12 cm. This method may be desirable if the mixture to be separated contains groups of compounds that have widely different properties.

Gradient Elution.—The chromatoplate is lowered into a jar containing a solvent, and then a second, usually, more polar solvent enters the chamber by means of a buret. The eluent is continually stirred and, as chromatography progresses, its polarity is slowly modified by the incoming solvent. This technique is particularly useful for fractionating compounds of widely different properties.[37]

Continuous Development.—Continuous development is usually done by forcing the solvent to run over the edge of the chromatoplate where it can be collected instead of being left to evaporate.[38] This method often is conducted by descending techniques, but it can also be applied in, for example, the BN-chamber. Continuous development

[35] Malins, D. C., and Mangold, H. K., J. Am. Oil Chemists' Soc., **37,** 576, 1960.
[36] Randerath, K., and Weimann, G., Biochim. Biophys. Acta, **76,** 129, 1963.
[37] Wieland, Th., Lüben, G., and Determann, H., Experientia, **18,** 430, 1962.
[38] Bennett, R. D., and Heftmann, E., J. Chromatog., **12,** 245, 1963.

combines some features of column chromatography with those of thin-layer chromatography. Separated compounds can be isolated by collecting the elute from the end of the plate.

Two-dimensional Development.—Square chromatoplates may be developed in two dimensions. A sample is spotted in a corner of the plate and the plate is developed, consecutively, in two directions, either with the same solvent, or with two different solvents. Particularly good separations are achieved, if two different solvents are used.

Chromatography on Discontinuous Layers.—Two different principles of chromatography may be employed on a single plate. For example, a mixture of compounds is spotted in a corner of a square plate coated with an adsorbent layer. After chromatography, the unused major portion of the layer is impregnated with silicone or paraffin oil, and the fractions obtained by adsorption chromatography are resolved further by reversed-phase partition chromatography in the second dimension.[39]

Chromatography on Gradient Layers.—Gradient layers plates can be utilized in three directions, each resulting in a characteristic separation. This is evident from Fig. 39-10 with the example of a gradient layer made from an active and an inactive adsorbent. With the use of gradient layers (*a* in Fig. 39-10), it is possible to determine

FIG. 39-10. The Three Possibilities of Applying Gradient Layers.

the optimum proportion of two different coating materials or an additive, such as an acid, base or salt. The use of a gradient in the direction of development (*b* and *c* in Fig. 39-10) often affords separations of mixtures that cannot be resolved on uniform layers.

Chromatography in Shaped Areas.—Thin layers can be divided into various shaped areas, as shown in Fig. 39-11. During development, the solvent is forced to expand into wider areas. As a result, the fractions appear as narrow bands, and discrete separations can be effected between compounds having almost identical migration rates. Furthermore, minor constituents in mixtures can be more easily fractionated from large amounts of other substances.

The SRS-Technique (Separation-Reaction-Separation).[40]—Two-dimensional thin-layer chromatography can be used for studying chemical reactions on the plate. The sample is first fractionated in one dimension and then the resolved fractions are transformed by exposure to UV. light and/or oxygen or by reaction with a reagent solution. The unchanged portions of the various fractions and the reaction products are chromatographed in the second dimension. An example of the application of this method is shown in Fig. 39-12.

[39] Kaufmann, H. P., and Makus, Z., Fette, Seifen, Anstrichmittel, **62,** 1014, 1960.
[40] Stahl, E., Arch. Pharm., **293,** 531, 1960.

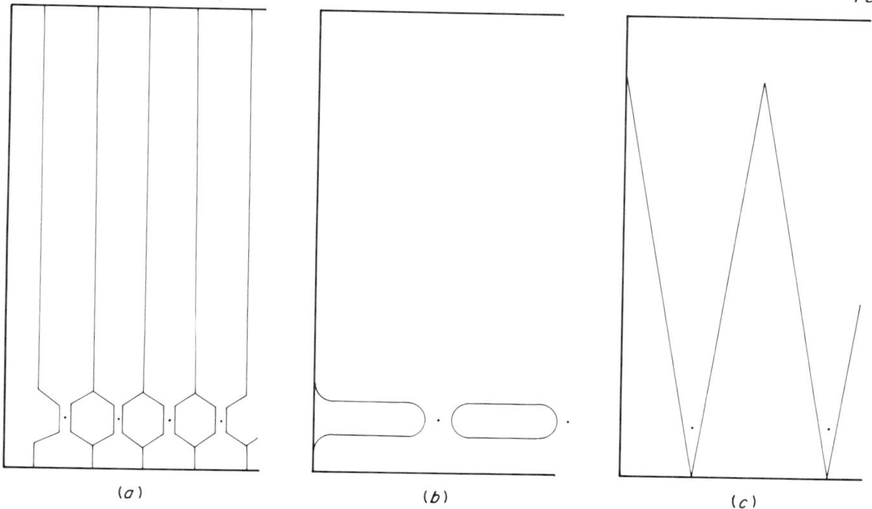

FIG. 39-11. Thin-layer Chromatography in Shaped Areas.

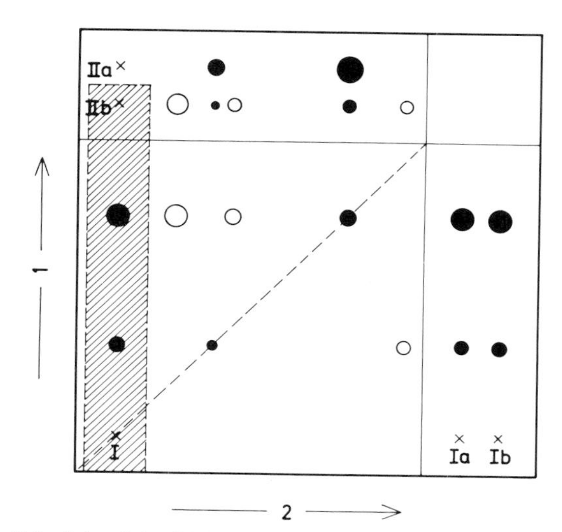

FIG. 39-12. The Principle of the SRS Technique: Fractions Resolved by Chromatography in One Direction are Reacted (Shaded Area) Before Development with the Same Solvent Is Continued in the Second Direction. The various fractions are identified by comparison with standards which are run along the edges of the plate (Ia and Ib, in the first direction, IIa and IIb in the second direction).

COATING MATERIALS AND SOLVENTS; APPLICATIONS

A survey of the principles of chromatography is presented in Table 39-2. This synopsis should aid in selecting the principle of chromatography which is particularly suitable for the resolution of a particular mixture, and it should facilitate choosing suitable coating materials and solvents. The information contained in Table 39-2 is presented more extensively in the following paragraphs.

Several representative examples of thin-layer chromatography are described here. For a more profound study of specialized applications, Thin-Layer Chromatography, edited by Stahl, should be consulted.

Procedures employing thin-layer chromatography which have been described in other chapters of Standard Methods of Chemical Analysis are:

1. Chapter 45, Volume III, Amino Acids.
2. Chapter 47, Volume III, Instrumental Methods in Clinical Medicine.
   a. Amino acids
   b. Barbiturates
   c. Serum lipids
3. Chapter 56, Volume III, Pesticide Residue Analysis.
   a. Chlorinated pesticides
   b. Organophosphate pesticides
4. Chapter 58, Volume III, Plastics.
   a. Separation of additives in polymers

ADSORPTION-TLC

Chromatography on adsorbents such as silica gel and alumina is used primarily for the fractionation of mixtures of rather nonpolar substances into classes of compounds that migrate at different rates by virtue of their respective polarities, *i.e.*, according to type(s) and number(s) of functional group(s) per molecule. Hydrocarbons, for example, may be separated as a class, from other classes of compounds, such as alcohols or aldehydes or acids. In neutral solvents, the adsorption affinity of various classes of compounds increases in the following sequence: hydrocarbons $<$ ethers $<$ nitro-compounds $<$ tert. amines $<$ esters $<$ prim. amines $<$ alcohols $<$ amines $<$ carboxylic acids.[41] Subfractionations within classes occur only when large differences in chain lengths and degree of unsaturation exist: short-chain compounds of a class are more strongly adsorbed than the corresponding long-chain compounds. Similarly, the highly unsaturated constituents of a class are more strongly adsorbed than are the saturated members, and compounds containing *trans* double bonds are more strongly adsorbed than are their *cis*-isomers. As a general rule, two or more functional groups in a molecule have an additive effect on the rate of migration, but steric effects between functional groups, *e.g.*, the formation of hydrogen-bonding, can be also highly influential in determining the rate of migration of a compound.

Thin-layer adsorption chromatography is particularly useful for the fractionation and analysis of petroleum products,[42] fats and waxes,[43] essential oils,[44] carotenoids,[45] fat-soluble vitamins,[46] some groups of steroids,[47] and certain alkaloids,[48] fat-soluble

[41] Brockmann, H., and Volpers, F., Chem. Ber., **82,** 95, 1949.
[42] Kucharczyk, N., Fohl, J., and Vymetal, J., J. Chromatog., **11,** 55, 1963.
[43] Mangold, H. K., J. Am. Oil Chemists' Soc., **41,** 762, 1964.
[44] Schantz, M. V., Farmaseuttinen Aikakauslehti, **2,** 52, 1962.
[45] Stahl, E., Bolliger, H. R., and Lehnert, L., in 7. Symposium der Deutschen Gesellschaft für Ernährung, Steinkopff Verlag, Darmstadt, 1963.
[46] Strohecker, R., and Henning, H. M., Vitamin-Bestimmungen, Erprobte Methoden, Verlag Chemie G. m. b. H., Weinheim, Germany, 1965.
[47] Neher, R., Steroid Chromatography, Elsevier Publishing Co., Amsterdam, London, New York, 1964.
[48] Waldi, D., Schnackerz, K., and Munter, F., J. Chromatog., **6,** 61, 1961.

dyes,[49] and insecticides.[50] Highly polar and water-soluble compounds may be separated by this type of chromatography, as less polar derivatives. For example, sugars may be chromatographed as acetyl derivatives,[51] and mixtures of other polyhydroxy compounds may be resolved after nitration.[52]

Adsorbents.—Materials used for thin-layer chromatography may contain 1–5 percent starch or 5–15 percent plaster of Paris (calcium sulfate) as a binder. Preparations without binding agents must be used if these additives react with compounds to be separated. Silica gel is used most frequently as an adsorbent.

A number of common adsorbents available for thin-layer chromatography are listed in Table 39-4; the addresses of manufacturers and suppliers are given.

TABLE 39-4. COATING MATERIALS FOR ADSORPTION-TLC

Silicic acid (silica gel)	1, 2, 3, 4[a]
Aluminum oxide (alumina)	1, 2, 3, 4
Kieselguhr (diatomaceous earth)	3, 4
Hydroxyl apatite	1

[a] Numbers refer to the following list of suppliers:
1. Bio-Rad Laboratories, 32nd and Griffin Avenue, Richmond, California.
2. Fluka, A. G., Buchs, S. G., Switzerland. U. S. Representative: International Chem. and Nuclear Corp., 13332 Torch Street, City of Industry, California.
3. E. Merck, A. G., Chemische Fabrik, Darmstadt, Germany. U. S. Representative: C. A. Brinkmann and Co., Inc., Cantiague Rd., Westbury, L. I., New York. Representative in England: Anderman & Co., Ltd., Battlebridge House, 87–95 Tooley Street, London S.E.1.
4. Research Specialties Co., 200 South Garrard Blvd., Richmond, California.

Layers 0.25 mm. thick are usually prepared by spreading an aqueous slurry of adsorbent with a commercial applicator (Table 39-3) on glass plates. Such a slurry may be made by thoroughly mixing in a mortar, 25 g. of Silica Gel G (Merck), which is the most commonly used adsorbent, with 50 ml. of distilled water. For the preparation of "thick" layers (1–2 mm.), Silica Gel G should be slurried with water in a ratio of 25:40, w/v. Moreover, silica gel preparations from different manufacturers, and adsorbents other than silica gel require more or less water. The instructions of the suppliers should be followed. After allowing them to air dry, adsorbent layers are activated by heating to 110°C. for 2 hours.

Solvents.—A typical solvent mixture[53] for adsorption thin-layer chromatography is given in Table 39-5. Also listed is a series of pure solvents, which are arranged in order of increasing eluting power.

By the use of the appropriate solvents, mixtures containing compounds of low adsorption affinity, *e.g.*, hydrocarbons and ethers, and high adsorption affinity, *e.g.*, alcohols and amides, may be readily separated into classes.

An Application of Adsorption-TLC.—Figure 39-13 shows, as an example of adsorption thin-layer chromatography, the fractionation of human tissue lipids on Silica Gel G.[54]

[49] Montag, A., Z. Lebensm. Untersuch.-Forsch., **116,** 413, 1962.
[50] Bäumler, J., and Rippstein, S., Helv. Chim. Acta, **44,** 1162, 1961.
[51] Tate, M. E., and Bishop, C. T., Can. J. Chem., **40,** 1043, 1962.
[52] Wekell, J. C., Houle, C. R., and Malins, D. C., J. Chromatog., **14,** 529, 1964.
[53] Mangold, H. K., and Malins, D. C., J. Am. Oil Chemists' Soc., **37,** 383, 1960.
[54] Tuna, N., and Mangold, H. K., in Evolution of The Atherosclerotic Plague, R. J. Jones, Ed., The University of Chicago Press, Chicago, 1963, p. 85.

TABLE 39-5. SOLVENTS FOR ADSORPTION-TLC

n-Hexane-Diethyl ether-Acetic acid, 90:10:1, v/v/v
n-Hexane*
Benzene*
Chloroform (96%)*
Ethyl acetate*

* Any two of these solvents may be mixed to yield developing systems of intermediate eluting power. In any case, 1–5% acetic acid or 1–5% diethylamine should be added if free acids or free bases, respectively, are to be chromatographed.

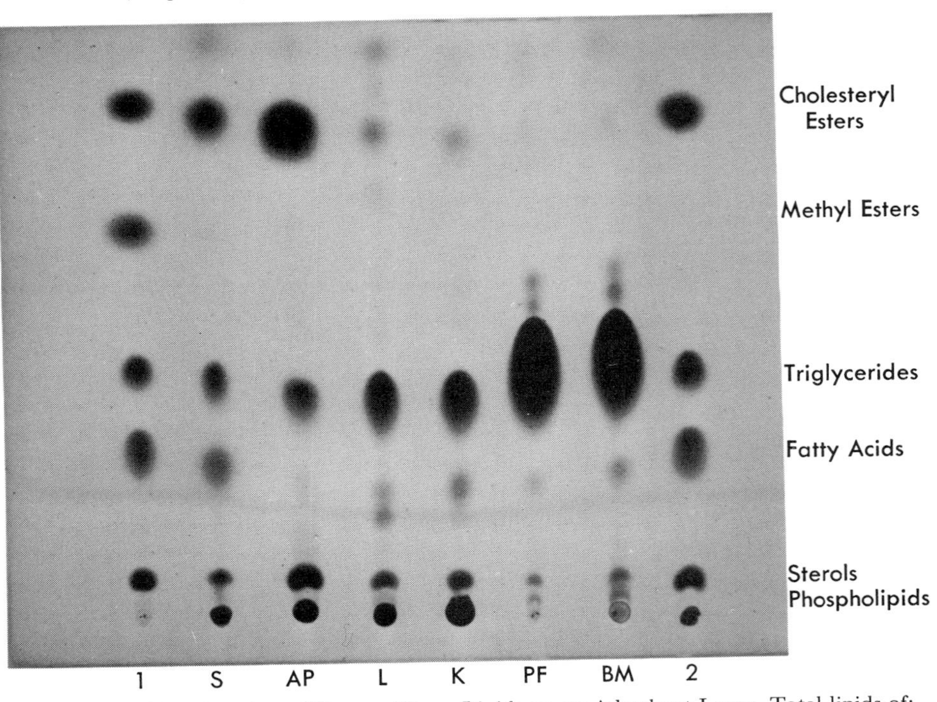

FIG. 39-13. Fractionation of Human Tissue Lipids on an Adsorbent Layer. Total lipids of: *S*, serum; *A.P.*, aortic plaque; *L*, liver; *K*, kidney; *P.F.*, perinephric fat; *B.M.*, bone marrow. Standard mixtures of: 1, cholesterol, oleic acid, triolein, methyl oleate, cholesteryl oleate; 2, lecithin, cholesterol, oleic acid, triolein, cholesteryl oleate. Adsorbent: silica gel G. Solvent: petroleum hydrocarbon:diethyl ether:acetic acid, 90:10:1, v/v/v. Indicator: charring after spraying with chromic sulfuric acid solution.

TLC ON ADSORBENTS CONTAINING SILVER NITRATE

Unsaturated compounds that differ in configuration, or in the degree of unsaturation can be fractionated by chromatography on adsorbents impregnated with silver nitrate.[55,56] Separations of mixtures are based upon the formation of π complexes

[55] Barrett, C. B., Dallas, M. S. J., and Padley, F. B., Chem. and Ind. (London), 1050, 1962.

[56] Morris, L. J., Chem. and Ind. (London) 1238, 1962.

between the double bond of the unsaturated constituents and the silver salt. The equilibrium of this reaction is reached in the course of chromatography. The complexes of unsaturated compounds migrate at a slower rate than do saturated components. Complexes derived from *cis*-unsaturated compounds are more stable than those derived from their *trans*-isomers and, therefore, pairs of *cis-trans*-isomers of unsaturated substances can be separated by adsorption chromatography on thin layers of silver nitrate-impregnated adsorbents.

This type of thin-layer chromatography is suitable for the fractionation of petroleum hydrocarbons, fats and waxes, essential oils, carotenoids, fat-soluble vitamins, and steroids. A review on the rather new technique has appeared recently.[57]

Coating Material.—Any of the adsorbents listed in Table 39-4 should be suitable. However, Silica Gel G (Merck) has so far been used almost exclusively.

Chromatoplates are usually prepared from a slurry of 23.75 g. Silica Gel G with 50 ml. of water in which is dissolved 1.25 g. of silver nitrate.[57] The use of a plastic applicator is recommended because metal applicators corrode after prolonged use with slurries containing silver nitrate. The coated plates are dried and activated at 110°C. for 2 hours.

Adsorbent layers can be expediently impregnated by placing freshly coated and briefly air dried chromatoplates on edge in an aqueous silver nitrate solution which is allowed to ascend the height of the plates.[58]

Solvents.—Chloroform is often used,[57] but all solvents and solvent mixtures listed in Table 39-5 can be used. As a rule, the more unsaturated the sample is, the more polar the solvent should be.

An Application of Adsorption TLC on Silica Gel Containing Silver Nitrate.—The fractionation of cashew nut shell liquid is shown in Fig. 39-14 as an example of thin-layer chromatography on silica gel impregnated with silver nitrate.

ION-EXCHANGE-TLC

The rate of migration of a compound in an ion-exchange system is determined by the total charge of the ionized groups per molecule. Consequently, ion-exchange chromatography can be used profitably for the separation of ionic from nonionic compounds, and also for the fractionation of the former species according to types and numbers of ionizable groups per molecule. The degree to which subfractionation occurs in the separation of a class having the same type and number of ionic groups depends upon the pH and the ionic strength of the developing solvent as well as the adsorptive properties of the ion-exchange material.

Ion-exchange-TLC can be employed for the separation of short-chain carboxylic acids,[58] sugar phosphates,[59] amino acids,[60] nucleotides,[61] and detergents.[62] It is in the resolution of such substances that this method has advantages over other types of chromatography. Neutral compounds may be fractionated by ion-exchange-TLC as their ionic derivatives. Borate complexes of sugars, for example, are easily resolved by this technique.

Ion-Exchange Material.—Preparations employed in thin-layer chromatography usually are cellulose derivatives, such as DEAE cellulose and ECTEOLA cellulose; polyethyleneimine (PEI) cellulose and polyphosphate cellulose are used most widely.

[57] Morris, L. J., in New Biochemical Separations, A. T. James and L. J. Morris, Ed., D. Van Nostrand Company, Ltd., London, Princeton, 1964, p. 295.
[58] Cubero, J. M., and Mangold, H. K , Microchem, J., **9,** 227, 1965.
[59] Dietrich, C. P., Dietrich, S. M. C., and Pontis, H. G., J. Chromatog., **15,** 277, 1964.
[60] de la Llosa, P., Tertrin, C., and Jutisz, M., J. Chromatog., **14,** 136, 1964.
[61] Randerath, K., Angew. Chem., Intl. Ed., **1,** 553, 1962.
[62] Mangold, H. K., unpublished material.

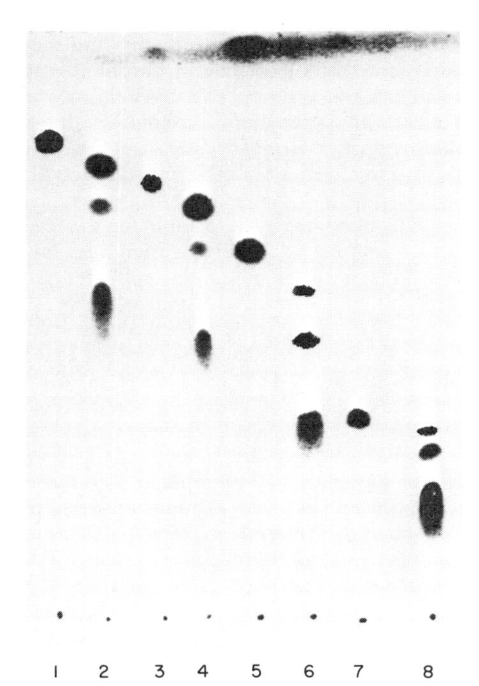

Fig. 39-14. Fractionation of Cashew Nut Shell Liquid on an Adsorbent Layer Impregnated with Silver Nitrate. Samples: 1, hydrogenated anacardic acid; 2, anacardic acid; 3, hydrogenated cardanol; 4, cardanol; 5, hydrogenated alkyl-substituted phenol; 7, hydrogenated cardol; 8, cardol. Adsorbent: Silica Gel G containing 5% (w/w) of silver nitrate. Solvent: diethyl ether:petroleum hydrocarbon:formic acid, 30:70:1, v/v/v. Indicator: charring after spraying with 50% aqueous sulfuric acid solution.

A list of commercially available ion-exchangers for thin-layer chromatography is given in Table 39-6, together with the addresses of the manufacturers and suppliers.

Layers, 0.5 mm. in thickness, of PEI cellulose are made with a commercial spreader (in Table 39-3) from a suspension which has been prepared by homogenizing 30 g. of

Table 39-6. Coating Materials for Ion-Exchange-TLC

Polyethyleneimine (PEI) cellulose	4[a]
Cellulose phosphate	2, 3
DEAE cellulose	1, 2, 3, 4
ECTEOLA cellulose	1, 2, 3, 4

[a] Numbers refer to the following list of suppliers:

1. Bio-Rad Laboratories, 32nd and Griffin Avenue, Richmond, California.
2. Macherey, Nagel & Co., Düren-Rhld., Germany. U. S. Representative: C. A. Brinkmann and Co., Inc., Cantiague Rd., Westbury, L. I., New York. Representative in England: Camlab (Glass), Ltd., Milton Road, Cambridge.
3. Research Specialties Co., 200 S. Garrard Blvd., Richmond, California.
4. Serva Entwicklungslabor, Heidelberg, Römerstr. 118, Germany. U. S. Representative: Gallard-Schlesinger, Chemical Manufacturing Corp., 580 Mineola Ave., Carle Place, L. I., New York.

TABLE 39-7. SOLVENTS FOR ION-EXCHANGE-TLC

Solvent
Aqueous hydrochloric acid solution, 0.001–1 *N*
Aqueous sodium hydroxide solution, 0.001–1 *N*
Aqueous sodium chloride solution, 0.001–1 *N*
Aqueous lithium chloride solution,* 0.001–1 *N*

* This solvent is particularly useful in two-dimensional TLC, as lithium chloride can be washed of the dry layer with abs. methanol before the plate is developed, with another solvent, in the second dimension.

cellulose powder MN 300 (Macherey, Nagel & Co.) in an electric mixer, for 30 sec., with 200 ml. of a dialized 1 percent polyethyleneimine hydrochloride solution.[63] The layers are used air-dried.

Commercial preparations of ion-exchangers differ widely in their properties, and separations achieved on such material often are difficult to reproduce.

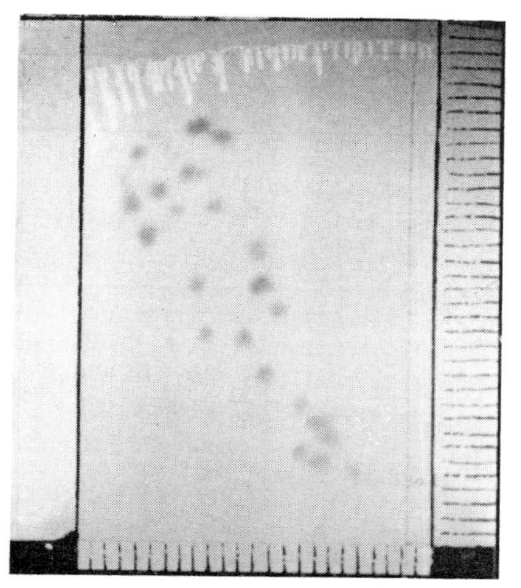

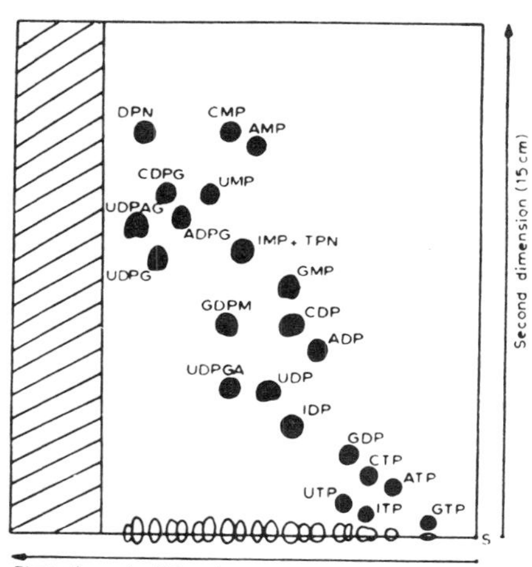

FIG. 39-15. Fractionation of a Mixture of Nucleotides on an Ion-exchange Layer. Sample: synthetic mixture of 23 ribo-nucleotides. Ion-exchanger: PEI-Cellulose (0.5 mm.). Solvents: 1st direction: 0.2 *M* lithium chloride solution (2 min.); 1.0 *M* lithium chloride solution (6 min.); 1.6 *M* lithium chloride solution ($>$1 hr.). These three solvents are run stepwise, without intermittent drying. After the third development, lithium chloride is removed by laying the plate in a flat dish filled with anhydrous methanol. After drying, the chromatoplate is developed in the second dimension. 2nd direction: 0.5 *M* formic acid-sodium formate buffer, pH 3.4, (0.5 min.); 2.0 *M* formic acid-sodium formate buffer, pH 3.4, (2 min.); 4.0 *M* formic acid-sodium formate buffer, pH 3.4 (1 hr.). Indicator: photographed in UV. light. *a* shows the actual chromatogram. The various nucleotides are identified in *b*.

Solvents.—In ion-exchange chromatography, aqueous solutions of acids, bases, and salts are used as developing solvents. A number of solvents are described in Table 39-7.

An Application of Ion-Exchange-TLC.—Figure 39-15 shows the fractionation of a mixture of nucleotides on a layer of PEI cellulose.[64]

[63] Randerath, K., Biochim. Biophys. Acta, **61,** 852, 1962.
[64] Randerath, E., and Randerath, K., J. Chromatog., **16,** 126, 1964.

PARTITION-TLC

In normal partition chromatography, the stationary phase is a polar liquid that is held by a solid support, such as cellulose or a weak adsorbent. Separation of a mixture is effected by virtue of differences in the solubilities of its components in the developing solvent and the stationary liquid phase, which may be water, formamide, polyethylene glycol, or a polyester. Normal partition chromatography, unlike adsorption chromatography, is useful for the fractionation of hydrophilic substances. Mixtures of classes of hydrophilic compounds that differ considerably in their solubilities in the two immiscible liquid phases may be separated according to class by this method. Partition chromatography, however, is more profitably applied to the resolution of members of homologous series.

Partition-TLC can be utilized for fractionating mixtures of carbohydrates,[65] glycosides,[66] water-soluble vitamins,[67] sterols,[68] alkaloids,[69] and dyes;[70] amino acids,[71] peptides,[72] and detergents[73] may be resolved as well.

Stationary Phases.—Cellulose powder and "wet" (air-dried) adsorbents are usually used as coating materials (Table 39-8). For the resolution of sterols and of weakly polar alkaloids, the layers are impregnated with formamide or polyethylene glycol.

TABLE 39-8. COATING MATERIALS FOR PARTITION-TLC

Cellulose	1, 2, 3, 4[a]
Kieselguhr (diatomaceous earth)[b]	
Hydroxyl apatite[b]	
Silicic acid (silica gel)[b]	

[a] Numbers refer to the following list of suppliers:
1. Machercy, Nagel & Co., Düren-Rhld., Germany. U. S. Representative: C. A. Brinkmann and Co., Inc., Cantiague Rd., Westbury, L. I., New York. Representative in England: Camlab (Glass), Ltd., Milton Road, Cambridge.
2. Research Specialties Co., 200 S. Garrard Blvd., Richmond, California.
3. H. Reeve Angel & Co., Ltd., 9 Bridewell Place, London E.C.4, England. U. S. Representative: Scientifica, P. O. Box 1084, Clifton, New Jersey.
4. C. Schleicher & Schüll, Dassel, Krs. Einbeck, Germany. U. S. Representative: C. Schleicher & Schuell Co., 543 Washington Street, Keene, New Hampshire.

[b] For commercial suppliers see Table 39-4.

Layers of cellulose, about 0.5 mm. thick, can be prepared with a commercial spreader (Table 39-3) from 15 g. of cellulose MN 300 which has been homogenized with 90 ml. of water in an electric mixer. The layers are dried at 105°C. for a quarter of an hour.

Formamide-impregnated layers are prepared by immersing plates coated with cellulose in a 20 percent solution of formamide in acetone. The solvent is removed with a stream of warm air.

[65] Stahl, E., and Kaltenbach, U., J. Chromatog., **5,** 351, 1961.
[66] Stahl, E., and Kaltenbach, U., J. Chromatog., **5,** 458, 1961.
[67] Strohecker, R., and Henning, H. M., Vitamin-Bestimmungen, Erprobte Methoden, Verlag Chemie G. m. b. H., Weinheim, Germany, 1965.
[68] Vaedtke, J., and Gajewska, A., J. Chromatog., **9,** 345, 1962.
[69] Teichert, K., Mutschler, E., and Rochelmeyer, H., Deut. Apotheker Ztg., **100,** 477, 1960.
[70] Wollenweber, P., in Thin-Layer Chromatography, G. B. Marini-Bettõlo, Ed., Elsevier Publishing Company, Amsterdam, London, New York, 1964, p. 14.
[71] von Arx, E., and Neher, R., J. Chromatog., **12,** 329, 1963.
[72] Studer, R. O., Vogler, K., and Lergier, W., Helv. Chim. Acta, **44,** 131, 1961.
[73] Mangold, H. K., and Kammereck, R., J. Am. Oil Chemists' Soc., **39,** 201, 1962.

Solvents.—The Partridge-mixture[74] is used more often than any other developing solvent. This and other systems are listed in Table 39-9.

TABLE 39-9. SOLVENTS FOR PARTITION-TLC

1-*Butanol-Acetic acid-Water, 40:10:50, v/v/v*
1-Butanol-Acetone-Diethylamine-Water, 10:10:2:5, v/v/v/v
2-Propanol-Formic acid-Water, 40:2:10, v/v/v
2-Butanol-Methyl ethyl ketone-Dicyclohexylamine-Water, 10:10:2:5, v/v/v/v
Phenol-Water, 75:25, w/w
(+7.5 mg NaCN per 100 g./solvent; gas phase saturated with 3% aqueous ammonia)

For the chromatography of weakly polar compounds in formamide-impregnated layers, hexane, benzene, chloroform, and mixtures thereof are used as developing solvents.

An Application of Partition-TLC.—A thin-layer chromatogram of a mixture of amino acids, an example of partition-TLC, is shown in Fig. 39-16.[75]

REVERSED-PHASE PARTITION-TLC

This type of chromatography differs from normal partition chromatography in that the stationary phase is nonpolar and the mobile phase is polar. Reversed-phase partition chromatography is used almost exclusively for the separation of classes into their constituents. In contrast to adsorption and normal partition chromatography, the more polar constituents of a class migrate ahead of the less polar substances, and unsaturated compounds migrate more rapidly than saturated components of the same class and the same molecular weight. Mixtures of saturated and unsaturated compounds that form "critical pairs" in reversed-phase partition chromatography at room temperature, may often be resolved at depressed temperatures.[76] As a general rule, reversed-phase partition chromatography is not well suited to the separation of *cis-trans*-unsaturated compounds.

Reversed-phase partition-TLC is valuable for the fractionation of mixtures of lipophilic substances, such as hydrocarbons and other nonpolar petroleum products,[77] fats and waxes,[78] terpene alcohols,[79] carotenoids,[80] fat-soluble vitamins,[81] steroids,[82] and fat-soluble dyes.[83] Groups of compounds that cannot be separated by adsorption are usually easily resolved by reversed-phase partition chromatography and *vice versa*.

Stationary Phases.—Thin layers used in reversed-phase partition chromatography are usually prepared by impregnating layers of silic acid or kieselguhr with nonpolar liquids. The most commonly used stationary phases are listed in Table 39-10.

Layers for reversed-phase partition chromatography are best prepared by allowing

[74] Partridge, S. M., Biochem. J., **42,** 238, 1948.
[75] von Arx, E., and Neher, R., J. Chromatog., **12,** 329, 1963.
[76] Malins, D. C., and Mangold, H. K., J. Am. Oil Chemists' Soc., **37,** 576, 1960.
[77] Badger, G. M., Donnelly, T. K., and Spotswood, T. M., J. Chromatog., **10,** 397, 1963.
[78] Anker, L., and Sonanini, D., Pharm. Acta Helv., **37,** 360, 1962.
[79] Stahl, E., in Thin-Layer Chromatography, E. Stahl, Ed., Springer-Verlag, Berlin, and Academic Press, New York, 1965, p. 196.
[80] Stahl, E., Bolliger, H. R., and Lehnert, L., in 7. Symposium der Deutschen Gesellschaft für Ernährung, Steinkopff Verlag, Darmstadt, 1963.
[81] Strohecker, R., and Henning, H. M., Vitamin-Bestimmungen, Erprobte Methoden, Verlag Chemie G. m. b. H., Weinheim, Germany, 1965.
[82] Peereboom, J. W. C., and Beekes, H. W., J. Chromatog., **9,** 316, 1962.
[83] Wollenweber, P., J. Chromatog., **7,** 557, 1962.

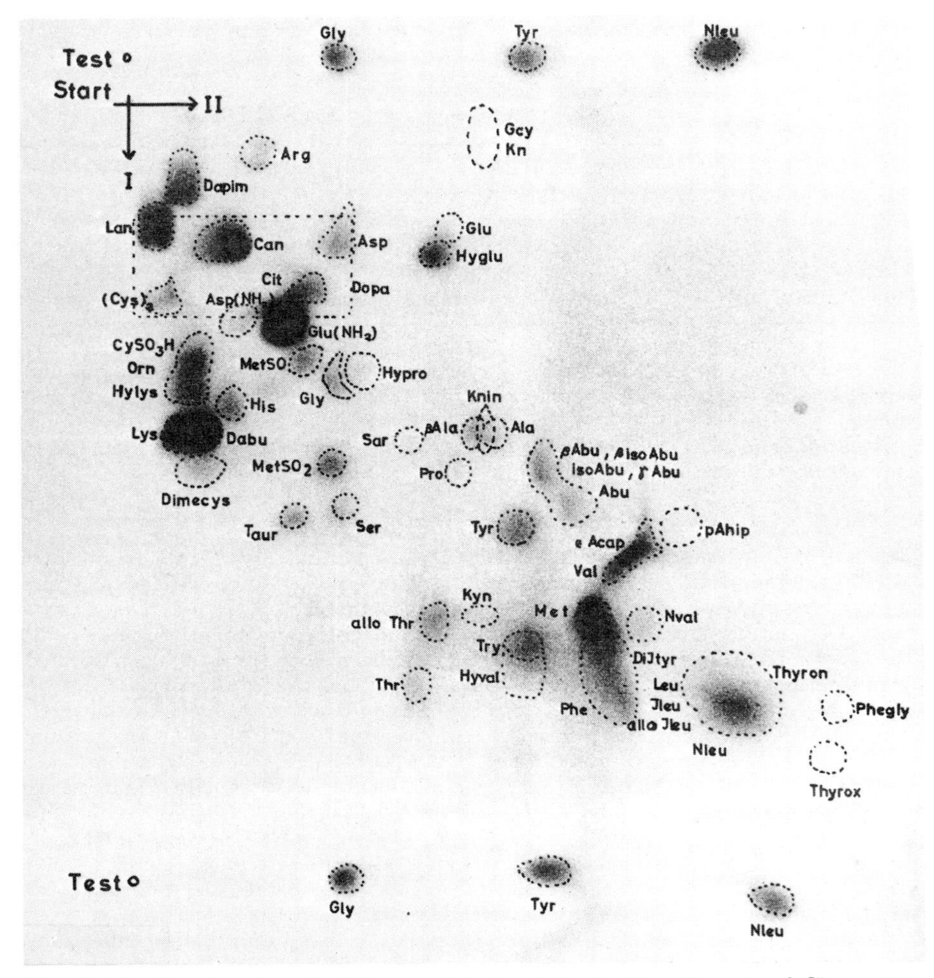

FIG. 39-16. Fractionation of a Mixture of Amino Acids by Two-dimensional Chromatography on a Cellulose Layer. Sample: synthetic mixture of 57 amino acids. Stationary phase: cellulose powder MN 300 (0.25 mm.). Solvents: *n*-butanol:acetone:diethylamine:water, 10:10:2:5, v/v/v/v. (I); isopropanol:formic acid (99%):water, 40:2:10, v/v/v. (II). Indicators (on three separate chromatoplates): *a*, ninhydrin-s-collidin in acidic ethanol, heating to 90°C.; *b*, isotin in pyridine-isopropanol; *c*, Pauly's diazo reagent.

a 5 percent solution of "paraffinum subliquidum" [84] in diethyl ether to migrate the length of the plate. After evaporation of the ether, the plates are ready for use.

Solvents.—A mixture of chloroform-methanol-water[85] is used most often. This and other solvent systems are listed in Table 39-11. Overlapping saturated and unsaturated

[84] E. Merck A. G., Chemische Fabrik, Darmstadt, Germany. U. S. representative: C. A. Brinkmann and Co., Inc., Cantiague Rd., Westbury, L. I., N. Y. Representative in England: Anderman & Co., Ltd., Battlebridge House, 87–95 Tooley Street, London S.E.1.

[85] Kaufmann, H. P., and Makus, Z., Fette, Seifen, Anstrichmittel, **62,** 1014, 1960.

TABLE 39-10. COATING MATERIALS FOR REVERSED-PHASE PARTITION-TLC

Paraffin oil (on silicic acid[a] or kieselguhr[a])	4[b]
Silicone (on silicic acid[a] or kieselguhr[a])	1
n-Tetradecane (on silicic acid[a] or kieselguhr[a])	2
Acetylated cellulose	3

[a] For commercial suppliers see Table 39-4.
[b] Numbers refer to the following list of suppliers:
1. Dow Corning Corp., Midland, Michigan.
2. Fisher Scientific Co., 633 Greenwich Street, New York 14, New York.
3. Macherey, Nagel & Co., Düren-Rhld., Germany. U. S. Representative: C. A. Brinkmann and Co., Inc., Cantiague Rd., Westbury, L. I., New York. Representative in England: Camlab (Glass), Ltd., Milton Road, Cambridge.
4. E. Merck A. G., Chemische Fabrik, Darmstadt, Germany. U. S. Representative: C. A. Brinkmann and Co., Inc., Cantiague Rd., Westbury, L. I., New York. Representative in England: Anderman & Co., Ltd., Battlebridge House, 87–95 Tooley Street, London S.E.1.

compounds ("critical pairs") can be separated with mixtures of acetic acid-peracetic acid (10 percent)-water[86] or acetic acid-water-perhydrol (10 percent).[87] Saturated compounds are well resolved with such developing solvents whereas all unsaturated constituents are oxidized in the course of chromatography and migrate in bulk with the solvent front.

TABLE 39-11. SOLVENTS FOR REVERSED-PHASE PARTITION-TLC

Chloroform-Methanol-Water, 75:25.5, v/v/v
Acetic acid-acetonitrile-water, 10:70:25, v/v/v
Acetic acid-acetonitrile, 50:50, v/v
Acetic acid-water, 75:25, v/v
Acetone-water, 60:40, v/v

An Application of Reversed-Phase Partition-TLC.—An example of reversed-phase partition-TLC is presented in Fig. 39-17.[88] It shows the fractionation of various fats and oils.

TLC ON POLYAMIDES

Powdered ε-polycaprolactam can be employed for the fractionation of mixtures of phenols and for the separation of phenols from quinones. The fractionation of phenols on this material is based on the hydrogen bonding that they form with the peptide bonds of the polyamides. Quinones react irreversibly with the free amino groups of polyamides. Aromatic nitro compounds can also be fractionated on polyamides. The nitro compounds are reversibly bound by the free amino groups of the polyamide.

Chromatography on thin layers of polyamide is useful for fractionating tannins,[89] coumarins,[90] flavone glycosides,[91] gallic acid esters, and other antioxidants,[92] also for

[86] Malins, D. C., and Mangold, H. K., J. Am. Oil Chemists' Soc., **37**, 576, 1960.
[87] Mangold, H. K., Fette, Seifen, Anstrichmittel, **61**, 877, 1959.
[88] Anker, L., and Sonanini, D., Pharm. Acta Helv., **37**, 360, 1962.
[89] Stadler, P., and Endres, H., J. Chromatog., **17**, 587, 1965.
[90] Bhandari, P. R., J. Chromatog., **16**, 130, 1964.
[91] Egger, K., Z. anal. Chem., **182**, 161, 1961.
[92] Davidek, J., and Pokorny, J., Z. Lebensm. Untersuch.-Forsch., **115**, 113, 1961.

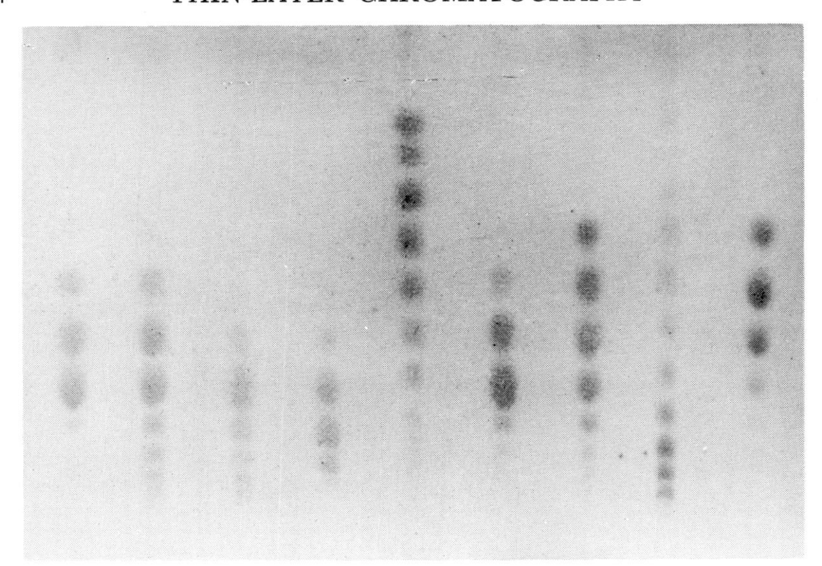

Fig. 39-17. Reversed-phase Partition Thin-layer Chromatogram of Fats and Oils. Samples from left to right: (1) almond oil; (2) peanut oil; (3) hardened peanut oil; (4) cocoa butter; (5) linseed oil; (6) olive oil; (7) sesame seed oil; (8) rape seed oil; and (9) cotton seed oil. Stationary phase: paraffin oil on Kieselguhr G. Solvent: acetic acid. Indicator: iodine vapors, followed by starch solution.

aromatic nitro compounds, including DNP-amino acids,[93] sulfonic acids, and their amides.

Polyamides.—Commercial preparations of polyamides for thin-layer chromatography are listed in Table 39-12. These materials are used without a binding agent.

Table 39-12. Polyamides for TLC

ε-Polycaprolactam	1, 2, 3, 4[a]
Acetylated ε-polycaprolactam	
Polyacrylonitrile	3
Mixtures of ε-polycaprolactam and polyacrylonitrile	

[a] Numbers refer to the following list of suppliers:
1. Mann Research Laboratories, Inc., 136 Liberty Street, New York 6, New York.
2. E. Merck A. G., Chemische Fabrik, Darmstadt, Germany. U. S. Representative: C. A. Brinkmann and Co., Inc., Cantiague Rd., Westbury, L. I., New York. Representative in England: Anderman & Co., Ltd., Battlebridge House, 87–95 Tooley Street, London S.E.1.
3. Research Specialties Co., 200 S. Garrard Blvd., Richmond, California.
4. M. Woelm, Eschwege, Germany. U. S. Representative: Alupharm Chemicals, 616 Commercial Pl., P. O. Box 755, New Orleans, Louisiana. Representative in England: L. Light & Co., Ltd., Poyle Colnbrook, Bucks.

Polyamide powders usually are applied to glass plates as slurries with chloroform-methanol, 40:60, v/v, in a ratio of 5 g. polyamide to 45 ml. of solvent. The plates are used after having been air-dried over night.

[93] Endres, H., and Hörmann, H., Angew. Chem. Int'l. Ed., **2,** 254, 1963.

Table 39-13. Solvents for TLC on Polyamides

Water-Ethanol, 50:50, v/v
Water-Acetone, 50:50, v/v
Water-Ethanol-Acetic acid-Dimethylformamide, 30:20:10:5, v/v/v/v
Dimethylformamide-Benzene, 3:97, v/v

Solvents.—Several typical developing solvents for thin-layer chromatography on polyamide are listed in Table 39-13.

An Application of TLC on Polyamide.—An example of a thin-layer chromatogram on ε-polycaprolactam is shown in Fig. 39-18.[94]

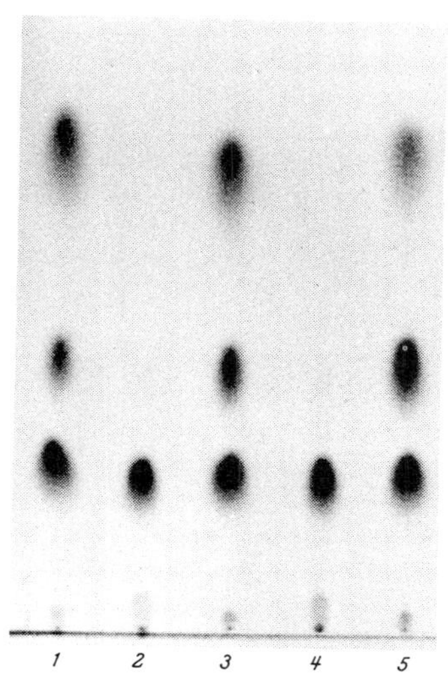

Fig. 39-18. Fractionation of Glycosides on a Polyamide Layer. Samples: 1, robinin, rutin, quercitrin; 2, myricitrin; 3, robinin, K-3-rhgl., quercitrin; 4, myricitrin; 5, robinin, rutin, quercitrin. Stationary phase: ε-Polycaprolactam. Solvent: water:ethanol:methyl ethyl ketone:acetyl acetone, 65:15:15:5, v/v/v/v. Indicator: photographed in UV. light.

TLC ON DEXTRAN GELS

Dextran gels are formed by the addition of water to semisynthetic preparations; they comprise a three-dimensional network of polysaccharide chains. Such gels can be used as molecular sieves for the chromatographic fractionation of mixtures of water-soluble substances. As an aqueous solution of the sample moves through the gel, the small molecules diffuse into the gel particles and are thus held back, whereas the larger molecules are eluted at a fast rate. The degree of cross-linking in the gel essentially determines the discreteness of separation.

Thin-layer chromatography on dextran gels is useful for the fractionation of mixtures of proteins differing in molecular weights.[95]

Coating Materials.—Commercial preparations of dextran gels for thin-layer chromatography are listed in Table 39-14.

Table 39-14. Dextran Gels for TLC

Sephadex G-25, Superfine® [1]
Sephadex G-50, Superfine® [1]
Sephadex G-75, Superfine® [1]
Sephadex G-100, Superfine® [1]

[1] Supplied by Pharmacia, Uppsala, Sweden. U. S. Representative: Pharmacia Fine Chemicals, Inc., 501 Fifth Avenue, New York 17, New York. Representative in England: Pharmacia (Great Britain), Ltd., Sinclair House, The Avenue, West Ealing, London W 13.

[94] Egger, K., Z. anal. Chem., **182,** 161, 1961.
[95] Wieland, Th., Lüben, G., and Determann, H., Experientia, **18,** 430, 1962.

TABLE 39-15. SOLVENTS FOR TLC ON DEXTRAN GELS

Aqueous acetic acid solution, 0.01–0.1 N
Aqueous ammonia, 0.01–0.1 N
Aqueous ammonium acetate buffer, pH 4.5, 0.01–0.1 M
Aqueous sodium phosphate buffer, pH 7.0,[a] 0.01–0.1 M

[a] Very dilute solutions should contain 0.1–0.2 M sodium chloride.

Dextran layers are prepared as follows:[96] 10 g. of "Sephadex G-25, Super Fine" are suspended in 50 ml. of buffer, *e.g.*, 0.2 M sodium phosphate, pH 7, and allowed to swell for 5 hours. The gel is applied with a commercial spreader (Table 39-3). The coated plates are ready for chromatography. They may be stored in a moist chamber. Layers that have dried out can be used after having been sprayed with buffer solution.

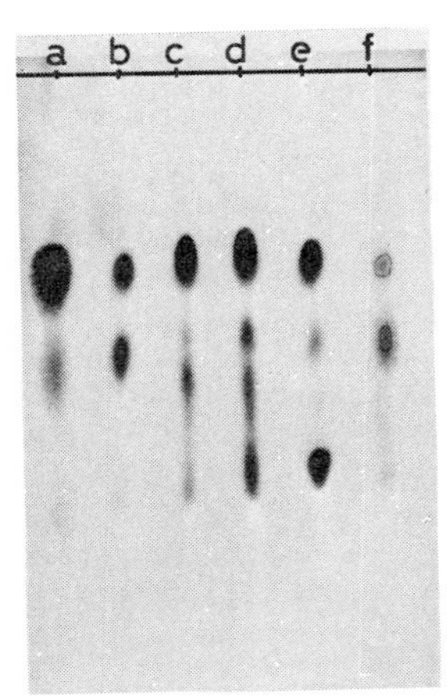

FIG. 39-19. Fractionation of Blood Serum Proteins on a Layer of Dextran Gel. Samples: *a*, normal serum; *b*, myeloma serum of γ_{ss}-globulin type; *c,d*, γ_{1A}-myeloma sera; *e*, serum containing a pathological macroglobulin. Coating material: Sephadex G-200, Superfine ®, (0.5 mm.). Solvent; 0.02 M sodium phosphate buffer, pH 7.0, containing 0.2 M sodium chloride. Indicator: amidoblack 10 B, saturated solution in methanol: acetic acid:water, 80:10:10, v/v/v. Encircled zones showed fluorescence in UV. light.

Solvents.—Aqueous solutions of weak acids and bases, and dilute salt solutions are used as developing solvents. Typical examples are given in Table 39-15.

An Application of TLC on a Dextran Gel.—Figure 39-19[97] shows the separation of proteins on a layer of a dextran gel.

THIN-LAYER IONOPHORESIS AND THIN-LAYER ELECTROPHORESIS

These techniques permit the separation of inorganic ions and of organic substances with ionizable groups. Thin-layer techniques offer several advantages over paper methods: in most applications, thin layers are prepared from slurries of silica gel with buffer solutions. These layers have a higher capacity than paper, and diffusion is minimized, which results in improved separation and greater sensitivity of detection.

The consecutive use of thin-layer electrophoresis and thin-layer partition chromatography—"fingerprinting"—is particularly rewarding. Amino acid hydrolyzates, for example, can be resolved on one plate: electrophoresis is applied in the first dimension and chromatography in the second direction.[98,99] A review of applications of thin-layer ionophoresis and thin-layer electrophoresis has been published.[100]

[96] "Sephadex® Thin-Layer Gel Filtration Superfine Beads," Pharmacia Fine Chemicals, Inc., 800 Centennial Ave., Piscataway, New Market, N. J.
[97] Johansson, B. G., and Rymo, L., Acta Chem. Scand., **18**. 217, 1964.
[98] Stegemann, H., and Lerch, B., Anal. Biochem., **9,** 417, 1964.
[99] Wieland, Th., and Georgopoulos, D., Biochem. Z., **340,** 476, 1964.
[100] Grassini, G., in Thin-Layer Chromatography, G. B. Marini-Bettōlo, Ed., Elsevier Publishing Company, Amsterdam, 1964, p. 55.

Apparatuses for thin-layer electrophoresis are available commercially.[101,102,103,104] An example of a "fingerprint" of a mixture of amino acids is shown in Fig. 39-20.[105]

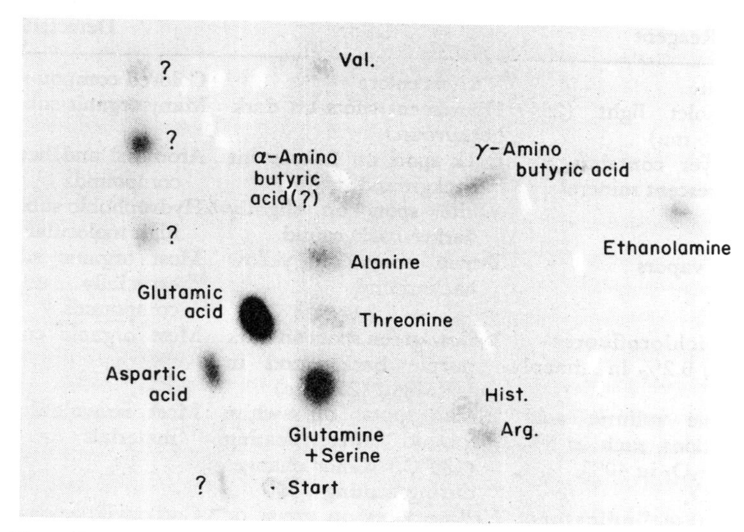

FIG. 39-20. "Fingerprint" of a Mixture of Amino Acids. Sample: extract of sugar beet leaves. Coating material: cellulose MN 300. Electrophoresis: 1200v./20 cm. (25 min.) in pyridine:acetic acid:water, 3:12:235, v/v/v. Chromatography, solvent: *n*-butanol:acetic acid:water, 40:10:10, v/v/v (15 hr.). Indicator: 0.2% ninhydrin in acetone.

METHODS OF DETECTION AND DOCUMENTATION

Most indicators used in paper chromatography are suitable for thin-layer chromatography also. In many instances, the sensitivity of these detection methods is increased one hundredfold when applied on a thin-layer chromatogram.

The consecutive use of two or several detection methods, on the same plate, increases the probability that no substance remains undetected. Corrosive spray reagents, such as chromic-sulfuric acid, may be used, eventually, for charring most organic compounds on inorganic layers, over a hot plate.

A number of common physical detection methods and spray reagents that have been used in thin-layer chromatography are listed in Table 39-16.

Extensive compilations of more specific reagents have been published.[106,107,108]

[101] C. Desaga, G. m. b. H., Heidelberg, Hauptstr. 60, Germany. U. S. representative: C. A. Brinkmann and Co., Inc., Cantiague Rd., Westbury, L. I., N. Y. Representative in England: Camlab (Glass), Ltd., Milton Road, Cambridge.

[102] K. Markgraf, Berlin, Germany.

[103] Research Specialties Co., 200 S. Garrard Blvd., Richmond, Calif.

[104] Shandon Scientific Co., 65 Pound Lane, London N.W.10, England. U. S. representative: Colab Laboratories, Inc., Chicago Heights, Ill.

[105] Stegemann, H., and Lerch, B., Anal. Biochem., **9,** 417, 1964.

[106] Bobbitt, J. M., Thin-Layer Chromatography, Reinhold Publishing Co., New York, 1963.

[107] Anfärbereagenzien für Dünnschicht—und Papier—Chromatographie, E. Merck A. G., Darmstadt, Germany.

[108] Waldi, D., in Thin-Layer Chromatography, E. Stahl, Ed., Springer-Verlag, Berlin, and Academic Press, New York, 1965, pp. 483–502.

Table 39-16. Some Common Detection Methods

Reagent	Color	Components Detected
1. Daylight	Various colors	Colored compounds
2. Ultraviolet light (254 and 366 mμ)	Fluorescent spots on dark background	Many organic substances
On layer containing a fluorescent mineral	Dark spots on fluorescent background	Aromatic and heterocyclic compounds
3. Water	White spots on slightly darker background	Hydrophobic substances of high molecular weight
4. Iodine vapors	Brown spots on yellow background	Most organic substances, especially unsaturated compounds
5. 2′,7′-Dichlorofluorescein, 0.2% in ethanol	Yellow-green spots on dark purple background in UV. light (254 mμ)	Most organic compounds
6. Chromic sulfuric acid solutions, such as 5% $K_2Cr_2O_7$ in 40% H_2SO_4	Black spots on white ground after heating (180°C.). Color changes during heating	Most nonvolatile organic materials
7. Acid-base indicators, such as 0.1–0.5% Bromocresol Green in ethanol made alkaline or Bromophenol Blue in 0.01 *N* aqueous citric acid or Bromothymol Blue in 0.01 *N* aqueous sodium hydroxide	Yellow spots on green or blue background	Carboxylic acids
8. Antimony chlorides: 50% $SbCl_3$ in glacial acetic acid	Various characteristic colors	Steroids, alicyclic vitamins, carotenoids
25% $SbCl_5$ in carbon tetrachloride	Various characteristic colors	
9. Ninhydrin, 0.3% in *n*-butanol containing 3% acetic acid	Pink to purple spots on white background	Amino acids, amines, and other substances
10. Diphenylboric acid β-aminoethyl ester 1% in ethanol[a]	Various characteristic colors	Many natural products

[a] Fluka A. G., Buchs S. G., Switzerland. U. S. Representative: International Chemical and Nuclear Corp., 13332 E. Torch St., City of Industry, California.

Biological methods can be useful for visualizing antibiotics[109] and other biologically active compounds.

For detection of radioactively labeled compounds, autoradiography is the most

[109] Brodasky, T. F., Anal. Chem., **35**, 343, 1963.

convenient method.[110] X-ray prints of thin-layer chromatograms are obtained, after complete evaporation of the developing solvent, by exposing the plates in the dark to "No-Screen Medical X-Ray Safety Film" [111] for 2 hours to 1 week. A convenient cartridge for making autoradiographs of chromatoplates is available commercially.[112] The films are developed, *e.g.*, with "Super-Mix Developer" [113] for 4–6 minutes and fixed for half an hour, *e.g.*, with "Acid Fixer." [114] Several instruments for scanning thin-layer chromatograms of radioactive material are on the market.[115,116,117,118,119] A very useful zonal scraper for transfer of small zones of coating material from glass strips has been described.[120] The scraped-off zones are assayed by liquid scintillation counting.[121]

Information obtained from viewing a thin-layer chromatogram, such as the pattern of separation—the sizes, shapes, and colors of the various spots—and the approximate quantity of each fraction, is not easily recorded in narrative form. Consequently, methods have been developed for the reproduction and preservation of thin-layer chromatograms.

Reproductions may be obtained by making tracings of the spots on transparent paper. Photographs, however, provide the most authentic records. Apparatus for taking photographs of chromatoplates in reflected and transmitted visible light, or in short (254 mμ) or long (365 mμ) wave length UV. light, are commercially available.[122,123] Copying devices, such as the "Copease" [124] and "Xerox 914," [125] can be employed for the reproduction of thin-layer chromatograms. Sometimes, however, small or weakly stained spots do not reproduce well, and blurring may occur. Clear photostats can be obtained after spraying the thin layer with a solution of paraffin in diethyl ether, 50:50, v/v.

The use of x-ray films for obtaining autoradiographs of chromatoplates has been discussed above.

A permanent record of a thin-layer chromatogram, or a photostat thereof, can be obtained by scanning with a photodensitometer that is designed to move the plate, manually or automatically, over a small hole or a narrow slot located between the light source and the photocell. X-ray prints can be similarly scanned. Several instruments, especially built for evaluating thin-layer chromatograms, are available commercially. Radio-scanners, too, can be used to obtain permanent records of thin-

[110] Mangold, H. K., Kammereck, R., and Malins, D. C., Microchem. J., Sympos., **2,** 697, 1962.
[111] Eastman Kodak Co., Rochester 3, N. Y.
[112] Analabs, Analytical Engineering Laboratories, Inc., Post Office Box 5215, Hamden 18, Conn.
[113] General Electric, X-Ray Department, Milwaukee 1, Wisc.
[114] Eastman Kodak Co., Rochester 3, N. Y.
[115] Atomic Accessories, Inc., Subsidiary of Baird-Atomic, Inc., 811 W. Merrick Rd., Valley Stream, N. Y.
[116] Baird & Tatlock (London), Ltd., Freshwater Road, Chadwell Heath, Essex, England.
[117] C. Desaga, G. m. b. H., Heidelberg, Hauptstr. 60, Germany. U. S. representative: C. A. Brinkmann and Co., Inc., Cantiague Rd., Westbury, L. I., N. Y. Representative in England: Camlab (Glass), Ltd., Milton Road, Cambridge.
[118] Nuclear Chicago Corp., 351 E. Howard Ave., Des Plaines, Ill.
[119] Packard Instrument Co., Inc., Box 428, La Grange, Ill.
[120] Snyder, F., Anal. Biochem., **9,** 183, 1964.
[121] Snyder, F., and Stephens, N., Anal. Biochem., **4,** 128, 1962.
[122] W. Bälz & Sohn K. G., Heilbronn a. N., Germany.
[123] C. Desaga, G. m. b. H., Heidelberg, Hauptstr. 60, Germany. U. S. representative: C. A. Brinkmann and Co., Inc., Cantiague Rd., Westbury, L. I., N. Y. Representative in England: Camlab (Glass), Ltd., Milton Road, Cambridge.
[124] Copease Corp., 425 Park Ave., New York, N. Y.
[125] Xerox Corp., Rochester 3, N. Y.

layer chromatograms of radioactive materials. Such instruments are commercially available (see p. 773).

Thin-layer chromatograms can be preserved by spraying the layers with a solution of plastic material, such as a 4 percent solution of collodian in 7.5 percent aqueous glycerol.[126] For the same purpose, aqueous dispersions of polyacrylates and similar polymers are available as aerosol sprays.[127,128,129] After the plastic film has set, the layer may be peeled off the glass plate; coated sheets are retained intact.

For the preservation of smaller areas of a chromatogram, adhesive cellophane tape, which is available in various widths,[130] may be pressed against the surface of the thin layer to lift it from the plate. The tape containing the coating material can then be placed directly in a notebook. Alternatively, another strip of adhesive tape may be attached to the undersurface of the layer so that the chromatogram is completely enclosed. Microchromatoplates are best preserved by wrapping them with transparent adhesive tape.

QUANTITATIVE THIN-LAYER CHROMATOGRAPHY

There are two basic techniques employed for the quantitative analysis of substances separated on chromatoplates: the various fractions can be measured *on the plate;* and fractions can be determined *after elution* from the coating material.

A subsequent chromatographic method may be employed for assessing the composition of fractions resolved on plates, thereby yielding quantitative analysis of the total in an indirect fashion.

The errors encountered in the various methods of quantification are claimed to be from 3 to 10%, depending upon the procedures employed and the types of compounds measured.

Analyses on the Plate.—These techniques are perhaps the most desirable because of their simplicity. Analyses of fractions on chromatoplates can be done by (a) visual comparison with standards; (b) the precise measurement of spot areas or spot sizes, and (c) photodensitometry. Quantification via reproductions often is more precise than analysis of fractions on the plate itself.

Radioactive substances can be assayed by (a) photodensitometry of x-ray prints, (b) by liquid-scintillation counting in suspension, and (c) by direct radio-scanning of chromatoplates.

Analysis Based upon Area-Weight Relations.—The size of a spot is mainly determined by the amount of substance applied to the plate. Additional significant and often critical factors that influence the size, shape, and color of a spot are: the nature of the solvent used for dissolving the sample, the way in which the solution is put on the layer, the composition and the thickness of the layer, the composition of the developing solvent, the conditions in the chromatojar, and the distance the spot has traveled. It is hardly possible to standardize the experimental conditions to the extent that the results from different chromatograms can be combined. In order to minimize the

[126] Barrollier, J., Naturwissenschaflen, **48,** 404, 1960.

[127] Camag A. G., Muttenz B. L., Homburgerstr. 24, Switzerland. U. S. representative: Microchemical Specialties Co., 1825 Eastshore Hwy., Berkeley 10, Calif. and A. H. Thomas Co., Vine St. at Third, Philadelphia 5, Pa. Representative in England: Griffin & George, Ltd., Chromatography Division, Ealing Road, Alperton, Middlesex.

[128] Fluka A. G., Buchs S. G., Switzerland. U. S. representative: International Chem. & Nuclear Corp., 13332 Torch Street, City of Industry, California.

[129] E. Merck A. G., Chemische Fabrik, Darmstadt, Germany. U. S. representative: C. A. Brinkmann and Co., Inc., Cantiague Rd., Westbury, L. I., N. Y. Representative in England: Anderman & Co., Ltd., Battlebridge House, 87–95 Tooley Street, London, S.E.1.

[130] Mann Research Laboratories, Inc., 136 Liberty St., New York 6, N. Y.

influence of the various factors affecting spot size and spot area, it is mandatory to chromatograph a series of mixtures of known composition on the same plate with the unknown sample. Model mixtures can be prepared from reference materials that were isolated, by preparative thin-layer chromatography, from the sample to be analyzed. All reference substances should be pure according to the parameters employed in the chromatographic separation.

In quantitative analysis, all samples should be applied to the plates as solutions in *one operation* and as equal volumes.[131]

Chromatoplates are always developed in a saturated atmosphere, *i.e.*, in jars lined with filter paper.

The edges of the spots, especially the tailends, usually are not very sharp. Therefore, spot areas are best determined, by planimetry, on a photostat of the chromatoplate.[132] The photographic emulsion of the high-contrast paper arbitrarily sets the limit between spot and background.

Graphical Methods.—As the spot area does not increase linearly with the amount present, it is advisable to use a calibration curve that is obtained by plotting the areas of spots formed by reference material *vs.* their weights (Figs. 39-21 and 39-22).[133] A

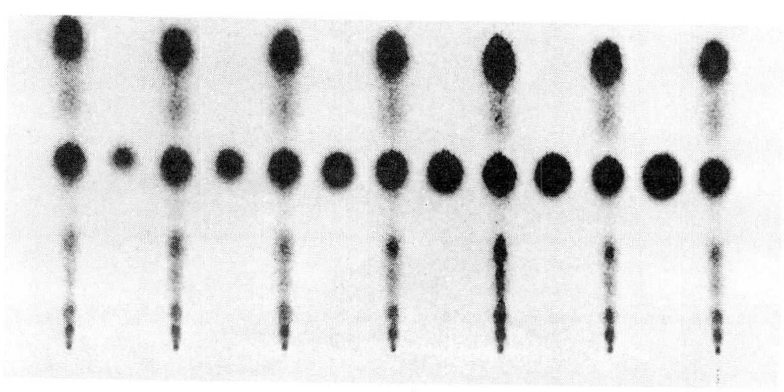

Fig. 39-21. Photograph of a Chromatoplate on which the Nonsaponifiable Fraction of Wool Wax Was Run with Different Amounts of Cholesterol.

new calibration curve must be prepared for each plate.[134] The amount of the unknown fraction is determined by relating its area to the calibration curve.

In adsorption chromatography and in partition chromatography, the square root of the spot area is a linear function of the logarithm of the weight of the material present.[135] Thus, *straight* calibration curves are obtained by plotting the log of the weights (W) *vs.* the square roots of the areas (A) (Fig. 39-23).[136] This relation is valid only in a certain range of material, and this range must be determined for each compound. The calibration curve shown in Fig. 39-23 is plotted using the data obtained from Fig. 39-21.

Algebraic Methods.—There are two methods, both of which are based on the linearity of the relation between log W and $\sqrt{A}$.

[131] Purdy, S. J., and Truter, E. V., Analyst, **87,** 802, 1962.
[132] Seher, A., Fette, Seifen, Anstrichmittel, **61,** 345, 1959.
[133] Purdy, S. J., and Truter, E. V., Laboratory Practice, **13,** 500, 1964.
[134] Seher, A., Nahrung, **4,** 466, 1960.
[135] Purdy, S. J., and Truter, E. V., Chemistry & Industry (London), 506, 1962.
[136] Purdy, S. J., and Truter, E. V., Laboratory Practice, **17,** 500, 1964.

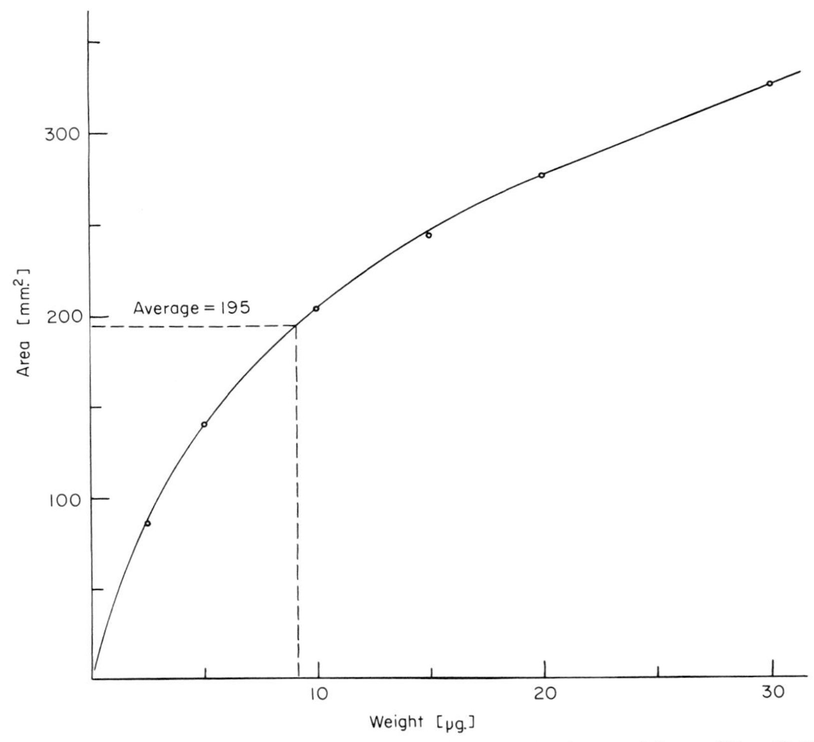

FIG. 39-22. Calibration Curves Obtained by Plotting the Areas of Spots (Fig. 39-21) *vs.* the Weights of the Material They Contain.

In the first method, equal volumes of the sample solution, a dilute sample solution, and a standard solution of reference material, are chromatographed side by side on a plate. The weight W of material contained in an "unknown spot" can be calculated from the formula:[137]

$$\log W = \log W_s + \left(\frac{\sqrt{A} - \sqrt{A_s}}{\sqrt{A_d} - \sqrt{A}}\right) \log d$$

where: A = spot area of the unknown;
A_d = area of the corresponding spot in a dilute sample;
d = dilution factor;
A_s = spot area of the standard; and
W_s = weight of the standard.

In the second method, equal volumes of the following solutions are chromatographed: a solution of the sample, a dilute solution of the sample, and a dilute solution of the same concentration as the first but containing in addition a certain amount of the

[137] Purdy, S. J., and Truter, E. V., Analyst, **87,** 802, 1962.

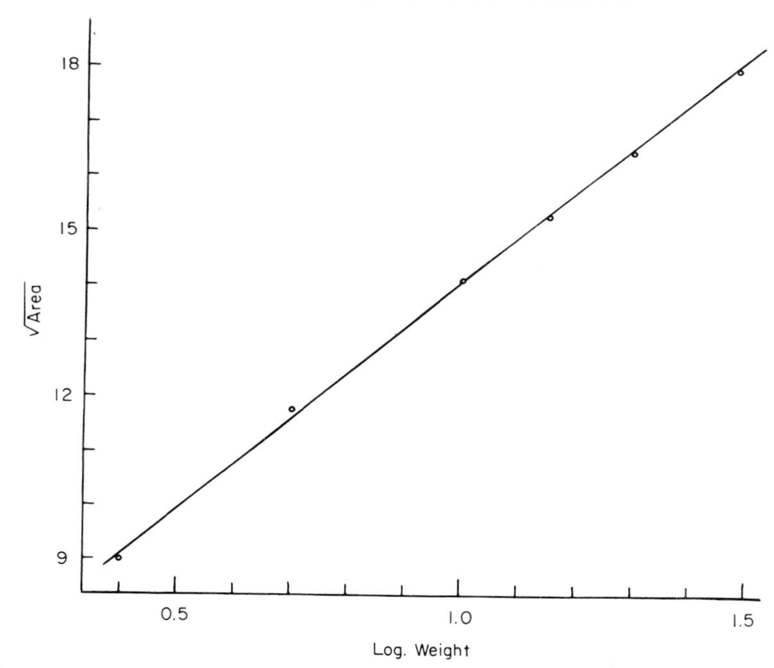

FIG. 39-23. Calibration Curves Obtained by Plotting the Square Roots of Spot Areas (Fig. 39-21) *vs.* the Logarithms of the Weights of the Material They Contain.

material to be determined. The weight of the fraction to be analyzed can be calculated from the formula:[138]

$$\log\left(\frac{Wd + a}{W}\right) = \left(\frac{\sqrt{A_+} - \sqrt{A}}{\sqrt{A_d} - \sqrt{A}}\right)\log d$$

where: A = spot area of the unknown;
A_d = area of the corresponding spot in the first dilute sample;
d = dilution factor; and
A_+ = spot area of the dilute sample solution containing reference material.

Analysis by Photodensitometry.—Densitometers built for scanning paper chromatograms and paper electrophoresis strips are readily adapted to use with chromatoplates. Instruments especially designed for scanning thin-layer chromatograms are available from several commercial houses.[139,140,141,142]

[138] Purdy, S. J., and Truter, E. V., Analyst, **87**, 802, 1962.
[139] Joyce, Loebl and Co., Gateshead on Tyne, England. U. S. representative: National Instrument Laboratories, Inc., 12300 Parklawn Dr., Rockville, Md.
[140] Photovolt Corp., 1115 Broadway, New York 10, N. Y.
[141] Shandon Scientific Co., 65 Pound Lane, London N. W. 10, England. U. S. representative: Colab Laboratories, Inc., Chicago Heights, Ill.
[142] Carl Zeiss, Optische Werke, Oberkochen Germany, U. S. representative: Carl Zeiss, Inc., 444 Fifth Ave., New York, N. Y.

Measurements may be made using transmitted light by moving the plate manually or automatically in 1-mm. steps over a small hole or a narrow slit (0.1 mm.) located between the light source and the photometer. However, the rather thick glass plates generally used in thin-layer chromatography diffract considerably the light beam going through the chromatoplate. It is advantageous, therefore, to scan photographs of thin-layer chromatograms or to scan the plates in reflected light.[143]

A very promising new technique is the determination of remission spectra on thin layers and the quantitative evaluation of chromatoplates in remission.[144,145] An instrument built for this type of work is available.[146]

Curves recorded by photometric methods are an expression of both the color intensities and the areas and shapes of the spot on a chromatoplate. Other factors that influence results obtained by use of this technique are the volatility of the compounds under investigation, and, if spray reagents are employed, whether color-formation takes place at a uniform rate. Some of these variables can be assessed and controlled by the prudent use of internal standards.

Suspension Counting of Radioactively Labeled Substances.—The various fractions are scraped off the plates and added to vials containing liquid scintillation solution. Prior elution of the radioactive substances from the coating material is not required. The liquid scintillation mixtures contain a gelling agent which holds the scrapings in suspension.

The following "cocktails" for liquid-scintillation counting have been found useful:[147,148]

a) 5 g. of 2,5-diphenyloxazole ("PPO"),[149] 0.3 g. of dimethyl-1,4-bis[2(5-phenyloxazol)-benzene], ("dimethyl-POPOP").
40 g. of "Cab-O-Sil," a thixotropic silica gel powder.
Make up to 1 liter with toluene. Fifteen ml. of this suspension is used, per counting vial, at a temperature of 6°C.

b) 7 g. of "PPO," 0.3 g. of "dimethyl-POPOP," 100 g. of naphthalene, and 40 g. of "Cab-O-Sil." Make up to 1 liter with dioxane. This suspension is mixed with water in a ratio of 15:3, v/v. An assay volume of 15 ml. is used per counting vial. Radioactivity is measured at 6°C.

In the authors' experience, quantitation by liquid-scintillation counting is the best all-around method. As it can be employed only with radioactive materials, consideration should be given to the possibility of labeling "cold" samples with a radioactive reagent.[150]

ANALYSIS OF ELUTED FRACTIONS

Quantitative determination of substances after elution from the plates is possible by gravimetric, volumetric, spectrophotometric, colorimetric, fluorometric, biological, or radiometric techniques. In all of these methods, a blank area of the layer, adjacent and equal in size to the area containing the fraction, should be analyzed. The amount of material found in the fraction to be analyzed must be corrected by the blank value.

[143] Hefendehl, F. W., Planta Med., **8,** 65, 1960.
[144] Jork, H., paper read at the 3rd Symposium on Chromatography, Brussels, 1964.
[145] Klaus, R., J. Chromatog., **16,** 311, 1964.
[146] Carl Zeiss, Optische Werke, Oberkochen, Germany. U. S. representative: Carl Zeiss, Inc., 444 Fifth Ave., New York, N. Y.
[147] Snyder, F., and Stephens, N., Anal. Biochem., **4,** 128, 1962.
[148] Snyder, F., Anal. Biochem., **9,** 183, 1964.
[149] "PPO," "Dimethyl-POPOP," and "Cab-O-Sil" are available from Packard Instrument Co., Inc., Box 428, La Grange, Ill.
[150] Mangold, H. K., Kammereck, R., and Malins, D. C., Microchem. J., Sympos., **2,** 697, 1962.

Substances fractionated on chromatoplates may be recovered in the following way: an area of the layer is piled up on the plate with a razor blade. The scrapings are transferred into a flask, slurried several times with a solvent and filtered through a sintered glass funnel. A suitable eluting solvent for a substance can be found by chromatographing it with different solvents on plates. Solvents that carry a fraction with the solvent front are suitable eluants. An apparatus[151] for eluting fractions on a disc of sintered glass is available commercially.[152] A very useful simple glass aspirator[153] for collecting a scraping by suction, and washing and filtering it over a plate of sintered glass is also being offered.[154]

The complete recovery of fractions from thin layers remains erratic. This is a serious shortcoming of all methods requiring elution. In some cases it is possible to overcome this handicap by carrying out a chromogenic reaction without prior extraction of the substance to be determined.[155,156]

PREPARATIVE THIN-LAYER CHROMATOGRAPHY

Thin-layer chromatography is often used as a preparative tool when difficult separations cannot be accomplished by other methods, or if the properties of the material to be fractionated prohibit handling large amounts. However, only adsorption thin-layer chromatography has been used to any extent for preparative purposes.

To scale up the process, thin-layer chromatography is often carried out with *larger plates*, measuring 40 × 20 cm.[157] and 100 × 20 cm.[158] Such plates are available from commercial houses.[159,160]

The coating materials used in analytical thin-layer chromatography (Tables 39-4, 39-6, 39-8, 39-10, 39-12, 39-14) are also employed for preparative separations. Silica gel containing a fluorescent mineral (but *no* plaster of Paris) is used most frequently. Layers 0.5 to 2 mm. in thickness usually are prepared by means of special applicators (see Table 39-3). Slurries for making such "thick" layers require less water than those used in coating plates with layers 0.25 mm. thick. Also, in order to avoid cracking of thick layers, they have to be air-dried for one or several hours before they are placed in an oven.

It must be emphasized that the efficiency of separation greatly diminishes as the thickness of the layer increases. In general, the thickness of the coating material should not exceed 1 mm. in order to eliminate overlapping of fractions due to differences in migration rates between the two faces of the layer.

Often the most efficient approach to the fractionation of a complex mixture is to chromatograph a sample first on a layer 0.5 to 1 mm. thick and then to rechromatograph each fraction in smaller amounts on standard layers 0.25 mm. in thickness.

A solution of the sample to be fractionated is applied to the plate as a row of closely spaced spots or as a thin streak across the plate. The application of large volumes of

[151] Komarek, R. J., Jensen, R. G., and Pickett, B. W., J. Lipid Res., **5**, 268, 1964.
[152] A. H. Thomas Co., Vine St. at Third, Philadelphia 5, Pa.
[153] Goldrick, B., and Hirsch, J., J. Lipid Res., **4**, 482, 1963.
[154] Kopp Laboratory Supplies, Inc., 70–13 35th Rd., Jackson Heights 72, N. Y.
[155] Gänshirt, H., Koss, F. W., and Morianz, K., Arzneimittel-Forsch., **10**, 943, 1960.
[156] Habermann, E., Bandtlow, G., and Krusche, B., Klin. Wochschr., **39**, 816, 1961.
[157] Stahl, E., Lab. Practice, **13**, 498, 1964.
[158] Halpaap, H., Chem.-Ing. Technik, **35**, 488, 1963.
[159] C. Desaga, G. m. b. H., Heidelberg, Hauptstr. 60, Germany. U. S. representative: C. A. Brinkmann and Co., Inc., Cantiague Rd., Westbury, L. I., N. Y. Representative in England: Camlab (Glass), Ltd., Milton Road, Cambridge.
[160] Shandon Scientific Co., 65 Pound Lane, London N.W.10, England. U. S. representative: Colab Laboratories, Inc., Chicago Heights, Ill.

such solutions by hand, however, is both tedious and time consuming. A simple and readily-made apparatus for the simultaneous application of 30 spots to a 20 × 20 cm. plate has been described,[161] and is available commercially.[162] This device (Fig. 39-24) consists of a "U-shaped" base frame over which a transverse metal bar is supported by

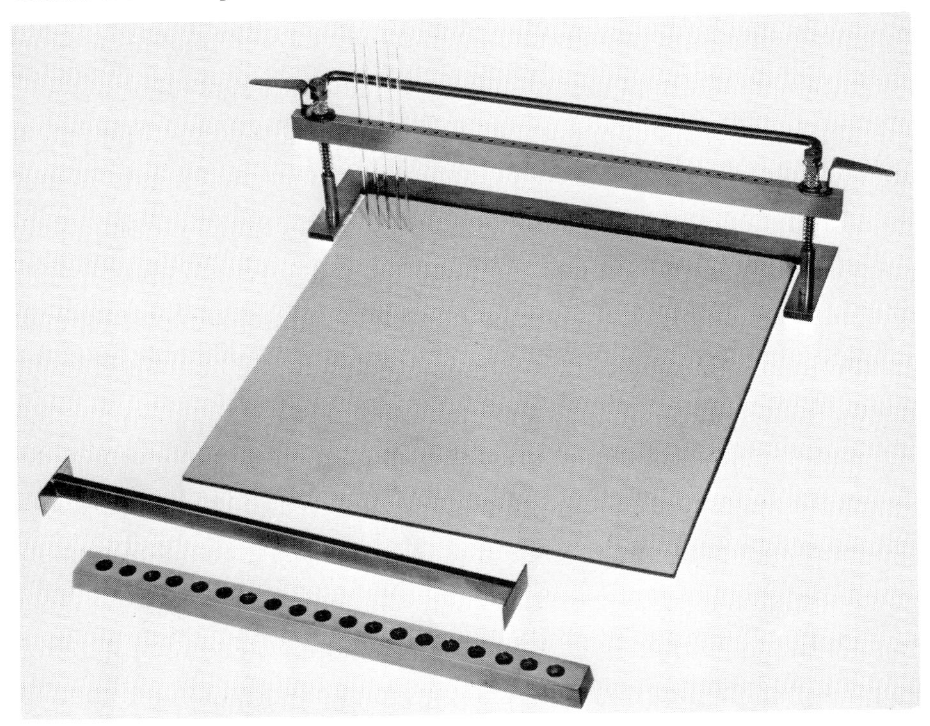

Fig. 39-24. Multiple Spot Applicator.

coiled springs. Disposable glass capillaries, which are mounted on the metal bar, are filled by dipping them into a trough containing a solution of the sample. By use of this applicator, the sample is delivered as a uniform series of spots as the capillaries are lowered onto the surface of the layer. A picture of this apparatus is shown in Fig. 39-24.

Most discrete separations are inevitably obtained if the sample is applied as a thin, even band. An instrument for applying the sample solution as a streak across a plate, 40 × 20 cm., has been devised;[163] it is also commercially available.[164] This electro-mechanical sample applicator (Fig. 39-25) utilizes a syringe equipped with a screw top and an adjustable pressure valve mounted on a movable support. The solution containing the sample is gently sprayed on the starting line, under a slight pressure of nitrogen, as the syringe moves back and forth across the plate.

[161] Morgan, M. R., J. Chromatog., **9,** 379, 1962.
[162] A. H. Thomas Co., Vine St. at Third, Philadelphia 5, Pa.
[163] Ritter, F. J., and Meyer, G. M., Nature, **193,** 941, 1962.
[164] C. Desaga, G. m. b. H., Heidelberg, Hauptstr. 60, Germany. U. S. representative: C. A. Brinkmann and Co., Inc., Cantiague Road, Westbury, L. I., N. Y. Representative in England: Camlab (Glass), Ltd., Milton Road, Cambridge.

A sample solution may also be applied, very conveniently, by using a syringe to which is attached a polyethylene tubing that has been tapered by heating over a small flame. As this flexible capillary is drawn gently over the plate, the solution containing the sample is applied with no damage to the layer surface.[165] Still another simple tech-

Fig. 39-25. Electromechanical Sample Applicator.

nique is to cover the thin layer with glass strips so that only a gap of 2 mm. remains along one edge of the plate, and then to apply the sample solution with a microspray gun from a distance of 1 to 2 cm.[166]

The solvents used in analytical work (Tables 39-5, 39-7, 39-9, 39-11, 39-13, and 39-15) are also employed in preparative thin-layer chromatography.

As in analytical thin-layer chromatography, fractionation can be achieved by developing a plate once, with a single solvent, or by multiple development, stepwise development, or continuous development. In preparative work, multiple and stepwise development are used almost exclusively; chromatography on gradient layers is also profitably employed as it yields particularly good separations. In the authors' experience, development in plain jars is advantageous.

In some cases a compound is more readily isolated as a derivative, especially if the derivative has a significantly different migration rate with respect to impurities from which it is to be separated. Hydroxy compounds, for example, are more easily separated from complex mixtures of other polar compounds as their weakly polar acetyl derivatives[167] or nitrate derivatives.[168] After purification by preparative thin-layer chro-

[165] Habermann, E., private communication.
[166] Stahl, E., Lab. Practice, **13,** 498, 1964.
[167] Mangold, H. K., Fette, Seifen, Anstrichmittel, **61,** 877, 1959.
[168] Wekell, J. C., Houle, C. R., and Malins, D. C., J. Chromatog., **14,** 529, 1964.

matography, these derivatives may be quantitatively recovered by alkaline saponification or by catalytic hydrogenation, respectively.

Volatile compounds may be fractionated on thin layers as their derivatives. Generally, satisfactory melting points of derivatives of volatile compounds, isolated by preparative thin-layer chromatography, can be obtained without further purification by other techniques, such as crystallization.[169]

Indicators used in preparative thin-layer chromatography should be nondestructive (Table 39-16, Nos. 1, 2, 3, 5, 7), but any suitable reagent can be employed if the major center portion of the plate is covered with a glass plate and only strips, about 2 cm. wide, along both vertical edges of the plate, are sprayed with the reagent solution. By use of this technique, the position of the various fractions in the covered part of the layer can be accurately predicted, provided the layer is of even thickness throughout.

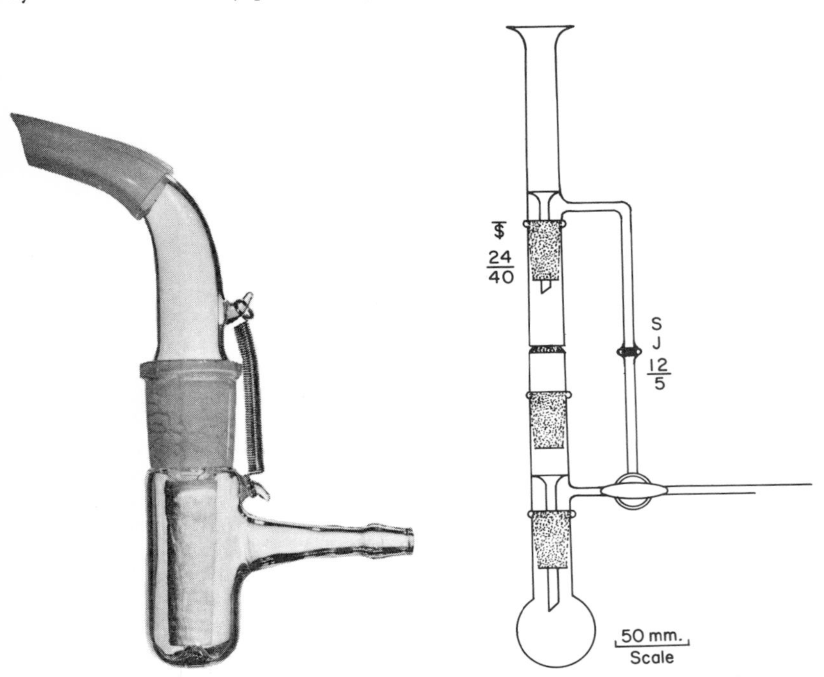

Fig. 39-26. Vacuum Zone Collector.

Fig. 39-27. Apparatus for Extracting and Filtering.

Substances separated by preparative thin-layer chromatography can be scraped off the plates with a spatula or a razor blade. It is more convenient, however, to employ a vacuum zone collector.[170] Such an apparatus is connected to an aspirator and the coating material containing the desired fractions is sucked into an extraction cylinder. A commercial model[171] of a vacuum zone collector is shown in Fig. 39-26.

[169] Malins, D. C., and Wekell, J. C., J. Chem. Educ., **40,** 531, 1963.
[170] Ritter, F. J., and Meyer, G. M., Nature, **193,** 941, 1962.
[171] C. Desaga, G. m. b. H., Heidelberg, Hauptstr. 60, Germany. U. S. representative: C. A. Brinkmann and Co., Inc., Cantiague Rd., Westbury, L. I., N. Y. Representative in England: Camlab (Glass), Ltd., Milton Road, Cambridge.

Many compounds which are not altered during chromatography will undergo degradation changes when they are on a dry (adsorbent) layer. Therefore, fractions should be recovered from the plates immediately after chromatography. The fractions are extracted by shaking with a suitable solvent and the resulting suspension is filtered through sintered glass. The residual coating material is re-extracted at least twice. A filtering apparatus (Fig. 39-27) especially designed for use in thin-layer chromatography has been designed[172] and is available commercially.[173]

A set of microchemical implements for work with small amounts of substances isolated by thin-layer chromatography has been described.[174] This set is available through a laboratory supply house.[175]

It is sometimes possible to isolate a fraction by sublimation. For this purpose, a cooled plate, kept about 1 mm. above the heated chromatogram, is quite satisfactory, as shown by Baehler.[176]

Regardless of the method used for recovering the components of a mixture, it is generally advisable to check by analytical thin-layer chromatography on a standard layer, the purity of each fraction isolated. Furthermore, a final judgment regarding the purity of a fraction recovered, *e.g.*, by adsorption thin-layer chromatography, should be reserved until that fraction has been examined further by complementary chromatographic techniques, such as reversed-phase partition chromatography on paper or a thin layer,[177] or by gas-liquid chromatography.[178,179] The purity of "chromatographically pure" substances should be ascertained by elemental analysis, by determinations of their physical constants, and by spectral analyses.

CONCLUSION

The thin-layer technique affords an elegantly simple procedure for chromatographing in all kinds of solid-liquid and liquid-liquid systems. Hence, this versatile tool can be applied to almost the entire spectrum of chemical compounds. It can be practiced on an analytical as well as on a preparative scale. Because of its speed, thin-layer chromatography can be employed for checking the course of chemical reactions in the laboratory and for following syntheses in industrial process control. Because of its great resolving power, thin-layer chromatography can be employed for uncovering adulteration of foods as well as decomposition of foods and drugs caused by improper storage or incorrect use.

The sensitivity of the method makes it possible to detect readily compounds which usually are encountered only in trace amounts, such as drug metabolites, narcotics, air pollutants, and pesticides. In botany, thin-layer chromatography can be employed as an aid in chemical taxonomy. In the clinical laboratory, morphological appearance of tissues can be associated with their chemical composition, as manifested by the chromatographic patterns of tissue extracts. Pathological changes often can be substantiated by abnormal chromatographic patterns of tissues.

The great advantages of thin-layer chromatography are often most profitably exploited when the technique is used in conjunction with other methods of analysis.

[172] Komarek, R. J., Jensen, R. G., and Pickett, B. W., J. Lipid Res., **5,** 268, 1964.
[173] A. H. Thomas Co., Vine St. at Third, Philadelphia 5, Pa.
[174] Schilcher, H., Z. anal. Chem., **199,** 335, 1964.
[175] Carl Roth OHG, 75 Karlsruhe, Herrenstrasse, Germany.
[176] Baehler, B., Helv. Chim. Acta, **45,** 309, 1962.
[177] Mangold, H. K., Kammereck, R., and Malins, D. C., Microchem. J. Sympos., **2.** 697, 1962.
[178] Stahl, E., and Trennheuser, L., Arch. Pharm., **293,** 826, 1960.
[179] Mangold, H. K., and Kammereck, R., Chem. & Ind. (London), 1032, 1961.

SELECTED BIBLIOGRAPHY

Books on Chromatography

Heftmann, E., Ed., Chromatography, Reinhold Publishing Co., New York, and Chapman & Hall, Ltd., London, 1966.

Lederer, E., Ed., Chromatographie en chimie organique et biologique, Vols. I and II, Masson et Cie, Paris, 1959, 1960.

Books on Thin-Layer Chromatography

Bobbitt, J. M., Thin-Layer Chromatography, Reinhold Publishing Co., New York, and Chapman & Hall, Ltd., London, 1963.

Randerath, K., Thin-Layer Chromatography, Verlag Chemie, Weinheim, with Academic Press, New York, 1963.

Stahl, E., Ed., Thin-Layer Chromatography; A Laboratory Handbook, Springer-Verlag, Berlin-Heidelberg-New York, with Academic Press, New York, 1965.

Truter, E. V., Thin Film Chromatography, Cleaver-Hume Press, Ltd., London, 1963.

Chapter 40

SEDIMENTATION ANALYSIS

By Gerson Kegeles
Department of Chemistry
Clark University
Worcester, Massachusetts

INTRODUCTION

Ultracentrifugation was originally devised by Prof. T. Svedberg as a tool for the separation and analysis of complex colloidal mixtures.[1] In its original conception, the ultracentrifuge was not so much an extremely high speed device as it was a centrifuge specially designed to be free of disturbing vibrations which would remix the partially separated fractions.

Methods of Separation.—It will not be the purpose of this chapter to provide details as to design of major equipment, since detailed descriptions exist elsewhere, and this is the province of a very few laboratories and commercial manufacturers. The applications of many alternative techniques, using a variety of accessories, become the province of the individual investigator, and will be described.

For direct-recording analytical purposes, a heavy rotor (Fig. 40-1) containing a chamber or chambers for transparent sample cells is driven by an oil turbine,[1,2,3] an air turbine,[4,5,6,7] a direct electrical drive,[8] or an electrical drive with magnetic suspension.[9] Analysis may also be performed by more conventional techniques of sampling, ordinarily at the completion of an experiment. Convection-free cells must be designed and oriented so that their side walls constitute planes lying along radii drawn from the axis of rotation (Fig. 40-2).[2,3] Cells essentially free of convection, which allow for optical observation of separations, followed by separation and sampling, have been designed by Tiselius, Pedersen, and Svedberg,[10] and by Yphantis and Waugh.[11]

A somewhat different design, which does not permit direct-recording analysis, but reduces convection, especially during deceleration and prior to sampling, is the "swinging-bucket" rotor.[12]

The traditional angle-head rotor (Fig. 40-3) for preparative work is also used for analyses based on partial separations. Convection is always present in its use, but this does not necessarily interfere with its application as a practical tool.

[1] Svedberg, T., and Rinde, H., J. Amer. Chem. Soc., **45,** 943, 1924.
[2] Svedberg, T., Colloid Chemistry, 2d Ed., D. Van Nostrand Co., Princeton, N. J., 1928.
[3] Svedberg, T., and Pedersen, K. O., The Ultracentrifuge, Oxford University Press, 1940.
[4] Henriot, E., and Huguenard, E., Compt. rend., **180,** 1389, 1925.
[5] Beams, J. W., Rev. Sci. Instr., **1,** 667, 1930.
[6] Beams, J. W., and Pickels, E. G., Rev. Sci. Instr., **6,** 299, 1935.
[7] McBain, J. W., and O'Sullivan, C. M., J. Amer. Chem. Soc., **57,** 780, 1935.
[8] Pickels, E. G., Machine Design, **22,** 102, 1950.
[9] Beams, J. W., Dixon, H. M., III, Robeson, A., and Snidow, J. Phys. Chem., **59,** 915, 1955.
[10] Tiselius, A., Pedersen, K. O., and Svedberg, T., Nature, **140,** 848, 1937.
[11] Yphantis, D. A., and Waugh, D. F., J. Phys. Chem., **60,** 630, 1956.
[12] Kahler, H., and Lloyd, B. J., J. Phys. Chem., **55,** 1344, 1951.

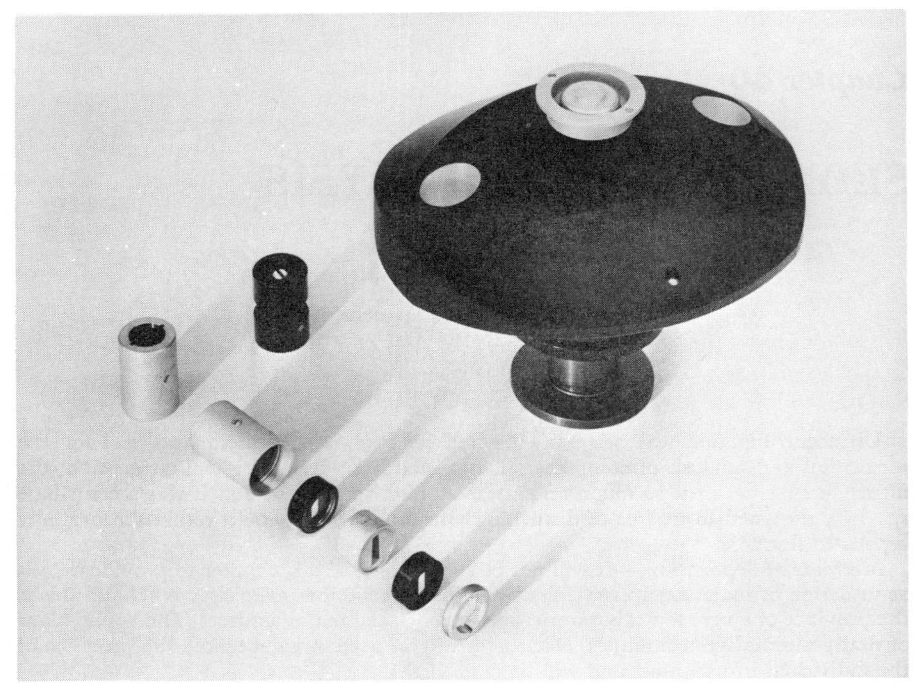

Fig. 40-1. (Courtesy Spinco Div., Beckman Instruments, Inc.)

In differential sedimentation with either the angle-head or swinging-bucket rotor, separations are achieved by collecting the sediment, or pellet, under prescribed conditions of gravitational field and time of sedimentation, resuspending in solvent, and sedimenting again and collecting sediment under altered conditions. The procedure,

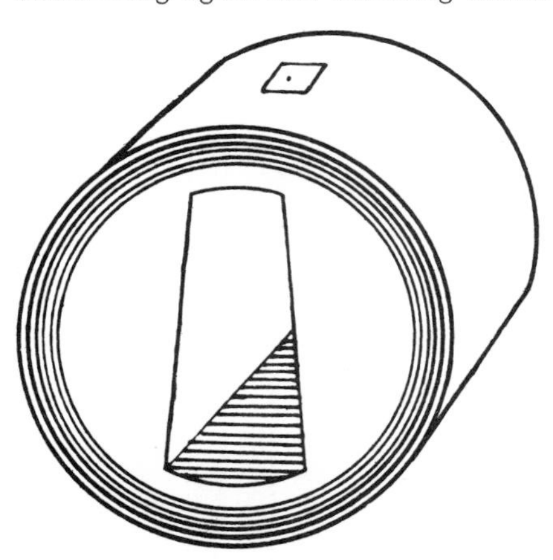

Fig. 40-2. (Courtesy S. M. Klainer.)

Fig. 40-3. (Courtesy Spinco Div., Beckman Instruments, Inc.)

while somewhat arbitrary, has had considerable practical use.[13] Primarily to avoid the effects of convective mixing, superposed concentration gradients of a neutral solute such as sucrose have been employed.[14]

Partial separations are also achieved in the establishment of sedimentation equilibrium, a steady state in which flow due to sedimentation in the centrifugal field is balanced by backward diffusion toward the axis of rotation as a result of the established concentration gradient. In practice, such experiments are performed at relatively low angular velocities. Such partial separations are also achieved during the period of approach to sedimentation equilibrium. Although analysis during the period of approach to equilibrium requires conditions for convection-free sedimentation, there is no such requirement for the final equilibrium condition, which may be employed analytically in a cell of any shape.

Separations based upon even very small differences in density may be achieved effectively by application of a centrifugal field in the presence of a density gradient.[15,16,17,18,19] These separations have been studied with direct-recording optical methods.

Methods of Analysis.—The traditional methods of collecting samples from different parts of the sample tube and subjecting them to chemical or biological assay, or to measurements of physical properties, are not without difficulty. Convective disturbances are essentially avoided with small samples only, in the Tiselius[10] and Yphantis-Waugh[11] partition cells, or are minimized by the superposition of density gradients upon larger samples held in swinging-bucket or angle-head rotors. Moreover, when the rotor is decelerated, the effects of diffusion tend to remix the fractions before they are sampled. For the partial characterization of biologically active entities in complex mixtures, these methods nevertheless remain invaluable.

However, for more highly purified solute systems, direct-recording optical methods which do not disturb the sample during the course of the experiment are highly preferable. These usually have very wide applicability, but sometimes suffer thereby in not being specific for certain solutes of interest.[20]

Historically, the methods based on light absorption were developed first.[1,2,3] With the advent of a number of methods based upon refractive index,[21,22,23,24,25,26,27,28,29,30,31,32] and capable of providing a detailed record related to concentration or concentration-gradient distribution, the light absorption method fell into disuse. Interest in nucleic

[13] de Duve, C., and Berthet, J., Int. Rev. Cytology, **3,** 225, 1954.
[14] Hogeboom, G. H., and Kuff, E. L., J. Biol. Chem., **210,** 733, 1954.
[15] Brakke, M. K., J. Amer. Chem. Soc., **73,** 1847, 1951.
[16] Anderson, N. G., in Physical Techniques in Biological Research, Vol. III, G. Oster and A. W. Pollister, Eds., Academic Press, New York, 1956.
[17] Meselson, M., Stahl, F. W., and Vinograd, J., Proc. Nat. Acad. Sci. U. S., **43,** 581, 1957.
[18] de Duve, C., Berthet, J., and Beaufay, H., Progr. Biophys. and Biophys. Chem., **9,** 325, 1959.
[19] Oster, G., and Yamamoto, M., Chem. Rev., **63,** 257, 1963.
[20] Johnston, J. P., and Ogston, A. G., Trans. Faraday Soc., **42,** 789, 1946.
[21] Lamm, O., Z. physik. Chem., **A 138,** 313, 1928.
[22] Tiselius, A., Pedersen, K. O., and Eriksson-Quensel, I. B., Nature, **139,** 546, 1937.
[23] Philpot, J. St. L., Nature, **141,** 283, 1938.
[24] Andersson, K. J. I., Nature, **143,** 720, 1939.
[25] Svensson, H., Kolloid-Z., **87,** 181, 1939; **90,** 141, 1940.
[26] Wolter, H., Ann. Physik, **7,** 182, 1950.
[27] Trautman, R., and Burns, V. W., Biochim. Biophys. Acta, **14,** 26, 1954.
[28] Calvet, E., Comptes rend. Acad. Sci., **220,** 597, 1945.
[29] Philpot, J. St. L., and Cook, G. H., Research, **1,** 234, 1948.
[30] Svensson, H., Acta Chem. Scand., **3,** 1170, 1949.
[31] Labhart, H., and Staub, H., Helv. Chim. Acta, **30,** 1954, 1947.
[32] Beams, J. W., Snidow, N., Robeson, A., and Dixon, H. M., III, Rev. Sci. Instr., **25,** 295, 1954.

acids and their separation,[17] the need for specific methods of analysis in mixtures,[20] and the advent of recording rapid-scanning photomultipliers,[33] which help to eliminate some of the difficulties earlier encountered in standardization of photographic techniques, have all contributed to a revival of interest in the light absorption technique, which can be made more powerful by the addition of spectrophotometric equipment.[34] For greatest sensitivity at low concentration, the light absorption methods are the methods of choice for many systems of biological origin. On the other hand, for most general applicability, for high absolute accuracy at moderate concentration levels, and for work with most synthetic polymer systems, scale,[21] Schlieren[23,24,25,26,27] or interferometric[28,29,30,31,32] optical systems, based upon refractive index, are required.

CHARACTERIZATION BY ULTRACENTRIFUGATION

This section will attempt to suggest very briefly the most frequently intended objectives and their attainability in the study of various types of solute systems, classified according to the type of ultracentrifuge experiment and the type of solute system.

SEDIMENTATION VELOCITY METHODS

Pure Solutes.—The sedimentation coefficient $s = (dx/dt)/\omega^2 x$ is determined as a function of concentration (x is distance from center of rotation, t is time, ω is angular velocity). In the most precise work, s is extrapolated to zero concentration.

Pauci-Disperse Nonreacting Mixtures.—The relative amounts of the various species, as well as their sedimentation coefficients, are desired. If it is not possible to determine separate sedimentation coefficients, a weight-average value may be obtained from the rate of movement of the x-coordinate defined by

$$\sqrt{\overline{x^2}} = \left[\int x^2 \frac{dn}{dx} dx \bigg/ \int \frac{dn}{dx} dx\right]^{1/2}$$

where: n is the refractive index;
x is the distance from center of rotation; and
$\frac{dn}{dx}$ is the refractive index gradient.

The integration is made over the entire boundary region, and a region of homogeneous liquid is required both above and below the boundary region.

Polydisperse Nonreacting Solutes.—The distribution of sedimentation coefficients is often desired. In less ambitious studies, the weight-average sedimentation coefficient, as defined above, may be desired.

Chemically-reacting Solute Systems.—The relative amounts of the various species, and from these the equilibrium constants for the chemical reactions, are often desired. When the chemical reactions are either very slow or very fast, compared to the rate of separation of species, these objectives are attainable in favorable cases.

SEDIMENTATION EQUILIBRIUM METHODS

Pure Solutes.—The molecular weight is desired and obtained, in the range from less than 100 to about 10^6. For nonideal solutions, the activity coefficient of the solute may be obtained as a function of the concentration.

Pauci-disperse Nonreacting Systems.—The molecular weight of each species is de-

[33] Riley, J. F., and Lyons, P. A., J. Amer. Chem. Soc., **77**, 261, 1955.
[34] Schachman, H. K., Biochemistry, **2**, 887, 1963.

sired, and is attainable in favorable cases. Alternatively, the weight-average molecular weight and the Z-average molecular weight (molecular weight averaged over a quantity equal to the product of weight times molecular weight) are obtained.

Polydisperse Nonreacting Systems.—The distribution of molecular weights is desired, and is attainable in the absence of extensive thermodynamic nonideality. Alternatively, the weight-average and Z-average molecular weights for the mixture are obtained.

Chemically-reacting Solute Systems.—The equilibrium constants for the chemical reactions may be obtained in the absence of extensive thermodynamic nonideality.

APPROACH TO SEDIMENTATION EQUILIBRIUM METHODS

Pure Solutes.—The molecular weight is desired and obtained, in the range from less than 100 to about 10^6. For nonideal solutes, activity coefficients may be obtained.

Purified Solute Systems.—The ultracentrifuge field relaxation technique provides an easily applied and extremely delicate criterion for assessing the presence of very small amounts of heavy impurities. On the other hand, the use of higher speeds, and of data from the top of the column only, ignores such impurities and gives the molecular weight of the major solute component.

Pauci-disperse Nonreacting Systems.—The molecular weight of each species is desired, and attainable in favorable cases. Alternatively, the weight-average molecular weight is readily obtained in rapid experiments (usually from 30 minutes to 2 hours).

Polydisperse Nonreacting Systems.—The weight-average molecular weight and the non-ideality (virial coefficient) are desired and attainable even for highly nonideal solutions.

Chemically-reacting Solute Systems.—The equilibrium constants for the chemical reactions may be obtained in the absence of extensive thermodynamic nonideality.

DENSITY GRADIENT SEDIMENTATION EQUILIBRIUM

Pure Solutes.—The density and the molecular weight in the presence of the gradient are desired and obtained.

Pauci-disperse Nonreacting Systems.—The densities and molecular weights of the individual species separated in the presence of the gradient are desired and obtained.

Polydisperse Nonreacting Systems.—A distribution of species primarily on the basis of densities should be attainable.

Chemically-reacting Solute Species.—It is predicted that the method may provide an invaluable analytical tool whenever the reactants and product are even slightly different in density (or partial specific volume).

ANALYTICAL PROCEDURES

This section will attempt to outline some of the experimental requirements for application of the characterization methods discussed above. Classification is made again according to the type of experiment and the type of solute system. The state of the art is such that there is seldom agreement among active investigators as to attainable accuracy using various techniques. Thus, only a few statements as to accuracy will be made. In addition to the specific references to be cited below, the general references are recommended for background and information.

SEDIMENTATION VELOCITY METHODS

Pure Solutes, Using Schlieren Optics.—A homogeneous solution of about 0.5 percent to 2 percent concentration is normally adequate for each experiment. For the usual

12-mm. thick cell with a single 4° sector angle (Fig. 40-2), approximately 0.8 ml. are required. For a 12-mm. thick, 2° sector angle cell the requirement can be reduced to as little as 0.2 ml. Under favorable conditions, accuracy is somewhat better than 1 percent.

Pauci-disperse Nonreacting Solutes, Using Schlieren Optics.—Requirements are essentially those for pure solutes, except that the lowest concentration may need to exceed 1 percent to search for small impurities as indicated by boundary separation.

Polydisperse Nonreacting Solutes.—For weight-average sedimentation coefficients from the movement of

$$x = \sqrt{\overline{x^2}} = \left[\int x^2 \frac{dn}{dx}\,dx \bigg/ \int \frac{dn}{dx}\,dx\right]^{1/2}$$

using Schlieren optics,[35,36] requirements are essentially those for pure solutes, except that, in the case of long-chain or stiff polymers, extrapolation must be made to much lower concentrations. For this purpose 30-mm. thick cells are desirable. In the case of nucleic acids, or colored solutes, the light absorption method is more sensitive at very low concentrations. For obtaining the distribution of sedimentation coefficients,[37,38] several experiments in the range 1 percent to approximately 0.2 percent should be performed, and the curves extrapolated to zero concentration, as well as to long times. The experiments at the lowest concentrations are most easily performed in a 30-mm. thick cell (for a 4° single sector cell approximately 2 ml. of solution are required).

Chemically-reacting Solute Systems.—Requirements are essentially those for a single pure solute, except that the range of concentration should be extended in both directions. In the event of boundary separation, the partial resolution of the boundaries can serve to determine the sedimentation coefficient of the monomer and the polymer in a reversibly polymerizing system forming a single polymeric species.[39,40] In the case of very slowly reacting systems, equilibrium constants for the chemical reaction may be estimated from a study of relative areas under separated boundaries, provided that several experiments are performed over a range of total concentration.[41,42] In the event of no boundary separation in a rapidly interconverting solute system, it is sometimes possible to estimate sedimentation coefficients of both slower and faster species by careful measurements over a range of total concentration, and by extrapolation of linear portions of the s *vs.* c diagram to zero concentration.[43]

Synthetic Boundary Experiments.—The solvent is layered over the solution while the rotor is in operation. This procedure was conceived and first developed into an operative technique by the author.[44] An alternative design was shortly thereafter developed elsewhere[45] as a result of the private communication of details of the author's cell design and successful results, prior to their publication. For a 2° sector angle, 12-mm. thick cell, as modified by the author (Fig. 40-4), approximately 0.15 ml. of solution and 0.12 ml. of solvent are required. Other adaptations may require up to twice these volumes, but some are capable of use with interferometric optical systems. Direct ob-

[35] Goldberg, R. J., J. Phys. Chem., **57,** 194, 1953.
[36] Trautman, R., and Schumaker, V. N., J. Chem. Phys., **22,** 551, 1954.
[37] Signer, R., and Gross, H., Helv. Chim. Acta, **17,** 726, 1934.
[38] Williams, J. W., Baldwin, R. L., Saunders, W. M., and Squire, P. G., J. Amer. Chem. Soc., **74,** 1542, 1952.
[39] Gilbert, G. A., Disc. Faraday Soc., **20,** 68, 1955; Proc. Roy. Soc., **A 276,** 354, 1963.
[40] Nichol, L. W., and Bethune, J. L., Nature, **198,** 880, 1963.
[41] Singer, S. J., and Campbell, D. H., J. Amer. Chem. Soc., **74,** 1794, 1952.
[42] Squire, P. G., and Pedersen, K. O., J. Amer. Chem. Soc., **83,** 476, 1961.
[43] Schwert, G. W., J. Biol. Chem., **179,** 655, 1949.
[44] Kegeles, G., J. Amer. Chem. Soc., **74,** 5532, 1952.
[45] Pickels, E. G., Harrington, W. F., and Schachman, H. K., Proc. Natl. Acad. U. S., **38,** 943, 1952.

servation of the sedimentation of slowly sedimenting solutes is facilitated. The refractive index change across the boundary region is used to determine original concentration, by measuring areas under Schlieren curves or by counting fringes from Rayleigh optical systems (a double channel synthetic boundary cell is used).

Transport Methods.—For biologically active materials, even in impure mixtures, bioassay methods may be used in partition cells, or in swinging-bucket rotors, or possibly in angle-head rotors in the presence of superposed density gradients of inert solutes. Optical analysis may be used for purer substances.[46,47,48] In the latter, the requirements are essentially those for ordinary sedimentation, except that it is advisable to introduce approximately 0.05 to 0.1 ml. of a dense immiscible transparent liquid which layers itself below the fluid column, when data are desired from the region near the cell bottom. This method is most suitable, in aqueous solution, for species with molecular weights below several thousand.

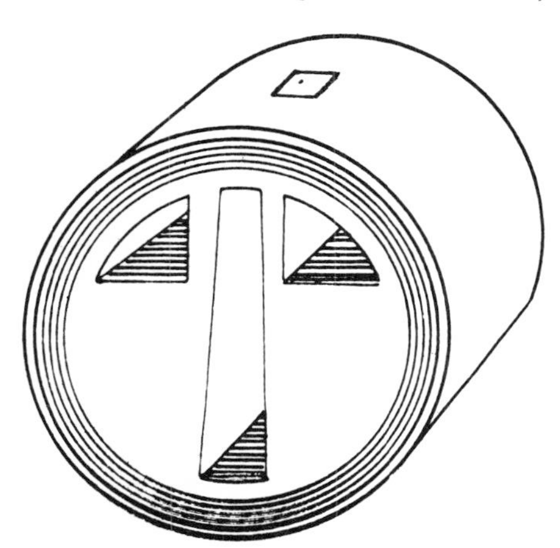

Fig. 40-4. (Courtesy S. M. Klainer.)

SEDIMENTATION EQUILIBRIUM METHODS

Pure Solutes.—For molecular weights of 1000 or less, a long column (10 to 15 mm.) of liquid may be used and equilibrium attained in approximately 2 days. A short column (less than 5 mm.) may be used to shorten very materially the time required for equilibrium,[49] but less data are obtained. For molecular weights of several thousand or more, it is preferable to use short columns and Rayleigh or Jamin interferometric optical systems. Experiments may be performed with as little as 0.1 ml. of solution, at concentrations from 0.1 to 2 percent. At the lowest concentrations, 30-mm. thick cells may be required. It is often desirable to use a rotor containing a large number of samples.[50] For thermodynamically nonideal solutions, it is necessary to extrapolate results to infinite dilution, which is most effectively accomplished by a series of short column experiments at different concentrations. Suitable rotor speeds vary from 60,000 revolutions per minute for solutes with molecular weights below 100 to only a few hundred revolutions per second in the 10^6 molecular weight range. The partial specific volume of the solute must be determined by independent measurements. In the most favorable cases, the accuracy is better than 1 percent.

Pauci-disperse Nonreacting Solutes.—The experimental conditions are similar to those for pure solutes; in the case of extensive thermodynamic nonideality, short column experiments designed to produce relatively small differentials of concentration between the top and the bottom of the column are virtually essential.

Polydisperse Nonreacting Solutes.—The experimental conditions are again similar to those just described. However, in the case of attempts to arrive at a distribution of

[46] Gutfreund, H., and Ogston, A. G., Biochem. J., **44,** 163, 1949.
[47] Baldwin, R. L., Biochem. J., **55,** 644, 1953.
[48] Webber, R. V., J. Amer. Chem. Soc., **78,** 536, 1956.
[49] van Holde, K. E., and Baldwin, R. L., J. Phys. Chem., **62,** 734, 1958.
[50] Yphantis, D. A., Ann. N. Y. Acad. Sci., **88,** 586, 1960.

molecular weights,[51,52] it is essential that thermodynamic nonideality be suppressed. This is accomplished in the case of proteins in aqueous solution by adjusting the pH to isoelectric conditions and working in the approximate range of 0.1 to 0.3 ionic strength. In the case of synthetic polymer solutions this is accomplished by dissolving the polymer in a solvent which has a θ-temperature[53] for the solute in the readily attainable range of the instrument (many ultracentrifuges operate satisfactorily up to 150°C. or higher, at the relatively low speeds ordinarily required—5000 to 20,000 r.p.m.). Very little experimental leverage can be obtained for the determination of molecular weight distributions unless the investigator has suitable apparatus and is willing to take the necessary pains to obtain successful experiments with long columns (approximately 15 mm.), which may imply experiments of as long as two weeks duration.

Chemically-reacting Solute Systems.—The required experimental conditions are essentially those for pure solutes, with the exception that a range of concentration (perhaps tenfold or more) should be covered to obtain equilibrium constants,[54,55,56] assuming no appreciable thermodynamic nonideality. This can be accomplished in one or two experiments using long columns, or in a large series of experiments at different starting concentrations, using short columns and Rayleigh or Jamin interferometry. If nonideality is present, it is virtually impossible to solve the problem without assuming that redistribution of the sample causes no local changes in nonideality;[57] however, this assumption is quite probably at variance with the real situation.

APPROACH TO SEDIMENTATION EQUILIBRIUM METHODS

Pure Solutes.—The methodology is based upon theoretical developments by Archibald,[58] and was applied to several problems subsequent to his publication.[59,60,61] The experimental technique has now become reasonably standardized.[62,63,64] Approximately 0.3 ml. of solution at a concentration of 0.5 percent to 2 percent are sufficient for a single molecular weight determination in an experiment of less than 2 hours duration, in the event of no appreciable thermodynamic nonideality. This solution may be layered over 0.05 ml. to 0.1 ml. of a denser immiscible liquid to make it possible to obtain data from the bottom of the column.[65] In a standard 12-mm. thick, 4° sector angle cell, 0.75 ml. or less of solution are required. This requirement may be reduced to about 0.15 ml. by use of a 12-mm. thick, 2° sector angle cell. In the event of strong nonideality, several determinations and an extrapolation to infinite dilution are required. For this purpose, a 30-mm. thick, 4° sector angle cell is very useful. The molecular weight is computed from values of the concentration gradient and the concentration (in refractometric units) extrapolated to both ends of the fluid column (Fig. 40-5), according to the equation of Archibald,[58]

[51] Rinde, H., dissertation, University of Uppsala, Sweden, 1928.
[52] Wales, M., Adler, F. T., and van Holde, K. E., J. Phys. Colloid Chem., **55,** 195, 1951.
[53] Flory, P. J., Principles of Polymer Chemistry, Cornell University Press, 1953.
[54] Squire, P. G., and Li, C. H., J. Amer. Chem. Soc., **83,** 3521, 1961.
[55] Adams, E. T., Jr., Ph.D. thesis, Univ. of Wisconsin, 1962.
[56] Jeffrey, P. D., Ph.D. thesis, Univ. of Adelaide, Australia, 1965.
[57] Adams, E. T., Jr., and Fujita, H., in Conference on Ultracentrifugal Analysis in Theory and Experiment, J. W. Williams, Ed., 119–128, Academic Press, New York, 1963.
[58] Archibald, W. J., J. Phys. Colloid Chem., **51,** 1204, 1947.
[59] Li, C. H., Tiselius, A., Pedersen, K. O., Hagdahl, L., and Carstensen, H., J. Biol. Chem., **190,** 317, 1951.
[60] Porath, J., Acta Chem. Scand., **6,** 1237, 1952.
[61] Brown, R. A., Kritchevsky, D., and Davies, M., J. Amer. Chem. Soc., **76,** 3342, 1954.
[62] Klainer, S. M., and Kegeles, G., J. Phys. Chem., **59,** 952, 1955.
[63] Klainer, S. M., and Kegeles, G., Arch. Biochem. Biophys., **63,** 247, 1956.
[64] Klainer, S. M., M. A. thesis, Clark University, 1955.
[65] Ginsburg, A., Appel, P., and Schachman, H. K., Arch. Biochem. Biophys., **65,** 545, 1956.

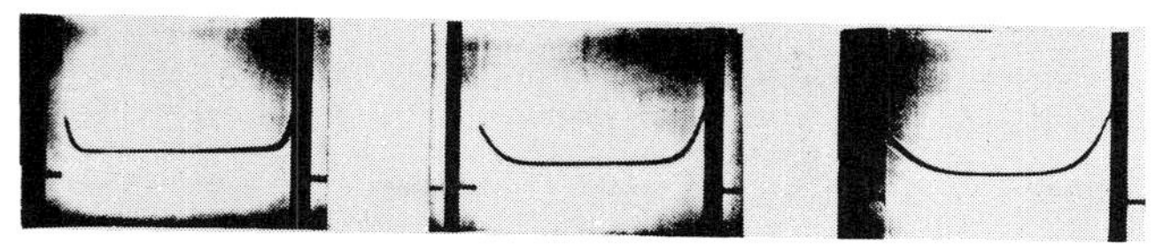

FIG. 40-5. (Courtesy S. M. Klainer.)

$$M = \frac{RT(dc/dx)}{(1 - V\rho)\omega^2 xc} = \frac{RT(dn/dx)}{(1 - V\rho)\omega^2 x(n - n_0)}$$

where: V is the partial specific volume of solute;
ρ is the density of the solution;
ω is the angular velocity of the rotor in radians per second;
x is distance from center of rotation to appropriate end of fluid column;
n is the refractive index of the solution; and
n_0 is the refractive index of the solvent.

In Figs. 40-5, 40-6, 40-7, and 40-8, centrifugal sedimentation proceeds from left to right. The patterns have been obtained in a Schlieren optical system.

For the concentration at the ends, the procedure and equations developed by Klainer and the author[62,63] are recommended, in which solvent (including all buffer ions, if any) is layered over solution in the ultracentrifuge (see Fig. 40-6), in a cell of the same thick-

FIG. 40-6. (Courtesy C. L. Sia, Clark University.)

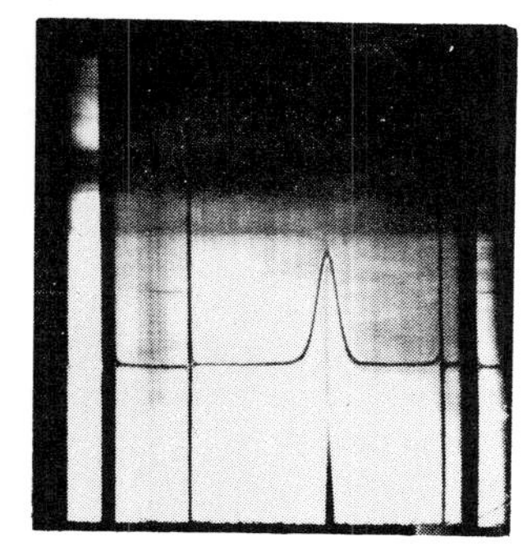

FIG. 40-7. (Courtesy C. L. Sia, Clark University.)

ness as that employed in the main run. For synthetic boundary cells of other than 12-mm. thickness, and for most work with organic solvents, it is necessary to modify the required standard dural centerpieces according to the author's procedure (Fig. 40-4).[44] The required drilling of blind holes in one face of a standard centerpiece of any size can be done by an engraver, from a template of an enlarged scale drawing. The original reference[62] and the M.A. thesis of S. M. Klainer[64] should be referred to for complete details of measurement and computation. It is also possible to avoid the synthetic boundary reference run in simple systems, by plotting results from a series of photographs at recorded times of sedimentation,[66] thereby gaining information about purity. It is

[66] Trautman, R., J. Phys. Chem., **60**, 1211, 1956.

strongly recommended that the Schlieren optical arrangement, equipped with a phase contrast diaphragm[26,27,62] be used, and that the source slit for the optical system be centered on the axis of the lens system.[27] As in the sedimentation equilibrium methods, partial specific volume measurements are required. The rotor speed should be selected

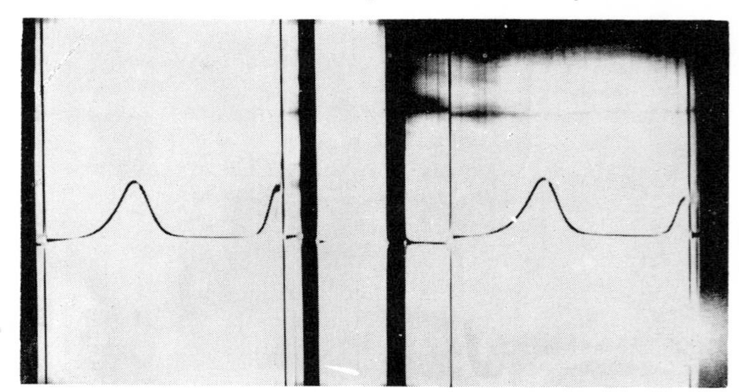

Fig. 40-8. (Courtesy C. L. Sia, Clark University.)

so as to provide a relatively gentle rise of the refractive index gradient function at the ends of the cell, as otherwise extrapolation becomes exceedingly difficult. The accuracy appears to range from about 5 percent for molecular weights of the order of magnitude 50 to 200 to close to 1 percent for very careful work in the range of molecular weights from 500 to 200,000. For still higher molecular weights, it becomes increasingly difficult to maintain the required constant, slow rotor speed, except with magnetically suspended rotors. For very high molecular weights, complications begin to occur when the centrifugal field employed is no longer large compared to the earth's gravitational field. For nonideal solutions, the apparent molecular weight is equal to

$$M \Big/ \left(1 + c\,\frac{\partial \ln y}{\partial c}\right)$$

where: c is a concentration; and
y is an activity coefficient on the same scale.

This permits the determination of activity coefficients with this technique. Two additional variations in technique will be described below, neither of which permits gathering of data from both ends of the cell.

Purified Solute Systems.—The modification described by Ehrenberg[67] uses higher speeds, and obtains data from the top of the cell only. A standard cell or a synthetic boundary cell operated as a standard cell is used for the main run, and the acceleration schedule, and time at full speed, are carefully noted. Just before a free peak begins to form at the upper meniscus, the refractive index gradient curve becomes horizontal, and a photograph is taken at this time (Fig. 40-7). In the reference run, solvent, including all buffer ions, is layered over solution in a synthetic boundary cell, and the identical acceleration schedule and time of centrifugation at full speed are followed as before. A photograph is taken at the same time. The area under this Schlieren curve measures the "plateau region" concentration, from which is subtracted the area above the "plateau region" in the main run, to provide the meniscus concentration. The Archibald condition

[67] Ehrenberg, A., Acta Chem. Scand., **11**, 1257, 1957.

is used to calculate molecular weights. Because these experiments must be performed at relatively high speed, it is recommended that the consequent window distortions be minimized by using the same synthetic boundary cell in both runs, a procedure found to be unnecessary in the usual low speed applications of the Archibald technique. The combination of two high speed runs serves to sediment high molecular weight impurities out of the recorded region of the cell, and out of consideration by the investigator. This often constitutes an excellent method for the molecular weight of the major component in a highly purified protein preparation, but, by the same token, it must not be employed as a criterion of purity.

A complementary method developed by Sia and the author[68] utilizes data from the bottom of the cell only. Approximately 0.05 ml. to 0.1 ml. of a dense, immiscible liquid are inserted with the solution. Solvent is then layered over solution (in a synthetic boundary cell), and the rotor is taken very briefly to a speed which causes sedimentation (20,000 r.p.m. for 1 to 2 minutes for a protein of molecular weight 70,000). The speed is then slowly relaxed to about 3000 to 6000 r.p.m., and a photograph is taken when the refractive index gradient curve at the lower meniscus is approximately horizontal (Fig. 40-8). The area under the free boundary plus the area from the region near the cell bottom measure the concentration at the lower meniscus, and molecular weights are calculated from the Archibald relation at the cell bottom. No reference experiment is required, and the entire experiment requires 1 hour or less. The heavy impurities ignored by the Ehrenberg technique and lost in part in the Archibald experiments are overwhelmingly in evidence in this ultracentrifugal field relaxation method. It is very difficult to prepare a protein which satisfies the size homogeneity criterion of this method: independence of the results on the time or rotor velocity at the higher speed. However, experience has shown that such preparations do exist, and the method is one of the simplest and most delicate known for proteins. It is likely to supplant the classical observation of a "single symmetrical peak" in sedimentation velocity experiments as the best criterion of homogeneity by ultracentrifugal analysis,[68a] whenever investigators submit their preparations to the stringent requirements of this delicate and easily applied test method.

Pauci-disperse Nonreacting Solute Systems.—As shown by Archibald,[58] the weight-average molecular weight is obtained for ideal solutions at both ends of the cell, and the molecular weight representative of the original mixture is obtained by extrapolating both sets of results to zero time, where they should intersect. For nonideal solutions, the resulting apparent molecular weight should be extrapolated to infinite dilution. The experimental requirements and conditions are otherwise as indicated for pure solutes.

Polydisperse Nonreacting Solute Systems.—Experimental conditions for the application of the Archibald method are essentially those outlined above for single pure solutes. It is essential that data from both the top and the bottom of the cell be obtained and correlated, either by operation at low speed and photographing at early times or, preferably, by extrapolating to zero time as originally recommended by Archibald. For nonideal solutions, such apparent molecular weights (or their reciprocals) are extrapolated to zero concentration to give the true weight-average molecular weight, and the slope of the plot at low concentrations is a measure of the nonideality of the solution, as originally demonstrated by the author and his colleagues.[69] Application to synthetic polymer systems has continued,[70] and the nonideality coefficient at low concentrations has been demonstrated to correlate, theoretically and experimentally, with the light-

[68] Sia, C. L., and Kegeles, G., Biochemistry, **2,** 906, 1963.
[68a] Rao, M. S. N., and Pandit, M. W., Biochim. Biophys. Acta, **94,** 238, 1965.
[69] Kegeles, G., Klainer, S. M., and Salem, W. J., J. Phys. Chem., **61,** 1286, 1957.
[70] Fujita, H., Inagaki, H., Kotaka, T., and Utiyama, H., J. Phys. Chem., **66,** 4, 1962.

scattering virial coefficient for the sample. It is urgent to re-emphasize here that the method is similar to light scattering in being able to examine a nonredistributed sample, in contrast to the sedimentation equilibrium method, which is not capable of exact treatment for polydisperse, highly nonideal polymers.

Chemically-reacting Solute Systems.—Data are obtained for such systems under conditions similar to those for single pure solutes, except that results from the bottom and the top may be separately plotted *vs.* the instantaneous local value of the concentration. For rapidly reversibly interacting solutes, the study of Rao and the author should be consulted for details.[71] A series of separate experiments covering a large concentration range should be performed to obtain equilibrium constants. For proteins in dilute aqueous solution, the method is found to be much easier to apply than is light scattering, because of the extreme sensitivity of the latter to stray dust particles.

DENSITY GRADIENT SEDIMENTATION EQUILIBRIUM

Pure Solutes.—The density gradient is produced by a (hopefully) inert substance, either externally or within the cell. For externally produced gradients, schemes similar to those used in chromatography[72] are used, and the solution from a small mixing chamber is flowed into the cell. Dense salts such as cesium and rubidium chlorides and sodium bromide have been sedimented to equilibrium to produce self-generated density gradients within the cell.[17] A small amount of the solution containing the solute to be examined is introduced into the cell through the filling hole by syringe or may be mixed with the gradient-forming salt before filling, or may be introduced by means of a synthetic boundary cell during the early stages of the rotor operation. For light absorption optics with nucleic acids, using ultraviolet light at 260 mμ wavelength, as little as 3 μg. of nucleic acid can be studied by this method. Equilibrium is obtained in about 24 hours at speeds of 20,000 to 40,000 r.p.m. The density of the solute of interest is obtained from the location of its band at equilibrium in the calculated gradient of density (or sampled and measured density) of the self-generated density gradient, in the arrangement of Meselson, Stahl and Vinograd,[17] and the number-average molecular weight is obtained from the width of (or, more precisely, the distribution of concentration across) the band. (To a first approximation, the zones have the shapes of Gaussian error curves, but digital computer studies by the author lead to the conclusion that no gradient can be found which will allow a concentration zone to persist in the exact shape of a Gaussian error curve.) Refractometric optical methods may also be used, but are not the methods of choice here, as they require much larger amounts of the solute of interest (perhaps 100 times as much), and they are sensitive to the gradient of concentration of the inert substance responsible for the density gradient.

Pauci-disperse Noninteracting Solutes.—These systems may be separated, based on density differences of only a few hundredths of a gram per milliliter, provided that the density gradient of the surrounding solution is adjusted correctly.[73] Experimental conditions are essentially as described for single solute systems. If externally produced density gradients are filled into the cell, they may be varied to attempt to improve separations. If gradients of density are produced internally, they may be made steeper, for example, by an increase of initial salt concentration, or by means of a higher rotor speed.

Polydisperse Noninteracting Solutes.—Synthetic polymers may be separated on the basis of density differences in organic solvents containing a density gradient. These will be generally mixed solvents in which the polymer system can be distributed. Since the

[71] Rao, M. S. N., and Kegeles, G., J. Amer. Chem. Soc., **80,** 5724, 1958.
[72] Bock, R. M., and Ling, N. S., Anal. Chem., **26,** 1543, 1954.
[73] Rolfe, R., and Meselson, M., Proc. Natl. Acad. Sci. U. S., **45,** 1039, 1959.

stereochemistry of the polymerization process has a marked effect on the density of the product, this is likely to develop into a useful method of analysis.[74]

Chemically-reacting Solutes.—Chemically-reacting systems which involve reactants and products having appreciably different densities will be banded in a density gradient with at least partial separation of species. The experimental conditions for such separations and analyses are unknown, but will probably differ appreciably for each system to be investigated. Computations are under way by the author and his colleagues to predict conditions under which the method may help elucidate the nature of chemical processes, as well as to determine whether unsuspected chemical reactions may seriously complicate the interpretation of analyses in density gradients.

SELECTED BIBLIOGRAPHY

Finson, B., "An Introduction to Density Gradient Centrifugation," Spinco Technical Reports, Spinco Division, Beckman Instruments, Palo Alto California, 1960. Also available from Spinco is technical literature on commercially available rotors, cells, and accessories for analytical ultracentrifugation.

Fujita, H., Mathematical Theory of Sedimentation Analysis, Academic Press, New York, 1962.

Nichol, L. W., Bethune, J. L., Kegeles, G., and Hess, E. L., in The Proteins, H. Neurath, Ed., Vol. III, Chapter 9, Academic Press, New York, 1964.

Schachman, H. K., in Methods in Enzymolgoy, S. P. Colowick and N. O. Kaplan, Eds., Vol. IV, Academic Press, New York, 1957.

Schachman, H. K., Ultracentrifugation in Biochemistry, Academic Press, New York, 1959.

Svedberg, T., and Pederson, K. O., The Ultracentrifuge, Oxford University Press, 1940.

Williams, J. W., Ed., Conference on Ultracentrifugal Analysis in Theory and Experiment, Academic Press, New York, 1963.

"Conference on the Ultracentrifuge," Ann. N. Y. Acad. Sci., **18,** 173–252, 1942.

[74] Hermans, J. J., and Ende, H. A., "Density Gradient Sedimentation," in Newer Methods in Polymer Characterization, B. Ke, Ed., Interscience, New York, 1964.

Chapter 41

PARTICLE SIZE ANALYSIS

By Brian Howard Kaye
Senior Physicist, Fine Particle Section
Applied Chemistry Division
IIT Research Institute
Chicago, Illinois

INTRODUCTION

The physical properties of powders and powder-fluid systems are related to the size distribution of the grains of the powder. To obtain information on the size distribution of the particles, many different physical phenomena have been utilized. Thus (by making certain assumptions), the quantity of gas adsorbed by a sample of the powder can be related to the surface area of the powder, or the concentration changes occurring within a settling suspension of the powder can be related to the size distribution of the powder. The theory and practice of methods for measuring the fineness of powders is usually referred to as Particle Size Analysis. Inasmuch as it is a relatively new field of activity, some of the nomenclature is confused, and apparently contradictory statements concerning the methods which appear in the literature can often be harmonized by careful definition of the terms employed. This is particularly true of the use of the word "accurate." The demands of technical workers in various industries for precision in their analytical methods differ, and the accuracy of the methods are judged by the precision required. A civil engineer needs to know the type of soil on which he is to build the new road. Because of the heterogeneous nature of the soil over the area he will operate, and the suitability of any given construction method for a wide range of soils, any analytical method giving a precision of 20 percent on the mean diameter of the size distribution will usually be adequate. The relatively cheap techniques of the pipet and hydrometer sedimentation methods are therefore accurate for this purpose. Against this, the powder metallurgist attempting to discover the difference between two metal powders, one of which sinters to 80 percent and the other to 90 percent of the theoretical density, finds that the confidence limits of the size distribution function of either powder, as determined by the pipet method, embrace any difference between the two size distributions and a more adequate technique must be found.

Confusion also arises from the fact that for particles other than spheres different methods of analysis measure different characteristic dimensions of a particle. For example, consider the particle shown in Fig. 41-1. If this particle is viewed on a microscope slide it could be in several positions, and the two-dimensional image could have various apparent diameters. If any measured diameter is reported as the size, it can be seen how confusion arises. If the particle is examined by measuring its falling speed in a viscous fluid, the parameter calculated from the data can again be reported as a size, and it will differ from any of the linear dimensions of the particle, and from the microscope sizes discussed above. In some of the earlier publications in the field of size analysis it was not fully realized that the various methods measure different quantities, and considerable effort was made to obtain correction factors to facilitate conversion of data obtained by one technique for comparison with data obtained by a different technique. It is now realized that the differences in the dimensions of particles as obtained by methods based upon various physical principles depend upon the shape, *i.e.*, spatial

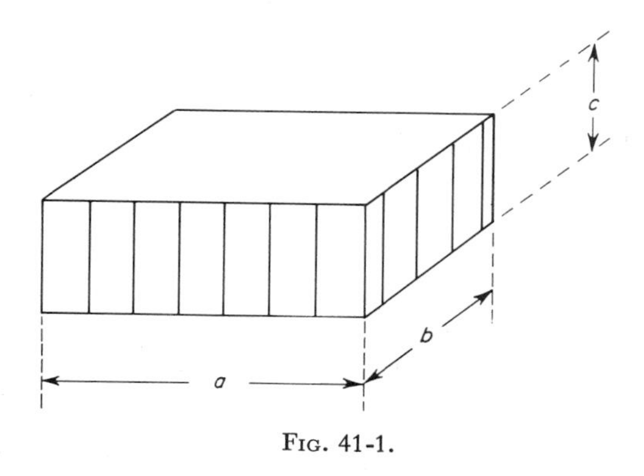

Fig. 41-1.

configuration, of the particles. The trend now is to exploit the differences between the data obtained by diverse methods in order to obtain information on the shape of the particles.

A useful classification of methods of analysis is according to the physical principles employed, and this is the scheme followed here. When selecting a method of analysis it is desirable to use a system comparable to that in which the powder is to be employed. Thus, if the covering power of a paint pigment is being investigated, microscope examination of the projected surface areas of the pigment particles is a direct measure of this property. On the other hand, if the store stability of the pigment is the main interest, a sedimentation technique that gives information on the settling velocities of the particles should be used.

It is sometimes helpful to distinguish between control and research methods of size analysis. In the initial investigations of a powder, elaborate techniques may have to be employed in measuring the size distribution, but once the material is established as an item in a production line, simpler methods of analysis may be used for control purposes. In the discussion of the methods given below some control methods are described and modifications to other methods, which facilitate design of control techniques, are given.

MICROSCOPE EXAMINATION

One of the earliest methods of particle size analysis was evaluation of particle parameters from an examination of the magnified image of particles by optical or electron microscope techniques. Particle diameters ranging from several millimeters to 0.1 μ can be measured by these techniques. Microscope examination methods have the advantage that they yield direct information on the shape, structure, and surface characteristics of a powder, and they require only a small sample. The major disadvantages are as follows: the methods of preparing the slide for examination can affect the degree of dispersion obtained; the large number of particles to be measured to obtain high precision entails extended viewing times; and precautions must be taken to prevent operator fatigue. If it is desired to compare results obtained by different operators, extensive training schemes are required.[1] Also, because of the very small sample used, great care must be exercised both in sampling the powder (preparative sampling error), and in selecting particles to be measured (analytical sampling error).

To minimize preparative sampling error, a comprehensive bulk sampling program should be followed to obtain a representative laboratory sample. In the writer's experience, apparently ludicrous results reported by the analyst to the technologist are often real enough, the source of trouble being inadequate sampling on the production line. A good maxim is that the analyst should control all sampling procedures prior to analysis. The laboratory sample should then be reduced to approximately 1-g. quantities, using an efficient sample reduction device.[2] Several slides should then be prepared, each from a different subsample, and particles to be counted selected from each slide. No general technique for dispersing the particles on the slide can be given; each powder has to be treated according to its physical and chemical properties.[3] The writer has found that an inert viscous mineral oil is often useful: a few drops are added to a small cone of dry powder and the resultant slurry is spread out with a glass rod.

Inasmuch as it is absolutely essential to avoid bias in selecting the particles to be measured, fields of view should be selected at random, and all particles of the size being investigated that are present in the field of view should be measured. If the size range of particles present is small, a straightforward series of measurements on, say, 500 particles, is usually sufficient; but if the size range is extensive, a stratified sampling procedure must be followed. The reason can be understood by considering a simple distribution by weight as illustrated in Fig. 41-2. In this distribution, there is the same percentage weight of particles in each size range, but a first-order approximation shows that the relative number of particles in each size group are as given in Table 41-1. If only 500 particles are counted indiscriminately, it can be seen that the chances of including the large particles in the count, in the correct proportions, are very low. In this case it is better to use a stratified sampling procedure, *e.g.*, measure 250 particles less than, say, 4 μ, then 250 greater than 3 μ and combine the data using the 3 μ to 4 μ as the correlation size group. As a rough guide, if the size range present is equal to or greater than 10:1, a stratified sampling procedure should be used. The design of an efficient procedure, *i.e.*, one which gives the maximum information for the minimum effort, is difficult and the aid of a statistician is usually necessary.[4]

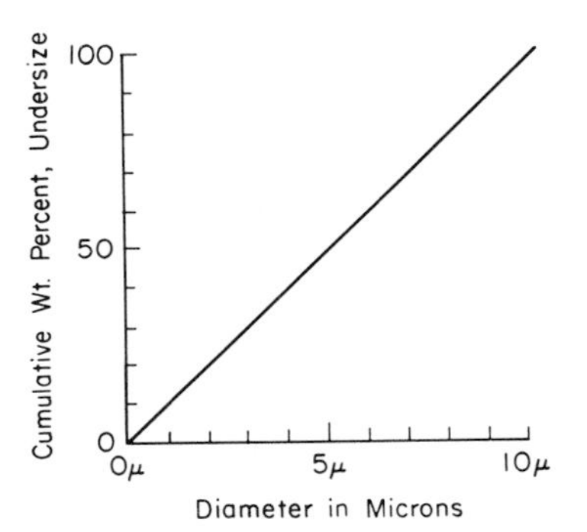

FIG. 41-2. Simple Cumulative Undersize by Weight Particle Size Distribution.

Many devices which facilitate microscope particle size analysis have been developed. One of the simplest aids is the graticule, a special, small grid which can be inserted into the eyepiece of the microscope. The various types of scale used in commercial graticules are illustrated in Fig. 41-3. In this diagram the outlines of several particles are shown, so that the function of the various scales can be described. The large square grid is used

[1] Watson, H. H., and Mulford, D. F., Brit. J. Appl. Phys., Suppl. **3**, 5105–5108, 1954.
[2] Kaye, B. H., Powder Metallurgy, **9**, 213–234, 1962.
[3] Herdan, G., "Small Particle Statistics", 2nd Ed., Butterworths, England, 1960.
[4] Kaye, B. H., Res. & Dev. for Ind., **29**, 19, January, 1964.

TABLE 41-1. RELATIVE NUMBER OF PARTICLES IN EACH SIZE GROUP FOR DISTRIBUTION GIVEN IN FIG. 41-2

Size Range, μ	*No. of Particles*
0–1	9514
1–2	352
2–3	76
3–4	28
4–5	13
5–6	7
6–7	4
7–8	3
8–9	2
9–10	1

to select the particles to be measured. If all particles intersecting the grid were counted, this would mean that a bias in favor of the larger particles would be introduced. An unbiased selection procedure is to select those particles whose geometric centers fall within the grid. Thus in Fig. 41-3, only one of the particles that intercept the selection grid would be included in the measurements.

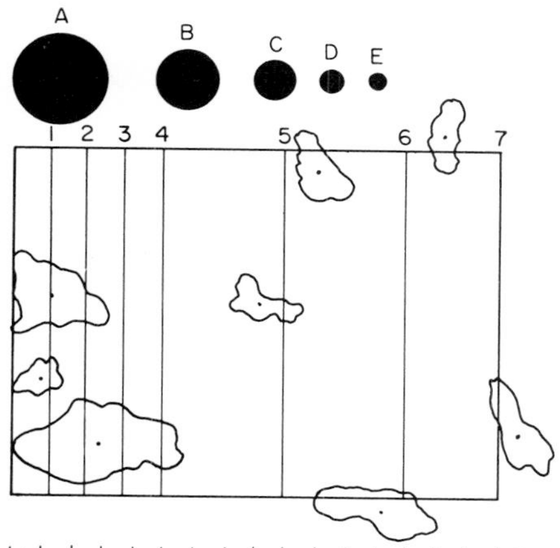

FIG. 41-3.

The first type of measurement which can be carried out with the graticule scales shown in Fig. 41-3 is the measurement of the diameter of the sphere with the equivalent projected area. This is achieved by comparing the image of a particle with the shaded circles marked A, B, C, D and E. This type of measurement is particularly vulnerable to operator error, and it will probably be superseded in many laboratories by the use of the Zeiss Endter particle size analyzer.[5] In this equipment, the area of a projected beam of light is compared directly with the image of a particle, as recorded on a photomicrograph. The area of the beam can be varied by means of an iris diaphragm, and facilities are provided with the equipment for recording the diameter of the beam when the image and beam areas are equal.

The second type of measurement is the measurement of the dimensions of the particle directly, using the linear scale F or the series of lines numbered 1 to 6. The series of lines have the advantage that the particles can be assigned rapidly to the appropriate size group if less exact information is sufficient. To avoid frequent movement of the graticule in aligning the scale and the image to measure any particular dimension of a particle, the concept of statistical diameters has been developed. Two statistical diameters which have been widely used in microscope particle size analysis are Martin's and Feret's diameters. These are defined as follows:

[5] Endter, F., and Gebauer, H., Optik, **97,** 13, 1956.

Martin's diameter: The mean length of a line intercepting the profile boundary of the image of the particle and dividing the image into two portions of equal area. The bisecting line is always taken parallel to the direction of traverse.

Feret's diameter: The mean length of the distance between two tangents on opposite sides of the image of the particle, the tangents being usually drawn perpendicular to the direction of traverse.

It can be seen from these definitions that statistical diameters are mathematical conventions used to describe readily measured averages. The magnitudes of these statistical diameters are related to the dimensions of the particles, but calculation of the conversion factors is not easy for nonspherical particles.[3]

In Fig. 41-4, a set of uniform triangles, in random array, has been drawn to illustrate that individual particles do not have a unique "statistical diameter." Theoretically, all

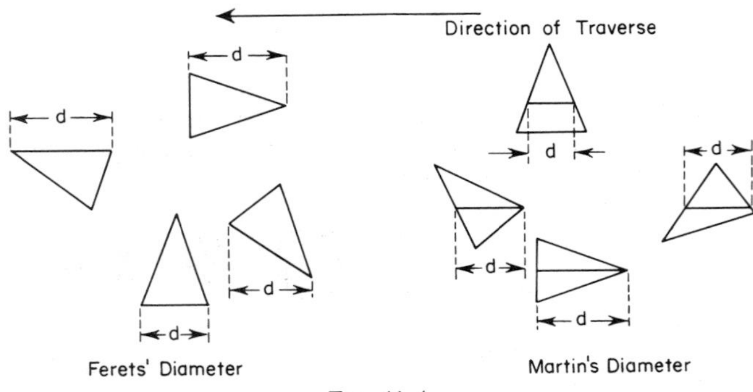

FIG. 41-4.

orientations are equally probable, and so by considering all possible values, the average value of the statistical diameters for any particular shape can be computed. When statistical diameters are utilized in a microscope count, all particles selected by the grid, in a straight line, traverse, are measured.

Double-image Microscopy.—A very important technique for particle size analysis by microscopic examination is based upon the use of double-image microscopy. A beam-splitting device is placed between the objective and the eyepiece of the microscope, so that two identical images of the object are formed in the field of view. A means of moving these images apart, with a device for measuring the movement, is provided. In the Timbrell microscope,[6] an electro-optical beam splitter is used and the frequency of oscillation of the splitter is chosen so that persistence of vision enables the two images to be seen. The size of a particle is measured by separating the images until there is no overlap. The main advantage of this method of measurement is that operator fatigue and variation between operators are greatly reduced, since the decision on the separation of the image is easier to make and is less subjective than estimation of areas and lengths. When using double-image microscopy, three types of diameter can be measured:

1st. Double-image Diameter.—The diameter obtained by separating images in the field of view, irrespective of their orientation to the direction of separation, until there is no image overlap. (This is, in fact, a statistical diameter.)

2nd Double-image Diameter.—This is measured by orientating the particles so that the maximum dimension lies along the direction of image separation before taking measurements.

[6] Timbrell, V., Nature, **170,** 318, 1952.

3rd Double-image Diameter.—The breadth of a particle as measured by image separation.

The method of making the measurements and the three types of double image diameter are illustrated in Fig. 41-5.

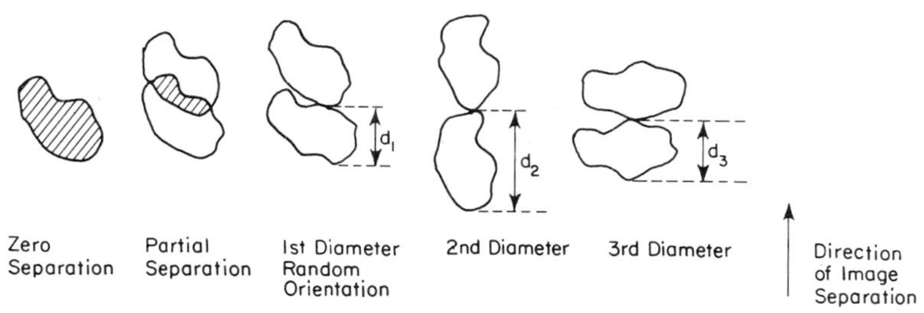

Fig. 41-5. Double-image Microscopy Diameters.

Several fully automatic microscopes for particle size analysis have been developed, but a discussion of these instruments is beyond the scope of this chapter. An up-to-date review of these instruments has been given by Connor.[7]

Optical microscope measurements on particles smaller than 1 μ are difficult, and electron micrographs have to be taken of the particles. The size of the particles is then assessed from measurements on the particle profiles. The Zeiss Endter equipment is useful for this type of measurement. All the statistical considerations outlined for the optical measurements apply to the interpretation of the electron microscope pictures.[8]

Membrane Filters as an Aid with Microscope Methods.—If the particulate matter to be examined under the microscope is a sample of dust, smoke, etc., from the atmosphere, or grit and dirt from gasoline or diesel fuel, then the use of membrane filters to collect the sample can simplify the subsequent analysis. Membrane filters are made of thin layers of cellulose esters, perforated by tiny uniform holes.[9] Particles collected from fluid streams passed through the filters remain on the surface of the membrane. The filter is then placed under the microscope. A few drops of immersion oil on the filter makes its surface transparent and allows the particles to be viewed directly.

SIEVE ANALYSIS

In sieve analysis the size distribution of a powder is obtained by measuring the weight of the fractions of the powder retained on a series of grids of decreasing aperture size. The grids can be manufactured either by punching holes in sheet metal, electroforming, or using woven wire cloth. The most appropriate method of manufacture depends, at present, on the size of aperture. Thus, wire woven sieves are usually used from approximately 40 μ up to 1 in., and electroformed from 40 μ downward. However, the technology of manufacture is constantly changing, and no definite guide can be given. When reporting a sieve analysis, it is important to specify the nature of the sieving surface since this influences the sieving process. Sieving techniques are used in particle size analysis over a size range of diameters from 18 μ up to greater than 1 in.

Advantages of sieve analysis are that large quantities of powder can be used, thus

[7] Connor, P., Ind. Chemist, 1–6, February, 1963.
[8] Brit. Standard 2406, Part 4, 1962.
[9] Cadle, R. D., Particle Size Determination, Interscience Publishers, Inc., New York, 1955.

minimizing the sampling error; and the equipment is cheap, easily maintained, reasonably robust, and simple to use.

The major disadvantage is that of determining when the separation of particles on the sieves is complete, and since this depends upon the loading of the sieve (*i.e.*, the amount of powder on the sieving surface) and the method of shaking, the technique is vulnerable to operator error. When using the finer wire mesh sieves, it is easy to damage the sieving surface.

The accuracy with which sieves can be manufactured is often the limiting factor on the precision of an analysis. Standard specifications for the construction and use of sieves have been prepared in several countries. Table 41-2 lists some of the important national

TABLE 41-2. NATIONAL STANDARD SPECIFICATIONS CONCERNED WITH SIEVES

Country	*Standard*	*Size Range Covered, μ*[a]
Britain	B.S. 410 and 1796	53–3353
United States	ASTM E/11/39	37–5660
Netherlands	N 480	50–850
Germany	D.I.N. 1171	60–5000
France	AFNOR NFX 11-501-1938	40–5000

[a] μ = microns.

standards. In addition, there is the Tyler standard series of sieves. This series has been prepared by the W. S. Tyler Company of Cleveland, Ohio, who were pioneers in the manufacture and standardization of test sieves. The Tyler sieve series is widely used. Recommendations for the calibration of test sieves are given in some of the national standards. Carpenter and Deitz recommend the use of standard glass beads.[10] A widely

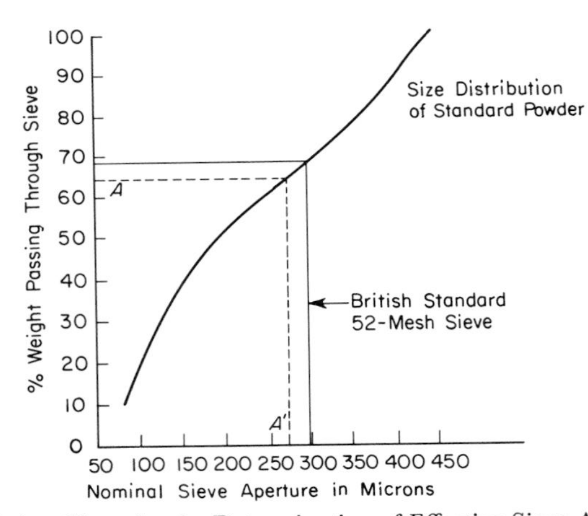

FIG. 41-6. Chart for the Determination of Effective Sieve Apertures.

used method of calibrating sieves empirically is to measure the effective aperture of the sieve. The method requires a supply of standard powder for which the size distribution, as measured under specified conditions, is known. Then from the data available, the chart given in Fig. 41-6 is drawn up. To illustrate the principle of the technique, con-

[10] Carpenter, F. G., and Deitz, V. K., J. Research Natl. Bur. Standards, **47**, 139, 1951.

sider the calibration of British Standard 52-mesh sieve. The nominal aperture size for this sieve is 295 μ. From the two lines drawn for this size on the chart, the percentage of the standard powder which should pass the sieve is 69 percent. If now the measured percentage passing for the sieve to be calibrated is 65, the effective aperture of the sieve is found by drawing the lines AA' and is approximately 265 μ. This type of sieve calibration is very useful when the production of large quantities of the same powder has to be monitored. It should be realized that the effective aperture of a sieve is not a unique property. It depends upon the quantity of powder present in the size range of apertures in the sieving surface and the exact details of the sieving process used in the experimental measurements.[11]

Experimental procedures to be followed when carrying out a sieve analysis vary according to the nature of the powder, the range of sizes present, and the accuracy required. For wide-range powders, and when the precision required is not too high, a nest or stack of sieves can be used in conjunction with machine shaking. The stack of sieves is assembled in increasing fineness from the top downward. The sample of powder is placed on the top sieve and, when the stack is vibrated, the powder works down through the nest of sieves until the finest fraction is collected in the container placed at the base. After sieving for a specified time, the residue remaining on each sieve is measured. It is widely recognized that removal of the finest fraction from the powder, prior to the analysis, greatly increases the speed at which the particles pass down through the nest of sieves.[7] Increased precision can be obtained by sieving the powder through each sieve in turn, by hand. However, different operators can obtain widely different results.

When sieving by machine or by hand, the sieve should be checked to see that no blinding is occurring. Blinding of sieve, *i.e.*, the blockage of the sieve apertures by oversized particles wedged into them, causes random variations in the available sieving surface and introduces uncertainty into the time required to eliminate subsieve particles. Changes in the sieving action are usually sufficient to avoid blinding. Methods of using micromesh sieves have recently been reviewed by Irani and Callis.[12]

When sieving small quantities of fine powders and when high precision is required, a rate method of sieve analysis can be used. This method is based on the fact that it has been demonstrated experimentally that the closing stages of a sieving process are governed by the equation:

$$\log_{10} (R_t - R_\infty) = At + B$$

where R_t = the residue on the sieve at the time t
R_∞ = the theoretical sieve residue, and
A and B = constants for a given sieve analysis.

The operator's method of shaking, variation in the sieve loading, and the characteristics of the sieve only affect the values of A and B. The equation is solved graphically from a series of values of t and R_t. An estimate is made of the value of R_∞, denoted by R_∞', and then the values of $(R_t - R_\infty')$ are plotted on a logarithmic scale against t. If the value of R_∞ has been overestimated, the curve will change sharply and become asymptotic to $-\infty$ (see Fig. 41-7). If the estimate is less than the true value, the plot will be asymptotic to the time axis. Thus, the initial plot enables the first estimate to be corrected. The value which gives the straight-line relationship is taken as the measured value. A full description of the method is given by Kaye.[13]

[11] Heywood, H., Trans. Inst. Min. Met., **55,** 391, 1946.
[12] Irani, R. R., and Callis, C. F., Particle Size Measurement, Interpretation and Application, John Wiley and Sons, Inc., New York, 1963.
[13] Kaye, B. H., Powder Metallurgy, **10,** 199, 1962.

For cohesive powders, *i.e.*, powders which cake and form loose agglomerates on the sieving surface, or for powders which become electrostatically charged, wet sieving should be considered. The particles are washed through the sieve with a gentle stream of fluid. It should be noted, however, that wet sieving should always be followed by a

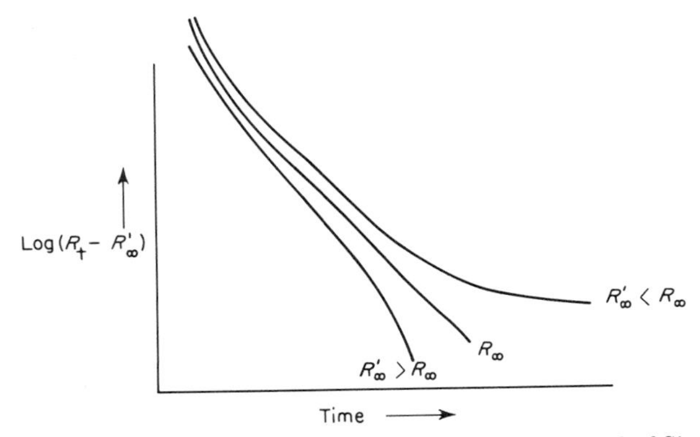

FIG. 41-7. Illustration of the Basic Steps in the Rate Method of Sieve Analysis.

short period of dry sieving, since some of the near mesh particles, which should just pass the sieve, are held in the mesh apertures by surface tension forces during the wet stage.

A recently developed instrument, which has solved many problems encountered when sieving very fine powders, is the Alpine Air Jet sieve. The principle of this instrument is outlined in Fig. 41-8. The sieve is sealed with an airtight plastic lid and fitted into the

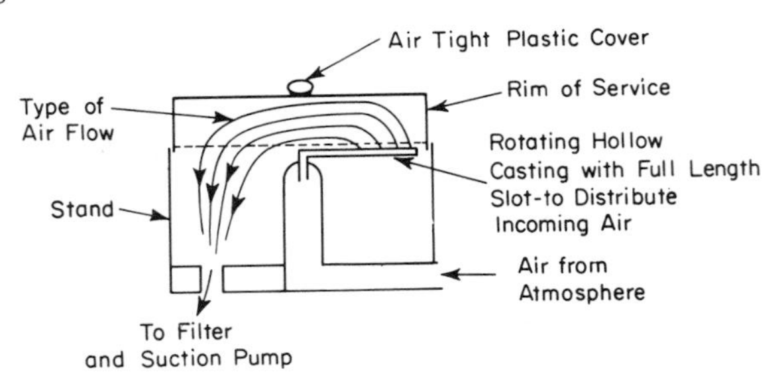

FIG. 41-8. Basic Principles of the Alpine Air Jet Sieve.

cylindrical stand. Air is sucked through the device by means of a normal vacuum pump. The air entering the device is distributed through the base of the sieve by a set of rotating nozzles, and the air flow is as illustrated. When the powder is placed on the sieving surface the air jets clean the sieve apertures immediately above them, and the return flow of air aids the passage of fines through the sieve. The fines are collected by a filter inserted between the stand and the pump. The general turbulence created on the sieving surface by the rotating jets also helps to break down agglomeration.[14]

When sieving friable materials, the vibration and movement of the sieve should not be of such a magnitude that the powder breaks down during the analysis. Conversely,

[14] Lauer, O., Staub., **20**, 69, 1960.

when sieving abrasive materials, care should be taken that the apertures of the sieve are not damaged during the analysis. The sieve should never be overloaded, since bowing of the surface will alter the effective apertures of the sieve.

SEDIMENTATION METHODS

General Theory.—In sedimentation methods the size distribution of the powder is determined by studying concentration changes occurring within a settling suspension. Two basic systems are employed in these methods. In the first group of methods, changes occurring within an initially homogeneous suspension are measured; and in the second group, a layer of suspension is added to the top of a column of fluid. These two groups are commonly known as *homogeneous techniques* and *two-layer techniques*. In practice, it is usual to distinguish between *incremental* and *cumulative methods*. In the first group, variations in concentration with time are studied at any specified depth in the body of the suspension; and in the second, the accumulation of sediment at the base of the sedimentation column is studied.

To interpret the changes occurring within the suspension, it is usually assumed that Stokes equation applies to the individual particle trajectories. A convenient form of this equation is:

$$d^2 = 18\eta h/(\rho_p - \rho_L)g\cdot t$$

where d = diameter of a sphere, in cm., falling freely under gravity,
η = viscosity (in poise) of the liquid through which the particle is falling,
ρ_p = density of the sphere in g./cc.,
ρ_L = density of the liquid in g./cc.,
g = acceleration due to gravity,
t = time of fall in seconds, and
h = height of fall.

When the particles start to fall, there will be an initial period of accelerated motion, but since this is small it can usually be neglected. This formula is applicable only for low rates of fall, *i.e.*, for streamline flow conditions; therefore, it is usual to select the variables of the system such that the Reynolds number for the largest particle present is less than 0.3. Reynolds number is defined by the equation:

$$\mathrm{Re} = \frac{v\cdot\rho_L\cdot d}{\eta}$$

where v = velocity of fall,
ρ_L = density of liquid,
d = diameter of particle, and
η = viscosity of liquid.

Several workers have investigated falling speeds of particles for systems of higher Reynolds number,[15] but in practice it is simpler to restrict analysis systems to low Reynolds numbers. There is some information available on the falling speeds of nonspherical particles, but in particle size analysis it is common practice to apply Stokes equation to nonspherical particles. The value of d calculated is then termed the Stokes diameter of the particle.

[15] Heywood, H., Proceedings of Symposium on Interaction between Fluids & Particles, London Inst. of Chem. Engr., 1962, p. 1.

An important restriction on the validity of Stokes equation is that the particles should be falling freely, *i.e.*, without interference from other particles in their vicinity or from the walls of the containing vessels. In the various sedimentation methods which have been devised, many different solids concentrations are used. As each method is discussed, the question of satisfying the conditions for free fall will be considered in detail.

In all sedimentation methods, the falling speeds of even the largest particles present are low, *i.e.*, of the order of cm./per minute. Also, especially in the case of very fine powders, it is sometimes necessary to extend measurements over a period of several hours. The sedimenting system must, therefore, be protected against thermal and mechanical disturbance. The elimination of mechanical disturbance, such as vibration, is a self-evident precaution, but in some cases the dangers of thermal instability are not fully recognized. In many systems, a sedimentation vessel with an open surface is placed in a constant temperature bath, as shown in Fig. 41-9. In this situation, although the

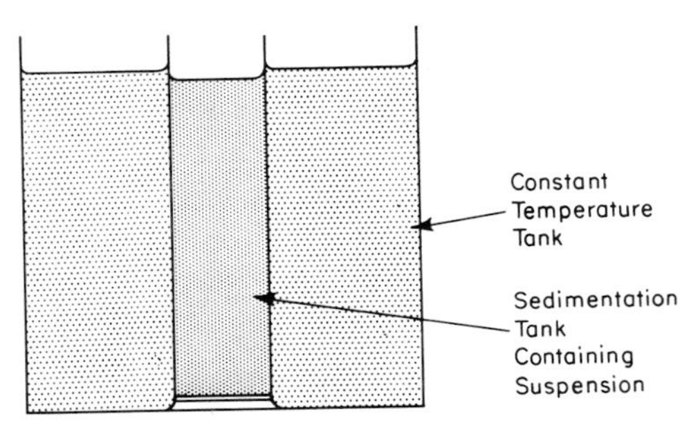

FIG. 41-9. Thermally Unstable Sedimentation Tank.

tank is at the same temperature as the bath, a temperature difference exists with respect to the room, and surface cooling occurs causing convection currents from the surface downward. A second mechanism that can aggravate this type of disturbance is surface evaporation, which again results in surface cooling. Whenever possible, the sedimenting system should be sealed. If it is not possible to provide a mechanical seal, an effective thermal buffer for aqueous systems can often be obtained by floating a layer of low volatility mineral oil on the top of the sedimenting system.[16]

A problem common to all sedimentation methods is the adequate dispersion of the powder sample. When the sedimenting fluid is a gas, the powder is often dispersed with the aid of high velocity gas jets. When the disperse phase is a fluid, vigorous mechanical agitation is rarely sufficient, and a surface active agent has to be used. The physical and chemical properties of the fluid and particles are very important in choosing the correct agent for any given system, and no general guidance can be given in selecting the appropriate substance. The amount of surface active agent required will normally be related to the surface area of the powder. The best procedure when adding the surface active agent is to mix sufficient of a solution of the agent with the dry powder to form a stiff paste. The high shearing forces which can be applied to the paste by stirring greatly aid dispersion of aggregates.

The severity of the dispersion process applied in any given case should be of the same order of magnitude as that to which the powder will be subjected when in the process under consideration.

[16] Kaye, B. H., and Treasure, G. R. C., Materials Research and Standards, ASTM, Philadelphia, 1965.

Incremental-homogeneous Suspension Methods.—The basic theory of this group of methods can be understood by considering the system illustrated in Fig. 41-10. In this

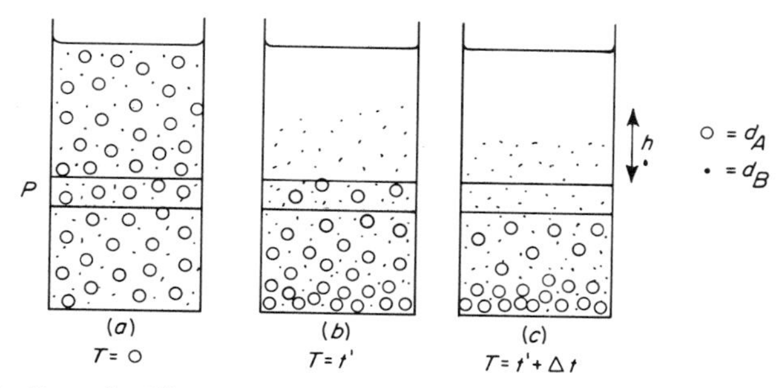

FIG. 41-10. Settling of a Homogenous Suspension Containing Two Types of Suspensions.

simplified system only two sizes are considered. These are spherical particles of diameter d_A and d_B. At the commencement of settlement ($T = 0$) both sizes are uniformly dispersed as shown in Fig. 41-10a. It is assumed that the particles fall freely. Consider the horizontal section P at the depth h. If the time required for particles of size d_A to fall from the surface through the height h is t', then, until this time, the concentration in the section P remains constant. This is because as many particles of each size enter the section as leave it. The section P is defined as the sampling zone. If Δt is the time for the particles of size d_A to pass through the section P, then in the time interval t', $t' + \Delta t$, there will be a change in concentration ΔC.

Let C_t be the concentration of particles in the section of any time t. It follows that

$$C(d_m) = C_{t'} - C_{t'+\Delta t}$$

where $C(d_m)$ is the concentration of particles with diameters in the range $d_{t'} \rightarrow d_{t'+\Delta t}$, the diameters being calculated from Stokes equation by inserting the two time values. Although derived for the simple case of two size groups, the equation is valid for a system containing a wide range of sizes. An alternative method of handling the data is as follows:

Let C_0 and C_t be the particle concentrations, at times 0 and t, in the section P:

$$\frac{C_t}{C_0} \times 100 = R(d_t)$$

where $R(d_t)$ is the percentage of particles less than d_t, the size of particle which falls from the surface in the time t.

In the first group of incremental homogeneous suspension methods of analysis, changes in concentration within the suspension are followed by extracting samples from the sampling plane. The solids concentration of the sample is then measured physically or chemically. The group is known generally as pipet methods of analysis. The essential features of equipment used in pipet methods are shown in Fig. 41-11. At time t a pipet is inserted into the suspension at the depth h and a sample withdrawn. Theoretically the sample is withdrawn from the horizontal section of thickness D (Fig. 41-11a), but in practice the shape of the sampling zone will approximate that of the sphere S, the center of which is coincident with the mouth of the pipet. This factor must be taken into account when comparing data obtained by the pipet technique with results obtained by other methods.

Many variations on the basic equipment outlines in Fig. 41-11a have been described. Probably one of the simplest and most widely used is that due to Andreasen.[17] The equipment is shown in outline in Fig. 41-11b. The sedimentation tank is cylindrical and made of glass. The stem of the pipet is fused to a bell-shaped dome which has a ground-

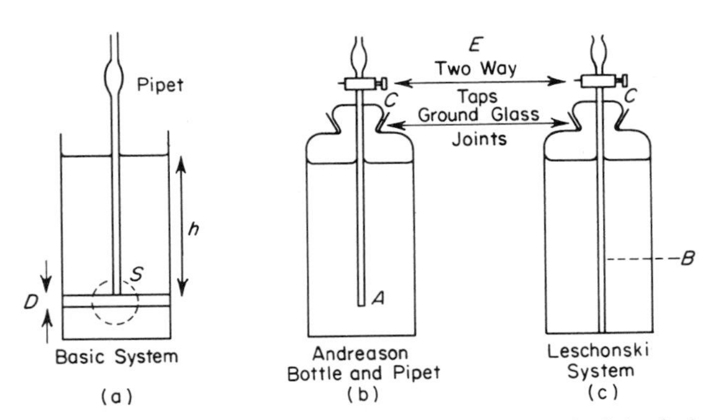

Fig. 41-11. **Equipment Used in the Pipet Method of Analysis.**

glass joint which matches that of the sedimentation vessel. To enable samples to be withdrawn from the vessel with the pipet in position, the air valve *C* is provided. When the suspension has begun to settle, a series of samples are withdrawn at specified time intervals. Each sample is discharged through the two-way tap *E*. The main objections to this system are, first, that the general assumption that the withdrawal of a sample does not affect the general behavior of the settling suspension other than to alter the distance of fall to the sampling zone may not always be valid. Secondly, the presence of the pipet in the system during the analysis disturbs the settling behavior of the suspensions. The portion of the suspension in the region *A* under the end of the pipet (Fig. 41-11b) becomes less dense than the surrounding regions due to the fact that particles leaving the region *A* are not replaced from above. This density difference initiates turbulent convection currents under the tip of the pipet and error is introduced into the measurements. A piece of equipment described by Leschonski[18] seems to overcome two of the major objections to pipet analysis. It is shown in outline in Fig. 41-11c. As can be seen, it is basically the same as the Andreasen apparatus. To overcome the density convection currents, the stem of the pipet is continued to the base of the vessel, thus eliminating the region *A* of Fig. 41-11b. Suspension is sucked into the pipet through a series of holes at *B*, arranged around the circumference of the stem. The sampling zone for this pipet thus consists of a series of small spheres clustered round the pipet and is therefore a better approximation to the theoretical horizontal section sampling zone.

General factors which can influence the precision of a pipet method of analysis are the shape and volume of the pipet, the ratio of the diameter of the sampling sphere to the depth at which measurements are made, and the rate at which samples are withdrawn, which should be closely controlled.[19] If the concentration of the samples is determined by drying the solids and weighing, care must be taken to allow for the weight of surface active agent present. The presence of the surface active agent on the surface of

[17] See Brit. Standard 3406, Part 2, 1962.
[18] Leschonski, K., Staub., **22,** 475–486, 1962.
[19] Johnson, R., Brit. J. Appl. Phys., Suppl. **3,** S.26, 1954.

the dried powder can cause serious error if the agent is hydroscopic. Leschonski has described a special dish, for use with the pipet method of analysis, which can reduce this source of error. It consists of a low weight, shallow polythene cup, the base of which is replaced by a membrane filter.[18] The sample of suspension is fitted in the cup and the surface active agent removed from the powder by washing with a suitable fluid. The low weight of the container greatly assists the weighing operation. The characteristics of the membrane filter can be obtained from the manufacturer, and this type of dish should not be used if the membrane contains apertures approaching the size of the finest particles in suspension.

The advantages of pipet methods are as follows: The equipment is cheap and relatively robust, requiring little or no maintenance. The experimental procedure is simple and operators can be relatively unskilled. The main theoretical disadvantage, especially if gravimetric estimation of the samples are made, is that the solids content of the initial suspension is often too high for free-fall conditions to apply.[20] However, provided conditions are standardized, *i.e.*, solids concentration maintained with very close limits, this need not be a disadvantage for control and empirical investigations. A second theoretical disadvantage is that the system is continually being disturbed as samples of suspension are withdrawn. A practical disadvantage can be that relatively large powder samples are required for an analysis to be carried out, *i.e.*, 3 to 5 g. compared to the milligram quantities required for photosedimentation or Coulter Counter analysis.

A second group of incremental-homogeneous suspension methods is known as hydrometer techniques. In these methods concentration changes within the suspension are determined by measuring the density of the suspension at certain depths with the aid of hydrometers. The simple system on which the method is based is shown in Fig. 41-12a.

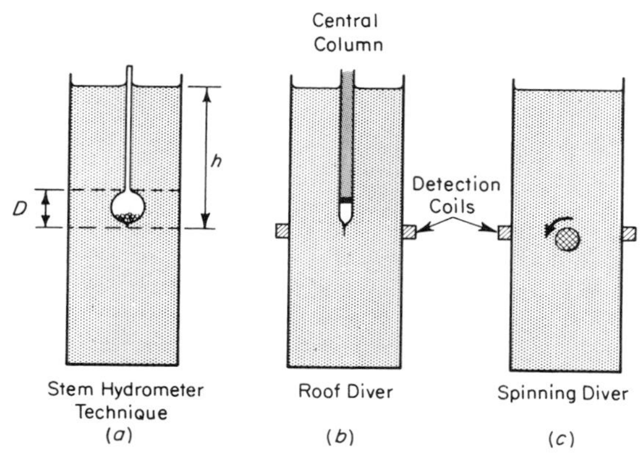

FIG. 41-12. Equipment Used in the Hydrometer Method of Size Analysis.

At time t the hydrometer is inserted into the suspension. It sinks to the depth h and it follows, from the theory of hydrometers, that the specific gravity registered on the stem is the average value of the density of the suspension over the horizontal section D. It can be shown[21] that the density of a settling suspension at a depth h after time t is given by:

[20] Kaye, B. H., and Boardman, R. P., Proceedings of Symposium on Interaction Between Fluids & Particles, London Inst. of Chem. Engr., 1962, p. 17.
[21] Berg, S., ASTM Special Technical Publication No. 234, 143, 1958.

$$R_{ht} = \frac{\rho_{sht} - \rho_L}{\rho_{si} - \rho_L} \times 100$$

where R_{ht} = percentage of particles smaller than d_{ht}, which is the Stokes diameter calculated by substitution, of h and t in Stokes equation,
ρ_{sht} = density of suspension at depth h below the surface at time t,
ρ_{si} = initial density of suspension, and
ρ_L = density of the dispersing fluid.

It follows from this equation that if the density of the initial suspension is fixed, the stem of the hydrometer can be made to give percentage solids direct. Because of this factor, and since the equipment is relatively cheap and robust, the technique has been widely adopted for the control of raw materials in the ceramic industry, and for soil testing.[22]

To determine the particle size distribution of the powder in suspension, it is necessary to take a series of readings over an extended period of time. Because of powder settling on the shoulders of the hydrometer, which would change its specific gravity, the hydrometer has to be withdrawn from the suspension after each reading is taken. The disturbance of the suspension each time the hydrometer is inserted and withdrawn introduces systematic errors into the experimental data. The resolution of the technique is not good when using ordinary type hydrometers since the bulb height, *i.e.*, the sampling zone width D, is an appreciable proportion of the sedimentation height. To overcome problems of resolution, suspension disturbance and powder settlement, Berg developed equipment using a series of small hydrometers of fixed density which could be completely submerged in the suspension and detected magnetically.[21] These miniature hydrometers are known as divers. A weakness of Berg's original technique is that the divers are drawn to the side of the suspension to be observed. This itself causes disturbance to the suspension and possibly distorts the true location of the diver. Two later modifications of Berg's method which avoid this difficulty are illustrated in Figs. 41-12b and c.

In the Roof Diver technique developed by Jarrett and Heywood, the divers have hollow brass cases and contain a permalloy strip. The series of divers is assembled in a hollow central column which is placed in the suspension as shown in the figure. Immediately below the end of the column on the outside of the sedimentation vessel is a detecting coil which is part of an a.c. inductance bridge. The time at which a diver moves from the base of a column and through the detection coil is the time at which the density of the suspension just falls below that of the diver. A disadvantage of this system is that in the zone beneath the column there will be density convection currents (see discussion of pipet methods). Also, it is usually necessary to vibrate the central column to ensure that the diver moves away from the column at the correct time.[23]

In the spinning diver technique a spherical diver is constructed by gluing two hollow Duralumin hemispheres together. By this method of construction the center of rotation is made to coincide with the center of gravity, the diver being completely symmetrical with respect to the center of gravity. Any single particle settling on the diver should initiate rotation, and once rotating it will shed all powder settling on it. The diver is detected electromagnetically as it passes through a coil connected to a high-frequency a.c. bridge. For a full description of the method, see Kaye and James.[24] A general disadvantage of the hydrometer type of analysis is that at the low-solids concentrations which are required for free-fall conditions, for the individual particles, to be satisfied, the density changes to be detected are so small that the construction and calibration of

[22] See Brit. Standard 1377, 1948.
[23] Jarrett, B. A., and Heywood, H., Brit. J. Appl. Phys., Suppl. **3,** S21, 1954.
[24] Kaye, B. H., and James, G., Brit. J. Appl. Phys., **13,** 414–419, 1962.

the hydrometers or divers are very difficult. At the higher-solids concentrations, the magnitude of systematic error involved by the disturbance to free-fall conditions would have to be determined for each specific situation.

In the third group of incremental-homogeneous suspension methods, concentration changes are measured by passing a beam of light through the suspension and recording the changes occurring within it. These methods are known as photosedimentation techniques. Because of the high sensitivity of optical methods of measuring concentration changes, only very small samples are required for analysis. At the low concentrations used, the particles in suspension are sufficiently far apart for free-fall conditions to apply to the system. An important advantage of photosedimentation methods is that, usually, the experimental measurements are obtained as electrical signals, in a form suitable for automatic recording of the data. The major theoretical difficulty which must be overcome when interpreting the results obtained by photosedimentation, arises from the complex optical properties of fine particles. When the particles in suspension are of the same order of magnitude as the wavelength of light, the simple laws of geometric optics cannot be used to calculate the opacity of the suspension. Historically there have been three different approaches to the problem of allowing for the optical behavior of fine particles. These different solutions of the problem will be discussed in connection with each of the three types of equipment in common use. It can be shown that, provided there is negligible reflection from the surface of the particles, and if the laws of geometric optics can be applied to the system, the opacity of a suspension is given by the equation:

$$\log_{10} \frac{I_0}{I_T} = K \sum_{i=1}^{i=x} n_i d_i^2 \qquad (1)$$

where I_0 = transmission of light through pure dispersing liquid,
I_T = transmission of light through the suspension diameter of particles,
d_1 = diameter of smallest particle present,
d_x = diameter of largest particle present, and
n_i = number of particles of diameter d_i in unit volume of the suspension.

K is a constant for any given suspension and is dependent on the length of the light path through the system, and on the shape of the particles.

A full discussion of this equation, together with the assumptions made in its derivation, is given by Rose.[25] The quantity $\log_{10} \cdot (I_0/I_T)$ is defined as the optical density of the suspension.

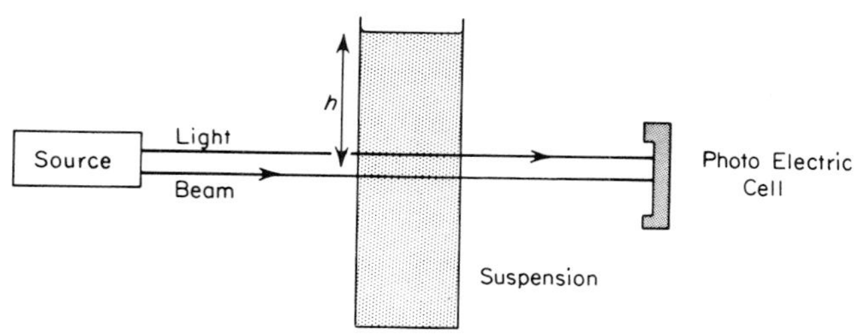

FIG. 41-13. Basic Photosedimentometer System.

Consider a light beam passing through a suspension at a depth h, as in the system shown in Fig. 41-13.

[25] Rose, H. E., The Measurement of Particle Size of Fine Powders, Chemical Publishers Co., Inc., New York, 1958.

If D_t is the optical density at time t, then

$$D_t = K \sum_{i=1}^{i=t} n_i d_i^2 \tag{2}$$

where d_t is the Stokes diameter of the largest particle present in the sampling zone, calculated by inserting the values of t and h in the Stokes equation. At time t' where $t' - t$ is small,

$$D_t - D_{t'} = K \left(\sum_{i=1}^{i=t} n_i d_i^2 - \sum_{i=1}^{i=t'} n_i d_i^2 \right) \tag{3}$$

If n_a is the number of particles in the range $d_t - d_{t'}$, and if the difference is sufficiently small that particles in this range can be regarded as having diameters given by:

$$d_a = \frac{d_t + d_{t'}}{2}$$

then Equation (2) can be written in the form:

$$D_t - D_{t'} = K n_a d_a^2$$

Thus

$$(D_t - D_{t'}) d_a = K n_a d_a^3 = K'(W)_{t \to t'} \tag{4}$$

where $(W)_{t \to t'}$ is the weight of particles with diameters in the range $d_t \to d_{t'}$, and K' is a constant.

From Equation (4) it can be shown that:

$$R(d_T) = \sum_{t=S}^{t=T} (D_t - D_{t'}) d_a \Big/ \sum_{t=S}^{t=L} (D_t - D_{t'}) d_a \tag{5}$$

where $R(d_T)$ = percentage by weight, of particles of diameters less than d_T.
S = time of fall of smallest particle present, from the surface of the suspension to the sampling zone, and
L = time of fall of largest particle present from the surface of the suspension to the sampling zone.

Using Equation (5), the size distribution of the powder can be calculated from a record of the intensity of transmission of the light beam through the suspension. As previously indicated, the simple theory outlined above has to be modified for particles which have diameters of the same order of magnitude as the wavelength of light. For particles smaller than approximately 50μ, diffraction effects are of the same order as the actual obstruction of the beam by the particle. In the case of transparent particles, refraction of the beam will in general occur, and there will be interference effects between light passing through and near the particle.

One approach to this basic defect of the simple theory has been to continue to use it to interpret the data obtained. The method is then regarded as a technique capable of high relative reproducibility, but of unknown absolute accuracy. If this approach is adopted, then recent work has shown that a white light source should be used in conjunction with a wide frequency response photoelectric cell, and wide-angle acceptance detection should be used.[26] Morgan gives a full description of the equipment used for routine analysis.[27]

[26] Kaye, B. H., and Allen, T., The Analyst, **90,** 147, 1965.
[27] Morgan, V. T., Brit. J. Appl. Phys., Suppl. **3,** S207, 1954.

An alternative approach to the problem is to modify the simple theory to allow for the optical properties of small particles. To do this a factor known as the extinction coefficient must be introduced into the derivation of the basic equation. By definition, the extinction coefficient, K_i, of a particle of diameter d_i is the ratio of the light obscured by the particle to the light which would have been obscured by the particle if the laws of geometric optics had been valid.[28] The extinction coefficient of a particle depends upon its diameter, the wavelength of the incident light, and the refractive index of the particle and the fluid. Using the concept of extinction coefficient, Equation (5) is modified to the form:

$$R(d_T) = \sum_{t=S}^{t=T} (D_t - D_{t'})d_a \cdot K_a / \sum_{t=S}^{t=L} (D_t - D_{t'})d_a K_a \tag{6}$$

where the symbols have the same meaning as before and K_a is the mean value of the extinction coefficient for the range $d_t - d_{t'}$. It is essential that the K-term does not change rapidly over the range $d_t - d_{t'}$. When the values of the extinction coefficient are known, Equation (6) can be used to calculate the size distribution.

A great deal of literature is available on the scattering of light by small particles, and several formulas have been suggested for use in calculating the extinction coefficients of spheres.[29] All the formulas are based on the assumption that no scattered light is received by the measuring device. If it is desired to construct equipment to carry out photosedimentation analysis, for which the necessary extinction coefficients are to be calculated theoretically, it is essential that the beam of light passing through the tanks be plane parallel, and that no scattered light be accepted by the detector. If a white light source is used, then the appropriate extinction coefficient will have to be calculated by considering the combined effects of the response characteristics of the detecting device, the wavelength distribution of the source, and the energy distribution within the spectrum of the source. It is also necessary to consider changes in refractive index of the particles and supporting fluids. The full complexity of the problem was not realized when some of the early work in this field was undertaken. Any published correction curves to be used in particle size analysis should be carefully examined to ensure that all the relevant factors were taken into account when deriving the curves. The writer is of the opinion that, at the present time, the work required to calculate extinction coefficients from the relevant theory is prohibitive and that, until further developments in light-scattering theory or in the use of computers to solve this type of problem, the values of K_i should be measured experimentally. Experimental determination of K_i is discussed later in this section.

In a third group of photosedimentation methods of analysis the optical properties of fine particles are taken into account by calibrating a given piece of equipment with known concentrations of particles of a given size. In fact, this group of methods is based upon the experimental determination of K_i, although this is not usually stated in the discussion of the methods. The equipment and technique developed by Musgrave and Harner is typical of this group of methods. The equipment is shown in outline in Fig. 41-14.[30] A strong converging beam of white light is passed through the suspension and received by a relatively wide-angle detection unit. (The aperture may appear small but it is large compared with the value of 0.00024 steradian used in photosedimentometer design by Rose[25]). The equipment is calibrated by measuring the equivalent hiding factor for each of the size ranges of interest.

[28] Lewis, P. C., and Lothian, G. F., Brit. J. Appl. Phys., Suppl. 3, S71, 1954.

[29] Van de Hulst, H. C., Light Scattering by Small Particles, Chapman & Hall, London, 1957.

[30] Musgrave, H. R., and Harner, J. R., ASTM Special Technical Publication No. 234, 172, 1958.

The equivalent hiding factor of size $d_A - d_B$ is defined as the fractional weight of particles of this size which have the same hiding power in suspension as unit weight of some standard size, usually the largest particle present in suspension. An implicit assumption in this definition is that the concentration of each increment of d in the range $d_A - d_B$

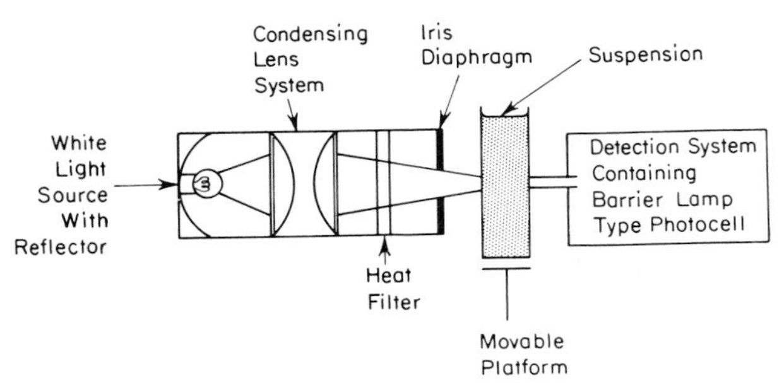

FIG. 41-14. Schematic Representation of the Musgrave and Harner Sedimentometer.

is the same. It follows that if the reference diameter is sufficiently great so that the extinction coefficient is unity (*i.e.*, greater than say 60 μ), then a relationship between the extinction coefficient and the equivalent hiding factor can be calculated.

For example, in the simple case of spherical particles:

$$K_a = \text{effective area}/(\pi/4)d_a^2 \tag{7}$$

where K_a is the average value of the extinction coefficient for the particle range $d_A \rightarrow d_B$

$$d_a = \frac{d_A + d_B}{2}$$

One way of interpreting Equation (7) is to consider the particles to have an effective diameter d_E, which differs from d_a. Using this interpretation, Equation (7) can be written in the form

$$K_a = \frac{d_E^2}{d_a^2} \tag{8}$$

If the laws of geometric optics were valid for the suspension system, it can be shown that

$$(E_T)_a = \frac{d_a}{d_R}$$

where d_R = diameter of the reference size, and
$(E_T)_a$ = theoretical equivalent hiding factor of particles of diameter d_a.

Then if $(E_M)_a$ is the measured equivalent hiding factor, it can be shown that

$$(E_M)_a = \frac{d_a^3}{d_R d_E^2} \tag{9}$$

From Equations (8) and (9) it follows that

$$\left(\frac{E_T}{E_M}\right)_a = K_a \qquad \text{for the range } d_A \rightarrow d_B$$

The values of E_M and K_a are quite specific for a given range of sizes and no extrapolation is permissible. Thus, if E_M were known for the ranges $10 \rightarrow 20\ \mu$ and $20 \rightarrow 30\ \mu$, it would not be valid to calculate the 15–25 μ factor, as the halfway value. This is because the value of K_i fluctuates considerably for a change in diameter of the same order of magnitude as the wavelength of the incident light. Again, if the geometry of the optical system of the photosedimentometer is changed, the values of E_M and K_a will change.

When constructing and using a photosedimentometer it is important to take into account the characteristics of the photoelectric device used, and possible fluctuations in the output of the source.

In attempts to overcome the difficulties associated with the light-scattering properties of small particles, electromagnetic radiation of shorter wavelength, such as x-rays and gamma rays, have been used.[31,32]

Cumulative-homogeneous Suspensions.—When an initially homogeneous suspension settles under the force of gravity it can be shown[33] that

$$W_t = W_{th} + t\frac{dw}{dt} \tag{10}$$

where W_t = the weight of particles settled onto the bottom of the sedimentation tank at time t,

t = time the suspension has been settling,

h = distance from the surface of the suspension to the base of the tank, and

W_{th} = weight of particles of diameter greater than d_{th}, calculated by inserting $t + h$ into Stokes equation.

Equation (10) can also be written in the form:

$$W_{th} = W_t - \frac{dw}{d(\ln t)} \tag{11}$$

From either Equation (10) or (11) the particle size distribution of a powder can be calculated from a record of the weight of the accumulated sediment at the base of the sedimentation column. When the record is obtained on a pen recorder as a function of time, Equation (10) is more convenient. If the readings are taken manually at fixed intervals of time, Equation (10) is plotted directly against ln t and therefore Equation (11) can be applied directly.

In the first group of cumulative-homogeneous suspension methods, the sediment is measured by direct weighing. Various types of equipment, termed sedimentation balances, for this type of measurement are shown in outline in Fig. 41-15. An advantage of this group of instruments is that a positive register of the largest particles in suspension is obtained. If very large particles are present when carrying out a photosedimentation, they may have cleared the beam before measurements are taken, but this cannot happen with a sedimentation balance method. A second advantage of this group is that direct mass measurements are made. Some of the simpler systems are ideal for control purposes. It is possible to make very precise and accurate measurements with some of the specialized instruments.

The simple system shown in Fig. 41-15 has the following disadvantages: As the balance pan sinks through the suspension, the displaced fluid flows up past the pan and inter-

[31] Brown, J. F., and Skrebouski, J. K., Brit. J. Appl. Phys., Suppl. **3**, S21, 1954.
[32] Ross, C. F., Anal. Chem., **31**, 337, 1958.
[33] Bostock, W. J., J. Sci. Inst., **29**, 209, 1952.

feres with the settling of the particles. Secondly, the suspension under the pan is stripped of particles more rapidly than the surrounding regions, the resulting density difference initiating turbulent convection currents around the edges of the pan. It has been established experimentally that the usual effect of density convection currents is to prevent a measurable proportion of fines from reaching the balance pan.[18] If an ordinary beam

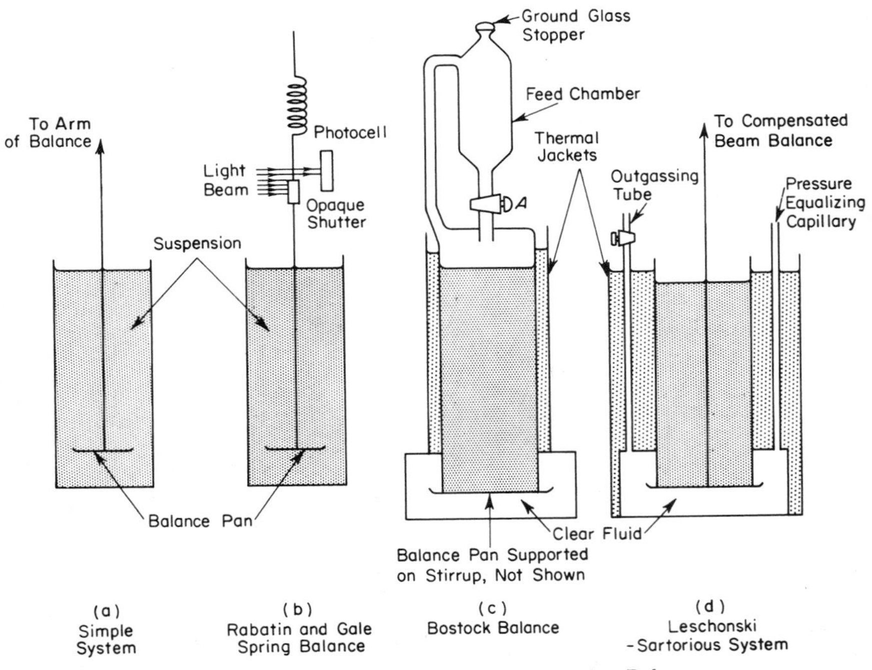

FIG. 41-15. Outline of Various Sedimentation Balances.

balance is used, the concentrations of solids required can exceed the upper limit for free-fall conditions in the suspension. A second effect which must be allowed for, if high solids contents are used, is that the density of the suspension is changing significantly with time, and therefore the bouyancy effect on the balance pan is changing. A further disadvantage of the simple system is that the support rod passes through the suspension and disturbs the free fall of the particles.

In the instrument shown in Fig. 41-15b, effects due to density convection currents are minimized by making the "dead space" under the balance small and by restricting the width of the annulus formed by the pan and the sedimentation tank.[34] The use of a sensitive spring balance and an optical method of recording its movement makes it possible to use low solids concentrations and to make the total movement of the pan through the suspension small. As the spring balance is extended by the solids settling on the pan, an opaque shutter moves across a beam of light and the signal received by a photoelectric cell is recorded. The system can either be calibrated with known weights or, if the response of the photocell is linear with energy received, the signal output can be taken as being directly proportional to weight.

[34] Rabatin, J. G., and Gale, R. H., Anal. Chem., **29**, 1314–1326, 1956.

In Fig. 41-15c the Bostock sedimentation balance is shown. This equipment is also known as the Gallenkamp sedimentation balance.[33] To overcome the problem of density convection currents, the balance pan is suspended in clear fluid beneath the sedimentation column. It is supported by a stirrup (not shown) which avoids the disturbance of the suspension due to the presence of a connecting rod. The suspension is introduced via the feeding chamber according to the following procedure. The pan is clamped to the base of the sedimentation column and the suspension placed in the feeding chamber. Then, with the ground-glass stopper in position, the tap A is opened. When the suspension has run into the column, the pan is freely suspended. The suspension will fall slightly until the drop in pressure above the surface is sufficient to balance the hydrostatic pressure of the suspension. The balance pan is connected to the arm of a torsion balance so that high sensitivity can be attained, with low solids content and small total movement of the pan. However, it has been reported that there are still discrepancies between the ultimate settled solids and the theoretically predicted value, and this should be taken into account when calculating the size distribution of the powder.

Leschonski has described a sedimentation balance with which it is claimed 98 percent of the theoretical settle solids is achieved. The system used, which is a modification of a commercial equipment (manufactured by Sartorious Werke, Germany) is shown in outline in Fig. 41-15d.[18] As in the case of the Bostock balance, the balance pan is suspended in clear fluid, to counteract the effect of density convection currents. The elevated rim of the pan acts as a guard ring to the base of the sedimentation column. To prepare the equipment for an experimental run, the pan is clamped against the base of the column. The clear fluid beneath the balance pan is then outgassed through the tube shown. This operation is necessary to prevent small bubbles forming under the balance pan and introducing error into the recorded weight. When outgassing is complete, the tube is closed, the column filled with suspension, and the pan freely suspended from the arm of an automatically compensated beam balance. The surface of the suspension falls slightly until the pressure of the column is balanced by means of the pressure equalization capillary. The movement of the balance pan is very small, because of the automatic compensation mechanism, and low solids concentrations can be used.

In a second group of cumulative-homogeneous suspension methods, the settled solids are removed periodically from the base of a sedimentation column. One form of this equipment, developed by Stairmand, has been included in the British Standards Methods for sedimentation analysis.[35] Full details of the method are given in the Standard specification. A different form of the apparatus, developed by Koback and Loveridge, is shown schematically in Fig. 41-16. The glass sedimentation vessel is tapered at the bottom, with the tip of the taper ground flat at right angles to its axis. With the exception of the internal diameter of the tip, which needs to be 1 to 2 mm., the dimensions of the tube are not critical. The small sample collection tubes are approximately 1.5 cm. deep and 1 cm. in diameter, thus having a capacity of about 1 ml. At the beginning of an experiment, the flexible rubber connection is attached to the tip and sealed with a clip. The funnel is fitted to the top of the column and the suspension added. The clip is opened and the suspension stirred with compressed air. When stirring is complete, the air supply is stopped, the funnel removed, and the stopper, with the tap open, is inserted into the top of the sedimentation tube. Sufficient suspension should be added to fill completely the sedimentation tube when the tap is closed. The time of settling out is measured from the moment the air supply is stopped. When the tap is closed, the bottom end is opened. The liquid is held in the tube by the atmospheric pressure, a meniscus is formed across the tip, and sediment collects at the hole. When clear sedimenting fluid contained in the small tube is brought into contact with the meniscus, the meniscus then

[35] Brit. Standard 3406, Part 2, 1962.

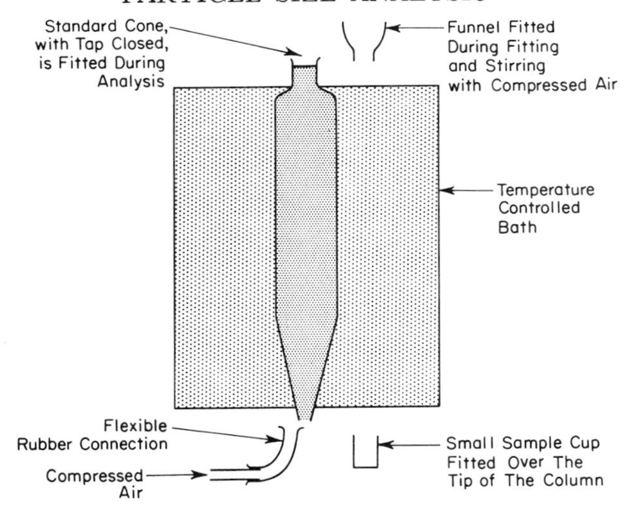

Fig. 41-16. Koback and Loveridge Sedimentation Column (not to scale).

breaks down and sediment passes into the tube. The sediment is taken away for gravimetric or chemical estimation at a series of times, the sealing meniscus reforming each time the tube is removed. The effect of the taper on the free-fall condition of the particles will have to be taken into account for absolute measurements.[36]

Cumulative Two-layer Systems.—First it should be noted that, as far as the writer is aware, there have been no reports of incremental two-layer suspension systems settling under gravity. The basic system on which the two-layer techniques are based is shown in Fig. 41-17. A layer of suspension of the powder under test is floated onto the top of a

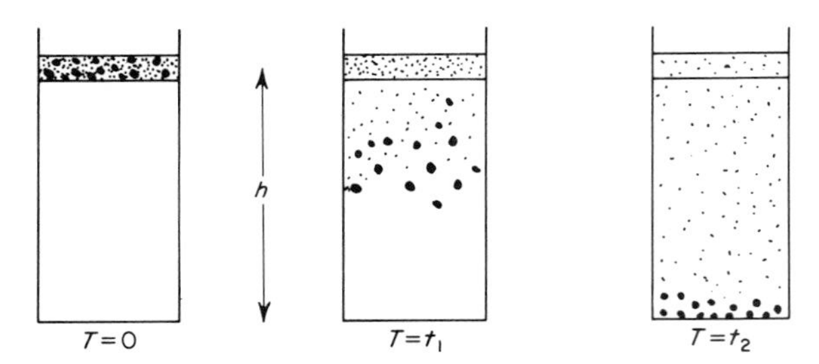

Fig. 41-17. Two-Layer Suspension Systems.

column of clear sedimentation fluid. To the first order of approximation all the particles start from the same position. At the time $T = t_1$, the front of the largest particles present will be passing down the tube as shown. The first register of particles reaching the base of the column will occur at the time $t = t_2$ when the largest particles have settled through the height h. The diameter of the largest particle present is calculated from Stokes law equation by the insertion of the appropriate values. The weight of particles reaching the bottom of the tube in the time interval t' to t'' is equal to the weight of particles with

[36] Koback, J., and Loveridge, D. J., J. Sci. Inst., **37**, 266, 1960.

the size range $d_{t'}$ to $d_{t''}$, these Stokes diameters being calculated from the values of t' and t''. It can be seen that data interpretation is simpler for the two-layer systems than for the homogeneous suspensions. The main difficulty of the techniques is the forming of a stable layer on top of the column of clear fluid. It is usual to employ a special feeding chamber, and often the density of the sedimentation fluid has to be higher than the layer suspension; *e.g.*, the layer suspension is made with water and floated onto a column of sugar solution of higher density. To obtain true free-fall conditions for the particles, there are some indications that concentrations as low as 0.05 percent by volume have to be used in the floated suspension.[20] If concentrations exceed this, the powder appears coarser than by other methods.

A widely used method of analysis based upon a two-layer cumulative system is that developed by Whitby.[37] The special tube used in this technique is shown in Fig. 41-18. It is designed so that the analysis can be continued for the fine sizes by centrifugal sedimentation. This aspect of the technique will be discussed in the next section. The layer of suspension is placed in the column with the aid of a feeding chamber. The rate of sediment accumulation is measured by determining the height of the sediment in the capillary at the base of the tube. The method of measurement is based upon the fact that the voidage of monosized particles of the same shape is independent of the size of the particles. Since each portion of the sediment is essentially monosized as it accumulates, this is a valid assumption to make, provided that the shape of the particles does not change with decreasing size. In assessing the absolute accuracy of the method, the effect of the taper at the base of the tube must be taken into account. For routine measurements, the distance through which the particles fall is taken from the middle of the floated suspension layer to the mid-point of the latest increment of sediment.

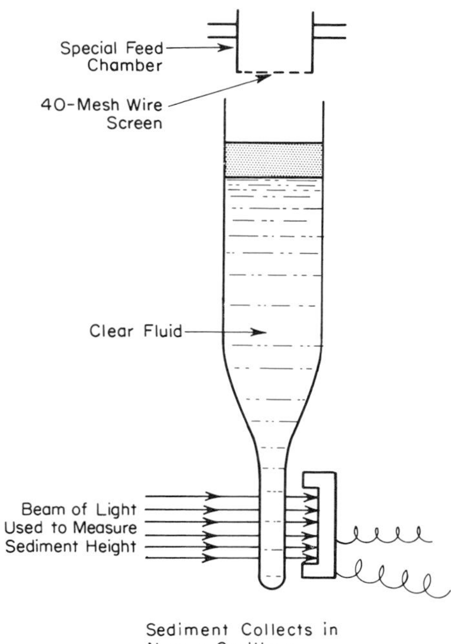

FIG. 41-18. Whitby Sedimentation Tube.

A second instrument in which a two-layer cumulative measurement system is used is the Sharples Micromerograph. The basic system of this instrument is shown in Fig. 41-19. A small sample of the powder is placed in the sample holder and balasted with compressed nitrogen gas through a narrow slit into the top of a tall sedimentation column. Thus the top layer is a well dispersed cloud of the powder. The sedimentation column is thermally insulated and the particles fall through the column onto the balance pan placed at the base. The length of the column is chosen so that the width of the injected zone is negligible compared to the height of fall. As the particles are collected on the balance pan, a slight rotation of the balance beam on its torsion suspension occurs. A sensing device applies a signal to the electronic control of the balance, which in turn applies a current to a restoring force coil on the other side of the beam balance. It can

[37] Whitby, K. T., Am. Soc. Heating & Air Cond. Eng., **66**, 33–50, 449–462, 1955.

be seen that the current required to keep the balance in equilibrium is a continuous measure of the weight of sedimented particles.[38]

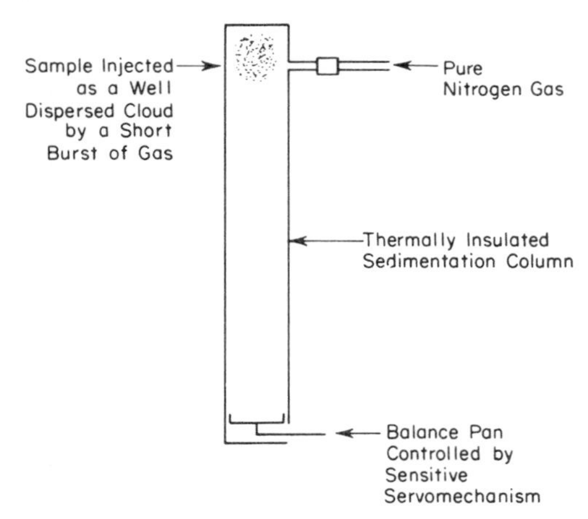

FIG. 41-19. Basic System of the Sharples Micromerograph.

Difficulties can arise with this equipment if the particles become electrostatically charged. If this happens, some of the particles become attached to the side of the column and never reach the balance pan. If the loss due to electrostatic charge occurs in a representative manner, *i.e.*, a constant fraction of all sizes is lost, then the effect can be allowed for. However, if there is a loss of powder during the analysis, the effect must be carefully investigated.

Centrifugal Sedimentation Techniques.—For very fine particles, the times required for sedimentation through a measurable height is too long for convenient analysis. Even if the long settling times can be used, problems associated with the thermal stability of the system became very difficult.[16] The sedimentation times can be considerably reduced by using centrifugal techniques. For particles settling through a viscous fluid, under centrifugal forces, the modified form of Stokes equation is:

$$d_s = \sqrt{\frac{18\eta \cdot \ln R/S}{(\rho_p - \rho_L)\omega^2 t}}$$

where d_s = Stokes diameter of the particle,
S = distance of the particle from the center of rotation at $t = 0$,
R = distance of the particle from the center of rotation at the time t,
ω = angular velocity of centrifuge in radians per second,
η = the viscosity of the fluid in poise,
ρ_p = density of particle, and
ρ_L = density of fluid.

If an initially homogeneous suspension is used, the calculation of the particle size distribution from the concentration changes occurring within the suspension is very difficult. This is because particles of the same size starting at different distances from the center of rotation are subjected to different forces. For a full discussion of the mathematical treat-

[38] Eadie, F. S., and Payne, R. E., Iron Age, **174,** No. 10, 99–107, 1954.

ment, see the discussion by Kamack.[39] The early methods of analysis were based upon the use of the ordinary laboratory bucket centrifuge. This type of equipment has the advantage that it is cheap and readily obtainable. However, it has two major disadvantages. First, since the particles travel along radial paths, they will strike the sides of the walls, and the effect of this on the final analysis is difficult to predict. Second, the stopping and starting of the centrifuge causes severe currents in the suspension (due to the changing momentum of the fluid) which will often resuspend the particles which have settled out. However, provided that all the conditions are carefully standardized, bucket centrifuge techniques can be used for control type analysis or for empirical investigations.[40]

Because of the difficulty of handling the data obtained using homogeneous suspensions, two-layer techniques are widely used in centrifugal methods of analysis. In the Whitby technique, the suspension tube has a specially shaped base. The volume of settled suspension is determined from the height of the solids collected in the capillary (see Fig. 41-18). The weight of slurry collected at any time t is the weight of particles less than d_t, the Stokes diameter, calculated from Equation (12), where S is now the distance of the suspension layer from the center of rotation and R is the distance of the top of the settled solids from the center of rotation. The specially shaped capillary serves two purposes: it facilitates the measurement of the settled solids, and it minimizes the swirling effects of the stopping and starting of the centrifuge.

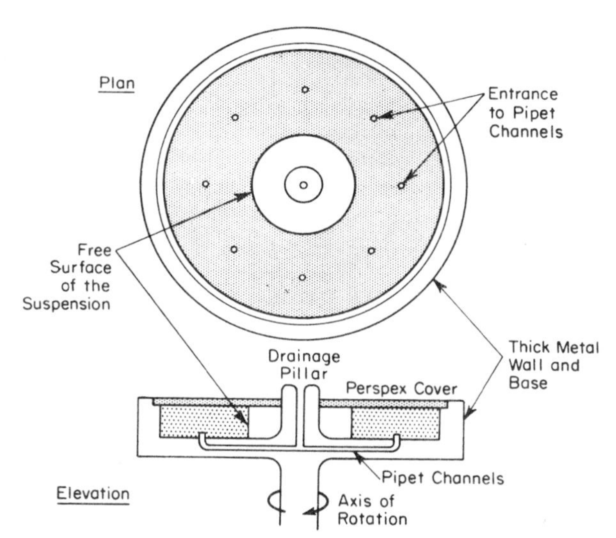

Fig. 41-20. Outline of Slater and Cohen Disc Centrifuge.

To overcome the effect of the walls of the bucket-type centrifuge, several disc centrifuges have been developed. The discussions in this chapter will be restricted to two of the simpler ones. These are the Slater and Cohen disc centrifuge and the Kaye disc centrifuge.[41,42] The basic system of the Slater and Cohen centrifuge is shown in Fig. 41-20. It is essentially a centrifugal pipet method. The centrifuging chamber is a hollow

[39] Kamack, H. J., Anal. Chem., **23,** 844–850, 1951.
[40] Jacobsen, A. E., and Sullivan, W. F., Ind. Eng. Chem., Anal. Ed., **18,** 360–364, 1946.
[41] Slater, Cohen, J. Sci. Inst., **39,** 614, 1962.
[42] Groves, M. J., Kaye, B. H., and Scarlett, B., Brit. Chem. Eng., **9,** 743, November, 1964.

disc with a central pillar as shown. Through the base of the disc are drilled several holes from the central pillar, which terminate in a series of apertures equally spaced around the perimeter of a circle concentric with the axis of rotation. The disc is partly filled with suspension and rapidly accelerated to the speed at which the analysis is to be carried out. Under centrifugal forces the free surface of the suspension is a cylinder concentric with the axis of rotation. After a given time of centrifuging, a sample of suspension is withdrawn through the base by applying suction to the drainage pillar. The solids concentration of the sample is then determined directly. The process is repeated at a series of times. For a full discussion of the method and the treatment of the data, see the article by Slater.[41]

The Kaye disc centrifuge is essentially a centrifugal photosedimentometer.[42] The basic system is shown in Fig. 41-21. In the simplest equipment which has been described, the

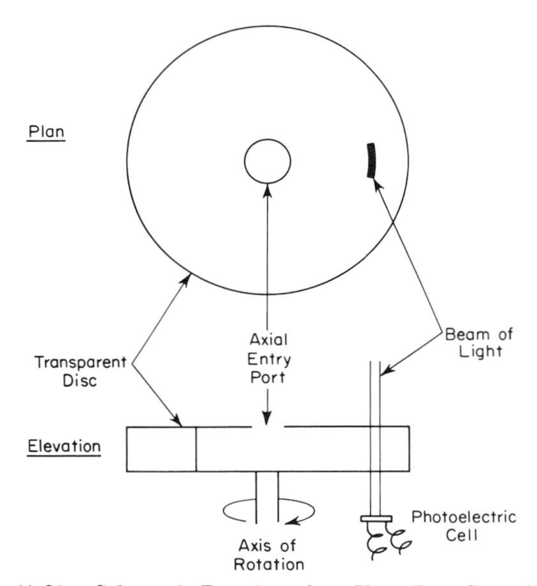

FIG. 41-21. Schematic Drawing of the Kaye Disc Centrifuge.

centrifuge chamber is a hollow, transparent disc (made for example from polymethylacrylate) with an axial entry port. A beam of light is passed through this tank as shown. Difficulties caused by stopping and starting the centrifuge are overcome by carrying out the analysis at constant speed. For this to be possible the inertia of the centrifuge must be high, so that injection of fluid into the tank will not significantly change the momentum of the system. Particle size analysis using this type of centrifuge can be carried out in two ways.

In the first technique, the suspension under test is added to the empty centrifuge while it is running at the speed at which the analysis is to be carried out. As in the case of the Slater and Cohen disc centrifuge, the free surface of the suspension is virtually a cylinder coaxial with the axis of rotation. The injection of the suspension can be carried out very rapidly through the wide entry port. As the particles sediment outward, measurements of the variations in concentration of the suspension are measured by means of the light beam. The calculation of size distribution from data obtained in this way is the same as for the Slater-Cohen disc centrifuge.

An alternative method of using the Kaye disc centrifuge is a modified form of the two-layer technique. For this type of analysis, the centrifuge disc is partially filled with clear fluid and allowed to attain the required running speed. As before, the free surface of the liquid under centrifugal forces is a cylinder coaxial with the axis of rotation. A small amount of suspension is then injected through the entry port.

Because of the angular momentum of the rotating fluid, the injected suspension cannot immediately penetrate the clear liquid and it forms a uniform layer on top of it. Once the layer has attained the velocity of the centrifuge (which in practice occurs very quickly), the particles start to sediment outward along radial paths. If the band of suspension is thin relative to its distance from the measuring zone, all particles can be regarded as starting from the same position. This means that each size of particle reaches the measuring position at a definite time. By measuring the changes in light intensity as the particles cross the beam, the concentration of each size group is measured continuously. If automatic recording devices are used, the trace from the recorder can be compared directly with the trace from a standard powder, and for control purposes there is no need for further data treatment. A further advantage of this modified two-layer technique is that several analyses can be carried out in succession without stopping the centrifuge, since, once the smallest particle has passed the sampling zone, the tank is effectively empty of particles and the next sample can be injected. For a full discussion of the technique, see the article by Kaye *et al.*[42]

ELUTRIATION TECHNIQUES

Elutriation is the process of separating powders into fractions of different mean diameter by suspending the particles in a moving fluid. (The root of the word "elutriate" comes from a Latin verb meaning "to wash out.") In a vertical elutriator the fluid moves upward through a column. For a specific velocity, particles smaller than a given size move upward with the fluid, while the larger particles settle to the bottom and the particles are thus separated into two fractions. Size analysis by elutriation is carried out by separating the powder into several fractions, using different fluid velocities, and then the weight of powder in each fraction is calculated directly. Elutriation methods of particle size analysis have the advantage that the prepared fractions of powder can be examined directly by secondary methods of analysis, such as microscope examination. In this way a great deal of valuable information can be obtained. The major disadvantages of the group of methods is that the fractionation of the individual particles does not always occur sharply with respect to the theoretical partition diameter, and it is not usually practicable to take fractions at $<5\ \mu$. The low cost of the basic equipment, however, is often an advantage.

A form of air elutriator which is widely used in particle size analysis, the Roller elutriator, is shown in outline in Fig. 41-22. The powder to be analyzed is placed in the Pyrex feed tube. The elutriating chamber, made from stainless steel, is connected flexibly to the feed tube and the exit filter tube as shown. The dry air, which elutriates the powder, enters the equipment via the flow meter through a small jet. During an analysis the feed tube is rocked, the combined effect of this motion and the gas flow causes turbulent conditions in the powder sample, and the particles are entrained in the gas stream entering the elutriating chamber. At the upper end of the chamber steady flow conditions persist, the large particles fall back into the sample tube while the fines are carried out of the chamber and collected in the filter. If Stokes law can be applied to the particles in the elutriating chamber, the critical size is given by:

$$d_c = \frac{18\eta v}{(\rho_p - \rho_F)g}$$

where v = linear velocity of fluid through the chamber,
g = acceleration due to gravity,
η = viscosity of the fluid (in poise),
ρ_p = density of powder particles, and
ρ_F = density of fluid.

The time required for the complete elimination of the particles smaller than d_c from the feed tube depends, in practice, on the magnitude of d_c. For the finest critical diameter,

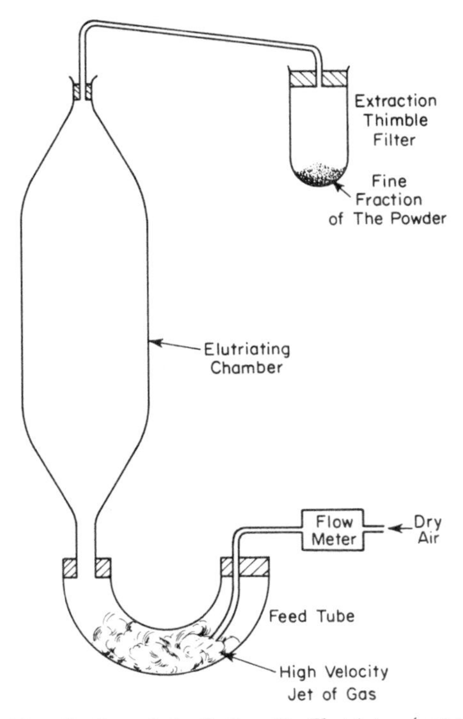

FIG. 41-22. Outline of the Roller Air Elutriator (not to scale).

say 5 μ, the time is approximately an hour, compared with 10 to 30 min. for the larger sizes. To aid fractionation of the powder, the equipment is usually supplied with four interchangeable elutriating chambers of different diameter. In the commercial form of the equipment, motor-driven, leather-tipped hammers are provided with which to vibrate the elutriating chamber. This prevents particles from clinging to the walls and so aids efficient fractionation.[43]

Another form of air elutriator is the Haultain infrasizer. In this equipment the air stream is passed, at a constant rate, through six cones of different diameter. Part of the

[43] Roller, P. S., J. Am. Ceram. Soc., **20**, 167–74, 1937. See also: Brit. Standard 3406, Part 3, 1962; and ASTM Special Technical Publication No. B293–54T, 1954.

system is shown in outline in Fig. 41-23. The critical diameter for each cone is calculated from the maximum diameter at the top of the cone. The cones are made of stainless steel and the diameters at the top increase in a $\sqrt{2}$ progression. The special feature of this equipment is the use of ball and cone valves to disperse the powder efficiently at the

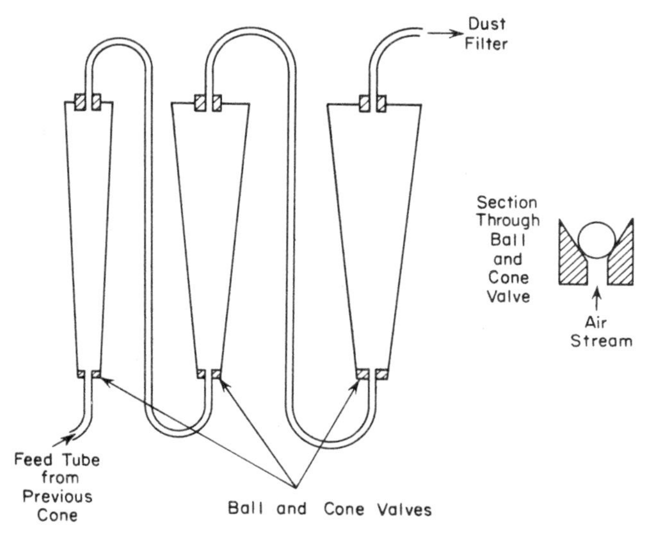

FIG. 41-23. Components of the Haultain Infrasizer.

beginning of each elutriation chamber. The valve consists of a special ball, resting in a cone. As the air stream enters, the ball is lifted to form a narrow annulus. The ball spins and this, combined with the high velocity gas flow in the annulus region, causes vigorous turbulence which results in efficient dispersion of the particles in the gas stream.[44]

A convenient type of liquid elutriator is the Blythe elutriator.[45] This usually consists of six elutriating chambers of the shape shown in Fig. 41-24. Each unit of the elutriator constitutes a syphon, and the suspension flows through the system at a constant rate. At the start of an analysis the powder is placed in the first "sump," and eventually clearly defined fractions are obtained in each of the beakers. One precaution which must be taken with this equipment is that, if the powder requires the use of a surface active agent for efficient dispersion, this agent must be added to the feed stream. If this is not done, eventually the dispersing agent is flushed out of the system and the originally dispersed powder will flocculate in the sumps.

STREAM METHODS OF ANALYSIS

In these techniques of particle size analysis, a stream of fluid, carrying particles to be measured, is passed through a sensing device, and measurements are made on individual particles. Different physical techniques are used to measure the particles in the sensing zone, light scattering, electric measurements, radiation adsorption, or sound detection. Stream methods of analysis are currently the subject of intense development programs

[44] Haultain, H. E. T., Trans. Can. Min. Met., **40,** 229, 1937.
[45] Pryor, E. H., Blythe, H. N., and Eldridge, A., Min. Met., **11,** 1953.

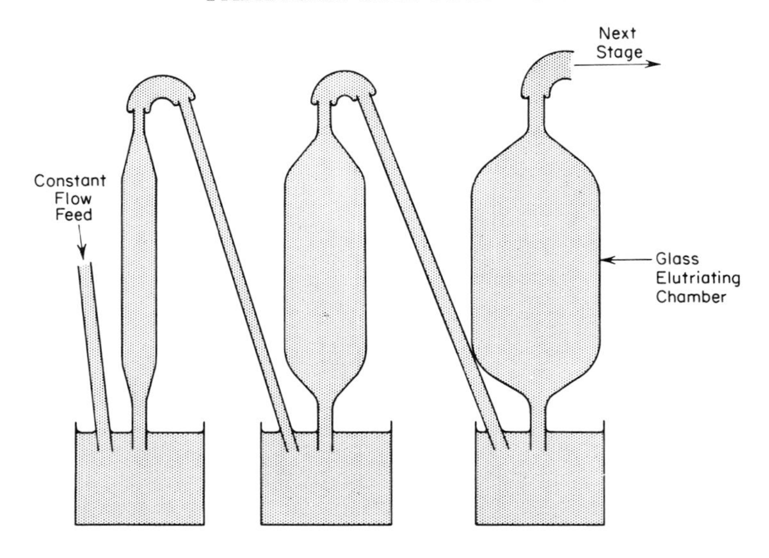

FIG. 41-24. Components of the Blythe Elutriator.

and it is to be expected that some of the systems being used in specialized laboratories will be widely used, in the near future, as standard methods of analysis. As a group, these are particularly suited for the monitoring of fluids with low concentrations of particle impurities, *i.e.*, air pollution measurements, dirt in fuel oil, etc. They are also useful when only a small sample of the powder is available. One method of stream analysis

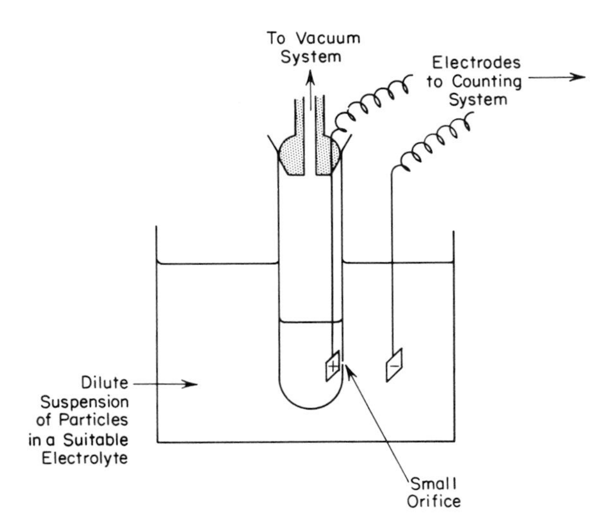

FIG. 41-25. Basic System of the Coulter Counter.

which is widely used is based on a proprietary instrument, the "Coulter counter." [46] The basic system of this equipment is shown in Fig. 41-25. The sensing zone is a small orifice between two portions of a suspension contained in a wide-diameter outer vessel open to the atmosphere, and a smaller vessel connected to a vacuum system. Two electrodes, one on either side of the hole, are used to measure the electrical resistance of the orifice system. The suspension, which must be electrically conductive, is drawn through the orifice by means of the vacuum system. As each particle of the suspension passes through the orifice, it replaces its own volume of electrolyte, and there is a change in resistance between the electrodes. While the particle is passing through the aperture, there is a voltage pulse of short duration between the electrodes. Provided that the particle diameter is relatively small with respect to the diameter of the orifice, and that the shape of the particle is not extreme, the magnitude of the pulse is proportional to particle volume. In practice, the manufacturers state that when precise measurements are required, the particle diameters, which can be sized with a given orifice, range from $1\frac{1}{2}$ to 30 percent of the orifice diameter. Many different sizes of orifice are available. The series of voltage pulses produced as the suspension passes through the orifice is electronically amplified, scaled, and counted. In the commercial equipment there are facilities for drawing small known amounts of suspension through the orifice.

Difficulties which arise from the method are the choice of the suitable electrolyte, the elimination of background electrical noise from the counting circuits, and the selection of a representative sample. By careful attention to detail these difficulties can be overcome. However, operators should be aware that variations in the experimental technique, or environment, can introduce systematic errors into the measurements. For instance, the introduction of a faulty stirrer motor into the laboratory can cause electrical noise in the counting circuit, when the equipment is used at its lower limits, if the instrument is not adequately shielded. Particle resistivity rarely requires consideration, because it is usually many orders of magnitude greater than that of the electrolyte. When sizing particles greater than, say, 20 μ, care must be taken that the agitation in the outer vessel is sufficient to ensure that the largest particle present has an opportunity of passing through the sensing zone. Properly used, this equipment is very useful in obtaining, directly, volume measurements of the powder in suspension and it can be a rapid method of analysis.

SURFACE AREA DETERMINATIONS BY PERMEABILITY TECHNIQUES

General Considerations.—The surface area of a powder can be calculated from the permeability of a powder bed, *i.e.*, the ease with which the powder bed permits the passage of a fluid. It must be stressed that the physical property measured is the permeability of the bed and that the validity of the measured surface area derived from such a procedure is no better than the validity of the assumptions made when interpreting the permeability data. As a group, the permeability methods of measuring surface area have the following advantages: (1) The size of sample required is of the order of several grams, and therefore sampling problems are relatively simple; (2) the equipment required is cheap and robust, compared with many other methods of size analysis; and (3) experimental data can be obtained quickly.

The main disadvantage is that, because the permeability of a powder bed depends upon its pore structure, anomalous results can be obtained if materials with widely divergent size or shape distributions are compared. For example, the measured surface

[46] Kubitschek, J., Research, **13**, 129, 1960.

area of a powder could apparently decrease by removing coarse particles from it. The reason for this is that the interpacking of large and small particles could give a dense powder bed of low permeability, *i.e.*, a high surface area would be recorded. The removal of the large particles leaves a loosely packed powder bed of high permeability, and thus a low surface area would be indicated. The methods are widely used for control purposes and, provided that due care is exercised when interpreting the results, they form a very useful group of techniques.

Darcy put forward the first permeability equation, which states: The rate of flow of fluid through a porous medium is directly proportional to the pressure gradient causing the flow. This can be expressed in the form

$$\frac{dQ}{dt} = (p_1 - p_2)K$$

where dQ/dt = rate of flow of fluid,
p_1 and p_2 = pressures on each side of the sample of porous material, or the powder bed, and
K = a constant dependent upon the experimental conditions.

This relationship only holds for streamline flow conditions. Later, Kozeny derived an equation in which a relationship between K and the powder bed characteristics was established. It was derived by considering the pore space of the powder bed to be equivalent to a bundle of capillaries of equal hydraulic radii and having a cross-sectional shape representative of the average pore cross section. (N.B. The hydraulic radius is a concept used in determining the resistance offered to the flow of fluid through a pipe. It is defined as the cross-sectional area of the pipe divided by the perimeter wetted by the fluid flowing through the pipe.) It was further assumed that the path of a streamline of the fluid through the bed will be tortuous with an average length L_e which would be greater than L, the nominal length of the bed. A modified form of Kozeny's equation, due to Carman, is the basis of most methods of determining surface area by permeability measurements. This so-called Kozeny-Carman equation is usually written in the form:

$$\mu = \frac{\epsilon^3}{(1 - \epsilon)^2} \cdot g \cdot \frac{\Delta p}{B\eta L S_w^2 \rho^2}$$

where μ = linear velocity of fluid through the powder bed,
ϵ = porosity of powder bed = (volume of bed − volume of particles)/volume of bed,
g = acceleration due to gravity,
Δp = pressure difference across the bed,
η = viscosity of fluid (poise),
L = thickness of bed,
ρ = density of powder particles,
S_w = specific surface area of the powder per gram, and
B = a dimensional constant which includes the tortuosity factor (Le/L).

Using a powder of known size characteristics and composed of spherical particles, Carman found $B = 5.0 \pm 0.5$. This value of B is almost always used when calculating surface area, and it is obviously a source of systematic error when nonspherical particles are used. If the fluids flowing through the powder is a gas at low pressure, and if the dimensions of the pores are of the same order as the mean free path of the molecules, then a modified formula has to be used:

$$\mu = \frac{g\,\Delta p}{B\eta L}\left\{\frac{\epsilon^3}{(1-\epsilon)^2 S_w^2 \rho^2} + \frac{\epsilon^2}{(1-\epsilon) S_w \rho} Zl\right\}$$

where the symbols have the same meaning as before, and l is the mean free path of the gas. Lea and Nurse found Z to have a mean value of 3.3.[47] From either the Kozeny-Carman equation or the modified formula, the measured surface area should be independent of the porosity of the powder bed. However, on this point the simple deviation is not adequate, and it has been experimentally determined that for many powders there is a tendency for S_w to increase with decreasing values of ϵ. In fact, a working committee of the American Society for Testing Materials proposed that, for cement, the basic Kozeny-Carman equation be modified by the substitution of

$$\frac{1}{(0.85-\epsilon)^2} \quad \text{for the} \quad \frac{1}{(1-\epsilon)^2}$$

term to allow for the dependence on porosity.[48] In practice it is usual to standardize the value of the porosity at which the measurements are taken. There is generally a reasonably wide range of values over which the measured surface areas do not change to any marked extent, and the standardized value is usually in this range, thus minimizing small variations in experimental technique. The various methods of analysis differ in the fluid used, the technique for measuring the fluid flow through, and the pressure drop across, the powder bed. The method of preparing the powder bed is usually determined by the nature of the powder. Care must always be taken to ensure that the bed is homogeneous, *i.e.*, does not contain fissures and cracks which would have the effect of bypassing portions of the bed.

Gooden and Smith Technique.—(A commercially available instrument based on this method is known as the Fisher subsieve sizer). The basic system of this equipment is shown in Fig. 41-26.[49] The air supply is passed through a surge tank, to smooth fluctua-

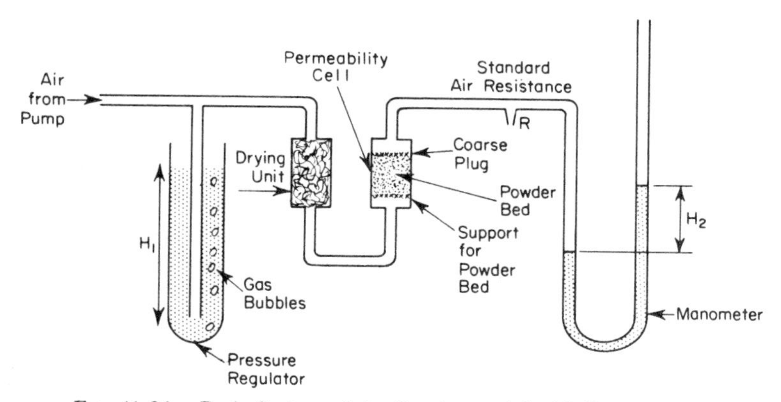

FIG. 41-26. Basic System of the Gooden and Smith Permeameter.

tion due to the pumping action. The pressure of the air flowing through the powder bed, prepared in the permeability cell, is adjusted to any required value by altering the height

47 Lea, F. M., and Nurse, R. W., J. Soc. Chem. Ind., **58,** 278, 1939.
48 ASTM, Special Technical Publication 234, 1958.
49 Gooden, E. L., and Smith, C. M., Ind. Eng. Chem., Anal. Ed., **12,** 479, 1940.

of fluid H_1. When the pressure exceeds the given value, gas bubbles escape, as shown. The pressure should be adjusted until a slow, steady stream of bubbles form. The powder bed is supported by a coarse metal gauze on which a filter paper is placed. The permeability cell is detachable from the rest of the circuit, and a smooth plunger is used to press the powder to form a homogeneous bed. (To enable a patent calculator to be used with the commercial equipment, it is necessary to use a weight of powder which, in grams, is numerically equal to the density of the particles of the powder.) When the powder bed is in the circuit, the pressure of the air drops to atmospheric through the standard air resistance R, shown in the figure. This is usually a gem crystal with a fine hole bored through it. Assuming that the basic Kozeny-Carman equation can be applied to the system, then rearranging the equation, we obtain

$$S_w^2 = \frac{\epsilon^3}{(1-\epsilon)^2} \cdot g \cdot \frac{(\Delta p)'}{B\eta \cdot L\rho^2\mu}$$

where $(\Delta p)' \equiv$ pressure drop across powder bed.

Let Q be volume of fluid flowing per second equal to μA, where A is the cross section of the powder bed:

$$S_w^2 = \frac{\epsilon^3}{(1-\epsilon)^2} \cdot g \cdot \frac{(\Delta p)'}{B\eta Q\rho^2}$$

Now for the standard resistance R, it follows that:

$$Q = K(\Delta p)''$$

where $(\Delta p)'' \equiv$ pressure drop across the resistance, and
$K =$ a constant characteristic of the resistance.

$$\therefore S_w^2 = \frac{\epsilon^3}{(1-\epsilon)^2} \cdot g \cdot \frac{(\Delta p)'}{K(\Delta p)''B\eta\rho^2}$$

If the fluids in the manometer and the pressure regulator are the same, this formula simplifies to:

$$S_w^2 = \frac{\epsilon^3}{(1-\epsilon)^2} \cdot g \cdot \frac{(H_1 - H_2)}{H_2} \cdot \frac{1}{BK\eta\rho^2}$$

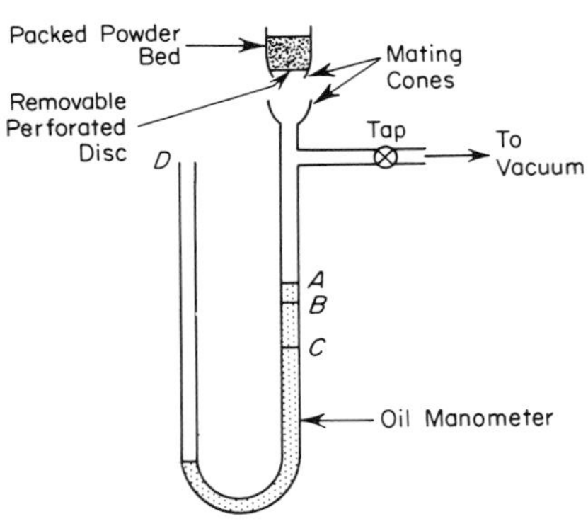

FIG. 41-27. Basic System of the Blaine Fineness Tester.

The unknowns in this equation can be obtained either by using a standard powder, or by using a flowmeter to find K. The range of surface areas which can be measured can be extended by having two or more standard resistances of different values. The Lea and Nurse permeameter is essentially the same as the Gooden and Smith equipment, the main difference being that a capillary flow meter is substituted for the standard air resistance.

The Blaine Fineness Tester.—This simplified air permeameter is widely used for control purposes. The basic system is shown in outline in Fig. 41-27. The permeameter cell is a small metal cylinder into which is fitted a removable, perforated metal disc. This disc rests on a rim near the base of the cell, and a filter paper is placed on top of the disc. The powder is placed in the cell and compacted with a sliding piston. This piston usually has a groove down one side to permit the escape of air as the powder bed is pressed down. When the preparation of the bed is complete, the cell is fitted to one end of a U-tube, which usually has a bore of the order of 1 cm. The liquid level in the manometer is now displaced by opening the tap. (It is important that the level be displaced this way and not by applying pressure to the arm D of the manometer, since this would cause air flow upward through the plug which could rupture the powder bed.) When the manometer level has risen to the point A, the vacuum tap is closed. The time for the manometer level to fall from B to C is measured. An assumption which is made to simplify the calculation is that the linear velocity of flow of the air through the powder bed is given by the expression:

$$\mu = \frac{ha}{T}$$

where h = distance between B and C,
a = cross-sectional area of the manometer tube, and
T = time of fall of manometer level between B and C.

If this value is substituted in the Kozeny-Carman equation, it can be shown that for a given instrument:

$$S_w = \frac{K'}{\rho} \frac{\epsilon^{3/2}}{1 - \epsilon} \cdot T^{1/2}$$

where K' = a constant characteristic of the instrument,
ρ = the particle density,
ϵ = the porosity of the powder bed, and
S_w = the surface area per gram of the powder.

It is usual to calibrate the instrument using a standard powder. For control purposes, if a standard porosity is used for the same material, the surface area is directly proportional to the square root of T. If the timing is done electronically, a scale, reading directly in *surface area*, can be constructed.[50, 51]

SURFACE AREA BY GAS ADSORPTION

Various methods for measuring the surface area of a powder from a study of gas adsorption have been devised. A complete study of gaseous adsorption is, in itself, a complete branch of surface chemistry, and only an outline of the basic principles and methods can be given here.[52] The theoretical treatment of an adsorption process is considerably simplified when an inert gas or nitrogen is adsorbed at low temperatures, *e.g.*, the temperature of liquid nitrogen boiling at atmospheric pressure. The discussion of methods will be restricted to this type of system. The basic concept involved in surface area determinations by gas adsorption is that, if the quantity of gas required to cover a powder with a complete monolayer of gas molecules is known, the powder surface area can be calculated, using the cross-sectional area of the gas molecules.

Gas adsorption methods are very important because they measure directly the surface area of powder available for chemical or physical reaction. However, any derived measure of particle size, such as a "mean particle diameter" quoted from gas adsorption data, must be interpreted with great care. This is due to the fact that, in the calculation of

[50] Blaine, R. L., ASTM Standards, Part 4, C204–55, 140, 1958.
[51] Spillane, F. J., Analyst, **82**, 712, 1957.
[52] ASTM Special Technical Publication No. 234, 1958.

the mean size, assumptions have to be made concerning the shape, density, and porosity of the particles of the powder. This point can be appreciated from the consideration of cube of granular sugar. Because of its high porosity it has, effectively, a high surface area available for solution. If, however, a mean diameter were calculated from the surface area available for solution, it would be very much smaller than the dimensions of the cube. Until recently, major disadvantages of gas adsorption techniques were the time required for an analysis, and the expense and complexity of the necessary equipment. The new gas flow methods, based on the original work of Nelsen and Eggertsen,[53] seem to offer the prospect of overcoming most of these difficulties. An important consideration in all gas adsorption studies is the state of the surface at the commencement of the experiment. The powder should always be carefully outgassed and the gas used chemically pure. For very high precision, the whole of the vacuum system should be outgassed.

Many theories on gaseous adsorption have been put forward, but the one which is widely used in surface area determinations is that due to Brunauer, Emmett, and Teller.[54] By considering the dynamics of a gas adsorption process, they deduced an equation which can be written in the form:

$$\frac{p}{V(p_S - p)} = \frac{1}{V_m C} + \left(\frac{C-1}{V_m C}\right)\frac{p}{p_S}$$

where V = volume of gas adsorbed at pressure p,
p_s = saturation vapor pressure at temperature of experiment,
V_m = volume of gas adsorbed when the entire surface is covered by a monomolecular layer, and
C = a constant.

Therefore, for systems to which this equation can be applied, a plot of $p/V(p_S - p)$ *vs.* p/p_S should give a straight line. From the intercept and slope of this line $1/(V_m C)$ and $(C - 1)/(V_A C)$ can be found, and hence C and V_A calculated. It should be noted that, if the data is plotted in this way, a resultant straight line is not sufficient proof that the theory can be applied to the system. It is also necessary that the value of C is in reasonable agreement with its value as predicted from thermodynamic considerations, *i.e.*,

$$C = \exp\left(\frac{E_1 - E_e}{RT}\right)$$

where E_1 = the heat of adsorption of the first adsorbed layer,
E_e = the heat of liquefaction of the adsorbing gas,
R = the gas constant, and
T = the absolute temperature.

Although the Brunauer, Emmett, and Teller theory (usually known as the B.E.T. theory) has been criticized, it has proved very reliable for interpreting adsorption studies when nitrogen gas is adsorbed onto a powder at the temperature of liquid nitrogen, provided that $0.05 < (p/p_S) < 0.35$.

B.E.T. Method of Measuring Surface Area.—If the adsorption isotherm for a gas is measured, and the surface area determined using the theory of Brunauer, Emmett, and Teller, the technique is known as the B.E.T. method.

An outline of a typical system for determining the adsorption isotherm is shown in Fig. 41-28. The sequence of operations is as follows: With taps A, B, and C closed, the sample tube is fitted to the equipment and held firmly by the springs. Tap A is then

[53] Nelsen, F. M., and Eggertsen, F. T., Anal. Chem., **30**, 1387, 1958.
[54] Brunauer, C., Emmett, P. H., and Teller, E. J., J. Am. Chem. Soc., **60**, 309, 1938.

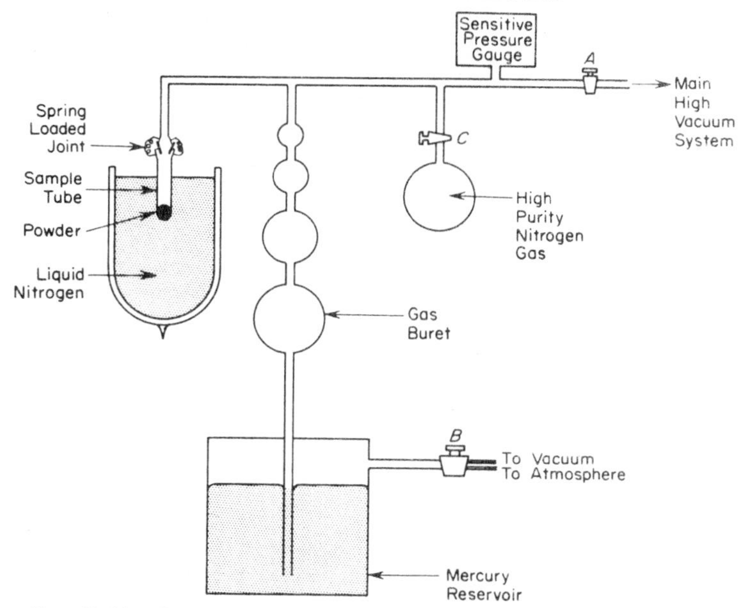

FIG. 41-28. Basic System for Determining Gas Adsorption Isotherms.

opened and the system evacuated. This is continued until the powder sample is completely outgassed and is often one of the longest operations of the sequence, sometimes requiring as long as 12 hr. Because of this, provision is often made in a more complicated system for the simultaneous outgassing of several sample tubes which can be put into the measuring circuit separately. During the outgassing operation the sample tube is at room temperature, or sometimes even surrounded by a small electric heater. When the measuring system has been evacuated to the required level, tap *A* is closed. Tap *C* is then opened briefly to charge the measuring system with pure gas, and the sample tube is immersed in liquid nitrogen. When the apparatus has attained thermal equilibrium, the pressure is recorded. The volume of each bulb and the gas space beyond the smallest bulb is accurately known from preliminary experiments. By opening tap *B* slightly to the atmosphere, each bulb of the gas buret is flooded in turn, and thus a series of corresponding pressure-volume data can be obtained and the isotherm plotted. The flooding of each bulb must be carried out slowly to minimize thermal effects which would occur if the nitrogen gas were compressed adiabatically. At all stages in the series of measurements, duplicate pressure readings should be taken at different times after the flooding operation, to ensure that thermal and physical equilibrium has been attained. For a detailed discussion of equipment of gas adsorption measurements, see the article by Fries.[55]

Gas Flow Adsorption Measurements.—Recent developments in instruments for measuring adsorption isotherms have eliminated the need for high vacuum systems by employing the principles of gas chromatography. The new system developed initially by Nelsen and Eggertsen is shown in Fig. 41-29. A known mixture of nitrogen and helium is passed through the sample tube. The helium functions as a carrier gas. The

[55] Fries, R. J., ASTM Special Technical Publication 234, 259, 1958.

ratio of helium to nitrogen can be altered by means of the valves, and the exact ratio is determined by means of the thermal conductivity cells A and B. The equipment is purged using the mixture of nitrogen and helium with the sample tube at room temperature. This stage corresponds to the outgassing procedure when using a vacuum system,

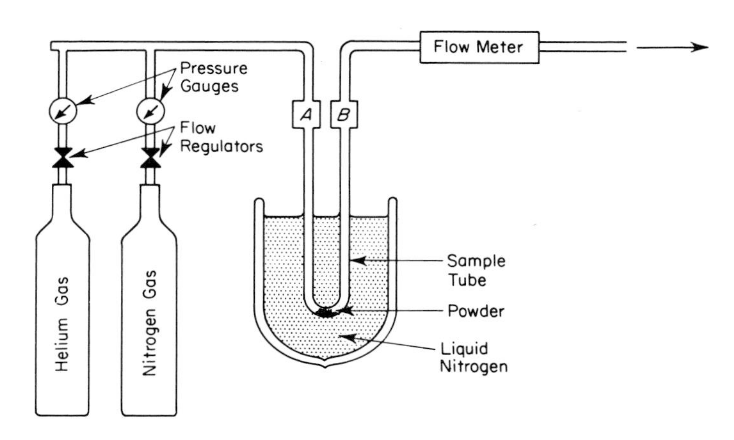

FIG. 41-29. Gas Flow Apparatus for the Determination of the Surface Area of a Powder. A and B are thermal conductivity cells for determining the percentage of nitrogen in the gas stream entering and leaving the sample tube.

and great care must be taken to ensure that the purging is complete. The thermal conductivity cells are connected to a recording potentiometer so that the gas mixture is continually monitored. When purging is complete, the sample is cooled in liquid nitrogen. The sample then adsorbs nitrogen, and this adsorption is indicated by a peak on the recorder chart. After equilibrium is established, the pen returns to its original position. On removing the coolant, desorption occurs. For a complete adsorption–desorption cycle, the record from the chart is as shown in Fig. 41-30. Provided low flow rates are

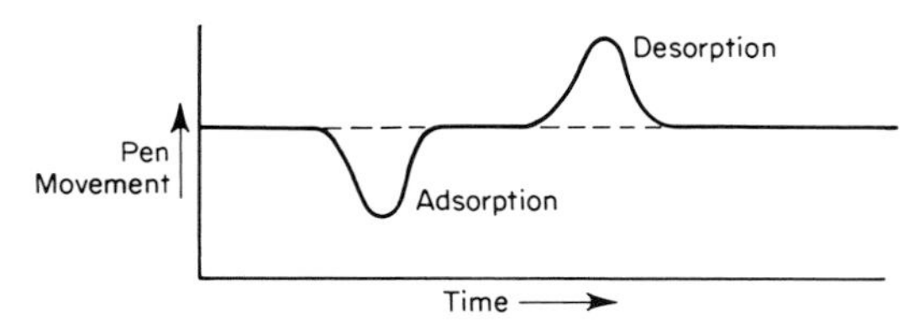

FIG. 41-30. Typical Chart Record for Adsorption-Disorption Cycle.

used and the peak height is not too large, it can be shown that the area of the adsorption and desorption peaks is a direct measure of the nitrogen adsorbed or desorbed. The apparatus can be readily calibrated using a sample of known surface area. Alternatively, a series of experiments can be carried out using several different gas mixtures where the normal B.E.T. isotherm can be plotted. In this case the partial pressure of the nitrogen is the appropriate value of p to use in the formula.

Pressure Differential Techniques for Measuring Surface Areas.—The equipment for determining the surface area of powders from gas adsorption, by a method described by Schlosser,[56] is shown in Fig. 41-31. This technique has the disadvantage that it requires a high vacuum system, but it enables a continuous record of the adsorption iso-

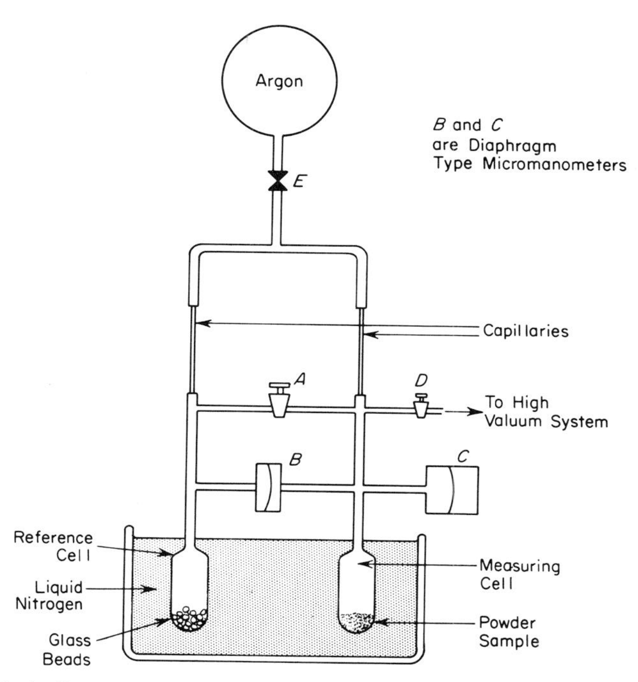

Fig. 41-31. Basic System for Measuring Surface Areas by the Pressure Differential Technique (equipment of this type known as Betograph). *B* and *C* are diaphragm type micromanometers.

therm to be obtained directly. The equipment is available commercially under the name Betograph.[57] The adsorption of gas by the powder is measured by comparing the pressure rise in the measuring cell with that in a reference cell of the same volume, when gas at a given pressure is fed into both of them from the Argon reservoir. The gas volume of the reference cell must always be the same as that of the measuring cell, and, for different powder samples, the volume of the reference cell is adjusted by means of coarse glass beads of negligible surface area. The system is evacuated by closing tap *E* and opening taps *A* and *D*, with both glass cells at room temperature. This is continued until the powder sample is degassed. Then taps *A* and *D* are closed. The two glass cells are now immersed in liquid nitrogen. When temperature equilibrium has been established, tap *E* is opened slightly. As the gas flows into the cells through the capillaries, the pressure in the reference cell rises faster than that in the measuring cell because of the adsorption of gas, in the latter, by the powder. The pressure difference between the two cells is a direct measure of the adsorbed quantity of gas.

[56] Schlosser, E. G., Chem. Ing. Tech., **31,** 799, 1959.
[57] Manufactured by Atlaswerke, A. G., Bremen, Germany.

The two-diaphragm-type micromanometers, B and C, record the differential pressure and the absolute pressure in the measuring cell, respectively. These micromanometers are connected to pen recorders, and a permanent record of the pressure changes enables the adsorption isotherm to be calculated.

Part II

INSTRUMENTAL METHODS FOR INDUSTRIAL PRODUCTS AND OTHER SPECIAL SUBSTANCES

Chapter 42

AIR POLLUTANTS

By Robert J. Bryan
Director of Technical Services
Los Angeles County Air Pollution Control District
Los Angeles, California

Introduction.—The objectives involved in conducting air pollutant analyses may include (1) provision of continuous warning systems against the accumulation of toxic contaminants, (2) the defining of the nature and degree of pollution from specific sources, (3) the establishment of pollutant trends in community air quality, (4) the measurement of air pollutants in support of studies in atmospheric chemistry, and (5) the identification of pollutants responsible for specific types of injury, nuisance, or damage. Recent strides in the development and use of analytical instrumentation have stimulated the use of such methods in the analysis of air pollutants.

The instrumental methods described in this chapter are broadly subdivided as either manual instrumental methods or automatic instrumental methods. They will further be classified according to technique, which will permit convenient cross-reference to Part I of this volume, which uses the same nomenclature and instrumental classifications.

MANUAL INSTRUMENTAL METHODS

Manual instrumental methods, as defined here, include the detection of a direct physical property of the material of interest, or of a reaction product of the material of interest by instrumental means. It does not involve sample collection, concentration, or processing steps.

VISIBLE AND ULTRAVIOLET SPECTROMETRY

These methods generally include the detection of a reaction product which will absorb light in the visible or ultraviolet region of the spectrum. The measurement is made by the use of commercially available colorimeters or spectrometers. Jacobs[1] has described a number of methods of analysis in this category including those for sulfur dioxide, hydrogen sulfide, nitrogen oxides, ammonia, ozone, benzene, and phenols. Noncolorimetric methods to be found in the aforementioned chapter are those for settled particulate matter, suspended particulate matter, sulfuric acid aerosol, carbon monoxide, aldehydes, and acetylene.

[1] Jacobs, M. D., in Welcher, F. J., Ed., Standard Methods of Chemical Analysis, Vol. II, 6th Ed., Chapter 23, D. Van Nostrand Company, Inc., Princeton, N. J., 1963.

INFRARED SPECTROMETRY

HYDROCARBONS

The instrumental methods used for hydrocarbons in air pollution work are those of infrared spectrometry and gas-liquid partition chromatography. Due to the complexity of the hydrocarbon mixture usually present in the ambient atmosphere, infrared techniques are capable of only semiquantitative and qualitative measurements. However, when such limitations are taken into consideration by the analyst, the technique can provide an abundance of analytical information. Atmospheric analyses by infrared methods are especially favored when large surveys are undertaken and there is a need for a simple, rapid means of analysis. The hexane equivalent technique as suggested by Mader, Heddon, Lofberg, and Koehler[2] is suitable for rapid quantitative work.

Hydrocarbons in the atmosphere are collected in a fire brick-packed, stainless steel U-tube immersed in liquid oxygen. Methane is not captured, but recovery is good for C_2's and higher. For industrial emission sampling where concentrations are greater, samples may be collected in double stopcock sampling containers and then introduced directly to the instrument.

Analysis is based on the absorption due to the C-H stretching vibration at approximately 3.3 to 3.5μ as measured with an infrared spectrometer equipped with an appropriate gas cell. The instrument is calibrated with *n*-hexane for analysis of unknown samples with results being reported in terms of parts per million as hexane. Aromatics, and to some degree olefinics, are not effectively measured because of the relatively poor absorbance at the wavelength used.

Apparatus. **Collection.**—For sampling atmospheres below the 5 p.p.m. level (10-meter cell) or 50 p.p.m. (1-meter cell), the collection train consists of a drying tube packed with Ascarite and a magnesium perchlorate plug; a $\frac{1}{2}$ inch o.d., 20 inch long U-tube made of 316 stainless steel with valves and fittings on either end, packed to a depth of 3 inches in both arms with C-22 fire brick, 30–60 mesh; a Dewar flask for liquid oxygen, an air pump; and a wet test gas meter. For higher concentrations a suitable double stopcock sampling container may be used.

Analytical.—An accurate infrared spectrometer, preferably double beam, equipped with at least a 1-meter gas cell. A 10-meter folded path cell will provide greater sensitivity.

Procedure.—Assemble the equipment in the sequence described. Add liquid oxygen to the Dewar flask slowly to within $\frac{1}{2}$ inch of the top. Sample at a rate of 3 liters per minute until approximately 60 liters are collected. At the end of each sampling period, while the tube is still in the liquid oxygen, close the valves at each end of the sampling tube and remove from the liquid oxygen. Place the collection tube in a beaker water bath at 80°–90°C. a few minutes before making the transfer to the cell in the infrared spectrometer. Evacuate the spectrometer cell and close the valves to the pump and mercury manometer. In order to purge the trap, open the valve of the stainless steel collection tube attached to the gas cell, close it again, and open the valve to the instrument air purge line and allow the collection tube to fill with air. Close the valve to the air line and then open the line to the spectrometer cell until the pressure has been equalized. Repeat this procedure several times until the pressure in the cell and the collection tube are close to atmospheric pressure. Finally, open both valves on the collection tube and allow the system to reach atmospheric pressure. Run an infrared scan from four to three μ. Run a blank scan on dry ambient air. Calculate the absorbance of the sample.

[2] Mader, P. P., Heddon, M. W., Lofberg, R. T., and Koehler, R. H., Anal. Chem., **24,** 1899, 1952.

Calibrate the infrared spectrometer by preparing a series of samples of *n*-hexane in air at different concentrations and run an infrared scan as before. Prepare a calibration curve by plotting the corrected absorbance of the known samples *vs.* the concentration of *n*-hexane on rectangular coordinate graph paper. The slope of this curve is called the calibration factor.

Calculation.—The concentration of hydrocarbons in parts per million as hexane for the air sample may then be ascertained by comparison of the absorbance reading to known values, and adjusting for sample volume. Generally, no temperature corrections are made on sample volumes unless the temperature goes above about 100°F. or below about 50°F.

EMISSION SPECTROMETRY

METALS

To determine the metals content of the atmosphere, suspended particulate matter is collected on a tared filter, which has been dried and weighed, by passing a known volume of air through the filter. The sample collection procedure used should be that given by Jacobs[3] in the method for "Suspended Particulate Matter." The glass filter web used by the National Air Sampling Network of the U. S. Public Health Service, Division of Air Pollution is most commonly used as the filter medium. The filters are charred, acid extracted, and a spectrographic analysis run on the dried residue from the extract to determine the metals content. The method of the County of Los Angeles Air Pollution Control District[4] or that of the National Air Sampling Network of the Public Health Service[5] have been found to be satisfactory.

Apparatus.—Arc-spectrograph (1.5-meter grating spectrograph, 7A./mm., Model 2060, with 35-mm. camera, Applied Research Laboratories, Glendale, California) with Multi-source unit (Applied Research Laboratories, Model 22), densitometer (Applied Research Laboratories Model 42), high purity spectrographic graphite electrodes (lower electrode, platform type; upper electrode, regular tip with undercut), developing facilities for films.

Reagents. **Film.**—35 mm. Spectrum No. 2 film.

Developer.—Kodak D-19.

Acetic acid (5 percent).—Dilute 50 ml. of glacial acetic acid to 1 liter with water.

Rapid Liquid Fixer.—Kodak rapid liquid fixer.

Standard Solutions. *Lithium Chloride-Graphite Mixture.*—Mix 1 part of lithium chloride with 2.5 parts spectrographic grade graphite. This is an internal spectrographic standard.

Stock Solution.—A stock solution containing salts of the metals to be analyzed is prepared by weighing accurately the quantities of each salt necessary to give the highest concentration required, and diluting with water. The ratios of the metals used should approximate those to be found in the ambient air sample.[6]

Working Standard Solutions.—A series of dilutions of the stock solution are prepared for the working standards. Successive reductions of fifty percent are convenient because of the logarithmic nature of the film calibration. The most dilute working standard should be about 1/1000th the concentration of the stock solution.

[3] Chapter 23 in Volume II.

[4] Laboratory Methods, Air Pollution Control District, County of Los Angeles, California, 1958.

[5] Air Pollution Measurements of the National Air Sampling Network, Analyses of Suspended Particulates, 1957–1961, Public Health Service Publication No. 978, 1962.

[6] For example, the ratio of zinc to beryllium used in the United States Public Health Service procedure is 200:1.

Film Calibration.—It is necessary to calibrate the film to be used in the analysis. By means of this calibration the operator will be able to convert percent transmission on the densitometer to relative intensity. This is accomplished by exposing films to an iron spectrum, using the step sector method described in the Laboratory Methods of the County of Los Angeles Air Pollution Control District[7] or the two-line procedure described by Churchill.[8] The film emulsion curve relating the relative intensity (logarithm of exposure) to the densitometer reading (percent transmission) is prepared.

Procedure.—High volume particulate sample collected as described in the aforementioned method for suspended particulate matter is muffled at 500°C. for 1 hour to burn off organic matter. Two extractions with 40 ml. of 1:1 redistilled nitric acid are made at slightly below the boiling point for 1-hour periods. Resulting extractions are filtered through Whatman #42 filter paper, the filtrate is evaporated to about 4 ml., and then made up to 10 ml. with demineralized water. Blanks are similarly prepared. Electrodes are prepared by securing an appropriate aliquot of the sample and solutions together with the lithium internal standard to the crater portion of the electrode. They are then dried and arced to completion in the spectrograph using a direct current arc. The spectra are recorded on film which is developed for three minutes at 70°F., acid stopped, and fixed. Repeat the arcing and photographic procedures for standards and blanks. Line transmissions are read on the densitometer.

Convert the percent transmission to relative intensity using the film calibration data. Obtain the intensity of the line for each element being measured in respect to the lithium standard as unity. Prepare working curves for each of the elements contained in the standards by plotting micrograms of each element *vs.* the intensity ratio of each of the dilutions of the standard solutions against the lithium internal standard. By means of the densitometer read the percent transmission for the line of each element in the unknown samples and blanks at the same wavelengths used for the standards. Compute the intensity ratio for each line in the same manner as the described for the standard. Read the micrograms of each element present in the unknown samples and blanks from the appropriate working curves.

GAS CHROMATOGRAPHY

HYDROCARBONS

Volatile hydrocarbons may be determined both quantitatively and qualitatively by the use of gas chromatography. Separation is achieved by exposing the injected sample to selective fractionating agents. In general, this fractionating agent is held in an elongated column with individual components of the sample being moved through the fractionating agent at differential rates by a nonadsorbable carrier gas such as helium.

The determination of individual hydrocarbon pollutants in the ambient atmosphere is usually accomplished by the use of partition (gas-liquid) chromatography. In this case the selected fractionating agent is a nonvolatile liquid film placed upon an inert solid support. A comprehensive treatment of gas chromatographic techniques and methods has been prepared by Dal Nogare and Juvet.[9] When properly selected columns, sample introduction systems, and flow rates are used, individual hydrocarbons are discretely separated prior to reaching the detector.

Flame ionization detectors are usually used for hydrocarbon analysis as this type of detector is insensitive to inorganic and fixed gases such as helium, oxygen, nitrogen,

[7] *Op. cit.*
[8] Churchill, J. R., Ind. Eng. Chem., Anal. Ed., **16,** 653, 1944.
[9] Dal Nogare, S., and Juvet, R. S., Jr., Gas-Liquid Chromatography, Interscience Publishers, Inc., New York, 1962.

hydrogen, carbon dioxide, and carbon monoxide. This simplifies separation and detection procedures. Qualitative detection is measured by retention time with quantitative measurement being accomplished by the measurement of peak height or area under the peak on the produced chromatograph.

***Apparatus.* Collection.**—Collection of ambient air samples for gas chromatographic analysis using flame ionization detection equipment requires relatively simple sampling apparatus. In some cases direct injections of nonconcentrated samples collected in precision syringes are all that is necessary. In other cases it is desirable to introduce a concentration step. In this event collapsible, chemically inert bags of polyester film, such as "Mylar" or aluminized "Scotch-Pak" have been successfully used. Samples are collected by the use of nonlubricating air pumps in a conveniently sized (approximately 10-liter) bag. A portion of the collected sample is then transferred to an evacuated 2-liter flask with approximately 1 liter from the 2-liter flask being concentrated in a $\frac{1}{4}$-inch stainless steel U-tube collection trap, 24 inches in total length, packed with 42–60 mesh fire brick coated with a fractionating agent, which is immersed in liquid nitrogen contained in a Dewar flask.

NOTE.—Caution must be exercised in the use of liquid nitrogen for the cold trap, as oxygen will concentrate in the collector. Sampling should be conducted at reduced pressures with a final pressure reduction to 2 mm. mercury (abs.) before removal from the cold trap being suggested.

Analytical.—Suitable gas chromatographic equipment for the analysis of hydrocarbon air pollutants is available from a number of manufacturers. Depending upon the number of individual constituents to be analyzed, and the convenience desired, single- or two-stage chromatographs may be used. Hydrogen flame ionization detectors are preferred for chromatographic equipment used in ambient air hydrocarbons analysis.

Calibration.—For calibration, known quantities of highly purified individual hydrocarbons are injected into the gas chromatograph by means of a precision microsyringe. Using the mode of operation that will be used in the analysis of the air sample, retention distance on the resulting chromatogram obtained by use of a strip chart recorder is used to identify the individual component peaks. The area under the peak is directly related to the eluted sample weight.

Procedure.—The collected sample, whether concentrated or not, is connected to the sample injection system on the gas chromatograph. The sample system introduces the sample to a flowing carrier gas which transports the sample through the partition column selected for use in the analysis. In the case of a single-stage instrument, the individual hydrocarbons will be resolved with the ultimate limitation being based upon the time available for analysis and the number of calibration hydrocarbons used, as a great number of isomers are possible with hydrocarbons having carbon numbers greater than six. The resulting chromatogram, together with the calibration data relating the area under the peaks to hydrocarbon quantity, is used for the determination of quantities of individual hydrocarbons. In the case of two-stage instruments, one of the stages may be isolated following a suitable length of time with the carrier gas continuing to flow through the other stage, and the resulting chromatogram produced. By means of this system, greater flexibility is attained for the analysis of more complex hydrocarbon systems. Abstractor columns may be used at the end of the separation column to separate hydrocarbon classes if desired. For example, mercuric perchlorate may be used to remove aromatic and olefinic hydrocarbons.

Developments in this field continue at a rapid pace, with great selection available in partition column packing and sample introduction systems. Primary limitations in this method involve the identification of unknown peaks and the resolution of overlapping peaks in highly complex systems. Great care must be exercised in the operation of all components of the system in order that reproducibility of measurement may be obtained.

TURBIDIMETRY AND NEPHELOMETRY

SULFATES

Water-soluble sulfates in the atmosphere have been used as an indicator of industrial polution. They include sulfuric acid aerosol and reaction products of sulfuric acid aerosol with alkaline materials, sulfate compounds emitted directly to the atmosphere, and naturally occurring sulfates. They are determined by collection on a high volume filter, subsequent extraction by hot water, precipitation by barium chloride, and determination by either turbidimetric or nephelometric procedures such as that given by the Public Health Service in their Publication No. 978[10] in a colorimeter or spectrometer adapted to this type of analysis.

Apparatus. **Collection.**—A high-volume filter such as that described by Jacobs[11] in the method for "Suspended Particulate Matter" in Chapter 23, Volume II, is suitable for this procedure. The fibrous glass web filter media, such as used by the National Air Sampling Network of the U. S. Public Health service, may be used.

Reagents. **10 *M* Hydrochloric acid.**—Eighty ml. of concentrated hydrochloric acid is diluted to 100 ml. with distilled water.

Glycerin-alcohol Solution.—One volume of glycerin is mixed with 2 volumes of 95 percent ethanol.

Barium Chloride Crystals.—High-quality 20–30 mesh crystals are used.

Stock Standard Solution (1000 μg. SO_4/ml.).—1.48 g. of anhydrous sodium sulfate are dissolved in distilled water and diluted to 1 liter.

Working Standard Solution (100 μg. SO_4/ml.).—Ten ml. of stock standard are diluted to 100 ml. with distilled water. This solution should be prepared daily.

Procedure.—The entire filter media or suitable aliquot of the sample is placed in a 125-ml. flask, and 50 ml. of distilled water are added. The mixture is refluxed for 90 minutes, cooled, and filtered through Whatman #1 paper. The extraction is repeated with 10–15 ml. of water, and the mixture is heated only a few minutes without a condenser. The solution is filtered through the same filters; flask and filter are washed until the total volume of filtrate is 80 ml. Twenty ml. of the water extract of the sample are pipetted into a clean, dry cuvet; 1 ml. of 10 *M* hydrochloric acid and 4 ml. of the glycerin-alcohol solution are added, and the solution mixed well. The optical density is read at 500 mμ against the blank. This reading is subtracted from the final reading as a correction for unmatched cuvets and impurities in the sample. Approximately 0.25 g. of barium chloride crystals are added and mixed until dissolved. After the mixture stands for 40 minutes, the optical density is read at 500 mμ against the reagent blank. Any spectrometer that accommodates cuvets with a light path of 25 or 50 mm. should be satisfactory. The sulfate content of the 20-ml. sample is determined by referring to the calibration curve.

Calculation.—The sulfate content of the atmospheric sample (assuming use of the entire filter) reported in terms of micrograms per cubic meter of air is determined as follows:

$$\mu\text{g. sulfate/cu. meter} = \frac{\mu\text{g. sulfate in 20 ml. sample} \times 4}{\text{cu. meter of air sampled}}$$

NOTE.—Factor of 4 in the equation above must be adjusted when an aliquot of the sample is used other than the entire filter.

[10] *Op. cit.*
[11] *Op. cit.*

Standardization.—A series of standards (starting with the working standard solution) is prepared based upon the expected range of sulfate concentration. The procedure for analysis of sample, starting with the addition of hydrochloric acid, is followed. For the calibration curve, micrograms of sulfate in the standard are plotted against the optical density. On graph paper with rectangular coordinates, the result should be a straight line.

AUTOMATIC INSTRUMENTAL METHODS

Automatic instrumental methods, for the purpose of this chapter, are defined as including those which involve the use of continuous analyzers in which the sample collection, processing, and analytical determination are carried out continuously in the proper sequence, with the results of such continuous determination being displayed on a suitable recorder. The American Conference of Governmental Industrial Hygienists have prepared a compendium of commercially available instruments.[12]

There are also available automatic analysis trains such as the "Auto-analyzer" manufactured by Technicon. This type of instrument performs only the sample processing and analysis operations by automatic means. It is useful when large numbers of samples must be analyzed, which may originate from a number of sources, and for which continuous time sequence of information is not absolutely necessary.

For the most part the automatic analyzers described in the following section apply similar instrumental principles for methods of analysis in the detection operation as are described in the previous section on manual instrumental methods. Again, these automatic analysis procedures are classified according to instrumental detection procedure utilized.

VISIBLE AND ULTRAVIOLET SPECTROMETRY

OZONE AND OXIDANTS

Ozone in the atmosphere is absorbed in a neutral buffered potassium iodide reagent in a continuous flow counter-current absorption column with the iodide being oxidized to iodine. The tri-iodide ion, which is produced in stoichiometric proportion, is determined in a continuous flow, dual-cell colorimeter which, in conjunction with the slide wire circuit of the recorder, gives a ratio recording of the optical transmittance of the reacted solution and air path blank. The recorder is calibrated in parts per hundred million ozone.

The use of a neutral buffered 10 percent potassium iodide solution has been found to minimize the interference of nitrogen dioxide, as compared to the 20 percent potassium iodide solution originally suggested by Littman and Benoliel.[13] Recent studies have shown that using the 10 percent reagent, 10 p.p.m. of nitrogen dioxide will give a response as 1 p.p.m. ozone.[14] Sulfur dioxide, if present, will give a quantitative negative interference.

[12] Air Sampling Instruments, 2nd Ed., American Conference of Governmental Industrial Hygienists, Cincinnati, Ohio, 1962.

[13] Littman, F. E., and Benoliel, R. W., "Continuous Oxidant Recorder," Anal. Chem., **25**, 1480, 1953.

[14] Bryan, R. J., and Cherniack, I., "A Comparison Study of Ozone and Oxidant Detectors Which Are Used for Atmospheric Air Sampling," J. of Air Poll. Control Assn., **15,** No. 8, 1965

Apparatus.—The apparatus used consists of a suitable assembly of a sampling probe, combination absorption and reaction column, reagent metering pump, air pump, flow meters, activated carbon reagent filter column, dual cell colorimeter, and servotype recorder. The absorption and reaction column used for this instrument consists of a 9-mm. i.d. glass tube, 53 mm. in length, which has a glass spiral on its inner surface. The reagent flows so as to wet the inner wall of the column. The air flow is counter-current to the reagent flow, and is measured by use of a variable area flow meter. The reagent flow is metered through the use of a constant displacement pump. The colorimeter assembly consists of a single mercury vapor lamp, a Corning optical filter, which transmits a narrow band of radiation in the 360-mμ, region, and two barrier layer cells. The 20-mm. Pyrex sample cell, through which the reacted reagent flows, is located in front of one of the barrier layer cells, while an adjustable beam attenuator is interposed in the reference path to the other.

The two barrier layer cells are connected in a ratio-measuring circuit to a 10 millivolt potentiometric recorder. The effective range of the instrument is 0–80 p.p.h.m. ozone on a logarithmic scale which may be adjusted by increasing the liquid flow rate while reducing the air flow rate.

Absorbing Solution.—Dissolve 200 g. of potassium iodide, 40.4 g. of disodium hydrogen phosphate ($Na_2HPO_4 \cdot 7H_2O$), 5.4 g. of monopotassium dihydrogen phosphate (KH_2PO_4) in distilled water, and dilute to 2 liters with water.

Calibration.—The calibration of the instrument is accomplished by both static and dynamic methods. The static method involves passing a standard solution of iodine in the filtered potassium iodide reagent through the sample cell and noting the recorder response. The dynamic method involves the use of a known concentration of ozone as determined by chemical means. The ozone is prepared from air, which has been passed through an Ascarite and activated carbon filter, by irradiation with an ultraviolet lamp. The stream is separated, with one portion going to the instrument and the second going to a set of chemical impingers containing a 2 percent aqueous iodide solution. The chemical reference test is conducted at an air flow rate of 1 liter per minute for a 45-minute period, with the contents of the two impingers being combined and acidified with sulfuric acid and immediately titrated with 0.002 *N* sodium thiosulfate, using starch as an indicator. A calibrated scale which should be nearly linear on semilog paper is prepared. In the case of static reagent calibration, the concentration on the scale must be calculated using air and reagent flow rates.

Procedure.—A fresh supply of reagent is added to the light-proof reagent reservoir. Liquid flow is established at 7 ml. per minute by means of the adjustable stroke positive displacement pump. Air flow rate is established at 3.7 liters per minute by measurement on the variable orifice meter and controlled by a bypass at the air pump. The reagent is freed of any iodine by filtration through a granular activated charcoal filter immediately before entering the contact column. Instrument zero is adjusted at a convenient point on the chart (approximately 5 percent of full deflection) by completely bypassing the sample air and adjusting the position of the beam attenuator in the reference path. All connections should be established as being air- and liquid-tight. Routine servicing should be performed as suggested by the manufacturer; it should also include periodic cleaning of glassware, checking of joints, replacing activated carbon in the reagent filter, and checking pH of the recirculating reagent. All adjustments made in flow rates, blank values, and any changes made in reagent and instrument parts, should be duly noted on the recorder chart. Charts are read periodically against the scale prepared from the calibration operation. Blank values should be subtracted from the gross scale reading to obtain the net ozone concentration.

NITROGEN OXIDES

Nitrogen dioxide by direct means, and nitric oxide by indirect means, are determined in the atmosphere by the formation of an azo dye by a modification of the Griess-Ilosvay diazotization reaction in a continuous flow concurrent absorption column, with subsequent colorimetric determination of the pink colored compound formed. The reaction, which is specific for nitrogen dioxide, or more specifically the nitrite ion, involves the diazotization of sulfanilic acid and coupling with N-(1-naphthyl)-ethylenediamine dihydrochloride.[15] In the case of nitrogen dioxide, an equivalence factor for the nitrite ion must be determined by calibration, as experimental evidence indicates that this factor exceeds the theoretical factor of 1 mole of nitrogen dioxide being equivalent to one-half mole of nitrite. The determination of nitric oxide is as nitrogen dioxide after oxidation by acidified potassium permanganate. In either case, the azo dye formed is determined in a continuous flow colorimeter system which, in conjunction with the slide wire circuit of the servotype recorder, gives a ratio recording of the optical transmittance of the reacted and blank solutions.

Apparatus.—The apparatus used consists of a suitable assembly of sampling probe, continuous concurrent-flow absorption column, potassium permanganate bubbler, liquid-holdup reaction tube, reagent metering pumps, air pump, flow meters, activated carbon reagent filter column, triple cell colorimeter, and potentiometric recorder. In the dual instrument for determining both nitrogen dioxide and nitric oxide, two separate absorption columns consisting of a 13 turn helix of 6-mm. i.d. tubing wound over a 4-inch mandrel are required. The reagent flow is metered through the use of constant displacement piston pumps with air flow being concurrent to the reagent flow and measured with the use of a variable area flow meter. This system is used to minimize turbulent diffusion and channeling of the colored reaction product as compared to the earlier used counter-current glass helice-packed vertical absorption column.[16] The colorimeter assembly consists of a single tungsten lamp focused on three optical cells: the blank reagent cell, the nitrogen dioxide sample cell, and the nitric oxide sample cell. Located between these cells and their respective barrier layer detectors are Corning filters which transmit light in the 550-mμ range. The barrier layer cells are connected to a two-point potentiometric recorder so that alternate readings of the nitrogen dioxide and nitric oxide are obtained. The normally used concentration rage is 0–5 p.p.m. on a logarithmic scale. Shorter or longer path optical cells may be used to change the range.

***Reagents.* Absorbing Solution.**—Dissolve 100 g. of sulfanilic acid in 15 liters of a good grade of distilled water. Add 2670 ml. of glacial acetic acid. Add distilled water to make a total volume of 20 liters.

Coupling Agent Stock Solution.—Dissolve 1 g. of N-(1-naphthyl)-ethylenediamine dihydrochloride in distilled water, and make up to 1 liter with water.

Permanganate Oxidizing Solution.—Dissolve 6.25 g. of potassium permanganate in approximately 100 ml. of distilled water. Add 3.4 ml. of concentrated sulfuric acid. Add water to make up to 250 ml.

Calibration.—Routine calibrations are performed by using stock solutions of sodium nitrite because of the difficulties in handling nitrogen dioxide for dynamic gas calibration operations. The nitrite calibration procedure requires the assumption of an equivalence

[15] Saltzman, B. E., "Colorimetric Microdetermination of Small Amounts of Nitrogen Dioxide in the Atmosphere," Anal. Chem., **26**, 1949, 1954.

[16] Thomas, M. D., MacLeod, J. A., Robbins, R. C., Goettelman, R. C., Eldridge, R. W., and Rogers, L. H., "Automatic Apparatus for Determination of Nitric Oxide and Nitrogen Dioxide in the Atmosphere," Anal. Chem., **28**, 1810, 1956.

factor for nitrogen dioxide as compared to sodium nitrite. The commonly assumed factor is the one described by Saltzman.[17] He states that 1 mole of nitrogen dioxide produces the same color intensity as 0.72 mole of sodium nitrite. This factor exceeds the theoretical factor of 0.5 mole of sodium nitrite, and is assumed to be a result of a portion of the nitrogen dioxide reacting directly with the sulfanilic acid without first being converted into nitrous and nitric acids. Because of differences in absoprtion columns, this factor should be obtained for each instrument. Calibration is performed by introducing a standard solution of sodium nitrite in absorbing solution into the measuring cells while the reference cell contains the same reagent, free of any nitrite. Concentrations over the range of interest should be used as there may be some departure from Beer's law at higher concentrations. Dynamic gas calibrations have been performed by the use of nitrogen dioxide, starting from high concentrations and using a cascade dilution system, or by preparing tanks of dilute nitrogen dioxide using evacuated cylinders and high precision syringes to introduce the microquantities of nitrogen dioxide necessary. It is more difficult to obtain a variety of concentration ranges with the latter procedure. Care must be taken to account for the equilibrium factor between nitrogen dioxide and nitrogen tetroxide. A calibrated scale which should be nearly linear on semilog paper is prepared. In the case of static reagent calibration the scale concentrations must be calculated using air and reagent flow rates.

Procedure.—A fresh supply of reagent is added to the reagent reservoir (usually a 6-gal. polyethelene container). Sufficient coupling agent stock solution to make the reagent 0.002 percent in N-(1-naphthyl)-ethylenediamine dihydrochloride (400 ml. in 20 liters) is added just prior to introducing the reagent to the instrument. Liquid flow is established at 2.16 ml. per minute in each separate reagent flow system by means of the adjustable stroke positive displacement pump. The air flow rate is established at 225 ml. per minute by measurement on the variable orifice meter and controlled by a bypass at the air pump. If a recirculating reagent system is used, a reagent containing the developed reaction product is first filtered through an activated carbon column system. Because the coupling agent is also removed by the activated carbon, it is necessary to use a two reservoir system when recirculating reagent, so that coupling agent can be added in the proper quantity to the recovered reagent. Otherwise, the spent reagent may be dumped. The air flow sequence involves passing the ambient air sample through the nitrogen dioxide absorption column and thence through a midget bubbler containing the acidified potassium permanganate oxidizing solution, where the nitric oxide is oxidized to nitrogen dioxide. The air stream then passes through the nitric oxide (equivalent nitrogen dioxide) column. The zero adjustments are manually made by means of a beam attenuator in all three light paths.

All connections should be established as being air and liquid tight. Routine servicing should be performed as suggested by the manufacturer, but should also include periodic cleaning of all glassware, replacing activated carbon in the reagent filter, and testing of the recirculated reagent. If the packed type absorption columns are used, particular attention is necessary to prevent channeling and buildup of reaction products in the column. Frequent cleaning with potassium hydroxide and alcohol reduces this tendency. All adjustments made in flow rates, blank values, and any changes made in reagent and instrument parts should be duly noted on the recorder charts. Charts are read periodically from a scale prepared from the calibration operation. Blank values should be subtracted from the gross recorder readings to obtain the net nitrogen dioxide and nitric oxide concentrations.

[17] *Op. cit.*

CONDUCTOMETRY

SULFUR DIOXIDE

Sulfur dioxide in the atmosphere may be measured using the continuous conductivity metering technique as described under "ASTM Designation D1355-60, Method A Conductivity Method." [18] In this procedure sulfur dioxide is absorbed in a counter-current wetted wall column designed so as to minimize the collection of potentially interfering aerosols. In a reagent which consists of a dilute solution of hydrogen peroxide and sulfuric acid, sulfur dioxide is converted to sulfuric acid with a continuous recording of the increase in electrical conductivity being a measure of the sulfur dioxide concentration. The method is not specific for sulfur dioxide, with soluble gases that yield electrolytes in solution causing the greatest interference. Most hydrogen halides interfere quantitatively, but in normal atmospheres this class of compounds would not be expected to be present in significant quantities. Weak acidic gases, such as hydrogen sulfide, give negligible interference because of slight solubility and poor conductivity. Sulfuric acid aerosol is extremely low in interference because of the poor collection efficiency for aerosols in the absorption unit. Alkaline gases such as ammonia interfere by neutralizing the acid, yielding low results unless the ammonia is present in extremely high concentrations, in which case the results would be high.

Apparatus.—The apparatus consists of a suitable assembly of sampling probe, absorber, gas flow meter, air pump, liquid pump, conductivity electrodes, and conductivity recorder. Two general types of apparatus under this general category have been used. The first type is described as an accumulative type of analyzer in which a definite volume of air is bubbled through a fixed volume of absorbent during a discrete time interval. This is a cyclic procedure which gives integrated sulfur dioxide values over the sampling period. The instantaneous type of analyzer is one in which a metered stream of absorbent is introduced to a continuous flow wetted wall absorption tube with a counter flow of sample air from which the sulfur dioxide is absorbed. The absorbing solution flows continuously past a conductivity cell of small volume, thus giving an instantaneous conductivity trace related to the sulfur dioxide concentration. The absorber for the instantaneous type absorber is a straight glass tube, 8- to 9-mm. i.d. and 70–75 cm. long. The tube is packed with a 6 pitch spiral made by twisting together two pieces of #26 Nichrome or equivalent wire. More recent versions of analyzers equivalent to that described in the ASTM method utilize a positive displacement reagent pump[19] in place of the suggested gravity flow system controlled by a fixed capillary. Analyzers in which there is no temperature control chamber for the conductivity electrodes require a temperature compensator for the recorder giving a 1.6 percent per degree centigrade correction for the range from 5–45°C.

Absorbing Solution.—To 5 gallons of a good grade of distilled water add the following: 10 ml. of 0.1 *N* sulfuric acid, 10 ml. of Dowicide solution (1 g. Dowicide per 500 ml. water), 10 ml. of 9 percent hydrogen peroxide.

Calibration.—Recorder calibration can be performed both statically and dynamically. Experience has shown that both procedures give equivalent results. The static

[18] Sulfur Dioxide Content of the Atmosphere, Continuous Analysis and Atomatic Recording of, ASTM Designation D1355-60, ASTM Standards on Methods of Atmospheric Sampling and Analysis, 2nd Ed., American Society for Testing and Materials, Philadelphia, 1962.

[19] Cherniack, I., "Development of a Prototype General Purpose, Portable Gas Analyzer," Fifth Conference, Methods in Air Pollution Studies, Calif. Dept. of Public Health, Los Angeles, 1963.

method is performed by introducing a series of sulfuric acid solutions of known concentration, assuming a stoichiometric relationship between sulfur dioxide and the acid solutions used, and preparing a scale in terms of parts per million based upon the liquid and air flow rates used. The dynamic calibration method involves the use of a synthetic mixture of air and sulfur dioxide with simultaneous sampling of the stream for reference analysis. The reference method used is that of West and Gaeke,[20] also described by Jacobs.[21] A fresh supply of absorbing solution is placed in the reservoir, which may be a polyethylene or glass container, and the analyzer operation is started. Air and liquid flow rates are adjusted with the normal values being 3.33 ml. per minute of absorbing solution, and 9.5 liters per minute of air sample. Care must be taken to eliminate formation of bubbles in the flow system which causes erratic response by the conductivity cells and interference with the liquid flow. The operating temperature range in the case of the thermostated instruments should be 120°F. ± 2°F. While the operation of this instrument is reasonably trouble free, liquid and air flow rate checks should be made from time to time, the glassware and conductivity cells should be cleaned, the pump motor and recorder should be serviced, along with other maintenance procedures suggested by the manufacturer. The reagent in this instrument is not recovered for re-use.

COULOMETRY

Several types of electrometric instruments are available for the continuous analysis of air pollutants. One type involves the principle of galvanic coulometry in which a self-generating current serves as the measure of the constituent in the sample. In the widest sense, this class of instrumentation may be described as a fuel cell. Another type of analyzer coming under the general heading of coulometry is the amperometric coulometric type of analyzer in which there is an applied e.m.f. An example of both types of instrument will be described in this section, with ozone analysis being the subject of each. As a matter of fact, many other types of substances, including air pollutants, may be susceptible to this type of analysis, including halogens, oxides of nitrogen, and carbon monoxide, to name a few.[22]

OZONE

GALVANIC COULOMETRY METHOD

Ozone is measured by the release of a halogen from an electrolyte solution which is reduced galvanically at a filter electrode, with the generated current in the external circuit being a measure of the concentration.

Apparatus.—The apparatus consists of a sample probe, air pump, galvanic cell assembly, and recorder to measure the voltage drop resulting from the generated current flow across a calibrated resistor. The cell assembly involves a compartment for the liberation of bromine, and another compartment containing the graphite yarn cathode and an activated coconut carbon powder anode. Air flow is measured through the use of a variable air flow meter with liquid flow being accomplished by the use of the air lift pump principle. Consequently, there is no metering required for the reagent which is continuously regenerated by the cell action.

Reagent.—Dissolve 14.2 g. of disodium hydrogen phosphate (Na_2HPO_4), 13.6 g. of monopotassium dihydrogen phosphate (KH_2PO_4), 357.1 g. of potassium bromide, and 0.17 g. of potassium iodide in distilled water. Add water to a volume of 1 liter.

[20] West, P. W., and Gaeke, G. C., Anal. Chem., **28,** 1816, 1956.
[21] *Op. cit.*
[22] Hersch, P., Galvanic Analysis, Advances in Analytical Chemistry and Instrumentation, Vol. 3, John Wiley & Sons, Inc., New York, 1964.

Calibration.—A calibrated scale is prepared by the dynamic procedure, using generated ozone as described under the colorimetric procedure for ozone earlier in the chapter. The scale produced should be linear, as the cell behavior is coulometric with ozone.

Procedure.—A fresh supply of reagent is introduced to the cell system and instrument operation is started. The air flow rate is adjusted as indicated by the variable orifice meter. In the commercially available instruments this flow rate is 149 ml. per minute. Because the cell current is linearly related to the air flow rate, minor adjustments may be made to retain the same scale calibration. The blank value for the scale is determined by passing the inlet air stream over an activated charcoal bed or a manganese dioxide catalyst tube which will decompose the ozone in the air stream. Little attention is necessary for this instrument except to maintain the proper flow rate. There is some loss of water from the reagent by evaporation, so that occasional adjustment of liquid level is necessary by the addition of distilled water. After a long period of time the carbon anode may need replacing as there is a net oxidation effect of the carbon at this point. Components exposed to reagent should be cleaned from time to time.

AMPEROMETRIC COULOMETRY METHOD

Ozone is determined in the atmosphere by the reaction with iodide to form iodine, which in turn reacts with hydrogen at the cathode of a cell having a small constant applied potential. The resulting polarization current tending to re-establish the hydrogen layer is a measure of the quantity of ozone passing through the cell. This method is not specific for ozone, as Bryan and Cherniack[23] have shown that nitrogen dioxide responds as a positive interference and sulfur dioxide as a negative interference, in a similar fashion to other methods of ozone analysis in which the oxidation-reduction reactions between ozone and a halide are involved.

Apparatus.—The apparatus includes a suitable sampling probe, a microcoulomb cell such as that developed by Brewer,[24] having a cathode of many turns of platinum wire over a glass stem and an anode with a single turn of platinum wire at the base of the stem, a source of applied potential, an air pump, a liquid pump, and a recorder. A commercial version of this analyzer is designed for portable operation. A small oscillating piston type air pump is used along with a bellows pump for reagent delivery and metering.

Reagent.—Dissolve 20 g. of potassium iodide, 50 g. of potassium bromide, 7.49 g. of disodium hydrogen phosphate ($N_2HPO_4 \cdot 7H_2O$). Add distilled water to make a total volume of 1 liter.

Procedure.—Fresh reagent is introduced into a glass reservoir provided in the instrument, and the analyzer operation is started. The air sampling rate is adjusted to 140 ml. per minute by means of a suitable, externally mounted, variable orifice meter. No air flow meter is provided with the analyzer. The bellows type liquid pump delivers approximately 1.5 ml. per hour. This flow rate is not critical as the cell should operate coulometrically and, thus, is dependent upon the mass of ozone transported across the cell electrode per unit time only. Care must be taken so that the platinum wire cathode is well wetted by reagent. Inasmuch as the potential across the cell is supplied by a mercury battery, no adjustment is necessary for this parameter. Normal operation involves essentially no operational adjustments unless a dual-range recorder is used. Routine maintenance requires the occasional cleaning of the cell, periodic changing of the reagent, and changing of the mercury battery as required. The analyzer is designed to operate unattended for approximately 3 days. Periodic checks of the air flow rate

[23] *Op. cit.*

[24] Brewer, A. W., and Milford, J. R., "The Oxford Ozone Sonde," Proc. Roy. Soc. (London), Ser. A, **256,** 470, 1960.

should be made to be certain that the delivery rate remains constant, as any deviation will affect the calibration scale.

Calibration.—This analyzer should be dynamically calibrated with ozone. It is the same procedure as described earlier in this chapter under the colorimetric continuous analyzer procedure. It is necessary to measure the air flow rate at which the scale is prepared, as this is a direct function of the mass of ozone passing through the cell per unit time.

NONDISPERSIVE INFRARED PHOTOMETRY

The principle of infrared absorption for the analysis of single components exhibiting rather strong infrared absorption spectra has been used with success by means of nondispersive photometric analysis. In most systems using this principle, sometimes known as the Luft principle,[25] the difference between the total infrared absorption in a sample cell containing the component of interest and that in a reference cell containing a gas which is optically transparent to infrared radiation in the same range is used as the means of detection. By alternating the source of infrared energy from the sample cell to the reference cell, unequal amounts of energy are transmitted to the detector cell at a regular frequency. This difference in infrared energy is proportional to the concentration to the component of interest in the sample. In the detector cell is contained the gaseous component of interest, which alternately expands and contracts at the same frequency as the alternating infrared source. This expansion and contraction causes an oscilating movement of a diaphragm condenser, which generates an electrical signal which is then amplified and fed to a recorder. In some cases it is necessary to reduce the interference from other substances which overlap in their infrared absorption spectra as compared to the component of interest. For purposes of further discussion of the method, an instrument for the analysis of carbon monoxide will be described. Instruments which are nearly identical except for the detector gas and interference cells are available for carbon dioxide and other gases which absorb rather strongly in the infrared region.

CARBON MONOXIDE

Apparatus.—The apparatus consists of a suitable sampling probe, an analysis unit containing the infrared source; filters if needed; a chopper for the infrared beams; the sample and reference cells; the detector cell; control unit containing power supply, amplifier, zero, and calibration controls; compressor or air pump; pressure gauges; and a servotype recorder. These components are usually mounted on a single chassis, although the analyzer unit may be placed at a remote location, with some limitations in distance.

Reagents. **Calibration Gas.**—A pressure cylinder equipped with suitable two-stage pressure regulators and gauges, and containing a mixture of carbon monoxide in nitrogen at a concentration near the high range of interest, should be available for regular span checks.

Zero Gas.—A pressure cylinder equipped with suitable two-stage pressure regulators and gauges, and containing a very low but known concentration of carbon monoxide in nitrogen, should be available for zero checks.

Procedure.—The instrument operating switches are turned to the "on" position and a warm-up time equal to that recommended by the manufacturer is allowed prior to the start of recording operation. A voltage test is then made. Following the instrument warm-up period, the span and zero checks are made by introducing the respective gases

[25] Hartz, N. W., and Waters, J. L., "An Improved Luft Infrared Analyzer," ISA Nat. Conf., Houston, 1951.

to the sample cell. The recorder readings are adjusted to indicate the correct values. Following this operation, the instrument is ready for operation on the ambient air sample. With the selection switch in the "sample" position, a continuous ambient air sample is introduced to the sample cell at the pressure selected for instrument operation. This factor is important as the calibration is pressure dependent. On the other hand, the instrument is not flow rate dependent, except as related to speed of response. Under normal operation this speed of response is such that 90 percent of true full scale reading is obtained within a few seconds. In some cases where time averaged values are of more interest than short term peaks, it is permissible to introduce a sample mixing chamber in the sample line prior to introduction of the sample to the analyzer. The time constant of such an integration device should be experimentally determined. Proper operation of the infrared source, the chopper, and the amplifier are important in the successful use of this instrument. Maintenance problems are principally electronic in nature although occasional checks should be made for leak tightness of the reference and detector cells.

IONIZATION ANALYSIS

The capacity for gas molecules to be ionized at differential potentials has been used as a basis of certain gas analysis intrumentation. The most frequent application of these analyzers has been in conjunction with gas chromatographic separation equipment as the detector element. A number of sources of ionizing potential have been used, including the hydrogen flame, beta-ray radioactive sources, and radio frequency generators. Each system has its advantages and disadvantages, mainly related to sensitivity and specificity. The use of the hydrogen flame as the ionization method has an advantage for hydrocarbon analysis because the ionization potential is low enough so that very few compounds other than hydrocarbons are ionized.[26] Among those gases which are not ionized are oxygen, nitrogen, the rare gases, carbon monoxide, and carbon dioxide. Thus, direct continuous sampling for hydrocarbons is possible without the use of extensive separation steps.

HYDROCARBONS

Apparatus.—The apparatus required consists of a suitable sampling probe, a hydrogen flame burner for the production of the ionization potential, an electrode system for the collection of ions, a stabilized amplifier, flame ignitor system, zero and span controls, attenuator section, Teflon diaphragm air pump, pressure regulators and gauges for the hydrogen and combustion air cylinders, and a potentiometric recorder.

Reagents. **Hydrogen Fuel.**—Either pure hydrogen or 40 percent hydrogen in air may be used as the fuel supply. The use of the 40 percent hydrogen mixture permits the attaining of a zero by merely shutting off the sample air,[27] although the difficulty in obtaining reproducible hydrogen in air concentrations must be taken into account.

Combustion Air.—Compressed air having a relatively low hydrocarbon content is satisfactory.

Span Gas.—Compressed methane in air at a concentration near the high concentration range expected should be used.

Zero Gas.—The zero gas should consist of a cylinder of compressed air having a low but known concentration of methane present.

[26] Morris, R. A., and Chapman, R. L., "Flame Ionization Hydrocarbon Analyzer," J. Air Poll. Control Assn., **11,** 10, 1961.

[27] Bryan, R. J., "Instrumentation for an Ambient Air Animal Exposure Project," J. Air Poll. Control Assn., **13,** 254, 1963.

Procedure.—The hydrogen flame is ignited and the range attenuation selector is set for a range suitable for use with the span gas. The hydrogen fuel and combustion air flows must be regulated carefully to the preselected rates that were used in the original calibration of the analyzer as indicated by the pressure gauges. The flow rates recommended by the manufacturer usually are satisfactory, although studies on the optimum air-fuel ratio may be made by the user to obtain greater sensitivity or more stable operation. The air-fuel ratio affects the hydrogen flame temperature and, thus, the ionization efficiency of the flame. The unstable portion of the air-fuel ratio curve which results in substantial change in sensitivity with minor fluctuations in flow rate should be avoided. The span check of the instrument is then made by introducing the span gas sample to the analyzer and adjusting the range control so that the proper value appears on the recorder trace. This operation is repeated with the zero gas. The range attenuator switch is then placed in a position so that the average maximum expected hydrocarbon concentration would appear at approximately 80 percent of the full scale deflection on the recorder. If the instrument is attended, the attenuator selected may be adjusted from time to time to improve the readability of the trace. The ambient air sample is then introduced to the instrument for the obtaining of a continuous trace of hydrocarbon measurements. When this instrument is used as the detector system for a gas chromatographic analyzer, calibration is usually carried out using pure hydrocarbons so that each peak may be separately analyzed with a precise calibration factor known for each individual hydrocarbon. When operated in the ambient air without previous separation steps, the values recorded must be reported in terms of the span gas used. In the case of the method described here, hydrocarbon concentrations would be reported in terms of methane. Because the instrument essentially detects the number of carbon atoms rather than the gas molecules, 1 p.p.m. by volume of propane would be expected to give a scale indication of 3 p.p.m. when reported as methane. The individual operator may wish to reproduce the specific calibration factors for different hydrocarbons for any given instrument, although tables of such factors are available. Maintenance problems principally involve the replacement of the ignitor wire and cleaning of the collection electrode.

Chapter 43

ALLOYS: IRON, STEEL, FERRO-ALLOYS, AND RELATED PRODUCTS

By H. F. Beeghly
4423 Clairton Blvd.
Pittsburgh, Pennsylvania

Introduction.—Analytical data are the basis for all process metallurgical operation. This chapter is devoted to consideration of the instrumental techniques used to make the determinations necessary at each production step, beginning with the raw materials, through operations of the ore beneficiation plants, blast furnaces, production of alloys from the primary metal and conversion of these to products which conform to specified chemical compositions. Discussion will be restricted to techniques widely used primarily as a means for reducing the elapsed time per determination without sacrificing accuracy, or to those effectively used for a specific purpose in production, quality control or research.

The following general references will be helpful in considering what specific instrumental techniques should be used for a given application.[1] Also, the technical specialists of the instrument manufacturer can provide valuable details on equipment limitations and performance characteristics for a specific application.

The major instrumental techniques for ferrous metallurgical analysis are emission and x-ray spectrometry and the high temperature techniques involving oxidation or reduction under controlled conditions used for the determination of the nonmetallic constituents carbon, sulfur, and the gases hydrogen, nitrogen, and oxygen. Electrometric, chromatographic, neutron activation, and election microprobe techniques are valuable, but less extensively used.

Sampling, sample preparations, and use of reliable reference materials, always very important in analytical work, require special attention when instrumental techniques are used.

SAMPLING AND REFERENCE MATERIALS

Sampling is the extremely important first step in all analyses.

The maximum economy is realized from instrumental techniques when samples

[1] Beeghly, H. F., Ferrous Metallurgy, Reviews, Analytical Chemistry, **21,** 241–6, 1949; **22,** 235–8, 1950; **23,** 228–31, 1951; **24,** 252–8, 1952; **25,** 30–6, 1953; **27,** 611–4, 1955; **29,** 638–43, 1957; **31,** 706–12, 1959; **33,** 70–6R, 1961, **35,** 1963; **37,** 87R–92R, 1965.

Dal Nogare, S., and Juvet, R., Gas-Liquid Chromatography: Theory and Practice, Interscience, New York, 1962.

Ferraro, J. R., and Ziomek, J. S., Eds., Developments in Applied Spectroscopy, Proceedings of 13th Symposium on Spectroscopy, Plenum Press, New York, 1963.

Meites, L., Handbook of Analytical Chemistry, McGraw-Hill, New York, 1963.

Muller, W. M., and Fae, M., Eds., Advances in X-Ray Analysis, Proceedings of Annual Conferences, Plenum Press, New York.

representing the critical variables of the process on material can be delivered to the instrument quickly and in the exact physical form required for the analytical determination. A reference material with similar matrix and physical form, containing known quantities of the constituents of interest, can be presented to the instrument at the same time; within seconds or, at most, a few minutes, analytical data can be reported to the plant operating personnel quick enough for them to make process adjustments when these are required.

Attention to sampling practice, to sample delivery to the analysis site, to sample form and to sample and reference material preparation is fully as important to attainment of best economy and accuracy from instrumental methods as is the selection of a specific instrument. The value of analytical data is contingent upon the success with which a sample representative of the critical compositional variables is obtained upon the accuracy with which the sample is analyzed and upon the ability for the analytical data to the user in time for corrective action to be taken.

The sampling procedure is determined by the nature of the material to be sampled and by the instruments and accessories available or that can be made available in a given laboratory for analyzing the sample.

Ores, sinters, fluxes, and ferro-alloys generally must be bulk sampled either manually or by automatic samplers. The bulk sample is reduced to a manageable quantity and homogenized prior to analysis by passing it through a series of crushers, mixers, and dividers which finally deliver a few ounces of powder representative of an original lot of several pounds or tons. The powder may be briquetted or converted to a soluble form by fusion or solution in acid.

Molten metals, generally manufactured in large melts or heats, are especially difficult to sample; care must be exercised both to obtain a representative sample from the bath, and to prevent segregation during solidification of the sample. Homogenization of the sample by taking millings of the cast specimens and mixing them or dissolving them is possible but increases the elapsed time between sampling and reporting the analysis.

Finished commercial products are random sampled and converted to the necessary physical form by machining, milling, or grinding.

Volume II, Part A, Chapters 2 and 21 should be consulted for more detailed information on sampling.

Reference materials with composition values established by the classical analytical methods, provide the basis for comparison measurements which make most instrumental quantitative analytical techniques technically feasible and the most economical for the many exacting determinations required in metal manufacturing and utilization.

Ultimate or primary standards, important to all methods of analysis, assume a greatly increased role of importance in the practical use of instrumental methods; most instrumental methods are secondary or empirical methods which enable the chemical composition of a sample of unknown composition to be related to that of a reference specimen of known chemical composition, determined by other methods, and of similar matrix composition and physical form, to the sample of unknown chemical composition.

Reference materials are the basis for calibrating and establishing working curves for specific instruments; they are the means for establishing precision and accuracy values for a given analytical technique, sample form or sampling procedure; day to day accuracy and equipment or operator performance under normal laboratory operating conditions are checked within the laboratory, and on an interlaboratory or interplant basis by use of reference materials or primary standards. Reference materials can be prepared within a given laboratory or plant; often specialized grade or grades with a new chemical composition range, will be produced for which there has been no counterpart; in these instances the developer must prepare his own reference materials. Some companies make these materials available outside their own organization. These internal or company references are not primary standards certified by a recognized standardizing agency. They generally are limited in their use to internal productions or quality control analyses or to commercial transactions in which producer and consumer agree to their use in the interim until primary standards become available.

One of the major obstacles to the use of instrumental analytical techniques in checking conformity of metal alloys to specifications in commercial transactions has been the lack of sufficient industry-wide primary standard reference materials in the physical forms, concentration ranges, and amounts necessary to fill the rapidly changing and diverse needs of the metals-producing and -consuming industries. Continuous available reference standards, carefully characterized, of certified purity or chemical composition, from a common neutral source, are essential to the use of instrumental analytical techniques in applied analysis involving production and sale of ferrous alloys.

The following sources will be helpful in locating reference material for this preparation:

(1) Standard Materials, Miscellaneous Publication 241, National Bureau of Standards, United States Department of Commerce, Superintendent of Documents, Washington 25, D. C. This publication lists the standard materials issued by the National Bureau of Standards and provides information on their chemical composition, physical forms, and procurement. Included are steel, and iron alloy chemical, emission and x-ray spectroscopic standards, ferro-alloys, iron ores, refractories and limestones.

(2) Wilhelm, H. A., and McCarley, R. E., High Purity Metals Available from American Producers, ISC-1029 (Rer.), Office of Technical Service, United States Department of Commerce, Washington 25, D. C., 1963. This report contains analytical data based on information supplied by producers.

(3) Analyzed Samples of Iron Ore for Reference Work for Student Analysis, G. Frederick Smith Chemical Co., Columbus, Ohio; Analyzed Samples of Limestone and Dolomite for Reference Work and Student Analysis. Bulletins give details of chemical composition, method of preparation and analysis.

(4) Michaelis, R. E., Report on Availability of Standard Samples, Reference Samples, and High Purity Materials for Spectrochemical Analysis, STP-S8E, American Society for Testing and Materials, Philadelphia, Pa., 1963. Prepared primarily for use in spectrochemical methods of analysis, the testing and text also provides information of value for application to other instrumental methods for analysis of metals and their compounds.

(5) Battelle Memorial Institute, Production and Availability of Some High-Purity Metals, 1 PB No. 162226, Office of Technical Services, United States Department of Commerce, Washington, D. C. List is up-dated periodically.

(6) Bureau of Analyzed Samples, Ltd., Middlesborough, Yorkshire, England, British Chemical Standards and Spectrographic Standards. Reference standards include steels, slags, ores, and refractories.

TECHNIQUES

Emission and x-ray spectrometric methods handle the major proportion of applied analysis in production laboratories in which iron base materials are the principal samples to be analyzed. A desirable goal, not fully attainable at present, is use of a single sample for determination of all elements required and a single analytical technique.

The emission spectrometer and x-ray spectrometer (with vacuum or controlled atmospheres to extend the sensitivity range and increase the number of elements that can be handled) complement each other well and are steadily reducing the number of elements that must be determined by other techniques.

All metallic constituents in ores, fluxes, slags, and iron-base alloys may be determined by one or the other of these techniques. Most metallic elements over relatively wide concentration ranges can be determined by either method.

The wide variation in composition and physical form of the sample matrix and the large differences in the concentration range of the major alloying constituents of alloys are major sources of problems in the day to day use of spectrometry. Methods of correcting or compensating for interelement effects generally can be developed, or suitable reference materials can be prepared to compensate for them. The cost of their development may be prohibitive if the number of samples of a given type to be analyzed is small.

Spectrometric methods, generally are less useful for determining the nonmetallic constituents; large numbers of carbon and sulfur determinations continue to be made by direct oxidation of the sample at high temperature. Improved methods of measuring the evolved oxides and the much lower equipment costs keep direct oxidation methods in competition with even the improved spectrometric methods.

The gas contents of metals have been determined by use of the emission spectrometer. Most laboratories, however, use fusion at high temperature, under reducing conditions, and heating, below the melting point, respectively in vacuum or in a carrier gas to recover the oxygen and hydrogen from samples. Nitrogen also is determined by the fusion method but is determined more frequently by the solution distillation method.

Other major instrumental methods valuable but generally restricted to experimental use, are neutron activation for determining oxygen and trace constituents, the electron probe microanalyzer, and the mass spectrometer, identification and determination of segregated or minor constituents.

Valuable instrumental techniques in widespread use for which equipment is less expensive include chromatographic, electrometric, and absorptiometric (mainly visible or photometric).

Primarily for investigational or special purpose applications, x-ray diffraction, chemical and electron microscopic, radiochemical, and thermoanalytical techniques are used.

Selected procedures for use of these techniques follow.

EMISSION SPECTROMETRY

The emission spectroscope (spectrograph or spectrometer) is used in iron and steel works laboratories in two general ways *viz.*, (a) for guidance and control of primary metal production operations where the work load, the sample matrix, and the determinations per sample are reasonably predictable, and (b) for investigational or special analyses where the work load and sample matrix is not predictable, and a wide variety of elements must be determined in many different sample matrices. Separate, but complementary, spectrometric installations provide the maximum of economy and flexibility.

Process guidance and control instrumentation for steel production places primary emphasis on dependability, reproducibility, and maintenance of accuracy within prescribed tolerance limits, and the ability to deliver analytical data to the operating personnel in an elapsed time short enough so that it can be used as a basis for corrective action to be taken when necessary.

The emission method for steelmaking laboratory use has evolved from the initial installations in which the spectra were recorded on photographic emulsions, to the air spectrometer which in turn is being superseded by the vacuum spectrometer. In this instrument the specimen is sparked in an argon atmosphere and the intensity of selected spectral lines is measured in a vacuum chamber. In contrast to the air spectrometer the vacuum instrument can be used to determine the nonmetals carbon, phosphorus, and sulfur as well as the metallic constituents. Its advantage is that all elements generally required can be determined on a single sample, whereas, with the air spectrometer, carbon and sulfur must be determined by combustion on a separately prepared sample, and phosphorus must be determined by a chemical method. The vacuum spectrometer effects a significant reduction in the elapsed time and cost of an analysis. Vacuum spectrometers are available from several manufacturers; their cost is $40,000 or more. Analysis of a sample for ten to twelve elements, including carbon, phosphorus, and sulfur, can be completed in 4 to 6 minutes after receipt of a sample.

Flat samples $\frac{1}{2}$ to 1 inch thick by $1\frac{1}{2}$ to 2 inches across are used. The samples are obtained by dipping a spoonful of molten metal from the furnace and casting it into metal or ceramic molds. These cast samples are prepared for analysis by grinding them to a surface finish of 60 to 80 μ.

Details of the analytical procedure will vary from one installation to another. For each installation, the spectrometer receivers must be set for the elements and concentration ranges to be determined, and must be adequately calibrated by use of company reference materials, or preferably, with reference standards. The reference materials also are used to establish the excitation or sparking conditions necessary for each type of alloy to be analyzed. The instrument manufacturer supplies detailed instruction and technical assistance in setting up and calibrating the equipment. When supplied with operating requirements such as elements, concentration ranges, and alloy types to be analyzed and data recording and transmitting method to be used, at the time equipment is ordered, the manufacturer's technical assistance can be especially valuable.

The vacuum spectrometer can analyze for metal concentration ranges as low as a few thousandths of a percent up to 20 percent. Carbon can be determined over the concentration range of approximately 0.01 percent in steel to 4 or 5 percent in cast iron.

In general, the air spectrometer is operated in the same manner as the vacuum spectrometer, except that nonmetals cannot be determined; use of cast pins approximately $\frac{7}{32}$ inch in diameter instead of flat samples is more common with the air spectrometer. Generally the sample mold is designed so that drilling from a portion of the cast sample will provide material for determining carbon, phosphorus, and sulfur.

Either the air or vacuum spectrometer can complete analyses very rapidly and, with speedy sample transfer from furnace to laboratory and fast transmittal of data back to the melt shop, provide information quickly enough to be valuable to the open hearth and electric furnace steelmaking operator. In each of these processes, the operator can take a sample of metal and slag from the bath at any stage of refining without reducing the production rate, and send it to the laboratory for analysis.

In the basic oxygen steelmaking process, metal samples cannot be taken from the molten bath without delaying production. The analytical control of this new, extremely rapid and very important steelmaking process is made difficult by the inaccessibility of the bath for sampling during the refining operation. The most practical method to date is to sample the bath at the end of each blow, make a rapid analysis with the vacuum spectrometer, and report the data back in time for use in making the next heat. Other instrumental methods of analytical control which may supplement analysis of the metal will be discussed under miscellaneous methods later in the chapter.

The vacuum spectrometer also has been used for the rapid analysis of steelmaking slags. The analytical procedure is basically the same for slags as for steel alloys. Sample preparation is different. The elements of interest in slags generally are iron and the elements that determine basicity of the slag, *viz.*, silicon, calcium, phosphorus, magnesium, and aluminum. Sample preparation typically consists of the following: (1) pulverization of the slag (to pass through a 3600-mesh per square centimeter sieve); (2) weighing the slag, diluent, and internal standard (a graphite diluent, and nickel oxide internal standard is used in one procedure in the ratio of 2 slag: 7 diluent: 1 internal standard); (3) mixing the components; (4) pelletizing the homogenized components; and (5) abrading the pellet to an approximately 60-μ finish.

The spectrometer calibration is carried out with slags of known chemical compositions covering the maximum and minimum concentration ranges to be encountered in the slags to be analyzed. The reference calibration materials, diluent, and internal standards are mixed in the 2:7:1 ratio and pelletized in exactly the same manner as described for the slags. Details of spectrometer calibration and sample excitation will vary with the equipment used; all steps in the procedure must be carefully standardized, and the standardized procedure must be carefully followed.

The number of determinations and number of samples to be analyzed on a repetitive basis by a given laboratory must be relatively large to warrant the expenditures necessary for installation of one or more air or vacuum spectrometers.

Spectrometry came into use in industrial laboratories primarily to speed up analyses and ease the major burden of large numbers of repetitive determinations of the same element in essentially the same matrix. When used in this way, the inherently versatile instrument loses some of its versatility.

A valuable complement to the spectrometer is a spectrometer or spectrograph for analyzing the unusual, infrequent, or nonrecurring sample. Simple direct current, alternating current, or high voltage spark sources may be used for excitation and analysis of samples over which there can be no control of sample size or method of preparation. The nature of the sample and the elements, and the concentration ranges to be determined govern the choice of the technique to be used for the analysis. Generally, conversion of the sample into a suitable form for excitation requires more time and judgment than any other phase of the analysis. Usually, it is not feasible to make up working curves or sets of reference standards for the occasional sample. The most widely used techniques are: (a) conversion of the sample to a solution (which may be excited directly or converted to a mixture of dry oxides); (b) use of the sample as a dry powder mixed with a buffer (diluent) and an internal or reference material; and (c) use of briquetted samples. Graphite electrodes are used in most cases. Almost any type of sample or matrix material can be prepared for analysis by one of these methods, and reference materials can be used to make up samples of known compositions for comparison. A buffer or diluent material is almost always used with the occasional or nonrecurring sample. It greatly extends the compositional range and variety of materials that can be analyzed quantitatively with the spectrograph. The buffer may also serve as the internal standard in many cases. When relatively large amounts of buffer are used, it is essential that it be free from the elements to be determined in the sample. In addition to the spectrographic facilities, a small chemical laboratory should be available for preparation of samples; as a minimum, a hood with hot plate and drying oven, equipment for crushing and mixing samples and a briquetting press are necessary. Since analyses generally are for constituents present in small amounts or on aliquots from high concentration samples, great care to avoid contamination and assure accurate aliquoting is necessary.

The great variety of sample preparation techniques and equipment available make it impossible to outline a single best procedure that can be used. Illustrative examples will be given; the individual user may find them helpful, but will have to select the particular detailed procedure suited to his requirements and laboratory facilities. A good general reference is Methods for Emission Spectrochemical Analysis, American Society for Testing and Materials, Philadelphia, Pa., 1953, which contains detailed suggested methods for analysis of ceramics and slags and for analysis of many of the nonferrous alloys which the steel works laboratory occasionally is called upon to analyze.

***Sample Preparation Methods.* Slags, Ores, Refractories.**—(1) The sample is crushed to pass a 177-μ sieve, mixed with graphite powder and ammonium chloride in the ratios of 2 parts of sample: 1 part of graphite: 1 part of ammonium chloride. A 20-mg. sample of the mixture is packed in a graphite electrode for excitation.

(2) The sample is crushed to pass a 0:3-mm. mesh sieve, 250 mg. are added to a graphite crucible which contains 1.5 g. of buffer (composed of a mixture of lithium tetraborate ($Li_2B_4O_7 \cdot 5H_2O$) 90 g., boric oxide (B_2O_3) 13 g., strontium oxide (SrO) 9.5 g., cobalt oxide (Co_2O_3) 10 g., and beryllium oxide (BeO) 0.05 g.). The mixture is fused by heating in a muffler at 1150°C. for 3 minutes. The melt is cast on a water-cooled aluminum sheet, and carefully deformed with a steel spatula. After solidification, the fused cake is transferred to a disc type grinder containing 3.5 g. of graphite powder and milled for 2 minutes. The milled mixture is compressed at a pressure of 4 tons per square centimeter to form rods which are used for excitation.

Inorganic Materials, Metals, Corrosion Products.—The powdered sample is mixed with anhydrous barium chloride (in the proportion of 1 part of sample to 10 parts of diluent) by grinding thoroughly in an agate mortar. The powder is then comprised into pellets weighing 20 mg. ± 1 mg. each, and transferred to electrodes for excitation.

Alternately, the powdered sample can be mixed with a diluent flux composed of equal parts of iron(III) sulfate and ammonium sulfate, or with a graphite diluent.

The powdered sample may be obtained by crushing solid material or by dissolving the sample in acid, evaporating the excess acid, and igniting the remaining salts to oxides.

Soluble Samples.—Materials soluble in water, acids, or alkalis may be weighed, dissolved, a measured amount of an internal standard solution added, and the solution diluted to a definite volume. The solution is used to coat the end of an electrode, dried, and excited. Materials that are not soluble may be converted to a soluble form by fusion, the fused melt dissolved, and diluted to volume.

Excitation Conditions.—The excitation conditions differ with the nature of the specimen, power source characteristics and spectrographic equipment to be used. The most universally applicable method of excitation and, probably, most frequently used method of excitation for miscellaneous samples is the direct current arc. Detailed procedures must be worked out for a specific set of laboratory conditions and spectrographic equipment and once established, all details of the procedures strictly adhered to.

Methods have recently been described for the determination of trace constituents in cast iron and low-alloy steel[2] and in ferroalloys.[3,4]

X-RAY SPECTROMETRY

In many respects, emission and x-ray spectrometry complement each other. Use of vacuum or controlled atmosphere systems has strengthened the position of both by extending to high concentration ranges the applicability of the emission method and extending the x-ray method to lower concentration ranges and lighter elements.

The vacuum x-ray spectrometer can be used for determination of elements as light as atomic number 12; as many as 22 elements can be determined on a sample in 2 minutes; liquid, powder, briquetted powder, or solid samples, *e.g.*, billet cross sections, may be accommodated in the equipment.

Generally the instrument manufacturer engineers details of the equipment to suit the specific needs of the individual user's requirements. These may range from a single purpose, continuous, production line measurement and control instrument, or a

[2] Hartung, W., Giesserei, **48,** 579, 1961.
[3] Svehla, A., and Kvopkova, O., Hutnicke Listy, **16,** 588, 1961.
[4] Yokoyama, Yu, J. Chem. Soc. Japan, Pure Chem. Sect., **81,** 1411, 1960.

continuous or semicontinuous analysis of beneficiated and sintered iron ore to a multi-element analyzer which regularly and repetitively analyzes discs of complex high alloy steels for 20 or more elements with a total analysis time of approximately two minutes, per sample. X-ray excitation is nondestructive to specimens; reference standards, once obtained, are permanent unless contaminated or damaged by careless or excessive handling. The continuous, production line measurement of the thickness of tin for control of tin coating weight on steel was possibly the first applied use of x-ray spectrometry in the metals industry. X-ray spectrometry occupies a role of growing importance in applied analysis and production control in the metal-producing and -consuming industries. Development of equipment has progressed sufficiently that the user must evaluate plant needs very carefully in terms of work load, and elements and concentration ranges to be determined. This information is necessary in order that the apparatus suppliers can be provided with a sound basis for tailoring equipment to fill plant needs at minimum installation and operating cost to the user. Interelement effects must be considered, especially if small amounts of light elements are to be determined in samples in which one or more heavy elements may vary within relatively wide limits.

X-ray spectrometry is used for analysis of blast furnace materials such as pig iron, slag and sinters, and steels; the complex, highly alloyed corrosion- and heat-resistant steels can be analyzed by x-ray spectrometry more economically and, possibly, with better accuracy than by any other method.

Solid iron and steel samples in cast (or the latter may be forged or wrought) or ground or machined to a uniform surface for exposure to the x-ray beam.

Slags and sinters generally are ground to pass an 80-mesh sieve, mixed with a binder, and the mixture is then homogenized by further grinding until it will pass a 300-mesh sieve. The mixture is then compressed into a disc with a hydraulic press. A commonly used binder is chromatographic cellulose powder.

Reference discs containing known amounts of the elements to be measured in the unknown sample are prepared in exactly the same manner and used to calibrate the spectrometer. The reference discs, once prepared can be retained and used repeatedly for calibration and checking performance of the equipment. This regular use minimizes errors from interelement effects.

Minor constituents have been determined by x-ray spectrometry in low-alloy steels,[5] and in slags and iron ores.[6] High-alloy steels have also been analyzed for elements down to aluminum.[7] X-ray fluorescence has been used for elements aluminum through chromium.[8,9]

ABSORPTION SPECTROMETRY

Ultraviolet and infrared absorption spectroscopy have had relatively few applications in analysis of ferrous metals in contrast to visible absorption for which there are many uses.

Occasionally, corrosion products, oxide, or other gas-metal films have been studied by infrared methods. The specimens are prepared by incorporating them into a clear disc, usually of potassium bromide or chloride, or by mulling them into an organic carrier; mineral oil and chlorofluorocarbon gases have been used. Specimens that are sensitive to moisture or oxygen must be mulled in a protective chamber. Cooling the

[5] Agricult. Mech. College of Texas, Activ. Analysis Research Center, "Modern Trends in Activation Analysis," 1961 Int. Conf., College Station, Texas, 1961.

[6] Kopineck, H. J., and Schmitt, P., Arch. Eisenhüttenw., **32,** 19, 1961.

[7] Metallurgia, **64,** 53, 1961.

[8] Carter, G. F., Appl. Spectr., **16,** 159, 1962.

[9] Laffolie, H., Arch. Eisenhüttenw., **33,** 101, 1962.

discs or mulls sharpens the spectra. Infrared has been used primarily for identification purposes thus far. Growing in importance in the metals industry is the use of infrared methods for the rapid quantitative determination of gaseous compounds in effluent gases from steelmaking and heat treating operations; also, in high temperature laboratory analytical techniques, infrared methods of measuring are growing in importance.

Ultraviolet absorption probably is not used in metals analysis to the extent that it could be. Early absorption measuring devices were limited to the visual region. Comparisons of colorimetric methods are in very widespread use in metals analysis. In general these methods are primarily chemical, the spectrophotometer being used to measure the absorption of the metal-color complex as the final step of the analysis. Such procedures are described in Volume II. Many color procedures have been replaced by the emission or x-ray spectrometer.

HIGH TEMPERATURE OXIDATION

Except in laboratories which utilize a vacuum spectrometer, combustion in oxygen is used for determination of carbon and sulfur in steel, iron, and steelmaking raw materials. Volume II outlines procedures generally used for these analyses. Commercial use of more rapid steelmaking processes has necessitated a reduction in the elapsed time for a carbon analysis and stimulated development of a method, which by careful attention to design detail, has reduced the time for a carbon determination to approximately 2 minutes per sample.

Molten metal is removed from the steelmaking furnace in a spoon, a pin specimen is taken from the spoon with a glass tube of uniform bore, evacuated and sealed in advance or by suction at the time of use. The filled tube is chilled in water; the glass is removed from the spin sample and an exact, predetermined, length is cut with a dual wheel cutter. For best accuracy these pins are weighed, placed in the combustion furnace, and burned rapidly. The carbon originally in the steel is converted quantitatively to carbon dioxide. The carbon dioxide content of the combustion gases is measured by thermal conductivity or by its infrared absorption.

Details of the commercially available equipment vary. By one thermal conductivity procedure, the metal and sulfur oxides are removed from the combustion gases, and any carbon monoxide is converted to carbon dioxide before the thermal conductivity is measured; in another, the thermal conductivity change is measured as the combustion gases flow through the measuring cell. In still other procedures, the combustion gases are collected in a gas holder and the carbon dioxide content is measured by thermal conductivity or by means of the infrared absorption of carbon dioxide.

By each of these procedures, actual analysis time is less than 2 minutes; if the combustion unit is near the furnace, the elapsed time from removal of the molten sample from the bath to reporting of the carbon value is approximately 5 minutes.

Infrared absorption also is used to monitor the carbon monoxide and carbon dioxide contents of effluent and stack gases from steelmaking furnaces. For these applications, there are very serious problems in making the analyses quantitative because of the difficulty of getting an accurate material balance, of cleaning and sampling affluent gases, and of accurately measuring their volume.

HIGH TEMPERATURE REDUCTION

The analysis of steels for oxygen has become commonplace in research. The most generally applicable method is by fusion of the metal sample in graphite in an evacuated system, collecting the evolved gases, and analyzing them. Chapter 36 of Volume II describes these techniques which permit the determination of hydrogen and, with special precautions, nitrogen on the same sample.

Generally, the sample is introduced into molten iron or platinum contained in a graphite crucible. The oxygen is evolved as carbon monoxide and hydrogen and nitrogen in elemental form. Unless the oxygen value also is needed, nitrogen and hydrogen are usually determined by other methods; there is a growing tendency to determine each of the three elements separately by techniques that are more rapid than vacuum fusion.

Oxygen is determined by the inert or carrier gas technique in which the sample is fused in the presence of graphite, the oxygen is evolved as carbon dioxide, is then carried from the furnace by an inert gas, and measured. In some procedures, the carbon dioxide is frozen out and measured by allowing it to vaporize in a capillary manometer; in others, gas chromatographic or infrared methods are used.

Hydrogen is generally extracted from steel by heating below the melting point in vacuum, generally at a temperature in the range of 850 to 950°C., and measured. Thermal conductivity, diffusion through a palladium membrane, and gas chromatography are the methods most frequently used for measuring the hydrogen. By the hot extraction method, hydrogen is recovered from the sample in relatively pure form. Sampling and storage of samples to be analyzed for hydrogen poses a special problem because of the relatively rapid loss of abnormal hydrogen contents of steels in storage at room temperature.

Nitrogen is difficult to recover quantitatively from steels by the usual vacuum fusion procedures. Use of the chemical or solution-distillation procedure is more economical and the most frequently applied for the nitrogen determination.

The step in which nitrogen is liberated from the sample is the most difficult one in both the fusion and the solution-distillation method.

A number of papers have appeared recently describing vacuum fusion methods for the determination of gases in ferrous materials.[10,11,12,13,14,15]

MISCELLANEOUS TECHNIQUES

Neutron activation extends the limits of detection for a number of elements to levels lower than can be detected by other methods. Applications in the analysis of steel and steelmaking raw materials appear to have been experimental ones thus far: lack of neutron sources for "on site" laboratory use has delayed use of this method. Determination of oxygen by use of the $O^{16}(n,p)N^{16}$ reaction is meeting with encouraging success.

Activation analysis has been used for the determination of most elements in the analysis of steel,[16] and for the determination of minor constituents in high-alloy steels.[17]

Electrochemical methods for determining oxygen in gas streams are technically feasible, and equipment is commercially available for monitoring the oxygen content of gas streams continuously over a wide range of temperatures and pressures. These methods are used for direct continuous measurement of oxygen in liquid-metal systems; their feasibility for use in liquid steel at present is limited to experimental uses.

Mass spectrometric methods are used in research analysis of solid metals; further refinements in excitation methods and simplification will be necessary before extensive

[10] Kraus, T., Arch. Eisenhüttenw., **33,** 527, 1962.
[11] Wever, F., U. S. Patent 2,991,694, July 11, 1961.
[12] Klyachko, Ya. A., and Chistyakova, E. M., Zavodsk. Lab., **27,** 135, 1961.
[13] Limpach, R., and Marincek, B., Arch. Eisenhüttenw., **31,** 639, 1960.
[14] Yanagisawa, S., and Seki, M., Japan Analyst, **9,** 176, 1960.
[15] Moreau, L., and Talbot, J., Bull. Soc. Chim., France, 148, 1961.
[16] Coleman, R. F., Analyst, **86,** 39, 1961.
[17] Hoste, J., Pure and Appl. Chem., **1,** 99, 1960.

use will be made on an applied basis. Simplified, rugged mass spectrometers may find applied use for control in the vacuum melting and degassing of steels.

The x-ray and electron probe microanalyzers have promise for identification of segregated constituents of metals and for use in quantitatively analyzing *in situ* areas as small as 1 μ. in diameter. The electron probe analyzers have been available commercially for less than 10 years; their potential as analytical tools has not been fully developed. Sample and experimental conditions must be carefully selected in order that analytical data can be consulted in a meaningful way with significant production fabrication or other variables. One of the applications of the probe has been in the identification of inclusions in steels and cast irons, for studying alloy layers in coating to steel interfaces and for study of high temperature scaling and gas-metal and corrosion reactions.

A number of methods have been published for the use of the electron probe microanalyzer for the identification of the constituents of nonmetallic inclusions, segregations, and diffusion zones in ferrous metallurgical products.[18,19,20,21,22]

Thermogravimetric techniques have been useful in studying gas-metal reactions and in identifying nonmetallic compounds isolated from steels.

Gas chromatographic methods and ion exchange techniques have been especially useful in separation reactions preparatory to the final determination of metal constituents. Their applications generally have been in conjunction with other procedures; detailed descriptions of their use are given in Volume II and other chapters of Volume III.

SUMMARY

Iron and steel production methods are going through a period of great and rapid change which began approximately 10 years ago and is continuing. These methods place heavy demands on analytical methods and data for production guidance and control. To some extent, developments in production and analytical methods have kept up with each other. One of the major, and only partially solved, problems is identification of the critical variables for which control data are needed; development of means of delivering samples representative of these variables, once identified, to analytical equipment poses another serious problem. Solution of these will reduce the overall cost of operating the analytical laboratory, increase the amount of useful analytical data obtained, and, hopefully, reduce the number of determinations which, though accurate, are of questionable usefulness.

A summary of a number of instrumental methods for the determination of elements in ferrous materials is given in Table 43-1, beginning on page 864.

[18] Bondy, C., Chim. Anal., **44,** 25, 1962.
[19] Bruch, J., Arch. Eisnenhüttenw., **76,** 5, 1962.
[20] Burriel, I. P., Ramirez, J., and Carmen, J., Inst. Hierro. Acero., **14,** 518, 1961.
[21] Clayton, D. B., Smith, T. B., and Brown, J. R., J. Inst. Metals, **6,** 224, 1962.
[22] Seebold, R. E., and Birks, L. S., Anal. Chem. **34,** 112, 1962.

TABLE 43-1. INSTRUMENTAL METHODS USED IN THE ANALYSIS OF STEEL AND OTHER FERROUS MATERIALS

Element	*Method*	*Material*	*References*[a]
Aluminum	Activation analysis	Steel	69
	Atomic absorption		64
	Spectrometry		39, 86, 96
	Vacuum x-ray spectrometry		92
Antimony	Neutron activation		33
	Polarography		73
	Emission spectrometry		48
Arsenic	Neutron activation	Meteorites	33
	Polarography		26
	X-ray fluorescence		59
Bismuth	Emission spectrometry		9, 47
	Polarography		52
Cadmium	Polarography	Stainless steels	41
Calcium	Flame spectrometry	Slags	15, 27
	Polarography		58, 57
Carbon	Conductometry		71
	Emission spectrometry		17, 37, 53, 72, 94
	High temp. oxidation		16, 21, 30, 67
	Infrared		87
Chromium	Activation analysis	Steel	69
	Atomic absorption	Low alloy steels	45
	Polarography	Cast iron	79
	X-ray spectrometry	Alloy steels	34, 35
Cobalt	Amperometric titration		7
	Atomic absorption		56
	Isotope dilution		68
	Neutron activation		31, 62, 91
	Polarography		61, 91
Copper	Activation analysis	Steel	69
	Atomic absorption	Steel	44
	Polarography		74, 83
		High-carbon ferromanganese	63
Hydrogen	Spectrometry		50
Iron	Flame spectrometry	Slags	28
	Reflected β-radiation	Ores	40
	X-ray spectrometry	Slags	46
Lead	Atomic absorption		19
	X-ray spectrometry		43
Magnesium	Atomic absorption	Cast iron	3
		Slags	54
	Spectrometry	Cast iron	1
	X-ray spectrometry	Nodular cast iron	66
Manganese	Neutron activation		6, 69
	Reflected β-radiation	Ores	40
	X-ray spectrometry	Ferromanganese	36

TABLE 43-1 (cont.)

Element	*Method*	*Material*	*References*[a]
Molybdenum	Activation analysis	Steel	69
	Polarography		29
Nickel	Activation analysis	Steel	69
	Flame spectrometry		20
	Polarography		93
	Potentiometric titration		76
Niobium	Polarography	High-alloy steels	8, 51
Nonmetallic compounds	Activation analysis		14
	Differential thermal analysis	Steel	2
	Radiometric methods		12, 70
Oxygen	Neutron activation		13, 88, 89
Phosphorus	Emission spectrometry		17, 37, 53, 72, 94
	Neutron activation		5, 69
Rare earths	Emission spectrometry		78, 84, 85
Silicon	Activation analysis	Steel	69
	Emission spectrometry	Ferromanganese and silicomanganese	81
		Ferrotungsten	82, 95
		Cast iron	18
	X-ray spectrometry		97
Sulfur	Activation analysis	Steel	69
	Emission spectrometry		17, 37, 53, 72, 94
Tantalum	Neutron activation	Ferro-alloys	77
		Steel	60
Tin	Emission spectrometry	Iron and ferrotungsten	75
	Neutron activation		32
	Polarography	Ferrotungsten	49
Titanium	Activation analysis	Steel	69
	Polarography		22, 42
Tungsten	Isotope dilution	High-alloy steels	55
	X-ray emission	High-alloy steels	4
Uranium	Fluorometry		10
	Radiometric method		38
Vanadium	Amperometric titration		80
Zinc	Atomic absorption		24, 25
	Polarography	Ferromanganese and steel	65, 90
	X-ray spectrometry		11

[a] Numbers refer to the following works:

1. Argyle, A., Brit. Cast Iron Research Assoc., **9**, 364, 1961.
2. Bandi, W. R., Karp, H. S., Straub, W. A., and Melnick, L. M., Talanta, **11**, 1327, 1964.
3. Belcher, C. B., and Bray, H. M., Anal. Chim. Acta, **26**, 322, 1962.
4. Belohlavek, O., and Lavansky, J., Hutnicke Listy, **15**, 548, 1960.
5. Bouten, P., and Hoste, J., Anal. Chim. Acta, **27**, 315, 1962.
6. Bouten, P., and Hoste, J., Talanta, **8**, 322, 1961.
7. Bozsai, I., Nagyarken. Lapja, **15**, 423, 1960.

8. Brindley, D. J., Analyst, **85,** 877, 1960.
9. Bykova, T. V., Romanova, L. Ya., Rudhevskii, N. K., Khoklov, G. Ya., and Yakovlek, B. M., Zavodsk. Lab., **27,** 315, 1961; Ind. Lab., **27,** 318, 1961.
10. Callahan, C., Anal. Chem., **33,** 1660, 1961.
11. Carr-Brion, K. G., Analyst, **89,** 346, 1964.
12. Cochran, A. A., and Miller, V. R., U. S. Bur. Mines, Rept. Invest., 6256, 1963.
13. Coleman, R. F., Analyst, **87,** 590, 1962.
14. Crussard, C., Berg-Hüttenmaenn. Monatsh. Montan. Hochschule Leoben, **107,** 1, 1962.
15. Debras-Guedeon, J., and Voinovilch, I. A., Chim. Anal. (Paris), **43,** 267, 1961.
16. Dezirat, R., Rev. Met., **57,** 1125, 1960.
17. Eckhard, S., Graue, G., and Marotz, R., Arch. Eisenhüttenw., **33,** 145, 1962.
18. Ellenburg, J. Y., Anal. Chem., **34,** 230, 1962.
19. Elwell, W. T., and Gidley, J. A., Anal. Chim. Acta, **24,** 71, 1961.
20. Eshelman, H. C., and Dean, J. A., Anal. Chem., **33,** 1339, 1961.
21. Freiwillig, R., Novak, F., and Cadek, J., Hutnicke Listy, **15,** 632, 1960.
22. Fukui, S., and Arita, T., Japan Analyst, **11,** 295, 1962.
23. Gibbons, D., and Simpson, H., Pure Appl. Chem., **1,** 135, 1960.
24. Gidley. J. A. F., and Jones, J. T., Analyst, **85,** 249, 1960.
25. Gidley, J. A. F., and Jones, J. T., Analyst, **86,** 271, 1960.
26. Gomiscek, S., Rudarsko-Met. Zbornik, **1,** 51, 1959.
27. Goto, H., Ikeda, S., and Kimura, J., Sci. Rept. Res. Inst., Tohoku Univ., Ser. A. **15A,** 155, 1963.
28. Goto, H., and Sudo, E., Bunseki Kagaku, **9,** 213, 1960.
29. Grasshoff, K., and Hahn, H., Z. anal. Chem., **186,** 147, 1962.
30. Green, I. R., Still, J. E., and Chirnside, R. C., Analyst, **87,** 530, 1962.
31. Haerdi, W., Fogel, J., and Monnier, D., Helv. Chim. Acta, **43,** 1585, 1960.
32. Hamaguchi, H., Kawabuchi, K., Onuma, N., and Kuroda, R., Anal. Chim. Acta, **30,** 335, 1964.
33. Hamaguchi, H., Nakoi, T., and Endo, T., Nippon Kagaku, Zassi, **82,** 1485, 1961.
34. Hirokawa, K., and Goto, H., Sci. Rept. Res. Inst., Tohoku Univ., Ser. A **14,** 278, 1962.
35. Hirokawa, K., and Goto, H., Sci. Rept. Res. Inst., Tohoku Univ., Ser. A **14,** 294, 1962.
36. Hirokawa, K., and Shimanuki, T., and Goto, H., Sci. Rept. Res. Inst., Tohoku Univ., Ser. A **15,** 124, 1963.
37. Horscroft, W. H., Blast Furnace Steel Plant, **49,** 975, 1961.
38. Horwood, J. L., Dept. of Mines & Techn. Surveys, Ottawa, Mines Branch, Technical Bulletin 25, November 1961.
39. Ihida, M., Bunseki Kagaku, **9,** 276, 1960.
40. Jirkovsy, R., J. Anal. Chem. U.S.S.R., **184,** 35, 1961.
41. Karp, H. S., and Krapf, G., Talanta, **11,** 1365, 1964.
42. Kawahata, M., Mochizuki, H., Kajiyama, R., and Irikura, K., Japan Analyst, **11,** 312, 1962.
43. Kilday, B. A., and Michaelis, R. E., Appl. Spectry., **16,** 136, 1962.
44. Kinson, K., and Belcher, C. B., Anal. Chim. Acta, **30,** 180, 1963.
45. Kinson, K., Hodges, R. J., and Belcher, C. B., Anal. Chim. Acta, **29,** 134, 1963.
46. Kopineck, H. J., and Schmitt, P., Arch. Eisenhüttenw., **32,** 19, 1961.
47. Kotrbova, M., Hutnicke Listy, **15,** 802, 1960.
48. Kowkin, V. D., and Zhikhareva, V. I., Ind. Lab., **27,** 143, 1961.
49. Kral, S., and Rett, V., Hutnicke Listy, **15,** 638, 1960.
50. Kudelya, E. S., and Ryabushko, O. P., Tr. Komis. Analit. Khim. Akad. Nauk S.S.S.R., **10,** 183, 1960.
51. Kurbatov, D. I., and Skorynina, I. S., Zavodsk. Lab., **28,** 1061, 1962.
52. Kurobe, M., Tereda, H., and Tajima, N., Japan Analyst, **12,** 4, 1963.
53. Laffolie, H., Arch. Eisenhüttenw., **32,** 145, 1961.
54. Leithe, W., and Hofer, A., Mikrochim. Acta, 268, 1961.
55. Leliaert, G., Hoste, J., and Eeckhaut, Z., Rec. Trav. Chim. Pays. Bas., **79,** 557, 1960.
56. McPherson, G. L., Price, J. W., and Scaife, P. H., Nature, **199,** 371, 1963.
57. Maekawa, S., Japan Analyst, **9,** 811, 1960.
58. Maekawa, S., and Yoneyama, Y., Japan Analyst, **9,** 811, 1960.
59. Maekawa, Yoneyama, Y., and Fujimori, E., Japan Analyst, **11,** 493, 1962.
60. Marchart, H., Hecht, F., Wetternick, L., and Plockinger, E., Radex Rundschau, 55, 1964.
61. Monnier, D., Haerdi, W., and Vogel, J., Anal. Chim. Acta, **23,** 577, 1960.
62. Monnier, D., Haerdi, W., and Vogel, J., Helv. Chim. Acta, **43,** 675, 1960.
63. Morris, A. G. C., Analyst, **87,** 478, 1962.
64. Nikolaev, G. I., and Aleskovskii, V. B., Zh. Analit. Khim., **18,** 816, 1963.

65. Okubo, T., and Uehara, F., Japan Analyst, **11,** 761, 1962.
66. Papp, L., and Varalljay, L., Kohasz. Lapok, Ontode, **95,** 278, 1962.
67. Peterson, W. M., Anal. Chem., **34,** 575, 1962.
68. Ralph, W. D., Jr., Sweet, T. R., and Mencis, I., Anal. Chem., **34,** 92, 1962.
69. Reiser, W., and Schneider, H., Arch. Eisenhüttenw., **32,** 31, 1961.
70. Richardson, H. M., I.S.I. Spec. Rept., **77,** 57, 1963.
71. Rickard, E. F., Analyst, **89,** 235, 1964.
72. Romand, J., Bachet, C., and Berneson, R., Mem. Sci. Rev. Met., **58,** 481, 1961.
73. Rooney, R. C., Brit. Cast Iron Research Assoc. J., **10,** 446, 1962.
74. Scholes, P. H., Analyst, **86,** 116, 1961.
75. Scholes, P. H., Analyst, **86,** 372, 1961.
76. Silverstone, N. M., Metallurgia, **65,** 99, 1962.
77. Simkova, M., Hutnicke Listy, **18,** 357, 1963.
78. Sorokina, N. N., and Golubera, V. M., Sb. Tr. Tsentr. Nauchn.-Issled. Inst. Chern. Met., **31,** 41, 1963.
79. Stabryn, Hutnicke Listy, **15,** 302, 1960.
80. Studenskaya, L. S., and Songina, G. A., Zavodsk. Lab., **26,** 1102, 1960.
81. Sukrovtseva, N. M., and Bugrina, V. V., Zavodsk. Lab., **27,** 314, 1961.
82. Svehla, A., and Kvopkova, O., Hutnicke Listy, **16,** 588, 1961.
83. Tajima, N., and Kurobe, M., Japan Analyst, **9,** 801, 1960.
84. Takao, Z., Kawaguchi, T., Kudo, Y., and Matsumura, T., Tetsu to Hagane, **48,** 1511, 1962.
85. Takao, Z., Kawaguchi, T., Kudo, Y., and Matsumura, T., Tetsu to Hagane, **49,** 1513, 1963.
86. Takao, Z., and Miyoshi, S., Tetsu-to-Hagane Overseas, **1,** 28, 1961.
87. Tipler, G. A., Analyst, **88,** 272, 1963.
88. Thompson, B., Anal. Chem., **33,** 583–6, 1961.
89. Veal, D. J., and Cook, C. F., Anal. Chem., **34,** 178, 1962.
90. Vesala, M., Hutnicke Listy, **16,** 805, 1961.
91. Vogel, J., Monnier, D., and Haerdi, W., Helv. Chim. Acta, **43,** 1254, 1960.
92. Wagner, J. C., and Bryan, F. R., Advan. X-Ray Anal., **6,** 339, 1963.
93. Weiss, D., Z. anal. Chem., **185,** 273, 1962.
94. Woodruff, J. F., and Thomas, A. H., Appl. Spectry., **16,** 29, 1962.
95. Yokoyama, Yu., J. Chem. Soc. Japan, Pure Chem. Sect., **81,** 1411, 1960.
96. Yokoyama, Yu., J. Japan Ind. Metals, Sendai, **25,** 48, 1961.
97. Zeuner, H., Giesserei, **49,** 858, 1962.

Chapter 44

ALLOYS: NONFERROUS

By Dean I. Walter and Owen R. Gates
with the Staff of the Analytical Chemistry Branch
U. S. Naval Research Laboratory
Washington, D. C.

INTRODUCTION

In the field of metals and their alloy systems the term "nonferrous" excludes only iron and its alloys. A narrower scope may be ascribed to the term if it is used in the context of the other family names, such as refractory metals, high-temperature alloys, rare-earth metals, platinum metals, and light alloys. Since there is no separate treatment of these families of alloys in the present work, the larger scope of nonferrous alloys will be considered in this chapter.

It would be wrong to assume that adequate coverage can be given to all the alloys of research significance; it would be equally wrong to assume that these research alloys should be ignored in the interests of the more "practical" common alloys. The last several decades have taught us that the laboratory curiosity of today may be a critical component of tomorrow's technology, and that the alloy crystallizing in the mind of a modern physicist may be in the melting pots of the metallurgists before these pages reach the publisher.

The purpose of this chapter, then, must be restricted to providing assistance in the development of a practical philosophy of instrumental approach to the analysis of nonferrous alloys. It will draw upon experiences in the authors' laboratory in which samples are received from all areas of naval interest, from submarines to satellites, and in sample sizes from air-borne dust particles to aircraft carrier deck plates.

The Choice of Analytical Approaches.—There is no one instrument that has universal applicability for alloy analysis, neither is there one instrument that can be recommended for the determination of one element in all matrices. Further, it is not often that an instrument can achieve its greatest versatility without the assistance of some chemical separations, concentrations, standardizations, or a combination of these. There are specialists in certain fields of instrumental analysis who can extend the applicability of their instrumental approaches to cover wide concentration ranges and to include a very large number of elements. This is commendable, but for the average analytical chemist, not always practical. It is the opinion of the authors that for each new set of analytical requirements encountered, a selection of analytical approaches can be made that will be optimum for a particular laboratory.

The selection of a method of analysis and the necessary instrumentation depends upon: (1) the elements to be determined and the accuracy required, (2) the concentration range of the elements to be determined, (3) the number and concentration range of the elements *not* to be determined, (4) the number of samples of a similar nature to be analyzed, (5) the size of the samples available, and whether or not they may be consumed in analysis and, of course, (6) the nature of the instrumental facilities available.

Preliminary Examination.—Unless the exact metallurgical history of a sample is known, it is wise and often economically rewarding to subject the sample to a preliminary spectrographic examination. An optical emission spectrograph of general utility is best for most survey purposes. A qualitative or semi-quantitative survey of the unknown sample can provide information on the general character of the material, a feeling for approximate levels of concentration, and impurities of possible analytical significance. In the research development of high-purity materials, a spectrographic survey may detect the introduction of an impurity, or may be used to advantage to determine when a level of sufficient purity is reached to warrant more detailed analytical characterization. Experimental work on new alloy systems may be followed spectrographically to determine homogeneity or discover segregation, and thus save further analytical work on unworthy samples.

For elements whose optical emission spectra are very profuse, and thus escape detection in low concentrations, x-ray fluorescence surveys prove to be profitable. This non-destructive approach is also extremely useful when samples of limited size are available.

Chemical Preparations.—Chemical preparations, and in particular chemical separations, are frequently required for samples, before instrumental approaches can be applied. Separations are particularly important when analyses are required of trace amounts. The matrix metal may interfere with the instrumental analysis, or it may simply lower the limits of accurate measurement by dilution effect. Separation of the matrix from the elements desired also permits the effective use of larger samples with a resultant increase of sensitivity.

While the value of certain instrumental approaches may lie chiefly in the fact that they eliminate extremely difficult or tedious chemical separations, there may still be considerable advantage afforded by chemical preparation of such samples. Alloys of niobium, tantalum, hafnium and zirconium, while they immediately suggest x-ray fluorescence techniques, still require carefully compounded standards over the concentration ranges encountered. These standards are best prepared chemically and converted to oxides, making it necessary for the metals to be converted to the same form.

Preparation of Standards.—The preparation, sampling, analysis, and distribution of alloys that are suitable for use as standards is a complex and costly undertaking. It requires the facilities and financial resources of either government or a large industry. Even then the number of alloy types is limited to a few of the more common industrial ones. The National Bureau of Standards has the most complete line of standards within the United States that are available for both chemical and spectrographic use. It is impossible, however, even for the United States Government to prepare standards for all of the needs of research on materials.

Some analytical instruments require that the sample be in solution form. This simplifies standard preparation and makes possible the synthesis of almost any desired combination of elements. It also provides great flexibility of composition range which can be adjusted, if necessary, in the course of an analysis. When trace analysis is involved, extreme caution must be observed in the synthesis of standards to prevent contamination by environmental elements.

Conversion of the metal samples to salts or oxides, as previously cited, also finds a great usefulness in spectrographic analysis, and permits the synthesis of standards with almost as great ease as with solution techniques. It also permits the relation of powder-sample analyses to the original solid sample, and thus the development of solid-sample standards suitable for individual laboratory usage.

Without doubt the most difficult area of standardization lies in the field of gases in metals and alloys. These difficulties are discussed in this chapter under Determination of Gases and Carbon in Nonferrous Metals and Alloys.

Sample History.—The importance of knowing the history of any sample to be analyzed cannot be overemphasized. While the subject of statistical sampling is a science in itself, the problems of sampling metallurgical materials require additional attention. This is especially true if the analysis is to be made on the surface of a metal sample, and if a very small area or volume of sample is involved.

Any attempt at simplification of a complex problem is dangerous; however, the following simple rules, if observed, will eliminate many of the difficulties that arise from sampling. (1) Make certain that the portion of the material taken for analysis approaches, as nearly as possible, the identity of the portion that is to be used for other characterizing measurements and observations, and on which the analytical data are to have bearing. Ideally, all the characterizing measurements, electrical, mechanical, magnetic, and analytical should be made on the same sample. With certain types of nondestructive analysis, such as x-ray fluorescence, the analytical phase of this ideal situation is being met. (2) Make certain that the physical preparation of all samples and standards is the same in every possible detail. For example, the correlation of a metallographic observation with an electron probe micro-analysis may be meaningless, if the sample surface has been repolished between studies, or the oxygen value obtained by the vacuum fusion analysis of a pulverized metal sample may be vastly different from the oxygen content of the solid parent-metal.

SPECTROMETRIC METHODS

Every element, by virtue of its individual atomic structure, produces characteristic spectra when placed in a state of excitation by an appropriate form of energy input. The input energy may be electromagnetic, electrical, or thermal, and the output may cover the spectrum from gamma rays through the far infrared. The identification and quantification of elements by their characteristic spectra, either emitted or absorbed, is broadly termed analytical spectrometry.

The breadth of scope makes it possible, although not always practical, to determine all the elements by some form of spectrometry. This section will include general discussions and some specific applications of analyses related to the field of nonferrous alloys by three general types of emission spectrometry: (1) flame spectrometry, (2) optical emission spectrometry, and (3) x-ray spectrometry. Because of its comprehensive treatment in Chapter 28, gamma ray spectrometry and the field of neutron activation analysis will not be considered here. Atomic absorption spectrometry, a more recent and rapidly advancing form of spectrometry, will also be considered.

FLAME EMISSION SPECTROMETRY

Flame emission spectrometry encompasses that area of spectrometry that relies on the thermal energy of a gas flame to produce the spectra of the more easily excited elements, and which provides for resolution of the spectra for measurement of individual wavelengths.

Flame spectrometry enjoys many of the advantages offered by arc- or spark-emission spectrometry, and in some applications is superior. While the flame is a relatively low energy excitation source, the spectra produced are less complicated. Still another advantage accrues in the preparation of standards, since liquid synthetic standards can be prepared to match any desired constituent composition. The use of liquid samples and standards removes all problems of sample history and homogeneity.

Scope.—In the past the flame spectrometer found its greatest application as a tool for the analysis of the alkali metals. This in itself was sufficient justification for its development. These metals, falling at the end of the quantitative analysis scheme, can be analytically tedious even when occurring singly, and even more so when occurring in combination.

Recent improvements in flame assemblies and instrumentation have enlarged the scope of flame emission spectrometry to include many elements that were previously considered unamenable to this type of analysis.

A description of the published quantitative flame spectrometric procedures for the analysis of current nonferrous alloy systems would require more space than is reasonably available for this section. Even with a complete coverage of the subject, it is unlikely that the chemist seeking a procedure for a particular alloy would find something directly applicable to his problem.[1]

Several procedures will be described for the flame spectrometric determination of some of the elements in a few of the common nonferrous alloys. In addition, a method will be described for the flame spectrometric analysis of an alloy system (Mg—Ag—In), which is less common, but which is typical of the variety of alloy combinations that may be encountered in research metallurgy. In these descriptions it is hoped that sufficient procedural details and operational suggestions will be found to serve as a general guide for the application of flame spectrometry to nonferrous systems.

Table 44-1[2,3] lists most of the elements reported to have been studied flame spectrometrically. Many of the listed elements are used as alloying constituents in nonferrous alloys, and hence may possibly be determined by flame procedures. The ease with which they yield to this type of analysis will depend not only upon the element under test, but also upon the matrix and other alloying constituents.

In the Table of Detection Limits, the following symbols are used:

L = Atomic Line, offering the highest selectivity.
B = Molecular Band, usually offering good selectivity.
C = Broad Band or Continuum, without selectivity.
AH = Air-Hydrogen Flame.
OH = Oxygen-Hydrogen Flame.
OA = Oxygen-Acetylene Flame.
n = Best sensitivity obtained using a non-aqueous solvent.
i = Inner cone of flame (high excitation temperatures owing to nonequilibrium conditions).

[1] Dean, J. A., Flame Photometry, McGraw-Hill Book Co., Inc., New York, 1960, pp. 145–294, discusses many applications.

A fuller appreciation of the scope of flame emission spectrometry may be gained by a survey of the literature. The monumental work of Mavrodineanu in compiling an organized bibliography of the flame literature is most helpful. The references are compiled (1) according to publication date, (2) type of publication, (3) materials analyzed, and (4) elements determined. This bibliography, containing 1791 references and covering the years 1848–1960, first appeared in Applied Spectroscopy across a several-year span. It is now available in a single volume as Reprint R-100 from Beckman Instruments, Inc., Fullerton, California. The literature complete to 1964 and covering 3600 references included in Mavrodineanu, R., and Boiteux, H., Flame Spectroscopy, John Wiley and Sons, New York, 1964.

[2] Reproduced from Beckman Bulletin #736C, with permission of the Beckman Instruments Co., Inc., Fullerton, California.

[3] For a more complete list of wavelengths and their limits of detection, see Herrmann, R., and Alkemade, C. T. J., in Gilbert, P. T., Jr., Trans., Chemical Analysis by Flame Photometry, 2nd Ed., Interscience, New York–London, 1963, p. 260; also Gilbert, P. T., Jr., Flame Spectra of the Elements, Beckman Bulletin 753-A.

Table 44-1. Condensed Table of Detection Limits*

Element	*Most Sensitive Wavelength/mμ*	*Type of Emission*	*Detection Limit/p.p.m.*	*Best Flame*
Aluminum	396.2	L	0.4	OA n
	484.2	B	0.2	OA n
Antimony	252.9	L	[a]	OA i
Arsenic	235.0	L	[a]	OA i
Barium	493.4	L	0.1[b]	OA n
	553.6	L	0.1	OH n
	830	B	0.03[b]	OA n
Beryllium	471	B	25	OH
Bismuth	472.3	L	20	AH
Boron	518	B	0.2	OH
Cadmium	326.1	L	0.5	AH
Calcium	422.7	L	0.003	OH
	554	B	0.004	OH n
	622	B	0.004	OH
Cerium	481	BC	2	OH
Cesium	852.1	L	0.15[c]	OH
Chromium	357.9	L	0.01	OH n
Cobalt	345.4	L	1	OH
Copper	327.4	L	0.02	OH n
Dysprosium	526	B	1	OH
Erbium	546	B	2	OH
Europium	466.2	L	0.2	OH
Gadolinium	461.6	B	1	OH
Gallium	417.2	L	0.05	OH
Gold	267.6	L	5[d]	OA
Holmium	516	B	2	OH
Indium	451.1	L	0.03	OH
Iodine	530.8	B	[e]	
Iron	372.0	L	0.2	OH n
Lanthanum	743	B	0.005	OH n
Lead	405.8	L	1	OH
Lithium	670.8	L	0.002	OH
Lutetium	466.2	B	3	OH
Magnesium	285.2	L	0.1	OH
	371	B	0.02	AH
Manganese	403.3	L	0.01	OH
Mercury	253.7	L	6	OH n
Molybdenum	379.8	L	10[b]	OA i
	550–600	C	1	OH
Neodymium	712	B	1	OA
Nickel	352.5	L	0.3	OH
Niobium	450–550	C	2	AH
Palladium	363.5	L	0.1	OH
Platinum	265.9	L	8[d]	OH
Potassium	766.5	L	0.01	OH
Praesodymium	852	B	10	OA

TABLE 44-1 (cont.)

Element	Most Sensitive Wavelength/mμ	Type of Emission	Detection Limit/p.p.m.	Best Flame
Promethium	680	B	10[f]	OA
Radium	482.6	L	2[b]	OH
Rhenium	488.9	L	[a]	
Rhodium	369.2	L	0.7	OH
Rubidium	780.0	L	0.007[c]	OA
Ruthenium	372.8	L	0.3	OA
Samarium	653	B	3	OA
Scandium	603.6	B	0.5	OA
Silicon	248.7	B	[e]	
Silver	338.3	L	0.05	OH
Sodium	589.0	L	0.0002	OH
Strontium	460.7	L	0.01	OH
	680	B	0.01	OH
Tellurium	401	B	3	AH
Terbium	534	B	2	OH
Thallium	535.0	L	0.1[b]	AH
Thulium	534.7	B	3	OH
Tin	303.4	L	10[b]	OA i
	358.5	B	25	OH
Titanium	516.7	B	0.2	OH
Uranium	550	C	0.7	AH
Vanadium	573.7	BC	0.2	OH n
Ytterbium	398.8	L	0.2	OH
Yttrium	599	B	0.5	OH
Zinc	213.9	L	10	OH n
	520	C	0.8	OH n
Zirconium	564	BC	8	OH

* Reproduced from Beckman Bulletin 736C with the permission of Beckman Instruments, Inc., Fullerton, California.

[a] Known to be emitted in the flame, but no measurements available; intensity probably rather low.

[b] Estimates based on sound extrapolations. Data for some of the rarer elements have been similarly estimated, always conservatively.

[c] Owing to ionization, the detection limit becomes poorer at lower concentrations. A Farnsworth 16PM1 photomultiplier will give the best results.

[d] Calculated theoretically; probably reliable.

[e] Band systems known to be emitted in flame, but probably quite weak.

[f] Promethium has been determined with a Beckman flame photometer, but data not available. Wavelength and detection limit interpolated.

NOTE.—Listed here are the useful wavelengths for flame analysis and the detection limits in parts per million (p.p.m.) for some of the common elements determinable with the Beckman DU flame spectrophotometer. (For accurate quantitative analyses, the sample quantity should be from 10X to 100X the detection limit.)

The detection limit is here defined as the concentration of the element in solution, in parts per million or milligrams per liter, needed to give a net response equal to 1 percent of background when the background is made to read full scale under optimum conditions with the Beckman DU Spectrophotometer: with 1P28 Multiplier Phototube operated at the highest sensitivity, or beyond 650 mμ with the Red-Sensitive Phototube and the 10,000 megohm Load Resistor.

TABLE 44-2.[4] ANIONIC INTERFERENCES#

Emitting Element	Concentration of Emitter	Anion Content 0.0–0.1 *M*						Anion Content 0.1–4.0 *M*					
		Cl^-	ClO_4^-	NO_3^-	$SO_4^=$	$PO_4^{\equiv}$	Ac^-	Cl^-	ClO_4^-	NO_3^-	$SO_4^=$	$PO_4^{\equiv}$	Ac^-
Barium	500 p.p.m.	0	0	0	−100	−66	0	−26	−26	0	−100	*	*
Boron	500 "	0	−18	0	−20	−12	0	+1	*	+20	+35	*	*
Calcium	100 "	+30	+60	−29	−46	−68	−10	+46	+60	−26	−48	*	*
Chromium	1000 "	0	0	0	0	0	0	0	0	0	+120	*	*
Copper	1000 "	0	0	0	0	+10	0	+18	+5	+4	+6	*	+66
Lithium	100 "	0	−3	−5	−20	−20	0	−35	−23	−7	−35	−20	*
Magnesium	500 "	0	+14	0	−35	−57	−6	+25	+20	+15	−37	−59	*
Manganese	100 "	+3	+10	0	−26	−26	0	+24	+10	0	−17	+100	*
Potassium	100 "	0	−8	0	−18	−30	0	−43	−39	−9	−40	−81	*
Silver	500 "	+	0	0	0	+3	+4	+	0	0	+13	*	*
Sodium	100 "	0	0	0	−13	−5	+1	−18	−13	0	−27	−10	*
Strontium	100 "	+17	+23	0	−22	−82	−7	+23	+23	0	−82	*	*
Thallium	500 "	0	−2	0	−8	+	+9	0	−12	0	−40	*	*

[4] Dippel, W. A., PhD. thesis, Princeton University, 1956.

The measure of enhansive or depressive interference is listed in terms of percentage, based on the luminosity readings of water solutions of the nitrate salts.

* This symbol is used to indicate very strong enhancement (mostly immeasurable).

Interferences.—Probably the main reason that flame spectrometry was slow in evolving as a quantitative tool for many elements was the large number of ills associated with its infancy. Until adequate instrumentation became commercially available, each experimenter had to rely upon his own ingenuity to prepare and improve his equipment. Even the earlier commercially available instruments were limited in their excitation capabilities and hence restricted largely to the analysis of the alkali and some of the alkaline earth metals. Such items as atomization, flame constancy, photocell fatigue and other variations attributable to electronic circuitry still require careful attention.

In spectrophotometers in which the test solution is aspirated through a tube into the flame, the slightest amount of clogging will result in large changes in luminosity readings. Therefore, this tube should be kept free of dirt and salts. Clogging in the siphon tube is minimized by the use of a water rinse by aspiration after each sample and standard.

Interferences may be caused also by other sample constituents. Their resulting annoyances may become manifest as band spectra, adjacent line spectra, or continua near or through the wavelength of the element being determined. The presence of some cations may enhance or depress the emission of a given element. Anions may also be responsible for enhansive and depressive effects. Table 44-2 shows the relative flame spectrophotometer effects of the listed anions on the emission of some elements. Examination of the table generally would indicate that careful attention should be given to the anion and its uniformity of concentration in both samples and standards. Of all the anions listed, the nitrate appears to be the least offensive.

DETERMINATION OF COPPER IN ALUMINUM-, TIN-, AND ZINC-BASE ALLOYS[5]

Introduction.—In this procedure two types of calibration curves are used to obtain data. One consists of a plot of the copper concentrations against the corrected luminosity readings; the other utilizes the internal standard technique. (The internal standard technique is especially useful for samples whose components enhance or suppress the emission characteristics of the element being determined.)

For the determination of copper in the above alloys, silver makes an excellent internal standard, because it is seldom present as an alloying element. In addition, the silver 328.1 mμ line is relatively close to the copper lines (324.8 and 327.4), is subject to about the same degree of self-absorption, and involves a similar energy level transition.

Table 44-3 shows the effect of indicated amounts of various elements on the flame spectrometric determination of copper. Before proceeding with the application of a flame spectrometric procedure to a given type of alloy, a preliminary study should be made of the various possible interferents which are common to the alloy under study. An optical emission spectrogram will provide a semi-quantitative measure of the alloy constituents. Thence, a flame spectrometric study can be made that will reveal their effects upon the luminosity of the line or lines of the element to be determined.

Table 44-4 shows the effect of various concentrations of four inorganic acids upon the determination of copper. Should silver be used as an internal standard, hydrochloric acid cannot be used. At a concentration of 1 *M* or less, none of the acids shows appreciable interference.

Scope.—These procedures cover the determination of copper in the range 0.3 to 8.0 percent in the alloy types specified. For specific alloy compositions and typical analytical data, see Table 44-5.

[5] Dean, John A., Anal. Chem., **27,** 1224, 1955. Copyright 1955 by the American Chemical Society, and reprinted in part with permission of the copyright owner.

TABLE 44-3. INFLUENCE OF DIVERSE ELEMENTS

Element Tested	*Concentration, p.p.m.*	*Copper, p.p.m.*	
		Present	*Found*
Aluminum	1,000	20	20
	2,000	20	20
	5,000	20	20
Cadminum	2,000	40	40
	4,000	40	40
Chromium	1,000	20	20
	2,000	20	21
Cobalt	1,000	20	18
	2,000	40	34
Iron	1,000	40	40
	2,000	40	42
Lead	4,000	40	40
	10,000	40	40
Magnesium	1,000	40	41
	2,000	40	42
Manganese	100	20	20
	500	20	20
Nickel	1,000	40	40
	2,000	40	42
	4,000	40	45
Potassium	2,000	40	40
	5,000	40	40
Sodium	2,000	40	40
	5,000	40	40
Zinc	1,000	20	20
	3,000	20	20
	9,000	100	100

Apparatus. **Spectrophotometer.**—A Beckman Model DU quartz spectrophotometer with Model 922 flame attachment and photomultiplier unit and oxyacetylene aspirator-burner, or equivalent equipment.

About 20 special 5-ml. beakers to contain samples to be atomized.

Reagents. **Standard Copper Sulfate Solution (1 ml. = 1.0 mg. copper).**—Dissolve 3.942 g. of fresh crystals of Reagent-Grade copper sulfate ($CuSO_4 \cdot 5H_2O$) in demineralized water and dilute to 1 liter.

Standard Silver Nitrate Solution (1 ml. = 2.5 mg. silver).—Dissolve 3.94 g. of Reagent-Grade silver nitrate ($AgNO_3$) in demineralized water and dilute to 1 liter.

Demineralized Water.—Pass distilled water through a bed of Amberlite MB-3 resin.

Hydrobromic Acid (48 percent).

Bromine.

Preparation of Calibration Curves.—Two types of standard curves are compared in this work:

One consists simply of the plot of the concentration of copper present against the luminosity observed at the peak of each respective copper line, L, from which value is subtracted the background reading, H. The choice of wavelength from which to obtain the background reading, H, depends upon which other elements might be present. If

TABLE 44-4. INFLUENCE OF ACIDS

Acid Concentration, Moles/Liter	*Copper Found*[a]	
	324.8 mμ	*327.4 mμ*
$HClO_4$		
0.5	40	40
1.0	40	40
1.5	41	40
2.5	41	39
5.0	45	42
HCl		
0.5	40	40
1.0	40	40
2.5	39.5	40
5.0	43	38
HNO_3		
0.5	41	40
1.0	41	40
1.5	41	42
2.5	—	42
5.0	47	43
H_2SO_4		
0.5	40	40
1.0	40	39
1.5	38	37
2.5	38	36
5.0	36	35

[a] 40.0 p.p.m. of copper present in each solution.

none is present that emits lines at 325.0 and 327.0 mμ, then these two wavelengths are suitable for use with copper lines 324.8 and 327.4 mμ, respectively. Because of the increasing self-absorption at higher concentrations, the calibration curve (although initially a straight line) will gradually bend toward the concentration axis. Since this becomes manifest quickly with the copper 324.8 line, it is used to determine luminosities for solutions containing less than 90 p.p.m. of copper. Serious self-absorption does not occur with the copper 327.4 mμ line until the copper content reaches 300 p.p.m.

The second type of calibration curve is obtained by the method of internal standardization as follows: To each sample and standard solution (containing between 10 and 75 p.p.m. of copper), add 1 ml. of the standard silver nitrate solution to provide a 50 p.p.m. silver standard. Transfer to a 50-ml. volumetric flask and adjust to the mark. For solutions containing 75 to 400 p.p.m. of copper, add 2 ml. of the standard silver nitrate solution to provide a 100 p.p.m. silver standard. Silver additions are made in this manner because a fixed amount of silver serves ideally as an internal standard over only a limited range of copper concentrations.

The ratio of the average relative luminosity (L − H) of the copper line to that of the silver line (also L − H), for example,

$$\frac{\text{L of Cu 324.8} - \text{H at 325.0}}{\text{L of Ag 328.1} - \text{H at 328.3}},$$

is plotted against concentration of copper on log-log paper to give one calibration curve. The other is made similarly with the 327.4 mμ copper line.

***Procedure.* Aluminum- and Zinc-Base Alloys.**—Transfer an accurately-weighed sample containing 1 to 15 mg. of copper to a 150-ml. beaker. Cover and dissolve in a minimum amount of perchloric acid (1:1) or nitric acid (1:1). Heat if necessary. Raise cover glass with hooks and evaporate nearly to dryness to remove the excess acid. Add 25 ml. of demineralized water and transfer to a 50-ml. volumetric flask. Add 2.00 ml. of the standard silver solution and dilute to the mark with demineralized water, and mix. Transfer a portion of each sample and standard solution to a clean 5-ml. beaker. Atomize each solution in the flame, read and record the luminosity.

Bracket[6] the unknowns with a series of standards. Obtain the luminosities at the following wavelengths: copper at 324.8 mμ, background at 325 mμ; copper at 327.4 mμ, background at 327 mμ; and silver at 328.1 mμ, background at 328.3 mμ. Obtain the copper-minus-background luminosity, and also the net copper to silver luminosity ratio as directed under "Preparation of Calibration Curve" and determine the copper content of each sample using the appropriate calibration curve.

***Procedure.* Tin-Base Alloys.**—Transfer an accurately weighed sample containing 1 to 15 mg. of copper to a 125-ml. Erlenmeyer flask. Dissolve with a solution containing 20 ml. of 48 percent hydrobromic acid and 2 ml. of bromine. Cover and heat gently to dissolve each sample. Add 10 ml. of concentrated perchloric acid and heat while swirling in a well ventilated hood until heavy white fumes of perchloric acid first appear. Then heat moderately and intermittently to decompose any lead bromide and expel all hydrobromic acid. A stream of compressed air passed into the flask materially hastens the removal of stannic bromide and antimony bromide. For large amounts of tin it may be necessary to repeat the volatilization step with an additional 5 ml. of hydrobromic acid.

Evaporate nearly to dryness to remove the excess acid. Add 25 ml. of demineralized water and transfer to a 50-ml. volumetric flask. Add 2.00 ml. of the standard silver solution and dilute to the mark with demineralized water, and mix. Transfer a portion of each sample and standard solution to a clean 5-ml. beaker. Atomize each solution into the flame, and read and record the luminosity.

Bracket the unknowns with a series of standards and obtain the luminosities as directed under Aluminum- and Zinc-Base Alloys.

Appraisal of Data.—National Bureau of Standards samples were used in the original study and the flame spectrometric values obtained for copper are compared with the certified values which were obtained by careful wet-chemical analysis. Table 44-5 summarizes these results.

Examination of the spectrometric results shows good correlation between the certified values and the respective flame photometric values. The data further show that in these types of samples there is no advantage in using the internal standard technique. However, some alloys may be encountered which will require the use of it or perhaps the standard addition technique.[7] The Beckman flame spectrophotometer, being a single beam instrument, is more amenable to the latter technique.

[6] The bracketing procedure is used to minimize error due to luminosity drift.

[7] Chow, T. J., and Thompson, T. G., Anal. Chem., **27**, 910, 1955. The application of the standard addition technique for the determination of calcium in sea water and marine organisms is described.

TABLE 44-5. ANALYSIS OF BUREAU OF STANDARDS SAMPLES BY FLAME SPECTROMETRY

Standard Sample	*Concentration of Sample p.p.m.*	*Certified Cu Value, %*	*Values Found, %* L–H* *Method*	*Values Found, %* *Internal Standard*
Al Alloy, 85a (94Al, 2Mg)	1800	2.48 ± 0.01	2.52 ± 0.04	2.48 ± 0.04
Al Alloy, 86c	5000	7.92 ± 0.0	8.11 ± 0.13	8.19 ± 0.17
(90Al, 1Zn, 1Fe)	1250		8.00 ± 0.18	8.00 ± 0.20
Al Alloy, 87 (89Al, 2Zn)	20,000	0.30 ± 0.01	0.297 ± 0.006	0.293 ± 0.006
Sn Alloy, 54b (87Sn, 7Sb, 2Pb)	2500	3.19 ± 0.02	3.24 ± 0.06	3.18 ± 0.10
Sn Alloy, 54c (86Sn, 7Sb, 2Pb)	2000	4.30 ± 0.02	4.33 ± 0.08	4.34 ± 0.10
Zn Alloy, 94a	10,000	1.08 ± 0.00	1.10 ± 0.02	1.08 ± 0.03
(95Zn, 4Al)	5000		1.10 ± 0.03	1.09 ± 0.04

* Line minus background.
Each value given is the average of a series of results, with associated standard deviation.

DETERMINATION OF COPPER IN COPPER-RICH ALLOYS[4]

This procedure is included largely to point up the applicability of flame spectrometry to major constituent analysis. While greater accuracy, especially for copper in copper-base alloys, is attainable by electro-deposition,[8] some analytical requirements may permit sufficient freedom to warrant the use of the more rapid flame technique.

Apparatus. **Spectrophotometer.**—A Beckman Model DU spectrophotometer with flame attachment and a blue-sensitive photomultiplier tube, or an equivalent instrument

Special Beakers (for aspirating solutions into the flame).

Standards.—Prepare standard solutions of each constituent contained in the alloys under test. Combine appropriate aliquots of these to synthesize standard solutions, each of which contains the equivalent of 0.1 g. of total metal and which closely matches the sample under test.

If appropriate NBS standard samples are available, include these in the analysis scheme to serve as a further check on procedure reliability.

Treatment of Synthetic Standard Solutions.—Add 5 ml. of nitric acid[9] to each synthetic standard solution and evaporate just to dryness (do not bake). Take up each with 2 ml. of hydrochloric acid, transfer to a 100-ml. volumetric flask, dilute to the mark, mix, and transfer about 3 ml. of each to a clean special 5-ml. aspiration beaker.

Preparation of Calibration Curve.—Obtain and record the luminosity measurements for the synthetic standard solutions using the 324.8 mμ or 327.4 mμ copper spectral line. Obtain an appropriate adjacent low-background wavelength measurement for each solution. Deduct the background measurement from the copper spectral line measurement to obtain the net copper spectral line luminosity.

Prepare the curve by plotting the net luminosities against the respective copper percentages.

[8] See Table 26-2, Standard Methods of Chemical Analysis, Volume II, Part A, 6th Ed., D. Van Nostrand Co., Inc., Princeton, N. J., 1963, p. 868.

[9] The nitric acid addition and subsequent evaporation of the synthetic standard solutions may be omitted if it is established that the synthetic standards, diluted directly to 100 ml., give reasonably similar luminosity readings.

Procedure.—Transfer a 0.1000-g. sample of brass or bronze to a 100-ml. beaker and cover with a watch glass. Add 5 ml. of nitric acid and evaporate just to dryness (do not bake). Take up with 2 ml. of hydrochloric acid, transfer to a 100-ml. volumetric flask, dilute to the mark, mix, and obtain the luminosity measurement, using the same spectral line that was used to prepare the calibration curve. In careful analysis, obtain luminosity measurements by bracketing the sample with appropriately prepared synthetic standard solutions.

From the calibration curve, determine the percentage of copper in the unknown sample.

If desired, the manganese and nickel may be determined flame spectrometrically on the same sample solution. To do so, prepare suitable synthetic standard solutions to cover the range of each element and obtain the respective luminosity readings. The spectral lines, 403.3 mμ and 352.8 mμ, may be used to obtain the luminosity measurements for the manganese and nickel respectively. Proper background luminosity corrections must be applied in determining the manganese and nickel percentages.

Comments.—Table 44-6 compares the flame spectrometric values obtained by Dippel[4] for copper, manganese, and nickel and the average NBS certificate values for these same elements.

TABLE 44-6. RESULTS OF ANALYSIS OF NBS STANDARD ALLOYS BY FLAME SPECTROMETRY

Sample	*Element Determined*	*% Found*	*% Present*	*Av. Dev., %*	*Relative Error*
Mn-Bronze	Cu.	59.07			
NBS #62b		59.30			
		Av. 59.19	57.39	0.20	+3.0
	Mn.	1.26			
		1.38			
		Av. 1.32	1.29	4.5	+2.3
Ni-Cu Alloy	Cu.	29.23			
NBS #162		30.03			
		Av. 29.63	28.93	1.3	+2.4
	Ni.	66.35			
		67.37			
		Av. 66.86	66.38	0.76	+0.70
	Mn.	2.28			
		2.45			
		Av. 2.36	2.34	3.8	+0.86

DETERMINATION OF SILVER AND INDIUM IN MAGNESIUM-BASE ALLOYS[10]

Introduction.—This alloy system is presented because it represents a research-type alloy, and one not often encountered in ordinary nonferrous analysis. However, the

[10] Unpublished work of the U. S. Naval Research Laboratory, Washington, D. C.

alloying constituents may both be excited by the flame to provide their characteristic line spectra; and in this matrix both respond nicely to flame spectrometric analysis. This, like many other alloy systems, will require that synthetic standards be prepared and utilized to develop the calibration curve.

Scope.—This method covers the analysis of magnesium-base alloys containing silver and indium in equal weight percentages, over the range 0–10 percent.

***Apparatus.* Spectrophotometer.**—Beckman Model DU or equivalent, with flame attachment, blue-sensitive photomultiplier tube, and oxyhydrogen atomizer-burner.[11]

Special 5-ml. Beakers.—One for each solution.

In careful work, calibrated or certified pipets and volumetric flasks should be used.

***Reagents.* Magnesium Stock Solution (1 ml. = 10.0 mg. magnesium).**—Dissolve 2.00 g. of clean, purified magnesium ribbon or turnings as follows: Place the metal in a 300-ml. Berzelius beaker and cover with a watch glass. With the cover slightly ajar, cautiously add about 2 ml. of concentrated nitric acid and allow the reaction to proceed until the acid is almost spent. Make similar repeated additions of the acid until the magnesium is dissolved and a total of 30 ml. of nitric acid has been added. Boil gently for several minutes and cool. Transfer to a 200-ml. volumetric flask, dilute to the mark, and mix thoroughly.

Silver Stock Solution (1 ml. = 1.0 mg. silver).—Dissolve 0.7875 g. of Reagent-Grade silver nitrate in 300 ml. of water contained in a 500-ml. flask. Add 10 ml. of nitric acid, dilute to the mark, and mix thoroughly.

Indium Stock Solution (1 ml. = 1.0 mg. indium).—Dissolve 0.5000 g. of purified indium with 10 ml. of nitric acid. Dilute with 30 ml. of water, boil gently for several minutes. Cool, transfer to a 500-ml. volumetric flask, dilute to the mark, and mix.

Preparation of Primary Standards.—Prepare primary standards by diluting stock solutions as specified in Table 44-7.

Table 44-7. Primary Standard Preparation

Primary Standards	*Magnesium Stock 10.0 mg./ml.*	*Silver Stock 1.0 mg./ml.*	*Indium Stock 1.0 mg./ml.*	*Final Dilution*	*Percent Silver*	*Percent Indium*
A	6.0 ml.	20.0 ml.	20.0 ml.	100 ml.	20.0	20.0
B	8.0 "	10.0 "	10.0 "	100 "	10.0	10.0
C	9.0 "	5.0 "	5.0 "	100 "	5.0	5.0
D	9.6 "	2.0 "	2.0 "	100 "	2.0	2.0
E	10.0 "	—	—	100 "	0	0

Preparation of Working Standards.—Combine aliquots of the primary standards to provide various silver and indium percentages, as indicated in Table 44-8. The two luminosity columns at the right are included to serve as additional guides.

Preparation of Calibration Curve.—Prepare a curve for the 338.3 mμ silver line by adjusting the slit width[12] and sensitivity so that the highest silver standard gives a peak luminosity reading between 90 and 100. Adjust the instrument to zero luminosity with

[11] The oxyhydrogen flame (2700°C.) although not as hot as the oxyacetylene flame (3200°C.) is a cleaner flame and produces less background radiation in the visible spectrum. Flame temperatures may be increased considerably by using nonaqueous combustible organic solvents to convey the sample into the flame and thus provide improved detection limits for those elements that are not easily excited at lower temperatures.

[12] The authors prefer to determine the proper slit width (starting at or near zero mm.) by setting the luminosity at about 90 on the percent T. scale, excite the highest standard in the series, then gradually adjust the slit width to bring the null meter into balance (meter needle at zero).

TABLE 44-8. WORKING-STANDARD PREPARATION

Working Standards	*Primary Aliquots Combined*	*Percent*		*Luminosity*	
		Ag	*In*	*Ag**	*In**
AC	10 ml. A + 10 ml. C	12.5	12.5	88.4	100.0
AD	10 ml. A + 10 ml. D	11.0	11.0	81.7	90.0
B	10 ml. B + —	10.0	10.0	77.7	81.9
BC	10 ml. B + 10 ml. C	7.5	7.5	65.2	62.3
BD	10 ml. B + 10 ml. D	6.0	6.0	56.0	50.5
C	10 ml. C + —	5.0	5.0	49.0	42.0
CD	10 ml. C + 10 ml. D	3.5	3.5	37.1	29.6
CE	10 ml. C + 10 ml. E	2.5	2.5	29.0	21.1
D	10 ml. D + —	2.0	2.0	24.0	17.0
E	10 ml. E + —	0	0	3.0	1.0
Blank (H_2O)		0	0	0	0

* The silver line (338.3) and indium line (451.1) were used to obtain the luminosities.

water. Then with the wavelength selector peaked on the silver line (338.3 mμ), without further adjustment of the wavelength selector, aspirate and measure the standards in increasing order of their silver content, beginning with the blank. After each measurement, aspirate water through the siphon to reduce clogging and interference. Plot the relative luminosity against percentage of silver.

Prepare an indium calibration curve, using the 451.1 mμ line, and following the same procedure as outlined for silver. In the preparation of this indium calibration curve, with the exception of the 10, 11, and 12 percentage points, all should fall on a straight line. The higher figures indicate the beginning of self-absorption. This phenomenon is much more pronounced for silver.

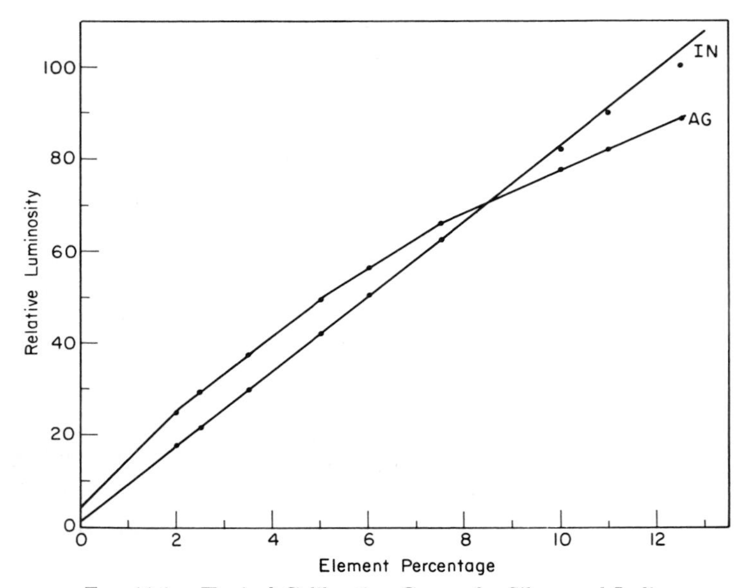

FIG. 44-1. Typical Calibration Curves for Silver and Indium.

Procedure.—Transfer 0.1000 g. of sample to a 100-ml. beaker and cover with a watch glass. Add 2 ml. of nitric acid and permit the sample to dissolve. Rinse the cover and inner wall of the beaker with distilled water. Boil gently for a minute to expel the oxides of nitrogen. Cool, transfer the solution to a 100-ml. volumetric flask, dilute to the mark, and mix. Transfer a small amount (about 4 ml.) of each solution of sample and standard to a clean properly-labeled 5-ml. beaker. (By providing a separate beaker for each solution, rapid atomization and interchange of samples and standards is realized and luminosity drift is less apt to be pronounced.)

Atomize and record the luminosity for both samples and standards, as was done for preparation and calibration curve. Refer readings to the appropriate calibration curve for the determination of the percentages present.

Appraisal of Data.—National Bureau of Standards samples are available for only a few of the most common nonferrous alloys. Therefore, it is necessary for the analyst to prepare synthetic standards for many of the alloy systems encountered. If analytically feasible, flame spectrometer data should be spot checked with data obtained from another acceptable procedure.

Table 44-9 compares the data obtained for various synthetic standards in which the

TABLE 44-9. COMPARATIVE ANALYSES FOR SILVER

Synthetic Sample	*Silver Present*	*Silver Found*	
		Titration	*Flame Photometry**
A	10.2%	10.15%	10.3%
B	10.0	10.05	10.0
C	4.0	4.1	4.1
D	0.4	0.3	0.4

* Percentages obtained from a straight line drawn through closest bracketing standard points.

silver content was checked by direct titration with standard ammonium thiocyanate, using ferric alum solution indicator.

Flame spectrometric values for indium compare so well with the synthetic standards that a refined gravimetric procedure is not considered necessary for cross checking.

The ability of the flame spectrometer to discriminate between synthetic standards whose silver and indium content differ by 0.1 or 0.2 percent is shown in Table 44-10.

TABLE 44-10. VARIATIONS IN LUMINOSITY FOR SMALL DECREMENTS IN ANALYTE CONTENT

Percentage Content, Silver or Indium	*Luminosity (% T. Scale)*	
	Silver	*Indium*
10.2	96.2	97.0
10.1	95.0	96.0
10.0	95.0	95.0
7.1	81.7	68.0
7.0	80.7	67.0
5.3	68.5	51.0
5.2	67.3	50.2
2.2	35.8	22.0
2.0	31.5	19.7

Comments.—This last technique is presented to suggest potentially wide applications of flame spectrometry to the analysis of flame-excitable constituents in a wide variety of nonferrous alloy systems. Depending on the constituents, matrix material, interferents, and accuracy requirements, it may be necessary to resort to standard addition or internal standard techniques in performing analyses; it may even be necessary to employ preliminary isolatory techniques. Regardless of the preliminary requirement, analysis of large numbers of samples by flame spectrometry (if applicable) is generally faster than conventional wet-chemical procedures.

In the field of alkali analysis it is an almost indispensable tool. Here it far surpasses many of the wet-chemical procedures which were necessarily used before the advent of refined flame spectrometry. For example, in 1955, the National Bureau of Standards issued revised percentage values for Na_2O and K_2O in various refractory materials. The revised flame spectrometric values (especially for sodium) are significantly different from those originally reported by wet-chemical methods.

Coverage of alkali metal analysis by flame spectrometric procedures is not attempted in this section. The chemist seeking guidance in the field of alkali metals analysis is referred to the vast flame spectrometric literature covering this area. It is very likely that specific procedures covering the pertinent analytical information will be found.

OPTICAL EMISSION SPECTROMETRY[13]

(OPTICAL EMISSION SPECTROCHEMICAL ANALYSIS)

Optical emission spectrometry in this chapter will be confined to that area of spectrometry in which the elements are excited electrically, or by a combination of electrical and thermal energies, and in which the spectra are resolved optically and recorded photographically.

This area of spectrometry has very broad applicability in the field of metals analysis and can accommodate both large and small samples in solid, powder, or solution form. It is especially useful in the lower percentage range of compositions; however, with proper calibration and standardization techniques, it is a vital industrial tool for alloy analysis.

Four general techniques are presented in this section to illustrate the application of optical emission spectrometry to nonferrous alloy analysis: (1) a method of broad applicability, illustrating the buffer method for powders, (2) a carrier-distillation method, (3) a point-to-plane method for solid samples, and (4) a porous electrode method for solutions.

Industrial alloy characterization, involving automated read-out processes for high speed control-type analysis, is beyond the scope of this work.

ANALYSIS OF NONFERROUS ALLOYS BY A METHOD OF BROAD APPLICABILITY[14]

BUFFER METHOD FOR POWDERS

General Considerations.—An important factor restricting the application of the spectrograph to the quantitative analysis of any and all kinds of materials, is the limited availability of suitable analyzed standards. In spite of the fact that there are available

[13] This section prepared by S. H. Cress, U. S. Naval Research Laboratory, Washington, D. C.

[14] Based on the method of Jaycox, Edwin K., Applied Spectroscopy, **12,** 87–89, 1958. Copyright 1958 by Applied Spectroscopy and reprinted in part with permission of the copyright owner.

a number of primary standards and many secondary standards, many available standards are useful only for the analysis of specific alloys. As an example, aluminum-base standards designed for the analysis of high-copper aluminum-base, are completely unsuited for the analysis of high-silicon aluminum-base, or other aluminum alloys. For precise quantitative work, standards must closely match the size, shape, composition and metallurgical history of the samples. From two to five reference points are required for each analysis, and it is obvious that hundreds of standards would be required for any laboratory concerned with a variety of materials. This, even if possible, is impractical because of the cost, the storage and indexing problems, and the analytical checking required on each standard.

To overcome these difficulties, the development of spectrochemical methods having broad applicability is almost a necessity. Samples are received in the analytical laboratory in the form of ingots, rods, sheets, foil, wire, millings, or finished piece parts. The total sample weight may vary from less than a milligram to several kilograms. In situations where the samples and standards are not compatible, it is necessary to convert both to a common form. This form in most cases is that of a dry salt or oxide powder. Solutions are sometimes used when all components are completely soluble in an appropriate solvent. In the procedure to be described, powdered samples are used exclusively.

For general spectrochemical work, the use of dry powders has a number of advantages: (1) almost all materials can be converted to a stable powder which can be stored indefinitely, (2) synthetic standards can be easily made from pure materials or by dilutions of, or additions to, certified standards, (3) powdered samples and standards can be buffered with other materials as needed, and (4) the spectral sensitivity of powders is generally high.

The principal disadvantage of powder methods is the sample preparation time. This may be one to two hours; however, a large part of this is inactive manhour time and the analyst can be conducting other work meanwhile.

The elimination of matrix effects is of primary importance, if the number of standards needed to analyze all the alloys in a given class is to be kept to a minimum. One of the best ways to accomplish this is to dilute both samples and standards with a buffer material to such a degree that the excitation and spectral emission characteristics of the buffered sample approach those of the pure buffer material. For the determination of the higher concentration constituents (>0.10 percent) the sample may be diluted with the buffer by a factor of 20, or even as much as 100. Under these conditions the buffer effectively wipes out the influence of the major components in the samples. With such large dilution factors, the sensitivity of the elements to be determined is greatly diminished, so that only such elements with concentrations greater than about 0.1 percent can be determined. On the other hand, if the dilution factor is reduced to 2 (1 part of sample to 1 part of buffer), good sensitivity is obtained, but the domination of the buffer on the sample matrix is greatly reduced. For this reason, the use of small buffer dilutions is confined to the analysis of single-base alloys (*e.g.*, copper-base, aluminum-base, etc.). This effectively yields a bi-component system, a metal and the buffer. As long as the principal component of the alloy is nearly the same in the samples and standards, the buffer (together with the principal metal-base component) is usually sufficiently dominant to offset the influence of most other constituents in the alloy.

It has been found that germanium dioxide (GeO_2) can be used successfully as the diluent buffer material and that it also serves as the internal standard for the determination of most elements. Germanium dioxide is chosen because it is readily available in very pure form, its behavior in the d-c arc is excellent, and the emission of its spectral lines is compatible with those of most of the elements to be determined. Also, its spectrum is relatively simple, minimizing spectral line interference.

Graphite powder of high purity (<100 mesh) is used as an additional buffer to promote smoother evaporation and excitation of the elements to be determined.

Apparatus.—Commercially available spectrographic equipment.

Excitation Source.—A direct-current arc source with an open circuit potential of 250 volts.

Spectrograph.—A spectrograph with sufficient resolving power and linear dispersion to separate clearly the analytical lines from other lines in the spectrum of the sample in the spectral region of 2300 to 4800 A.

Developing Equipment.—Developing, fixing, washing, and drying equipment as recommended by the photographic plate manufacturer.[15]

Microphotometer.—A microphotometer with a precision of ± 1.0 percent for transmittances between 5 and 90 percent.

Mortar and Pestle.—Mortar and pestle of material that will not contaminate the sample with any of the elements to be determined. (A dental amalgamator utilizing a plastic vial and a plastic ball is most satisfactory.)[16]

Preparation of Standards.—For each metal-base material, select standards containing the elements of interest covering the desired concentration ranges. National Bureau of Standards standard samples are recommended where appropriate. In some cases complete coverage may not be available. However, gaps in, and extensions of, available ranges may be supplemented by diluting the standards with unalloyed matrix metal, by combining available standards, or by adding pure elements. Additional elements, not available in pure metal form, may be added from standard solutions of their salts.

Convert the metal standards to drillings or millings, clean with a light acid-etch, wash, and dry. Drillings or millings are preferred over filings or sawings, because they are less likely to be contaminated by the cutting tools.

Weigh 600 mg. of metal standard and transfer to a Vycor evaporating dish. Dissolve[17] copper-base, lead-tin-base, magnesium-base, or zinc-base alloys with nitric acid (1:4); dissolve aluminum-base and titanium-base alloys with sulfuric acid (1:4). After dissolution is complete, add 600 mg. of pure germanium oxide (GeO_2) and 1200 mg. of pure graphite powder, Grade 2. (Do not add graphite to aluminum- or titanium-base alloys until after drying and baking.) Evaporate the standards to dryness on a medium hot-plate, then bake the various alloys salts as follows: for copper-, lead-tin-, magnesium-, and zinc-base alloys, 15 minutes at 400°C.; for aluminum-base alloys, 15 minutes at 600°C.; and for titanium-base alloys, 15 minutes at 800°C. After cooling, transfer the sample to a plastic vial mortar with a plastic ball pestle and mix for two minutes in a dental amalgamator. The plastic vial serves as a permanent storage container.

Preparation of Samples.—Weigh 200 mg. of sample drillings and transfer to a Vycor evaporating dish. Treat samples in the same manner as their comparable standards. If concentration ranges above 1 percent are to be determined, dilute the samples with unalloyed matrix metal. Apply the appropriate dilution factor in the final calculations.

To each sample add germanium dioxide, and graphite powder so that the final ratio is 1:1:2, as directed under Preparation of Standards.

Electrode System. **Lower Electrode (Anode).**—A $\frac{1}{4}$-inch diameter high-purity graphite rod, with a cup depth of $\frac{1}{16}$ inch and a diameter of $\frac{3}{16}$ inch.

[15] See also, Suggested Practices for Photographic Processing in Spectrochemical Analysis. (ASTM E2 SM2-1).

[16] A dental amalgamator suitable for this purpose is sold under the trade name, Wig-L-Bug, and is marketed by Spex Industries, Hollis 23, N. Y.

[17] Tin in high-tin alloys will precipitate as metastannic acid, which is converted to the oxide on baking. High silicon in aluminum-base alloys will also precipitate.

Upper Electrode (Cathode).—A $\frac{3}{16}$-inch diameter high-purity graphite rod with a flat exposed end.

Excitation and Exposure.—Fill 3 cup-electrodes level full with each sample and standard. Excite samples and standards in triplicate in the d.c. arc at 250 volts and 12.0 amp.

Exposure Conditions

Spectral Region	2300 to 4800 A
Slit width	0.01 mm.
Slit length	1.0 mm. per step
Filter	Three step neutral filter transmitting approximately 100, 20 and 5%.
Arc preburn	None
Arc exposure	6 sec.

Photographic Processing.—Process the emulsion as recommended by the photographic plate manufacturer.[18]

Photometry.—Determine transmittances of the spectral line pairs listed in Table 44-11 and convert them to relative intensities using an emulsion calibration curve pre-

TABLE 44-11. COPPER-BASE ALLOYS—ANALYTICAL LINE PAIRS

Element		*Analytical Line, A*	*Internal Standard Line, A*	*Concentration Range, Percent*
Aluminum	Al	2568.0 (A)	Ge2829.0 (B)	0.003 to 1.0
Antimony	Sb	2598.1 (B)	Ge2829.0 (B)	0.10 to 1.0
Arsenic	As	2349.8 (A)	Ge2829.0 (B)	0.03 to 1.0
Bismuth	Bi	2898.0 (A)	Ge2829.0 (B)	0.010 to 0.50
	Bi	3067.7 (B)	Ge2829.0 (B)	0.001 to 0.02
Iron	Fe(II)	2599.4 (B)	Ge2829.0 (B)	0.03 to 1.0
	Fe	3020.6 (A)	Ge2829.0 (B)	0.001 to 0.05
Lead	Pb	2663.2 (A)	Ge2829.0 (B)	0.01 to 1.0
	Pb	2833.1 (A)	Ge2829.0 (B)	0.001 to 0.02
Manganese	Mn	2949.2 (A)	Ge2829.0 (B)	0.10 to 2.0
	Mn(II)	2605.7 (B)	Ge2829.0 (B)	0.003 to 0.10
Nickel	Ni	2821.3 (A)	Ge2829.0 (B)	0.01 to 1.0
	Ni	3002.5 (A)	Ge2829.0 (B)	0.001 to 0.03
Silicon	Si	2506.9 (A)	Ge2829.0 (B)	0.01 to 1.0
	Si	2881.6 (A)	Ge2829.0 (B)	0.001 to 0.03
Silver	Ag	3382.9 (B)	Ge2829.0 (B)	0.001 to 0.02

(A) = 100% T Filter
(B) = 22% T Filter

pared as recommended by photographic plate manufacturer.[19] With the data obtained on the standards, plot an analytical curve relating:

Log percent concentration of x *versus* Log I_x/I_{Ge}, where x is the element sought, I_x is

[18] See also Suggested Practices for Photographic Processing and Photometry (ASTM E-2, E115-56T, E116-56T).

[19] See also Photographic Photometry in Spectrochemical Analysis (ASTM E-2, E116-56T).

the relative intensity of the spectral line of x, and I_{Ge} is the relative intensity of the germanium internal standard spectral line. From the average of triplicate determinations of Log I_x/I_{Ge} for each sample, determine the concentration of x from the analytical curve.

Table 44-12 summarizes typical deviation data obtainable on National Bureau of Standards copper-base alloys.

Table 44-13 summarizes typical data obtainable on two samples of aluminum-base alloys, one containing a high concentration of silicon, the other a high concentration of copper—two extremes in compositions.

Table 44-14 summarizes typical data obtainable on lead-tin-base alloys. The precision for the lead-tin-base alloys is not as good as that for the copper- and aluminum-base alloys, probably due to the very wide variation in composition of the samples used. These samples ranged from nearly-pure tin to nearly-pure lead, and included solders, lead- and tin-base alloys, some containing 10 percent antimony and 4 percent copper.

NOTE.—The method has been applied to the analysis of titanium. In this case, synthetic standards were used. Precision data were satisfactory, but accuracy data could not be established because analyzed standard samples were not available for comparison. It is significant to note that when the sulfate-plus-graphite was used without the germanium dioxide buffer, very poor analytical results were obtained. The addition of the germanium dioxide stabilizes this system appreciably.

TABLE 44-12. COPPER-BASE ALLOYS—SUMMARY OF PRECISION DATA

Element	*No. of Samples*	*Concentration Range, %*	*No. of Determinations*	*% Deviation From NBS*
Nickel	5	0.2 to 0.6	13	±5.8
Aluminum	3	0.01 to 1.0	8	±7.3
Lead	3	0.01 to 1.0	8	±6.3
Silicon	3	0.04 to 0.12	9	±6.0
Iron	5	0.03 to 0.82	13	±4.3
Silver	4	0.001 to 0.04	11	±3.5
Manganese	1	0.005	4	±5.4
			Average Percent Deviation	±5.1

TABLE 44-13. ALUMINUM-BASE ALLOYS—SUMMARY OF PRECISION DATA

Sample	*Element*	*No. of Determinations*	*Percent Chemical*	*Percent Found*	*Average Deviation*	*Average % Deviation*
SAC 95*	Cu	6	0.090	0.094	+0.004	+4.3
	Si	6	5.67	5.40	−0.27	−4.8
	Fe	6	0.46	0.50	+0.04	+8.7
	Mg	6	0.05	0.045	−0.05	−10.0
	Mn	6	0.05	0.055	+0.05	+10.0
SAC 105*	Cu	7	6.61	6.2	−0.41	−6.2
	Si	7	0.69	0.66	−0.03	−4.3
	Fe	7	0.67	0.68	+0.01	+1.5
	Mg	7	0.10	0.101	+0.001	+1.0
	Mn	7	0.11	0.104	−0.006	−5.4
					Average Percent Deviation	±4.7

* Standard samples of Aluminum Company of America.

TABLE 44-14. LEAD-TIN-BASE ALLOYS—SUMMARY OF PRECISION DATA

Element	*No. of Samples*	*Range, %*	*No. of Determinations*	*Average % Deviation From NBS*
Copper	4	0.01 to 0.20	9	±7.5
Nickel	3	0.002 to 0.02	8	±10.0
Bismuth	6	0.005 to 0.30	15	±3.6
Antimony	6	0.005 to 1.0	14	±9.7
Silver	5	0.0018 to 0.21	12	±6.7
Iron	2	0.001 to 0.033	10	±8.3

Average Percent Deviation ±7.7

ANALYSIS OF TANTALUM AND TANTALUM OXIDE[19]

CARRIER-DISTILLATION METHOD

The carrier-distillation method is used to volatilize and excite the impurity elements within a reasonable length of time, while burning as little of the refractory oxide as possible.

Scope.—This method covers the analysis of the following twelve elements in tantalum oxide in the parts-per-million range: aluminum, chromium, copper, iron, lead, magnesium, manganese, nickel, silicon, tin, titanium, and vanadium. The minimum detectability is 20 p.p.m. or less for all elements listed. See also Table 44-16.

Apparatus.—See Table 44-15.

TABLE 44-15. APPARATUS AND SPECTROGRAPHIC OPERATING CONDITIONS

Spectrograph	3-m. Baird Grating Spectrograph having a dispersion of 5.55 A/mm. in the first order.
Excitation Unit	Baird Source Power Unit
Current, D.C.	10 amp. (short circuit)
Pre-arc	None
Exposure	90 sec.
Sector wheel	6% transmission
Filter	None
Slit	25 μ
Analytical gap	4 mm.
Sample electrode	UCP No. 1990 on pedestal electrode UCP No. 1964.
Counter electrode	UCP No. 1992
Spectral range	2200–3500 A
Photographic emulsion	Eastman SA-1
Developer	Kodak D-19, 68°F., 5 min.
Plate calibration	Two-step method, iron-arc exposure
Densitometer	Baird Densitometer-Comparator

[19] Based on the method of Laib, Roger, D., Applied Spectroscopy, **17**, 160–162, 1963. Copyright 1963 by Applied Spectroscopy, and reprinted in part with permission of the copyright owner.

TABLE 44-16. MINIMUM DETECTABLE LIMITS AND PRECISION OF ANALYTICAL LINES

Element	*Wavelength, A*	*Min. Detectable Limit, p.p.m.*	*Concentration Range, p.p.m.*	*Coefficient of Variation, %*
Al	3082	5	50–600	
	2575		50–1000	7.6
	2660		150–1000	
Cr	3021	20	30–500	
	2843		50–1000	6.1
	2780		250–1000	
Cu	3247	1	5–50	3.0
Fe	3021	10	10–500	
	2832		500–5000	
	2744		50–4000	6.4
	2598		1000–5000	
Mg	2802	8	8–200	5.8
Mn	2576	5	15–400	7.6
Ni	3003	20	30–1000	7.6
Pb	2833	20	30–800	8.6
Si	2881		150–1000	
	2519		100–1500	
	2524		150–1000	4.0
Sn	2840	10	15–1000	6.1
Ti	3086	20	20–500	5.9
	3078		40–1000	
	2599		500–5000	
V	3185	7	20–400	8.7
	3102		50–1000	

Carrier.—A mixture of 30 percent silver (300-mesh), 20 percent barium fluoride, and 50 percent silver chloride. Silver chloride is prepared fresh, and dried in the dark with methanol to obtain a soft, friable product. The three ingredients of the carrier are

TABLE 44-17. ACCURACY OF ANALYTICAL DATA

Element	*Concentration Added, p.p.m.*	*Concentration Found, p.p.m.*	*Error, %*
Al	87	82	6
Cr	82	90	10
Cu	22	25	13
Fe	92	100	9
Mg	209	210	1
Mn	70	82	17
Ni	680	670	2
Pb	690	700	2
Si	170	180	6
Sn	72	70	3
Ti	87	95	9
V	77	84	9

weighed into a plastic vial and ground three minutes in a Wig-L-Bug Vibrator,[16] and stored in the dark until needed. As the ratio of the ingredients is critical, it should be observed faithfully.

Preparation of Standards.—Mix high-purity tantalum oxide with dilute sulfuric acid solutions of soluble compounds of the following elements: aluminum, chromium, copper, iron, lead, magnesium, manganese, nickel, silicon, tin, titanium, and vanadium. Prepare a set of six standards of varying concentrations plus an oxide blank. Carefully dry in platinum dishes and grind in plastic vials until thoroughly mixed.

NOTE.—A moving-plate study of the most concentrated standard, using 30-second exposure intervals to determine the volatilization patterns of the elements, revealed a 90-second exposure to be adequate for all elements. Using this exposure, the standards were arced in duplicate, then analytical curves were prepared, checked for linearity, and extrapolated for the concentrations of impurities in the base material.

Preparation of Sample.—Prepare the oxide of tantalum by heating the sample in a platinum dish with a Meeker burner. Caution should be observed in the ignition since tantalum sponge is pyrophoric. After the metal has ignited, place the dish in a muffle furnace at 900°C.[20] for ½ to 2 hours depending on the size of the sample. After cooling, pulverize the oxide in a polystyrene vial in the Wig-L-Bug Mixer. If lumps remain that appear to be incompletely oxidized, return these to the muffle for additional heating. (Very hard lumps of oxide may be ground in an agate mortar; however, this tends to contaminate the sample with silicon.)

For maximum efficiency in a carrier-distillation procedure, the sample and carrier must be intimately mixed in the correct proportions. To accomplish this, weigh 210 mg. of the sample and 90 mg. of the carrier-mix[21] into a 1-inch polystyrene vial, and grind for one minute on the Wig-L-Bug Vibrator. Mix standards in the same manner as described for the samples.

Procedure.—Transfer 100 mg. of each sample and standard into a separate deep-cup electrode, and pack with a rod machined to fit inside the electrode cup. To allow the gases to escape during the excitation without disturbing the sample, make a hole through the center of the packed cup with a large steel pin.[22]

Arc the samples and standards in duplicate, using the operating conditions shown in Table 44-15. After the characteristics of the analytical curves are checked initially, one spectrum of each standard is put on each plate. This eliminates the need for internal standards with subsequent calculation of intensity ratios.

Densitometry and Calculations.—From the density readings of the lines, draw new analytical curves each time for the complete set of standards. This is preferred to the usual manner of correcting previously drawn curves with one or two standards placed on each plate. It is possible to use element lines that are very close to tantalum lines because of the dispersion of the Baird Spectrograph. An example of this is Al 3082.1 and Ta 3081.8 A lines.

Plot the analytical curves on two cycle semi-log paper with the concentrations as ordinate and the density readings plotted directly on the abscissa. Read the sample concentrations from the curves, and average the duplicate values.

[20] Tantalum metal may also be converted to the oxide as follows: Place the platinum crucible containing the tantalum directly in a cold muffle furnace and gradually increase the temperature to 900°C.

[21] The balance pan should be made of platinum to avoid attack by the silver chloride with subsequent contamination of the sample.

[22] Nachtrieb, N. H., Principles and Practice of Spectrochemical Analysis, McGraw-Hill Book Co., Inc. 1950, p. 256, Fig. 12.8.

ANALYSIS OF ALUMINUM AND ALUMINUM-BASE ALLOYS[23]

POINT-TO-PLANE SPARK METHOD FOR SOLID SAMPLES

Scope.—This method covers the spectrographic analysis of aluminum and aluminum-base alloys for the following elements in the ranges indicated:

Element	*Concentration Range %*
Silicon	0.02 to 14.0
Copper	0.001 to 10.0
Magnesium	0.001 to 10.0
Zinc	0.03 to 8.0
Nickel	0.03 to 3.0
Iron	0.02 to 2.0
Manganese	0.005 to 2.0
Lead	0.03 to 0.7
Bismuth	0.03 to 0.7
Chromium	0.01 to 0.5
Titanium	0.01 to 0.5
Tin	0.01 to 0.5
Beryllium	0.0002 to 0.5
Calcium	0.0005 to 0.1
Sodium	0.0005 to 0.05

This method is applicable primarily to the analysis of chill-cast disks, but it may be extended, with proper precautions, to the analysis of samples in other forms on which a flat surface suitable for sparking can be machined. To be suitable, this flat surface must be at least $\frac{5}{8}$ inch wide, and must be compositionally representative of the material to be sampled. Because of the effects of matrix and metallurgical state, the scope of the method is limited by the standards available. Ideally, standards and samples should be of similar composition and metallurgical state; when they are not, corrections must be applied to compensate for these effects.

Summary of Method.—A flat surface is prepared on the sample. The sample is used as one electrode and a specially shaped graphite rod as the other electrode in a controlled spark discharge. The spectra are recorded photographically and the transmittance measurements of selected line pairs are obtained photometrically. Logarithmic intensity ratios are calculated by means of an emulsion calibration curve. Concentration is obtained by referring intensity ratios of the unknown samples to analytical curves prepared from standard samples.

Apparatus. **Excitation Source.**—A high-voltage spark unit, consisting of a transformer supplying power to a capacitor which is discharged periodically through a series circuit consisting of a relatively high inductance, minimum resistance, and the analytical spark gap.

The discharge is oscillating and of relatively long duration, which results in increased detectability for impurity elements, combined with good reproducibility. The unit should be capable of continuous, trouble-free operation at the power level employed.

Spark Stand.—A spark stand designed to accommodate a flat-disk electrode in opposition to a graphite counter electrode.

[23] Based on the methods of Churchill, J. R., ASTM Methods for Emission Spectrochemical Analysis, 1964, pp. 41–50. Copyright 1964 by ASTM, and reprinted in part with permission of the copyright owner.

Spectrographs.—Almost any of the commercial instruments offered for metallurgical work. Grating spectrographs having a 1.5-meter focal length for a 24,000-line grating, or a 2-meter focal length for a 15,000-line grating, are satisfactory.

Microphotometer.—A unit having precision of at least ±1.0 percent for transmittance readings between 10 and 90 percent.

Materials. **Graphite Rods.**—High-purity, 0.242-inch diameter.

Photographic Emulsion.—Either plates or films of an emulsion type suitable for the spectral range covered.

Photographic Processing Solutions.—The formulas recommended by plate or film manufacturer.

Standards. **Primary Standards.**—Primary standards for a few alloys are available from the National Bureau of Standards. These standards are in the form of transverse slices cut from 2.5-inch diameter rolled bars, and are issued with chemical compositions. These have the status of primary standards only in the analysis of commercial bar stock. For most other applications under this method, they must be re-evaluated locally to compensate for metallurgical differences between samples and standards. Under such conditions, they become secondary or tertiary standards.

Secondary Standards.—Secondary standard samples suitable for use in this method are available commercially.[24]

Tertiary Standards.—Standards of local origin, usually referred to as tertiary standards, are required when appropriate secondary standards are not available. These include chill-cast disks, sections of extrusions, sheet samples, and castings standardized by chemical means in the laboratory using them. Such tertiary standards are often required when the analytical sample differs metallurgically from available secondary standards.

Preparation of Samples. **(a) Fabricated Products.**—Machine the samples of extrusions, rolled bar, and sheet with a lathe to produce a flat surface suitable for sparking. On sheet samples, machine to a depth of 0.030 inch, or one-fourth the thickness of the sheet, whichever is smaller. On rolled bar, extrusions, and heavy plate, machine a cross-sectional surface for sparking, provided that a sufficiently large cross-section is available. If the cross-sectional area is insufficient, follow the procedure described for sheet.

(b) Castings.—The sampling of castings is generally more difficult and more critical than the sampling of other products. In general, the analytical sample should be cut from a region of rapid solidification. Machine a flat surface lying at least 0.050 inch below the original surface. Two or more samples may be cut from various locations on the casting to insure a representative analysis. The sampling problem is influenced by the alloy type, the size and shape of the casting, and the casting procedure. Each type of casting requires a certain amount of exploratory work before it can be analyzed accurately and efficiently.

(c) Pig and Ingot.—The sampling of pig and ingot for analysis varies with the compositions involved and the quality of the material. (A generally satisfactory procedure is to cut a cross-sectional slice at two locations spaced about one-third of the length of the pig or ingot from either end.) Machine each slice to a smooth finish on one side and analyze at from three to five locations equally spaced along a diagonal of this surface. This procedure is adequate for most commercial alloys. For low-grade secondary metal more extensive sampling, both longitudinally and cross-sectionally, may be required.

(d) Heterogeneous Samples.—When sampling by the techniques described is not

[24] Report on Available Standard Samples, Reference Samples, and High-Purity Materials for Spectrochemical Analysis, ASTM STP No. 58-E, American Society for Testing and Materials, 1964.

applicable, either because of nonuniformity or physical form, melt the sample and cast as chill-cast disks. Carry out the melting and casting operations as rapidly as possible, the melting preferably being performed in a small induction furnace. If the sample is in the form of turnings, thin sheet, or other finely divided material, remove grease with a suitable solvent and press into a briquet before melting to minimize oxidation and loss of volatile constituents. This method of preparing samples is not satisfactory for the determination of sodium and calcium. There is also a tendency for magnesium and zinc results to run low because of losses during melting. With increasing size of melt, losses of volatile elements diminish.

Electrode System.—Insert a freshly cut graphite rod in the Petrey spark stand and adjust vertically to give a gap distance of 3 mm. Place the sample, machined side down, on the Petrey stand in such a position that the spark will impinge on a central area of the machined surface. In the case of a sample having a peripheral sprue, orient the sample so that the spark does not fall within a 60-degree arc of the diameter passing through the center of the sprue. If the sample has been previously sparked, position it so that the two sparked areas do not touch. After carefully positioning the sample to conform to the above conditions, clamp it firmly in place so that good electrical contact is established between the sample and the top plate of the Petrey stand.

Focus an image of the spark on the grating or prism of the spectrograph by means of a spherical lens or by a cylindrical lens placed with the cylindrical axis parallel to the slit. On a stigmatic spectrograph, place the lens directly in front of the slit. On an astigmatic instrument, place the lens at the secondary (vertical) focus of the spectrograph. The focal length of this lens must be such as to produce an image either smaller or larger than the aperture of the grating or prism. The image must not approach equality of height with this aperture because of the high intensity gradient in the vicinity of the electrodes.

Excitation.—Select discharge parameters according to the source unit employed, as shown in the following tabulation:

(a) Feussner-Type Spark:	
Nominal power setting	2 kw.
Capacitance	0.021 μf.
Inductance	0.4 to 1.4 mh.
Resistance in series with gap	None
Nominal output voltage	17,500 v.
Primary voltage	75 v.
Primary current	6.6 amp.
Discharge per cycle	2
(b) Air-Interrupted Spark:	
Capacitance	0.009 to 0.012 μf.
Inductance	0.3 to 0.5 mh.
Resistance in series with gap	None
Primary resistance	9 ohms
Peak voltage, output	20,000 v.
Radio frequency current	9.5 to 12.5 amp.
Discharges per cycle	4
Air interrupter:	
Tungsten electrodes, diameter.	0.375 inch
Air orifice	0.25 inch
Air pressure	2 p.s.i.

(c) Rectified Spark With Rotary Interrupter:

Capacitance	0.007 μf.
Inductance	0.4 to 1.4 mh.
Resistance in series with gap	None
Peak voltage, output	20,000 v.
Primary voltage	250 v.
Primary current	4 amp.
Radio frequency current	6 to 12 amp.
Discharges per cycle	4

(d) Other Spark Units.—Excitation units on which the precise constants given in Tabulations (a), (b), and (c) are not available may be used within the following limits, provided that it can be shown experimentally that equivalent precision and accuracy are obtained:

Capacitance	0.005 to 0.025 μf.
Inductance	0.2 to 1.5 mh.
Resistance in series with gap	None
Peak voltage	10,000 to 30,000 v.
Radio frequency current	7 to 14 amp.
Discharge per cycle	1 to 4

Exposure.—Range of Conditions:

Slit width:	
Prism spectrographs	30 to 60 μ
Grating spectrographs	50 to 80 μ
Preburn	5 to 10 sec.
Exposure	10 to 30 sec.
Filters	as required

Slit Width.—Optimum slit width varies with the instruments used and the determinations made. On the prism instruments the maximum slit width is limited by interference effects, and the width chosen should give a smooth, single-maximum contour on microphotometric scanning. Optimum slit width varies even among prism instruments of the same make, and must therefore be determined for each spectrograph. On the grating instruments the main factor limiting slit width is line-to-background ratio. A slit width of 80 μ is satisfactory for most determinations, but slit widths as small as 50 μ may be used under this method when higher line-to-background ratios are desired. Determinations of minor impurities, in which slit widths as small as 10 μ are often used advantageously, are not within the scope of this method.

Exposure Time.—Exposure time, filter transmittances, and optical adjustments are interdependent. A minimum exposure of 10 seconds is required to obtain a representative sample of radiation. Exposure time, filter tranmsittances, and optical adjustments affecting line density shall be selected to give suitable line transmittances.

Filters.—Nominally neutral filters, grating apertures, collimator apertures, and external lenses of various focal lengths may be used for the purpose of adjusting optical speed. However, the effects of these variables on the sampling of the radiation and on the uniformity of spectrum lines must be taken into account by the use of standard samples.

Fixed or removable filters may be used to obtain more favorable intensity ratios. A removable filter may be used to provide a dual concentration range, thus reducing the number of different lines used.

Filters are best mounted immediately in front of the film or plate. Suitable filters of virtually any desired density are available commercially in the form of quartz plates bearing evaporated metal coatings. Any type of absorbing material of suitable physical form and having the desired transmittance at the particular wavelength involved is satisfactory for a filter medium, provided, of course, the transmittance does not change rapidly with time. No general specifications for filters can be given except in relation to a particular set of apparatus and a particular application.

Emulsion Calibration and Photographic Processing.—Follow recommendations supplied by film and plate manufacturers.

Photometry.—Use the Al 3059.93 A line as the internal standard for determinations in which an internal standard is required. Select wavelengths for the elements to be determined from Table 44-18. Indices given in Table 44-18 were obtained by the use of one or more spectrographs, but are not necessarily typical or average values for all spectrographs.

In selecting an analytical line for a particular determination, the factors to be considered are interference by other elements, the concentration index, proximity to the internal standard wavelength (Al 3059.93 A), and the transmittance of the line image under the conditions of test. Make the preliminary selection from Table 44-18 by selecting a line which has a concentration index near the concentration expected in the sample, and for which no interferences are indicated for the alloy being analyzed. If, on trial, the line is found to have too high a concentration index, that is, if the intensity ratio is too low in the spectrum of the sample, select a line of lower concentration index from the table. Similarly, if the concentration index proves too low, select a line of higher concentration index. The final selection must approximate the requirements shown in Table 44-19.

When filters are used on analytical lines, the concentration indices are increased in inverse proportion to the transmission of the filter. The use of such filters may be helpful in obtaining a satisfactory selection of wavelengths.

Calculation of Results.—At concentration of 0.05 percent or less, when the result is to be expressed to only one significant figure, estimate concentration by either visual or photometric comparison of the analytical lines in sample and standard spectrograms photographed on the same plate or film. The standards used should consist of a series covering the concentration range of the samples, preferably in approximately logarithmic progression, with a concentration ratio of 1.5 to 2.0 between successive standards. Also, the standards must be of the same general alloy type as the samples.

For concentrations in excess of 0.005 percent, and in all cases where results are to be expressed to two or more significant figures, calculate results by the internal standard procedure. Corrections for spectral background are optional but not recommended. The control of transmittance levels and the frequent use of standards largely eliminates the value of such corrections in this method.

Prepare analytical curves by plotting the logarithm of concentration against the logarithm of the intensity ratios of the analysis and internal standard lines for a series of standard samples. Prepare a separate analytical curve for each element in each general type of alloy and employ a sufficient number and variety of standards to establish clearly the contour of the analytical curve, if it shows curvature. Analytical curves found to be straight lines for one aluminum alloy may be assumed to be straight lines for all aluminum alloys within the same concentration range. In such cases, two standards representing concentrations near the top and bottom of the concentration range to be covered are sufficient to establish the analytical curve for a given particular alloy. Treat the analytical curve as having constant slope and with concentration index varying transversely from plate to plate or film to film. Determine the position of the analytical curve

TABLE 44-18. ANALYSIS LINES AND INTERFERING LINES

Element	*Analytical Line, A*	*Concentration Index with Respect to Al 3059.93 A, percent*	*Interfering Line, A*	*Interfering Concentration, percent*[a]
Silicon	Si 2987.65	15.0	Fe 2987.29	1.5
	Si 2435.16	3.0	Fe 2434.94	0.5
	Si 2519.21	0.9	Cr 2519.52	2.0
	....	....	Fe 2519.05	1.5
	Si 2528.52	0.6	....	....
	Si 2506.90	0.25	Cu 2506.27	4.0
	Si 2516.12	0.20	....	....
	Si 2881.58	0.15	Cr 2881.93	1.0
Copper	Cu 2961.16	7.5	....	....
	Cu 2824.37	6.0	Cr 2824.54	0.5
	Cu 2242.61	2.0	....	....
	Cu 2247.00	0.9	....	....
	Cu 3273.96	0.04	....	....
	Cu 3247.54	0.03	....	....
Magnesium	Mg 3329.93	10.5	Ti 3329.46	0.05
	Mg 3332.15	5.5	Ti 3332.11	0.05
	Mg 2915.52	5.0	Cr 2915.23	0.5
	Mg 3336.68	3.5	Cr 3336.33	0.5
	Mg 2778.29	0.9	Cr 2778.06	0.5
	....	....	Fe 2778.22	0.7
	Mg 2782.97	0.9	....	....
	Mg 2779.83	0.25	Cr 2780.30	0.5
	....	....	Fe 2779.30	1.0
	Mg 2790.79	0.05	....	....
	Mg 2852.13	0.01	Fe 2851.80	2.0
	Mg 2802.70	0.004	....	....
	Mg 2798.06	0.001	....	....
	Mg 2795.53	0.001	Mn 2794.82	0.1
Zinc	Zn 3075.90	5.0	Fe 3075.72	0.5
	Zn 2557.96	1.0	Mn 2557.54	0.5
	Zn 3282.33	1.0	Cu 3282.72	10.0
	....	....	Ti 3282.33	0.05
	Zn 3302.59	0.5	....	....
	Zn 3345.02	0.1	....	....
Nickel	Ni 2992.60	5.4	Cr 2992.45	2.0
	Ni 3315.66	4.2	Ti 3315.32	0.2
	Ni 3232.96	2.2	Fe 3232.79	3.0
	Ni 2437.89	1.5	Mn 2437.91	1.0
	Ni 3037.94	0.8	Fe 3037.39	0.2
	....	....	Mn 3038.50	1.0
	Ni 3433.56	0.75	Cr 3433.31	0.5
	Ni 3134.11	0.5	Cr 3134.31	0.5
	Ni 3492.96	0.35	....	....
	Ni 3414.76	0.15	....	....

TABLE 44-18 (cont.)

Element	*Analytical Line, A*	*Concentration Index with Respect to Al 3059.93 A, percent*	*Interfering Line, A*	*Interfering Concentration, percent*[a]
Iron	Fe 3037.39	2.5	Ni 3037.94	0.2
	....	....	Cr 3037.04	0.5
	Fe 3047.60	1.5	....	....
	Fe 2966.90	1.3	....	....
	Fe 2727.54	0.8	Cr 2727.26	1.0
	Fe 2743.20	0.65	Cr 2743.64	0.2
	Fe 2613.82	0.40	Pb 2614.18	0.2
	Fe 2598.37	0.35	Mn 2599.04	0.3
	Fe 2739.55	0.3	Cr 2740.10	1.0
	Fe 2755.74	0.2	....	....
	Fe 2749.32	0.2	Cr 2748.98	0.1
	Fe 2599.40	0.1	Mn 2599.04	0.3
Manganese	Mn 2722.08	4.0	....	....
	Mn 2900.16	2.0	....	....
	Mn 3228.09	1.5	Fe 3227.75	1.0
	Mn 2886.68	1.1	....	....
	Mn 2711.58	0.8	Fe 2711.65	1.0
	Mn 2708.45	0.7	....	....
	Mn 2705.74	0.45	....	....
	Mn 2889.58	0.4	Cr 2889.48	0.2
	Mn 2701.70	0.35	Cr 2701.99	2.0
	Mn 2933.06	0.1	Cr 2932.70	2.0
	Mn 2949.20	0.1	Cr 2949.44	2.5
	Mn 2593.73	0.03	....	....
Lead	Pb 4057.82	0.40	....	....
	Pb 2833.07	0.25	....	....
Bismuth	Bi 2897.98	0.90	Mn 2897.80	1.5
	....	....	Mn 2898.69	0.3
	Bi 3067.72	0.07	Fe 3067.24	0.2
Chromium	Cr 2966.05	3.5	....	....
	Cr 3017.57	0.7	Fe 3017.63	1.0
	Cr 2762.59	0.3	....	....
	Cr 2766.54	0.1	Cu 2766.37	4.0
	Cr 2843.25	0.1	....	....
	Cr 2835.63	0.07	....	....
	Cr 3593.49	0.04	....	....
Titanium	Ti 3252.91	0.35	....	....
	Ti 3248.60	0.30	Mn 3248.52	0.1
	Ti 3241.99	0.15	....	....
	Ti 3236.57	0.1	Mn 3236.78	0.3
	....	....	Ti 3236.12	0.1
	Ti 3239.04	0.1	Fe 3239.44	1.5
	....	....	Cr 3238.76	0.5
	Ti 3372.80	0.1	....	....

TABLE 44-18 (cont.)

Element	*Analytical Line, A*	*Concentration Index with Respe t to Al 3059.93 A, percent*	*Interfering Line, A*	*Interfering Concentration, percent*[a]
Titanium (*cont'd*)	Ti 3234.52	0.05	Cr 3234.06	0.5
	Ti 3361.21	0.05	Ni 3361.56	0.5
	Ti 3349.41	0.03	Ti 3349.04	0.01
Tin	Sn 3262.33	0.85	....	....
	Sn 3175.02	0.40	....	....
	Sn 2839.99	0.35	Cr 2840.02	0.02
Beryllium	Be 2650.62	0.02	Mn 2650.99	0.3
	Be 2348.61	0.003	Fe 2348.30	0.3
	Be 3131.07	0.0009	Ti 3130.80	0.1
	Be 3130.42	0.0005	Ti 3130.80	0.1
Calcium	Ca 4226.73	0.06	....	....
	Ca 3968.47	0.006	....	....
	Ca 3933.67	0.003	....	....
Sodium	Na 5889.95	(*b*)	....	....
	Na 5895.92	(*b*)	....	....

[a] Approximate minimum concentration of interfering element at which interference is observed.

[b] Used without internal standard on prism spectrographs. Al 3050.08, Al 3057.15, or Al 3066.16 used as internal standard in second order spectra on grating spectrographs.

for each plate or film with an analytical standard representing a concentration within plus one-half or minus one-third that of the sample analyzed. Adjust the analytical curve to the average position indicated by the average of four spectrograms of the standard, except when the following applies: If the analytical curve is in continual use

TABLE 44-19. APPROXIMATE LIMITS OF INTENSITY RATIO AND TRANSMITTANCE IN THE SELECTION OF SPECTRUM LINES

Concentration, percent	*Intensity Ratio*	*Transmittance, percent*
0.001 to 0.10	0.2 to 5.0	3 to 90
0.10 to 1.0	0.3 to 3.0	10 to 70
1.0 to 4.0	0.5 to 2.0	15 to 60
Over 4.0	0.6 to 1.5	25 to 50

(approximately daily) and there is no evidence of error when last used, adjust the curve midway between its previous position and the position indicated by a single spectrogram of the standard taken on the same plate or film with the sample. If the half correction so determined exceeds 3 percent of the concentration of the standard, discard the data, prepare new spectrograms, and determine the position of the analytical curve with a minimum of four standards without regard to previous data.

The conversion of microphotometer readings to concentrations may be effected through the use of graphical calculators such as the Dunn-Lowry calculator[25] or the

[25] This calculator was developed by Aluminum Company of America and is now commercially available. See Churchill, J. R., Selected Topics in Modern Instrumental Analysis, edited by Boltz, David F., Prentice-Hall, Inc., 1952, pp. 214–215.

multiple determination calculating rule. To do this, plot the emulsion calibration and analytical curves on logarithmic coordinates of the same physical dimensions. Project the numerical values of relative transmittance onto a line parallel with the exposure axis, and thus obtain a scale characteristic of the emulsion. Project the numerical values of concentration onto a line parallel with the intensity ratio axis to produce an analytical scale. These scales are used in alignment to obtain concentration values as follows:

Adjust the analytical scale to align the index with a pointer or indicator. This accomplishes the correction discussed in the third paragraph under Calculation of Results. Move the emulsion scale until the relative transmittance reading of the internal standard also aligns with this indicator. Opposite the transmittance reading of the element line read the concentration of that element from the analytical scale.

Precision and Accuracy.—The reliability of this method has been studied in a large number of cooperating laboratories and found to be satisfactory for most routine purposes. The precision of the method is such that coefficients of variation ranging from 2 to 4 percent are obtained at concentrations above 0.50 percent in repeat tests on the same material. Higher coefficients may be expected at low concentrations when weak lines are obtained, or when, as is usually the case, exposure conditions are adjusted to favor higher constituents.

Aside from precision, the accuracy of this method depends largely on the quality of the standards used and the degree to which they resemble the samples both chemically and physically. Errors amounting to several percent of the concentration determined may be introduced by comparing samples and standards of marked physical dissimilarity as, for example, in analyzing sheet products by comparison with cast standards. In the analysis of chill-cast disks with commercially available cast standards, the accuracy of the method becomes virtually equivalent to the precision as stated in the preceding paragraph.

ANALYSIS OF TRACE ELEMENTS IN MAGNESIUM BY SOLUTION TECHNIQUES[26]

POROUS ELECTRODE METHOD FOR SOLUTIONS

This method illustrates the porous-cup electrode technique, and is applied to the analysis of trace elements in magnesium. Elements that may occur in magnesium but do not lend themselves readily to solution techniques of analyses are included for information purposes and referenced for a suitable spectrographic approach.

Scope.—The following elements are determined by solution techniques in the trace concentration range, with the limits of detection listed:

Barium	0.0005%
Beryllium	0.0003%
Boron	0.001%
Lithium	0.002%

The following elements also may be determined spectrographically in magnesium by either the solid block or the pencil electrode techniques: aluminum, cadmium, calcium, cerium, copper, iron, lanthanum, lead, manganese, nickel, silicon, silver, tin, titanium, zinc, and zirconium.

See also Tables 44-21 and 44-22.

Solution Techniques.—Solution techniques may prove to be indispensable under circumstances where chemical analysis is difficult, tedious, or even impossible. With solu-

[26] Based on the method of Price, W. J., Spectrochim. Acta, **7**, 118–127, 1955. Copyright 1955 by Spectrochimica Acta, and reprinted in part with permission of the copyright owner.

tion technique, chemical analysis becomes unnecessary, since synthetic standard solutions are made up from the pure constituents and suitable solid standards may afterward be calibrated from these. Poor reproducibility of results from solid specimens which is often caused by heterogeneity, is generally improved by taking such samples into solution.

The procedure recommended is the porous-cup technique originated by Feldman.[27]

The porous cup electrode consists of a 0.25 × 1.5-inch right cylindrical graphite rod, with a 0.125-inch hole drilled along its axis to within 1.1 mm. of the other end. It is used as the upper electrode, with the open end up, and contains the liquid sample. The lower electrode is a solid 0.125-inch graphite rod. A synchronous spark or a 220-volt intermittent alternating or direct current arc is first applied for 5 or 10 seconds. The heat thus produced helps the liquid to soak through the bottom of the porous cup and reach the sparking surface. After a 15-second delay, the sparking is resumed and the exposure begun. The liquid feeds through the porous cup by wick action, constantly renewing the thin surface film of liquid as it is dispersed by the spark. Spattering does not occur, and with proper sparking conditions the liquid in the cup does not boil. A sample of 0.2 to 0.3 ml. lasts as long as 240 seconds.

Apparatus. **Spectrograph.**—A medium dispersion spectrograph, unless certain rare earths, thorium, or zirconium are present. If any of these is present, a higher dispersion instrument is needed.

Porous-Cup Electrodes.—Electrodes should conform to the specifications detailed under Solution Techniques.

Lower Electrode.—Solid 0.125-inch graphite rods of highest available purity.

Photographic Plates.—A high speed, fairly high contrast emulsion, with uniform contrast over the 2500–5000 A wavelength range.

Preparation of Standards.—Dissolve 2 g. of spectrographically pure magnesium in 30 ml. of hydrochloric acid (1:1). When dissolution is complete, add a further 20-ml. portion of the acid. Add appropriate aliquots of standard solutions of the elements to be determined, covering the composition ranges anticipated. Hydrochloric acid or water solutions of high-purity salts are preferred. After the requisite amounts of the solutions containing the trace elements have been added, dilute to 100 ml. with water.[28] A series of about seven standards is sufficient to cover a hundred-fold range of an element (*e.g.*, beryllium 0.001–0.1 percent), and a number of elements may be added to the same series of standards (in this work, barium, beryllium, and lithium).

Preparation of Samples.—Dissolve a 2-g. sample in 30 ml. of hydrochloric acid (1:1). When dissolution is complete, add an additional 20 ml. of acid and dilute to 100 ml.[28]

Electrode Filling.—Withdraw 0.2 to 0.3 ml. of the sample solution with a long fine-tipped pipet. Insert the pipet tip in the cup of the electrode so that the tip touches the bottom of the cavity. Allow the solution to drain into the cup as the pipet is withdrawn. (If air bubbles are entrapped in the liquid column, splashing and sample loss will result during sparking.) Use the same volume of solution for all samples and standards.

Excitation.—Select excitation conditions and line pairs from Tables 44-20 and 44-21. Determine exposure time experimentally to achieve maximum sensitivity and reproducibility.

[27] Feldman, Cyrus, Anal. Chem., **21,** 1041, 1949.

[28] It is necessary that the final solutions be at least 1 *N* with respect to the free hydrochloric acid to avoid both adsorption of some elements (particularly beryllium) on to the walls of the containing vessel, and chromatographic effects in the porous cup itself. Hydrochloric acid is preferred as the solution medium because of the high volatility of metallic chlorides. There is no reason why other acids could not be used, and they may even be better in some circumstances from the point of view of purity. It must be borne in mind, of course, that nitric acid is undesirable for tin, that hydrochloric acid cannot be used with silver, and that sulphuric acid is unsuitable for the determination of barium, calcium, and lead.

Table 44-20. Excitation Information

	SETTINGS				
Source Unit	*Secondary Voltage*	*Capacitance*	*Inductance*	*Resistance*	*Electrode Gap width*
Spark Source I for solution excitation	8 kv.	0.005 μf.	0.135 mh.	nil	2 mm.
Spark Source II for block sample	15 kv.	0.005 μf.	0.005 mh.	nil	4 mm.
Controlled arc source	—	200 μf.	0.50 mh.	7 ohms	4 mm.

NOTES ON THE DETERMINATION OF CERTAIN TRACE ELEMENTS IN MAGNESIUM ALLOYS

The methods and line-pairs given in Tables 44-21 and 44-22 are those which experimentally proved to give best overall sensitivity to trace quantities. The elements in Table 44-21 are augmented by the following remarks:

Aluminum.—Small amounts of aluminum occur in high-purity magnesium, zinc- and zirconium-containing alloys. In certain alloys, particularly zirconium-containing alloys, aluminum may be present in "soluble" and "insoluble" forms, thus giving rise to uneven distribution and poor analytical reproducibility.

Barium.—Barium can be determined down to 0.01 percent by the solution technique. Below this concentration, a cyanogen band-head at 4553.1 A causes serious interference with the most sensitive barium line 4554.0, if a low dispersion unit is used. This interference is eliminated by sparking the solutions in an atmosphere of commercially-pure oxygen. A simple glass shroud may be readily constructed for this purpose or a commercial Stallwood-type jet may be purchased from various manufacturers. Metal samples may also be used, but these must first be calibrated by the above solution technique, and in order to overcome the same band interference, pencil self-electrodes must be employed.

For the estimation of very low concentrations and blanks it may be preferable to plot the intensity ratio Ba 4554.0 underlying background, against concentration. A measure of the underlying background is obtained as the average of the background deflection taken at equal distances on each side of the line.

Beryllium.—Beryllium is remarkably sensitive in both arc and spark excitation, and is not easily determined by chemical procedures. Solutions or metal samples may be employed, the latter being standardized by the solution technique. If low concentrations of beryllium are to be determined in the presence of zirconium or the rare earths, a high dispersion spectrograph must be used to overcome the effects of line-interference.

Boron.—The determination of boron is important, since traces of this element present during the electrolytic extraction process for magnesium cause non-coagulation of the metal, and, hence, low recoveries.

Boron is calibrated for and determined by the solution technique. For samples of magnesia, magnesite, or magnesium chloride, the same standards and method as for magnesium metal are employed. For the lowest concentrations, boron-free graphite electrodes must be employed.

Calcium.—The determination of calcium is required in certain high-purity alloys. The most sensitive lines of calcium occur in the 3934 A region, where normal plate

TABLE 44-21. ANALYTICAL PARAMETERS FOR CERTAIN TRACE ELEMENTS IN MAGNESIUM

Element		*Sample Form*	*Excitation*	*Line Pairs*		*Detectable Limit, %*	*Notes*
Aluminum	(a)	Block	Arc	Al 3961.5*	Mg 4057.6	0.001	Zr interferes
	(b)	Block	Arc	Al 3944.0*	Mg 4057.6	0.005	Th interferes
Barium	(a)	Soln.	Spark I	Ba 4554.0	Mg 4703.0	0.01	Sparking in air
	(b)	Soln.	Spark I	Ba 4554.0*	Mg 4703.0	<0.0005	Sparking in oxygen
	(c)	Pencils	Spark II	Ba 4554.0*	Mg 4703.0	0.0002	Added inductance 0.135 mH
Beryllium	(a)	Soln.	Spark I	Be 3130.4	Mg 3074.0	0.0003	
	(b)	Block	Spark II	Be 3130.4	Mg 3074.0	0.001	
	(c)	Block	Arc	Be 3130.4	Mg 3074.0	<0.0001	
Boron	(a)	Soln.	Spark I	B 2497.7*	Mg 2660.8 or	0.005	Source unit as Table 44-20
	(b)	Soln.	Spark I	B 2497.7*	Mg 2776.7	0.001	Inductance 0.005 mh.
Calcium	(a)	Block	Spark II	Ca 3933.7	Mg 3329.9 or	0.002	
	(b)	Pencils	Arc	Ca 3933.7	Mg 3074.0	0.0003	
Lithium		Soln.	Spark I	Li 6707.8	Mg 5528.5	0.002	
Rare Earths	(a)	Pencils	Arc	Ce 3201.7	Mg 3074.0	0.01	Total Rare Earths limit: 0.02 percent
				La 3949.1	Mg 4057.6	0.005	
	(b)	Block	Arc	Ce 3201.7	Mg 3074.0	0.02	Total Rare Earths limit: 0.04 percent
				La 3949.1	Mg 4057.6	0.01	

* See note under Table 44-22.

Table 44-22. Solid Sample Methods for Trace Elements in Magnesium

Element	*Line-Pair*		*Lowest Limit of Detection, %* *Method* (1)	*Method* (2)	*Notes*
Cadmium	Cd 3261.1	Mg 3074.0	0.01	—	
Cadmium	Cd 2288.0	Adj. Bgd.*	0.001	0.0002	
Copper	Cu 3247.5	Mg 3074.0	0.0002	0.00005	
Iron	Fe 3020.6	Mg 3074.0	0.002	0.001	Zirconium interferes
Iron	Fe 2719.0	Mg 3074.0	0.005	0.003	
Iron	Fe 2483.3	Mg 3074.0	0.001	<0.001	
Lead	Pb 3639.6	Mg 3074.0 or Mg 3329.9	0.002	0.001	Uniform gamma plate necessary
Lead	Pb 2614.2	Mg 2736.5 or Mg 3074.0	0.001	0.001	
Manganese	Mn 2949.2	Mg 3074.0	0.002	0.002	
Manganese	Mn 2576.1	Mg 3074.0	0.0005	0.0002	
Nickel	Ni 3414.8	Mg 3329.9	0.001	0.001	Zirconium interferes
Nickel	Ni 3002.5	Mg 3074.0	0.002	0.002	
Silicon	Si 2881.6	Mg 3074.0 or Adj. Bgd.*	0.002	0.002	Background correction of Si line essential
	Si 2516.1	Mg 3074.0 or Mg 2736.5	0.001	0.001	
Silver	Ag 3382.9	Mg 3329.9	<0.001	<0.0001 †	† estimated Figure
Tin	Sn 3175.1	Mg 3074.0	0.002	0.001	
Titanium	Ti 3349.0	Mg 3329.9	‡	0.002	‡ Ordinary graphite contains some Ti
Zinc	Zn 3345.0	Mg 3329.9 or Mg 3074.0 Adj. Bgd.*	0.002	0.002	Uniform gamma plate preferred
Zirconium	Zr 3392.0	Mg 3329.9	0.005	<0.005	

Method (1) block samples with graphite counter electrode.
Method (2) pencil self-electrodes.

* Adjacent background, where this is reproducible from spectrum to spectrum (*e.g.*, where it originates from closely situated dense magnesium lines), may be employed as an internal standard intensity. The distance from the analysis line at which the background reading is taken must be carefully standardized.

gamma is too high for accurate evaluation. The use of a uniform gamma plate overcomes this problem, and incidentally simplifies the choice of an internal standard line.

All sparking surfaces must be freshly machined immediately before use to minimize contamination from atmospheric dust. Standard samples are conveniently analyzed by flame spectrometry.

Lithium.—Lithium is readily calibrated for and determined by the solution technique, but the occurrence of its strongest line at 6707.8 A necessitates the use of a panchromatic or special red-sensitive emulsion.

Rare Earths.—The spectrographic determination of low concentrations of rare earths is beset by two difficulties, namely, the lack of very sensitive emission lines, and the occurrence of most of the lines at wavelengths above 3500 A—a region of serious cyanogen-band interference. The best sensitivity is therefore obtained with pencil self-electrode samples, and a uniform gamma plate. A controlled atmosphere device, referred to under Barium, is also useful in eliminating cyanogen-band interference. Calibration is done by chemical analysis.

Other Elements.—The foregoing elements have all required individual methods for all or part of the range. Some elements listed in Table 44-22 are sought in the routine examination of all alloys and high-purity magnesium, and are determined by using a common set of conditions. Methods (1) and (2) in Table 44-22 refer to metal electrode systems as follows:

(1) Point-to-Plane System. *Sample.*—Block, not less than one quarter-inch thick, with a machined flat surface of at least one square inch for arcing or sparking.

Counter-Electrode.—Graphite rod, 4 mm. diameter, flat-end.

Gap Width.—4 mm.

Polarity.—Sample negative.

(2) Pencil Self-Electrodes. *Sample.*—Both electrodes are pencils, 6 mm. diameter, cast direct or machined from sample block. Sparking ends turned to 4 mm. diameter.

Gap Width.—4 mm.

X-RAY SPECTROMETRY[29]
(X-RAY SPECTROCHEMICAL ANALYSIS)

X-ray spectrochemical analysis covers that area of spectrometry in which wavelengths in the x-ray range of the spectrum are emitted, recorded, and interpreted as a means of obtaining composition information. The spectra are produced by irradiation of the specimen with x-rays or electron beams.

Diffraction crystals and sensitive detectors are used in a goniometer to measure the spectra and record characteristic line intensities. The intensity of the spectral lines is dependent on the amount of the particular element present. Standards, if not available, are easily prepared so that the line intensities related to calibration curves provide accurate quantitative determination of the amount of an element present. The method provides rapid and accurate analyses.

Scope.—The x-ray spectrochemical method is one of the few analytical methods that may be utilized when it is not permissible to destroy the sample. This is especially important in research projects in which the composition of a sample must be followed in the course of other measurements and treatments. It is also particularly useful where other methods of analysis are difficult due to the chemical similarity of elements, and when other methods are tedious and less accurate than the imposed analytical requirements.

Since the x-ray spectra originate in the inner electron shells of the atoms, the spectra are relatively simple, especially when compared to optical emission spectra. The applicability of x-ray spectrochemical analysis is very broad, as shown in Table 44-23 which designates those elements that may be determined.

The particular examples provided in this section will follow an organization based on sample preparation and instrumentation. This provides the broadest general applicability of the method to materials analysis. Instrumentation will include flat and curved crystal spectrometers, and the electron probe microanalyzer.

[29] This section prepared by E. J. Brooks, U. S. Naval Research Laboratory, Washington, D. C.

TABLE 44-23. ELEMENTS DETERMINABLE BY X-RAY SPECTROCHEMICAL ANALYSIS

H																	He
Li	Be											B	C	N	O	F	Ne
Na	Mg											Al	Si	P	S	Cl	A
K	Ca	Sc	Ti	V	Cr	Mn	Fe	Co	Ni	Cu	Zn	Ga	Ge	As	Se	Br	K
Rb	Sr	Yt	Zr	Nb	Mo	Tc	Ru	Rh	Pd	Ag	Cd	In	Sn	Sb	Te	I	Xe
Cs	Ba	*	Hf	Ta	W	Re	Os	Ir	Pt	Au	Hg	Tl	Pb	Bi	Po	At	Rn
Fr	Ra	Ac	Th	Pa	U												

* La, Ce, Pr, Nd, Pm, Sm, Eu, Gd, Tb, Dy, Ho, Er, Tm, Yb, Lu

Elements C to Sc; measure the X-ray K series spectra by special detectors with vacuum or He path.

Elements Ti to Ba; measure the X-Ray K series in air path.

Elements La to U; measure the X-Ray L series in air path.

Sample Form and Preparation.—This method of analysis is often research oriented, and the form of samples received for analysis may not be readily characterized or defined. As a result, the methods of sample preparation are varied.

No preliminary sample treatment is permitted for those samples whose complete identity must be retained throughout a research program.

When permissible, samples to be analyzed on an "as received" or "as is" basis, are given a minimum of surface treatment. This is accomplished by sanding the surface smooth and/or polishing and etching for orientation.

When analyses on such specimens are not sufficiently accurate due to specimen topography or due to the absence of suitable reference standards, the specimens must be reduced to a common form. To accomplish this, only the simplest treatment, which will result in sufficient sensitivity and accuracy, is employed.

The more common procedures for sample preparation and treatment to insure repeatability and to achieve accuracy and sensitivity in an analysis are listed:

a. compression of metal chips, turnings, drillings into a solid disc at high pressures,[30]

b. fusion with borax and chill-casting into discs,[31]

c. formation of metallic discs by button furnace melting,[32]

d. chemical reactions to convert entire sample to powder form for briquetting with a binder at high pressures,

e. chemical reactions involving separation and briquetting,

f. chemical reactions involving separation and filtration, and

g. separation by ion exchange reactions.[33,34]

Several of these preparatory procedures (d, e, and f) are described below, along with illustrative x-ray spectrochemical techniques.

POWDER PROCEDURE APPLIED TO HAFNIUM-ZIRCONIUM ALLOYS

This procedure illustrates the application of the x-ray spectrochemical method to the analysis of metals which may be reduced to powder form by means of chemical procedures. The essence of this procedure is the reduction of the sample and standards to powder form, recovery of the sample completely, and preparation of a sturdy homo-

[30] Cullen, T. J., Anal. Chem., **33**, 1342, 1961.

[31] Townsend, J. E., Applied Spectroscopy, **17**, 37, 1963.

[32] Tahlbusch, W. A., Applied Spectroscopy, **17**, 72, 1963.

[33] Romans, P. A., Niebuhr, W. J., and Hauger, J. R., Dept. of Interior, Bureau of Mines, RI 6483.

[34] Collin, R. L., Anal. Chem., **33**, 605, 1961.

geneous disc by pressing with an organic binder. The procedure has all the advantages described under Optical Emission Spectrometry, in the method, Analysis of Nonferrous Alloys by a Method of Broad Applicability. Additional advantages lie in the fact that the powdered samples are briquetted. This provides a permanent form of the samples and standards, if they are to be retained for future reference work; it also permits the powders to be recovered by removal of the organic binder by ignition.

The powder procedure is applied here to the determination of small amounts of zirconium in hafnium metal.

***Apparatus.* X-ray Tube.**—Tungsten-target Machlett OEG-type x-ray tube capable of operation at 50 kv. and 20 ma.

Analyzing Crystal.—Lithium fluoride.

Detector.—Geiger tube, scintillation counter, or proportional counter.

Goniometer.—Norelco Hi-Angle goniometer or equivalent.

Power Supply.—50 kv. – 50 ma. full-wave rectified x-ray tube power supply.

Briquetting Press.—Buehler press capable of 12000 p.s.i. on a 1-inch diameter piston.

***Reagents.* Hydrofluoric Acid (48 percent).**

Sugar Solution.—100 g. sugar in 100 ml. water.

Preparation of Sample.—Transfer a 0.200-g. sample to a 40-ml. platinum crucible. Add 5 ml. water, 1 ml. nitric acid, 1 ml. hydrofluoric acid to the crucible, and cover with a platinum lid. Place the crucible on an asbestos pad on a hot plate and warm. Allow the dissolution of the sample to proceed (do not boil). If the reaction is too slow, remove the crucible, add more hydrofluoric acid and again warm. Repeat this addition step until the dissolution is complete. Cool slightly and rinse the cover, catching the rinsings in the crucible, and evaporate the solution to dryness. Add 2 ml. of hydrofluoric acid and warm gently to dissolve the residue. The amount of hydrofluoric acid required will vary with different alloys. In each case, add sufficient hydrofluoric acid to redissolve the residue. Cool and add 10 drops of sulphuric acid (1:1). Evaporate to a volume of about 1 ml. Add 10 drops of the sugar solution and continue the evaporation until the sugar begins to carbonize. When the solution becomes black and viscous, carefully tilt and rotate the crucible (held in Blair-type crucible tongs) until most of the wall of the crucible is coated with the syrup. Continue the evaporation to dryness on the hot plate. To prevent spattering, carefully char the residue by heating the crucible on an asbestos-covered gauze over a Fisher burner. Ignite in a furnace at 550°C. To prevent the loss of metals such as molybdenum and tungsten through volatilization, do not permit the temperature to rise above 550°C. The remaining residue readily flakes off the crucible wall due to the sugar solution carbonization. Loosen the residue with a soft scraper and gently pulverize it in the crucible.

Briquetting Procedure.—Add a total of 1.5 cc. of methocellulose powder in 3 portions, using a platinum spatula in a stirring-grinding motion to insure a homogeneous mixture. Transfer the mixture to a 1-inch cylindrical mold. Level the surface of the powder and compact into a wafer at 12,000 p.s.i. in a Buehler press.

Preparation of Standards.—Weigh a total of 0.200 g. of high-purity hafnium and zirconium in the percentage ratio required for each standard into a 40-ml. platinum crucible. Proceed as directed under Preparation of Sample and Briquetting Procedure. If sufficiently-pure hafnium is not available, prepare standards by adding known weights of zirconium to weighed portions of the specimen. Determine the compositions by transposing the calibration curve to intercept zero.

In general, if the desired metal is not available in sufficient purity for use as a standard, a reliable "twin" calibration curve may be obtained by choosing an element with nearly the same x-ray parameters as the desired metal. In the analysis of hafnium for zirconium, for instance, tantalum was used as the "twin" for hafnium, since the tantalum excitation and absorption factors for zirconium very closely approach those of hafnium. Figure 44-2 shows typical calibration curves for both.

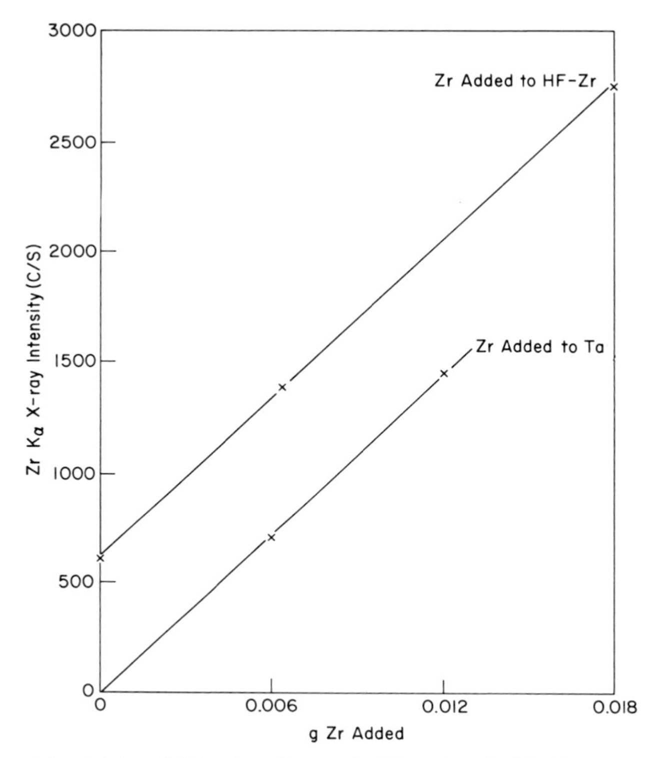

FIG. 44-2. Calibration Curves for Zirconium in Hafnium.

X-Ray Measurements.—Place the wafer in the specimen holder and insert in the x-ray spectrometer. Irradiate the sample with a tungsten-target OEG-50 type x-ray tube, operated at 35 kv. and 10 ma. Measure the intensity of Zr K_α x-ray line at $2\theta = 22.5°$. Determine the background intensity at $2\theta = 22.5°$ by scanning the spectrum from $2\theta = 20°$ to $2\theta = 24°$. Establish a calibration curve between the Zr K_α line intensity (minus the background intensity), and the weight percent of the standards.

SEPARATION AND PRECIPITATION PROCEDURE APPLIED TO THE DETERMINATION OF URANIUM IN COPPER

This procedure illustrates the application of the x-ray spectrochemical method to the determination of a minor alloying element (0.01 to 1.0 percent) which may be precipitated chemically after the removal of the bulk of the matrix metal. Uranium is the metal chosen to illustrate the method because of the broadening scope of uranium technology, and because it is a metal that is difficult to determine by optical emission spectroscopy and other instrumental approaches.

The matrix metal is removed by electrodeposition on platinum electrodes, after which the uranium is precipitated as the hydroxide in the presence of ammonium chloride.

The uranium precipitate, along with other precipitated hydroxides, is ignited, briquetted, and analyzed for uranium by x-ray fluorescence.

Apparatus.—As described in Powder Procedure Applied to Hafnium-Zirconium Alloys above.

Preparation of Sample.—Transfer a 1.00-g. sample to a 250-ml. beaker and dissolve carefully with 20 ml. of nitric acid (1:1). Determine the copper as directed in Volume II-A, page 816. To the electrolyte, add 10 g. of ammonium chloride. (If the amount of uranium to be determined is very small, add a few milligrams of iron to serve as a collector). Precipitate the uranium with ammonium hydroxide, and boil to coagulate. Filter, and ignite the precipitate at 800–850°C. Weigh the impure precipitate and briquette as described under Powder Procedure Applied to Hafnium-Zirconium Alloys.

NOTE.—This procedure should be applicable to many alloy systems. If other matrices or alloying constituents are involved which interfere with the ammonium hydroxide precipitation or produce interfering x-ray spectra, other isolatory procedures may be required. Using the mercury cathode electrolysis to remove iron from the sulfate solution, this procedure has been successfully applied to the determination of uranium in steels.

Preparation of Standards.—To three 1-gram samples of the matrix metal, add 2-, 10-, and 20-mg. portions of uranium metal or the appropriate amount of a standardized U_3O_8. Include a fourth 1-gram sample of the matrix metal as a blank. Carry the standards and blank through the procedure described for Preparation of Sample.

X-Ray Measurements.—Place the wafer in the specimen holder and insert in the x-ray spectrometer. Irradiate the sample with a tungsten-target OEG-50 type x-ray tube operated at 50 kv. and 40 ma. Measure the intensity of the U L_α line at $2\theta = 26.2°$. Determine the background intensity at 26.2° by scanning the spectra from $2\theta = 24.5°$ to $2\theta = 27.5°$. Establish a calibration curve relating the U L_α line intensity (minus the background intensity) and the weight of uranium in the standards.

FILTRATION PROCEDURE APPLIED TO THE DETERMINATION OF MERCURY IN ZINC

This procedure illustrates the application of the x-ray spectrochemical method to the rapid determination of a metal which may be separated from its matrix by chemical precipitation. Mercury is determined in zinc amalgam by x-ray examination of mercury sulfide immediately after its precipitation from an acid solution of the sample. The method is sensitive to microgram quantities of mercury.

***Apparatus.* Machlett OEG-50, Molybdenum-Target X-Ray Tube.**—Other x-ray measuring equipment as described in Powder Procedure Applied to Hafnium-Zirconium Alloys.

Millipore Filter Discs.[35]—White, plain, 25-mm. diameter with 0.45 μ porosity.

Filter Disc Holder.—A sheet of ¼-mil mylar film is stretched and taped to a cardboard frame, which is cut to fit the spectrometer specimen holder. A second sheet of film is stretched and taped to the frame over the disc, so that the disc is held flat. (A significant reduction in the spectrum background is achieved when the frame is cut so that the disc is essentially suspended in air when it is positioned in the specimen chamber.)

***Reagents.* Thioacetamide (2 percent Solution).**

Copper Sulphate Solution.—1 ml. = 0.001 g. copper.

Standard Mercury Nitrate Solution (1 ml. = 10 μg. mercury).—Into a tared 50-ml. beaker, weigh carefully about 1 g. of Reagent-Grade mercury. Cover with 20 ml. of water and add 15 ml. of nitric acid. Allow the mercury to dissolve, transfer to a 1000-ml. volumetric flask, dilute to the mark, and mix. Dilute a 10-ml. aliquot of this solution to contain 10 μg. of mercury per milliliter.

[35] Millipore Filter Corp., Watertown 72, Mass.

Preparation of Samples.—Transfer a 0.100-g. sample of the zinc metal, which has been exposed to mercury vapor, to a 250-ml. Erlenmeyer flask. Dissolve the metal in the minimum amount of hydrochloric acid (1:1), add 1 ml. of nitric acid, and boil until the solution becomes clear. Add 5 ml. of sulfuric acid (1:1) and evaporate to dense white fumes of sulfur trioxide. Cool and dilute carefully to 100 ml. Add exactly 2 ml. of the copper sulfate solution (1 ml. = 0.001 g. copper) and heat just to boiling. Add 1 ml. of thioacetamide solution (2 percent). Again, heat just to boiling, place in a hot water bath for 15 minutes, then cool for approximately 10 minutes. Filter through a Millipore disc, and hold between mylar sheets as described under Apparatus for measurement in the x-ray spectrometer.

Preparation of Standards.—Prepare a series of mercury standards containing 0 (blank), 50, 100, 150 and 200 μg. of mercury by adding the standard mercuric nitrate solution to 0.100-g. samples of Reagent-Grade zinc contained in 250-ml. Erlenmeyer flasks These standards cover a mercury range to 0.20% on a 0.1-g. sample basis.

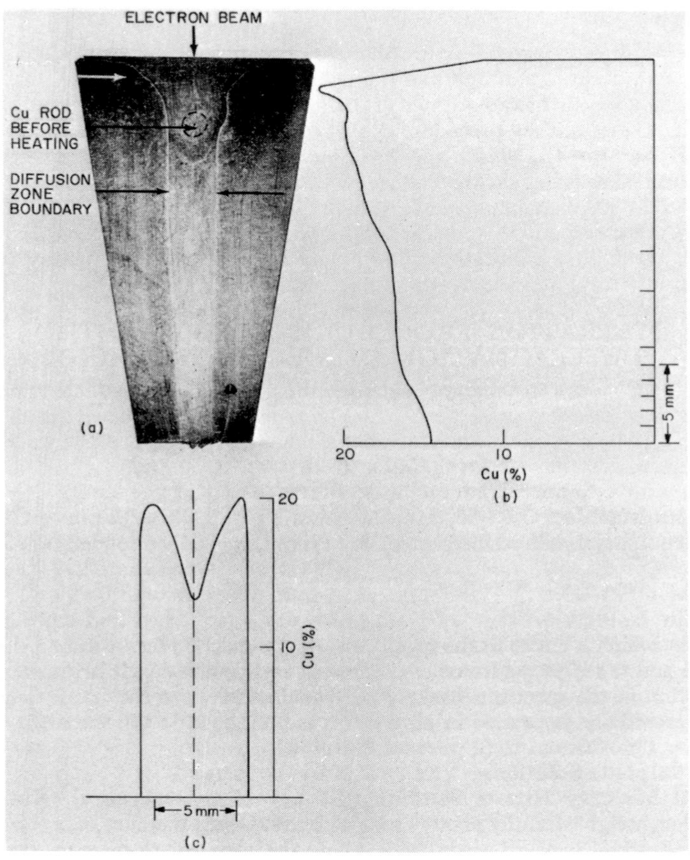

FIG. 44-3. (a) Micrograph of Electron Beam Melted Copper-Titanium Specimen. (b) and (c) Concentration Curves of Copper Distribution in (a).

X-Ray Measurements.—Insert the filter in the spectrometer. Irradiate the specimen with a molybdenum-target OEG-50 type x-ray tube operated at 50 kv. and 20 ma. Measure the intensity of the Hg L_α x-ray line at the mercury-line setting of $2\theta = 35.9°$ for each sample and standard. Measure the background intensity at a setting of $2\theta = 35°$ Correct the mercury intensity readings by subtracting the background.

Prepare a calibration curve from the standard sample readings, and determine the mercury concentrations in the samples by reference to the calibration curve. Better than 200 counts per second should be obtained for the highest standard.

THE MASKED WINDOW TECHNIQUE FOR *IN SITU* ANALYSIS OF SMALL AREAS

(*APPLIED TO COPPER DIFFUSION IN TITANIUM*)

The x-ray spectrochemical method may be applied to the analysis of small areas of specimens in such studies as diffusion, segregation, and corrosion. In these applications the atoms in areas as small as 0.5 mm. are excited by the radiation from a masked window x-ray tube. The masked window technique has been used to analyze compositions in diffusion regions of electron-beam welded metals with a resolution of 0.2–0.3 mm. Inasmuch as the analysis to be described is not apt to be duplicated in terms of specific samples and exact research requirements, the application will be reported in descriptive rather than directive format.

Background.—A titanium ingot with copper rods inserted in a $\frac{1}{16}$-inch hole was bombarded with an electron beam from a commercial electron-beam welder. The ingot was then sectioned lengthwise through the middle of the diffusion zone, and the area of interest was given a metallurgical polish to provide a flat surface. The problem was to determine the extent to which copper had diffused in the titanium ingot and the concentration distribution. Figure 44-3(a) is a micrograph of the polished surface of the sectioned specimen.

***Apparatus.* Curved Crystal Spectrometer of NRL Design.**[36]

Analyzer Crystal.—Lithium fluoride bent to a 40-cm. radius and ground to a 20-cm. radius.

X-Ray Tube.—Machlett OEG-50 tungsten-target, x-ray tube; window masked to achieve a 0.5-mm. x-ray beam.

Detector.—Scintillation counter.

X-Ray Measurements.—The sample was positioned and irradiated with the tube operating at 40 kv. and 20 ma. The curved crystal spectrometer was set at $2\theta = 45°$ to detect the Cu K_α line, the amplifier and pulse-height analyzer circuits were set to operate in integral mode. The specimen was translated before the beam in 0.5-mm. steps, traversing the diffusion zone. Several traverses were made across the specimen at different locations, and another traverse along the diffusion zone.

After x-ray examination of the specimen, a 0.0125-g. sample was drilled from a portion of the homogeneous region and, along with synthetic standards, was prepared for x-ray spectrochemical analysis by the chemical method described under Powder Procedure Applied to Hafnium-Zirconium Alloys. This carefully determined value served as a standard reference value for copper determination in the titanium matrix.

A concentration topograph was prepared, as shown in Fig. 44-3(b) and (c).

The copper value determined spectrochemically on the drillings was 18 percent. This concentration of copper gave a measurement of 200 counts per second with the curved crystal optics. The reproducibility was ±0.2 percent.

[36] Birks, L. S., Brooks, E. J. and Gourlay, G. W., Rev. Sci. Instr., **29**, 425, 1958.

THE ELECTRON PROBE X-RAY MICROANALYZER TECHNIQUE FOR *IN SITU* ANALYSIS OF VERY SMALL AREAS

(*APPLIED TO METALLIC PHASE IDENTIFICATION*)

The electron probe, described in detail in Chapter 10, provides analyses of materials with surface areas as small as one or two microns in diameter by virtue of a focused electron beam which excites the atoms to yield their characteristic x-ray spectra. The example cited is typical of the probe's application to the solution of problems involving the analysis of minute entities hitherto unapproachable by analytical tools. Again the format of presentation will be descriptive rather than directive.

Background.—Under metallographic examination, a niobium-zinc alloy revealed, in addition to the normally-expected phases, two distinct phases occurring in infrequent distribution, with one of the phases parasitic to the other. The problem was to determine the composition of the two unknown phases.

***Apparatus.* An Electron Probe X-Ray Microanalyzer.**—The associated x-ray optics employed a thin, bent lithium fluoride crystal in a transition modе, set to measure the Nb K_α line.

Standards.—Small specimens of high-purity niobium and high-purity zinc along with two niobium-zinc alloys of known composition were used.

Preparation of Sample.—The specimen of the niobium-zinc alloy was mounted along with the high-purity metals and the known alloys in a 1-inch plastic metallographic mount. The surfaces were prepared by the usual metallographic procedures. The plastic surface on the polished side was coated with a conducting silver paint to provide a ground circuit and thus eliminate electrostatic charging. A small area of each imbedded

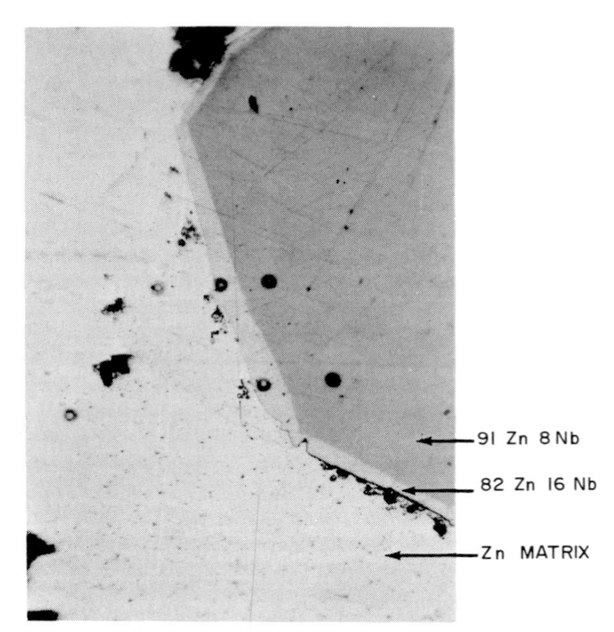

Fig. 44-4. Micrograph of Zirconium-Niobium Alloy Microanalyzed for Phase Identification.

metal was grounded by the silver paint, which in turn was wire-grounded through a microammeter to the chassis upon insertion of the specimen in the probe.

X-Ray Examination.—The plastic disc containing the specimen and standards was positioned on the stage of the probe, and the system evacuated to a pressure of about 10^{-5} mm. of mercury.

The probe was operated at 27 kv. and 1×10^{-8} amperes. Each phase was positioned under the beam, and the niobium and zinc x-ray intensities were measured and recorded. The x-ray intensities from the standards were used to establish the calibration curve.

Figure 44-4 is a micrograph of the specimen showing several phases in the metal and the contamination spots left by the electron beam at selected spots of analysis.

NOTE.—The procedures described in this section are intended to illustrate general approaches to analytical determinations. Numerous variations of the techniques have been reported in the literature for application to particular or unique problems. The methods of Nondispersive or Pulse-Height Analysis and associated techniques have not been described, since the sample preparations described here are generally applicable. For a general review of the method, the reader is referred to the Chapters on X-Ray Spectroscopy and the Electron Probe X-Ray Microanalyzer and the references therein cited.

ATOMIC ABSORPTION SPECTROMETRY[37]

Atomic absorption covers that area of spectrometry that involves the absorption, rather than the emission, of characteristic wavelengths in the optical region of the spectrum for the analytical characterization of elements.

Atoms absorb light energy of the same wavelength they emit. Sharp resonance line radiation energy at the characteristic wavelength absorbed by a specific element to be determined is provided by a hollow cathode lamp whose cathode contains that element (some cathodes contain more than one element). This energy is passed through a flame into which the sample solution is atomized. At the temperature of the flame, relatively few of the atoms are excited. These unexcited or ground state atoms of the element under test absorb the characteristic resonant energy emanating from the hollow-cathode lamp in direct proportion to their population in the flame. The intensity of the unabsorbed radiation is measured by a detection system consisting of a monochromator to isolate the wavelength of interest, an amplifying system containing a photomultiplier tube, and a recorder or millivolt meter. The percentage absorption, in the flame, of the characteristic light emitted by the hollow-cathode lamp then becomes a measure of the concentration of the element being determined. Its percentage concentration is established by referring to properly prepared calibration curves.

Providing a suitable sharp-line source is available to emit resonance radiation of the element or elements under test, atomic absorption spectrometry is applicable to many inorganic samples which can be dissolved or suspended in aqueous or organic solvents.[38] Because of its sensitivity, it is especially applicable as an analytical technique for the determination of certain trace constituents. It has been used considerably for the analysis of biological (clinical) and agricultural materials. The literature since 1962 indicates its extension to metallurgical materials and other commercial products.

While atomic absorption spectrometry is excellent for the analysis of certain materials and elements, it cannot compete with instrumental techniques which are capable of

[37] This section prepared by R. W. Black, U. S. Naval Research Laboratory, Washington, D. C.

[38] A. Walsh, in 1955, was the first to suggest the application of atomic absorption spectrometry to flame analysis. The first integrated instruments became commercially available in 1961. Since then variously designed instruments have become available from manufacturers of scientific equipment throughout the world.

determining many elements at one operation. Limits of detection vary from element to element, also some metals form refractory compounds in the flame.

Atomic absorption spectrometry is especially applicable to the analysis of metals and alloys for such trace elements as zinc, cadmium, magnesium, calcium, lead, gold, and silver, each of which has a very high sensitivity and few interferences. This technique may be very valuable for the standardization of samples to be used for the calibration of the emission or mass spectrograph, as well as the analysis of ultra-pure research materials.

Scope.—Because of the resolution attainable and the ease with which synthetic standard solutions can be prepared, atomic absorption spectrometry has become a popular instrumental tool in analytical chemistry. In addition to this, there are areas of analysis where atomic absorption spectrometry and flame spectrometry complement each other. The following tables are indicative of the scope and sensitivities attainable with atomic absorption spectrometry.

Table 44-25 lists those elements whose concentration in solution at or less than the

Table 44-24. Applicability of Atomic Absorption Spectrometry

H																	He
(Li)	(Be)											B	C	N	O	F	Ne
(Na)	(Mg)											(Al)	Si	P	S	Cl	A
(K)	(Ca)	Sc	(Ti)	(V)	(Cr)	(Mn)	(Fe)	(Co)	(Ni)	(Cu)	(Zn)	(Ga)	Ge	(As)	(Se)	Br	K
(Rb)	(Sr)	Yt	Zr	Nb	(Mo)	Tc	Ru	(Rh)	(Pd)	(Ag)	(Cd)	(In)	Sn	(Sb)	(Te)	I	Xe
(Cs)	(Ba)	*	Hf	Ta	W	Re	Os	Ir	(Pt)	(Au)	(Hg)	(Tl)	(Pb)	(Bi)	Po	At	Rn
Fr	Ra	Ac	Th	Pa	U												

* La	Ce	Pr	Nd	Pm	Sm	Eu	Gd	Tb	Dy	Ho	Er	Tm	Yb	Lu

Although hollow-cathode lamps are available for those elements enclosed in the heavy blocks, atomic absorption techniques have not been developed for some of the enclosed elements. With no interfering ions present, those elements surrounded by a circle have been detected at or less than one microgram per milliliter of solution. This degree of sensitivity has been attained with aqueous solutions of all circled elements except beryllium, aluminum, titanium, and vanadium which required an oxyacetylene flame in conjunction with organic solvents.

one p.p.m. level can be detected and determined by atomic absorption spectrometry. These values represent sensitivities which have already been obtained. Many of these sensitivities may be improved with the use of more sophisticated instruments and techniques. (Sensitivity is defined as that concentration of an element in solution which when sprayed into the flame will produce 1 percent absorption or double the background absorption.)

Some Difficulties or Limitations.—Being mainly a solution technique, sensitivities by atomic absorption may be less (due to dilution) than those attainable by techniques capable of obtaining analytical data on solid samples. Even with this dilution effect, some elements (zinc is an example) have lower detection limits via atomic absorption than by other spectroscopic techniques.

Cationic and anionic effects must be ascertained for each analytical application, particularly when microgram quantities of elements are to be determined. Free-acid effects must be determined. If no separations are made, it is also necessary to determine the effect of major constituents whose concentration may be 10,000 or 1,000,000 times greater than that of the element to be determined. Most elements produce characteristic continua. This may be negligible for low ratios of major-to-minor constituent components, but may cause gross errors when elements in the parts-per-million range are

TABLE 44-25. SENSITIVITIES OF VARIOUS ELEMENTS AT THEIR RECOMMENDED RESONANCE WAVELENGTHS

Element	*Resonance Line, Angstroms*	*Sensitivity Range, μg./ml.*
Antimony*	2311	0.2–1.0
Barium	5536	0.1–1.0
Bismuth*	3068	0.1–0.3
Cadmium	2288	0.001–0.01
Calcium	4227	0.01–0.1
Chromium	3579	0.01–0.2
Cobalt	2407	0.1–0.15
Copper	3247	0.005–0.01
Gallium	2874	1.0
Gold	2428	0.1
Indium	3040	0.1–0.7
Iron	2483	0.02–0.05
Lead	2833	0.02–0.3
Lithium†	6708	0.005–0.03
Magnesium	2852	0.001–0.008
Manganese	2795	0.005–0.02
Mercury	2537	0.5–1.0
Molybdenum*	3133	0.1–0.5
Nickel	2320	0.01–0.05
Palladium*	2476	0.01–1.0
Platinum*	2659	0.1–1.0
Potassium†	7665	0.005–0.01
Rhodium	3435	0.3
Rubidium†	7800	0.02–0.1
Selenium	2040	1.0–5.0
Silver	3281	0.02–0.1
Sodium†	5890	0.005–0.01
Strontium	4607	0.02–0.1
Tellurium*	2143	0.02–1.0
Thallium	2768	0.05–0.2
Zinc	2139	0.002–0.01

Common nonferrous alloy constituents which should be amenable to analysis by atomic absorption spectrometry are *italic*.

* Elements which may be determined under special circumstances.

† The alkali metals may be analyzed by atomic absorption spectrometry, however they may be more advantageously analyzed by flame spectrometry.

being determined. For this type of work it is necessary to check background emission which may be caused by emission-band spectra or continuous flame radiation.

Very few standards with accurate trace-element analyses are available for high-purity materials research work. This handicap is more easily overcome for atomic absorption spectroscopy than for many other instrumental approaches because of the ease of preparing synthetic standard solutions which closely resemble the solutions of the test samples. The reagents and water must be ultra-pure and special care exercised in all operations.

Applications.—The methods which follow describe typical applications of atomic absorption spectrometry for the analysis of nonferrous metallurgical materials.

Since zinc and magnesium are common nonferrous alloy constituents which are normally difficult to determine accurately at microgram levels by conventional chemical methods, procedures for their determination are presented.

DETERMINATION OF ZINC IN COPPER-, ALUMINUM-, AND ZIRCONIUM-BASE ALLOYS[39]

Zinc is found in many nonferrous alloy systems either as an alloying or trace constituent. Depending on the alloy system and analysis requirements, it is frequently determined by difference. Although often tedious, there are excellent techniques for the determination of macro amounts of zinc; but these do not necessarily apply to the determination of trace amounts. Because of its simplicity, atomic absorption spectrometry is extremely useful in determining both trace and macro amounts of zinc.

Preliminary Considerations.—As with other spectroscopic analytical procedures, certain precautions must be observed.

Drift.—Slight changes in the emission intensity of the hollow-cathode lamp and variations in atomization rate of the solution or standard are common causes of drift which become manifest through instrument response. Taking the mean of repeated measurements will minimize errors caused by slight variations in lamp emission intensity and in sample or standard atomization rate.

Effect of Anions.—Due consideration must be given the various anions used to prepare the samples and standards for atomization. When possible, use anions which produce the least measurable absorption at the wavelength being measured (in this instance, the zinc line at 2138 A). Tables 44-26 and 44-27 show the respective effect of various acid concentrations in the absence and presence of zinc.

TABLE 44-26. EFFECT OF ACID CONCENTRATION IN ABSENCE OF ZINC

Acid	*Concentration*	*Optical Density*
Nitric Acid	1:99	Nil
	1:19	Nil
	1:9	Nil
	1:3	Nil
Sulfuric Acid	1:3	0.028
Hydrochloric Acid	1:99	0.025
	1:19	0.075
	~1:19 (0.625 *N*)*	0.005
	1:9	0.21
	1:3	0.52

* Neutralized with sodium hydroxide before the measurement was made.

Each of the halogen acids produces an absorption band between 2100 and 2200 A. These are probably caused by molecular absorption.[40] The addition of sodium hydroxide to the change point of methyl red tends to minimize the absorption (see the optical density of neutralized 0.625 *N* hydrochloric acid in Table 44-26.

[39] Gidley, J. A. F., and Jones, J. T., Analyst, **85**, 249, 1960.

[40] According to Gidley, J. A. F., and Jones, J. T., Analyst, **86**, 271, 1961, it is generally agreed that oxide layers of the brass burner are attacked by the halogen acids and the reaction products are carried into the flame with the resulting absorption due to copper and zinc.

TABLE 44-27. EFFECT OF ACID CONCENTRATION ON THE DETERMINATION OF 5 P.P.M. OF ZINC

Concentration of Acid	*Zinc Found in p.p.m.**	
	in nitric acid	*in sulfuric acid*
1:49	4.95	4.60
1:19	4.85	4.30
1:9	4.65	3.77
1:3	4.30	2.90

* Standard zinc nitrate solution used for comparison purposes.

Effect of Cations.—The effect of cation interference was determined by adding a solution containing 0.1 g. of each potential interferent (in the least nitrate ion concentration) to a solution containing 0.5 mg. of zinc. Each resulting solution diluted to 100 ml. contained 5 p.p.m. of zinc and 1000 p.p.m. of the element whose cationic effect was appraised. No interference was observed from aluminum, antimony, arsenic, barium, bismuth, boron, cadmium, calcium, chromium, cobalt, copper, iron, lead, lithium, manganese, nickel, phosphorus, potassium, silver, sodium, strontium, thorium, tin, titanium, and zirconium.

The comparison data indicated a slight interference from magnesium (zinc recovery of 4.75 p.p.m. was obtained), but severe interference from silicon (zinc recovery of 2.85 p.p.m. was obtained).

Effect of Matrix.—The effect of various amounts of copper and aluminum on the determination of 5 p.p.m. of zinc is shown in Table 44-28.

TABLE 44-28. EFFECT OF COPPER AND ALUMINUM ON THE DETERMINATION OF 5 P.P.M. OF ZINC

Amount of Copper or Aluminum Present, g./100 ml.	*Zinc Found in Presence of*	
	Copper, p.p.m.	*Aluminum, p.p.m.*
0.05	4.98 to 5.05	5.10
0.20	4.90	5.08
0.25	4.93	—
0.50	4.82 to 4.85	4.95
1.00	4.75	4.48
5.00	4.30 to 4.47	—

Table 44-29 shows the zinc recoveries obtainable when various percentages of zinc are added to 0.05 to 1.0 g. of copper.

Apparatus.—A sensitive commercially available atomic absorption spectrometer.

Instrument Operation.—Turn on the hollow-cathode lamp and instrument. Adjust the slit width, photomultiplier voltage, and lamp current to conform to the manufacturer's specification (do not exceed the current rating specified for any given lamp; if possible operate lamps with the lowest adequate amperage). Set the wavelength selector at 2138 A., and allow sufficient time for the instrument to become stabilized. Adjust the air or fuel pressure and aspirate the solutions into the flame.

Reagents.[41] **Standard Zinc Stock Solution (1 ml. = 1.0 mg. zinc).**—Dissolve 1.000 g. of high-purity zinc in 100 ml. of nitric acid (1:1). Cool, dilute to one liter, and mix.

[41] Unless specified otherwise in the procedure, the use of concentrated acids is assumed.

TABLE 44-29. TYPICAL ZINC RECOVERIES FROM COPPER-ZINC SOLUTIONS

	Percent Zinc	
Copper Present, g.	*Added*	*Recovered*
1.0	Nil	0.0016
	0.001	0.003
	0.005	0.008
	0.010	0.010
	0.050	0.049
0.5	0.10	0.097
0.25	0.20	0.19
0.10	0.50	0.49
0.05	1.00	0.98

Standard Zinc Solution (1 ml. = 0.1 mg. zinc).—Transfer 100 ml. of the zinc stock solution to a 1-liter volumetric flask, dilute to the mark, and mix.

Secondary Standard Zinc Solution (1 ml. = 1 μg. zinc).—Transfer 10 ml. of the standard zinc solution (1 ml. = 0.1 mg. zinc) to a 1-liter volumetric flask. Add 500 ml. of water, 50 ml. of nitric acid, and 50 ml. of sulfuric acid. Allow to cool, dilute to the mark, and mix.

Hydrobromic Acid–Bromine Mixture (9 + 1).—Carefully add 10 ml. of bromine to 90 ml. of hydrobromic acid, and mix cautiously but thoroughly.

Acid Solvent Mixture.—Cautiously add 150 ml. of sulfuric acid to 700 ml. of water and cool. Then mixing after each addition, add 75 ml. of nitric acid and 75 ml. of hydrochloric acid. Cool to room temperature.

Hydrofluoric Acid.

Preparation of Calibration Curve.—Transfer 25-, 50-, 75-, and 100-ml. aliquots of the standard zinc solution (1 ml. = 0.1 mg. zinc) to appropriately identified 1-liter volumetric flasks. Dilute each to the mark and mix thoroughly. These solutions contain, respectively, 2.5, 5.0, 7.5, and 10.0 p.p.m. of zinc.

Make initial instrument response adjustments by aspirating water into the flame. Then aspirate portions of each solution into the flame, and measure the resulting absorbancy over a 30-second interval to average out short-term fluctuations in the output intensity of the lamp. Make a total of 10 such sets of measurements. From the mean of the measurements for each of the solutions, prepare a calibration curve[42] which relates the absorption to the respective zinc concentrations.

Procedure.—Transfer a sample containing 0.1 to 0.8 mg. of zinc to a 100-ml. beaker. For varying zinc percentages the following sample-weights are recommended:

Percent Zn	0.01/0.08,	0.04/0.16,	0.10/0.4,	0.2/0.8,	0.4/1.6
Sample Wt.	1.0 g.	0.5 g.	0.2 g.	0.1 g.	0.05 g.

For alloys containing greater than 1.6 percent zinc, decrease the weight of sample proportionally. For alloys containing less than 0.01 percent zinc, increase the weight of the sample proportionally. However, the use of a large sample tends to alter the solution viscosity to the extent that it may become necessary to prepare a new calibration curve with standard solutions which contain about the same amount of high-purity matrix material as is present in the sample under test.

In each set to be analyzed, include at least one standard which closely matches the samples under test.

[42] Plot the optical density against the zinc content of the standards. Optical density = $\log P_0/P_t$, where P_0 and P_t are measures of the output current of the photomultiplier tube for the water and standard zinc solution, respectively.

Copper-Base Alloys Containing No Tin or Silicon.—Dissolve the sample with 10 ml. of nitric acid (1:1), boil one minute to expel the oxides of nitrogen. Cool and dilute to 100 ml. in a volumetric flask.

Copper-Base Alloys Containing Tin.[43]—Dissolve the sample with 10 ml. of the hydrobromic acid-bromine mixture and evaporate to dryness. Repeat the evaporation to dryness with two separate 5-ml. additions of the hydrobromic acid-bromine mixture. Add 5 ml. of nitric acid, dropwise, warm to decompose the bromides, and again evaporate to dryness. Hydrobromic acid exhibits a definite absorption band over the wavelength used for making atomic absorption measurements for zinc; it is therefore important to remove all traces of this acid.[40] Dissolve the residue in 10 ml. of nitric acid (1:1). Transfer to a 100-ml. volumetric flask, dilute to the mark and mix.

Copper-Base Alloys Containing Silicon.—Transfer the sample to a platinum dish and add 10 ml. of nitric acid (1:1), 10 ml. of hydrofluoric acid, and 2 ml. of ulfuric acid. Evaporate to fumes of sulfur trioxide. Cool, dilute with water, transfer to a beaker, and warm until solution is complete (if present, remove lead sulfate by filtration). Transfer to a 100-ml. volumetric flask, dilute to the mark, and mix.

Aluminum-Base Alloys (Silicon <0.5 percent).—Dissolve sample with 25 ml. of the acid solvent mixture (use 10 ml. for samples weighing less than 0.1 g.). To avoid spitting, carefully evaporate to sulfur trioxide fumes. Cool, add 20 ml. of water, 10 ml. of nitric acid (1:1), and warm gently to dissolve the salts. Boil one minute, cool, transfer to a 100-ml. volumetric flask, dilute to the mark, and mix.

Aluminum-Base Alloys (Silicon >0.5 percent).—Transfer the sample to a platinum dish, add 10 ml. of water, and dropwise cautiously add hydrofluoric acid until the sample has been dissolved. Add 5 ml. of hydrofluoric acid, a few drops of nitric acid, and 2 ml. of sulfuric acid. Carefully evaporate to sulfur trioxide fumes. Cool, add 20 ml. of water, 10 ml. of nitric acid (1:1), and warm gently to dissolve the salts. Cool, transfer to a 100-ml. volumetric flask, dilute to the mark, and mix.

Zirconium-Base Alloys.—(Note. The specified maximum limits for zinc is usually 100 p.p.m.). Transfer a 1.0-g. sample to a platinum dish and add 5 ml. of water. Cautiously add hydrofluoric acid until the sample is dissolved. Add a few drops of nitric acid to dissolve copper and molybdenum, then 5 ml. of sulfuric acid. Under a radiant heater, evaporate to sulfur trioxide fumes. Cool, dilute with water, and add 5 ml. of nitric acid. Transfer to a 150-ml. beaker, warm to dissolve salts, cool, transfer to a 100-ml. volumetric flask, dilute to the mark, and mix.

NOTE.—When atomic-absorption measurements are made on such a solution, use the secondary zinc standard solution containing 1 p.p.m. of zinc in dilute sulfuric acid (1:19) and dilute nitric acid (1:19) to determine if it is necessary to apply a correction factor to evaluate the zinc content of the sample.

Sample Solution Atomization.—Aspirate the sample and standard solutions into the flame, and measure the absorption as directed in the second paragraph under Preparation of Calibration Curve.

Sample Evaluation.—From the calibration curve, convert the mean of the absorption measurements for each sample to percent zinc. The results obtained for the included standard or standards will determine if a correction factor should be applied to the percentages of zinc found in the samples.

Comments.—The work involved in developing an atomic absorption spectrometric procedure for the analysis of an element in one or more alloy systems may prove reward-

[43] Alternatively, treat the sample with 10 ml. of nitric acid (1:1) and boil to expel the oxides of nitrogen. Add 30 ml. of hot water and place on a steam bath for 30 minutes to permit the tin to settle. Filter through a tight paper into a 100-ml. volumetric flask. Wash with hot water, cool, dilute to the mark, and mix.

ing for the processing of a large number of samples. If only a few samples are to be analyzed, it may be advantageous to use the existing analytical procedure where they are adequate.

However, there are alloy systems which are difficult to analyze chemically. In addition, many analyses require the determination of elements in trace ranges which preclude the use of many chemical and instrumental procedures. In these areas of analysis atomic absorption spectrometry is especially useful and rewarding.

THE DETERMINATION OF MAGNESIUM IN NICKEL AND NICKEL ALLOYS[44]

The following procedure for the determination of magnesium in metallurgical materials by atomic absorption spectrometry is rapid and accurate. It is relatively free of many of the interferences associated with the determination of magnesium by other chemical and instrumental methods. The classical gravimetric pyrophosphate technique, which has been used so frequently for the determination of macro amounts of magnesium, requires considerable time. It cannot be applied to the determination of trace amounts of magnesium. Sensitive colorimetric techniques are available but their usefulness is limited largely to magnesium solutions from which most of the accompanying alloying constituents have been isolated.

Interferences.—The presence of 10 mg. of nickel per ml. has been shown to have a negligible effect on the determination of magnesium. In the presence of nickel, as much as 0.2 percent of aluminum or silicon causes negligible interference;[44] however, in the absence of nickel, aluminum and silicon cause severe interference.[45]

Apparatus.—A sensitive commercially available atomic absorption spectrometer.[46]

Instrument Operation.—Turn on the hollow-cathode lamp and instrument. Adjust the slit width, photomultiplier voltage, and lamp current to conform to the manufacturer's specification (do not exceed the current rating specified for any given lamp). Set the wavelength selector to 2852 A., and allow sufficient time for the instrument to become stabilized.[47]

Reagents. **Standard Magnesium Stock Solution (1 ml. = 100 μg. magnesium).**—Carefully add about 10 drops of nitric acid to a covered beaker containing 0.1000 g. of high-purity magnesium and allow a few minutes for the reaction to subside. Repeat the nitric acid additions until the sample is completely dissolved. Dilute to 50 ml. and boil to expel the oxides of nitrogen. Cool, transfer to a 1000-ml. volumetric flask, dilute to the mark, and mix.

Standard Magnesium Solution (1 ml. = 1 μg. magnesium).—Dilute a 10-ml. aliquot of the magnesium solution (1 ml. = 100 μg. magnesium) to 1000.0 ml.

Standard Nickel Solution (1 ml. = 2.5 mg. nickel).—Dissolve 2.5 g. of high-purity nickel with 20 ml. of nitric acid. Dilute to 50 ml. and boil to expel the oxides of nitrogen. Cool, transfer to a 1000-ml. volumetric flask, dilute to the mark, and mix.

Preparation of Calibration Curve.—To 10-ml. aliquots of the standard nickel solution, add aliquots of the standard magnesium solutions to cover the percentage range

[44] Andrews, T. R., and Nichols, P. N. R., Analyst, **87,** 25, 1962.

[45] Menzies, A. C., Anal. Chem., **32,** 898, 1960.

[46] The instrument used by Andrews and Nichols was a Uvispek spectrometer (Model H700-308) with associated atomic absorption attachment, hollow-cathode lamps and power supply, and a 1P28 photomultiplier and amplifier feeding into a modified 10-mv. Honeywell-Brown recorder.

[47] Andrews and Nichols used a lamp current of 9 ma. and a slit width of 0.25 mm. for their work.

of magnesium to be determined in the samples.[48] Include a blank containing only a 10-ml. aliquot of the standard nickel solution. Dilute each solution to 50.0 ml. and mix. Adjust the instrument to register zero absorbance while aspirating distilled water into the flame. Aspirate portions of the standard solutions into the flame and measure the resulting absorbance of each over a 30-second period.

Prepare a calibration curve which relates the absorption to the respective magnesium concentration.

Procedure.—Dissolve 25 mg. of sample with 2 ml. of nitric acid (1:1).[49] Transfer the solution to a 50-ml. volumetric flask, dilute to the mark, and mix. Aspirate a portion of the sample solution into the flame and measure the resulting absorbance over a 30-second interval to average the short term fluctuations in the output intensity of the lamp. In careful work it is well to bracket the sample solution with closely matching standard solutions—one containing slightly less magnesium and the other containing slightly more magnesium than the sample.

Use the calibration curve to convert the absorbance obtained for the sample solution to percent magnesium.

Comments.—Some nickel samples have been analyzed both by chemical means and by atomic absorption. These samples contained a maximum of: 0.1 percent each of aluminum, chromium, and titanium; 0.2 percent of copper; 0.3 percent of iron; 0.4 percent each of manganese and silicon; and 1 percent of cobalt. The results of these analyses are shown in Table 44-30.

TABLE 44-30. COMPARISON OF RESULTS OBTAINED FOR MAGNESIUM BY CHEMICAL AND ATOMIC ABSORPTION SPECTROMETRIC ANALYSIS

Nickel	*Magnesium Content*	
Sample	*Chemical, %*	*Atomic-Absorption, %*
1	0.118	0.113, 0.123
2	0.048	0.051, 0.051
3	0.021	0.023, 0.021
4	0.016	0.017, 0.016
5	0.007	0.006, 0.005
6	0.051	0.051, 0.051

Studies indicate that on a 0.25 g. nickel sample, as little as 0.0003 percent of magnesium can be determined with an estimated standard deviation of ± 0.00005 percent.

For routine work, in which the equipment is fed with sample solutions more or less continuously, the solution atomizing apparatus should be cleaned intermittently and the instrument response checked at frequent intervals with standard solutions.

For careful work, the previously mentioned bracketing technique should be utilized. This enables the analyst continuously to detect significant changes in the instrument response.

[48] A 10-ml. aliquot of the standard nickel solution contains 25 mg. of nickel (equivalent to the recommended sample weight), but only one-fifth as many nitrate ions as contained in the sample solution. If it is established that the nitrate ion interferes, proper adjustment must be made in preparing the standard solutions used to obtain the calibration curve.

[49] If the sample contains more than 0.15 percent of silicon, evaporate to dryness with 2 ml. of hydrochloric acid to dehydrate the silica. Then dissolve the residue with 2 ml. of nitric acid (1:1). Filter if necessary.

THE DETERMINATION OF ZINC IN ELECTROLYTIC COPPER[50]

Zinc may be determined in high purity copper with considerable ease by atomic absorption techniques. The removal of the copper matrix electrolytically and the concentration of the zinc-bearing electrolyte provides a means of extending the lower limit of zinc detectability to a point determined primarily by the purity of the reagents. In the procedure described for a 2.0-g. copper sample, differences as small as 0.5 p.p.m. are readily discernible.

In the presence of as much as 0.5 g. of copper, 1 or 2 μg. of zinc may be determined with relative ease. Data are presented which compare the effects of various analytical parameters.

Apparatus.—A sensitive commercially-available atomic absorption spectrometer. In this work the Jarrell-Ash Model 82-360 Atomic Absorption Spectrometer was used.

The settings were as follows:

Hollow cathode lamp current	14 ma.
Wavelength	2138 A
Photomultiplier voltage	750 v.
Slit width	25 μ
Air pressure	20 p.s.i.
Hydrogen pressure	10 p.s.i.
Time of atomization	30 seconds

Amplifier gain set to give zero absorption (on a scale of 100) with only the lamp emission passing through the flame.

Plastic Containers and Bottles.—Except where high temperatures or strong acids require the use of Pyrex glassware.

Reagents. **Nitric Acid (0.1 percent Solution).**—Dilute 1 ml. of nitric acid to 1000 ml.

Deionized Water.—Pass distilled water through a mixed-bed deionizer capable of providing water with a resistivity of 1.25×10^6 ohms per centimeter cube or better.

Standard Zinc Stock Solution (1 ml. = 100 μg. zinc).—Dissolve 25 mg. of high-purity zinc in 10 ml. of water containing a few drops of nitric acid. Boil to expel the oxides of nitrogen, dilute to 250.0 ml., and store in a plastic bottle.

Standard Zinc Solution (1 ml. = 1 μg. zinc).—Dilute 2.5 ml. of the standard zinc stock solution to 250 ml. Prepare fresh as needed.

Standard Copper Solution (1 ml. = 0.02 g. copper).—Dissolve 5 g. of high-purity copper[51] in 30 ml. of nitric acid (1:1). Boil to expel the oxides of nitrogen, cool, and dilute to 250 ml.

Procedure. **Copper Removed.**—Dissolve 2 g. of copper in a 150-ml. beaker with 15 ml. of nitric acid (1:1). Boil to expel oxides of nitrogen, dilute to 125 ml., add one drop of a 1 percent hydrochloric acid solution, and plate the copper on platinum electrodes. Evaporate the electrolyte containing the zinc and other impurities to a volume of 1 or 2 ml. (Exercise care to avoid contamination from any source.) Dilute to 10 ml. with water and again evaporate to a volume of 1 or 2 ml. Repeat the dilution and evaporation procedure. Finally adjust the volume to exactly 25.0 ml. (The resulting solution will have a pH of about 3.) Include both a water and reagent blank.

Table 44-31 shows relative zinc absorbances obtained for variously treated samples of high-purity copper following electrolysis.

[50] Unpublished work of the U. S. Naval Research Laboratory, Washington, D. C.

[51] In this work the zinc impurity content of Cu-B was 0.00015 percent and Cu-F was 0.0001 percent.

Table 44-31. Recovery of Zinc from High-Purity Copper after Electrolysis

Sample		Zinc Added		*Absorbance		Zinc Found			Recovery of Added Zn, %
Number	Weight	μg.	%	Total %	Net %	Total μg.	Net μg.	Total %	
1. (Water Blank)		—	—	1.3	—	—	—	—	—
2. (Reagent Blank)		—	—	8.3	7.0	1.45	—	—	—
3. Cu-B	2.0 g.	—	—	21.0	19.7	4.5	3.05	0.00015	—
4. Cu-F	2.0	—	—	18.0	16.7	3.5	2.05	0.00010	—
5. Cu-F	2.0	2.0	0.00010	25.3	24.0	5.75	4.3	0.00022	0.00012
6. Cu-F	2.0	6.0	0.00030	38.6	37.3	10.0	8.55	0.00043	0.00033

* Final dilution of aspirated solutions: 25 ml.

***Procedure.* Copper Present.**—To 10 ml. of water, and to a series of zinc standards, add 1 ml. of a 0.1 percent nitric acid solution. Dilute each solution to 50.0 ml. and store in a plastic bottle. (The resulting solutions have a pH of about 3.5.)

To 10 ml. of water, and to a similar series of zinc standards, add 2.5 ml. of the standard copper solution (1 ml. = 0.02 g. copper). Dilute each solution to 50.0 ml. and store in a plastic bottle. (The resulting solutions have a pH of about 2.5.)

Similarly prepare a third series of zinc standards each of which contains 25 ml. of the standard copper solution (1 ml. = 0.02 g. copper). Dilute each to 50.0 ml., and store in a plastic bottle. (The resulting solutions have a pH of about 1.8.)[52]

Turn the instrument on and allow sufficient time for it to become stabilized. With only the emission from the hollow-cathode lamp passing through the flame, set the instrument at zero absorbance (on a scale of 100). Then aspirate the blank and synthetic standard solutions into the flame and measure the respective absorbance of each over a period of 30 seconds.

Table 44-32 shows the relative absorbances of the various solutions.

Comments.—With proper consideration for the differences in dilution, a comparison of Tables 44-31 and 44-32 shows a greater sensitivity (Net Absorbance) for zinc in the absence of copper; however, in practical terms, zinc in the 1 to 2 p.p.m. range may be determined satisfactorily, without copper removal. Table 44-32 shows that when the zinc content is expressed in weight percent in the copper matrix, a ten-fold increase in sensitivity is achieved by a ten-fold increase in sample weight, up to 0.5 g. Although the background absorbance reading for samples containing 0.5 g. of copper is higher than for samples containing 0.05 g. of copper, the absorbance increments for corresponding amounts of zinc remain reasonably comparable.

LITERATURE

In addition to the procedures presented, the following are other selected reported applications of atomic absorption spectrometry to the determination of various elements in associated nonferrous metallurgical materials: cadmium in zirconium alloys;[52a] copper in aluminum alloys and in white metal;[52b] lead in bronze and zirconium alloys;[52a] magnesium in aluminum and its alloys,[52a, 52c, 52d] and zinc in bronze,[52a] gunmetal,[52e] and zirconium alloys.[52a]

[52] To minimize background interference in this procedure, a special effort has been made to maintain the nitric acid concentration within these pH values (1.5 to 3.5) without resorting to neutralization.

[52a] Elwell, W. T., and Gidley, J. A. F., Atomic Absorption Spectrometry, Pergamon Press, MacMillan Co., New York, 1962.

[52b] Wallace, F. J., Hilger Journal, **7**, 65, 1963.

[52c] Wallace, F. J., Analyst, **88**, 259, 1963.

[52d] Leithe, W., and Hofer, A., Microchimica Acta, 277, 1961.

[52e] Wallace, F. J., Hilger Journal, **7**, 39, 1962.

TABLE 44-32. ABSORBANCE MEASUREMENTS OF VARIOUS ZINC STANDARD SOLUTIONS

Item	*Copper*[0] *Content, g.*	*Zinc Added, μg.*	*Total Zinc Content, μg.*	**Total Absorbance, %*	*Net Absorbance, %*	*Total Zinc, %*
A-1 (Blank)	—	—	—	1.3	0	—
A-2	—	0.5	0.5	2.3	1.0	—
A-3	—	1.0	1.0	3.5	2.2	—
A-4	—	2.0	2.0	6.0	4.7	—
A-5	—	4.0	4.0	10.5	9.2	—
A-6	—	16.0	16.0	31.2	29.9	—
B-1	0.05	—	0.05	2.0	0	0.0001
B-2	0 05	0.5	0.55	3.0	1.0	0.0011
B-3	0.05	1.0	1.05	4.4	2.4	0.0021
B-4	0.05	2.0	2.05	6.3	4.3	0.0041
B-5	0.05	4.0	4.05	10.2	8.2	0.0081
C-1	0.5	—	0.5	7.5	0	0.0001
C-2	0.5	0.5	1.0	8.4	0.9	0.0002
C-3	0.5	1.0	1.5	9.2	1.7	0.0003
C-4	0.5	2.0	2.5	11.0	3.5	0.0005
C-5	0.5	4.0	4.5	14.0	6.5	0.0009

[0] Copper sample Cu-F (0.0001% Zn) used for additions.
* Final dilution of aspirated solutions: 50 ml.

Some reviews including extensive bibliographies on all phases of atomic absorption spectrometry have been published.[52f, 52g, 52h, 52i, 52j, 52k] In addition to this there are numerous newsletters and brochures published by equipment manufacturers relating to new developments in instruments and techniques.

POLAROGRAPHIC METHODS

Polarography covers that area of electrochemistry which relates the characteristic diffusion current of certain ions of a given element to the amount of that element in the solution being electrolyzed.

Since its discovery in 1922 by Heyrovsky at the Charles University of Prague, the polarograph (variously called polarograph, electropode, electro-chemograph, electro-polarizer, etc. in America for patent reasons) has been developed into a very dependable and versatile tool for the analytical chemist. It is especially valuable in trace metals analysis, but is not limited to this concentration range.

Scope.—Many of the alloying and trace constituents found in nonferrous alloys may be determined polarographically. Some are more amenable than others; much depends on factors such as the matrix metal, the voltage at which reduction or oxidation occurs,

[52f] Walsh, A., Advances in Spectrometry, Vol. II, Interscience, New York, 1961, pp. 1–22.
[52g] Robinson, J. W., Anal. Chem., **33,** 1067, 1961.
[52h] Allan, J. E., Spectrochimica Acta, **18,** 605, 1962.
[52i] Gilbert, P. T., Jr., Anal. Chem., **34,** 210R, 1962.
[52j] Scribner, B. F., and Margoshes, M., Anal. Chem., **36,** 337R, 1964.
[52k] David, D. J., Spectrochimica Acta, **20,** 1185, 1964.

and the combination of elements under test. Diffusion-current patterns are extremely important; some elements produce well-defined patterns, others produce poorly-defined patterns. The latter may often be improved by the proper choice of supporting electrolyte and/or the careful use of appropriate amounts of maximum suppressors.

Table 44-33[53] lists a few of the commonly used supporting electrolytes and the approximate half-wave potentials (referred to the saturated calomel electrode, S.C.E.) at which some associated constituents of nonferrous alloys undergo electrolysis.

The reader is cautioned that many elements, even though they are not listed in Table 44-33, produce unacceptable or interfering diffusion current patterns. If proper allowance cannot be made for these by complexing or by the choice of a suitable supporting electrolyte, chemical separation may be required. For a given electrolyte, some such provision must especially be made for major constituent ions which are reducible at a voltage near or positive to that of the element being determined.

Maxima Suppression.—As the phenomenon of maxima is encountered, it will be necessary to add a maximum suppressor to the solution to be electrolyzed. Gelatin is the most commonly used maximum suppressor.

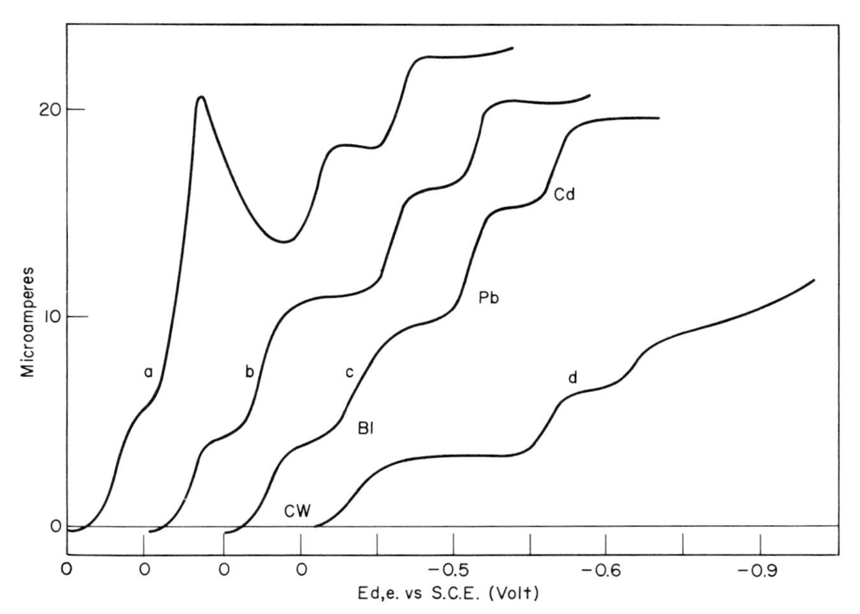

FIG. 44-5. Effect of Maximum Suppressor on the Diffusion Current Patterns of Bismuth. Mixture of about 0.8 millimolar copper, bismuth, lead, and cadmium in acidic tartrate medium of pH 4.5. Concentrations of gelatin were (a) 0, (b) 0.005, (c) 0.01, and (d) 0.03%. (Courtesy of Analytical Chemistry.)

Figure 44-5 shows how electrolytes containing various percentages of gelatin suppress a bismuth maximum and further affect the diffusion current patterns of lead and cadmium.

[53] For a more complete list of supporting electrolytes, polarographic half-wave potentials, and pertinent data, the reader is referred to Meites, L., Ed., Handbook of Analytical Chemistry, McGraw-Hill Book Company, New York, N. Y., 1963, pp. 5–53 to 5–99.

TABLE 44-33. SUPPORTING ELECTROLYTES AND REPORTED HALF-WAVE POTENTIALS

Supporting Electrolyte	*Possible Interfering Elements* $E_{1/2}$ *vs. S.C.E. > 0 Volts*[5]	*Possibly Determinable Elements* $E_{1/2}$ *vs. S.C.E. < 0 Volts (−Volts)*[55]
0.1 *M* $HClO_4$ or 0.1 *M* $NaClO_4$	Ag(I), Bi(III), Cu(II), Fe(III), Hg(I), Hg(II), Tl(III)	[Mo, Pb, Tl, V, In, As, Ni, Zn, Cr, Fe.] Mo(VI), −0.24; Pb(II), −0.38; Tl(I), −0.46; V(III), −0.5; In(III), −0.57; As(III) in 1 *M* HNO_3, −0.7; Ni(II), −1.0; Zn(II) in 1 *M* $NaClO_4$, −1.0; Cr(III), −1.46; Fe(II), −1.46
1.0 *M* HCl	Cu(II), Fe(III), Hg(I), Hg(II), V(V)	[Bi, Sn, Sb, Mo, Sb, As, Pb, Sn, Tl, V, In, Cd, V, Ti.] Bi(III), −0.09; *Sn(II)*, −0.1; Sn(IV), −0.1; Sb(III), −0.15; Mo(VI) in 0.3 *M* HCl, −0.26; Sb(V), −0.35; As(III), −0.43; Pb(II), −0.44; Sn(IV), −0.47; Tl(I), −0.48; V(III), −0.51; In(III), −0.56; Cd(II), −0.64; V(IV), −0.78; Ti(IV), −0.81
8.0 *M* HCl	As(III), Cu(II), Fe(III), Hg(II), Mo(VI), Sb(V), Sn(IV), Ti(IV), V(V)	[Sb, Bi, Pb, Ni, Tl, Cd.] Sb(III), −0.24; Bi(III), −0.34; Pb(II), −0.62; Ni(II), −0.67; Tl(I), −0.67; Cd(II), −0.8
0.1 *M* NaOH, 0.1 *M* KOH, or 0.1 *M* $(CH_3)_4NOH$		[As, Sb, Tl, Cr.] *As(III)*, −0.23; *Sb(III)*, −0.36; Tl(I), −0.46; Cr(VI), −0.97
1.0 *M* NaOH		[As, Cu, V, Sb, Tl, Bi, Sn, Pb, Cd, Cr, Fe, In, Co, Zn, Mn, Cr.] *As(III)*, −0.27; Cu(II), −0.41; *V(IV)*, −0.43; *Sb(III)*, −0.45; Tl(I), −0.48; Bi(III), −0.6; *Sn(II)*, −0.73; Pb(II), −0.76; Cd(II), −0.78; Cr(VI), −0.85; Fe(II), −0.9; In(III), −1.1; Co(II), −1.46; Zn(II), −1.53; Mn(II), −1.7; Cr(II), −1.94
1.0 *M* NH_4OH & 1.0 *M* NH_4Cl	Sn(IV)	[Cr, Cu, V, Fe, Tl, Co, Cd, V, Ni, Co, Zn.] Cr(VI), −0.2; *Cu(I)*, −0.22; Cu(II), −0.24; *V(IV)*, −0.32; *Fe(II)*, −0.34; Tl(I), −0.48; Co(III) in 2.5 *M* NH_4OH, −0.54; Cd(II), −0.81; V(V), −0.96; Ni(II), −1.1; Co(II), −1.29; Zn(II), −1.35

0.1 *M* NH_4Cl, 0.1 *M* KCl, 0.1 *M* LiCl, or 0.1 *M* $(CH_3)_4NCl$	Cu(II), Fe(III), Hg(II), Tl(III)	[Co, Cr, Pb, Tl, In, Cd, Cr, Ni, Co, Fe, Al.] $Co(NH_3)_6^{+++}$, −0.26; Cr(VI), −0.3; Cr(II), −0.34; Pb(II), −0.4; Tl(I), −0.46; In(III), −0.56; Cd(II), −0.6; *Cr(III)*, −0.61; Ni(II), −1.1; Co(II), −1.2; Fe(II), −1.3; Al(III), −1.75
1.0 *M* KCl	Cu(II), Hg(II), Tl(III)	[Cr, Pb, Tl, In, Cd, Zn, Co, Mn.] *Cr(II)*, −0.4; Pb(II), −0.4; Tl(I), −0.48; In(III), −0.6; Cd(II), −0.64; Zn(II), −1.0; Co(II), −1.2; Mn(II), −1.5
1.0 *M* KCN	Tl(I)	[Pb, Sb, V, Cd, Co, Mn, Cr, Co, Au.] Pb(II), −0.72; Sb(III), −1.1; V(III), −1.17; Cd(II), −1.18; Co(II), −1.3; Mn(II), −1.36; $Cr(CN)_6^{-3}$, −1.38; *Cr(II)*, −1.38; Co(III), −1.45; Au(I), −1.46
1.0 *M* KCNS	Ag(I), Bi(III), Cr(VI), Cu(II), Fe(III), Sb(III)	[Pb, Sn, Ti, Sn, Tl, Cd, As, Ni, In, Cr, Zn, Co, Mn.] Pb(II), −0.44; Sn(II), −0.46; *Ti(III)* in 0.1 *M* KCNS, −0.46; Ti(IV) in 0.1 *M* KCNS, −0.46; Sn(IV) in 0.02 *M* HCl, −0.5; Tl(I), −0.52; Cd(II), −0.65; As(III) in 0.001 *M* HCl, −0.68; Ni(II), −0.68; In(III), −0.72; *Cr(II)*, −0.8; Cr(III), −1.05; Zn(II), −1.06; Co(II), −1.08; Mn(II), −1.5
0.1 *M* Ethylene-diamine & 0.1–1.0 *M* KCl or 0.1–1.0 *M* KNO_3	Ag(I), Hg(II)	[V, Cr, Co, Cu, Pb, Cd, In, Zn, Ni, Mo.] *V(IV)*, −0.37; Cr(VI), −0.44; *Co(II)*, −0.45; Co(III), −0.48; Cu(II), −0.5; Pb(II), −0.65; Cd(II), −0.97; In(III), −1.1; Zn(II), −1.58; Ni(II), −1.6; Mo(VI), −1.95
0.1 *M* Pyridine & 0.1 *M* Pyridinium Chloride	Ag(I), Cr(VI), Cu(II)	[V, Mo, Pb, Tl, Sb, V, Cd, V, Ni, As, Cr, Bi, Zn, Co, Sn.] V(V), −0.11; Mo(VI), −0.24; Pb(II), −0.4; Tl(I), −0.45; Sb(III), −0.47; *V(II)*, −0.5; Cd(II), −0.62; V(IV), −0.63; Ni(II), −0.75; As(III), −0.9; Cr(III), −0.99; Bi(III), −1.0; Zn(II), −1.03; Co(II), −1.06; Sn(II), −1.12

TABLE 44-33 (cont.)

Supporting Electrolyte	*Possible Interfering Elements* $E_{1/2}$ *vs. S.C.E.* > 0 *Volts*[54]	*Possibly Determinable Elements* $E_{1/2}$ *vs. S.C.E.* < 0 *Volts* (−*Volts*)[55]
1.0 *M* Hydrazine & 1.0 *M* NH_4Cl & 1.0 *M* NH_4OH	Ag(I)	[Pb, Tl, Pb, Cu, Sn, Sb, Cd, In, Ni, As, Mn, Sn, V, Co, Zn, Cr, Fe, Bi, Mo.] Pb(II), −0.42; Tl(I), −0.49; Pb(II), −0.51; Cu(I), −0.52; *Sn(II)*, −0.63; Sb(III), −0.74; Cd(II), −0.84; In(III), −0.9; Ni(II), −1.08; As(III), −1.1; Mn(II), −1.1; Sn(IV), −1.13; V(V), −1.15; V(IV), −1.2; Co(II), −1.3; Zn(II), −1.33; Cr(III), −1.4; Fe(II), −1.47; Bi(III), −1.54; Mo(VI), −1.7
Saturated Citric Acid	Ag(I), Cr(VI), Cu(II), Fe(III), Mo(IV), V(V)	[Bi, Sn, Pb, Sb, Tl, Cd, In, As, Cr, Zn.] Bi(III), −0.03; *Sn(II)*, −0.05; Pb(II), −0.36; Sb(III), −0.38; Tl(I), −0.44; Cd(II), −0.51; In(III), −0.54; As(III), −0.58; Cr(III), −0.78; Zn(II), −0.93; Ni(II), −0.98
0.1 *M* Ammonium Citrate, pH = 6.1	Ag(I), Cr(VI), V(V)	[V, Cu, Fe, Bi, Sn, V, Tl, Pb, Cd, Ti, Cr, Mo, Cr, Zn, As, V, Sb, Mn.] *V(III)* in 1 *M* Na_3Cit., −0.1; Cu(II), −0.17; *Fe(II)*, −0.18; Fe(III), −0.22; Bi(III), −0.31; *Sn(II)*, −0.41; V(IV), −0.44; Tl(I), −0.51; Pb(II), −0.54; Cd(II), −0.7; Ti(IV) in 0.4 *M* Na_3Cit., −0.9; Cr(II), −1.0; Mo(VI), −1.0; Cr(III), −1.2; Zn(II), −1.3; As(III), −1.5; V(IV), −1.5; Sb(V), −1.6; Mn(II), −1.6
0.1 *M* Ammonium Tartrate & 0.1 *M* NH_4OH	Ag(I)	[Cu, V, Cr, V, Tl, Fe, Sn, Bi, Pb, Cd, Fe, Sb, Ni, In, Zn, Co, Mn, As, Sb.] Cu(II), −0.15; *V(IV)*, −0.21; Cr(VI), −0.24; V(V), −0.26; Tl(I), −0.47; *Fe(II)*, −0.47; *Sn(II)*, −0.53; Bi(III), −0.54; Pb(II), −0.54; Cd(II), −0.73; Fe(III), −0.83; Sb(III), −0.95; Ni(II), −0.96; In(III), −1.15; Zn(II), −1.2; Co(II), −1.22; Mn(II), −1.53; As(III), −1.57; Sb(V), −1.7.

[54] The elements shown above ($E_{1/2}$ *vs.* S.C.E. >0 volts) are listed alphabetically; their half-wave voltages are not listed. Their diffusion current waves occur at a potential so positive that they cannot be evaluated, because they merge with the wave produced by the oxidation of the electrode mercury. If present in appreciable amounts, their limiting diffusion currents can interfere with the determination of elements whose half-wave reduction potentials are negative with respect to the saturated calomel electrode; it may then be necessary to choose a more suitable electrolyte or resort to chemical separations.

[55] For any given supporting electrolyte, each element in this column is listed in the reported order of its negatively increasing half-wave potential ($E_{1/2}$) value, referred to the saturated calomel electrode (S.C.E.).

To make the elements and their order more apparent for a chosen supporting electrolyte, the first line (enclosed in brackets) contains the chemical symbols in their proper order.

An italicized chemical symbol indicates the ions of the element in that valence state produced an anodic diffusion current wave through the associated reported half-wave value.

No attempt has been made to specify wave types as being poorly defined or well defined. Nor has an attempt been made to identify waves which exhibit maxima; generally the presence of about 0.005 percent gelatin or 0.003 percent Triton X-100 in the supporting electrolyte will suppress most maxima.

Electrolysis Cell.—There are many types of cells available. A small cell is advantageous for many applications because it may be operated on a small volume of solution. This generally permits sufficient concentration of the sample solution to determine trace constituents. For this work significant concentration of the sample solution often requires the preliminary isolation (by extraction or other wet-chemical means) of the element to be determined. As the element to be determined is concentrated, so are the diverse accompanying ions that were not separated in the isolatory procedure. Their presence often causes "noise" which results in poorly-defined polarograms. Although much smaller cells are available for the analysis of extremely small samples, it is pointless to concentrate sample solutions to provide greater diffusion currents for the sought element unless acceptable polarograms are obtainable.

The cell shown in Fig. 44-6 has a capacity of about 2 ml. The head of the column of

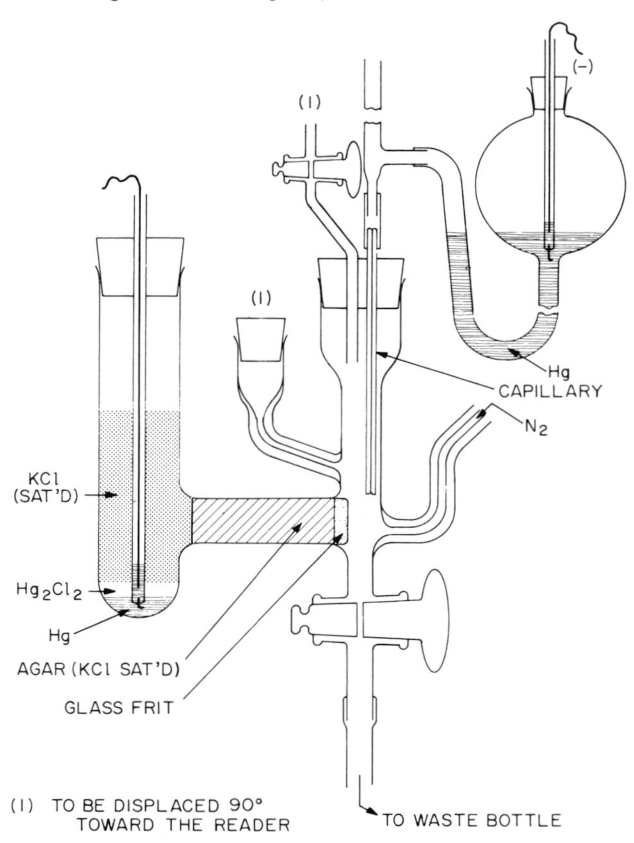

FIG. 44-6. Dropping-Mercury Electrode Cell Assembly.

mercury may be adjusted to regulate the dropping rate of the mercury from the capillary. The bore[56] of the capillary tubing should be about 0.05 mm. in diameter, and its length

[56] Capillary tubing, outside diameter about 6 mm. and bore about 0.05 mm., may be purchased from the E. H. Sargent Co., Chicago, Ill. The Corning Glass Works, Corning N. Y., sells a marine barometer tubing which is also suitable.

adjusted so it will deliver (when immersed in the electrolyte) one drop of mercury every 5 or 6 seconds when the head of the mercury column is about 30 cm.

When the proper length of the capillary tubing has been ascertained, it should be recorded and future cuts made accordingly. Sooner or later the capillary will become clogged and will have to be replaced. The clogged piece should be discarded as the capillary is so small it cannot be cleaned easily. Capillary replacement will be required less frequently if proper precautions are taken to prevent dust and dirt from getting into the mercury well and column area. The well should be connected to the column with clean, dry Tygon tubing. Only Reagent-Grade, triple-distilled mercury should be used in the well and column.

Figure 44-7 shows the advantage of working with a relatively small cell when a

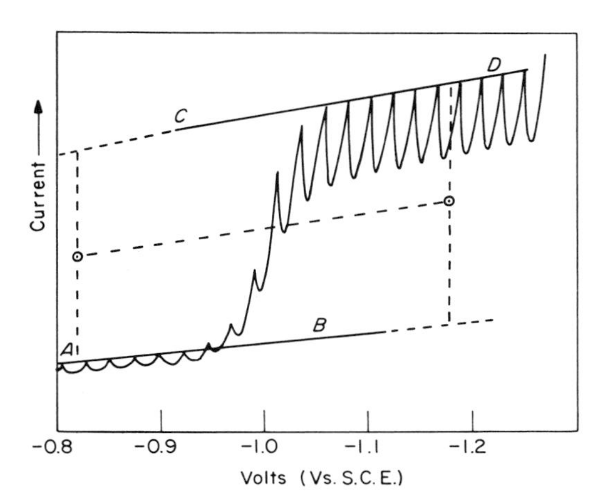

FIG. 44-7. Polarogram of a Solution Containing 20 μg. of Zinc in 5.0 ml. of 1 *M* NaCl. Line AB represents the tangent to the peaks of the residual current. Line CD represents the tangent to the peaks of the limiting current.

limited amount of sample is available. The polarogram was prepared with a solution containing 20 μg. of zinc in a total volume of 5 ml. The supporting electrolyte was 1 *M* sodium chloride. The instrument was set at maximum sensitivity and operated with a slight amount of damping.

Cell Operation.—Fill the cell once with the solution to be analyzed. Open the lower stopcock and discard this cell-conditioning solution. Close the lower stopcock and again fill the cell with the solution to be analyzed, making sure the dropping electrode is slightly immersed. Place the stopper in the side tube and bubble nitrogen (about one bubble per second) for 5 minutes through the cell to expel the dissolved oxygen. Stop the nitrogen flow and immediately close the nitrogen-exit stopcock. Electrolyze the solution contained in the cell.

Instrument Operation.—The recommended warm-up time may vary for different instruments. If this information is not available allow at least 20 minutes. Properly connect the electrode cable of the instrument to the cell. To adjust the instrument, load the cell with a standard solution which contains a low amount of the element to be determined, but which otherwise closely matches the sample solution. Select the voltage range which scans the half-wave potential of the element to be determined and run a trial electrolysis with the instrument set at or near its highest sensitivity, and with little or no damping.

The resulting polarogram will provide information regarding sensitivity attainable, and reveal interfering diffusion currents of other sample constituents,[57] assuming the standards are prepared to match closely the sample to be analyzed. Regarding interfering diffusion currents, it is recommended that Table 44-33 be examined for possible ion interferents; it should be further examined for a supporting electrolyte which may be used to provide an acceptable potential interval between the element to be determined and associated components. If no suitable electrolyte is listed, it may even become necessary to resort to further isolatory procedures.

Assuming an acceptable polarogram (either with or without preliminary chemical separation) has been obtained, the remaining samples, blank, and standards may be run with celerity. The introduction of a new sample into the cell should be preceded by several distilled water rinses. This is especially necessary if the percentage of the element to be measured is lower in the replacement solution than in the discharged solution. In this regard, it is advantageous, when possible, to arrange the electrolysis order of the samples and standards so that each successive solution contains a higher percentage of the element to be determined. By so doing, the cell need be conditioned with one or at most two rinses with each new solution to be electrolyzed; rinsing with distilled water may be omitted.

Isolatory Procedures.—Since many elements produce diffusion currents which overlap or are too close to each other to permit their accurate measurement (even when electrolyzed in a most favorable supporting electrolyte), the analyst must resort to chemical separation. Many isolatory techniques are available. Depending on the separation to be made, precipitation, liquid-liquid extraction, distillation, ordinary electrolysis, or mercury cathode electrolysis may be chosen to accomplish the desired separation. Whatever the technique, care must be exercised to prevent the partial loss of the sought constituent or constituents.[58] By the same token. contamination must be avoided.

Evaluation of Diffusion Currents.—The standard sample technique, a comparative method,[59] is frequently used for the polarographic evaluation of many new materials and alloy systems. For this type of work, it is generally quite easy to prepare synthetic standard sample solutions which closely match the materials being investigated.

Figure 44-7 illustrates one method of measuring diffusion current wave height. A straight line *AB*, is drawn through the peaks of the residual current. Similarly, line *CD* is drawn through the peaks of the limiting current. In an ideal polarogram these two lines are parallel or nearly so. If such be the case a nominal voltage value selected near the half-wave potential may serve as the voltage at which the diffusion current is measured. When a given voltage is selected, it should be used to measure the diffusion current for each succeeding standard solution or sample solution to be evaluated. (For the series of samples exemplified by the polarogram in Fig. 44-7, the recording was started at -0.8 v. *vs.* S.C.E. for each sample and standard solution.)

If the lines representing the residual current and limiting current are not parallel, it is obviously more important to obtain a measurement of the diffusion current at that point on the wave which corresponds to the half-wave potential. The greater the

[57] In developing a polarographic procedure, the seemingly innocent addition of indicators (*e.g.*, methyl red) may result in the formation of objectionable diffusion-current patterns which are noticeable on polarograms recorded at high sensitivity.

[58] Separations are treated in most quantitative analysis textbooks, including an extensive section in Volume II A of this work.

[59] Taylor, J. K., Anal. Chem., **19,** 368, 1947, discusses some aspects of the evaluation of diffusion currents by various Comparative Methods and also by the Absolute Method.

tendency for these lines to converge in a given direction, the greater is the necessity to determine the diffusion current at the half-wave potential. This may be done by drawing the tangent lines representing the residual and limiting currents as suggested previously, extending the former to a potential 0.3 or 0.4 volt more negative than the estimated $E_{1/2}$ values and the latter to a potential 0.3 or 0.4 volt more positive than the estimated $E_{1/2}$ value. Establish the midpoint between these two lines at two potential values separated by about 0.4 volt, each about an equal distance from the estimated half-wave potential. A line drawn through these midpoints will intersect the diffusion current at the half-wave potential (see dotted lines in Fig. 44-7).

As the slopes of the lines representing the residual and limiting currents vary, precision and accuracy suffer. Wide slope variations, assuming the sought constituent is normally capable of producing a well-defined diffusion current, suggest the need for the use of a more appropriate supporting electrolyte, or the use of a more refined isolatory technique for separating the sought constituent from its associated components.

Applications.—The polarographic literature[60] is extensive. Many of the references deal with the analysis of nonferrous alloy systems. Much work has been done on aluminum-, copper-, lead-, magnesium-, and zinc-base alloys. There are also references to the analysis of many other nonferrous materials. To acquaint the reader with the practical quantitative polarographic application to the analysis of some of these alloys and also with some of the difficulties encountered in sequence polarographic analysis, three detailed procedures are presented. Following these procedures, 20 selected abstracts of reported procedures are presented for the polarographic analysis of various nonferrous materials.

THE POLAROGRAPHIC DETERMINATION OF LEAD IN INDIUM[61]

This procedure was developed for the analysis of lead-indium binary alloys. Systems such as these which are prepared from relatively high-purity constituents, contain little or no impurities to produce annoying and interfering diffusion currents. With a supporting electrolyte capable of producing a well-defined diffusion current for the minor constituent, the polarographic analysis is rapid and straightforward.

Polarographic analysis of such materials becomes all the more attractive if it can be used as an alternative to existing tedious wet-chemical procedures.

Figure 44-8 illustrates the importance of the proper choice or adjustment of the supporting electrolyte. Curves (*a*) and (*b*) are unacceptable because the indium wave almost overlaps the lead wave. Although the diffusion current for lead in curve (*c*) is smaller than in curves (*a*) and (*b*), the diffusion current for lead is adequately separated from that of indium.

Apparatus. **Any Modern Commercially-Available Polarograph.**

Electrolysis Cell.—H-type cell and dropping-mercury electrode assembly similar to that shown in Fig. 44-6.

Reagents. **Tartaric Acid (20 percent Solution).**—Dissolve 200 g. of tartaric acid in water and dilute to 1000 ml.

[60] A comprehensive bibliography (listing over 6800 references of the polarographic literature which covers the years 1922 to 1955 has been prepared by the E. H. Sargent Co., 4647 West Foster Avenue, Chicago 30, Ill. It contains authors listed alphabetically with the respective papers of each arranged chronologically. In addition to this, there is a cross-referenced subject index. A revised Polarographic Bibliography, Cat. #S-29368, has been prepared by the E. H. Sargent Co. It contains 12,000 references covering the years 1922 to 1965.

[61] Unpublished work of the U. S. Naval Research Laboratory, Washington, D. C.

Sodium Hydroxide (20 percent Solution).—Dissolve 200 g. of sodium hydroxide in 500 ml. of water. Cool, dilute to 100 ml. and store in a polyethylene bottle.

Phenolphthalein (1 percent Solution).—Dissolve 1 g. of phenolphthalein in 100 ml. of ethyl alcohol.

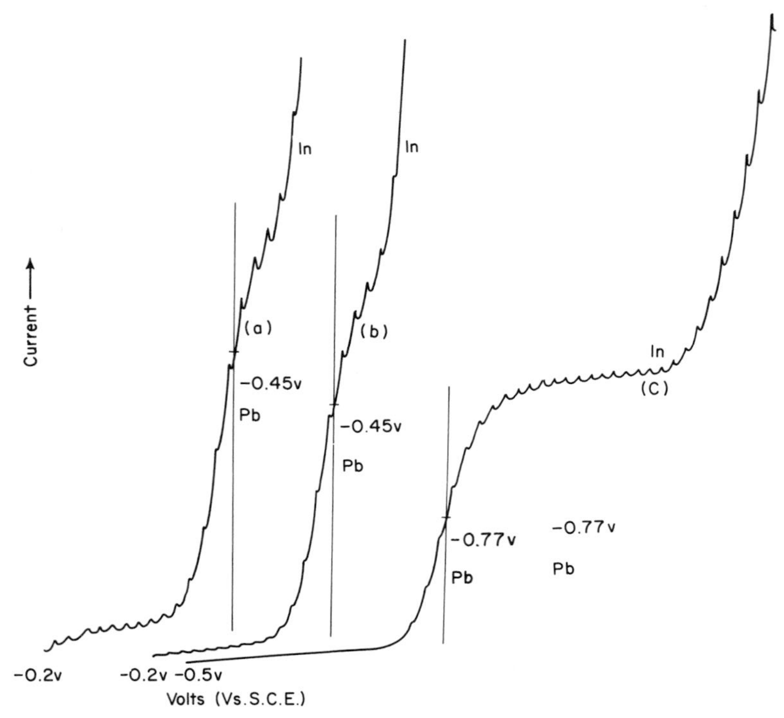

Fig. 44-8. Effect of Supporting Electrolytes on Lead-Indium Diffusion Currents. These polarograms were recorded for 3 solutions, each containing 0.001 g. of lead and 0.009 g. of indium dissolved with the same amount of nitric acid. Curve (a) was obtained by diluting to 25 ml. and electrolyzing, beginning at −0.2 v. *vs.* S. C. E. Curve (b) was obtained by adding 1 g. of tartaric acid, diluting to 25 ml. and electrolyzing, beginning at −0.2 v. *vs.* S. C. E. Curve (c) was obtained by adding 1 g. of tartaric acid, neutralizing with NaOH to pH 12, diluting to 25 ml. and electrolyzing beginning at −0.5 v. *vs.* S. C. E.

Standard Lead Solution (1 ml. = 0.0005 g. lead).—Dissolve 0.1000 g. of high-purity lead with 10 ml. of nitric acid (1:1). Dilute with 30 ml. of water and boil to expel the oxides of nitrogen. Cool, transfer to a 200-ml. volumetric flask, dilute to the mark, and mix.

Standard Indium Solution (1 ml. = 0.001 g. indium).—Dissolve 0.2000 g. of high-purity indium with 10 ml. of nitric acid (1:1). Add 30 ml. of water and boil to expel the oxides of nitrogen. Cool, transfer to a 200-ml. volumetric flask, dilute to the mark, and mix.

Standardization. **Reference Solutions (5 to 25 percent lead).**—To five clean 25-ml. volumetric flasks, numbered 1 through 5, add respectively the following aliquots of the standard lead solution (1 ml. = 0.0005 g. lead): 0, 1, 2, 3, and 5 ml. To these same flasks and, in the same order, add the following aliquots of the standard indium solution (1 ml. = 0.001 g. indium): 10, 9.5, 9, 8.5, and 7.5 ml. The total amount of lead + indium contained in each flask = 0.01 g.

Preparation of Supporting Electrolytes.—To each of the flasks containing the reference solutions, add 5 ml. of the 20 percent tartaric acid solution, and one drop of the phenolphthalein solution. Neutralize each carefully with the 20 percent sodium hydroxide solution. Add exactly 0.5 ml. of the sodium hydroxide solution in excess.[62] Dilute to the 25-ml. mark and mix.

Instrument and Cell Adjustment.—Warm up and check the instrument according to the manufacturer's recommendation.

With the electrode immersed in water, adjust the mercury well to provide about a 30-cm. head of mercury. Rinse the cell several times with the synthetic standard solution which contains no lead (blank). Then fill the cell with the same electrolyte so the lower tip of the dropping electrode is well immersed.

Insert a stopper in the filling tube, open the stopcock at the top of the cell, and bubble nitrogen (about one bubble per second) through the electrolyte for 5 minutes. Turn off nitrogen and close the nitrogen-exit stopcock.

Electrolysis.—As suggested under Instrument Operation, arrange the solutions so each succeeding sample will contain an equal or higher percentage of lead than its predecessor. (It may not be possible to do this with the unknown samples, but it is always possible with the standards.)

After observing that the dropping electrode is functioning properly and the electrode cable is properly attached, proceed with the initial electrolysis as follows: Set the instrument at or near its highest sensitivity and turn on the cell current. Adjust the chart paper until the recorder pen is directly over a heavy cross line, and identify it as the −0.4 volt[63] starting line. Set the polarizing voltage at −0.35 volt, and start the polarizer. At the instant that the scanning polarizer registers −0.4 volt, start the recorder and make a polarogram which scans through the diffusion-current range to about −1.1 volts. Stop the recorder and polarizer, and turn off the cell current.

Replace the solution in the cell with the next higher lead standard solution to be analyzed, but first condition the cell to the new solution by rinsing it at least once with the new solution. Remove the oxygen from the new electrolyte as previously directed and repeat the electrolysis procedure.

Preparation of Calibration Curve.—After all the standard solutions have been electrolyzed, determine their respective relative diffusion currents from the polarograms, and plot these against the lead percentages they represent. For wide percentage ranges use log-log graph paper.

Figure 44-9 shows a typical curve obtained for synthetic solutions containing up to 25 percent lead.

Procedure.—Transfer 0.1000 g. of sample to a 100-ml. beaker. Add 5 ml. of water, cover, and cautiously add 5 ml. of nitric acid. Warm, if necessary, to effect dissolution. Dilute to about 30 ml. with water and boil gently to expel the oxides of nitrogen. Cool, transfer to a 100-ml. volumetric flask, dilute to the mark, and mix.

Transfer a 10-ml. aliquot of the solution to a 25-ml. volumetric flask. Treat as directed for the reference solutions in Preparation of Supporting Electrolyte.

Determine the diffusion current for the sample solution, using the same means as was applied for determining the diffusion currents for the standard solutions. Obtain the lead percentage from the standard curve.

[62] A total of 4.0 ml. of the sodium hydroxide solution is generally required to neutralize and adjust each standard solution to about pH 12.

[63] Since the reference cell is a saturated calomel electrode (S.C.E.), this and following voltages will be referred to it.

Comment.—By using a 0.5-g. sample and adjusting the final volume of the total sample to 15 ml. it is possible to determine as little as 0.004 percent lead in indium without resorting to preliminary isolatory techniques. This order of sensitivity can be attained only with great difficulty by usual wet-chemical procedures.

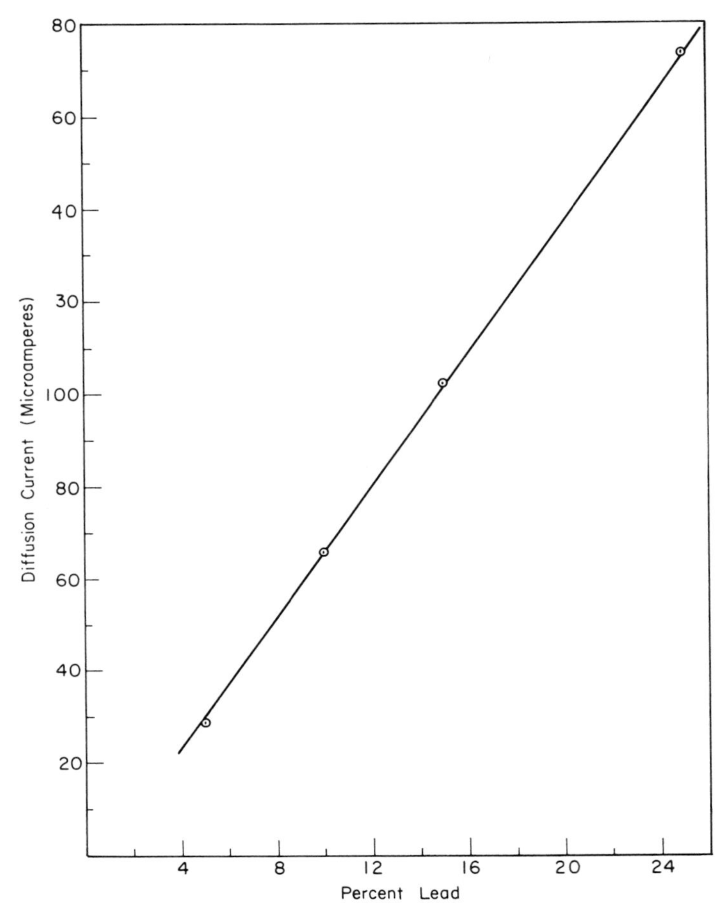

Fig. 44-9. Calibration Curve for Lead (5–25%) in Indium.

POLAROGRAPHIC ANALYSIS OF ALUMINUM ALLOYS FOR COPPER, LEAD, NICKEL, AND ZINC[64,65]

This method presents polarographic techniques for the determination of the metals cited in the composition ranges usually associated with their occurrence in aluminum

[64] Kolthoff, I. M., and Matsuyama, G., Ind. Eng. Chem., Anal. Ed., **17,** 615, 1945. Copyright 1945 by ACS and reprinted in part with permission of the copyright owner.

[65] For a rapid standard addition procedure for the individual polarographic determination of nickel and zinc, or copper in aluminum alloys, see Payne, S. T., Light Metals, **15,** 151, or 223, respectively, 1952.

alloys. The use of synthetic standards to match the alloy compositions and the aluminum matrix concentration eliminates variables due to the influence of one metal upon the diffusion current of another.

Apparatus.— Any modern commercially-available polarograph.

Reagents. **Bromocresol Green (0.1 percent Solution).**—To 100 mg. of bromocresol green (tetrabromo-*m*-cresolsulfonphthalein) in an agate mortar add 2.9 ml. of 0.05 *M* sodium hydroxide. Rub the solid until dissolved and dilute with water to 100 ml.

Dithizone (0.05 percent Solution in Carbon Tetrachloride).—Dissolve 500 mg. of dithizone (diphenylthiocarbazone) in 1000 ml. of carbon tetrachloride (U.S.P.).

Gelatin (0.5 percent Solution).—Soak 0.5 g. of gelatin in 100 g. of distilled water. Heat to the boiling point, cool to room temperature, and add a few drops of toluene as a preservative.

Hydrochloric Acid (0.1 *M* Solution).—Dilute 8.5 ml. of constant-boiling acid to 500 ml.

Hydroxylamine Hydrochloride (2 *M* Solution).—To 13.9 g. of hydroxylamine hydrochloride (recrystallized from water) add distilled water to make 100 ml.

Nitric Acid (1:1) Solution.—Mix 500 ml. of concentrated nitric acid with 500 ml. of distilled water.

Potassium Thiocyanate (2 *M* Solution).—To 19.4 g. of Reagent-Grade potassium thiocyanate, add distilled water to make 100 ml. of solution.

Sodium Citrate (1.25 *M* Solution).—To 184 g. of Reagent-Grade sodium citrate dihydrate, add distilled water to make 500 ml. of solution.

Sodium Citrate (Saturated Solution).—Dissolve 400 g. of Reagent-Grade sodium citrate dihydrate in 600 ml. of distilled water.

Sodium Hydroxide (1 *M* Solution).—To 5 ml. of saturated sodium hydroxide, add distilled water to make 100 ml.

Sodium Hydroxide (15 percent Solution).—Dissolve 150 g. of Reagent-Grade sodium hydroxide pellets in 850 ml. of distilled water.

Thymol Blue (0.1 percent Solution).—Rub 100 mg. of thymol blue (thymolsulfonphthalein) with 4.3 ml. of 0.05 *M* sodium hydroxide in an agate mortar. After the solid dissolves, dilute with water to 100 ml.

Pyridine.—Reagent Grade.

High-Purity Aluminum Solution (1 ml. = 0.02 g. aluminum).—Transfer 2.000 g. of high-purity aluminum to a 400-ml. beaker, cover, and slowly add 22 ml. of 15 percent sodium hydroxide. After the reaction subsides, heat the solution to effect completion of the reaction. Add 40 ml. of nitric acid (1:1) and heat to expel the oxides of nitrogen. Cool, transfer to a 100-ml. volumetric flask, dilute to the mark, and mix.

Nickel Solution (1 ml. = 0.001 g. nickel).—Dissolve 1.000 g. of high-purity nickel with 10 ml. of nitric acid, dilute with 50 ml. of water, and boil to expel the oxides of nitrogen. Cool, transfer to a 1-liter volumetric flask, dilute to the mark, and mix.

Zinc Solution (1 ml. = 0.001 g. zinc).—Prepare as directed for nickel.

Copper Solution (1 ml. = 0.001 g. copper).—Prepare as directed for nickel.

Lead Solution (1 ml. = 0.001 g. lead).—Prepare as directed for nickel.

Iron Solution (1 ml. = 0.001 g. iron).—Prepare as directed for nickel, except use 40 ml. of nitric acid (1:3) to dissolve the iron.

Procedure.[66] **Preparation of Sample.**—To 1.000 g. of sample in a 150-ml. beaker

[66] In the various procedures presented, the method of translating diffusion currents to respective component percentages is optional. Irrespective of the method of translation, for those determinations performed in the presence of large amounts of aluminum, the reader is reminded of the importance of preparing synthetic standard solutions whose aluminum contents closely resemble those of the sample solutions to be tested.

covered with a watch glass, slowly add 11 ml. of 15 percent sodium hydroxide. After the reaction subsides, heat the solution to effect completion of the reaction. Add 20 ml. of nitric acid (1:1), stir, and heat to expel the oxides of nitrogen. The alloy dissolves completely except for a little white residue which is probably metastannic acid and silica. Cool the solution to room temperature and dilute to 50.0 ml. in a volumetric flask. Use aliquot samples of this solution for the following analyses:

Determination of Copper in the Presence of Much Iron.—Pipet a 10-ml. aliquot of the sample solution into a 25-ml. volumetric flask. Add a drop of the 0.1 percent thymol blue indicator solution, neutralize with 1 M sodium hydroxide solution until the indicator changes to an orange color, and then add 1 ml. in excess. Add 0.5 ml. of the 2 M hydroxylamine hydrochloride solution, 0.5 ml. of the 2 M potassium thiocyanate solution, and shake gently until the red color of the iron thiocyanate disappears. Add a little water to wash down the side of the flask, 0.5 ml. of the 0.5 percent gelatin solution, dilute the solution to the 25-ml. mark with distilled water, and mix. Transfer a necessary portion of the solution to a polarographic cell and bubble nitrogen through the electrolyte for 5 minutes to remove oxygen. Record a polarogram from -0.2 to -0.6 volt (*vs.* S.C.E.) or measure the current at -0.3 and -0.5 volt (*vs.* S.C.E.). Correct the observations for the residual current and compare the corrected diffusion current with that of a standard sample solution.

Rapid Method for Determination of Nickel and Zinc.—Pipet a 15-ml. aliquot of the sample solution into a 50-ml. volumetric flask, add 5 ml. of 1 M sodium hydroxide solution, and mix thoroughly to make the precipitated aluminum hydroxide redissolve. Add 0.70 ml. of the 2 M hydroxylamine hydrochloride solution, 0.50 ml. of the 2 M potassium thiocyanate solution, and rinse down the neck of the flask with distilled water. Shake the solution in the flask until the red color of iron thiocyanate disappears, then add 5.0 ml. of the 1.25 M sodium citrate solution. Mix the contents of the flask thoroughly and add 0.50 ml. of pyridine, 2 drops of 0.1 percent bromocresol green indicator solution, and 15 percent sodium hydroxide solution until the indicator changes to a distinct green color (pH = 4.5). Add 1.0 ml. of the 0.5 percent gelatin solution and dilute to the mark with distilled water. Transfer a portion of the solution to a polarographic cell, bubble with nitrogen gas for 5 minutes, and record a polarogram from -0.4 to -1.4 volts (*vs.* S.C.E.). To determine the amount of nickel and zinc in the sample, compare their respective diffusion currents with those observed with standard sample solutions prepared by adding appropriate amounts of the standard nickel and zinc solutions to an amount of the high-purity aluminum solution which about matches the aluminum content of the unknown sample solution.

Separation Method for Determination of Nickel.—Electrolyze a suitable aliquot portion of the aluminum solution in nitric acid to remove copper. Transfer the solution to a 50-ml. volumetric flask, add 10 ml. of pyridine, dilute to the mark with distilled water, and shake vigorously. Filter the solution through a clean, dry funnel fitted with a coarse-porosity paper. Pipet a 20-ml. aliquot of the filtrate and 0.5 ml. of 0.5 percent gelatin to a 25-ml. volumetric flask. Dilute to the mark and mix. Transfer a portion of the solution to a polarographic cell, bubble with nitrogen for 5 minutes to remove oxygen, and record a polarogram from -0.6 to -1.0 volt (*vs.* S.C.E.). Compare the diffusion current with that of a standard sample solution to determine the amount of nickel present.

Separation Method for Determination of Zinc.—To facilitate the dithizone extraction of zinc, remove copper from the alloy solution before the extraction. Copper can be removed very simply by treating an aliquot portion of the alloy solution with hydroxylamine hydrochloride and potassium thiocyanate. (Alternatively a weighed sample of the alloy may be dissolved in hydrochloric acid, leaving the copper unattacked). The amount of alloy sample used does not affect the diffusion current constant, since the zinc is extracted from the solution. For most alloys, a 15-ml. aliquot sample of its solution may be treated with 0.5 ml. of the 2 *M* hydroxylamine hydrochloride solution and 0.5 ml. of the 2 *M* potassium thiocyanate solution to remove the copper (the copper thiocyanate precipitate need not be removed from the solution). For alloys of low zinc content, it is convenient to dissolve a 1-g. sample in 25 ml. of constant-boiling hydrochloric acid and filter the solution to remove the residue of copper, nickel, etc.

To the resulting copper-free solution, add thymol blue indicator, 10 ml. of the saturated sodium citrate solution, and ammonia until the indicator changes color to a greenish yellow. Transfer this solution quantitatively to a separatory funnel (the stopcocks of the separatory funnels should not be greased but wetted with water). Add 10 ml. of the 0.05 percent dithizone in carbon tetrachloride solution and shake for 1 to 2 minutes. (If appreciable amounts of lead and zinc are present, the carbon tetrachloride layer becomes a bright cherry red.) Withdraw the carbon tetrachloride phase into a clean 125-ml. separatory funnel, add 10 ml. of the 0.05 percent dithizone in carbon tetrachloride solution to the aqueous solution, and again extract as outlined above. Continue the extraction until the carbon tetrachloride phase remains green or becomes a brownish purple, then extract once more to ensure the complete separation of zinc and lead. (If a brownish-purple scum forms over the carbon tetrachloride during the extractions, do not transfer it to the 125-ml. separatory funnel. The scum is nickel dithizonate which is slightly soluble in carbon tetrachloride.) Shake the aqueous solution with two small portions of carbon tetrachloride to rinse out droplets containing zinc and lead. Add these to the 125-ml. separatory funnel and discard the aqueous solution. Add 25 ml. of water containing 1 drop of ammonia to the combined extracts and shake to wash the carbon tetrachloride. Withdraw the carbon tetrachloride phase to another 125-ml. separatory funnel, shake the ammonia solution with two small portions of carbon tetrachloride, and add these extracts to the main carbon tetrachloride extract. Discard the ammonia solution and clean the funnel.

To the combined extracts add 20 ml. of 0.1 *M* hydrochloric acid and shake for 2 to 3 minutes. (The carbon tetrachloride layer will turn green if no copper is present.) Withdraw the carbon tetrachloride phase to the other 125-ml. separatory funnel. Rinse the hydrochloric acid solution with two small portions of carbon tetrachloride and combine the latter with the carbon tetrachloride extract. Leave the hydrochloric acid solution in the separatory funnel with any scum and droplets of carbon tetrachloride.

Add 10 ml. of fresh 0.1 *M* hydrochloric acid to the carbon tetrachloride extract, shake for 2 to 3 minutes, and discard the carbon tetrachloride phase. Rinse the hydrochloric acid solution with two small portions of carbon tetrachloride and transfer it quantitatively to the separatory funnel containing the 20-ml. portion.

Shake the combined hydrochloric acid solutions with several small portions of chloroform until the chloroform remains colorless, and discard the chloroform. (The nickel dithizonate scum is soluble in chloroform and thus only a few droplets of clear chloroform should remain with the acid solution.) Transfer the acid solution quantitatively to a 100-ml. beaker and boil on a hot plate to expel all the chloroform. Cool the solution to room temperature and transfer it to a 50-ml. volumetric flask. Add 1 ml. of the 0.5 percent gelatin solution, 1 ml. of pyridine, and dilute to the mark with distilled water. Transfer a portion of the solution to a polarographic cell, bubble with nitrogen for 5 minutes to remove oxygen, and record a polarogram from -0.2 to -0.6 volt (*vs.* S.C.E.) to determine lead, and from -0.8 to -1.2 volts (*vs.* S.C.E.) to determine zinc. Compare the diffusion currents for lead and zinc with those observed for standard sample solutions prepared as follows: Combine known amounts of standard lead and zinc solutions with 30 ml. of 0.1 *M* hydrochloric acid, 1 ml. of pyridine, 1 ml. of the 0.5 percent gelatin solution, and dilute to 50.0 ml.

POLAROGRAPHIC DETERMINATION OF COPPER, NICKEL, COBALT, AND CHROMIUM IN TITANIUM ALLOYS[67]

This procedure emphasizes the advantages that may be realized by the use of an easily performed (not necessarily quantitative) isolatory technique to remove the bulk of the matrix material prior to polarographic analysis. Although this particular technique will not apply to many alloy systems, it is often possible to effect simple separations that will permit the polarographic determination of one or more of the alloying constituents.

***Apparatus.* A Modern Commercially-Available Polarograph.**

Solution Evaporators.—Moroney No-Bump type (Fisher Scientific Co.).

Platinum Crucibles or Dishes.—Capacity of 30-ml. or larger.

Plastic Dropper.—Polyethylene or polystyrene.

***Reagents.* Sulfuric Acid (20 percent Solution).**—Carefully add 200 ml. of sulfuric acid to 800 ml. of water.

Pyridine.—Reagent Grade (boiling point range, 113° to 116°C.)

Hydrofluoric Acid.—Reagent Grade (48 percent).

Gelatin (1 percent Solution).—Dissolve 1 g. of gelatin in 50 ml. of water by gently applying heat. Transfer to a 100-ml. volumetric flask and dilute to the mark. Use only a freshly prepared solution.

Gelatin (0.5 percent Solution).—Dilute a portion of the 1 percent solution with an equal portion of water.

Barium Chloride (10 percent Solution).—Dissolve 10 g. of barium chloride, in 100 ml. of water.

Iron.—Chromium-free Grade.

Silver Nitrate (0.25 percent Solution).—Dissolve 0.25 g. of silver nitrate in 100 ml. of water.

Ammonium Persulfate.—Reagent Grade.

Sodium Hydroxide (4 *M* Solution).—Dissolve 80 g. of sodium hydroxide in 500 ml. of water.

Hydrogen Peroxide (30 percent Solution).

Graphite.—Chromium-free Grade.

Standard Copper Solution (1 ml. = 0.001 g. copper).—Dissolve 1.0000 g. of high-purity copper in a minimum amount of nitric acid. Transfer to a 1-liter volumetric flask, dilute to the mark, and mix.

Standard Nickel Solution (1 ml. = 0.001 g. nickel).—Transfer 4.0501 g. of nickel chloride hexahydrate ($NiCl_2 \cdot 6H_2O$) to a 1-liter volumetric flask, dissolve with water, dilute to the mark, mix, and standardize.

Standard Cobalt Solution (1 ml. = 0.001 g. cobalt).—Transfer 4.0372 g. of cobalt chloride hexahydrate ($CoCl_2 \cdot 6H_2O$) to a 1-liter volumetric flask, dissolve with water, dilute to the mark, mix, and standardize.

Standard Chromium Solution (1 ml. = 0.001 g. chromium).—Transfer 2.8284 g. of National Bureau of Standards potassium dichromate to a 1-liter volumetric flask, dissolve with water, dilute to the mark, and mix.

Preparation of Calibration Curves.—Prepare calibration curves for copper, nickel, and cobalt by adding known amounts of standard copper, nickel, and cobalt solutions,

[67] Mikula, J. J., and Codell, M., Anal. Chem., **27,** 729, 1955. Copyright 1955 by ACS and reprinted in part with permission of the copyright owner.

respectively, to pure titanium, and carry them through all the steps of the procedure. The approximate half-wave potentials for the reduction of copper, nickel, and cobalt, respectively, occur at −0.25, −0.78, and −1.06 volts (*vs.* S.C.E.). Figure 44-10 shows typical calibration curves for these three elements.

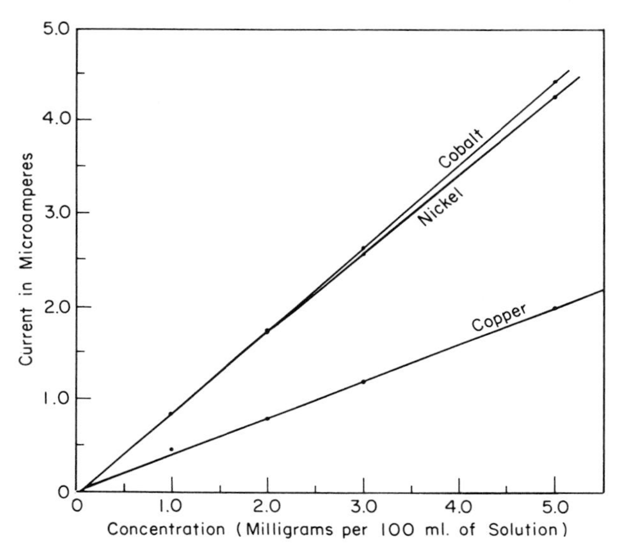

FIG. 44-10. Relation Between Diffusion Current and Concentration of Copper, Nickel, and Cobalt.

Prepare a series of standards for the determination of chromium by adding known amounts of standard chromate solution to separate 50-ml. volumetric flasks containing 1 ml. of the 0.5 percent gelatin solution and 1 ml. of sulfuric acid. Neutralize with 4 *M* sodium hydroxide, and add 20 ml. in excess. Dilute to volume and prepare polarograms.

Prepare separate standards for the determination of chromium in the presence of manganese as follows: Transfer 1 ml. of sulfuric acid and 1 ml. of hydrochloric acid to a 50-ml. volumetric flask. Add 5 ml. of water. Neutralize with 4 *M* sodium hydroxide and add a 20-ml. excess. Add an appropriate aliquot of the standard chromate solution and 1 ml. of the 0.5 percent gelatin solution. Dilute to the mark and prepare polarograms.

Determine the relative diffusion currents for each series of standard solutions and prepare a calibration curve for each element to be evaluated.

***Procedure*. Determination of Copper, Nickel, and Cobalt.**—Place a 0.1-g. sample in a 250-ml. beaker containing approximately 15 ml. of water. Using a plastic dropper, add 15 to 20 drops of hydrofluoric acid, place on hot plate, and warm gently until titanium is completely dissolved. Add 1 to 2 drops of nitric acid to oxidize the titanium. (A few additional drops of nitric acid may be required to dissolve some alloying constituents.) Add 2 ml. of perchloric acid, and evaporate to moist dryness, but do not bake. To ensure uniform heating and to prevent spattering, this operation should be performed in a No-Bump solution evaporator (see apparatus). Remove from the hot plate and cool to room temperature. Add exactly 2.0 ml. of concentrated hydrochloric acid, and swirl to dissolve salts. Wash the sample into a 100-ml. volumetric flask using 50 to

75 ml. of water. (If chromium is present, add 5 ml. of the 10 percent barium chloride solution at this point.) Add exactly 5.0 ml. of pyridine, shake gently, and let stand 2 minutes; then add 5.0 ml. of the 1.0 percent gelatin solution, dilute to mark with water, and mix. Allow the precipitate to settle, then electrolyze a portion of the supernatant liquid between 0.0 and −1.3 volts (*vs.* S.C.E.). Making proper allowance for the residual current in each instance, measure the diffusion currents for copper, nickel, and cobalt, respectively at or near −0.25, −0.78, −1.06 volts (*vs.* S.C.E.). Use the calibration curves to convert the associated diffusion currents to percent copper, nickel, and cobalt in the sample.

Determination of Chromium.—Transfer a 0.1 g. of sample to a platinum dish and add 25 mg. of chromium-free iron,[68] 5 ml. of 20 percent sulfuric acid, and 15 to 20 drops of hydrofluoric acid. If necessary, heat until the sample is dissolved. Add 2 to 3 drops of nitric acid, and gently heat to fumes of sulfuric acid. Continue heating 2 to 3 minutes longer, remove from hot plate, and cool. Use a stream of water from a wash bottle to transfer the sample into a 250-ml. beaker, and dilute to approximately 100 ml. Place on a hot plate and boil the solution for five minutes. (Titanium will hydrolyze at this point.) Add 5 ml. of silver nitrate solution, and cautiously add about 1 g. of ammonium persulfate. Boil 10 to 15 minutes to destroy the excess ammonium persulfate. (If the solution becomes pink, the procedure for Determination of Chromium in the Presence of Manganese should be followed.) If no pink color results, continue as follows: Remove from the hot plate and cool. Neutralize with 4 *M* sodium hydroxide until all the iron is just precipitated. Add 20 ml. of 4 *M* sodium hydroxide containing 25 to 30 drops of 30 percent hydrogen peroxide. Add a small amount of graphite to minimize bumping, and boil the solution until a volume of approximately 15 to 20 ml. remains. Cool and transfer the solution to a 50-ml. volumetric flask. Add 1.0 ml. of the 0.50 percent gelatin solution, dilute to the mark, and electrolyze a portion of the supernatant liquid between −0.4 and −1.6 volts (*vs.* S.C.E.). Use the calibration curve to convert the diffusion current (corrected for the residual current) to percentage chromium in the sample.

Determination of Chromium in the Presence of Manganese.—Follow the preceding chromium procedure to and including the 10 to 15-minute boiling period. Then add 1 ml. of 12 *M* hydrochloric acid, and boil 10 minutes longer. Filter on a medium paper and wash several times with hot water. Heat the filtrate to boiling, remove from the hot plate, and neutralize with 4 *M* sodium hydroxide until a slight permanent precipitate appears. Add 20 ml. of ammonium hydroxide and 20 ml. of saturated bromine water. Boil about 4 minutes, filter through a fast paper, and wash with warm 2 percent ammonium hydroxide solution. Boil the filtrate about 15 minutes, then cautiously add 20 ml. of the 4 *M* sodium hydroxide containing 25 to 30 drops of 30 percent hydrogen peroxide. Boil 10 minutes, filter through a medium paper, and wash with water. Add a small amount of graphite to the filtrate to prevent bumping, and boil until a volume of approximately 15 to 20 ml. remains. Cool and transfer the solution to a 50-ml. volumetric flask. Add 1.0 ml. of the 0.5 percent gelatin solution, dilute to the mark, mix, and electrolyze a portion of the supernatant liquid between −0.4 and −1.6 volts (*vs.* S.C.E.). Use the calibration curve to convert the diffusion current (corrected for the residual current) to percentage of chromium in the sample.

Discussion.—None of the elements, with the exception of chromium, which would be expected to be found in commercial titanium alloys, interferes with the simultaneous determination of copper, nickel, and cobalt. The interference of chromium is easily removed by the addition of barium chloride.

[68] The subsequent precipitation of titanium with sodium hydroxide is more complete in the presence of a small amount of iron. See Hillebrand, W. F., and Lundell, G. E. F., Applied Inorganic Analysis, 2nd Ed., John Wiley, New York, 1953, p. 597.

Satisfactory results are obtainable for copper, nickel, and cobalt over the range of 0.2 to 5.0 percent.

ABSTRACTED PROCEDURES WHICH APPLY OR MAY BE ADAPTED TO NONFERROUS ALLOY ANALYSIS[69,70]

The following abstracted procedures are presented for the polarographic determination of various elements (listed alphabetically) which may be encountered in nonferrous materials. With minor changes it may be possible to adapt a procedure for the analysis of a given element to nonferrous materials other than the one or ones listed. Each abstracted procedure contains valuable information regarding supporting electrolyte and wave form or half-wave reduction potential ($E_{1/2}$ *vs.* S.C.E.) reported in the literature for the listed element.

As with the foregoing procedures, the evaluation of each element to be determined is accomplished by comparing the diffusion current of its solution with the diffusion currents of synthetic standard sample solutions. A literature reference is given for each procedure, in case the procedural information in a given abstract is insufficient for a particular application.

ALUMINUM (0.01 TO 0.3 MG.) IN BRONZE[71]

Procedure.—Dissolve 1 g. of sample with 10 ml. of 5 *M* hydrochloric acid and 5 ml. of 30 percent peroxide. Evaporate to fumes with 10 ml. of 5 *M* perchloric acid. Cool and dilute to 50 ml. with water. If much tin is present, filter and wash with water. Electrolyze the filtrate with a mercury cathode. Dilute the electrolyte to 100.0 ml. and neutralize a suitable aliquot to pH 5 with 2.5 *M* sodium hydroxide. Add 1 ml. of 5 *M* perchloric acid, 5 ml. of 2 *M* sodium acetate, and 20 ml. of 0.05 percent Pontachrome Violet SW. Dilute to 50 ml. and analyze polarographically.

SE: 0.1 *M* acetic acid, 0.1 *M* sodium acetate, and 0.3 *M* sodium perchlorate.
WR: −0.1 to −0.8 v.

ANTIMONY (2.0 TO 5.0 PERCENT) IN LEAD[72]

Procedure.—Dissolve 0.2 g. of sample with 15 ml. of hydrochloric acid. Add 3 drops of bromine and boil. Dilute to 50 ml. with hydrochloric acid (1:1). To a 5-ml. aliquot, add 0.1 ml. of a 0.5 percent gelatin solution and analyze polarographically.

SE: 8 *M* hydrochloric acid.
$E_{1/2}$: −0.2 v.

BISMUTH (0.01 TO 1.0 PERCENT) IN ALUMINUM-COPPER-ZINC ALLOYS[73]

Procedure.—Dissolve 5 g. of sample with nitric acid (1:1), boil and add 5 g. of tartaric acid. Make ammoniacal, add 2 g. of potassium cyanide, and precipitate the bismuth and lead with sodium sulfide. Filter and dissolve the sulfides with nitric acid (1:1). Evaporate to dryness with 6 *M* hydrochloric acid. Take up with a little hydrochloric

[69] These abstracts were compiled from the cited references and from Meites, L., Ed., Handbook of Analytical Chemistry, McGraw-Hill Book Company, New York, N. Y., 1963.
[70] In the following abstracted procedures, SE, WR, and $E_{1/2}$ are respective abbreviations for supporting electrolyte, wave range, and half-wave reduction potential; unless otherwise stated WR and $E_{1/2}$ values are referred to the saturated calomel electrode.
[71] Willard, H. H., and Dean, J. A., Anal. Chem., **22,** 1264, 1950.
[72] Kraus, R., and Novák, J. V. A., Coll. Czech. Chem. Comm., **10,** 534, 1938.
[73] Krössin, E., Metall. u. Erz., **38,** 10, 1941.

acid (1:1), dilute to 50.0 ml. with 10 percent hydrochloric acid, and analyze polarographically.

SE: 3 *M* hydrochloric acid.
$E_{1/2}$: −0.9 v.

BISMUTH (>0.0005 PERCENT) IN CADMIUM[74]

Procedure.—Dissolve 5 g. of sample with nitric acid (1:1). Add a solution of iron(III) nitrate containing 30 mg. of iron, neutralize with ammonium hydroxide and add an excess. Filter and redissolve the precipitate with warm 8 *M* hydrochloric acid. Concentrate (if necessary) and add hydrazine hydrochloride until colorless. Adjust the volume to contain 3 *M* hydrochloric acid and analyze polarographically.

SE: 3 *M* hydrochloric acid.
$E_{1/2}$: −0.9 v.

CADMIUM (0.01 TO 5.0 PERCENT) IN ALUMINUM[75]

Procedure.—Cautiously dissolve 2 g. of sample with 4 ml. of 37 percent sodium hydroxide and add an excess of 16 ml. Boil, dilute to 50 ml., and carefully add 60 ml. of nitric acid (1:1). Again boil, cool, and add 10 ml. of a 50 percent solution of ammonium sulfate. Electrolyze with platinum electrodes to remove the copper and lead. Dilute the electrolyte to 200.0 ml. To a 20-ml. aliquot, add 0.1 ml. of 8 *M* hydroxylamine hydrochloride, then neutralize to pH 3 with a 20 percent solution of sodium carbonate. Heat to 80°C. for 10 minutes. Cool, add gelatin solution, dilute to 25 ml., and analyze polarographically.

SE: Ammonium sulfate.
$E_{1/2}$: −0.6 v.

CADMIUM (0.005 TO 0.1 PERCENT) IN ZINC[76]

Procedure.—Cautiously dissolve 9 g. of sample with 40 ml. of hydrochloric acid. Evaporate to near dryness, add 5 drops of hydrochloric acid (1:1), and dilute to 50 ml. To a 10-ml. aliquot, add 11 ml. of ammonium hydroxide and 1 ml. of a saturated sodium sulfite solution. Add gelatin, dilute to 25.0 ml., and analyze polarographically using a mercury pool anode.

SE: 7 *M* ammonium hydroxide with sodium sulfite.
$E_{1/2}$: −0.85 v.

COPPER (>0.1 PERCENT) IN COPPER, LEAD, TIN, AND ANTIMONY ALLOYS[77]

Procedure.—Dissolve 1.0 g. of sample with 10 ml. of hydrochloric acid and 10 ml. of hydrochloric acid which is saturated with bromine. Add 20 ml. of hydrochloric acid and 10 ml. of a saturated sodium sulfite solution, and dilute to 100.0 ml. To a 5-ml. aliquot, add 20 ml. of ammonium hydroxide (1:1), 2 ml. of a saturated sodium sulfite solution, dilute to 100.0 ml., and analyze polarographically.

SE: Ammonium hydroxide and sodium sulfite.
$E_{1/2}$: −0.2 v.

[74] Krössin, E., and Wagner, E., Metall. u. Erz., **38,** 199, 1941.
[75] Stross, W., Proc. 1st. Intern. Polarog. Congr., Prague, I, 397, 1951.
[76] Spálenka, M., Polarografické metody v metalurgii, SNTL, Prague, 1954.
[77] Cozzi, D., Ann. Chim. Appl., **29,** 474, 1939.

COPPER (0.005 TO 0.5 PERCENT) IN MAGNESIUM[78]

Procedure.—Dissolve 1.0 g. of sample with hydrochloric acid (1:1) and nitric acid (1:1). Add 10 ml. of a 25 percent citric acid solution, 8 g. of ammonium chloride, and dilute to 100.0 ml. with ammonium hydroxide (1:4). To a 10-ml. aliquot, add gelatin solution and analyze polarographically.

SE: Ammonium citrate and ammonium chloride.
$E_{1/2}$: −0.2 v.

INDIUM (>0.005 PERCENT) IN ZINC[79]

Procedure.—Add sufficient hydrochloric acid to dissolve the sample, then 1.7 ml. of 0.5 *M* ammonium chloride for each gram of sample used. Neutralize with ammonium hydroxide, filter, and wash with 1 percent ammonium hydroxide. Dissolve the precipitate with 10 ml. of a 10 percent tartaric acid solution and analyze polarographically.

SE: 10 percent tartaric acid solution.
$E_{1/2}$: −0.55 v.

IRON (UP TO 18 PERCENT) IN NICKEL-MOLYBDENUM-IRON ALLOYS[80]

Procedure.—Dissolve 0.2 g. of sample with 10 ml. of hydrochloric acid (1:1) and 4 ml. of 30 percent hydrogen peroxide, and dilute to 100.0 ml. To a 10-ml. aliquot, add 10 ml. of water, 5 ml. of 0.5 *M* triethanolamine, 10 ml. of ammonium hydroxide (1:1), and 3 ml. of 2 *M* ammonium chloride. Add 2 ml. of a saturated sodium sulfite solution, dilute to 50 ml., and analyze polarographically.

SE: 0.05 *M* triethanolamine, 1.5 *M* ammonium hydroxide, and 0.2 *M* ammonium chloride.
$E_{1/2}$: −0.5 v.

IRON (0.002 TO 2.5 PERCENT) IN NONFERROUS ALLOYS[81]

Procedure.—Dissolve 1 to 10 g. of sample with 25 ml. of hydrochloric acid and 10 ml. of nitric acid. Warm to dissolve, if necessary, and evaporate nearly to dryness. Add 10 ml. of hydrochloric acid and repeat the evaporation. Add 20 ml. of water and swirl to dissolve salts. Add 10 to 50 g. of amalgamated zinc and agitate 1 minute. (If the solution becomes turbid, add a few drops of hydrochloric acid.) Filter through a Whatman 41H, paper, and wash several times with water. (Reserve the unused amalgamated zinc for re-use.) To the filtrate add 0.2 *M* potassium permanganate until the pink color holds for 5 seconds. Add 2 ml. of a saturated oxalic acid solution, 5 g. of citric acid, 0.1 ml. of 0.1 percent methyl red, then ammonium hydroxide to the first color change. Dilute to 100.0 ml. and analyze polarographically. (*Note.* Use methyl red sparingly as it may be reduced at $E_{1/2} = -0.55$ v.).

SE: Oxalic acid, ammonium hydroxide, and 0.26 *M* citric acid.
$E_{1/2}$: −0.55 v.

[78] Mukhina, Z. S., Zavodskaya Lab., **14,** 153, 1948.
[79] Jentzsch, D., Frotscher, I., Schwerdtfeger, G., and Sarfert, G., Zeit. Anal. Chemie, **144,** 8, 1955.
[80] Wolfson, H., Nature, **153,** 375, 1944.
[81] Meites, L., Anal. Chem., **24,** 1374, 1952.

MANGANESE (>0.01 PERCENT) IN NICKEL AND MONEL[82]

Procedure.—Dissolve 1 g. of sample with 10 ml. of hydrochloric acid (1:1) and 5 ml. of nitric acid (1:1). Dilute to 100.0 ml. To a 10-ml. aliquot, add 2 ml. of ammonium hydroxide, 5 ml. of a 10 percent ammonium carbonate solution, and 2 ml. of 30 percent hydrogen peroxide. Filter and dissolve the precipitate with hydrochloric acid (1:1) and a 6 percent sulfuric acid solution. Dilute to 25 ml. with the supporting electrolyte and analyze polarographically.

SE: 0.15 *M* triethanolamine, 1.5 *M* sodium hydroxide, and oxidize with oxygen.
$E_{1/2}$: −0.49 v.

NICKEL (UP TO 20 PERCENT) AND ZINC IN BRASS AND BRONZE[83]

Procedure.—Dissolve 1 g. of sample with 25 ml. of nitric acid (1:1) and boil gently for 5 minutes. Dilute to 70 ml. with hot water and digest for 30 minutes. (If tin is present, filter and wash with hot 2 percent nitric acid.) Add 1 drop of 0.1 *M* hydrochloric acid and electrolyze with platinum electrodes to remove copper and lead. Dilute the electrolyte to 250.0 ml. To a 50-ml. aliquot, add 4 ml. of a 0.5 percent gelatin solution, 10 ml. of ammonium hydroxide, dilute to 100 ml., and analyze polarographically.

SE: 0.4 *M* ammonium nitrate and 1.5 *M* ammonium hydroxide.
$E_{1/2}$: −1.15 v. for nickel.
$E_{1/2}$: −1.38 v. for zinc.

NICKEL (>0.01 PERCENT) IN COBALT[84,85]

Procedure.—Dissolve 1 g. of sample with 15 ml. of nitric acid. Evaporate (to near dryness) three times with 10 ml. of hydrochloric acid. Add 2 ml. of hydrochloric acid, 20 ml. of water, and warm to dissolve salts. Cool and dilute to 50.0 ml. Transfer two 20-ml. aliquots to clean 50-ml. volumetric flasks. To one flask, add 5.0 ml. of a standard nickel chloride solution containing 2.0 mg. of nickel (standard addition technique). To each flask, add 2.5 ml. of pyridine, 2.5 ml. of a 0.2 percent gelatin solution, and dilute to volume. Analyze each polarographically.

Note.—Since the diffusion current for large amounts of cobalt commences before the limiting current for nickel is well established, choose a voltage (on the current-voltage curve) 0.10 to 0.12 volt beyond the half-wave potential of nickel to determine its limiting current.

SE: Pyridine
$E_{1/2}$: −0.78 v.

LEAD (>0.1 PERCENT) IN BRASS AND BRONZE[86]

Procedure.—Dissolve 2 g. of sample with 25 ml. of nitric acid. Boil, cool, and dilute to 50.0 ml. Filter a portion through a dry paper. To a 10-ml. aliquot, add 10 ml. of a 50 percent sodium sulfite solution and 16 ml. of a 13 percent potassium cyanide solution. Mix well, add 5 ml. of a 25 percent triethanolamine solution, 10 ml. of 10 *M* sodium hydroxide, 2 ml. of a 0.2 percent gelatin solution, and analyze polarographically.

[82] Spálenka, M., Hutnické Listy, **8,** 382, 1953.
[83] Alsopp, W. E., and Arthur, T. E., Anal. Chem., **23,** 1883, 1951.
[84] Lingane, J. J., and Kerlinger, H., Ind. Eng. Chem., Anal. Ed., **13,** 77, 1941.
[85] Jones, R. H., Analyst, **71,** 60, 1946.
[86] Milner, G. W. C., Metallurgia, **36,** 287, 1947.

SE: Triethanolamine and sodium hydroxide.
WR: 0 to −1.0 v.

LEAD (<0.01 PERCENT) IN ZINC[87]

Procedure.—Dissolve 5 g. of sample with 20 ml. of hydrochloric acid. Heat and add 3 drops of a saturated potassium chlorate solution. Boil, cool, and dilute to 20.0 ml. To a 5-ml. aliquot, add methyl violet and neutralize with ammonium hydroxide. Dilute to 7.0 ml. and analyze polarographically.

SE: Ammonium chloride.
WR: −0.2 to −0.8 v.

TIN (>0.2 PERCENT) IN ALUMINUM[88]

Procedure.—Dissolve 1 g. of sample with 35 ml. of 5 *M* hydrochloric acid and boil. Add 60 ml. of 5 *M* sodium hydroxide, boil, cool, and dilute to 100.0 ml. To a 10-ml. aliquot of the supernatant liquid, add 9 ml. of 5 *M* hydrochloric acid and analyze polarographically using a mercury pool anode. (*Note.* Lead interferes.)

SE: 1 *M* hydrochloric acid.
$E_{1/2}$: −0.29 v.

TITANIUM (0.06 TO 0.2 PERCENT) IN ALUMINUM[89]

Procedure.—Dissolve 2 g. of sample with 30 ml. of 6.5 *M* sodium hydroxide. Add 170 ml. of water, filter and wash. Dissolve the precipitate with 26 ml. of hot 4.5 *M* sulfuric acid and wash with water. Neutralize to litmus with ammonium hydroxide. Add 25 ml. of 2 *M* sulfuric acid, 15 g. of tartaric acid, dilute to 100.0 ml., and analyze polarographically.

SE: 1 *M* tartaric acid, 0.5 *M* sulfuric acid, and 1.2 *M* ammonium sulfate.
WR: 0 to −1.0 v.

ZINC[90,91] *(0.1 TO 2.0 PERCENT) IN ALUMINUM-COPPER ALLOYS*[92]

Procedure.—Dissolve 0.5 g. of sample with 10 ml. of 3.5 *M* sodium hydroxide. Boil and dilute to 20 ml. Add 15 ml. of a solution containing 53 g. of ammonium chloride, 350 ml. of ammonium hydroxide, and 650 ml. of water. Add 2 ml. of a saturated sodium sulfite solution and 2 ml. of a 0.5 percent gelatin solution. Dilute to 50 ml. and analyze polarographically.

NOTE.—Copper, iron, mercury, manganese, nickel, and silicon do not interfere.

SE: Ammonium hydroxide, ammonium chloride, and sodium sulfite.
WR: −0.6 to −1.6 v.

[87] Nickelson, A. S., and Randles, J. E. B., Polarographic and Spectrographic Analysis of High-Purity Zinc and Zinc Alloys for Die Casting, H. M. Stationery Office, London, 1945.
[88] Spectrochemical and Polarographic Analysis of Aluminum and its Alloys, British Aluminum Co., Ltd., London, 1943.
[89] Graham, R. P., and Hitchen, A., Analyst, **77**, 533, 1952.
[90] Zinc (up to 40 percent) in brass and bronze may be run simultaneously with nickel. (See the abstracted procedure for nickel and zinc in brass and bronze).
[91] For the determination of zinc (0.001 to 0.05 percent) in pig lead, soft solder, white metal bearing alloys, and die casting alloys, see Volume II A, p. 902.
[92] Spálenka, M., Zeit. Anal. Chemie, **128,** 42, 1947.

ZINC (20 TO 45 PERCENT) IN BRASS[93]

Procedure.—Dissolve 0.1 g. of sample with 2 ml. of nitric acid and dilute to 50.0 ml. To a 5-ml. aliquot, add 5.0 ml. of 4 *M* ammonium chloride, 5.0 ml. of 4 *M* ammonium hydroxide, and analyze polarographically.

SE:	Ammonium chloride and ammonium hydroxide.
WR:	0 to −1.6 v.

DETERMINATION OF GASES AND CARBON IN NONFERROUS METALS AND ALLOYS[94]

The determination of gases in metals was, until recently, confined largely to iron and steel, but within the past several decades interest has spread to almost all metal systems. As knowledge of the effects of oxygen, hydrogen, nitrogen, and carbon on the mechanical and electrical properties of metals increases, suppliers and processors of metals require more and faster analyses, and for advanced research efforts the limits of sensitivity must be extended to lower and lower levels. Laboratories devoted to metals analysis must plan in terms of these demands for determinations of gases in a range of metals extending from lithium to plutonium, singly, and in an endless variety of alloy combinations.

Scope.—Establishment of standard methods for gases in metals has progressed slowly, due in large part to the lack of suitable standard materials. For this reason, and because of the wide variety of metals that must be considered, a universal method suitable for all analyses cannot be recommended, nor is it practical here to recommend individual methods for specific metals and alloys. Instead, the methods in common use for gases-in-metals analysis are described briefly, with some discussion of their applications to particular metals. This information is intended to suggest a suitable approach to the analyst faced with a particular problem.

***Sample Preparation.* General Considerations.**—Sample preparation is often the most critical part of an analysis for gases in metals. Gases may be in the metal or on it; they may be in solid solution, combined with the metal, or entrapped physically in voids. Metals are not, as a rule, homogeneous, and the likelihood of introducing surface contamination militates against subdividing a large amount of material to obtain a representative sample; it is best to work with a single piece. Care must be taken in cutting to avoid surface contamination by reaction of friction-heated metal with air; conversely, some metals lose hydrogen when warmed in air. Removal of surface contaminants is done by abrading with a file or by acid cleaning. Final rinsing of the sample is done with organic solvents, acetone and carbon tetrachloride being among the more popular of these. Geometry of the sample, atmospheric conditions, method of storage, manner of introduction into vacuum analysis systems, and other variables can affect the amounts of gases in or on a sample at the time of analysis.

Standard Samples.—Because of the difficulties mentioned above, particularly that of obtaining homogeneous materials, standard samples for gases in metals are almost non-existent. Various task forces under ASTM Committee E-3, Division I, are working on methods of analysis and standardization of a wide range of metals and alloy systems. Information on available standards will be kept current by the chairman of this Division, who will be the best source of information on any particular metal system at any particular time.

[93] Schwarz, K., Z. anal. Chem., **115,** 161, 1939.

[94] This section prepared by William A. Fraser, U. S. Naval Research Laboratory, Washington, D. C.

METHODS

Methods in general use for determining gases or carbon in metals are described briefly below. Some of the methods and apparatus are described in detail in Volume IIB, Chapter 36 "Gas Analysis—Vacuum Techniques." Chemical methods for the determination of gases in metals are beyond the scope of this chapter. They are generally less satisfactory than instrumental methods, but the time-honored Kjeldahl method is the usual one for determining nitrogen in these metals and alloys. Current publications discuss at length methods in use for gases-in-metals analysis and provide comprehensive bibliographies of the literature.[95]

Vacuum Fusion.—In the vacuum fusion method the sample is fused in a graphite crucible that is heated by induction in a vacuum system. The crucible often contains a molten metal bath to facilitate quick release of the gases. Bath material added simultaneously with the sample is called a "flux." The temperature of fusion and extraction varies from 1000 to 2000°C., depending upon the metal to be analyzed and the bath or flux. Platinum and iron are the most common bath materials at high temperatures; tin may be used at lower temperatures. The gases—carbon monoxide (from oxygen reacting with graphite), hydrogen, and nitrogen—are pumped from the fusion chamber into an analytical system where the amount of each is determined. Vacuum fusion is widely used for determining oxygen and hydrogen. Complete extraction of nitrogen is sometimes possible, in which case the three gases can be determined simultaneously. Gettering of gases by metal vaporized from the crucible and deposited on the furnace wall is sometimes a problem. Aluminum and manganese are particularly suspect as getters in oxygen analysis.

Inert Gas Fusion.—In the inert gas fusion method, the sample is fused with platinum in a graphite crucible in a stream of inert gas, which carries the released gases into an analysis system. With this method, ordinarily used for oxygen only, hydrogen and nitrogen may be determined as well with suitable measuring systems.[96] Inert gas fusion temperatures (2000–2300°C.) are higher than those used in vacuum fusion, which makes it possible to determine oxygen and nitrogen in more refractory forms. This method also has the advantages of speed and reduced rate of vaporization of metal from the crucible, resulting in reduced gettering.

Vacuum Extraction.—In the vacuum extraction method the sample is heated in vacuum to a temperature below the melting point, and gases released are transferred into a measuring system. Vacuum fusion equipment may be used for analyses by this method, which depends on the rate of diffusion of the gas in the metal being great enough to permit complete extraction in a reasonable time. Where it can be applied, vacuum extraction has the advantage of relatively low operating temperature, with consequent lowering of the apparatus blank. This is the usual method for determining hydrogen alone, and it has been applied successfully to oxygen in some of the refractory metals.

Isotope Dilution.—In the isotope dilution method the sample, containing gas in the natural isotope ratio, is brought into contact with a known quantity of the gas enriched with respect to one of its isotopes. This is done by heating the sample with a known quantity of a "master alloy" containing the enriched isotope, or by heating the sample in an atmosphere containing the enriched isotope. When equilibrium is attained, a portion of the gas is extracted by vacuum fusion or hot extraction, and the isotope ratio of the mixture is measured by mass spectrometry. Complete extraction of the gas is not required for this method, which has been used for determining oxygen, hydrogen and

[95] James, J. A., Metallurgical Reviews, **9,** 93, 1964.
[96] Holt, B. D., and Goodspeed, H. T., Anal. Chem., **35,** 1510, 1963.

nitrogen. The time and effort required for determinations by isotope dilution do not recommend it as a substitute for vacuum or inert gas fusion, where these methods are satisfactory.

Emission Spectrometry.—In the emission spectrometric method the sample is fused in an argon atmosphere by a d.c. carbon arc, with simultaneous release and excitation of the gases. Amounts of the gases present are determined from the intensities of the resulting emission spectra. Fassel and co-workers have developed this technique and applied it successfully to determining oxygen, hydrogen, and nitrogen in a wide range of metals. Advantages of the method include speed of analysis and the very high temperature (above 3000°C.) of the sample melt, which rapidly breaks down even refractory oxides and nitrides.

Neutron Activation.—In the neutron activation method the sample is irradiated to convert part of the gas into radioactive species, the resulting radiation being a measure of the amount of gas present in the sample. The most widely used technique determines oxygen by using fast (14 m.e.v.) neutrons to produce the reaction $O^{16}(n,p)N^{16}$. Use of this method is limited to laboratories having access to a high-energy neutron source. Neutron activation avoids the problem of extracting the gas from the metal, and large samples can often be used, which may be an advantage when working with materials that may not be homogeneous.

Combustion Methods.—In combustion methods for the determination of carbon the sample is oxidized and carbon dioxide formed is measured. Variations of this basic technique are almost universally used for determining carbon in metals. Methods for carrying out the oxidation at atmospheric pressure and at low pressure are described in detail in Volume IIB, Chapter 36.

APPLICATION OF METHODS TO THE METALS

There are very few methods for determining gases in nonferrous metals that can be considered standard methods. In the absence of standard samples for checking results among laboratories, the most that can be done in many cases is to adopt a method that gives self-consistent results in one's own laboratory. Widely accepted methods are in use for a few metals, and in the discussion below these are described briefly for the metals concerned.

Vacuum fusion and inert gas fusion are the usual methods for determination of oxygen. Where applicable, specific conditions for analyses by these methods are given here. Inert gas fusion temperatures used by individual analysts are not as readily available as vacuum fusion temperatures; indeed, temperatures used for inert gas fusion analyses are frequently not reported at all. Vacuum fusion temperatures are lower than those used for inert gas fusion, so if extraction of oxygen is complete at the lower vacuum fusion temperature, the higher inert gas fusion temperature presumably affects only the speed of extraction. In using this information one must bear in mind that analysts do not always agree on details. For example, a number of laboratories may use vacuum fusion with a platinum bath to determine oxygen in a particular metal, but the temperatures used may vary over a range of 200°C. Such variations of conditions considered best for a given analysis may be due to differences in equipment from laboratory to laboratory, or they may simply reflect personal preferences of the analysts.

Hydrogen, when it is not determined with oxygen by vacuum fusion, is usually determined by vacuum extraction at a temperature well below the vacuum fusion temperature. Nitrogen is usually determined by the Kjeldahl solution-distillation method, and carbon by combustion methods. Because these methods for hydrogen, nitrogen, and carbon are of such wide applicability, they are not always mentioned here in the discussion of specific methods for the metals.

Copper and Copper-Base Alloys.—Oxygen in copper may be determined by vacuum fusion. Hydrogen and nitrogen are usually present in very small quantities relative to oxygen, and Harris and Hickam[97] took advantage of this to simplify the vacuum fusion apparatus for the determination of oxygen in copper. The sample is heated to 1150°C. in a furnace chamber which, with a manometer, forms a known volume. Since the total pressure may be assumed to be due to carbon monoxide (from oxygen in the metal) a more elaborate system for analyzing gases is not necessary. The method has been used for samples containing 0.01–0.5 percent oxygen by weight. Conventional vacuum fusion has the advantage of greater sensitivity.

Hydrogen may be present in copper dissolved in the metal, entrapped in voids as molecular hydrogen, or combined in water or hydrocarbons. Hot extraction in a graphite crucible can be used to determine entrapped or dissolved hydrogen. The sample must be fused if combined hydrogen is also to be determined. All surface oxide should be removed from samples for hydrogen determination by hot extraction, because hydrogen may react with the oxide to form water and escape measurement.

Beryllium.—Oxygen in beryllium may be determined by inert gas or vacuum fusion with a platinum bath or flux. Some vacuum fusion investigators claim better results with tin added to the bath or with a platinum bath and tin flux. Platinum-to-sample ratios vary from 4:1 to 50:1, and vacuum fusion temperatures from 1650–1950°C. Gettering of carbon monoxide by beryllium vaporized from the crucible and deposited on furnace walls is a problem in vacuum fusion that is minimized in inert gas fusion with its lower vaporization rates. Activation analysis with fast neutrons is also used for determining oxygen in beryllium, with sensitivity to 0.001 percent claimed. This method has the distinct advantage over fusion methods of minimizing the toxicity hazard.

Aluminum.—Methods for oxygen in aluminum are, at best, not very satisfactory. Aluminum reacts with graphite at 1200°C. to form the carbide, so container material for vacuum or inert gas fusion is a problem. If the oxygen content of the sample is high enough it can be added to an iron bath, giving, in effect, an aluminum-containing steel. A temperature of 1600°C. and a bath-sample ratio of 10:1 are used. Success has also been claimed for inert gas fusion at 1800°C. with a platinum flux. Preparing surfaces of samples for analysis is complicated by the ease with which aluminum forms oxides and hydrated oxides on clean surfaces. It is probably safer to determine oxygen in aluminum by one of the chemical methods in which the metal is dissolved and the aluminum oxide residue weighed.

Hydrogen in aluminum is determined by vacuum extraction from the solid at 500–575°C. or by vacuum fusion in a tin bath at 650°C.

Titantium, Zirconium, Hafnium.—Oxygen in titanium, zirconium and hafnium is determined by inert gas fusion or by vacuum fusion, with a platinum bath or flux (10:1 bath-to-sample weight ratio). Typical temperatures for vacuum fusion are 1950°C. for titanium, 2000° for zirconium and 2050° for hafnium. The Walter Method,[98] in which titanium reacts with graphite chips to form the carbide, was the first widely-accepted method for titanium. Hydrogen is determined in titanium and zirconium by vacuum extraction at 800–1400°C.

Molybdenum, Niobium, Tantalum, Tungsten, Vanadium.—Oxygen in these metals and their alloys is determined by inert gas fusion with a platinum bath, or by vacuum fusion with a bath of platinum or iron. Inert gas fusion temperatures are in the 2100–2250°C. range, vacuum fusion temperatures are about 1950°C. with platinum bath, and 1650–1850°C. with iron. The minimum bath-to-sample ratios range from 3:1 to 10:1. Vacuum extraction at about 2000°C. has been used to determine oxygen in

[97] Harris, W. F., and Hickam, W. M., Anal. Chem., **31**, 281, 1959.
[98] Walter, D. I., Anal. Chem., **22**, 297, 1950.

molybdenum and tungsten, the high diffusion rate of oxygen in those metals making its use possible. Hydrogen is determined by vacuum extraction or along with oxygen by vacuum fusion. Mallett[99] has published a review of the literature on determination of gases and carbon in molybdenum, niobium, tantalum, and tungsten.

Other Metals.—Methods for determining oxygen in other metals are not established, though many methods have been tried and the results published. Verification of the validity of these methods may be lacking, but in many cases they will be satisfactory in the laboratory. Hydrogen can usually be extracted from metals at temperatures practical in vacuum fusion equipment. Nitrogen is almost always determined by chemical means, but evidence that it can be extracted by vacuum fusion from some metals is gradually being accumulated. Chemical methods are used for oxygen in the alkali metals and calcium.

Theory and practice of gas-in-metal analysis have been treated at length by Turovtseva and Kunin.[100] A symposium consisting mostly of review articles contains much information as well as bibliographies arranged both by method and by gas or metal.[101] Methods for determining oxygen are covered in an annotated bibliography.[102]

[99] Mallett, M. W., Talanta, **9,** 133, 1962.

[100] Turovtseva, Z. M., and Kunin, L. L., Analysis of Gases in Metals, Consultants Bureau, New York, 1961.

[101] The Determination of Gases in Metals, Special Report No. 68, The Iron and Steel Institute, London, 1960.

[102] LePape, M., and Platzer, R., La determination de l'oxygene dans les metaux, Série Bibliographies No. 23, Service de Documentation du C.E.A., Centre d'Etudes Nucléaires de Saclay, B. P., No. 2, Gif-sur-Yvette (Seine-et-Oise), France, 1962.

Chapter 45

AMINO ACID ANALYSIS

By S. Mark Henry
Bristol-Myers Co.
Hillside, New Jersey

INTRODUCTION

An impressive variety of methods has been developed over the past half century for the determination of amino acids. The earliest procedures were purely chemical, usually relying on the isolation of amino acid derivatives and subsequent gravimetric or colorimetric estimation of quantity. The chemical methods, now seldom used, are described in detail by Block and Bolling.[1]

A sensitive but also little used procedure depends on the addition of a known quantity of amino acid labeled with nitrogen-15 to a hydrolyzate of a protein or to any amino acid mixture. The amino acid in question is then isolated and purified along with its isotopic analog from which it is inseparable by the usual laboratory procedures. The ratio of nitrogen-15 to normal nitrogen is then determined by means of a mass spectrograph. Since both normal and isotopic amino acid are lost to the same extent during the purification procedures, the amount of unlabeled amino acid recovered is proportional to the amount of labeled amino acid.

Until quite recently, microbiological assays were used in many laboratories, in addition to the chemical and physicochemical methods mentioned above. These consist of the addition of a protein hydrolyzate to a culture medium deficient in one of approximately twenty amino acids. One obtains a growth response curve commensurate with the amount of amino acid present. The technique is limited primarily in that closely related amino acids and other compounds may interfere, usually through a sparing action. Except in rare instances, protein hydrolyzates must be used. As in chemical assays, a standard curve is obtained, in this case by estimating the effect on growth when increasing quantities of pure amino acid are added to the media.

A convenient and rapid assay for arginine, histidine, lysine, or glutamic acid is based on the use of specific L-amino acid decarboxylases, which are available commercially. The carbon dioxide evolved is easily measured manometrically.[2,3]

By far the most widely used methods of amino acid analysis today are the chromatographic techniques. Details of an ion-exchange column chromatography method used successfully by the author are given in Volume II, Part A, page 937. References to improved procedures are given in the last section of this chapter. Block also gives details of methods for the qualitative and quantitative analysis of amino acids in protein hydrolyzates using paper chromatography (Vol. II, Part A, p. 920). The present chapter describes supplementary paper chromatographic techniques as well as thin-layer chro-

[1] Block, R. J., and Bolling, D., The Amino Acid Composition of Proteins and Foods, 2nd Ed., Charles C Thomas, Springfield, Ill., 1951.
[2] Gale, E. F., Biochem. J., **39,** 46–52, 1945.
[3] Frank, L. H., and DeMoss, R. D., Arch. Biochem. and Biophys., **67,** 387–397, 1957.

matography, paper electrophoresis, and gas chromatography. The latter methods are rapidly gaining respect as potentially valuable methods for the very rapid analysis of complex mixtures containing amino acids.

PAPER CHROMATOGRAPHY

The first great advances in the rapid separation and identification of amino acids were realized by the team of Martin, Consden, Gordon, and Synge[4] using *paper chromatography*, then in its infancy. Our knowledge of amino acids has paralleled refinements of their original procedures over the past two decades. Although other methods have been developed or improved simultaneously, paper-partition chromatography is still the method of choice for most amino acid investigations in the majority of laboratories. In virtually all laboratories it remains a valuable adjunct to the now completely automated column chromatographic method.

In general paper chromatographic methods used for protein hydrolyzates may be used also for analysis of the amino acids in tissue extracts or for other applications with few, if any, modifications. In addition, other systems of separation are available, some of which are discussed here. Regardless of the details of any one procedure, the method necessarily involves the following steps: preparation of sample; application of sample to paper; development of chromatogram using suitable solvent system; visualization of amino acids on the paper; identification and quantitative estimation. Each of these steps is discussed in detail elsewhere (Vol. II, p. 920; see also footnotes 5 and 6), and need not be repeated here. However, a few comments on each step will be helpful to the analyst who may be working with biological preparations other than protein hydrolyzates.

Sample Preparation. **Extraction from Tissues.**—On rare occasions, the analyst is presented with a preparation which can be chromatographed intact, *i.e.*, without removing substances which might interfere. Thus, with simple mixtures of low salt and lipid content, one may chromatograph directly. However, with most biological fluids, partial purification is required. Tissues of either animal or plant origin are generally extracted with 80 percent ethanol as follows:

To 1 g. of tissue add 4 ml. of ethanol. It is assumed that the tissue contains sufficient water to lower the alcohol content of the mixture to about 80 percent. Homogenize in a Waring Blendor, Virtis, Ten Broeck, or any other suitable tissue grinder. Transfer to a centrifuge tube, and place in water bath at 100°C. for 1 minute to precipitate proteins. Centrifuge at a speed sufficient to produce a pellet from suspended particles. Decant and save supernatant fluid. Suspend residue in 5–10 ml. of 80 percent ethanol, and centrifuge again. Combine supernatant liquids. Repeat extraction with 80 percent ethanol at least twice more. Concentrate on a rotary vacuum evaporator and reconstitute to a suitable volume for further fractionation.

It may be necessary to remove lipids from ethanolic extracts. This is done by dissolving the vacuum-dried extract in 10 percent (v/v) 2-propanol, to which is then added an equal volume of chloroform. A clear upper aqueous layer containing the amino acids is obtained on centrifugation.

Another widely used method is that described originally by Roberts, *et al.*[7] employing

[4] Consden, R., Gordon, A. H., and Martin, A. J. P., Biochem. J., **38**, 224–232, 1944.
[5] Henry, S. M., "Paper Chromatography," in Newman, D. W., Ed., Instrumental Methods of Experimental Biology, The Macmillan Co., New York, 1964, pp. 13–56.
[6] Heftmann, E., Chromatography, Reinhold Publishing Co., New York, 1961.
[7] Roberts, R. B., Abelson, P. H., Cowie, D. B., Bolton, E. T., and Britten, R. J., "Studies of Biosynthesis in Escherichia Coli," Carnegie Institute of Washington (Publication 607), Washington, D. C., 1955.

5 percent trichloroacetic acid. The trichloroacetic acid is easily removed from the extract with ether.

Desalting.—The high concentrations of salts present in biological fluids and extracts of tissues seriously interfere with both chromatographic separation and subsequent reaction of amino acids with ninhydrin and other detection reagents. Of the methods available for removing salts, treatment with an ion exchange resin is probably the most widely used. Most of the free amino acids are adsorbed on a column of Amberlite IR-120 (H^+), Dowex 50 (H^+), and similar resins. The strongly acidic amino acids, cysteic acid and taurine, pass through the column with other anions and nonionic material. The remaining amino acids are eluted from the column with 0.4 to 2.0 *N* ammonium hydroxide. Excess ammonia is removed from the elutriate *in vacuo*, and the sample is then percolated through an anion-exchange resin to remove the remaining cations. Amberlite IRA-410 ($CO_3^=$) or Dowex 1 (Cl^-) retain the amino acids, which are then eluted with dilute acid. Details of a procedure employing Dowex 50 but applicable to other resins are given by Plaisted[8] (also see Vol. II, p. 921).

A *chemical method for removal of salt* is described by McCollum.[9] The amino acid extract is adjusted to pH 4 to 5 with hydrochloric acid and is filtered and dried. The residue, ground to a fine powder, is suspended in 0.2 *N* DL-camphorsulfonic acid in acetone using 50 ml. of reagent per gram of amino acid. After 1 hour with continuous stirring, the insoluble amino acid-camphorsulfonates are removed by filtration and treated with dry ammonia gas to liberate the amino acids. The insoluble ammonium camphorsulfonate is then removed by filtration from aqueous solution. Additional chemical methods are listed by Block (Vol. II, p. 920).

Equally useful but less frequently employed for desalting are the electrodialytic and electrophoretic procedures all of which require somewhat expensive and elaborate equipment.[5,10,11]

Application of Sample to Paper.—Methods of applying aliquots of amino acid solutions to the chromatographic filter paper are adequately discussed elsewhere (Vol. II, p. 929). In addition to the several types of micropipets mentioned, the analyst should also be aware of the newer disposable pipets. These are accurately calibrated for quantitative delivery of 1–100 μl., and are simple and economical to use.

Solvent Systems.—In addition to the one-dimensional system described by Block for amino acids in protein hydrolyzates, several two-dimensional systems have met with general acceptance. The author has obtained excellent results with the following:

System A.[12]—Chromatograph in the first direction with *n*-butyl alcohol-acetic acid-water, 450:50:125 (v/v); and in the second direction with *n*-butyl alcohol-methyl ethyl ketone-water, 2:2:1 (v/v). A shallow dish containing 4 *N* ammonium hydroxide to replace the cyclohexylamine used by Mizell and Simpson is placed in the chromatographic chamber with the second solvent. See Table 45-1.

System B.[13]—Chromatograph in the first direction with ethyl alcohol-*tert*.-butyl alcohol-58% (w/v) ammonium hydroxide-water, 60:20:5:15 (v/v) and in the second direction with *tert*.-butyl alcohol-88% (w/v) formic acid-water, 14:3:3 (v/v).

A chromatographic map and relative positions for 40 sulfur compounds and a similar

[8] Plaisted, P. H., Contribs. Boyce Thompson Inst., **19**, 231–244, 1958.
[9] McCollum, E. V., and Rider, A. A., Arch. Biochem. Biophys., **40**, 20–21, 1952.
[10] Block, R. J., Durrum, E. L., and Zweig, G., Paper Chromatography and Paper Electrophoresis, 2nd Ed., Academic Press, New York, 1958.
[11] Smith, I., Chromatographic and Electrophoretic Techniques, Vol. 1, Chromatography, Interscience Publishers, New York, 1960.
[12] Mizell, M., and Simpson, S. B., Jr., J. Chromatog., **10**, 157–160, 1961.
[13] Margolis, D., and Mandl, R. M., Contribs. Boyce Thompson Inst., **19**, 509–512, 1958.

Table 45-1. Migration Characteristics of Some Amino Acids and Related Compounds

Amino Acid	R_f *in System A*[a]		$R_{proline}$ *in System B*[a]	
	First Solvent	*Second Solvent*	*First Solvent*	*Second Solvent*
Alanine	0.39	0.22	0.90	1.01
β-Alanine	—	0.16	0.65	0.90
Arginine	0.19	0.07	0.43	0.47
Aspartic acid	0.33	0.11	0.22	0.65
Cysteic acid	—	0.24	0.33	0.21
Cystine	0.17	0.16	0.22	0.13
Glutamic acid	0.37	0.12	0.29	0.82
Glycine	0.33	0.18	0.62	0.68
Histidine	0.19	0.25	0.64	0.34
Hydroxyproline	—	0.19	0.77	0.68
Leucine	0.72	0.57	1.37	1.29
Lysine	0.18	0.09	0.41	0.50
Methionine	0.57	0.46	1.09	1.12
Phenylalanine	0.66	0.63	1.33	1.21
Proline	—	0.24	1.00	1.00
Serine	0.31	0.26	0.65	0.64
Threonine	0.36	0.52	0.88	0.74
Tryptophan	0.61	0.60	1.05	1.06
Tyrosine	0.53	0.43	0.98	0.95
Valine	0.56	0.42	1.22	1.22

[a] The constituents of the solvent systems are described in the text. The paper must be dried thoroughly before developing with the second solvent. $R_{proline}$ values are given for System B since better separation is obtained when the solvent is permitted to drip off the end of the paper.

number of amino acids and related compounds are given by Margolis and Mandl (see Table 45-1).

Analysis by chromatographic methods frequently demands the use of several solvent systems and, in some cases, a variety of specific reagents. The identities of the sulfur-containing amino acids, for example, are verified by developing both in the Margolis-Mandl system (System B) and in System C.

System C.—Chromatograph in the first direction with methanol-pyridine-water, 20:1:5 (v/v); and in the second with *tert.*-butyl alcohol-formic acid-water, 70:15:15 (v/v).[14] See Fig. 45-1.

There is no single solvent system suitable for the separation of all amino acids and related compounds. The analyst is encouraged to consult the several excellent texts and such publications as the Journal of Chromatography for additional solvents and techniques for specific purposes.

Visualization.—Ninhydrin (triketohydrindene hydrate) is the reagent of choice for most amino acids. Prepared as a 0.25 percent (w/v) solution in acetone containing 5 percent (v/v) pyridine, distinctive colors are given by aspartic acid, asparagine, cystine, and other amino acids. Thus, the reagent locates and aids in identifying as well. Rapid color development is achieved by heating the chromatogram after spraying or dipping into the reagent. Caution must be observed when heating at temperatures

[14] Cotty, V. F., Henry, S. M., and Hilchey, J. D., Contribs. Boyce Thompson Inst., **19**, 379–392, 1958.

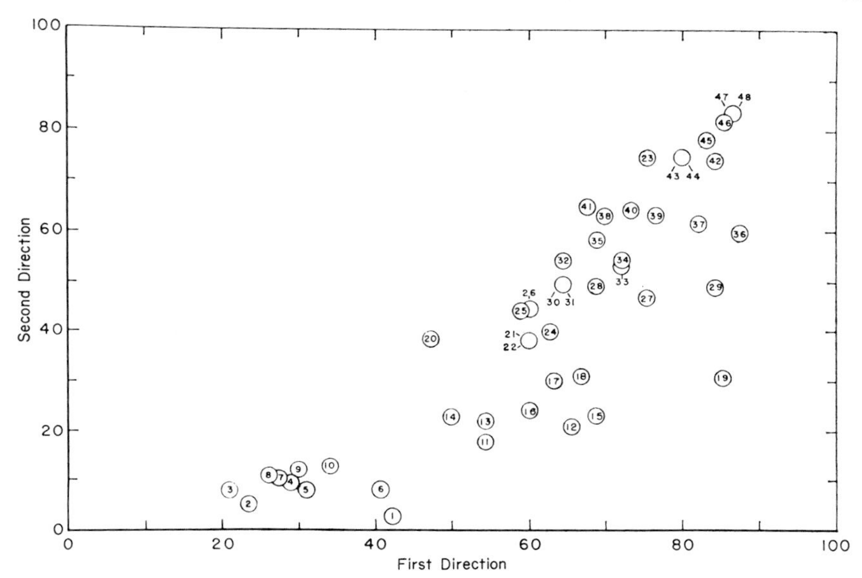

FIG. 45-1. A Two-dimensional Paper Chromatographic Map of Some Sulfur Compounds of Biological Importance. (26) *N*-acetyl-glutathione, (20) *N*-acetylglutathione—*N*-ethylmaleimide adduct, (46) *N*-acetylhomocysteine thiolactone, (1) coenzyme A, (15) cystamine, (8) cystathionine, (33) cysteamine, (37) cysteamine—*N*-ethylmaleimide adduct, (10) cysteic acid, (29) cysteine ethyl ester hydrochloride, (42) cysteine ethyl ester—*N*-ethylmaleimide adduct, (34) cysteine—*N*-ethylmaleimide adduct, (14) cysteinesulfinic acid, (4) cystine, (5) *meso*-cystine, (7) djenkolic acid, (17) ergothioneine, (27) ergothioneine—*N*-ethylmaleimide, (43) ethionine, (30) ethionine sulfone, (38) S-ethylcysteine, (28) glutamylcysteine—*N*-ethylmaleimide adduct, (2) glutathione (oxidized), (25) glutathione—*N*-ethylmaleimide adduct, (16) homocysteine, (40) homocysteine—*N*-ethylmaleimide adduct, (23) homocysteine thiolactone, (45) α-hydroxy-γ-(methylmercapto) butyric acid, (18) hypotaurine, (19) isethionic acid, (3) lanthionine, (47) 2-mercaptoethanol, (48) β-mercaptopropionic acid, (39) methionine, (22) methionine sulfone, (21) methionine sulfoxide, (13) methionine sulfoximine, (32) S-methylcysteine, (11) methyl methionine sulfonium chloride, (6) sodium sulfate, (36) sodium taurocholate, (12) taubine, (41) β-2-thienylalanine, (9) thiolhistidine, (24) thiolhistidine—*N*-ethylmaleimide adduct, (44) thiomalic acid, (35) thiouracil, (31) thiourea. R_f values are obtained by referring to scales at left and bottom. Origin is at lower left corner.

above 60°C., since background coloration is intensified with elevated temperatures as well as on standing at room temperature.

Identification and Quantitative Estimation.—The qualitative amino acid composition of whole animal protein hydrolyzates is more or less predictable. Moreover, bulk proteins are surprisingly similar quantitatively.[15] If one prepares standard two-dimensional chromatograms of the 18–20 amino acids usually recovered from acid hydrolyzates of protein, the *relative positions* of the amino acids on the resulting map may be used as a fairly accurate guide to identity following development with ninhydrin. In questionable cases there are a variety of specific reagents which may be used. The Sakaguchi reaction for arginine; the Folin reagent, sodium nitroprusside, *N*-ethylmalemide and others for sulfur amino acids; the Pauly reagent for histidine and tyrosine; Ehrlich's

[15] Vegotsky, A., and Fox, S. W., "Protein Molecules: Intraspecific and Interspecific Variations," in Florkin, M., and Mason, H. S., Eds., Comparative Biochemistry, Vol. IV, Academic Press, New York, 1962.

reagent for tryptophan; and countless others (Vol. II, p. 929 ff.) are used alone or in combination to obtain maximum information from a chromatogram.

Quantitative determinations on one-dimensional chromatograms are easily made by visual *comparison* or the *maximum color density* method outlined by Block (Vol. II, p. 933). Either method may be used for two-dimensional systems.[16] An alternate system consists in outlining the ninhydrin spots which are then cut out and weighed. The area or size of the spot is proportional to the quantity of amino acid. This method is subject to considerable error, particularly when one fails to obtain discrete, circular spots on the chromatogram.

A radiometric-colorimetric method of amino acid analysis has been used in conjunction with metabolic studies in a variety of organisms. Carbon-14 supplied as labeled glucose or carbonate[17] is incorporated into the amino acids, which are then isolated by the usual methods and chromatographed. Autoradiograms are prepared by placing a sheet of sensitive film (Kodak No-Screen X-Ray Film) in juxtaposition with the chromatogram. After a few days to several weeks, depending on the intensity of the radioactivity, the autoradiogram is developed. The amino acids responsible for the spots on the film are located on the overlying chromatogram and are outlined, cut out, eluted, reacted with ninhydrin, and estimated photometrically (see Vol. II, p. 924).[16]

THIN-LAYER CHROMATOGRAPHY

The technique of "open-column" chromatography recently redeveloped by Stahl (see footnote 17) and known as *thin-layer chromatography* (TLC) is particularly advantageous because of the rapidity with which one obtains separation. Although widely employed in lipid analysis, it is used also for amino acid analysis and, in fact, for as many types of compounds as have been separated on paper. Whereas a two-dimensional paper chromatogram takes a minimum of 2 days for completion, TLC separation can be accomplished in less than 5 hours. One-dimensional separation of simple mixtures is obtained in less than 2 hours. In addition, the technique is more sensitive and results in better separation. Techniques for layering the adsorbents on glass plates and procedures for development, etc. are discussed elsewhere in this volume (Chapter 39; also see footnotes 17 and 18). The following solvent systems are recommended.

One-dimensional.[19]

Adsorbent: silica gel G.

Solvent: methyl ethyl ketone-pyridine-water-acetic acid, 70:15:15:2 (v/v).

Dissolve the amino acids in 0.1 *N* hydrochloric acid to give 1–5 μg./μl. Develop with ninhydrin after thorough drying. Leucine and isoleucine, which normally have very close R_F values, are separated in this system.

Two-dimensional.[20]

Adsorbent: silica gel G.

Solvents: First direction in chloroform-methanol-17 percent ammonium hydroxide, 2:2:1 (v/v).
Second direction in phenol-water, 75:25 (w/w); add 20 mg. sodium cyanide per 100 g. of mixture.

[16] Porter, C. A., Margolis, D., and Sharp, P., Contribs. Boyce Thompson Inst., **18,** 465–476, 1957.

[17] Henry, S. M., Thin-Layer Chromatography, in Newman, D. W., Ed., Instrumental Methods of Experimental Biology, The Macmillan Co., New York, 1964, pp. 57–85.

[18] Randerath, K., Thin-Layer Chromatography, Academic Press, New York, 1963.

[19] Brenner, M., and Pataki, G., Helv. Chim. Acta, **44,** 1420–1425, 1961.

[20] Fahmy, A. R., Niederwieser, A.; Pataki, G., and Brenner, M., Helv. Chim. Acta, **44,** 2022–2026, 1961.

Oxidation of the sample with performic acid[21] converts methionine to methionine sulfoxide and cystine to cysteic acid. It is suggested that both oxidized and unoxidized aliquots be chromatographed as an aid in identifying sulfur amino acids. Development for a distance of 15 cm. gives excellent separation. The relative positions of the amino acids are shown in Fig. 45-2.

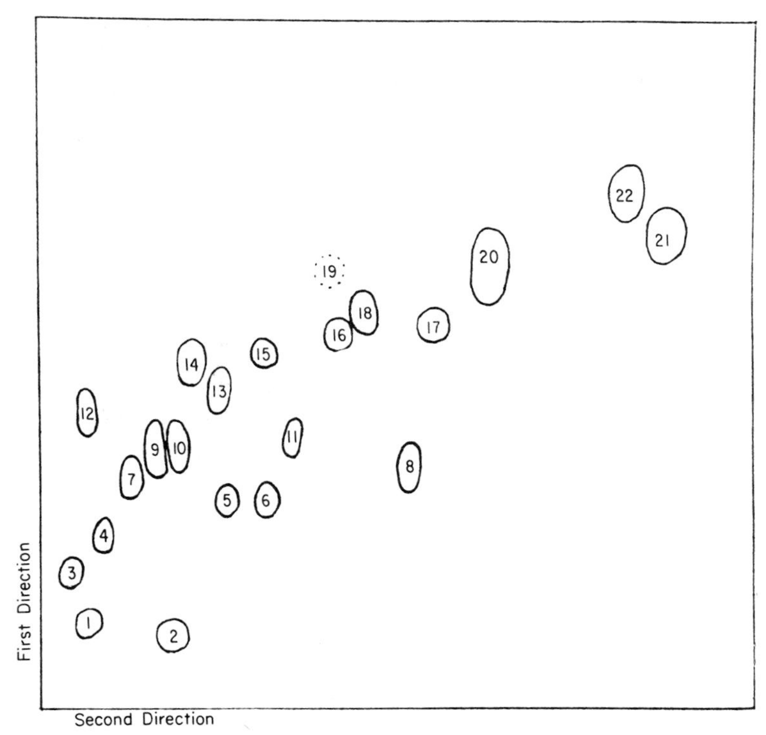

FIG. 45-2. A Two-dimensional Chromatogram of Amino Acids on Silica Gel G. (1) lysine, (2) arginine, (3) hydroxylysine, (4) glutamic acid, (5) β-alanine, (6) γ-amino-n-butyric acid, (7) serine, (8) proline, (9) glycine, (10) aspartic acid, (11) hydroxyproline, (12) cysteic acid, (13) alanine, (14) threonine, (15) histidine, (16) methionine sulfone, (17) tyrosine, (18) valine, (19) methionine—in unoxidized sample, (20) leucine + isoleucine, (21) tryptophan, (22) phenylalanine. Origin is at lower left corner.

Randerath[18] gives additional solvent systems for amino acids, dinitrophenylamino acids (DNP amino acids), and phenylthiohydantoins (PTH amino acids). The latter are widely used in end group analysis.

A useful modification of the glass chromatoplate is the Eastman *Chromagram* (Distillation Products Industries, Rochester, N. Y.), a sheet of inert polyester base which is coated with an absorbent. The ready-made plate is flexible and may be cut to any desired size with a pair of scissors. The author has obtained good separation of simple mixtures of amino acids on *Chromagram* Type K301 R (silica gel with fluorescent indicator) using *n*-butyl alcohol-acetic acid-water, 450:50:125 (v/v). Peculiarly, develop-

[21] Hirs, C. H. W., J. Biol. Chem., **219**, 611–621, 1956.

ment time was as long as with Whatman No. 3 paper, approximately 5 hours for 200 mm. However, the amino acid spots were more clearly delineated than on paper.

Analogous to TLC on plastic supports is glass fiber paper (GFP) chromatography. GFP sheets are available (Applied Science Laboratories, Inc., State College, Pa.) untreated or impregnated with various adsorbents.

Development time for amino acids with *n*-butyl alcohol-acetic acid-water, 450:50:125 (v/v) on GFP sheets impregnated with silicic acid is less than one-half that required for paper, and separation is somewhat better. Untreated and potassium silicate treated GFP sheets were unsatisfactory for amino acids with the above solvent.

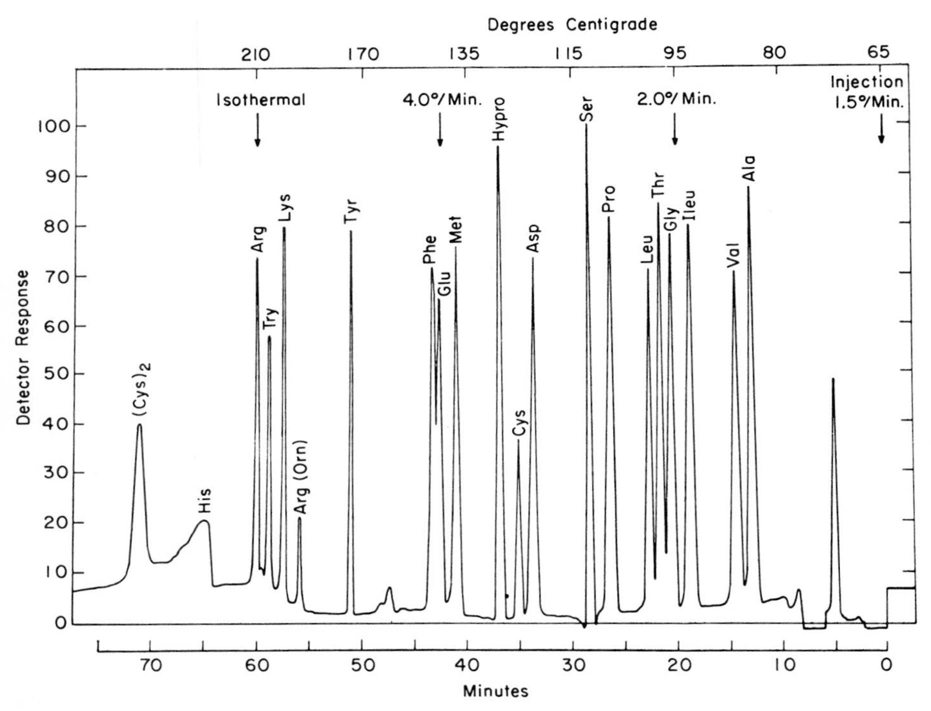

FIG. 45-3. Gas Chromatographic Separation of a Mixture of Trifluoroacetylated Amino Acid Methyl Esters. (Reprinted from Anal. Chem., **36**, 1191–1197, 1964. Copyright 1964 by the American Chemical Society and reprinted by permission of the copyright owner.)

GAS CHROMATOGRAPHY

Neither gas-liquid chromatography nor gas-solid chromatography (Vol. II, p. 225) can be considered at present to be among the *standard* methods of amino acid analysis.[22] Amino acids, as such, do not meet the basic requirements for gas chromatography, *i.e.*, a sufficiently low vapor pressure to be converted to a gas at relatively low temperatures. They must be converted either to esters or to volatile pyrolysis products. Since gas chromatography permits detection of minute quantities of substances in a very short

[22] Burchfield, H. P., and Storrs, E. E., Biochemical Applications of Gas Chromatography, Academic Press, New York, 1962.

period of time, an intensive search has been conducted for suitable procedures applicable to amino acids.

Conversion to *N*-acetylamino acid *n*-amyl esters[23] or *N*-trifluoracetylamino acid *n*-butyl esters[24] has met with considerable success. High yields in the conversion of 21 amino acids to trifluoroacetylated methyl esters are obtained using the technique of Cruickshank and Sheehan[25] described below.

Esterification.—Suspend up to 100 micromoles of amino acids in 5 ml. of methanol and saturate with anhydrous hydrochloric acid. Add 1 ml. of dimethyl sulfite, and heat under reflux on a steam bath for 30 minutes. Remove excess reagent under reduced pressure, and dry the amino acid methyl ester hydrochlorides *in vacuo.*

Trifluoroacetylation.—Add 1 ml. of trifluoroacetic anhydride to the amino acid esters in a flask, and reflux on a steam bath for 10 minutes. Remove excess reagent with a stream of dry nitrogen and redissolve residue in 1 ml. of trifluoroacetic acid for chromatography.

Apparatus.—Cruickshank and Sheehan use a Jarrell-Ash Model 700 Universal Chromatograph with an automatic temperature programmer and an argon diode ionization detector. The stainless steel, 2-foot column (1.5 mm. i.d.) is packed with Gas Chrom P coated with 5 percent neopentyl glycolsuccinate. Coat the support by suspending in a chloroform solution of the polyester and evaporating the solvent on a rotary concentrator. Heat to 100°C. at 0.1 mm. or a lower pressure. Wash the packed column with Argon at 225°C. at a flow rate of 18 ml./minute.

Chromatography.—Equilibrate column oven at 65°C. Inject a 2-μl. aliquot of the solution of amino acid derivatives into the flash heater held at 295°C. Maintain argon flow rate of 18 ml./minute. Increase temperature 1.5°C./minute. After 20 minutes increase rate to 2°C./minute and, after 42.5 minutes, to 4°C./minute to a final temperature of 210°C. Analysis is complete in 75 minutes.

Figure 45-3 illustrates the type of separation which may be obtained. The original publication[25] discusses alternate methods for preparing derivatives and gives details for quantitative analyses.

Pyrolysis of amino acids at 300°C. to yield characteristic amine profiles on gas chromatograms is accomplished according to the procedure of Winter and Albro.[26] With refinements in technique the method may prove to be a valuable adjunct to other methods of amino acid analysis since it does not require a hydrolyzate as a starting point; peptides and even proteins are pyrolyzed directly, and immediately subjected to gas chromatography. Thus, certain amino acids, which may be partially or completely destroyed during acid hydrolysis, may be detected.

[23] Johnson, D. E., Scott, S. J., Meister, A., Anal. Chem., **33**, 669–673, 1961.
[24] Zomzely, C., Marco, G., Emery, E., Anal. Chem., **34**, 1414–1417, 1962.
[25] Cruickshank, P. A., and Sheehan, J. C., Anal. Chem., **36**, 1191–1197, 1964.
[26] Winter, L. N., and Albro, P. W., J. Gas Chrom., **2**, 1–6, 1964.

Chapter 46

PORTLAND CEMENT

By Wm. G. Hime
Portland Cement Association
Research and Development Division
Skokie, Illinois

The chemical and engineering properties of portland cement are generally considered to depend upon the proportions of its major components. The analysis of portland cement, in contrast to steel analysis, seldom requires the determination of trace components, although recent work indicates that the effects of some constituents may be much greater than their proportions would indicate.

Most control and specification analyses must be made by methods giving mean errors of 0.1 to 0.3 percentage points or less, when the elements are calculated as the oxides. For the components calcium oxide and silicon dioxide, present in 60 and 20 percent concentrations, respectively, this fact implies a relative error of 0.5 percent. Such accuracies are beyond the capabilities of most instruments, except for x-ray emission spectrometers. Other components, however, may be analyzed by instrumental techniques with accuracies equal to or exceeding those obtained by conventional wet chemical methods.

Volume II[1] of this publication should be consulted for specifications and noninstrumental methods of analysis. Instrumental methods, as covered in this chapter, are not as yet part of ASTM[2] or U.S. Government specifications (the flame photometric determination of alkalies is an exception).

OPTICAL AND RELATED METHODS

INFRARED SPECTROMETRY

INORGANIC COMPONENTS

Although the individual components of portland cement (calcium silicates, aluminates, aluminoferrites, etc.) have distinctive infrared absorption patterns,[3,4] the spectrum of portland cement fails to reveal most of these components (due to their concentrations, mutual interferences and the overriding absorptions of sulfate, carbonate, and water).

A possible practical use for an infrared examination of portland cement is suggested

[1] Welcher, Frank J., ed., Standard Methods of Chemical Analysis, 6th Ed., D. Van Nostrand Co., Inc., Princeton, N. J., Vol. II, Part B, 1963, p. 1053.

[2] ASTM Specification C-114-63, ASTM Standards, Part 9, American Society for Testing and Materials, Philadelphia, Pa., 1965.

[3] Hunt, C. M., Doctoral Thesis, University of Maryland, Microfilm No. Mic. 59-2793, University Microfilms, Inc., Ann Arbor, Mich.

[4] Lehmann, H., and Dutz, H., Chemistry of Cement, Proceedings of the Fourth International Symposium, Monograph 43, Vol. 1, National Bureau of Standards, Washington, D. C., 1960, p. 513.

by the presence of a sharp absorption maximum (at 3640 cm.$^{-1}$) due to calcium hydroxide. Since the cement chemist's usual methods for "free lime" do not differentiate between calcium oxide and hydroxide, qualitative and quantitative procedures for one of these components are desired. A quantitative infrared procedure for calcium hydroxide in cement is not now available, and development of one will depend upon the availability of standards and the elimination of particle size effects.

ORGANIC COMPONENTS

Organic materials are not necessarily present in portland cement. Grinding aids and air-entraining agents, however, may be components of some cements. Organic materials are, more often, found in concretes. Infrared procedures for the detection and identification of many of the organic compounds most often added to cement, mortar, or concrete have been developed in the author's laboratory, and are described below. Successful analyses using such procedures are dependent upon such factors as the age of the sample, the concentration of the organic material, and the analytical equipment used.

Acid-Chloroform Extraction.—This procedure permits the identification of such materials as the abietate-type air-entrainers, tallow, most organic acids (stearic, benzoic, etc.), salts of weak acids (as the free acid) and, occasionally, lignosulfonates.

Place 40 g. of cement or concrete (48-mesh) in a 1-liter separatory funnel and mix it with 500 ml. of distilled water added in two approximately equal portions. Shake vigorously immediately after the addition of the first portion to effect complete dispersion. Then add the second portion and shake again. At once add rapidly 185 ml. of hydrochloric acid (concentrated). Stopper, invert, and shake the funnel briefly. (Violent shaking, which produces great internal pressures, should be avoided.) Immediately relieve any pressure by opening and closing the stopcock. Cool to room temperature rapidly by running tap water on the flask. Add 75 ml. of chloroform to the solution, stopper the funnel, shake vigorously for 5 min., and allow to stand until the water and chloroform layers separate (about 15 min.).

Draw off the lower chloroform layer, including scum and undissolved concrete, into a 125-ml. separatory funnel. Shake the funnel vigorously to ensure complete extraction of the scum. Draw the contents through a Büchner funnel fitted with a medium-textured filter paper. Place the filtrate in a clean 125-ml. separatory funnel. Draw off the chloroform into a 250-ml. beaker. Evaporate the chloroform at a low temperature (not over 63°C.) to dryness.

Infrared Analysis of the Residue.—If the residue is a solid of sufficient quantity, scrape it from the bottom of the beaker, and grind using a small mortar and pestle. This powder may be dried further in an oven at a low temperature. The extract is finally mixed with potassium bromide and pressed into a pellet. If the residue is an oil of sufficient quantity it may be pressed between two salt plates and analyzed directly.

If the residue is not of a quality or quantity necessary to permit the above preparations, add potassium bromide directly to the beaker containing the residue. Add a few ml. of chloroform. As the chloroform evaporates, the residue will be absorbed by the salt. Mix the solid thoroughly and press into a pellet.

Obtain the infrared absorption spectrum of the sample between about 2.5 and 15 μ (4000 to 650 cm.$^{-1}$). Identify the pattern by standard methods, or by the use of the table given below.

LIGNOSULFONATES

Lignosulfonate is one of the more common classes of organic materials likely to be found in concrete. Its detection depends upon the size and age of the sample, the procedure used, and the equipment available. The following method produces excellent spectra.

Extraction. **Cement.** Shake 50 g. of cement with 50 ml. of 10 percent sodium carbonate solution in a separatory funnel for 2 min. Filter the slurry through Whatman No. 41 paper (or its equivalent) using a Büchner funnel and suction flask. Discard the filter cake in the funnel, and keep the filtrate.

Paste, Mortar or Concrete.—Grind 100 g. of the hardened cement paste with mortar and pestle until it passes a 48-mesh sieve. Shake with 100 ml. of 10 percent sodium carbonate solution in a separatory funnel for 5 min. Filter the slurry through medium-texture filter paper using a Büchner funnel and suction flask. Remove the filter cake from the Büchner funnel and transfer back to the separatory funnel. Shake with 50 ml. of 10 percent sodium carbonate solution for 5 min., and then filter the slurry as described above. Once again remove the filter cake from the funnel and extract and filter as described immediately above. Combine the filtrates from the three extractions.

Neutralize the above filtrate with concentrated hydrochloric acid using litmus or pH paper, and then add about 0.5 ml. of the acid in excess. Cool to room temperature.

Anion Exchange.—Pass the acidified filtrate through an ion-exchange column (about 1 in. in diameter) containing about 10 ml. of an anion exchange resin (hydrated) of the strongly basic type, in the chloride form. It is important that the resin be of Analytical Grade and that it be washed with acid and with base to remove all soluble material. The manufacturer's literature generally gives a detailed procedure for purifying the particular resin used.

Since the affinity of the anion exchange resin for lignosulfonate is very great, a fairly fast flow rate from the column may be used. The filtrate need not be added dropwise to the column but can be added in large aliquots, or all at once, if the column is sufficiently large.

After all the filtrate has been passed through the column, add 0.50 M hydrochloric acid to the column until the effluent is free of sulfate (as indicated by the lack of a precipitate after the addition of a barium chloride solution). Discard this effluent. Elute the column with 15 to 20 ml. of 1:1 hydrochloric acid, which may be added to the column all at once. Use a flow rate such that the acid does not remain in contact

TABLE 46-1.

Material	*Characteristic Absorptions*[a]
Abietic acid derivatives (*e.g.*, Vinsol resin)	1030w, 960w, 825w, 755m, 700m
Benzoate salts (as benzoic acid)	1315s, 1280s, 1175m, 1120m, 1065m, 1020m, 930s, 800m
Dodecyl benzene sodium sulfonate	1200s, 1135m, 1050m, 1005m, 830m
Hydroxyamine-sulfonated hydrocarbon (*e.g.*, Darex)	1400w, 1375–1355db, 1270m, 1175w, 1030w, 900w, 815w, 715w, 650w
Lignosulfonates	1500w, 1450w, 1400w, 1300–1100s, 1030s
Oleic acid	1370w, 1270s, 1250–1200s, 1110w, 1080w, 960m, 930s, 720m
Polyvinyl acetate (acid extractions of lignosulfonates from concrete may, at times, give similar absorptions)	1430m, 1365s, 1230s, 1115m, 1015s, 940m
Stearate salts (as stearic acid)	1290s; identifying set of 5–1250w, 1230w, 1215w, 1195w, 1180w; 935s, 725 and 715 dbs

[a] b = broad; db = doublet; m = medium; s = strong; w = weak.

with the resin for more than about 5 min. Collect the effluent in a small clean beaker and evaporate to near dryness on a steam bath, and then allow to evaporate to dryness at room temperature (under vacuum if available) until all trace of acid has been removed.

Infrared Analysis.—To the residue in the beaker add several drops of water and enough potassium bromide (Infrared Grade) to give a pellet that contains about 1 percent of the residue. Mix the contents of the beaker thoroughly, using a small spatula to scrape the dried residue from the bottom of the beaker. Transfer the contents of the beaker (not necessarily quantitatively) to a small mortar and pestle, and grind for a few minutes until the residue is well dispersed in the potassium bromide. Dry the mixture in an oven at 110 C. until all traces of moisture have been removed. Without delay, press a pellet or disc from the mixture using an evacuable die. The pellet should be as clear as possible and free from moisture.

Obtain the infrared absorption spectrum of the pellet between about 2.5 and 15 μ (4000 to 650 $cm.^{-1}$). Identify the pattern by standard methods, or by the use of Table 46-1.

Table of Organic Spectra.—The organics in Table 46-1 have found some commercial application as additives to cement or admixtures to concrete. The extracted forms of these materials may be identified through their infrared absorptions, as listed in the table.

ATOMIC ABSORPTION SPECTROMETRY (ABSORPTION FLAME PHOTOMETRY)

To date, applications of atomic absorption spectrometry to cement analyses have been made only by instrument manufacturers. The method holds promise for several elements commonly present in cement, and may be of even greater value for the determination of such elements as zinc and lead in cement, mortar, and concrete. The latter two elements can seriously affect the setting time and the strength of mortar and concrete; thus methods for their detection and determination are desirable.

FLAME EMISSION SPECTROMETRY

Applicability.

The determination of the sodium and potassium contents of cement are frequently required. For this reason, flame photometers are now standard equipment in most laboratories performing cement analyses. The necessary presence of these flame photometers has inspired efforts to extend the applicability of such instruments to other analyses. Although these investigations do not indicate that determinations of the two major components of cement—calcium and silicon—can be made with an accuracy sufficient for control purposes, flame methods may be useful for the control analyses of other elements, and for research purposes.

DETERMINATION OF MAGNESIUM, MANGANESE, SODIUM AND POTASSIUM

A method by Ford[5] of this laboratory modified the ASTM procedure for alkalies[6] to include magnesium and manganese. This method has been further modified to make it applicable to flame photometers capable of measuring the flame intensities of these four elements.

[5] Ford, C. L., ASTM Bull. No. 250, 25, December 1960.

[6] ASTM Standard Method C-114, ASTM Standards, Part 9, American Society for Testing and Materials, Philadelphia, Pa., 1965.

***Reagents.* Calcium Chloride Stock Solution.**—Add 300 ml. of water to 112.5 g. of Primary Standard or "Low-alkali" Grade calcium carbonate. Slowly add, with stirring, 500 ml. of concentrated hydrochloric acid. Cool, filter into a 1-liter volumetric flask, and dilute to the mark. This solution contains 63,000 p.p.m. of calcium as the oxide.

Magnesium Stock Solution.—Introduce 50.4 g. of magnesium chloride hexahydrate into a 1-liter volumetric flask and add water to the mark. Mix to dissolve. This solution contains 10,000 p.p.m. of magnesium as the oxide.

Manganese-Alkali Stock Solution.—Introduce 1.886 g. of sodium chloride, 1.583 g. of potassium chloride, and 2.141 g. of manganese(II) sulfate monohydrate (all previously dried at 105 C. for 2 hr. or more) into a 1-liter volumetric flask and mix thoroughly. This solution contains 1000 p.p.m. each of sodium, potassium, and manganese as their oxides (the latter as manganese(III) oxide (Mn_2O_3)).

Flame Standard Solutions.—Prepare the solutions prescribed in Table 46-2.

TABLE 46-2. FLAME STANDARD SOLUTIONS

Solution No.	Concentration: % Equivalent in Cement		Composition			Final Vol. (ml.)
	MgO	Na_2O, K_2O, Mn_2O_3	Calcium Stock (ml.)	Magnesium Stock (ml.)	Manganese Alkali (ml.)	
1	5.00	1.00	200	100	200	2000
2	4.00	0.75	100	40	75	1000
3	3.00	0.50	100	30	50	1000
4	2.00	0.25	100	20	25	1000
5	1.00	0.10	100	10	10	1000
6	0	0	100	0	0	1000
7	0	1.00	0	0	100	1000

Calibration.—Set the instrument at the wavelength setting for the element to be determined, as follows:

Magnesium at 371 mμ
Manganese at 403.3 mμ
Sodium at 589 mμ
Potassium at 768 mμ

(No information is available as to the results that may be expected if a color filter instrument is used. The calcium interference on sodium, however, may be severe.)

Except for magnesium, determine the exact wavelength setting for maximum response by means of Solution No. 7. Set the instrument to zero or minimum transmission with the shutter closed (or with a water blank, if there is no shutter). Using either the sensitivity or slit width controls, or both, set the instrument to 100 percent transmittance, or maximum dial reading, while atomizing Solution No. 1. Repeat the zero and 100 adjustments until instrument readings are constant within usual tolerances.

Atomize the flame standard solutions. Record the transmittance readings for Solutions Nos. 1 to 5 as "gross luminosity," and as "background" for Solution No. 6.

Correct the "gross luminosity" readings for background emission and plot the resultant "net luminosities" as ordinates, and the corresponding "cement percentage" concentrations of the standards as abscissas.

Preparation of Sample.—Weigh 1.000 g. of cement into a beaker or, preferably, a platinum dish. Disperse with 20 ml. of water, add 5 ml. of concentrated hydrochloric acid and break up lumps with a rubber policeman or "mushroom" stirring rod. Rinse the policeman or rod with a small amount of water. Evaporate the contents of the vessel to dryness under an infrared lamp or on a steam bath (the former is more efficient). Cool and add 15 ml. of 1:1 hydrochloric acid. Digest on a steam bath for 15 min. and add 15 ml. of hot water. Add 1:1 ammonium hydroxide until alkaline to methyl red. Make just acid with hydrochloric acid, then repeat the addition of ammonia, drop by drop, until the solution just turns yellow, and then add one drop in excess. Filter through a medium-texture filter paper into a 100-ml. volumetric flask. Dilute to the mark with water and mix.

Flame Analysis.—For each of the elements, calibrate the instrument as described above, atomize the cement solution and record the transmittance. Atomize Flame Standard Solution No. 6 and record the transmittance as background. Correct the cement transmittance intensities for background emission, and determine percentage concentrations of the respective oxides from the calibration curves.

DETERMINATION OF SODIUM AND POTASSIUM

If the analyses for magnesium and manganese are not desired, or if the flame photometer is only capable of alkali analyses, the previous procedure may be modified as follows:

Reagents. **Calcium Chloride Stock Solution.**—See previous method.

Alkali Stock Solution.—Prepare as directed for the "Manganese-Alkali Stock Solution" in the previous method, omitting the manganese sulfate.

Flame Standard Solutions.—Prepare as in the previous method, except that only alkali and calcium solutions are used.

Calibration.—Calibrate as in the previous method.

Preparation of Sample.—Weigh out the cement and dissolve and dehydrate as in the previous method. Since silica does not affect the alkali intensities obtained with certain instruments, trials with NBS standards 1011 through 1016 may suggest elimination of the dehydration step. Take up in acid as previously directed, and filter into the volumetric flask without addition of ammonia.

Flame Analysis.—Proceed as in the previous method.

DETERMINATION OF ALUMINUM, BARIUM, CALCIUM, IRON, LITHIUM, MAGNESIUM, MANGANESE, POTASSIUM, SODIUM AND STRONTIUM

To be applicable to the determination of several elements, any single method of flame emission analysis requires minimization of chemical and radiation interelement effects. In addition, the flame emission intensities of certain elements must be increased. The use of 8-hydroxyquinoline (oxine) for the flame analysis of silicates[7] appears to accomplish both requirements.

Although accuracies and exact procedures depend upon the flame equipment available, an adaptation of the oxine procedure to permit cement analyses has been made in the author's laboratory.

Procedure.—Weigh 1.000 g. of cement into a platinum dish or glass beaker (the former is preferred), add 20 ml. of water and 5 ml. of concentrated hydrochloric acid. Evaporate to dryness and cool. Take up the residue with 20 ml. of 1:1 hydrochloric acid. Bring to a boil, filter into a 250-ml. volumetric flask, cool and dilute to the mark with water. Pipet 50 ml. into a 100-ml. volumetric flask, add 25 ml. of a 20 percent

[7] Debras-Guedon, J., and Voinovitch, I. A., Trans. Intern. Ceram. Cong., 8th, 29, 1962.

solution of oxine in 2:3 acetic acid. Add 10 ml. of 1:1 hydrochloric acid and mix. Make up to 100 ml.

Atomize the sample into an oxygen-acetylene flame. Determine the concentrations of the elements listed below, at the wavelengths given, by locating the observed intensities on a calibration curve constructed by analyzing NBS Standard Cement Samples Nos. 1011, 1013, 1014, 1015, and 1016 in a similar manner. For greatest accuracy, background intensities should be subtracted. The wavelength settings for such background measurements are best determined by scans in the region of the emission peak.

Elements Determined (as oxides)	*Wavelength ($m\mu$)*
Al_2O_3[a]	484.23
BaO[b]	455.40
CaO	422.67
Fe_2O_3	385.99
Li_2O[c]	670.78
MgO	285.21
Mn_2O_3	403.08
K_2O	404.41–404.72
Na_2O	589.00
SrO	460.73

[a] Aluminum determinations are possible only for high-alumina cements.
[b] The barium oxide contents of the NBS Standards have not been certified. They may be determined by a procedure given by Ford.[8] The barium contents of most cements are insufficient to give measurable flame intensities.
[c] The lithium contents of the NBS cements have not been certified.

EMISSION SPECTROMETRY

Applicability.—Emission spectrometry has apparently been applied to acceptance and control analyses only in countries other than the United States. Publications from the Soviet Union[9,10,11] indicate that such analyses are equal in accuracy to ordinary wet chemical procedures. However, neither the published data nor work in this country indicates that analysis by emission spectrometry is accurate enough for a sufficient number of elements to be of general value. Research applications may be more frequent.

The elements present in cement that may be analyzed by emission spectrometric methods, and the possible uses of such analyses, are as follows:

(1) Elements of general analytical interest, determined with an accuracy approximately equivalent to that obtained by ordinary methods—aluminum, iron, magnesium, manganese, sodium, and titanium.

(2) Elements of general analytical interest, analyzed with accuracies sufficient for semiquantitative purposes—calcium, phosphorus, potassium, and sulfur.

(3) Elements present in trace concentration, of research interest, analyzed with accuracies equivalent to or better than those obtained by usual procedures—chromium, copper, lithium, strontium, vanadium, and zirconium.

[8] Ford, C. L., ASTM Bull. No. 247, 77, July 1960.
[9] Massil'on, T. K., Trudy Gosudarst. Vsesoyuz. Inst. po Proekt. i Nauch. Issledovatel Rabotam v Tsement Prom., **1956** (19), 115, 1956.
[10] Massil'on T. K., Bulletin of the Academy of Sciences of the USSR, Physical Series, English Translation (Columbia Technical Translations), **19** (1) 95, 1955.
[11] Kel'tseva, Z. A., *ibid.*, 97.

Procedures.—A procedure described by a Soviet worker[10] involves the moving-lower-electrode method (a procedure that may make this method applicable to automated analysis). The cement (clinker, or raw material) sample is moistened with ethyl alcohol and coated in a thin layer on a copper plate. The latter serves as the moving stage electrode.

More accurate results are suggested,[12,13,14] if the cement is pelletized and used as the lower electrode. Graphite is added as a binder and stabilizer, cobalt oxide as an internal standard, and potassium nitrate or ammonium chloride as radiation buffers. The procedure suggested by Helz and Scribner is as follows: mix together

(1) 0.440 g. spectrographic graphite powder
(2) 0.050 g. cobalt oxide
(3) 0.0075 g. potassium nitrate
(4) 0.500 g. portland cement

Press the mixture into a suitable cylindrical pellet at about 40,000 p.s.i.

For the above procedures, NBS Standards 1011 through 1016 may be used to prepare suitable calibration curves.

X-RAY EMISSION

To date, the x-ray spectrometer has proven to be the only instrument capable of analyzing portland cement for its major elemental components with accuracies sufficient for control purposes. An ASTM Committee is presently studying such techniques for possible use as specification procedures.

ANALYSES FOR ALUMINUM, CALCIUM, IRON, MAGNESIUM, MANGANESE, POTASSIUM, SILICON, AND SULFUR

Several methods applicable to cement analyses have been proposed in the literature. These procedures differ almost entirely in their sample preparation procedures. Samples may be prepared by grinding only,[15,16,17] by fusions with borax or lithium tetraborate,[18,19] by fusions employing a heavy absorber,[20] and by the use of internal standards.[21]

From this variety of procedures, three methods, chosen as applicable to a wide range of instrumentation and accuracy requirements, are described.

Apparatus. **Tube Targets.**—Both chromium and tungsten target x-ray tubes have been used, with the former now generally preferred. All of the elements of interest to cement chemists are, with the exception of iron and manganese, lower in atomic number than chromium. A chromium target tube provides increased emission intensities for the lighter elements in comparison to intensities excited by a tungsten tube. The

[12] Mesbah, C., Bull. Soc. Franc. Ceram., **51**, 121, 1961.
[13] Helz, A. W., and Scribner, B. F., J. Research, Nat. Bur. Std., **38**, 439, 1947.
[14] Hasler, M. F., Harvey, C. E., and Barley, F. W., Proceedings, ASTM, **48**, 944, 1948.
[15] Kester, B. E., Rock Prod., **64** (3), 90, 1961.
[16] Palmer, K. E., Pit Quarry, **55**, 102, 1962.
[17] Allegre, R., Analysis of Calcareous Materials, S.C.I. Monograph No. 18, Society of Chemical Industry, London, 289, 1964.
[18] Anderman, G., and Allen, J. D., Advances in X-ray Analysis, Vol. 4, Plenum Press, New York, 1961, p. 414.
[19] Bean, L., and Mulligan, B. W., ASTM 1st International Conference on Materials, Preprints, American Society for Testing and Materials, Philadelphia, Pa., 1964, p. 36.
[20] Rose, H. J., Adler, I., and Flanagan, F. J., U. S. Geol. Survey, Profess. Paper 450-B, 1962, p. 80.
[21] Brown, O. E., Proceedings, ASTM, **63**, 904, 1963.

loss of iron intensity is insufficient to affect analyses significantly for this element, and manganese determinations are seldom required.

Optical Path.—Vacuum is preferred, with hydrogen or helium acceptable.

Analyzing Crystals.—Instruments that permit a crystal choice for each analyzed element may use crystals chosen from appropriate tables. For instruments that, in practice, permit only a few crystals to be used, or where a budget problem exists, ADP (ammonium dihydrogen phosphate) may be used for magnesium, and, if necessary, for the other elements. Preferably, however, elements of atomic numbers higher than magnesium should be analyzed with an EDDT (ethylenediamine ditartrate) or PET (pentaerythitol) crystal.

Pulse Height Analyzers.—Discussions with cement analysts indicate that difficulties have often arisen when pulse height analyzers were employed in the circuitry. Where an analyzer with very stable electronics is available, it should be used to improve signal to background ratios, especially for magnesium and aluminum radiations.

Sample Preparation and Analysis.—A procedure may be chosen from the three described below, in accordance with the time and equipment available, and the desired accuracy.

Background corrections will increase accuracies, but are generally unnecessary when materials of similar composition are used as standards.

Procedure	*Preparation Time (Min.)*	*X-ray Equipment*	*Application and Accuracy*
(1) Fine Powder	5 to 10	Any	All elements. Relative errors of 1% or greater often occur.
(2) Internal Standard	15 to 30	For channel instruments, channels for vanadium and chlorine	All elements. Relative errors less than 1% except for samples of widely varying composition.
(3) Fusion—Heavy Absorber	20 to 40	Any	All elements except, probably, magnesium and, possibly, aluminum. Errors about 1% or less over a very wide concentration range.

(1) Fine Powder.—Grind 5.000 g. of cement and 0.2500 g. of dodecyl sodium sulfate (other grinding aids may be used, as experience dictates) for 6 min. in an efficient grinding mill. A "rotating puck" mill has been found by cement analysts to be excellent for this operation. Press at about 8000 p.s.i. into pellets of a size suitable for the available equipment.

Accumulate sufficient counts for the desired accuracies, using Kα radiation. Prepare a calibration curve by analyzing NBS standards 1011, 1013, 1014, 1015 and 1016 in the same manner, plotting emission intensities (*e.g.*, counts per second) against elemental or oxide percentages. Use this calibration curve to determine the desired percentages for the analysis samples.

(2) Internal Standard.—As suggested by Brown, mix together

5.0000 g. cement
0.1000 g. vanadium pentoxide
0.1000 g. sodium chloride
0.2500 g. dodecyl sodium sulfate

Grind the mixture for 6 min. in an efficient mill and press at 8000 p.s.i. into pellets of a size suitable for analysis. Prepare a reference sample of cement in a similar manner.

For both the unknown and the known samples, determine the emission intensities for the elements of interest. Also determine the intensities, on both samples, of the appropriate internal standard elements, given below. When the instrument design permits, simultaneous determinations of the intensities of unknown and reference samples, or analyzed element and internal standard element, or both, should be made. Otherwise such determinations should be made successively, before analyses for other desired elements are made.

Compute intensity ratios for each element, as follows:

$$R = \frac{UA}{RA} \times \frac{RIS}{UIS}$$

where R = the intensity ratio,
UA = the counts per second of element A in the unknown sample,
RA = the counts per second of element A in the reference sample,
RIS = the counts per second of the appropriate internal standard element in reference sample, and
UIS = the counts per second of the appropriate internal standard element in the unknown sample.

Vanadium is used as the internal standard for determinations of calcium, iron, manganese, and potassium.

Chlorine is the internal standard for magnesium, aluminum, silicon, and sulfur.

Using NBS Standards 1011, 1013, 1014, 1015, and 1016, analyzed as above, prepare calibration curves, with intensity ratios plotted as ordinates and elemental or oxide percentages as abscissas.

Determine the unknown elemental or oxide percentages with the use of the calibration curves.

The calibration curves should provide good analyses over a period of weeks, on condition that the same standard reference sample is used. The standard should be protected from the air during storage.

(3) Fusion-Heavy Absorber.—The procedure suggested by Rose, Adler, and Flanagan[20] has been modified in the laboratories of the Portland Cement Association to provide greater accuracies. For most instrumentation, the concentration of heavy absorber used in the original procedure is too great to permit accurate magnesium and aluminum analyses in a reasonable time. The modified procedure permits good aluminum results, although magnesium accuracies may still be insufficient for referee analyses.

Mix 1.000 g. of sample, 0.5000 g. of lanthanum oxide, and 6.000 g. of lithium tetraborate. Fuse at 750°C. for 1 min. Raise the temperature to 1000°C. and hold for 1 min. Pour into a suitable weighing vessel, cool, and weigh. Add boric acid to bring the weight to 7.8 g. Grind in a mill for 5 min., and press in a suitable die at 25,000 p.s.i.

A "one-standard" procedure provides accuracies suitable for control purposes and possibly for more stringent requirements, provided that the sample is similar in composition to the standard. For this method, the calculation is as follows:

$$\text{Percent element in unknown} = \frac{\text{counts per sec., unknown}}{\text{counts per sec., standard}} \times \%\ \text{element in standard}$$

For samples of widely varying composition, prepare a calibration curve with the use of NBS Standards 1011, 1013, 1014, 1015, and 1016. For each element plot the emission intensities of the Standards against the corresponding elemental or oxide percentages.

X-RAY DIFFRACTION

Experimental Difficulties.—The analysis of portland cement for its compound composition may eventually be routinely accomplished by x-ray diffraction methods. At present, however, a number of factors stand in the way of such procedures.

In addition to the usually difficult application of x-ray diffraction methods to quantitative analysis, portland cement presents four problems largely peculiar to this material. First, certain components of both unhydrated and hydrated cements may exist partially in an amorphous form, at least as far as x-ray diffraction is concerned. Calcium hydroxide may be such a component, although recent work indicates the possibility that such "amorphous" calcium hydroxide may be in loose chemical combination with other materials.

A second problem is that calibration standards are not commercially available—neither individual components of cement (or its hydration products), nor cements having known compound compositions. Availability of the latter is complicated by a lack of accurate independent methods for obtaining such information.

A third problem is that, both for portland cement and its hydration products, some of the phases exist as solid solutions, with varying compositions. Thus the alite phase in cement, although primarily tricalcium silicate, does not give a diffraction pattern identical with that of tricalcium silicate. Indeed, the polymorphic forms of alite give rise to shifts in diffraction peaks, and thus present a calibration problem.

A fourth concern is the lack of suitable peaks for diffraction analysis. Some of the components of cement have only a few lines, and, in many cases, the lines from the various compounds overlap.

Experimental Approaches.—Approaches to methods for the solution of the above problems have been made by Copeland and coworkers. Their x-ray diffraction studies were concerned with quantitative techniques,[22] cement analysis,[23,24,25] and investigations of hydrated cement pastes.[26] Also, a number of other investigators, including von Euw,[27] Smolczyk,[28] and Midgley,[29] have developed procedures for cement or clinker analyses. Moore[30] has compared compound composition data obtained by x-ray diffraction microscopy and wet-chemical methods. Her paper gives an excellent summary of analytically valuable diffraction peak positions for cement compounds. She also compares internal standards, and reports the coefficients of variation that were obtained in these analytical studies.

Frohnsdorff and Harris[31] have applied an electronic computer to the difficult calculation problems that arise due to the presence of overlapping diffraction peaks.

Practical Applications, Present and Future.—X-ray diffraction methods may be

[22] Copeland, L. E., and Bragg, R. H., Anal. Chem., **30,** 196, 1958.

[23] Copeland, L. E., Brunauer, S., Kantro, D. L., Schulz, E. G., and Weise, C. H., Anal. Chem., **31,** 1521, 1959.

[24] Brunauer, S., Copeland, L. E., Kantro, D. L., Weise, C. H., and Schulz, E. G., Proceedings, ASTM, **59,** 1091, 1959.

[25] Kantro, D. L., Copeland, L. E., Weise, C. H., and Brunauer, S., J. Res. Develop. Lab., Portland Cement Assoc., (1), 20, 1964.

[26] Kantro, D. L., Copeland, L. E., and Anderson, E. R., Proceedings, ASTM, **60,** 1020, 1960.

[27] von Euw, M., Silicates Ind., **23,** 643, 1958.

[28] Smolczyk, H.-G., Chemistry of Cement, Proceedings of the Fourth International Symposium, Monograph No. **43,** Vol. 1, National Bureau of Standards, Washington, D. C., 27, 80, 1962.

[29] Midgley, H. G., Fletcher, K. E., and Cooper, A. G., Analysis of Calcareous Materials, S.C.I. Monograph No. 18, Society of Chemical Industry, London, 362, 1964.

[30] Moore, A. E., *ibid.*, p. 372.

[31] Frohnsdorff, G. F. C. and Harris, P. H., *ibid.*, p. 320.

useful for the solution of some manufacturing control problems. Although precise and accurate procedures may not yet be available, the concentrations of cement compounds, relative to concentrations in a reference cement, may be estimated in certain cases. The reference cement may be a production sample suitable for producing quality concrete.

Information important in studies of the rheological properties of concrete may be deduced from a knowledge of the state of hydration and the crystallinity of the calcium sulfate components of the cementitious material. Anhydrite, plaster, and gypsum can be detected by x-ray diffractometry when these materials are present in concentrations of at least a few percent. Semiquantitative analyses are often possible. The sharpness of the diffraction peaks is influenced by, and therefore a measure of, degrees of perfection and sizes of diffracting crystals.[32]

In the future, x-ray diffraction analysis equipment might become part of automatic production and control systems. Even without automation, rapid, precise diffraction analysis methods for compound composition may replace those conventional techniques that provide less informative elemental concentration data.

The work of Seligmann and Greening,[33] adapting diffraction methods to a study of early hydration reactions, should find practical application.

ELECTROMETRIC AND RELATED TECHNIQUES

POTENTIOMETRIC TITRATIONS

Applications of potentiometric titrations to cement analysis appear to be limited to determinations of calcium and magnesium,[34] chlorine, iron, and manganese. Accuracies claimed for the calcium and magnesium procedure, employing EDTA, do not indicate that the method will compete seriously with methods that utilize colorimetric indicators. Potentiometric methods for iron and manganese, likewise, do not appear to offer significant advantages over chemical indicator methods of end-point detection, although they present automation possibilities.

However, analysis for chloride in cements (and more often, in mortars and concretes), is more easily and accurately made by potentiometric methods than by other procedures. The procedure in use at the author's laboratory is described.

ANALYSIS FOR CHLORIDE

Apparatus. **Potentiometer.**

Glass Electrode.

Silver-silver Chloride Electrode.

Procedure.—Weigh 5 to 10 g. of sample into a 250-ml. beaker. Disperse with 20 ml. water, add 15 ml. concentrated nitric acid, stir to break up lumps, and dilute with water to about 100 ml. Bring just to a boil. Check with litmus paper to be sure that the solution is acid (add nitric acid if not); then filter through a medium-texture filter paper (or fritted glass crucible). Titrate with 0.1000 *M* silver nitrate solution, recording the potential after each 0.10-ml. addition. Determine the potential break and its corresponding volume of titrant. Calculate the percentage of chloride in the sample as follows:

$$\text{Percent chloride} = \frac{\text{ml. } AgNO_3 \times 0.3546}{\text{weight of sample}}$$

[32] Greening, N. R., private communication.
[33] Seligman, P., and Greening, N., Highway Research Record No. 62, 80, 1964.
[34] Roueche, A., and Monnier, D., Anal. chim. Acta, **31,** 426, 1964.

THERMOANALYTICAL TECHNIQUES

DIFFERENTIAL THERMAL ANALYSIS

Although equipment for differential thermal analysis has only recently become commercially available, the technique has been applied to cement research studies for over a decade. Early uses include studies of some of the silicate phases of cement as reported by Jeffrey,[35] and Kalousek's work on hydration and calcium hydroxide.[36]

Recent work with more sophisticated equipment has been concerned with studies of portland cement, its constituent compounds, and their hydration products.[37,38] None of these studies has demonstrated a practical application of DTA to routine analyses of portland cement. Longuet and Courtault,[39] however, suggested that the alite phase could be determined in cement clinkers by this method.

As sensitivities are increased through improved instrumentation and technique, it would appear possible to use differential thermal analysis for qualitative and quantitative determinations of several cement components—components difficult to determine by other methods. Examples might include calcium sulfate hemihydrate and gypsum, calcium hydroxide, water, and carbonates.

[35] Jeffrey, J. W., Proceedings of the Third International Symposium on the Chemistry of Cement, Cement and Concrete Association, London, 1952, p. 30.
[36] Kalousek, G., *ibid.*, pp. 296, 334.
[37] Webb, T. L., and Kruger, J. E., Analysis of Calcareous Materials, S.C.I. Monograph No. 18, Society of Chemical Industry, London, 1964, p. 419.
[38] Petzold, A., and Goehlert, J., Tonind. Ztg. Keram. Rundschau., **86,** 228, 1962.
[39] Longuet, P., and Courtault, B., Silicates Ind., **28,** 28, 1963.